D0001499

BILE PIGMENTS

Chemical, Biological, and Clinical Aspects

BILE PIGMENTS

Chemical, Biological, and Clinical Aspects

TORBEN K. WITH

Centrallaboratoriet
Svendborg Centralsygehus
Denmark

Translated by J. P. Kennedy

Central Basic Research Laboratories
Esso Research and Engineering Co.
Linden, New Jersey

1968

ACADEMIC PRESS   New York and London

612·35 W

UNIV. COLL. OF
LIBRARY
S. WALES & MON.
CARDIFF

COPYRIGHT © 1968, BY ACADEMIC PRESS INC.
ALL RIGHTS RESERVED.
NO PART OF THIS BOOK MAY BE REPRODUCED IN ANY FORM,
BY PHOTOSTAT, MICROFILM, OR ANY OTHER MEANS, WITHOUT
WRITTEN PERMISSION FROM THE PUBLISHERS.

ACADEMIC PRESS INC.
111 Fifth Avenue, New York, New York 10003

United Kingdom Edition published by
ACADEMIC PRESS INC. (LONDON) LTD.
Berkeley Square House, London W.1

Originally published in the German language under the title "Biologie der
Gallenfarbstoffe" and copyrighted in 1960 by Georg Thieme Verlag,
Stuttgart

LIBRARY OF CONGRESS CATALOG CARD NUMBER: 67-22781

PRINTED IN THE UNITED STATES OF AMERICA

OCO2046492

To the memory of my father
Carl Johannes With, M.S., M.D., Zoologist and Dermatologist
December 11, 1877–June 16, 1923

and

To my wife Kamma, née Bentsen

with thanks and gratitude

Preface

The aim of this monograph, which is probably the largest existing one of its type, is to cover as completely as possible the chemical, biological, and clinical aspects of bile pigments, and to review all of the literature in this field irrespective of language and place of origin. It is intended for all workers in the field of bile pigments, particularly clinical chemists, and for those in related disciplines, including biologists, biochemists, physiologists, pathologists, physicians, surgeons, veterinarians, zoologists, botanists, and microbiologists, and for chemists with a special interest in pyrrole pigments.

The field has broadened considerably in recent years. It has been recognized that bile pigments are not merely waste products of porphyrin biosynthesis and degradation, but that they have biological functions of their own dating back to pre-Cambrian times. The first conference dealing exclusively with bile pigments was held in 1966.

The literature in the text has been covered through mid-1966. At this point it became impossible to incorporate additional new work in the text. However, titles of important papers published since that time are listed as Additional Readings at the conclusions of the appropriate chapters. Because of the rapidly expanding literature on bile pigments it became necessary to add many new references on galley proof. These references are asterisked in the text and appear in the Supplementary Bibliography.

The first version of this work was started in 1945 when Dr. Eggert Møller, Professor of Internal Medicine, Copenhagen University, my chief at that time, suggested that I collate in book form my original papers on bile pigments in man. It became clear to me that it was not a book on my personal studies which was needed, but a comprehensive monograph on the entire complicated and controversial field of bile pigments. This work was completed in 1954, and 300 copies of it were produced in mimeographed form and distributed by A. Frost-Hansen, Copenhagen. It consisted of 583 pages and 2118 references. It was favorably received. A second, abbreviated and completely rewritten version was published in German by G. Thieme Verlag, Stuttgart in 1960. This work was also well received by the reviewers.

In all three versions I have attempted to point out current theories that are obviously misleading and those areas in which existing knowledge is insufficient. Experimental work which should be performed has also been delineated, and I have noted, with gratitude, that some of the suggestions made in the first two versions have actually been carried out.

The reader may be surprised by the criticism of some generally acknowledged theories and methods. It is, however, my opinion that "Traditional theory calls for more critical scrutiny than it has received" (M. E. Bitterman, in "The Evolution of Intelligence," *Scientific American,* January, 1965, page 92) and that a more philosophical attitude is needed in biology as a complement to the explosive development of experimental data—ideas expressed by several leading biologists during recent years as pointed out admirably in *The Lancet* (1962, **I,** 1342) in the introduction to the group of purely speculative articles called "Hypothesis," and also by me in the columns of *Nordisk Medicin* (1960, **63,** 816–817).

I am indebted to numerous investigators in the field for generously supplying reprints, for interesting and friendly correspondence, and for many visits and personal meetings in my own laboratory, in other laboratories, and during various congresses. These contacts are an important basis of this book. My special thanks are due to my wife who typed my first handwritten English manuscript, to Mr. Aage Ritter who admirably performed the difficult task of mimeographing the first version, to Mr. Arne Frost-Hansen who agreed to distribute the quite untraditional first version, to Professor Dr. H. A. Kühn who arranged my contact with G. Thieme Verlag, to Dr. Annemarie Clotten who translated the manuscript of the second version into German, and to G. Thieme Verlag, Stuttgart, Germany. Finally, I want to thank the staff of Academic Press for their splendid cooperation.

It is my sincere hope that this version of "Bile Pigments" will be as well received as its predecessors.

December, 1967 TORBEN K. WITH

Contents

BILE PIGMENTS

Chemical, Biological, and Clinical Aspects

CHAPTER I

The Chemistry of Bile Pigments

Introduction

For knowledge of the chemistry of bile pigments we are indebted mainly to Hans Fischer and his school. The results of their research were published in the monograph "Die Chemie des Pyrrols" (The Chemistry of Pyrrole).

A short survey of pyrrole compounds follows. For details the reader should consult the works of H. Fischer and Orth (1937), Fischer and Stern (1940), C. J. Watson (1938, 1942), Siedel (1939, 1940, 1943, 1944), Fischer and von Dobeneck (1947), Lemberg and Legge (1949), Bénard et al. (1949a), and Gray (1953, 1961a). For questions involving absorption spectra, he should refer to the works of Geiger (1936), Pruckner and Stern (1937), A. Stern and Pruckner (1938), and Pruckner and von Dobeneck (1942).

A. Structure and Nomenclature

True bile pigments, the bilirubinoids, are linear tetrapyrroles. They are derivates of the porphyrins which are cyclic tetrapyrroles. Because of physiological considerations, however, certain dipyrroles are regarded as bile pigments by some authors. For a better understanding of the biology of bile pigments, a short discussion of the structure of porphyrins is in order.

Porphyrins are derived from porphin. They consist of four pyrrole rings attached to each other by four methine bridges (—CH=). The four rings are designated I to IV and the bridges α, β, γ, and δ. In positions 1 to 8, the H-atoms can be replaced by various radicals. The more common substituents are methyl (M), vinyl (V), ethyl (E), —CH_2CH_2COOH (P), and —CH_2COOH (A).

The two formulas (Fig. 1) indicate resonance between two equivalent structures (mesomerism). The true structure of porphin is an intermediate one. Its electronic state is a composite of these two formulas (Zeile, 1956). The structure of porphin and porphyrins exhibits considerable stability because of the mesomerism. By substitution, a variety

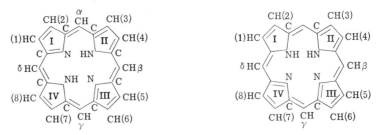

Fig. 1. Resonance states of porphin. The two formulas indicate mesomerism. The compound corresponds to an electron position intermediary between the two formulas. There are four methine bridges (α–δ) and H-atoms 1–8 where substitutions can take place.

of porphyrins can be obtained. Thus, etioporphyrin is obtained by substituting the hydrogens with four methyl and four ethyl radicals; four methyl and four —CH$_2$CH$_2$COOH (propionic acid) radicals yield coproporphyrin, and four —CH$_2$COOH (acetic acid) and four —CH$_2$CH$_2$COOH yield uroporphyrin. All these porphyrins exist in four isomeric forms symbolized by I to IV. The formulas for the four coproporphyrins are shown in Fig. 2.

Etioporphyrins are derived from coproporphyrins by substituting four —CH$_2$CH$_2$COOH groups with four ethyl radicals. Similarly, the four uroporphyrins are constructed by substituting the four methyl groups of the coproporphyrins with —CH$_2$COOH radicals. In nature only isomers I and III are found.

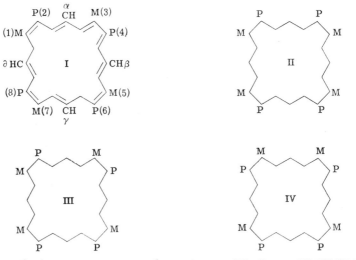

Fig. 2. The four isomeric coproporphyrins. M = —CH$_3$; P = —CH$_2$CH$_2$COOH.

By substituting two of the —CH_2CH_2COOH groups of coproporphyrin with vinyl, ethyl, or hydrogen, dicarboxylic porphyrins are obtained. These porphyrins, containing three different substituents in the porphyrin nucleus, exist in 15 isomeric forms, but only the form known as IX exists in nature (cf. Fig. 3). Protoporphyrin IX is a derivative of uroporphyrin III (Fischer and Stangler, 1927; Fischer and Orth, 1937, p. 409).

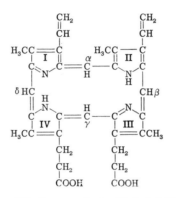

FIG. 3. Protoporphyrin IX. Protoporphyrin IX is 1,3,5,8-tetramethyl-2,4-divinyl-6,7-dipropionic acid porphin. If the two vinyl groups are replaced by two ethyl groups, mesoporphyrin IX is obtained; if they are replaced by two H-atoms, deuteroporphyrin IX results.

When the porphyrin ring is opened by cleavage of a methine bridge, linear tetrapyrroles or bilirubinoids are obtained. These consist of four pyrrole rings, connected by three bridges, either methine (—CH=) or methene (—CH_2—). These bridges were formerly characterized by the symbols α, β, and γ. These symbols do not always correspond with similar signs used to designate the bridges of the parent porphyrins.

Depending on the number of symmetry planes present in its molecule, a porphyrin can yield two, three, or four different linear tetrapyrroles. These are designated α, β, γ and δ, depending on which of the methine bridges of the porphyrin is broken. As mentioned above, the Greek letters designating the porphyrin bridges are not practical to characterize the bridges in bile pigments. Thus, following a proposition of Lemberg and Legge, (1949, p. 107), bile pigment bridges are called a, b, and c (see Figs. 4, 6, and 7).

The expression "bile pigments" can be used in a wider sense than "bilirubinoids" (Siedel, 1939, pp. 81–144). According to this nomenclature, the term bile pigment includes all compounds of pyrrole, including chromogens, formed during the physiological degradation of hemoglobin. Therefore, certain dipyrrole pigments will be grouped

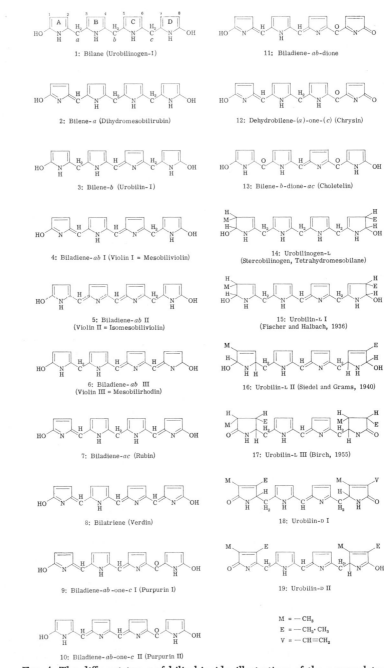

1: Bilane (Urobilinogen-I)

11: Biladiene-*ab*-dione

2: Bilene-*a* (Dihydromesobilirubin)

12: Dehydrobilene-(*a*)-one-(*c*) (Chrysin)

3: Bilene-*b* (Urobilin-I)

13: Bilene-*b*-dione-*ac* (Choletelin)

4: Biladiene-*ab* I (Violin I = Mesobiliviolin)

14: Urobilinogen-ʟ
(Stercobilinogen, Tetrahydromesobilane)

5: Biladiene-*ab* II
(Violin II = Isomesobiliviolin)

15: Urobilin-ʟ I
(Fischer and Halbach, 1936)

6: Biladiene-*ab* III
(Violin III = Mesobilirhodin)

16: Urobilin-ʟ II (Siedel and Grams, 1940)

7: Biladiene-*ac* (Rubin)

17: Urobilin-ʟ III (Birch, 1955)

8: Bilatriene (Verdin)

18: Urobilin-ᴅ I

9: Biladiene-*ab*-one-*c* I (Purpurin I)

19: Urobilin-ᴅ II

10: Biladiene-*ab*-one-*c* II (Purpurin II)

M = —CH₃
E = —CH₂·CH₃
V = —CH=CH₂

$$M = \text{—CH}_3$$
$$E = \text{—CH}_2\cdot\text{CH}_3$$
$$V = \text{—CH}=\text{CH}_2$$

FIG. 4. The different types of bilirubinoids; illustrations of the nomenclature used in this volume. The compounds are all presented as bis-lactim forms (OH on positions 1′ and 8′, cf. Fig. 7). Most of their properties are, however, best accounted for by bis-lactam notation as exemplified in Figs. 6 and 18.

4

with the bile pigments. Other bile pigments which are found in lower animals are derived from chlorophyll (Chapter X). Lemberg and Legge as well as Gray, however, use the expression "bile pigments" exclusively for linear tetrapyrroles and exclude dipyrrole pigments.

Bile pigments of higher animals, as far as is known, are all derivates of protoporphyrin IX. Similar compounds derived from other porphyrins have been synthesized, for example, coprobilirubin from coproporphyrin. These pigments may possibly occur in lower animals.

The bilirubinoids are named with the same numbers as the porphyrins from which they are derived. The signs α, β, γ, or δ indicate the methine bridge where the porphyrin ring is opened (Siedel and Fischer, 1933; Fischer and Haberland, 1935; Siedel, 1935). Thus, bilirubin is called protobilirubin IXα because it is formed from protoporphyrin IX by opening at the α-bridge.

Depending on the nature of the bridges, bilirubinoids are grouped into bilanes with three methene bridges (—CH$_2$—), bilenes or bilienes with one methine (—CH=) and two methene bridges, biladienes with two methine and one methene bridge, and bilatrienes with three methine bridges. This nomenclature, proposed by Lemberg and Legge will be used subsequently in this book. The symbols added in parentheses correspond with those proposed by Siedel (1937; 1939, pp. 96 and 123). When one of the —CH= bridges in a triene is oxidized to —CO—, a bilenedione (dioxobiliene) is formed. The formulas in Fig. 4 illustrate this nomenclature.

Another system, retaining the symbols I and IV and 1 to 8 from the parent porphyrins, was used by Thorpe (1955) and West and Todd (1956). This is illustrated by Fig. 5.

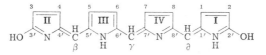

FIG. 5. Bilatriene formula with porphyrin nomenclature.

Because hydroxypyrroles, the building units of bile pigments, are really pyrrolenones, Gray *et al.* (1958) proposed a nomenclature based on the completely unsaturated structure "bilenone" (Fig. 6).

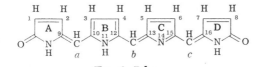

FIG. 6. Bilenone.

Complete skeleton formulas of the most important types of bile pigment, according to the most commonly accepted nomenclature, are given in Fig. 7.

It has been tacitly assumed that all natural tetrapyrrole bile pigments have structure of the type IXα. However, Gray *et al.* (1958) found that there was no analytical evidence corroborating this assumption. Consequently, they investigated natural tetrapyrrole bile pigments by oxidizing with alkaline permanganate solution and identifying degradation products (monopyrroles) by paper chromatography. In this manner,

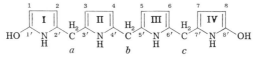

Bilane skeleton

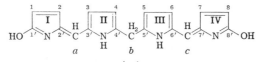

Biladiene-(*ac*) skeleton

Bilatriene skeleton

Fig. 7. Complete skeleton formulas of the common bile pigment types according to the most commonly employed nomenclature.

they could determine only degradation products of the IXα type tetrapyrroles and thus substantiated current concepts. Further, Petryka *et al.* (1962) showed that fission of the porphyrin ring at sites other than the α-bridge actually takes place during *in vitro* degradation of hemin in aqueous pyridine solution, containing hydrazine and sodium hydroxide, by passage of oxygen at 60°C. The biliverdin formed was isolated in crystalline condition and subjected to oxidation with alkaline permanganate, and the resulting pyrrole carboxylic acids were identified by means of paper chromatography (Nicolaus, 1960). The monopyrrole carboxylic acids present in the degradation products proved that fission must have taken place not only at the α-bridge, but at least at one of the other bridges too. This is contrary to results of *in vivo* degradation of the porphyrin ring where fission only takes place at the α-bridge.

Of the bilanes only mesobilane (urobilinogen IXα) and its tetra-hydro derivative (stercobilinogen) and urobilinogen-D are known. Dihydromesobilirubin is a bilene-*a*. Mesobilene-*b* (urobilin IXα) is a bilene-*b*. Among the biladienes-*ab*, the violins, three different types are known: mesobiliviolin (type I), isomesobiliviolin (type II), and mesobilirhodin (type III) (see Fig. 4). Biladienes-*ac* are called rubins; of these, bilirubin, mesobilirubin, and dihydrobilirubin are known. Bilatrienes are called verdins; of these, biliverdin and mesobiliverdin (glaucobilin) are known.

There is not complete agreement on details concerning the structure of bile pigments. The structures presented in Fig. 4 are of the classic bis-lactim form employed by Fischer, Siedel, and Lemberg. Modern investigators prefer the bis-lactam notation (cf. ÓhEocha, 1965a*). Figures 6 and 18 exemplify bis-lactam formulas. The uncertainties concerning the structure of the bilenes are discussed in Section E of this chapter. The structure No. 6 in Fig. 4, originally ascribed to mesobilirhodin by Siedel and Möller (1939), really constitutes the structure of the algal bile pigment phycoerythrobilin and not mesobilirhodin according to ÓhEocha *et al.* (1964*).

Biladiene-*ab*-ones-*c* are oxidation products formed during the Gmelin reaction of bile pigments. Of these, two types are known: (I) the bilipurpurins and mesobilipurpurins of Siedel, called biliviolins, type II by Lemberg; and (II) the isomeric bilipurpurins and mesobilipurpurins of Siedel (9 and 10, respectively, in Fig. 4). Biladiene-*ab*-diones (Fig. 4, No. 11) are Lemberg's biliviolins type III. Dehydrobilene-*a*-ones-*c* are Lemberg's chrysins. Bilene-*b*-diones-*ac* are called choletelins and mesocholetelins.

The structure of bile pigments makes possible certain forms of tautomerism shown in Fig. 8.

In rings I and IV (rings A and D in Gray's pyrrolenone nomenclature), keto-enol tautomerism is possible in bilanes, bilenes, and violins and lactam-lactim tautomerism in rubins, violins, and verdins.

It has been generally assumed that the rubins exist in the bis-lactam form rather than in the bis-lactim form because they do not form Zn complexes. This assumption is, however, not valid since Ó'Carrá (1962) has shown that the rubins actually form Zn complexes. Rubins can, consequently, exist also as a bis-lactim form containing two pyrrolenine N groups capable of complexing with Zn ions.

To explain the reactions of bile pigments, especially their diazo reaction, Mendioroz (1953c) considered mesomerism.

---

* References designated by an asterisk can be found in the Supplementary Bibliography.

Mendioroz' theory is based on the work of Pauling (1938) and postulates that bile pigments are resonance hybrids of a number of electronic structures. Besides the classic formulas, two reactive electronic configurations (with one free electron on the C-atom) are considered. Classic structures do not allow a combination with diazonium (see Fig. 25, Section J, this chapter). As shown in Fig. 9, five electron structures of pyrrole are postulated. On the basis of these formulas, nine different electron structures of the tetrapyrrole chain are possible (see Fig. 9). When electron-repulsive groups are substituted in the pyrrole units, only structures I, II, and III are possible, of which I corresponds with the classic formulas. The three electronic configurations of the pyrrole ring possible in verdins and rubins are given in Fig. 10.

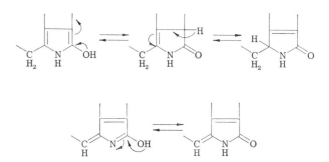

FIG. 8. Tautomerism of bile pigments. Top row: Keto–enol tautomerism of rings I and IV (A and D) of bilanes, bilenes, and violins. Bottom row: Lactim–lactam tautomerism of rings I and IV (A and D) of verdins, rubins, and violins.

Pullman and Perault (1959) performed calculations of the resonance energy of protoporphyrin and biliverdin by means of the molecular orbital method (L.C.A.O. approximation) and found very high values— 210 kcal/mole for protoporphyrin and 200 kcal/mole for biliverdin.

Certain dipyrroles, the pentdyopents and the bilifuscins, are often included with the bile pigments. These dipyrrole bile pigments are dipyrrylmethanes, which have a methene bridge between the two pyrroles, or dipyrrylmethenes which have a methine bridge. Their basic structures are presented in Figs. 11 and 12.

The symbol α,α' denotes a bridge involving C-atoms in the α-position in both pyrrole rings (i.e., those linked to the N-atom).

Modern chemical nomenclature for dipyrrole pigments requires some explanation because of the use of the notation 1*H*-pyrrole. It is possible to have more than one notation for the pyrrole molecule. Usually the structure is written with an NH and double bonds between carbon atoms 2 and 3 as well as 4 and 5; this is called 1*H*-pyrrole. But it can also be writ-

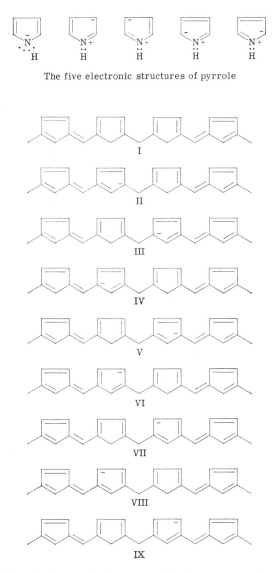

The five electronic structures of pyrrole

I

II

III

IV

V

VI

VII

VIII

IX

The nine electronic structures of the tetrapyrrole chain
Biladienes-(a, c)

FIG. 9. Mesomerism of bile pigments. With substitutions in the pyrrole rings as in natural rubins, however, only structures I, II, and III are possible. I accounts for ca. 85% of the resonating system. II and III are diazotable.

ten with N (without H in position 1), and two H atoms at position 2, and double bonds between positions 1 and 5 as well as 3 and 4 which is called 2*H*-pyrrole. 3*H*-Pyrrole has two H at position 3 and double bonds be-

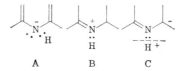

A   B   C

FIG. 10. Possible electron structures of pyrrole in verdins and rubins.

tween positions 1 and 2 as well as 4 and 5. Although these notations are of no importance for simple compounds because of resonance and tautomerism, they are of real importance in more complicated systems such as the dipyrrylmethenes. For example, the compound in Fig. 12 is a (2,2′)-1*H*-dipyrrylmethene and the structure of a 1′,5′-dihydro-(2,2′)-1*H*-dipyrrylmethene is derived from Fig. 12 by adding two H atoms to ring II in positions 1′ and 5′ and removing the double bond between 1′ and 5′. The designation 2,2′ refers to the linkage of the two pyrrole rings by means of a bridge in the positions 2 and 2′ (for further examples see Fig. 23a–d).

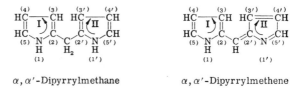

α, α′-Dipyrrylmethane   α, α′-Dipyrrylmethene

FIGS. 11 and 12. Illustration of two types of dipyrrole bile pigments: dipyrrylmethanes (left, Fig. 11), and dipyrrylmethenes (right, Fig. 12).

The occurrence of intramolecular

$$\text{NH} \ldots \text{N}$$

H-bonding in dipyrrylmethenes and its absence in dipyrrylmethanes was pointed out by Badger *et al.* (1962*). Furthermore, intramolecular H-bonding is possible between the pyrrole NH and the carboxyl groups of the side chains in both dipyrrylmethenes and dipyrrylmethanes, i.e.,

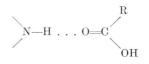

Summary

The structure and nomenclature of bile pigments and their relation to porphyrins are discussed. The term "bile pigment" includes not only pigments, but chromogens as well. Lemberg and Legge (1949) and Gray

(1953, 1961a) consider only linear tetrapyrroles, or bilirubinoids, as real bile pigments. Siedel (1939), however, uses this term for all pyrrole compounds which are formed during hemoglobin degradation in animal organisms. Thus, he includes some dipyrroles. We prefer Siedel's definition because, from the biological standpoint, it is the most descriptive one. The chemical nomenclature of Lemberg and Legge (1949) is to be preferred on most points, and is followed below with a few modifications. The tautomerism and mesomerism of bile pigments are discussed.

B. General Chemical Properties; Degradation and Synthesis

Bile pigments are ampholites because they contain pyrrole nitrogen as well as carboxyl groups. They are soluble in acids as well as in dilute alkali solutions. Whereas all bilirubinoids are water insoluble, their solubility varies in organic solvents.

The bile pigments form esters with various alcohols and acids, e.g., glucuronic acid and sulfuric acid (see Chapter V,F), and metal complexes with such ions as Cu, Zn, Ni and Fe.

The color of bile pigments varies greatly and some are colorless chromogens. Color and absorption spectra depend mainly on the number of double bonds in the bridges a, b, and c. Because of the absence of double bonds in the bridges, bilanes and dipyrrylmethanes are colorless. Similar to monopyrroles, dipyrroles have their ultraviolet (UV) absorption maxima at about 280 nm. The molar extinction of the latter is about double that of the monopyrroles. The UV absorption of bilanes has not been investigated.

The dipyrrylmethenes are yellow substances with a main peak between 400 and 450 nm and a UV peak between 250 and 300 nm. The exact location of these peaks depends on the nature of the substituents in positions 2,5 and 2',5'. A few exceptions are known; thus, the propentdyopents, which are dipyrrylmethenes, are colorless.

Addition of protons or metal ions on the pyrrole N in dipyrrylmethenes yields salts (ions) or metal complexes. This increases the extinction coefficient significantly and simultaneously displaces the peaks about 50 nm toward higher wavelengths.

Among the tetrapyrroles the bilanes are colorless, the bilenes are yellow, the biladienes are red or violet, and the bilatrienes are blue or green. Their absorption curves will be discussed later, together with the various substances. The absorption varies with the pH of the solution, but less than is the case for porphyrins. This phenomenon has been carefully studied in stercobilin (Gray, 1953, pp. 35–36) and bilirubin (Fog, 1960, pp. 59–60). By altering the pH in the range of 5–10, the form of the absorption curves changes considerably. Gray emphasized the usefulness of this phenomenon in the study of bile pigments.

A valuable summary of some properties of a series of important bile pigments was compiled by ÓhEocha (1965*) in Table I.

Investigations on spectrophotometric titration curves of bile pigments are due to Gray *et al.* (1961*) who examined solutions of bilenes, rubins, violins, verdins, and dipyrrylmethenes in aqueous buffer solutions (McIlwain's buffers and veronal-acetate buffers, the latter having constant ionic strength, $\mu = 0.1$). The two buffer systems employed yielded almost identical results in the pH range of 1–12. These curves illustrate the variation of spectral absorption with pH (300–550 nm range for bilenes, 250–700 nm range for verdins, violins, and rubins) as well as the variation of extinction at the spectral maximum with pH in the range 1–12 based on titration measurements. Bilenes, violins, and verdins exhibit greater maximal absorption at low pH than at high pH, and their maximum becomes broader and lower with increasing pH. In contrast the maximal absorption of the rubins increases and their peak becomes higher and more narrow with increasing pH accompanied by a distinct shift of the maximum toward shorter wavelengths. This finding contradicts earlier observations on bilirubin (Williams and Cabello Ruz, 1943; Martin, 1949).

The titration curves showed a well-marked increase in density at maximum in the pH range of 6–8 for bilenes, a moderate increase in the pH range of 4–6 for violins, and a minor increase in the pH range of 2–4 for verdins. Contrary to this the rubins exhibited a moderate decrease of density at maximum in the pH range of 6–8.

These findings clearly indicate that the bilenes, violins, and verdins are basic, whereas the rubins are acidic compounds. The pK of the corresponding conjugate acids was found to be 7.2–7.6 for the bilenes (7.2 for U-D, 7.4 for U-I, and 7.6 for U-L). The stronger basic character of U-L (stercobilin) is ascribed to its saturated rings A and D giving rise to a higher electron density about the pyrroline N of its central dipyrrylmethene chromophore; this N constitutes the spectroscopically active nucleophilic center of the chromophore and is undisturbed by effects from the remoter parts of the stercobilin molecule because of the saturation of rings A and D (cf. Figs. 4, 6, 15–17). Consequently the nucleophilic center is more readily available for external coordination (protons, metals) than in the nonsaturated bilenes.

Mesobilivioin exhibits a basic chromophore with pK = 4.0 for its conjugate acid. This lesser degree of basicity is explained by its more extensive chromophore which covers three pyrrole rings. To this is added the acidic group C=O in ring D of the bis-lactam form.

TABLE I

Properties of Some Bile Pigments[a]

Name	Class and structure number	Structure[b]	Absorption maxima (mμ) and millimolar absorbancy index[c]			Color of fluorescence of zinc complex salt	pK of conjugate acid
			Free pigment	Protonated pigment	Zinc complex salt		
Biliverdin (R:—CH=CH₂)	Bilitriene	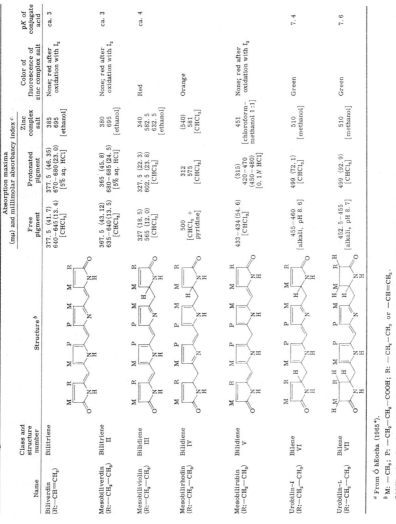	377.5 (41.7) 640–645 (13.4) [CHCl₃]	377.5 (46.35) 670–680 (23.0) [5% aq. HCl]	385 695 [ethanol]	None; red after oxidation with I₂	ca. 3
Mesobiliverdin (R:—CH₂—CH₃)	Bilitriene II		367.5 (43.12) 635–640 (13.5) [CHCl₃]	365 (45.8) 680–685 (24.5) [5% aq. HCl]	380 695 [ethanol]	None; red after oxidation with I₂	ca. 3
Mesobiliviolin (R:—CH₂—CH₃)	Bilidiene III		327 (18.5) 565 (12.0) [CHCl₃]	327.5 (22.3) 602.5 (23.8) [CHCl₃]	340 582.5 632.5 [ethanol]	Red	ca. 4
Mesobilirhodin (R:—CH₂—CH₃)	Bilidiene IV		500 [CHCl₃ + pyridine]	312 575 [CHCl₃]	(540) 581 [CHCl₃]	Orange	
Mesobilirubin (R:—CH₂—CH₃)	Bilidiene V		433–434 (54.6) [CHCl₃]	(315) 420–470 (450–480) [0.1 N HCl]	451 [chloroform– methanol 1:1]	None; red after oxidation with I₂	
Urobilin-i (R:—CH₂—CH₃)	Bilene VI		455–460 [alkali, pH 8.6]	499 (72.1) [CHCl₃]	510 [methanol]	Green	7.4
Urobilin-L (R:—CH₂—CH₃)	Bilene VII		452.5–455 [alkali, pH 8.7]	499 (92.9) [CHCl₃]	510 [methanol]	Green	7.6

[a] From Ó hEocha (1965*).

[b] M: —CH₃; P: —CH₂—CH₂—COOH; R: —CH₂—CH₃ or —CH=CH₂.

[c] Millimolar absorbancy index given in parentheses where available; solvent system given in brackets.

The verdins are much weaker bases than the violins. Measurements of the pK of the conjugate acids, especially that for mesobiliverdin, are difficult because of their instability between pH 2.5 and 5. The approximate pK value is 3. This behavior is to be expected because of the extensive resonating system of the verdins incorporating all four pyrrole nuclei as well as the two acidic C=O groups in the bis-lactam form.

The acidic nature of the rubins is in agreement with the opinion of Lemberg and Legge (1949) that these pigments do not form metal complexes and hydrochlorides in contrast with the basic bilirubinoids (bilenes, violins, and verdins). Gray et al. (1961*) explains this by the bis-lactam form of the rubins which has NH groups in all four pyrrole rings. From the titration curves the following pK values were obtained: bilirubin 7.1, dihydrobilirubin 7.2, and mesobilirubin 7.3. The values are only approximate, however, because of the instability of the pigments.

In contradiction to the view of Lemberg and Legge (1949) and Gray et al. (1961*) that rubins form no metal complexes, O'Carrá (1962) and van Roy and Heirwegh (1965*) found that bilirubin really forms Zn complexes although much less readily than the basic bilirubinoids (cf. this Chapter, Section E). This suggests that the bis-lactam structure cannot completely explain the properties of the rubins.

By various chemical treatments of bilirubinoids, a number of dipyrroles or monopyrroles can be obtained. On the basis of the structure of these substances, conclusions have been drawn as to the structure of bilirubinoids.

Thus, hematinic acid is formed on oxidation of bilirubin with chromic acid. After long reduction with HI in glacial acetic acid, small amounts of cryptopyrrole are obtained. When bilirubin is reduced with sodium amalgam, mesobilane is formed. The latter yields methyl ethyl maleic imide and hematinic acid on chromic acid oxidation. This indicates the existence of two types of pyrrole rings in bilirubin. One type yields hematinic acid on oxidation; the other has to be reduced with amalgam before it yields methyl ethyl maleic imide on oxidation. In addition, reduction stabilizes the bilirubin chain so that it cannot be degraded completely to monopyrroles. Stabilization is achieved by reduction of vinyl groups to ethyl groups, i.e., the meso compounds (containing ethyl) exhibit the highest stability (see Fig. 13).

On mild reduction with HI in glacial acetic acid, bilirubin yields chiefly bilirubic acid (Fig. 14). This forms hematinic acid and methyl ethyl maleic imide on oxidation with PbO_2 or HNO_3. When bilirubin is treated with alkaline permanganate solution, xanthobilirubic acid is obtained. This can be reduced back to bilirubic acid with HI and glacial acetic acid. When the reduction is carried out for a longer period of time,

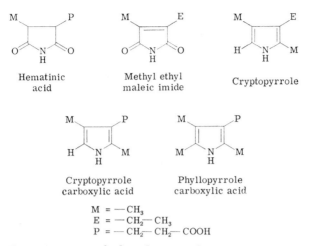

$$M = -CH_3$$
$$E = -CH_2-CH_3$$
$$P = -CH_2-CH_2-COOH$$

Fig. 13. Monopyrrole degradation products of bilirubinoids.

cryptopyrrole and its carboxylic acid are formed. Treatment with potassium methoxide yields phyllopyrrole carboxylic acid. When bilirubin is hydrogenated in the presence of colloidal palladium, mesobilirubin is obtained. When mesobilirubin is treated for a short time with boiling resorcinol and the mixture is introduced into water, neoxanthobilirubic acid is formed (see Fig. 14). This has the same structure as xantho-

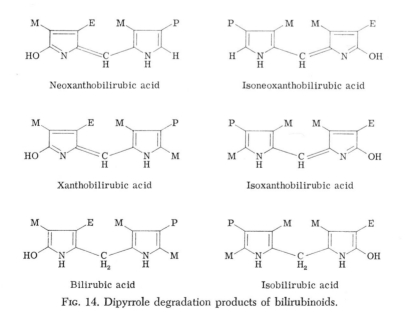

Fig. 14. Dipyrrole degradation products of bilirubinoids.

bilirubic acid, except for the methyl group in the α-position in the second ring.

It has been shown that the three above-mentioned dipyrrole compounds exist in two isomeric forms (see Fig. 14).

Recently, Nicolaus (1960) described a micromethod for identification of bile pigments based on oxidation with $KMnO_4$ in alkaline solution. In this way, monopyrrole carbonic acids are formed which can subsequently be identified by paper chromatography.

Nicolaus studied 65 different monopyrrole carbonic acids and determined their R_f values in five solvent systems: butanol–2 N NH_3, 1:1; butanol–ethanol–33% NH_3–water, 10:10:1:4; ethanol–33% NH_3–water, 80:4:16; butanol–glacial acetic acid–water, 4:1:5; propanol–33% NH_3–water, 60:30:10. The spots were made visible by spraying with diazotized sulfanilic acid and by subsequent treatment with alkali. The method makes possible identification of pyrrole carbonic acids in quantities below 5 μg.

The method of Nicolaus is not only of value in the study of the constitution of bile pigments, but also in porphyrins, melanins, and certain other natural products.

Synthesis of bilirubinoids can be achieved by condensation of the corresponding dipyrrole degradation products (see Fig. 14) with formaldehyde. But synthesis of vinyl-containing bilirubinoids—such as bilirubin and biliverdin—requires dipyrrole compounds with vinyl instead of ethyl, and such are difficult to obtain.

Most bile pigments have been obtained synthetically. Mesobiliverdin was synthesized by Siedel (1935); urobilin IXα by Siedel and Meier (1936); mesobilirubin by Siedel (1937); mesobiliviolin and mesobilirhodin by Siedel and Möller (1939); bilirubin and biliverdin by Fischer and Plieninger (1942). Recently, Kay et al. (1963) in C. J. Watson's department,[*] synthesized ($\pm$)-urobilin-L (stercobilin) by hydrogenation of bilirubin in the presence of large quantities of 10% palladium charcoal catalyst in glacial acetic acid at 60°C in an atmosphere of hydrogen. The direct synthesis of mesobilane (urobilinogen) and stercobilinogen (tetrahydromesobilane) has not been accomplished.

C. Biladienes-ac or Rubins

This group includes bilirubin and mesobilirubin. The former has two vinyl groups in positions 2 and 8 (in porphyrin nomenclature, 4 and 2; see Fig. 5), the latter carries two ethyl groups in the same positions (see Fig. 4, No. 7). Bilirubin and mesobilirubin thus show the same mutual relation as protoporphyrin and mesoporphyrin. A rubin

[*]Department of Medicine, University of Minnesota, Minneapolis, Minnesota.

containing vinyl in position 2 and ethyl in position 8 is formed as an intermediary product during hydrogenation of bilirubin to mesobilirubin and is known as dihydrobilirubin.

The formula for bilirubin is $C_{33}H_{36}O_6N_4$ and its molecular weight is 584.7.

The term bilirubin was coined by Städeler (1864). Previously, the terms biliphaeine and cholepyrrhine had been used for the red bile pigment (see Maly, 1868; Thudichum, 1868).

Bilirubin is ordinarily obtained from bile stones of oxen, where it is found as the fairly pure calcium salt. Lowry et al. (1953) proposed a useful method for obtaining bilirubin from human feces. However, the intestinal flora first has to be suppressed with antibiotics. Ascorbic acid addition inhibits oxidation during alkaline extraction in this process. Bilirubin can also be obtained from bile (Porsche et al., 1939; Schwartz and Watson, 1942; Garner, 1955). Larger amounts of crystalline, N^{15}-labeled bilirubin have been obtained from feces of a patient with hemolytic icterus. Prior to administration of N^{15}-labeled glycine, the patient was treated with Terramycin (Watson et al., 1954). Radioactive bilirubin-C^{14} was prepared by Ostrow et al. (1961) and bilirubin-H^3 by Grodsky et al. (1962). Recently, Sato (1962) described in detail methods for preparing pure bilirubin from human pigmented gall stones. These calculi contained 22.3–44.2% bilirubin, making up the largest component of the stones. The bilirubin was nearly entirely combined with inorganic bases such as water-insoluble salts and was readily freed from the salt by dilute acid.

A method for large-scale preparation of bilirubin-C^{14} with high specific activity was described by Custer et al. (1964*). Erythrocytes from ducks treated with acetylphenylhydrazine were incubated with glycine-2-C^{14} to produce radioactive hemoglobin. The hemoglobin solution was injected intravenously into a dog with biliary fistula and the bilirubin-C^{14} was isolated from the bile.

Lester and Klein (1966*) described a relatively simple and inexpensive method for preparation of bilirubin-H^3 with a specific activity of 10 μC per millimole. They fed H^3-ALA* specifically labeled at positions C-3 and C-5 to rats and isolated the bilirubin excreted with their bile for the following 24 to 48 hours. This bilirubin was labeled at the stable and nonionizable positions of the molecule, namely, the three bridges a, b, and c and the four side chains (vinyl and propionic acids) at the C atom closest to the pyrrole ring.

Bilirubin is a red-brown microcrystalline substance. It is insoluble in distilled water and dilute acids, easily soluble in dilute alkalies, and

---

* ALA: δ-Aminolevulinic acid.

sparingly soluble in neutral salt solutions. It is insoluble in most non-polar organic solvents, but soluble in $CHCl_3$ and acetone. Most commercial bilirubin preparations are incompletely dissolved in $CHCl_3$, giving a certain insoluble residue which dissolves in dilute alkalies, forming solutions that give a positive diazo reaction. This shows that the insoluble residue contains bilirubin (Michaëlsson, 1961, p. 19). The solubility and stability of bilirubin in $CHCl_3$ depends on the quality of the $CHCl_3$ (Brodersen and Vind, 1963a). In CCl_4, bilirubin is hardly soluble at all (Harboe, 1965).

The best solvent for bilirubin is pyrrole, which dissolves about 25 mg per milliliter. The very polar solvent formamide, which can be mixed with water in all proportions, dissolves about 1 mg bilirubin per milliliter (Harboe, 1965). Thus the solubility of bilirubin cannot be a simple question of polar or nonpolar solvents, as is the general belief at present. The solubility in formamide is perhaps due to the special capacity of this solvent to form hydrogen bonds with carboxylic acids (Mandel and Decroly, 1964).

Quite recently N. M. G. Harboe (personal communication to the writer, 1964) found that cyanide solutions are by far the most powerful solvents for bilirubin. A $0.1\,M$ solution of KCN in formamide dissolves as much as 27 g bilirubin per liter and is stable, i.e., the loss is, at the highest, 1% per day when placed at 5°C in darkness. Pure formamide dissolves only 0.85 g bilirubin per liter, a $0.50\,M$ aqueous solution of KCN only 1.15 g per liter, and a $0.05\,M$ aqueous KCN solution 0.85 g per liter. Further, the loss of bilirubin in the aqueous KCN solutions is considerable, about 10% per day for the $0.5\,M$ and about 2% per day for the $0.05\,M$ KCN solution.

By neutralization of solutions of bilirubin in dilute alkalies, neutral colloidal suspensions or brown amorphous precipitates of bilirubin are formed. The colloidal suspensions can be obtained by adding a saturated solution in acetone dropwise to distilled water at 80°C and removing the acetone by evacuation (Varela Fuentes and Recarte, 1934b). Jirsa and Šponar (1955), as well as Jirsa and Sedlaček (1956), prepared colloid suspensions by adding redistilled water to bilirubin solutions in dioxan.

The solubility of bilirubin in water was studied in detail by Overbeek *et al.* (1955a,b,c) by means of potentiometric titration with glass electrodes. The extremely low solubility of 5×10^{-11} mole or 0.03 μg/liter was found for undissociated bilirubin. The ions are much more soluble. Burnstine and Schmid (1962) studied the solubility of bilirubin in phosphate buffers of pH and ionic strength within physiological ranges (pH 7.1–7.9, ionic strength 0.02–0.474). They found a considerably higher solubility than Overbeek *et al.*, who worked with a much lower ionic strength. At the ionic strength of extracellular fluid (about 0.15), the solubility was of the order of magnitude 5 mg/100 ml at pH 7.4, but decreased rapidly with falling pH.

The solubility of bilirubin was a main question during the general discussion on bilirubin metabolism at the symposium held at The Royal Free Hospital, London, July 1966 (Bouchier and Billing, 1967, pp. 141–142). It was pointed out that bilirubin is much less soluble than the related verdins and urobilins. According to Nicholson one reason for this difference is that the bilirubin molecule is flatter than the verdins and bilenes, the structure of the latter being rather helical owing to internal H bonding (cf. this Chapter, Section E). Fog pointed to the strong tendency toward H-bonding between bilirubin molecules—from the keto group of one of the terminal rings in one bilirubin molecule (bis-lactam form) to the NH group in one of the terminal pyrrole nuclei in another bilirubin molecule. Further, Fog pointed out that the bilirubin molecule probably exists as a ring structure very similar to the porphyrin ring because of a hydrogen bond between one keto group in ring A and one hydroxy group in ring D, with the H oscillating between the two oxygens (mono-lactam form, as in Figs. 17c,d).

The partition of bilirubin between organic solvents and aqueous buffers with and without protein was studied by D. Watson (1964b). When solutions of bilirubin in ethyl acetate, mesityl oxide, or cyclohexanone were shaken with borate buffers (0.05 M, pH between 7.6 and 10.0), some pigment moved into the aqueous layer in amounts increasing with increasing pH. If human plasma was added to the buffer solution (50 μliters for every 2 ml), maximum transference of bilirubin occurred at pH 8.5–9.0. With ethyl acetate and mesityl oxide, bilirubin transference was increased a little by the presence of plasma, but with cyclohexanone the presence of plasma slightly inhibited the transference of bilirubin to the aqueous layer. The use of $CHCl_3$ was avoided because of its tendency to denature plasma proteins. Solutions of styrene, cumene, and ethylene dichloride containing bilirubin showed, after equilibration with aqueous borate buffers, a weaker affinity for bilirubin. Maximum transference of bilirubin to the aqueous phase took place at pH above 9. Again, little difference was observed after addition of plasma albumin. With benzene or xylene, maximum bilirubin transference took place at pH 9.1, but if albumin was added, maximum transference took place at pH 8.6. Partition of bilirubin between xylene (1 volume) and diluted plasma (0.4 volume; dilution 1:40) frequently resulted in a fine precipitate at the interface with the plasma. This precipitation was eliminated by addition of ethylenediaminetetraacetic acid (EDTA) to the buffer.

Titration curves of bilirubin with NaOH and HCl were published by

Overbeek *et al.* (1955b), who found that one mole of bilirubin consumed two equivalents of base, and by Lucassen (1961,* p. 46), who performed titrations in both aqueous and acetone-water solutions and found that aqueous titrations of sodium bilirubinate solutions with HCl gave non-reproducible results corresponding to between two and four equivalents of HCl consumed per mole of bilirubin.

Bilirubin has no absorption bands in the visible spectrum. However, in $CHCl_3$, and also in 95% alcohol–$CHCl_3$, a peak appears at 450 nm. Its alkali salts in aqueous solution show a maximum at 420 nm. When small amounts of serum are added to the solution, the peak is displaced to 450 nm. Figure 15 shows absorption curves of bilirubin in aqueous alkaline solution in the presence and absence of serum.

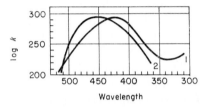

FIG. 15. Absorption spectrum of bilirubin in aqueous solution. (1) Pure aqueous alkaline solution. (2) Aqueous alkaline solution with addition of serum.

Absorption curves were thoroughly investigated by Heilmeyer (1931a), Heilmeyer and Toop (1932), P. Müller and Engel (1931a,c), Roy and Boutaric (1941), Penati and Pagliardi (1943), With (1945a,c), and Bénard *et al.* (1949c). Measurements are difficult in pure alkaline aqueous solutions on account of the rapid oxidation of bilirubin. Using a fast-working Hilger spectrograph with echelon cells, With found $E_{1\,cm}^{1\%}$ of 900–950 at maximum for $CHCl_3$ solution, 750–850 for alcoholic–$CHCl_3$ solution (95% alcohol), and 800–850 for aqueous alkaline solutions (0.1 N NaOH). The only recent measurement of the extinction coefficient for aqueous alkaline bilirubin solutions is due to Fog and Bugge-Asperheim (1964*) who found maximum 440 nm with $E_{1\,cm}^{mM} = 55.0$ corresponding to $E_{1\,cm}^{1\%} = 945$.

Williams and Cabello Ruz (1943) and Bénard *et al.* (1949b,c) found a dependence of absorption maximum on pH. They measured a maximum of 420 nm in 0.1 N NaOH and 430 nm in 0.01 N NaOH. The same maximum was obtained in 0.01 N Na_2CO_3. An absorption maximum of 440 nm was observed at pH 4–6 where incomplete precipitation already occurs.

UV absorption has been investigated by Henry-Cornet and Henry

(1936, 1937), Williams and Cabello Ruz (1943), Bénard *et al.* (1949b), and Hosokawa (1956b). The maxima measured showed a considerably lower extinction than those found in the visible region. Williams and Cabello Ruz found different UV maxima in aqueous solutions at various pH values.

Watson *et al.* (1960) found that bilirubin and other vinyl-containing bile pigments as well as protoporphyrin exhibit a sharp infrared absorption maximum at 10,080 nm.

Martin (1949) demonstrated the validity of Beer's law in aqueous bilirubin solutions in the region of the absorption maximum in both the presence and absence of proteins.

Barac (1949) prepared various alkali derivatives of bilirubin. He found that not only the —COOH groups but also the HO— and possibly the —NH groups can react with alkali. Thus di-, tetra-, and hexa-alkali compounds seem to be possible.

Absorption spectra have also been studied by Hunter (1951, p. 93 and Fig. 9). His curves show a maximum for serum-containing solutions at 460 nm with $E_{1\,cm}^{1\%} = 980$. In aqueous alkaline solution without serum the maximum was 430 nm, but here he reports no quantitative data.

Henry *et al.* (1953) determined the maximum to be 450 nm in $CHCl_3$ solution with $E_{1\,cm}^{mM} = 60$ (millimolar extinction coefficient) and $E_{1\,cm}^{1\%} = 1030$. In aqueous alkaline solutions containing serum, they noted a maximum of 460 nm with $E_{1\,cm}^{mM} = 45.5$ ($E_{1\,cm}^{1\%} = 795$). Najjar and Childs (1953) found $E_{1\,cm}^{mM} = 56.3$ at maximum 550 for bilirubin in $CHCl_3$ and 43.3 (maximum 560 nm) for aqueous bilirubin solutions containing serum albumin. This corresponds to $E_{1\,cm}^{1\%}$ of 965 and 740, respectively. O'Hagan *et al.* (1957) studied bilirubin preparations of various origin, laboratory preparations as well as commercial ones, and found $E_{1\,cm}^{mM}$ between 43.5 and 59.8 in $CHCl_3$ (maximum 453 nm). They emphasized the necessity of specifying the extinction values of bilirubin standard preparations.

Henry *et al.* (1960) described a method of purification of bilirubin and recommended the figure 60 for $E_{1\,cm}^{mM}$ of pure bilirubin in $CHCl_3$ at 453 nm. Plachý *et al.* (1961) prepared bilirubin from human bile by the method of Hawk *et al.* (1947) and found that its properties corresponded closely with German commercial bilirubin from Homburg Ltd. They controlled the purity by means of paper chromatography and drew attention to the lack of commercial bilirubin preparations that comply with valid standards of homogeneity. Michaëlsson (1961, p. 20) determined $E_{1\,cm}^{mM}$ for commercial bilirubin from British Drug Houses in $CHCl_3$ at 450 nm and found values between 57.6 and 60.2 (average of 8 determinations: 58.7), whereas Nosslin (1960) found 58.9–61.9 (60.4 on the average) in similar studies.

Fog (1960) emphasized that standardization of spectrophotometers is necessary if exact determinations are wanted. It is more necessary to standardize the spectrophotometer used than to employ a standard preparation of more or less questionable purity! He found a flat maximum at 454–456 nm for bilirubin in $CHCl_3$.

Recently Fog (1964) discussed the purification of bilirubin in detail. He dissolved the preparations in analytical grade $CHCl_3$, which was purified by washing first with aqueous $Na_2S_2O_3$ and then several times with water, and followed by drying over anhydrous Na_2SO_4 and finally distillation. This $CHCl_3$ dissolved approximately 1 mg bilirubin per milliliter when boiled for 5–15 seconds under reflux. This solution was filtered through a column of anhydrous Na_2SO_4 shielded from light. This column retains impurities including biliverdin. After this, more than half the $CHCl_3$ is removed by distillation until crystallization starts. Crystallization proceeds rapidly and the distillation has to be stopped immediately. The hot solution is filtered and cooled to $-20°C$ for 24 hours. Then equal volumes of ethyl ether ($-20°C$) are added to bring out nearly all the bilirubin remaining in the mother liquor. The crystals are collected by filtration or centrifugation and washed with ethyl ether ($-20°C$) until the ether is colorless, after which the crystals are stored in a vacuum desiccator with P_2O_5 in the dark. The yield of crystals is about 60% of the starting material.

For purity control, Fog dissolved 1.5–6.5 mg bilirubin in boiling $CHCl_3$ under reflux in dim light and diluted to 500 ml at 20°C in a measuring flask. Extinctions were read in a Beckman B spectrophotometer standardized with K_2CrO_4 dried on P_2O_5 and dissolved in 0.05 N KOH. Fog found the following E_{1cm}^{mM} values for different commercial bilirubin preparations at 454 nm: British Drug Houses, 59.3—after recrystallization, 59.1—after purification, 61.3; Hoffmann-La Roche, 56.3—57.6—60.5, respectively; L. Light & Co., 57.2—57.5—60.3; Dr. Theodor Schuchardt, 56.4—59.5—61.2; Pfanstiehl, 59.4—60.4—60.1; average of the five preparations studied, 57.7 (± 1.52)—58.8 (± 1.25)—60.7 (± 0.54). The standard deviation is added in parentheses. Fog found that the typical absorption curve of bilirubin in $CHCl_3$ is useless as a measure of purity.

Newbold and LeBlanc (1964[*]) studied the quality of five different commercial bilirubin preparations. The moisture percentage varied between 0 and 1.5% and the loss of weight following heating at 60°C for 5 hours varied from 3.9 to 11.7%. The color varied from bright orange to deep red-brown, but showed no relation to the purity. The preparations did not exhibit a definite melting point. Generally they began to shrink at about 195°–215°C and blanched and decomposed at 240°–250°C. The solubility in $CHCl_3$ varied. For one preparation (Pfanstiehl) 10 mg dissolved completely in 50 ml $CHCl_3$ at room temperature, while the others did not dissolve completely but left a brown residue. On heating on a steam bath for 15–20 minutes they were, however, completely dissolved in $CHCl_3$. The $E_{1cm}^{1\%}$ at 454 nm varied from 1006 to 1027 and the E_{1cm}^{mM} from 58.7 to 60. It is emphasized that the extinction constant is a good criterion of purity, but that it cannot be accepted as completely reliable.

Clarke (1965*) isolated pure crystalline bilirubin from gallbladder bile of humans, calfs, hogs, and dogs and compared it to commercial bilirubin preparations. The extinction coefficients (E_{1cm}^{mM}) in $CHCl_3$ at 450–453 nm varied from 60.0 to 61.0. Meites and Traubert (1965*) found the following extinction value (E_{1cm}^{mM} 453 nm in $CHCl_3$) for American commercial bilirubin preparations: Pfanstiehl 60.1 and 60.7 (two preparations), Warner-Chilcott 60.0, Nutritional Biochemicals 60.2, Harleco 59.1, the average being 60.0 with a standard deviation of 0.58. Martinek (1966*) studied five commercial preparations (Eastman-Kodak, Fisher, Mann, Hoffmann-La Roche, and Pfanstiehl) and found the extinction constant varying between 58.0 and 60.4. Jackson *et al.* (1966*) found that E_{1cm}^{mM} in $CHCl_3$ at 450 nm was as high as 66.8 for a bilirubin preparation from Weddel Pharmaceutical Ltd. Kuenzle *et al.* (1966b*) found E_{1cm}^{mM} at maximum 440 nm $=$ 60.8 for pure unconjugated bilirubin in a mixture of 9 volumes of 0.1 N NaOH and 1 volume of 10% aqueous Na-dithionite.

The effect of molecular aggregation—monomolecular state against colloidal state—on the absorption of bilirubin was investigated by Jirsa and Šponar (1956). In strong alkali (pH ca. 12), the maximum was 430 nm. Neutral salts caused association of bilirubin molecules with a simultaneous shift of the maximum to 470 nm, considerable flattening of the curve, and lowering of the extinction. Surface active agents transformed colloidal bilirubin solutions into real solutions exhibiting steeper absorption maxima and higher extinctions.

Fog (1960, pp. 59–60) found that a change of pH from 8.3 to 7.4 was followed by a shift of the maximum from 465 to 460 nm and a decrease of the extinction of about 9%.

Hosokawa (1956b) prepared molecular compounds of bilirubin with amino acids. Absorption spectra of these compounds did not differ appreciably from that of bilirubin. However, the diazo reaction was either negative or slightly positive. Bilirubin–protein compounds and glucuronic acid esters of bilirubin will be discussed later (Chapter V,B and F).

Kahán (1964a,b) found in electrophoresis experiments at pH above 7 that bilirubin forms a compound with EDTA differing from bilirubin in electrophoretic behavior and spectral absorption. Solutions of bilirubin in 0.15 N EDTA at pH 8.45 exhibited a maximum at 425 nm, whereas solutions in phosphate buffer at the same pH showed one at 435 nm. Further, the EDTA solutions had a lower extinction.

Mesobilirubin is darker yellow and more soluble in $CHCl_3$ than bilirubin. It has a substantially greater stability against oxidizing reagents. The absorption maximum of mesobilirubin is 425 nm in $CHCl_3$ (Heilmeyer, 1943, p. 104; Hosokawa, 1956a). The situation is about the same in dioxan (Pruckner and Stern, 1937). Mesobilirubin can be obtained from bilirubin by mild hydrogenation (Fischer and Niemann, 1923, 1924). Whereas bilirubin has two vinyl groups in positions 2 and 8 (4 and 2 in porphyrin nomenclature), mesobilirubin has two ethyl groups in the same positions. When bilirubin is mildly hydrogenated with palladium as a catalyst, dihydrobilirubin is formed first (with one vinyl and one ethyl group); later, mesobilirubin is obtained (Fischer and Haberland, 1935). Strong hydrogenation with sodium amalgam yields mesobilane in which the bridges are also hydrogenated. Hosokawa (1956a) investigated the dimethyl esters of mesobilirubin.

Ó'Carrá (1962) demonstrated that bilirubin and mesobilirubin form Zn complexes like other bile pigments. To 5 ml of a 10^{-5} M solution of bilirubin in $CHCl_3$–CH_3OH (1:1), a drop of 2% Zn acetate was added. This was followed by color change from yellow to saffron and a shift of the absorption maximum from 452 to 476 nm. The solution remained nonfluorescent in UV light. On addition of a drop of concentrated HCl, the color changed back to yellow. Mesobilirubin showed a similar behavior, the maxima being 430 and 451 nm. These observations can only be explained by a reversible reaction of Zn^{++} with the rubins.

Similar findings were reported by van Roy and Heirwegh (1965[*]) who added 50 μl of a bilirubin solution in $CHCl_3$ to 5 ml of a mixture of 10 volumes of ethanolamine and 0.1 ml of an aqueous Zn acetate solution to obtain a solution with a final molarity for bilirubin 0.0196 mM and Zn(II) 0.0065–0.0784 mM. Absorption was recorded in the range 240–540 nm with a Beckman DB spectrophotometer with a linear and log potentiometric recorder. The maximum was markedly depressed and displaced toward longer wavelengths after the addition of Zn. The changes were reversed on addition of the powerful chelating agent EDTA.

Tvaroha (1961a,b,c) succeeded in separating bilirubin from mesobilirubin by means of polarography. In mixtures, the two pigments were determined quantitatively with an accuracy of ±5%. His method is valuable in determining contamination of bilirubin preparations.

Brodersen and Vind (1963b), described a quantitative method for determination of mesobilirubin in serum (see Chapter V,D,2).

Pearson and Watson (1963*) reported a chromatographic method for the separation of bilirubin and mesobilirubin that detected concentrations of mesobilirubin as low as 0.5 mg/100 ml in the presence of much higher bilirubin concentrations.

Bilirubin can easily be oxidized, especially in aqueous alkaline solutions. Oxidation can be inhibited by redox agents, for example, ascorbic acid (Sauerbruch, 1937; Barac, 1939; 1946f,h, 1957; Lambrechts and Barac, 1939). The molecule is fairly stable in pure $CHCl_3$, and under refrigeration it can be stored for weeks without appreciable losses. Small amounts of serum added to the aqueous solutions have a similar stabilizing effect (see Chapter V,B,5). By oxidation of bilirubin, the green biliverdin is formed (see Section D, this chapter). Takeuchi (1959) found that bilifuscins are formed on further oxidation of bilirubin in aqueous solution. The oxidation of bilirubin is greatly enhanced by X-rays (Barac *et al.*, 1961a,b; Beaumariage *et al.*, 1961) in both aqueous and $CHCl_3$ solutions. This process is effectively inhibited by ascorbic acid and serum albumin.

Fog and Bugge-Asperheim (1964*) studied the stability of bilirubin and pointed out that Küster (1909) had observed that crystalline bilirubin changes with time. Newly crystallized bilirubin dissolves immediately in $CHCl_3$ at room temperature, but older preparations only dissolve completely on heating under reflux and then leave an insoluble residue when treated with $CHCl_3$ at room temperature. This phenomenon is explained either by isomerization of bilirubin to dihydrobiliverdin—due to displacement of the π electrons from the vinyl groups to the central CH_2-bridge (Gray *et al.*, 1961*)—or by transition between two crystalline states, the less soluble being the more stable. Dissolved in pure $CHCl_3$ bilirubin is stable for hours even in diffuse daylight; this stability is ascribed to intramolecular hydrogen bonds (cf. Fig. 17). In alkaline aqueous solutions bilirubin is extremely unstable because these H-bonds are broken and the molecule can be dehydrogenated at the central CH_2-bridge due to either isomerization (cf. above) or oxidation. This process is catalyzed by metals which form complexes with the biliverdin chromophore (cf. below). The well-known stabilization of alkaline aqueous solutions following addition of serum albumin is presumably due to re-establishment of the intramolecular H-bonds of bilirubin. Also, addition of chelating agents like EDTA to alkaline bilirubin solutions (a few millimoles of EDTA per liter) has a highly stabilizing effect.

The stability of bilirubin was also studied by De Ewenson *et al.* (1966*) who found that verdinoid pigments were formed when bilirubin was treated with sodium epoxide. Identical pigments were formed after long exposure to visible light. This transformation of bilirubin to ver-dinoid pigments in the absence of oxidizing agents is explained by a shift of π electrons from one of the vinyl groups to the central bridge (Gray *et al.*, 1961*; Gray, 1961b). Alkaline bilirubin solutions were allowed to stand with Zn acetate or complexing agents (EDTA) and the formation of verdinoid pigment was studied by following the change in optical density at 450 nm in a spectrophotometer with a time-drive attachment. Further, the initial and the final components were examined by infrared spectrophotometry which did not reveal any new functional groups, thus confirming the prototropic nature of the reaction. If a is the initial optical density at 450 nm and $(a - x)$ is the density at time t, $\log [(a - x)/a]$ can be plotted against time. Working under conditions minimizing the catalytic effects of light it was established that the reaction is first-order in alkaline solution with EDTA (rate constant, min^{-1}; $K_1 = 3.4 \times 10^{-6}$) and without EDTA ($K_2 = 2.0 \times 10^{-5}$). If traces of Zn acetate were present in the solution the reaction curve exhibits a slope indicating that several steps occur. Probably there is a fast initial reaction in which Zn acetate acts as a catalyst. The addition of small quantities of EDTA slows down the rate of transformation of bilirubin in the Zn-containing alkaline solution. Similar reaction constants were measured for the processes following irradiation of bilirubin in alkaline solution. At pH 10–11 the rate constant (min^{-1}) was 1.7×10^{-3}; when EDTA was added the rate constant was 1.2×10^{-3}. In CHCl$_3$ solution it was 5.5×10^{-3}. The high rate constant in CHCl$_3$ solution is probably due to the production of phosgene or HCl by irradiation of the CHCl$_3$. The authors concluded that a first-order reaction of a prototropic nature can occur in the transformation of bilirubin, but that intramolecular H-bonds play an important role in the stability of bilirubin.

Both bilirubin and mesobilirubin give positive Gmelin and diazo reactions. In addition, bilirubin shows a red coloration with concentrated HCl which has a maximum at 495 nm (Heilmeyer, 1938). A *new color reaction* with 3-methyl-2-benzothiazolon-hydrazone-chloride (MBTH) was described by Fog and Jellum (1962). A mixture of 0.5 ml of a bilirubin solution in CHCl$_3$, 4 ml of isopropyl alcohol, and 1 ml of 0.4% aqueous MBTH solution was allowed to stand for 5 minutes at room temperature. Then 1 ml 1.3% FeCl$_3$ in 0.25 N HCl was added. After 1 hour spectrophotometry was carried out. Pure bilirubin gives a blue-green color with a broad maximum at 635 nm and $E_{1\,\text{cm}}^{\text{mM}} = 119$, a figure considerably higher than that of its diazo reaction (ca. 81). Fog (1964) gives the figure 120.13 for $E_{1\,\text{cm}}^{\text{mM}}$ of the bilirubin MBTH color reaction at 635 nm. Pure azobilirubin also reacts with MBTH, giving an absorption maximum at 615 nm with $E_{1\,cm}^{mM} = 80$. Biliverdin and urobilins also gave color reactions with MBTH.

The structure of bilirubin has been disputed for a long time. Städeler (1864) and Küster (1899, 1906, 1909, 1912, 1915, 1917, 1922a,b,c) obtained it first in crystalline state. Its close relation to hemoglobin was first proved by Küster (1899). Küster *et al.* (1914), Küster (1915, 1917), and Fischer (1915) mentioned two possible isomers. Fischer and Niemann (1923), as well as Fischer and Haberland (1935), suspected that the difference between the hypothetical forms involves the IV pyrrole ring. They attributed configurations IV A and IV B to the ring as shown in Fig. 16. Fowweather (1932) and Halbach (1938), however, assumed a lactam-lactim tautomerism (mentioned previously by Küster, 1922c) and thought that the isomeric pyrrole rings have configurations IV A and IV C.

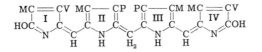

Bilirubin IX α

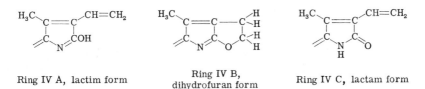

Ring IV A, lactim form   Ring IV B, dihydrofuran form   Ring IV C, lactam form

FIG. 16. Different structures proposed for bilirubin.

The vinyl groups on ring IV is always hydrogenated before the vinyl group on ring I for which dihydrobilirubin contains vinyl in position 2 and ethyl in position 8. Therefore, Fischer and Haberland (1935) believed structure IV B to be the correct one. Later, however, Fischer *et al.* (1941) and Fischer and Plieninger (1942), after having succeeded with the synthesis of bilirubin, thought that structure IV A corresponds with pyrrole ring IV. It is now believed that a lactim form with OH in rings I and IV is formed during biosynthesis but subsequently tautomerizes to a lactam form with O in both these positions (Gray, 1961a; see Fig. 8). The role of mesomerism was discussed above.

Recently, Fog and Jellum (1963) have pointed out that bilirubin itself is much more stable than its esters and they explained this difference by the existence of intramolecular hydrogen bonds in free bilirubin. Such bonds can link one carboxyl group with the N of the corresponding pyrrole or with that of the other pyrrole, i.e., two different intermolecular H-bond patterns are theoretically possible (cf. Fig. 17). They supported their theory with observations in the infrared spectra of bilirubin, meso-bilirubin, and mesobilirubin dimethyl ester.

The latter exhibited a displacement of the infrared bands toward higher wave numbers than expected and the two former toward lower wave numbers than expected. This observations seem to indicate that the carboxyl groups are engaged in H-bond formation.

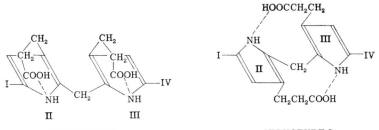

STRUCTURE 1   STRUCTURE 2

Fig. 17. The two bilirubin structures differing in intramolecular H-bonds. The differences are found in pyrrole rings II and III, which contain the propionic acid groups. In structure 1 the hydrogen bond links the carboxyl groups to their corresponding pyrrole N; in structure 2, they are linked to the opposite pyrrole N.

In mass spectrometric studies Jackson *et al.* (1966*) found that commercial bilirubin consists mainly of one molecular species with the expected molecular weight of 584 and some products of higher hydration.

D. Bilatrienes or Verdins

This group includes biliverdin (dehydrobilirubin) and glaucobilin (mesobiliverdin, dehydromesobilirubin). These compounds stand in the same relation to one another as do bilirubin and mesobilirubin, i.e., the former has two vinyl groups, whereas the latter carries two ethyl groups in positions 2 and 8 (4 and 2 in porphyrin nomenclature; see Fig. 5).

The question of the correct structural formula of bilatrienes, i.e., the classic bis-lactim notation, given in Fig. 4, No. 8 and Figs. 5 and 7, or the bis-lactam notation given in Fig. 6, was recently studied by Nomura *et al.* (1966*) who used measurements from infrared spectrum (3100–3600 cm⁻¹) and nuclear magnetic resonance spectrum of solutions of biliverdin dimethyl ester. They concluded that the ester exists in the bis-lactam form and eliminated the possibiliy of the existence of appreciable amounts of enolic and dihydrofuran tautomers (cf. Fig. 16).

Biliverdin is a dark green, microcrystalline substance. It is insoluble in water, dilute acids, ether, and $CHCl_3$, but dissolves in dilute alkali solutions by salt formation. It is easily soluble in glacial acetic acid and methyl, ethyl, and amyl alcohol. Biliverdin can be partially extracted from 0.5% HCl solutions with ethyl acetate, and completely so with $CHCl_3$. Extraction with ether is not possible. The addition of neutral salts (sodium acetate, ammonium sulfate, sodium chloride) facilitates the transfer into organic solvents (Ichikawa, 1956,3).

Berzelius (1841a,b) discovered biliverdin in the bile of oxen. It is found mainly in herbivorous mammals, and in the urine and serum in certain cases of icterus. Crystalline biliverdin was first prepared by Küster (1909), but his crystals were badly contaminated (Lemberg and Legge, 1949, p. 114). The first bona fide crystallization was performed by Lemberg and Barcroft (1932). Because of its presence in egg shells and in the placenta, biliverdin is sometimes called ooverdin or uteroverdin. Garner (1955) described a method of biliverdin preparation from ox bile. The crystalline biliverdin methyl ester obtained by him had a melting point of 205–210°C. Biliverdin is an intermediate during the biological degradation of hemoglobin to bilirubin (see Chapter II,B). The prosthetic group of the enzyme catalase contains up to 25% of biliverdin (K. G. Stern, 1935; Sumner and Dounce, 1938; Lemberg, 1938).

Biliverdin is an oxidation product of bilirubin. It can be obtained by leaving aqueous alkaline bilirubin solutions exposed to air, or on treatment with hydrogen peroxide. Solutions of biliverdin are green and show a broad absorption maximum at 700 nm and a narrow one in the ultraviolet region at 300–370 nm (Lemberg and Barcroft, 1932; Pruckner and Stern, 1937; Williams and Cabello Ruz, 1943). When serum is added to biliverdin solutions, an absorption displacement can be observed similar to the shift known to occur with bilirubin (Penati and Pagliardi, 1943). Details on absorption spectra have been reported by Lemberg and Legge (1949, pp. 116–118). Sakamoto (1956c) described absorption maxima for biliverdin preparations of varying purity. Gray (1961a) found maxima at 377 and 680 nm in solutions in 5% HCl in methanol.

The oxidation of biliverdin is enhanced by X-rays; the pigment, like bilirubin, is transformed to propentdyopent (Barac and Beaumariage, 1964*).

Biliverdin gives the Gmelin reaction, but its diazo reaction is negative (Ehrlich, 1884; Küster, 1922b; Lemberg, 1932, 1934a,b,c). Methods for its quantitative determination have been worked out by Engel (1940), Lemberg *et al.* (1941b), Amada (1941), Lemberg and Legge (1941), Larson *et al.* (1947) and Larson and Watson (1949).

Gardikas *et al.* (1950) and Garay and Argerich (1963) oxidized biliverdin to bilipurpurin with iodine and determined its zinc salt using a fluorimetric method, a technique which is claimed to be highly specific and sensitive.

Biliverdin, like bilirubin, forms water-soluble conjugates with glucuronic acid. The separation and purification of these conjugates by chromatographic methods was described by Noir *et al.* (1965*).

Glaucobilin (mesobiliverdin) differs from biliverdin by forming a blue solution. It exhibits maxima at 373 and 670 nm in 5% HCl in methanol (Gray, 1961a). The isolation of glaucobilin from vertebrates has not been achieved, but it occurs in lower animals and red algae (see Chapter X).

Pearson and Watson (1963) introduced a method for spectroscopic distinction between biliverdin and glaucobilin based on the Zn complexes of their oxidation products, that of biliverdin exhibiting a maximum at 635–640 nm, that of glaucobilin having one at 625–628 nm.

Radioactive biliverdin was prepared by Goldstein and Lester (1964*) by treating C^{14}-bilirubin with $FeCl_3$.

E. Bilanes and Bilenes (Urobilinogens and Urobilins)

The term "urobilin" was introduced by Jaffe (1869), who recognized the bilic origin of this urinary pigment. He was able to prove its formation by oxidation of a chromogen from urine or feces (Jaffe, 1871). Older literature is discussed in detail by With (1954, p. 14). Knowledge about these pigments accumulated slowly and progress was impeded by many errors, as summarized by C. J. Watson (1957, 1959, 1963).

Fischer (1911) and Fischer and Meyer-Betz (1911) reduced bilirubin with sodium amalgam and obtained a crystalline product. Initially, this compound was called hemibilirubin, but later the name was changed to mesobilirubinogen. The same authors were able to isolate a similar colorless substance from pathological urine believed to be mesobilirubinogen. This explained why urobilinogen of urine was thought to be mesobilirubinogen for a long time. Not before 1932 did C. J. Watson (1932a,b), from Fischer's laboratory, succeed in isolating and crystallizing the fecal pigment. The following year he was also able to isolate this substance from pathological urine (Watson, 1933a). However, a few years later it was found that the fecal pigment and the product obtained by reduction of bilirubin are dissimilar (Fischer *et al.*, 1935; C. J. Watson, 1935a,b,c, 1936a). It was pointed out later that Fischer (1911), without knowing it, had already isolated stercobilin in crystalline form (Baumgärtel, 1950b).

Hammarsten (1907) proposed using the term urobilinoid for all urobilin pigments, including chromogens. This terminology will be employed here, although it is used differently in the literature. Thus, Baumgärtel (1950b, p. 90) distinguished between "urobilinoids" and "stercobilinoids." C. J. Watson (1935a,b) proposed calling the fecal pigment (stercobilin) "urobilin." Lemberg et al. (1938b) suggested discarding the term stercobilin and proposed to call mesobilirubinogen (urobilinogen IXα) "mesobilinogene" and to call urobilin IXα "mesobilene-b." This nomenclature caused some confusion; for example a well-known investigator claimed that stercobilin and classical urobilin (urobilin IXα) were identical (Drabkin, 1942).

C. J. Watson et al. (1954), Watson and Lowry (1956), and Lowry et al. (1956) proposed a simplified nomenclature. Since urobilin IXα and its chromogen are optically inactive, they called them "i-urobilin" and "i-urobilinogen." The levorotatory stercobilin and its chromogen were called "l-urobilin" and "l-urobilinogen." The dextrorotatory urobilinoids isolated by Watson et al. were called "d-urobilin" and "d-urobilinogen." This terminology was attacked by Stich (1957) and Siedel (1957) who pointed out that it contradicts generally accepted principles of chemical nomenclature. According to this, l-urobilin and d-urobilin should be enantiomorphs and i-urobilin should be their racemate. This is, however, not the case.

Later, C. J. Watson (1959) proposed the symbols i-U, d-U, and l-S. To avoid the above-mentioned conflict with chemical nomenclature, we shall here employ the following terms: Urobilin-ɪ (U-ɪ), Urobilin-ᴅ (U-ᴅ), and Urobilin-ʟ (U-ʟ); and for the chromogens, UG-ɪ, UG-ᴅ, and UG-ʟ.

The following nomenclature will be used in this treatise: All urobilins (U) and their chromogens (UG) will be called "urobilinoids." They are divided in three groups: the first including U-ɪ (urobilin-ɪ; urobilin IXα; mesobilene-b) and its chromogen UG-ɪ (urobilinogen-ɪ; urobilinogen IXα; mesobilirubinogen); the second, U-ʟ (urobilin-ʟ; stercobilin; tetrahydromesobilene-b) and UG-ʟ (urobilinogen-ʟ; stercobilinogen; tetrahydromesobilane); the third, U-ᴅ (urobilin-ᴅ) and UG-ᴅ (urobilinogen-ᴅ).

Urobilins (bilienes-b) are brown pigments. They were considered amorphous substances until C. J. Watson (1932,a,b, 1933,a,b), and Rudert and Heilmeyer (cited in Heilmeyer and Krebs, 1934a,b) obtained them in crystalline form. They are soluble in ethyl alcohol amyl alcohol, and $CHCl_3$ an somewhat soluble in ether. Urobilins are almost completely insoluble in distilled water, but somewhat soluble in dilute solutions of neutral salts. They are precipitated from aqueous alkaline solutions by acids, saturated ammonium sulfate, Zn, Pb, and phosphotungstic acid (Méhu, 1878). They can be extracted from $CHCl_3$ solutions with dilute alkali. Their Zn salts show a characteristic green fluorescence, the so-called Schlesinger reaction, which was discovered by Jaffe (1869) and introduced into clinical chemistry by Schlesinger (1903).

Urobilins develop intensive red color on treatment with $HgCl_2$, the sublimate reaction (A. Schmidt, 1895). This color develops slowly, requiring 3–4 hours for completion at room temperature. The reaction product is insoluble in most solvents except alkalies (Goiffon, 1920a,b). However, this reaction has not been sufficiently investigated on pure materials. Urobilins do not react with Ehrlich's aldehyde reagent.

Urobilinogens (bilanes) are colorless substances that can be converted to the corresponding urobilins by mild oxidation. UG-I can easily be obtained in crystalline form, but crystalline UG-L has not yet been prepared (Lowry et al., 1956). UG-I is obtained by hydrogenation of bilirubin with sodium amalgam or by reduction of mesobiliviolin (biladiene-ab; Möller, 1939). The synthesis of U-L was recently achieved by Kay et al. (1963), but that of UG-L has not yet been achieved.

All urobilinoids occurring in fresh urine or feces are chromogens (Saillet, 1897; Steensma, 1907; Fischer and Libowitzky, 1939), and are partly oxidized to urobilins when exposed to air.

Urobilinogens are readily soluble in ether, ethyl acetate, amyl alcohol, and $CHCl_3$. On saturation with ammonium sulfate they precipitate from aqueous solutions and from urine. After acidification with glacial acetic acid, they can easily be extracted from aqueous solutions with ether or petrol ether. Their Zn salts do not show green fluorescence. They give a strong red color with Ehrlich's aldehyde reagent, i.e., p-dimethylaminobenzaldehyde in strong aqueous HCl (see Section K, this chapter). With diazo reagent they give a yellow color (see Section J, this chapter).

Methods for the preparation of crystalline urobilins have been presented in detail by C. J. Watson (1935c; 1953), C. J. Watson et al. (1953), and Iwado (1957a). C. J. Watson (1953) gave a simplified method for the preparation of crystalline U-I from bilirubin, and Moolenar (1960) one for preparation of crystalline U-L from feces.

Radioactive urobiligen-I (C^{14}-UG-I) was prepared by Lester and Schmid (1965*) from C^{14}-bilirubin with 40–60% yield. The preparation exhibited high specific activity which did not change on recrystallization. It remained colorless for 2–3 weeks while stored in high vacuum in the dark. The preparation was highly hygroscopic.

Depending on solvent and on pH, urobilins show various absorption bands between 485 and 510 nm (C. J. Watson, 1935c; A. Stern and Pruckner, 1938; Lemberg and Legge, 1949, pp. 139–140 and 142–143;

Hosokawa, 1956a). According to Lemberg *et al.* (1938c), the absorption spectra of U-I and U-L differ only insignificantly. This finding was corroborated by C. J. Watson and Lowry (1956) who found the maxima 495.2, and 492.7, and 495.2 nm, respectively, for the hydrochlorides of U-I, U-L, and U-D in dioxan. Additional spectrometric data are reported by Iwado (1957b).

Henry *et al.* (1961) studied the spectral absorption of commercial and laboratory preparations of urobilins. The commercial preparations were far from pure. The best laboratory preparations showed a maximum at 492–494 nm with $E_{1\,\mathrm{cm}}^{1\%} = 1350$–1570 in 3% HCl in methanol.

Type I-, L-, and D-urobilinoids cannot be distinguished on the basis of their spectral absorption, their solubility, or their Schlesinger or Ehrlich reactions. However, they can be differentiated according to their optical rotation. Thus, Fischer *et al.* (1935) and Fischer and Halbach (1936) have shown that U-L hydrochloride (stercobilin-HCl) has an exceptionally high rotation $[\alpha]_{589\,\mathrm{nm}}^{20°} = -3500$, whereas U-I has no optical rotation.

Schwartz and Watson (1942) found a strongly dextrorotatory urobilin in microbially decomposed human fistula bile and called it *d*-urobilin. This compound (U-D) shows even higher specific rotation (+ 4000) than U-L. Its empirical formula was $C_{33}H_{40}N_4O_6$ and that of UG-D was $C_{33}H_{42}N_4O_6$. C. J. Watson and Lowry (1956) and Lowry *et al.* (1956) give the following values for the specific rotation ($[\alpha]_{589\,\mathrm{nm}}^{20°}$) of the various urobilinoids: U-D +5000°; U-L −3500°; UG-D +74°; UG-L −16.7. The extraordinarily high specific rotation of these compounds is not quite satisfactorily explained, but Gray (1961a) points out that an important factor is that their absorption maxima are situated close to the wavelength of the light used in measuring the optical rotation.

In the tabulation below W. J. Cole *et al.* (1965*) gave the following values for the specific rotations.

Form	Free pigment	Hydrochloride	Zn Complex	Urobilinogen
U-L	−870	−4000	+467	−17
U-D	+910	+5000	+740	+74
U-I, dextrorotatory	Not known	+5000	+1420	—

The highest specific rotations are found for the hydrochlorides dissolved in $CHCl_3$.

Recently Jackson *et al.* (1966*) found the following specific rotations: fecal U-L hydrochloride, $[M]_D^{CH_3} = -24.8 \times 10^3$; fecal U-D, $[M]_D^{CHCl_3} = +27.4 \times 10^3$. Further they gave the following values for the molecular absorption coefficients at the spectral maxima: U-L, $\epsilon = 93.0 \times 10^3$ at 496 nm; U-D, $\epsilon = 93.0 \times 10^3$ at 499 nm; and U-I, $\epsilon = 60.8 \times 10^3$ at 496 nm.

The *chemical basis of this optical activity* was recently studied by Moscowitz *et al.* (1964*) in the United States and by W. J. Cole *et al.* (1965*) in England. According to Moscowitz (1961*) optically active chromophores can be divided into two groups: "inherently dissymmetric," and "inherently symmetric, but asymmetrically (more generally dissymetrically) perturbed." Moscowitz *et al.* (1964*) pointed out that the extremely high optical activity of urobilins points to an inherently asymmetric chromophore, but this is not a sufficient explanation. Also, a dissymmetric environment created by the parts of the molecule outside the chromophore is necessary to account for such an extremely high optical activity. They studied molecule models (space-filling Stuart-

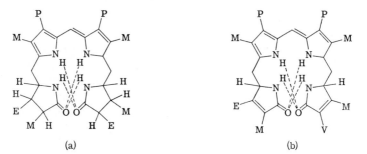

(a)   (b)

Figs. 17a and b. Structure of U-L (a) and U-D (b) according to Moscowitz *et al.* (1964*).

Briegleb type) and found that the models suggested a twisted chromophore of fixed chirality due to intramolecular hydrogen bonding. These considerations also explain the relatively low optical activity of the urobilinogens because the hydrogenation of the *b*-bridge destroys the conjugated π system involving the B and C pyrrole nuclei and hence excludes the possibility of achieving an inherently dissymmetric chromophore (cf. Fig. 17a,b).

Moscowitz *et al.* (1964*) tested this hypothesis by adding compounds with strong H-bonding capacity to $CHCl_3$ solutions of the hydrochlorides of U-L and U-D. The substances added were methanol, trifluoroacetic acid, and trichloroacetic acid. The strong external hydrogen bonding introduced in this way was expected to reduce the internal hydrogen bonding inside the molecule with resulting stretching of the helically twisted chromophore. This expectation was fulfilled as the solutions exhibited a marked decrease in optical activity for U-L as well as U-D after the addition of the H-bonding compounds. This effect was reversible for it disappeared after addition of suitable bases, such as piperidine.

In England the group working with C. H. Gray studied the same problems by means of molecule models and included the simpler dipyrryl compounds in their investigations. Both urobilinogens and the analogous dipyrrylmethanes show a steric interaction between the central CH_2-bridge and the proximal C-atom of one of the β-propionic acid groups, an effect which, although small, is sufficiently large to give noncoplanarity between the adjacent pyrrole nuclei (B and C) in the urobilinogens. Similar effects probably take place between the pyrrole nuclei A and B and between C and D. According to W. J. Cole *et al.* (1965*) accurate models of the urobilin molecules cannot be constructed because of the hybrid nature of C-atoms taking part in the central —CH=-bridge, but the bond lengths here must be less than at the central CH_2-bridge in the urobilinogens for which the above-mentioned steric effects must be enhanced in the urobilins.

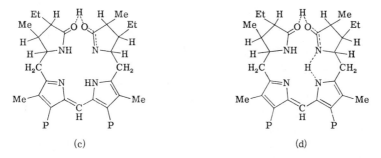

(c)   (d)

Figs. 17c and d. Different mono-lactam forms of U-L according to Gray *et al.* (1961*).

Already Gray *et al.* (1961*) suggested a mono-lactam structure for U-L because this, unlike the bis-lactam and bis-lactim forms, provides two NH-groups with replaceable H and two electron-donating N-atoms and accounts for the inclusion of one metal atom in each molecule of metal complex. This structure also provides an opportunity for an extra hydrogen bond and exhibits no unsaturation in the end rings to restrain by resonance effect the electrons participating in the H-bonding which is particularly strong (Figs. 17c,d, and 17e).

Although the terminal pyrrole rings of U-L are saturated, all four rings of U-I and U-D are unsaturated; the electrons at their N-atoms are less localized than is the case in U-L and are less ready to engage in H-bonding. This contributes to the high stability of the U-L molecule.

According to W. J. Cole *et al.* (1965*) both urobilins and their

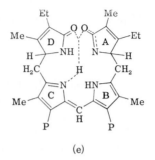

(e)

Fig. 17e. Structure of U-I according to W. J. Cole *et al.* (1965*).

chromogens exhibit asymmetric C-atoms in the central α-positions in the two terminal rings, i.e., the C-atoms numbered 9 and 16 in Fig. 6 (cf. also Fig. 18). These asymmetric C-atoms are the main cause of the optical activity of urobilins, and the central dipyrrylmethene chromophore is of importance because its absorption maximum is close to the sodium-D line at which standard measurements of optical rotation are performed.

Because of these circumstances the dipyrrylmethene chromophores of urobilins exhibit the so-called Cotton effect, a phenomenon subjected to closer study by W. J. Cole (1963*). If the optical rotation is read in monochromatic light at different wavelengths and the molecular rotation plotted against the wavelength, optical rotatory dispersion curves result. Such curves may be of two types: (1) they may be plain (Fig. 17f), i.e., without maxima or minima plain positive (Fig. 17f, A and B) or plain negative (Fig. 17f, C)—or (2) they may be anomalous (Fig. 17g). Such anomalous curves exhibit maxima and minima; in Fig. 17g, curve A

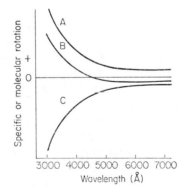

Fig. 17f. Typical plain rotatory dispersion curves (A and B, positive; C, negative). From W. J. Cole (1963*).

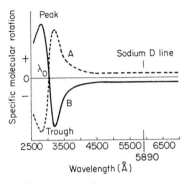

Fɪɢ. 17g. Typical anomalous rotatory dispersion curves (A, positive Cotton effect; B, negative Cotton effect). From W. J. Cole (1963*).

illustrates a positive Cotton effect and curve B a negative Cotton effect. Curve A is characteristic of a substance with a chromophore which has an absorption maximum (λ_0) that is approximately the mean of the maximum and the minimum wavelengths of the dispersion curve.

The stereoisomeric states of U-ɪ are still obscure (W. J. Cole *et al.*, 1965*). U-ᴅ racemizes readily in alkali (Gray and Nicholson, 1958c), and since U-ɪ has been obtained only by a reduction process involving the preliminary reduction of bilirubin in alkaline solution, it seems likely to assume that U-ɪ must be a racemate. To test this W. J. Cole *et al.* (1965*) prepared U-ɪ by catalytic reduction of bilirubin in neutral solution followed by oxidation with ethereal iodine. The product was optically inactive at 589 and 546 nm. Therefore, molecular asymmetry is lacking in bilirubin, which is optically inactive, and consequently production of optically active urobilins is most likely to be caused by asymmetric activity of enzymes. W. J. Cole *et al.* (1965*) also discussed the possibility of optical activity in other bile pigments and pointed out that this is theoretically possible because violins and rhodins possess one asymmetric C-atom.

C. J. Watson *et al.* (1965*) isolated crystalline UG-ɪ from human feces 5–6 days after discontinuation of oral administration of tetracyclin and found it identical with synthetic mesobilirubinogen in melting point, mixed melting point, crystal structure, and X-ray crystal powder patterns. The two substances were both optically inactive throughout the range 200–600 nm. The U-ɪ prepared from natural UG-ɪ was resolved by fractional crystallization into a crystalline dextrorotatory component ($[\alpha]_D^{20} = +5280°$) and a levorotatory mother liquor ($[\alpha]_D^{20} = -1870°$). Partial resolution of synthetic U-ɪ into strongly positive and negative rotating forms was also achieved.

Additional methods of differentiation between the urobilinoids are melting point determinations (C. J. Watson and Schwartz, 1942; Schwartz and Watson, 1942), certain color reactions, determination of degradation products after oxidation, and paper electrophoresis (Kahán, 1958; Lozzio *et al.*, 1963a,b). C. J. Watson and Lowry (1956) give the following figures for the melting points of the free urobilins and their hydrochlorides in crystalline form: U-I 159–164°; U-L 157–162°; U-D 162–165°; U-I, HCl 175–177°; U-L, HCl 234–236°; U-D, HCl 172–174°.

U-I and UG-I give, on boiling with concentrated HCl containing a little $FeCl_3$, a blue or violet color due to mesobiliviolin, the meso-biliviolin reaction (Lemberg, 1934a,b,c; Siedel and Meier, 1936; C. J. Watson, 1936b; Lemberg *et al.*, 1938b). This reaction is negative with U-L and UG-L, but U-D and UG-D develop a blue-green color (C. J. Watson and Lowry, 1956). The reaction will be discussed in Section F, this chapter.

U-I and UG-I can also be differentiated from U-L and UG-L by the pentdyopent reaction (see Section H, this chapter) which is positive with U-I and UG-I and negative with U-L and UG-L (Fischer and von Dobeneck, 1940). Fischer (1912) and Fischer and Libowitzky (1939) found that U-I gives a violet color with an alkaline copper sulfate solution, while this copper reaction is negative with U-L. According to Baumgärtel (1950a; 1950b, pp. 78–79), this reaction depends on formation of copper complexes with decomposition products. That it is negative with U-L only indicates that this compound is more stable than U-I.

U-D gives a specific color reaction with dioxan and HCl. This reaction is negative for U-I and U-L (C. J. Watson and Schwartz, 1942). U-D is less stable and less soluble in petrol ether than U-L.

Gray and Nicholson (1957a,b, 1958a,b,c) investigated the structure of U-D. They demonstrated that it can be derived from U-I by replacing the ethyl group in position 8 with a vinyl group (cf. Fig. 4, No. 18). Treating a solution of U-D in 1.25 N NaOH with H_2O_2, they obtained racemic U-D (1958a,b,c). Urobilinogen formed when U-D was reacted with hydrogen and colloidal Pt in methanol or acetic acid solution. Four H-atoms were taken up per molecule. Oxidation of this chromogen gave a dextrorotatory urobilin exhibiting $[\alpha]_{589\,nm}^{20°} = 4950$ in $CHCl_3$. After hydrogenation this compound behaved like U-I and not like U-D. It was therefore considered to be a dextrorotatory U-I. Gray and Nicholson think that levorotatory U-I also exists. Because of the existence of racemic U-D and optically active U-I, the chemistry of urobilinoids can be regarded as extremely complicated.

U-L and UG-L are considerably more stable than U-I and UG-I (C. J. Watson, 1933a,b, 1942; Baumgärtel, 1949a). Urobilin-L yields only acidic composition products on oxidation with chromic acid, whereas U-ɪ yields both alkaline and acidic compounds (Fischer and Wenderoth, 1939).

U-ʟ is oxidized to propentdyopent by irradiation of its aqueous solution with X-rays. This effect is more marked in alkaline than in neutral solutions (Barac and Beaumariage, 1964*).

Small differences in solubility also exist between these two urobilin types. UG-ɪ can be extracted from aqueous acidic solutions with $CHCl_3$, but it goes into the aqueous phase at alkaline reaction (Fischer and Meyer-Betz, 1911). Contrary to this, UG-ʟ cannot be extracted with water from $CHCl_3$. This was used by Baumgärtel (1947a) to separate the two substances. According to him, the findings of Fischer and Meyer-Betz, that the urobilinogen of normal urine cannot be extracted with $CHCl_3$, indicate that it cannot be UG-ɪ.

The structure of urobilinoids is shown in Fig. 4: No. 1 is UG-ɪ, No. 3 is U-ɪ, No. 14 is UG-ʟ, Nos. 15, 16, and 17 the formulas proposed for U-ʟ, and Nos. 18 and 19 are those proposed for U-ᴅ. The formulas of U-ʟ and U-ᴅ are still disputed.

Gray and Nicholson (1958a,b) maintained that U-ᴅ and UG-ᴅ have a vinyl in position 8, whereas Siedel (1957) doubted this (cf. Fig. 4, No. 19). C. J. Watson et al. (1960) could not find the characteristic infrared absorption of vinyl in U-ᴅ or its reactants in the mesobiliviolin reaction, but Gray and Nicholson (1960) answered their criticism by pointing out that the mesobiliviolin reaction of U-ᴅ is extremely sensitive to minute variations in the experimental technique. Further, Gray and Nicholson (1958a,b) supported their theory of the structure of U-ᴅ with the observation that it can be transformed into a mesobiliviolinoid substance without oxidation as shown in Fig. 18.

Ó'Carra et al. (1964*) studied the relation between the algal bile pigment phycoerythrobilin and urobilin-ᴅ and found a close resemblance. Phycoerythrobilin is isomerized by $10\,M$ HCl to a mesobiliviolin and a urobilin which differs from both U-ɪ and U-ᴅ by forming refractory covalent linkages with thiol compounds. A pigment obtained from U-ᴅ by isomerization is also closely related to phycoerythrobilin and considered to be its side-chain isomer. Because U-ᴅ failed to react with cysteine, it probably does not contain a vinyl group.

The biological hydrogenation of bilirubin to UG-ʟ proceeds, according to Siedel, over the intermediates shown in Fig. 19.

For U-ʟ, three different structural formulas have been proposed (cf. Fig. 4, Nos. 15, 16, and 17). Fischer and Halbach (1936) proposed the first one (No. 15), but this was criticized by Siedel and Grams (1941) who proposed the second formula (No. 16). Birch (1955) proposed the

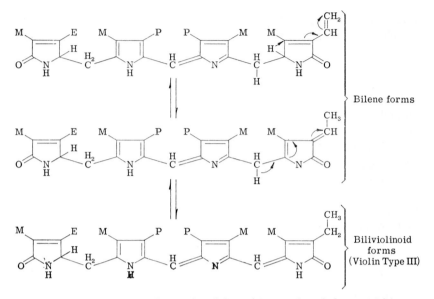

FIG. 18. The tautomeric forms of urobilin-D (Gray and Nicholson, 1958b).

third formula (No. 17) because it accounts for the great stability of U-L. Gray and Nicholson (1957a,b, 1958a,b) believe that this formula is the correct one. In spite of the fact that paper chromatography and contercurrent distribution gave evidence for only one homogeneous U-L, these authors still discuss the possibility of an equilibrium between the three formulas.

It should be further mentioned that Kay *et al.* (1963) succeeded in synthesizing racemic stercobilin ($\pm$-U-L) by hydrogenation of bilirubin, and that Lester and Schmid (1963) report the preparation of radiochemically pure C^{14}-UG-I by hydrogenation of bilirubin-C^{14} in C. J. Watson's laboratory.

Ó'Carra (1962) prepared a urobilin from algal biliproteins and called it *phycourobilin.* It is not released on treatment of the biliprotein with concentrated HCl, but it is obtained in low yield from chromopeptides formed by tryptic digestion, followed by centrifugation, separation on Sephadex G-75, and finally purification on an Al_2O_3 column.

Jackson *et al.* (1966[*]) published mass spectrometric studies on urobilins employing an A.E.I. "MS 9" mass spectrometer equipped with a direct inlet and operated at temperatures up to 250°C. They studied the hydrochlorides of U-L, U-D, and U-I prepared from human feces as well as U-I prepared from bilirubin. Bilirubin was also studied and found to consist mainly of a single molecular species having a molecular weight

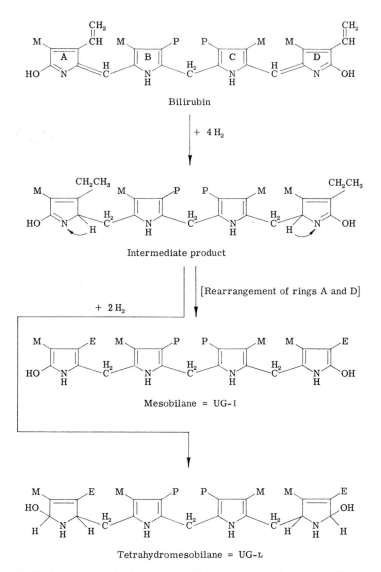

Bilirubin

+ 4 H₂

Intermediate product

[Rearrangement of rings A and D]

+ 2 H₂

Mesobilane = UG-I

Tetrahydromesobilane = UG-L

FIG. 19. Hydrogenation of bilirubin to urobilinogen-L according to Siedel (1957).

of 584 corresponding to accepted values. The urobilins all behaved, however, as mixtures. U-D consisted of a major compound with a molecular weight of 588, but also contained considerable quantities of a compound with molecular weight 590. Fecal U-I contained in addition to the expected compound with molecular weight 590 substantial quantities of a compound with molecular weight 592, and the same was true for synthetic U-ı from bilirubin. U-ʟ contained very little of the expected compound with molecular weight 594, but it contained two compounds with molecular weights of 592 and 596. These results were later proved to be due to artifacts (Gray, 1966, personal communication), a possibility already pointed out by the authors in a footnote. Heringová *et al.* (1964a*) described the isolation from the feces of infants of a hydroderivative of bilirubin different from both U-ı and U-ᴅ which was probably not a racemate of the dextrorotatory U-ı described by Gray *et al.* Heringová *et al.* believed that it was most likely a new type of urobilin not isolated previously.

Berendson *et al.* (1964*) isolated a urobilin of a type hitherto not described from the feces of a patient with dyserythropoietic jaundice (cf. Chapter II, Section A). Its properties were briefly described only; its absorption spectrum and its reaction with FeCl₃ closely resembled those of U-ᴅ, but it was optically inactive at 589 nm.

It should also be mentioned that W. C. Meyer (1947a,b,c) found a "third urobilin" in normal and pathological stool and urine. This substance was, however, not isolated. According to Baumgärtel (1949a, 1950b), this substance is the chlorophyll compound phylloerythrinogen.

The biliene-*a* dihydromesobilirubin was isolated from the stool of a patient with hemolytic icterus by Görges and Gohr (1954). This compound differs from the urobilins which are bilenes-*b* (cf. Fig. 4, Nos. 2 and 3). Dihydromesobilirubin is soluble in CHCl₃, methanol, and alkali, and has an absorption maximum in chloroform at 485–510 nm. Its Zn salt does not show fluorescence, but it gives violet color with Ehrlich's aldehyde reagent. The compound is diazo positive. On careful oxidation, a violet color develops due to mesobiliviolin formation, e.g., with FeCl₃ and concentrated HCl. Dihydromesobilirubin was also studied by Susuki (1958a,b).

F. Biladienes-*ab* or Violins; The Mesobiliviolin Reaction

Fischer and Niemann (1924) prepared mesobiliviolin by oxidation of urobilin-ı with FeCl₃ in HCl. This compound has intensive violet color. C. J. Watson (1932b, 1933a) found a similar substance in stool, called "copromesobiliviolin." Reinert (1948) was also able to demonstrate it in feces. Garner (1954) isolated it from ox bile. Lemberg (1928, 1929, 1930a,b) and Lemberg and Bader (1933a,b) found similar substances in red algae (see also Lemberg and Legge, 1949, pp. 128 and 147). These substances were further studied by ÓhEocha (see Chapter X). Related pigments were also isolated from lower animals (cf. Chapter X).

The term "violin" is used differently by Lemberg and by Siedel. Lemberg *et al.* (1941a,b) called the red-violet pigments that form during the Gmelin reaction "biliviolins." Siedel (1939), however, called these substances "purpurins," and used the term "mesobiliviolins" for biladienes-*ab*. He did not employ the term "biliviolin." Lemberg and Legge (1949, p. 123) included under "biliviolinoid substances" mesobiliviolin, mesobilirhodin (= mesobilierythrin), phycoerythrobilin of algae, and all the biladiene-*ab*-ones-*c* that are formed in the Gmelin reaction.

Siedel (1935) synthesized mesobiliviolin IXα, and obtained two isomeric materials which differed only in the position of the double bonds. One of them was red-violet, and its Zn salt gave a red fluorescence (mesobiliviolin). The other isomer was brownish-red and the Zn salt showed yellowish-brown fluorescence (mesobilirhodin). Lemberg and Legge (1949, p. 128) called the latter mesobilierythrin. The mesobiliviolin prepared from UG-ı (mesobilane) is a mixture of mesobiliviolin and mesobilirhodin and can be separated by chromatography. Siedel and Möller (1940) were able to identify the synthetic and natural products. Mesobiliviolin, as well as mesobilierythrin, yield mesobilane on reduction with sodium amalgam. The bilene-*a*, dihydromesobilirubin, forms on catalytical reduction of mesobiliviolin with platinum oxide (Siedel and Möller, 1939). In addition, a third isomeric biladiene-*ab*, isomesobiliviolin, was synthesized by Siedel and Möller (1940). The formulas of the three isomeric mesobiliviolins are given in Fig. 4, Nos. 4, 5, and 6.

Ó'Carra *et al.* (1964[*]) recently published studies on the spectral properties of violins with special regard to phycocyanobilin, the prosthetic group of phycoerythrin, and concluded that phycoerythrobilin has the biladiene structure (Fig. 4, No. 6) formerly ascribed to mesobilirhodin by Siedel (1935). Phycoerythrobilin was found to be isomerized by concentrated HCl to a mesobiliviolin and a urobilin, which differs from U-ı and U-ᴅ in forming refractory covalent linkages with thiol compounds including the apoprotein of the phycoerythrins. A pigment obtained from U-ᴅ by isomerization was found to be closely related to phycoerythrobilin although not identical with it; these two pigments are considered to be side-chain isomers.

Violins have a tendency for *polymerization*. The products are reddish-brown and amorphous. The polymerization product of mesobiliviolin is called ψ-mesobiliviolin. Its Zn salt shows red fluorescence (Siedel and Möller, 1940). On standing longer, it transforms to dioxytripyrroles (Siedel and Grams, 1941). Thus, transformation from tetrapyrroles to tripyrroles occurs during oxidative degradation.

Mesobiliviolin forms during the $FeCl_3$ or mesobiliviolin reaction (Stich, 1952a,b,c; Gohr, 1954). Certain bilanes and bilenes (UG-ı, U-ı, UG-ᴅ, U-ᴅ, dehydromesobilirubin) give positive reactions, but UG-ʟ and U-ʟ do not react. The reagent consists of a dilute solution of $FeCl_3$

in 24% HCl. The reagent is added dropwise to the alcoholic solution of the sample. The sample (urine, bile, stool) is acidified with acetic acid and extracted with $CHCl_3$. The extract is filtered and dried in vacuum. The dry material is suspended in alcohol and the boiling reagent added. The mesobiliviolin reaction was thoroughly discussed by K.-H. Brandt (1957, p. 81) and by C. J. Watson (1959).

These authors studied the reaction with mixtures of crystalline preparations of U-ɪ and U-ʟ and found that the resulting color depended on the ratio U-ɪ to U-ʟ. The reaction was found suited for determination of the two urobilinoids in biological material after $CHCl_3$ extraction. By long-continued oxidation, glaucobilin was formed. U-ᴅ and UG-ᴅ give violinoid substances without oxidation (Gray and Nicholson, 1958a,b; cf. Section E, this chapter).

C. J. Watson (1960*) pointed out that U-ᴅ yields predominantly glaucobilin with $FeCl_3$ oxidation, whereas U-ɪ gives variable mixtures of mesobiliviolin, mesobilirhodin, and glaucobilin. A blue color with the mesobiliviolin reaction can thus be caused by different substances or mixtures.

Jirásek and Jirsa (1960) found that the mesobiliviolin reaction is suitable for separation of U-ɪ and UG-ɪ from U-ʟ and UG-ʟ in biological materials. Lack of confidence in the reaction is due to the fact that analysis sometimes is performed without previous $CHCl_3$ extraction. Difficulties that arise when both pigments are present simultaneously also have to be taken into account. For this purpose, Jirásek and Jirsa developed a paper chromatographic separation method. On long-continued oxidation with $FeCl_3$, a blue pigment is formed which was identified as glaucobilin on paper chromatography.

Messmer and Dengler (1962) also used the mesobiliviolin reaction for differential urobilinoid analysis in biological material. They extracted with acetic acid–$CHCl_3$, evaporated the solvent, extracted the residue with ethanol, added $FeCl_3$ in 25% HCl, and heated for 3 minutes on boiling water bath. The solution was then subjected to paper chromatography of the ring type in a Desaga round filter developer DBEM No. 330.† It is important to saturate the atmosphere in the chamber with the solvent for at least 1 hour before the run. The duration of the run is 2.5 hours at 20°. The solvent is a 10% aqueous pyridine solution. The ring chromatograms were always reproducible under constant working conditions. First, a brown ring is formed; if mesobiliviolin is present, a violet one—mesobiliviolin—follows, which overtakes the first one in 30 minutes. Fluorescence after preparation with Zn salts is valuable in

† Manufactured by Desaga GbmH, Heidelberg, Germany; U.S. representative, C. A. Brinkmann Co., Inc., Cantiague Road, Westbury, N.Y.

identification of the rings. The paper of Messmer and Dengler contains several beautiful color photographs.

Lozzio *et al.* (1964a,b) described a method for quantitative determination of mesobiliviolin based on the fluorescence of its Zn salt and paper chromatographic identification.

The reaction mixture of the mesobiliviolin reaction becomes reddish-violet if UG-I or U-I are present, bluish-green with U-D or UG-D, and brownish with U-L or UG-L. The latter color is not a result of oxidation but due to complex formation with Fe. If mesobilirubin is present, it gives a blue color because of oxidation to glaucobilin, and if bilirubin is present a green color develops because of biliverdin formation.

Watson (1959) was able to determine U-I, U-D, and U-L semiquantitatively in mixtures with spectrophotometric measurements of the mesobiliviolin reaction.

The algal bile pigments, the *phycobilins,* were subjected to penetrating studies (original investigations as well as reviews) by ÓhEocha and his collaborators (ÓhEocha, 1962*, 1963*, 1965a*,b*, 1966*). The phycobilins are discussed in Chapter X.

G. Dipyrrole Bile Pigments: Fuscins and Leukans

Fuscins are dipyrrylmethenes biologically related to the bilirubinoids. Mesobilifuscin is formed from a chromogen called promesobilifuscin or mesobilileukan. The latter occurs in the form of its polymerization product as a decomposition product of hemoglobin (see Stich, 1957); in porphyrias, similar substances are excreted in the urine and deposited in the bones as by-products of porphyrin synthesis (With, 1958b,c).

In his early work, Fischer (1911) described a substance obtained as a by-product of the reduction of raw bilirubin with sodium amalgam. He called it *"Körper II"* ("compound II"). Only when Meldolesi *et al.* (1939) suceeded in isolating a similar product in stool was the compound further investigated. Siedel and Möller (1939, 1940) purified this fecal product by column chromatography and determined its structure, although they were not able to crystallize it. They showed that the mother compound is not bilirubin but bilifuscin, an impurity of raw bilirubin already investigated by Städeler (1864), von Zumbusch (1901), and Weinberger (1936). Siedel and Möller (1939) prepared bilifuscin from bile stones and obtained "compound II" by reduction with sodium amalgam. Weinberger (1936) isolated bilifuscin from human bile stones.

It was first believed that bilifuscin is formed during stepwise degradation of myoglobin, because Meldolesi detected this substance as a chromoprotein (myobilin) exhibiting green fluorescence in stool of patients with muscular dystrophy. Mesobilifuscin is liberated from myobilin with HCl–methanol. Engel (1940) and Siedel *et al.* (1947) established bilifuscin as a normal degradation product of hemoglobin which is excreted with the bile and reduced to mesobilifuscin in the large intestine. This is corroborated by the findings of Perkoff and Tyler (1950), who found the same myobilin concentration in normal subjects and patients with muscular dystrophy. Siedel *et al.* (1947) also found mesobilifuscin in normal stool.

The yellow pigment "xanthorubin" (cf. Chapter II,C) occurring in the serum of hepatectomized animals as well as the yellow "nonbilirubin" of normal serum (cf. Chapter V,C,3) may contain fuscin. Lemberg and Legge (1949, p. 150), however, found differences between the spectral absorption of xanthorubin and bilifuscin. The pyrrole pigment of wool, "lanaurin," described by Rimington and Stewart (1932) possibly belongs to this class.

The structure of mesobilifuscin was investigated by Siedel and Möller (1939). They established that this substance is a mixture of two isomeric dioxydipyrrylmethenes, i.e., mesobilifuscin I and II.

Fuscins differ from other dioxydipyrrylmethenes in their color intensity and in their ability to give the pentdyopent reaction (cf. Section H, this chapter). Siedel and Möller (1939) explained this by postulating two tautomers, a lactim and a lactam (cf. Fig. 20).

Siedel *et al.* (1947) pointed out that the specific structure of fuscins causes their deep brown color and amorphous form. They synthesized two isomers of mesobilifuscin and the corresponding bilifuscins. Furthermore, they prepared mesobilifuscin from stool of normal subjects kept

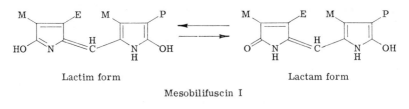

Lactim form   Lactam form

Mesobilifuscin I

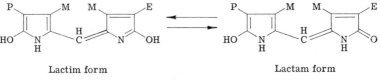

Lactim form   Lactam form

Mesobilifuscin II

Fɪɢ. 20. Mesobilifuscins I and II.

on a diet free from meat and chlorophyll. This indicates that mesobilifuscin is a product of normal pyrrole metabolism. Watson (1942) was
also able to identify mesobilifuscin in relatively high concentration in
the stool. He thought that the substance copronigrin isolated by him
(C. J. Watson, 1932b) earlier was identical with mesobilifuscin.

According to Siedel *et al.* (1948) and Bingold and Stich (1949),
fecal fuscins exist mainly as the chromogen promesobilifuscin, also
called mesobilileukan. It can be extracted with water or dilute alkali
from stool. From such solutions brown, amorphous mesobilifuscin can
be precipitated by acids. Promesobilifuscin is formed from bilirubin,
mesohemin, hemin, or hemoglobin by oxidoreduction with sodium
amalgam and oxygen in ammoniacal solutions. Similarly, pentdyopent
yields promesobilifuscin by reduction with sodium amalgam. It is also
formed by action of liver "brei" on bilirubin, or of *Streptococcus viridans*
on blood agar.

Promesobilifuscin in a dipyrrylmethane. It does not give any of the
chemical identification reactions of bile pigments. It is soluble in water,
dilute alkali, butyl and amyl alcohol, hardly soluble in $CHCl_3$ and ether,
and insoluble in benzene and liquid paraffin. On treatment with hydrogen
and especially at higher temperatures, promesobilifuscin polymerizes to
mesobilifuscin.

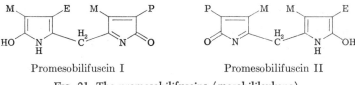

Promesobilifuscin I   Promesobilifuscin II

FIG. 21. The promesobilifuscins (mesobilileukans).

Siedel *et al.* (1948) proposed the formulas in Fig. 21 for the two
isomeric promesobilifuscins. The existence of probilifuscins (bilileukans)
—i.e., compounds differing from bilfuscins by having a vinyl group
instead of the ethyl group—has not been established.

Siedel *et al.* (1948) were able to isolate a number of mesobilifuscins
by chromatography, which they considered as various grades of polymerization. Stich and Stärk (1953) distinguished between water soluble and
water insoluble mesobilifuscins. The latter were further divided, on the
basis of solubility of their methyl esters, into $CHCl_3$ soluble, methanol
soluble, and amyl alcohol soluble forms. These authors further subdivided
the $CHCl_3$-soluble fraction into forms A, B, and C, depending on the
eluation of the esters by $CHCl_3$ from an Al_2O_3 column.

Von Dobeneck (1948a,b, 1949), however, doubted the findings of
Siedel *et al.* and Stich and Stärk and did not consider their structural

formulas of bilifuscin and mesobilifuscin sufficiently substantiated. He found that "compound II" contains less hydrogens than suggested by Siedel's formulas. Siedel's findings were published only in short preliminary notes (see C. J. Watson, 1956a,b,c), and are therefore difficult to evaluate.

The normal urinary pigment "urochrome B," which contributes about 50% of the color of urine, may be a fuscin. Stich and Stärk (1953) isolated this compound from numerous normal and pathological urines and identified it as a mesobilifuscin. Except in one case of polycythemia where type C dominated, type B was usually found.

It is an interesting question whether fuscins excreted in stool and urine under normal and pathological circumstances are derivatives of hemoglobin decomposition or whether they are by-products of pyrrole synthesis. The presence of considerable amounts of nonporphyrin pyrrole pigments in the urine and organs of porphyria patients seems to indicate that fuscins can be formed as by-products of porphyrin synthesis (compare With, 1958b). An observation by C. J. Watson (personal communication, 1956; but see Gilbertsen et al., 1957) corroborates this view. He and his colleagues administered glycine-N^{15} to patients and were able to isolate stercobilin and mesobilifuscin from stool. During the first peak of stercobilin excretion, a definite increase of mesobilifuscin-N^{15} was encountered, whereas the excretion of mesobilifuscin during the second peak of stercobilin, appearing after 120 days, was considerably lower. This second peak corresponds to the bile pigment formed by hemoglobin disintegration. Therefore, Watson's observations indicate (Gilbertsen et al., 1957) that mesobilifuscin from stool is a product of porphyrin synthesis rather than of hemoglobin disintegration (compare Chapter II,A); see also C. J. Watson (1957*).

Gilbertsen et al. (1957) described a method of extraction and purification of mesobilifuscin. Garay et al. (1964a*) used this method in the study of mesobilifuscin in human meconium. Only in one case did they obtain a characteristic spectral curve with a maximum at 400 nm, and they emphasized the considerable difficulties inherent in the determination of fuscin pigments.

More recent studies on fuscins have been made by Netoušek and his collaborator Moravec at Prague (see Moravec and Netoušek, 1963; Moravec, 1964). They discuss the analytical methods and propose their own method for isolation and determination of mesobilifuscin in stool. They used 20 g fresh stool, collected after placing the patient on a diet poor in chlorophyll and meat. They also proposed their own methods for isolation of mesobilifuscin from urine and bile.

The feces were extracted first with $CHCl_3$ (to remove bilirubin), then with dilute alkali (to remove mesobilileukans), and finally with petrol ether after acidification (to remove urobilinoids and porphyrins). The $CHCl_3$ extract was evaporated and made alkaline with NaOH, after which its bilirubin was precipitated with $CaCl_2$; subsequently, its mesobilifuscin was extracted with butanol–acetic acid (10:1). The fecal sample, purified by the previous extractions, was then extracted with butanol–acetic acid (10:1); three extractions were performed. The pooled extracts were concentrated *in vacuo* and diluted with 150 ml methanol. Then NaOH was added to pH 7 and Al_2O_3 powder added to adsorb the mesobilifuscin. The Al_2O_3 was then washed with 1% aqueous NaOH, and the mesobilifuscin was eluated with butanol–acetic acid. The eluate was evaporated and subsequently extracted with the following solvents: (1) $CHCl_3$; (2) amyl alcohol; (3) distilled water; (4) methanol; (5) butanol; (6) glacial acetic acid. The fractions were then subjected to adsorption chromatography on Al_2O_3 columns and eluated from the columns with butanol–acetic acid (10:1) which is the most powerful eluent for mesobilifuscins. The purified fractions were read spectrophotometrically at 450 nm.

For urine, bilirubin was first removed by precipitation with $CaCl_2$, and the urobilinoids by extraction with petrol ether–acetic acid. The urine thus purified was diluted three times with water, after which Al_2O_3 powder was added until the urine became completely colorless. The adsorbate was washed and eluted with butanol–acetic acid (10:1). Then the eluate was evaporated and subjected to further purification by washing with $CHCl_3$ and petrol ether. Then the mesobilifuscin was dissolved partly in methanol, partly in glacial acetic acid, and the two fractions subjected to chromatography on Al_2O_3 columns.

The fuscin chromogens—mesobilileukans—are lost with this method, which determines only the fuscins proper. The chromogens can be extracted from the stool with dilute NaOH and from the urine with isoamyl alcohol, and subsequently transformed to fuscins by heating with concentrated HCl.

This shows that isolation and determination of fuscins are exceedingly complicated matters. Nevertheless, the study of fuscins is necessary for complete understanding of the pyrrole metabolism.

Netoušek and Moravec (1965*) reported observations on mesobilifuscin excretion in 54 cases of various liver diseases.

The occurrence of dipyrrole pigments in *gallstones* was studied by Suzuki (1965a*, b*). The black pigments of dark human gallstones was found to be closely related to bilirubin and different from melanins. If commercial bilirubin or synthetic calcium bilirubinate or finely ground pigmented gallstones were heated with 20% HCl for several days a black pigment was formed. This pigment was washed with distilled water, dried, and then washed with $CHCl_3$ to remove unchanged bilirubin. The synthetic pigment formed in this way was compared to the black pigment extracted from dark human gallstones and purified similarly. The infrared absorption spectra of the synthetic and the natural black pigments were practically identical and behaved in a similar way after addition of various reagents. The infrared spectra of melanins differed markedly.

It was concluded that the black pigment of dark gallstones is a pyrrole pigment closely related to bilirubin and that it is a high molecular polymer. In view of the pronounced tendency of fuscins and propentdyopents to polymerize it seems likely that the black pigment is a polymerized dipyrrole pigment.

It cannot, however, be looked upon as an established fact that it is formed from bilirubin. It could also be formed from bilifuscins which have formed during hemoglobin degradation or as a by-product of heme synthesis. Presumably this can be elucidated by means of studies with labeled heme precursors.

Summary

Fuscins are an important, yet not well understood, group of bile pigments. They are dipyrrylmethenes, and have a strong tendency to polymerization. They do not crystallize, and give negative color reactions for bile pigments. Thus, their quantitative analysis is difficult. They occur in the body as the corresponding chromogens, the promesobilifuscins (mesobilileukans) which are dipyrrylmethanes. These are found in stool and urine of normal and sick subjects. Like tetrapyrrole bile pigments, they form during hemoglobin degradation. However, some observations indicate that they are mainly by-products of pyrrole synthesis.

H. Dipyrrole Bile Pigments: Pentdyopents, Propentdyopents, and the PDP Reaction (Stokvis Reaction)

Stokvis (1870, 1872a,b,c), and 60 years later Bingold (1932, 1941), observed that urine samples with high bilirubin content give intensive red color on reduction in alkaline solution. Because this red pigment had an absorption maximum about 525 nm, Bingold introduced the term "pentdyopent reaction" (5-2-5 = pent-dyo-pent, in Greek), or better the "direct PDP reaction."

Fischer and Müller (1937), Fischer and von Dobeneck (1940, 1947), and von Dobeneck (1941a,b, 1942, 1948a), who thoroughly studied the phenomenon, found that it is a group reaction. Verdins, rubins, bilenes-*b*, and bilanes as well as certain porphyrins, give positive reactions when they are previously treated with H_2O_2, the "indirect PDP reaction."

Various dipyrrylmethenes and oxydipyrrylmethenes give the direct PDP reaction—i.e., without previous treatment with H_2O_2. U-L and UG-L do not give the indirect PDP reaction. Fischer and von Dobeneck (1940) recommended the term "Stokvis reaction" since the absorption maxima of various substances differ and none of the well-defined PDP compounds showed a maximum at exactly 525 nm.

The substances which form during this reaction are α,α'-dioxydipyrylmethanes. Von Dobeneck (1948a,b) calls them briefly DPA. DDPA seems, however, a more fitting term. They are colorless and form intensely red alkali salts. The latter are extremely soluble in water and crystallize readily. DDPA are very sensitive to oxygen. They can occur in native urine, but mainly they are obtained from propentdyopents in alkaline solution.

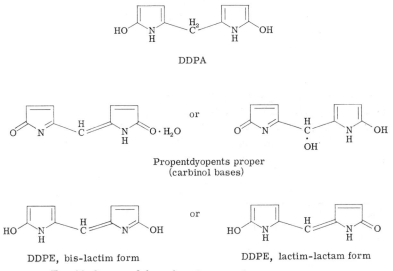

DDPA

Propentdyopents proper
(carbinol bases)

DDPE, bis-lactim form   DDPE, lactim-lactam form

Fig. 22. Structural formulas of propentdyopent compounds.

Propentdyopents occur in two forms: carbinol bases (propentdyopents proper) and dioxydipyrrylmethenes (DDPE). The latter can be easily benzoylated to yield corresponding monobenzoxy compounds (von Dobeneck, 1948a). Their structures are showed in Fig. 22.

Substitution with vinyl, ethyl, methyl, and propionic acid groups in positions 4, 3, 3', and 4' yields natural substances (see Figs. 11 and 12).

Propentdyopents are colorless materials which are extremely water soluble and crystallize easily. Carbinol bases crystallize with uptake of water. DDPE derivatives give red compounds with concentrated alkali, but this color is different from the pentdyopent reaction. In alkaline solution, reduction occurs and a new absorption appears (von Dobeneck, 1941b).

Propentdyopents of bile stones are exclusively carbinol bases (Fischer and von Dobeneck, 1940). In urine there are also DDPE compounds. This is why some urines give red color with alkali even without oxidation (von Dobeneck, 1942). Urine with a very high carbinol base concentration develops red color on addition of alkali (von Dobeneck, 1948b).

Six different pentdyopents can be formed from heme, bilirubin, and urobilinogens (-ɪ and -ᴅ). They are depicted with numerals 1 to 6 in Fig. 23. Except for 1 and 3, von Dobeneck (1942) was able to synthe-

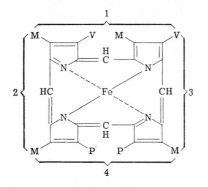

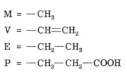

Protoheme IX

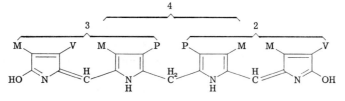

Bilirubin IXα

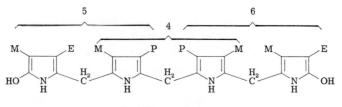

Urobilinogen-I

Fɪɢ. 23. The six different propentdyopents (DDPE).

size them as esters. Substance 1 has no COOH ($P = -CH_2CH_2COOH$) and thus is basic, whereas 2, 3, 5, and 6 have one, and 4 has two COOH groups. As the formula suggests, substance 1 can be formed only from uncleaved protoporphyrin and not from linear tetrapyrroles of type α.

DDPE compounds of types 5 and 6 are identical with mesobilifuscins I and II (see Fig. 20). Contrary to all other DDPE derivatives, these compounds do not give the PDP reaction. Von Dobeneck (1941a) found that pentdyopents, obtained from bilirubin, contain vinyl groups. He was able to isolate such compounds from bile stones of men and oxen. Type 4 originates from U-I, i.e., it does not contain vinyl groups, and it has not been isolated from natural substrates. However, it is postulated that it be formed in urines that contain no bilirubin but do contain UG-I. Preparation of pentdyopent compounds from bilological material is difficult, because of their instability and exceeding solubility in water (Fischer and von Dobeneck, 1940; von Dobeneck, 1941a,b). Thus, quantitative determinations of these compounds which claim accuracy have to be evaluated carefully (C. J. Watson, 1942).

The mode of formation of propentdyopents in the body is not uniformly interpreted. Bingold (1941) thought that they are formed from hemoglobin. However, this cannot be correct because hemoglobin is protected by catalase under physiological circumstances and this theory was refuted by Fischer and von Dobeneck (1940, p. 40), W. C. Meyer (1947a), and Brugsch and Allies (1948).

It is difficult to decide whether propentdyopents form primarily in metabolism or secondarily in bile and urine. They can form very easily and rapidly from bilirubin and UG-I in biological liquids. Here formation proceeds much more rapidly than in pure aqueous solutions (von Dobeneck, 1942). It is equally difficult to decide how much bilirubin and urobilinoid present in urine or bile will be transformed into propentdyopents. Watson (1942) mentions an experiment in which a patient was given more than 100 g hemoglobin by blood transfusion. The amount of urobilinoid excreted did not correspond to the administered amount of Hb, but a strongly positive PDP reaction was obtained.

According to their structure the various types of propentdyopents differ in their absorption bands. Von Dobeneck (1942) found 529–541 nm (maximum at 535 nm) for type 1, 532–536 nm (maximum 529 nm) for types 2 and 3, 517–529 nm (maximum 523 nm) for type 4, and 514–527 nm (maximum 525 nm) for types 5 and 6. The bands are rather diffuse.

The technique of the PDP reaction and its clinical applicability were thoroughly discussed by Stich (1952a,b,c). The indirect PDP reaction differentiates reacting urobilinoids (types I and D) from nonreacting urobilinoids-L (stercobilin type). The direct PDP reaction occurs in most urines containing bilirubin as well as in some urines from patients with liver disease in spite of absence of pathological bilirubin concentrations. A maximum at 525 nm suggests urobilin pentdyopent (types 5 and 6). Paper chromatographic and electrophoretic pentdyopent analyses have been carried out by Heikel (1958) and Garay et al. (1964*).

The studies of propentdyopent compounds of Hans Fischer and his school were revived after a pause of 17 years by von Dobeneck and his collaborators in a series of papers: VI–XI. "Mitteilung zur Stokvis-Reaktion" in Z. Physiol. Chem. (von Dobeneck and Klötzer, 1959; von Dobeneck et al., 1962a*,b*; von Dobeneck and Brunner, 1965a*,b*; von Dobeneck et al., 1965*) summarized in a review by von Dobeneck (1966*).

Von Dobeneck and Klötzer (1959) prepared basic propentdyopents by treating mesohemin and hemin with hydrogen peroxide in alkaline medium. This shows that the degradation of hemes is symmetrical under these conditions. From hemin IX, divinyl propentdyopent (first structure in Fig. 23) was formed. Attempts to crystallize the basic propentdyopents were unsuccessful; they rapidly underwent secondary reactions (oxidation, polymerization).

The original belief that the pentdyopents proper are formed by reduction of propentdyopents to dihydroxy-dipyrrylmethanes in NaOH has now been abandoned (von Dobeneck et al., 1962a*). The appearance of the typical PDP absorption spectrum is now believed to be due to oxidation of dihydroxy-dipyrrylmethanes to 5-hydroxy-5'-oxo-5'H-dipyrrylmethanes. If these compounds are dissolved in NaOH solutions from which the oxygen has been removed by boiling, then the pentdyopent spectrum appears immediately. The question whether the pentdyopents themselves are disodium salts of dihydroxy-dipyrrylmethanes or monosodium salts of 5-hydroxy-5'-oxo-5'H-dipyrrylmethanes has not been decided (von Dobeneck et al., 1962a*).

According to their process of formation the propentdyopents should be 5,5'-dihydroxy-(2,2')-dipyrrylmethenes, but they behave both chemically and optically like 5-hydroxy-5'-oxo-(2,2')-5'H-dipyrrylmethanes (von Dobeneck et al., 1962a*) (cf. Fig. 22, bottom right).

Von Dobeneck et al. (1962b*) introduced a new synthesis of tetramethylpropentdyopent—by action of bromine on 5,5'-dicarboxyl-dipyrrylmethane in methanol. The brief action of elementary bromine at low temperature gave 2–10% yield of tetramethyl-dicarboxy-dipyrrylmethane, a colorless compound with a strongly positive PDP-reaction. This compound exhibited an infrared spectrum very closely related to, but not identical with that of tetramethylpropentdyopent. Elementary analysis showed that the composition of the new substance differed from tetramethylpropentdyopent; the former having a mole of methanol, the latter a mole of water. Consequently the two substances were called *"methanol propentdyopent"* and *"water propentdyopent."* If the former is dissolved in methanol containing 10% water and the methanol is driven out with acetone, then methanol propentdyopent is transformed into water propentdyopent.

By heating water propentdyopent with acetic anhydride a red color is formed which changes to a brown color. With methanol propentdyopent the red color turns greenish blue. If the heating of the water propentdyopent solution in acetic anhydride is stopped during its red phase by rapid cooling, an intense yellowish-red crystalline substance is obtained that is stable in air. With Zn acetate the substance reacts immediately to Zn propentdyopent (von Dobeneck *et al.*, 1962b*).

Von Dobeneck *et al.* (1965*) found that OH-, NH-, SH-, and CH-acidic compounds, as well as oxygen will add to propentdyopent. The most important properties of propentdyopents are their capacity to add various compounds and their strong tendency to polymerize. These properties probably explain the fact that the living body does not contain any crystallizable pyrrole compounds with less than four pyrrole nuclei. Further, the lack of exact quantitative agreement between the amount of porphyrin compounds degraded in the organism and the identifiable pyrrole metabolites formed can be ascribed to these properties of the propentdyopents (cf. Watson, 1956a,b,c).

Von Dobeneck and Brunner (1965a*) identified the following four types of propentdyopents by means of their visible and UV absorption maxima: (*a*) classic type, (*b*) neo-type, (*c*) pro-type, and (*d*) aza-type.

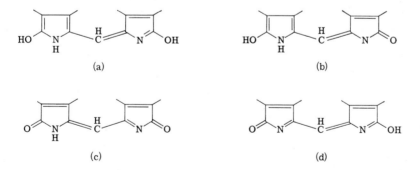

Figs. 23a–d. (a) (2,2′)-1*H*-Dipyrrylmethene, classic type (bis-lactim). (b) 5′-Oxo-1,5′-dihydro-(2,2′)-1*H*-dipyrrylmethene, neo-type (lactim-lactam). (c) 5,5′-Dioxo-5,5′-dihydro-(2,2′)-1*H*-dipyrrylmethene, pro-type (bis-lactam). (d) 5-Oxo-(2,2′)-5*H*-dipyrrylmethene, aza-type (lactam-lactim). For explanation, see pp. 8–10.

Of these four types, three (Figs. 23a,b,c) have been synthesized, but the aza-type has not yet been synthesized (von Dobeneck, personal communication, 1966).

The neo-type is unable to form metal complexes (like the rubins) because it is devoid of electron-donating N-atoms.

Water-propentdyopent has the structure given in Fig. 23e. This compound is extremely water-soluble because it contains three O-atoms as well as the two carboxyl groups in the side chains.

In a similar way CH—, OH—, SH—, NH—, and other acidic groups can be added. On reduction of "classic" dibromo-pyrrylmethanes in glacial acetic acid with K acetate hydrogen-propentdyopent is formed (Fig. 23f).

(e)   (f)

Figs. 23e and f. (e) Water-propentdyopent. (f) Hydrogen-propentdyopent.

Methanol-propentdyopent has a quite similar formula, i.e., the H in the 2-position in Fig. 23f is replaced by an —OCH$_3$ group (von Dobeneck, personal communication, 1966).

Pure propentdyopents were found to exhibit a very strong paramagnetism and their polymers showed an electron spin resonance much higher than all other known organic compounds (von Dobeneck, 1966*). This may be used as a very sensitive method for demonstrating the presence of these compounds in biological materials. Further, von Dobeneck (1966*) pointed out that propentdyopent compounds can cause photosensitization of the skin like the porphyrins, a very interesting proposal deserving further investigation.

According to von Dobeneck (1966*) it has not been finally decided whether or not propentdyopents are formed from heme in the organism, whether they occur in the blood, or whether they are only formed in the urine.

I. The Gmelin Reaction (Oxidation Tests)

As early as 1826 Tiedemann and Gmelin reported that they obtained a characteristic sequence of colors when they added fuming HNO$_3$ to bilirubin dissolved in CHCl$_3$. The initially yellow solution became green, then blue, violet, red-orange, and yellow again. This reaction is shown by bilirubin, dihydrobilirubin, mesobilirubin, artificial tetrapyrroles with relatively stable chains (Fischer and Orth, 1937, p. 712), and some bile pigments found in lower animals (see Chapter X). Similar behavior is experienced in aqueous solution and by using other oxidizing agents. With mild oxidation only the first stages of the color sequence are obtained, giving a green or blue final solution. A series of oxidation tests, using a variety of reagents, has been proposed (see Chapter VI,A,1). The blue and violet stages of the reaction were earlier called "bilicyanin" and "biliviolin." Today these terms are used for other purposes.

In the oxidation tests described bilirubin is oxidized under *acidic conditions*. Under alkaline conditions biliverdin could not be identified as an intermediary oxidation product of bilirubin (Ostrow *et al.*, 1961*). The oxidation seems to progress rapidly toward colorless compounds under alkaline conditions.

This reaction was investigated especially by Fischer's collaborator, Siedel (see Siedel and Fröwis, 1939, 1941; Siedel and Grams, 1941; Siedel, 1943a,b). The green color is due to biliverdin. If mesobilirubin is used, the initial green color is due to a mixture of yellow mesobilirubin and blue glaucobilin, and the blue color following the initial green one is due to glaucobilin itself. With bilirubin, the blue hue is due to a mixture of green biliverdin and the reddish purpurins. Lemberg called the purpurins biliviolins, but later agreed to use Siedel's terminology (Lemberg and Legge, 1949, pp. 130–131).

The orange-red color stage is caused by a mixture of purpurins and the next reaction products, the choletelins. The term choletelin was introduced by Maly (1869). Heinsius and Campbell (1871) thought that choletelin and urobilin were identical.

The Gmelin reaction was investigated with the help of artificial symmetrical bilirubinoids (glaucobilin XIIIα methyl ester) and bromomethanol; see Figs. 4 and 24.

The color of an organic substance depends mainly on its number of conjugated double bonds occurring in succession in a chain and forming so-called chromophores.* Thus the following types arise:

$$[\ldots =CH— \ldots]—CH_2—[\ldots —CH= \ldots]$$

in the first line of Fig. 24; in the second line

$$[\ldots =CH— \ldots —CH= \ldots —CH= \ldots]$$

in the third line

$$[\ldots =CH— \ldots —CH= \ldots]—CO— \ldots$$

---

* Marked with brackets [   ]; . . . designates a pyrrole ring.

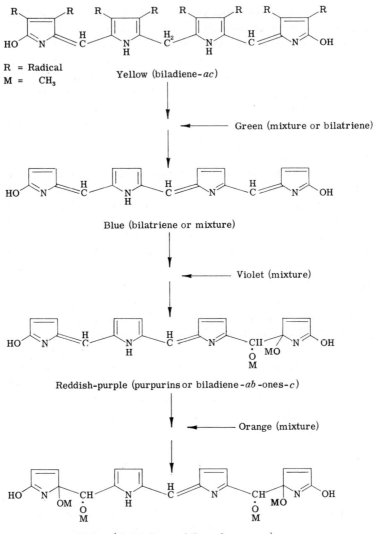

Yellow (choletelins or bilene-*b*-ones-*ac*)

Fig. 24. Course of the Gmelin reaction.

and in the last line

$$\ldots -CO-[\ldots -CH= \ldots]-CO- \ldots$$

Brackets designate chromophore groups; three dots, pyrrole rings. In the chromophore formulas, CO is used as it occurs in the Gmelin reaction of natural bilirubinoids; the CHOM in Fig. 24 occurs in the artificial reaction described.

This concept of chromophorous groups is, however, a simplified one because the pyrrole rings also contain double bonds. The correct picture is obtained by counting the number of double bonds in succession on Fig. 4. Bilanes (Nos. 1 and 14) containing only two conjugated double bonds in succession are colorless, rubins (No. 7), bilenes (Nos. 2, 3, 15, 16, 17, 18 and 19), chrysins (No. 12), and choletelins (No. 13) containing five are yellow, violins and purpurins containing six (No. 6), seven (Nos. 5 and 10) or eight (Nos. 4, 9, and 11) are violet or purple, and verdins (No. 8) containing ten conjugated double bonds in succession are green or blue.

As oxidation progresses, the last double bond in the chain disappears and colorless substances form. Oxidation first attacks the central methene bridges (—CH$_2$—) and transforms them into methine bridges (—CH=). Next, the outer methine bridges are oxidized by adding two methoxy groups (OM) or by transformation into —CO—. Finally the last methine bridge is also transformed in the same fashion. The OM is replaced by OH if HNO$_3$ is used instead of bromomethanol. Dehydrogenation transforms the CHOH bridges to —CO—.

According to Lemberg and Legge (1949, p. 131) dihydroxy-*c*-biladienes-*ab* type compounds form during the second stage of the reaction. These compounds are unstable and can be easily transformed into dehydrobilane-*a*-ones-*c* or chrysins. These will be easily oxidized to biladiene-*ab*-ones-*c* (also called bilipurpurins type 2; see Fig. 4).

Because of its characteristic color sequence, the Gmelin reaction is a valuable qualitative test for rubins and verdins. Stepwise conversion of various color stages, however, renders it less suitable for quantitative purposes. Peterman and Cooley (1933a,b) and Amada (1941) investigated its use in quantitative determinations. The reaction is difficult to control and can progress until colorless substances are formed.

Spectrophotometric investigations of the oxidation products of bilirubin have been carried out by Zak *et al.* (1954). For oxidation, they used FeCl$_3$ in a mixture of H$_2$SO$_4$, glacial acetic acid, and HClO$_4$. Dilute pure bilirubin solutions gave stable colors. Constant spectral maxima were obtained which followed Beer's law. Dilution with an equal volume of water caused changes in color and spectral curves. The substances formed during this process, however, have not been purified and isolated. Hosokawa (1956a) described absorption curves for mesobilipurpurin and mesocholetelin in CHCl$_3$.

J. The Diazo Reaction

The diazo reaction was discovered by Ehrlich (1883). He mixed 0.1% diazobenzene sulfonic acid in HCl-alcohol with a solution of bilirubin in CHCl$_3$. This gave rise to a red color which on addition of concentrated HCl changed through violet to blue. With biliverdin, the reaction was negative. Pröscher (1900a,b) obtained the reaction product in crystalline form. Orndorf and Teeple (1905) found that a mixture of two azo compounds is involved. According to Hijmans van den Bergh and Snapper (1913) and Hijmans van den Berg (1918), the reaction can be carried out with sulfanilic acid-HCl in aqueous solution. Fischer and Barrenscheen (1921) employed diazotized tribromoanilin and diazobenzene chloride. According to Fischer and Niemann (1923), mesobilirubin and its methyl ester also give the reaction. In 1935 Fischer and Haberland discovered that a positive reaction is obtained with various synthetic bilirubinoids, for example protobilirubins IIIα and XIIIα, coprobilirubin IIα, as well as with the natural ones, bilirubin (protobilirubin IXα) and mesobilirubin (mesobilirubin IXα).

They demonstrated that the reaction proceeds in two steps, shown in Fig. 25. First the bridge b is hydrolyzed. In the next step, one of the reaction products reacts with the diazonium, whereas the other, plus another half containing —CH_2OH, combine to form bilirubin again.

Hydrolysis may occur on both sides of bridge b. Thus, equal amounts of the two possible azo compounds, called azobilirubin-AB and azobilirubin-DC in Fig. 25, are formed. The mixture of the two is known as azobilirubin. Also, certain α- and β-oxypyrroles and dipyrrylmcthenes can react with diazo reagents. The latter, similar to bilirubin, split hydrolytically (Fischer and Orth, 1937, pp. 717–723).

More recently, the kinetics of the diazo reaction have been investigated by Overbeek *et al.* (1955a,b,c), Amatuzio (1960), Brodersen (1960), and Lucassen (1961*).

Overbeek *et al.* (1955c) studied the reaction occurring between bilirubin and *p*-diazobenzene sulfonic acid in a mixture of water, alcohol, and $CHCl_3$. One molecule of bilirubin reacts with two molecules of diazonium to form two molecules of azobilirubin. Contrary to the postulate of Fischer and Haberland (1935), it was shown that the hydroxypyrromethene carbinol molecule (A—B—CH_2OH or D—C—CH_2OH in Fig. 25) formed by the cleavage of bilirubin reacts directly with diazonium. There is no bilirubin synthesis prior to this reaction. They determincd the reaction constants for both stages, i.e., (a) hydrolysis to one molecule of azobilirubin and one molecule of hydroxypyrromethene carbinol, and (b) reaction of the latter with one more molecule of diazonium to yield a second azobilirubin molecule. They employed 2,4,6-tribromobenzene diazonium hydrosulfate instead of *p*-diazobenzene sulfonic acid and found that the main reactions proceed similarly with both reagents.

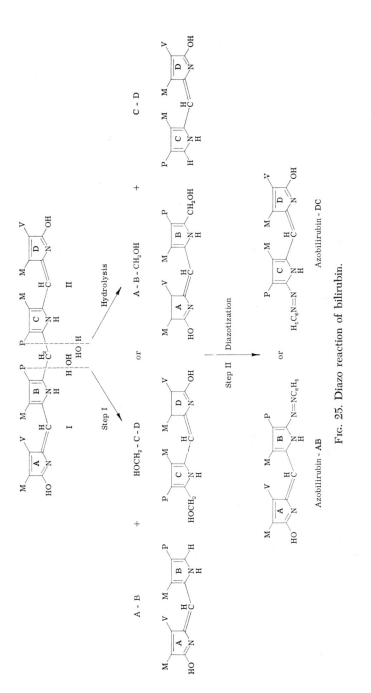

Fig. 25. Diazo reaction of bilirubin.

Amatuzio (1960) spectrophotometrically followed the progress of the diazo reaction at 535 nm at $27° \pm 0.02°$ (water bath). He used a 0.025 M stock solution of sulfanilic acid (4.33 g sulfanilic acid + 1.325 g sodium carbonate in 1000 ml). Ten ml of this stock solution were mixed with 10 ml 0.075 M HCl and, after cooling down to 4°, with 10 ml of 0.025 M sodium nitrite (1.73 g liter). The mixture was kept at 4° for 30 minutes and then diluted to a final concentration of either 0.50 or 0.33 mM diazonium per liter. The reaction was performed with 1 ml dilute serum (1:5), 18 ml 8.7 M acetic acid, and 1 ml of the diluted diazonium reagent. The blank had the same composition without added diazonium solution. Two calibration curves were constructed with 0.01, 0.02, 0.04, 0.06, 0.08, and 0.10 mg bilirubin in the reaction mixture (20 ml). Measurements were performed after diluting the reaction mixture with 8.7 M acetic acid to 20 ml.

Sera from newborns as well as bilirubin glucuronide solutions obtained from bile were studied. Free bilirubin was investigated in the concentration range of 0.9–1.70 mM/liter. It was found that the reaction is bimolecular within this concentration range. The rate constant was 201–226. Bilirubin glucuronide reacted too quickly to be studied under these experimental conditions. The reaction was complete within 5 minutes. The optimum pH was at 1.6–1.9.

In contrast to Overbeek *et al.* (1955a,b,c), who studied the reaction in alcohol-CHCl$_3$-water mixtures, and to Amatuzio (1960), who followed it in relatively strong acetic acid, Brodersen (1960) investigated the reaction conditions in aqueous solutions. He determined the amount of diazonium compound consumed by means of coupling with N-(1-naphthyl)-ethylenediamine hydrochloride and spectrophotometric measurements at 530 nm. Crystalline bilirubin was dissolved in CHCl$_3$ and was extracted with dilute serum after addition of various amounts of petrol ether. HCl up to a concentration of 10 mM/liter was added to the mixture. The diazo reagent used by Brodersen (1960) was prepared from sulfanilic acid and HCl, as is customary in clinical chemistry. However, its diazonium concentration was ten times higher than that of the usual diazo reagents, i.e., it was 1 mM/liter instead of 0.1 mM/liter. In this way he achieved a reaction fast enough to permit mathematical analysis of the curves obtained. Further, the excess of diazonium compound was so much larger than the bilirubin concentration (0.02 mM/liter) that the former could be considered constant during the entire reaction. The diazonium concentration was determined by adding 0.2 ml 0.1% aqueous N-(1-naphthyl)-ethylenediamine hydrochloride and 2 ml distilled water to 0.1 ml of the reaction mixture. In this manner, a red azo pigment was formed which reached its maximum extinction within 3 minutes. The diazonium concentration was proportional to the extinction determined at 530 nm when the data were corrected by subtracting the blank extinction.

Brodersen found that the diazonium concentration decreased immediately after the addition of diazo reagent to the serum. This "initial diazonium drop" was independent of the presence of bilirubin; it also occurred in sera free from bilirubin. It amounted to 20–50% of the initial diazonium concentration, depending on the serum-to-reagent ratio. The magnitude of the drop varied from serum to serum.

The reaction kinetics of the diazo reaction of free bilirubin acid and bilirubin diglucuronide were subjected to a detailed investigation by Lucassen (1961*) (cf. Chapter V). He employed purified *p*-diazobenzene sulfonic acid and determined the concentration of this reagent spectrophotometrically by means of its β-naphthol complex (β-naphthol orange). Purified preparations of bilirubin diglucuronide were employed, and the azo pigments of bilirubin and its diglucuronide were purified as reference substances. An apparatus for automatic spectrophotometric recording of the reaction velocity during the first 60 seconds was constructed and described. Measurements of the reaction velocity were performed on aqueous solutions, in water-acetone mixtures (1:1, v/v), and in $CHCl_3$-ethanol-water mixtures (3:6:1, v/v/v). Further, the effects of electrolytes (salt effect) and serum albumin on the course of the reaction were studied, and the activation energy of the first step of the diazo reaction was determined.

It was emphasized that the instability of azobilirubin at pH higher than 5 makes quantitative measurements at such pH values impossible, unless *caffeine*, which inhibits the degradation of azobilirubin, is added. Also, excess of diazo reagent was shown to cause degradation of azobilirubin; caffeine is necessary if an excess of this reagent is used.

Finally, Lucassen proposed a modified scheme for the intermediary steps of the diazo reaction based on measurements of the reaction constants.

Only bilirubinoids with a *central methene bridge* ($-CH_2-$) give a positive diazo reaction. Thus, bilanes and bilenes-*a* (dihydromesobilirubin) react positively like the rubins (biladienes-*ac*), whereas biladienes-*ab* (violins) and bilatrienes (verdins) do not.

Ehrlich (1884) and Oppenheimer (1885) observed a yellow diazo reaction in urine under various pathological circumstances. K. Thomas (1907a; 1907b, p. 41 ff.) was able to obtain this reaction in bile and stool extracts and showed that it is due to urobilinogen. Varela Fuentes and Canzani (1938, 1939), Lopez Garcia (1941), and Castex and Lopez Garcia (1941) investigated this yellow diazo reaction in serum and compared its absorption curve with that of the diazo reaction of purified UG-I.

Görges and Gohr (1954) found that the diazo reaction is positive with dihydromesobilirubin, but did not specify the color of this reaction.

Hosokawa (1956c) substantiated the necessity of the presence of a central methene ($-CH_2-$) bridge for the positive diazo reaction. He investigated bilirubinoids by use of certain microqualitative reactions specific for active methene groups (treatment with sodium-1,2-naphthoquinone-4-sulfonate followed by addition of $0.5\,N$ NaOH; see also Yamaoka *et al.*, 1956a).

Hijmans van den Bergh and Müller (1916) discovered that the reaction proceeds faster in the presence of alcohol than in aqueous solution. They also reported that certain sera give this fast reaction even without addition of alcohol. This discovery caused great interest, and since then a diazo reaction without alcohol is customarily referred to as a *direct* diazo reaction; when alcohol is added, the reaction is called an *indirect* diazo reaction (see Chapter V,D). As well as with bilirubin, the direct and indirect diazo reaction is given with other rubins, including synthetic ones (Fischer and Orth, 1937, p. 720). In the absence of alcohol the reaction proceeds extremely slowly in aqueous solution, but it nevertheless takes place. A true negative reaction occurs in neutral aqueous colloidal bilirubin solutions (Varela Fuentes and Recarte, 1934a,b). Acetone and glacial acetic acid have the same accelerator effect on the diazo reaction as alcohol (cf. Fischer and Orth, quoted above).

The spectral absorption of the diazo reaction was first investigated by Heilmeyer and Krebs (1930). The investigations of Amada (1941), With (1945b), Künzer (1951a p. 30–34), and Lowry *et al.* (1953) followed, and finally the investigation of Fog (1957), on changes due to various pH values. The ultraviolet absorption of the diazo reaction has been studied by E. Torp-Pedersen, unpublished results, 1948, who found that the reagents themselves have a definite ultraviolet absorption. Thus the ultraviolet absorption of azobilirubin can only be studied with purified preparations.

The diazo reaction does not take place in strongly acid or alkaline solutions. Consequently, it can be stopped by adding larger amounts of acid or alkali. Reaction termination, however, does not occur instantaneously; Deenstra (1948a) has shown that when strong alkali is added to bilirubin solutions which contain serum, the reaction rate increases initially. After this initial increase, the reaction stops completely. According to Bungenberg de Jong (1937, 1943), the optimum rate of the diazo reaction in serum-containing bilirubin solutions occurs at pH 4–5.

The reaction is influenced by pH and the presence of electrolytes and certain organic compounds (for example, benzoates and urea). At high ascorbic acid concentrations, it becomes negative (Sauerbruch, 1937). A thorough discussion of the effect of pH, alcohol, electrolytes, etc., on the diazo reaction is given in Chapter V,C,5. Most investigations have been carried out in solutions containing protein. Only a few data exist on the reaction in protein-free solutions. Most important are Fog's (1957, 1960) studies of the indicator properties of azobilirubin. According to this work, absorption maxima in neutral, strongly acid, and strongly alkaline solutions are at 520, 560, and 580 nm, respectively. Similar findings are reported by Jirsa and Jirsová (1959).

Fog especially studied the changes occurring in the quotient: E_{560}/E_{520} in acid medium, and E_{580}/E_{520} in alkaline medium. The results are shown in Figs. 26 and 27.

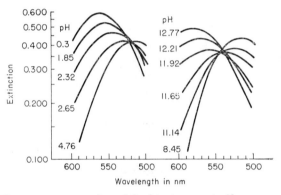

FIG. 26. Absorption curve of azobilirubin in protein-free aqueous solution at varying pH levels (Fog, 1957).

Jirsa and Jirsová (1959) found maxima of 510–520 nm in neutral aqueous solutions, 560 in acid, and 570–580 in alkaline. The maximal extinction values occurred at pH below 2 and at pH 8. Addition of methanol or proteins or both enhanced the extinction. In protein-free solutions methanol caused a shift of the maximum toward shorter wavelengths.

Kaneda (1963b*) studied the spectral absorption of the diazo reaction of solutions of bilirubin in $CHCl_3$ after addition of methanol. Using 2 ml of bilirubin solution, 3, 4, 5, or 6 ml of methanol, and 0.1, 0.2, 0.5, 1.0, or 2.0 ml of diazo reagent he studied the extinction curves after 1 minute and until the curves became stable. The spectral maximum of the reaction was at 560 nm and already dominated after 1 minute if 1 ml or more of diazo reagent was added. If only 0.5 ml of diazo reagent was added the absorptivity at 560 and that at 420 nm (peak for unchanged bilirubin) were about equal after 30–60 seconds. With lower diazo concentrations the azobilirubin peak at 560 nm was definitely lower than the bilirubin peak at 420 nm after 1 minute. As the reaction progressed, the absorptivity at 560 nm increased parallel with the decrease in absorptivity at 420 nm. With 2 ml of bilirubin solution, 3 ml of methanol, and 1 ml of diazo reagent the 420 nm maximum was completely eliminated after 10 minutes; with 2 ml, 6 ml, and 0.5 ml, respectively, the 420 nm maximum disappeared after 20–30 minutes, whereas the absorptivity persisted after 60 minutes with lower diazo concentrations.

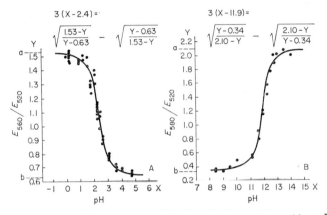

FIG. 27. Variation of the quotients E_{560}/E_{520} (acid reaction; A) and E_{580}/E_{520} (alkaline reaction; B) of azobilirubin with pH (Fog, 1957). The extinction ratios are plotted along the ordinate axis, the wavelengths along the abscissa.

The diazo reaction of mesobilirubin and bilirubin-dimethyl ester behaved similarly, but the maxima were different—550 nm for mesobilirubin azo pigment and 390 nm for unchanged mesobilirubin, 540 nm for bilirubin dimethyl ester azo pigment and 410 nm for the ester itself. If the reaction mixture was left standing at room temperature for hours the diazo maximum gradually flattened, and this flattening was more pronounced if a higher volume of diazo reagent was used. After addition of appropriate volumes of HCl the azo maximum changed to 580 nm for all three pigments investigated, and the spectral absorption of the acid solutions remained unchanged after storage at room temperature for at least 1 week.

The *extinction constants* of the diazo reaction of bilirubin have been studied by several investigators, employing various purified bilirubin preparations.

With (1945b) found the following values for $E_{1cm}^{1\%}$: 1200–1300 in strongly acid (blue) solution using filter S 57 of a Pulfrich photometer and caffeine-sodium benzoate as an accelerator. In weakly acid solution (red) he found the figure 800 with filter S 52, and in strongly alkaline solution the figure 1100 with filter S 59. When alcohol was used as an accelerator the $E_{1\,cm}^{1\%}$ values were about 5% higher. If serum was added to the solutions, the values increased 6–12%. This indicates that azobilirubin, like bilirubin, is connected to serum albumin. From the data of Lowry *et al.* (1953), $E_{1\,cm}^{1\%}$ of the diazo reaction can be calculated for a solution of pure bilirubin in a mixture of 6 volumes of methanol, 1 volume of $CHCl_3$, and 1 volume of diazo reagent; the maximum was 540 nm and $E_{1\,cm}^{1\%} = 760$. O'Hagan *et al.* (1957) found $E_{1\,cm}^{mM}$ values of 42.9–55.6 for various bilirubin preparations (azobilirubin in $CHCl_3$-alcohol; maximum, 532 nm). The highest value was obtained with Hoffmann-La Roche bilirubin, the lowest with Eastman Kodak bilirubin. As the molecular weight of bilirubin is 584, $E_{1\,cm}^{mM} = 584 \times E_{1\,cm}^{1\%} \times 10^{-4}$, i.e., $E_{1\,cm}^{mM} = 55.6$ corresponds to $E_{1\,cm}^{1\%} = 945$, and 42.9 corresponds to 735.

Brückner (1959) reported the high value of $E_{1\,cm}^{mM} = 71.97$ at maximum 569 nm using a diazo reagent with 1% sulfanilic acid, a coupling reagent with antipyrine and urea, and reading in alkaline methanolic solution. Witmanns *et al.* (1961) presented data from which $E_{1\,cm}^{mM} = 46$ can be calculated for serum-containing solutions with caffeine-sodium benzoate as an accelerator and reading in alkaline solution. Henry *et al.* (1960) reported the value of $E_{1\,cm}^{mM} = 64.0$ at 545 nm for pure azobilirubin in slightly acid methanolic-aqueous solution with Malloy-Evelyn's method (1937). Small amounts of $CHCl_3$ were found to inhibit the reaction. The ratio between the spectral absorption of bilirubin in $CHCl_3$ and that of its diazo reaction varied from 0.87 to 1.01 for different commercial bilirubin preparations, but was 0.93–0.96 for purified laboratory preparations.

Clarke (1965*) gives spectrophotometric data for azobilirubin solutions corresponding to a bilirubin concentration of 5.5 μg per milliliter. The absorptivities at maxima and at various pH's are given for solutions in 50% aqueous methanol and aqueous solutions. From the absorptivities given the values for $E_{1\,cm}^{mM}$ can be calculated (see tabulation).

Solvent	pH	Maximum (nm)	$E_{1\,cm}^{mM}$
Methanol, 50%	1.0	542	71
	3.0	520	68
Water	5.0	510	61.5
	9.0	510	60.5
	11.0	530	57.5
	13.0	580	87

Meites and Traubert (1965*) studied the diazo reaction of bilirubin in $CHCl_3$-methanol solution using varying volumes of $CHCl_3$ and methanol, bilirubin solution containing 8 mg/100 ml, and a constant volume of diazo reagent. One milliliter of diazo reagent was added to 0.1–2.4 ml of $CHCl_3$ and 0–4.0 ml of water; then methanol was added to volume 10 ml. The absorptivity of the azobilirubin was not influenced by $CHCl_3$ concentrations up to 24% (v/v) with 10% water. They found maximum 560 nm with $E_{1cm}^{mM} = 70.3 \pm 0.28$. The absorptivity of azobilirubin prepared from bilirubin added to serum was found to be essentially the same (69.5 ± 0.75).

Fog (1964) performed a thorough study of the extinction of the diazo reaction of a number of bilirubin preparations before and after purification and compared the results with measurements of the "yellow extinction" of bilirubin and the MBTH reaction (cf. Section C, this chapter) of the same preparations. For the purified preparations, the ratio $E_{470}^{azo}/E_{454}^{yellow}$ varied between 1.37 and 1.43, and E_{1cm}^{mM} was 85.0 ± 0.02 for the diazo reaction at 470 nm.

Bilissis and Speer (1963) proposed a stable artificial standard for colorimetric measurements of azobilirubin consisting of N-(1-naphthyl)-ethylenediamine dihydrochloride in aqueous solution. A solution containing 6.45 mg/100 ml is approximately equivalent to the diazo reaction of 5 mg bilirubin per 100 ml. The spectral curves of the solutions are closely similar; the maximum of the standard solution is 530 nm, like that of azobilirubin in slightly acid solution. The standard solution is stable for at least 2 months at 4°.

Pittera and Cassia (1962) and Cassia and Pittera (1962) fractionated the azo pigment prepared from crystalline commercial bilirubin and diazobenzene sulfonic acid in alcoholic solution by means of partition chromatography on Al_2O_3 columns. The solvent mixture consisted of 12.5 volumes of n-butanol saturated with $1.5 M$ glycine buffer (pH 2) and 7.5 volumes of methyl ethyl ketone, the glycine buffer constituting the mobile phase. Five different fractions of azo pigment could be separated, but isolation and identification of the fractions were not achieved. The appearance of five fractions in azobilirubin from bilirubin is difficult to understand, but it may be explained by the use of commercial preparations without previous purification.

Lins (1950, 1953) studied the behavior of various sulfonamides as substitutes for sulfanilic acid in the diazo reaction. He found the strongest reaction with sulfametazine and with 4,4'-diaminodiphenyl sulfone ($NH_2C_6H_4SO_2C_6H_4NH_2$). Hosokawa (1956b) investigated the diazo reaction of compounds of bilirubin with amino acids. The bilirubin–glycine compound gave a negative diazo reaction.

Fog *et al.* (1962) studied the diazo reaction with 25 different primary aromatic amines. The absorption maximum in acid solution and the extinction at maximum were determined and the latter expressed as per cent of that found with diazotized sulfanilic acid. Sulfanilamide (113%) and 2-aminoanthraquinone (103%) were the only ones exhibiting extinctions exceeding that of sulfanilic acid (100%). The range of variation was from below 40% to 113% and the absorption maxima varied from 520 to 600 nm. Rand and di Pasqua (1962) employed diazotized 2,4-dichloroaniline (cf. Chapter V,C,4).

Kahán (1964a,b) studied the influence of EDTA on the diazo reaction of bilirubin. An accelerator effect of EDTA on the diazo reaction could be observed when using $5 M$ EDTA (pH 7.2). If EDTA was present only in an equimolar ratio to bilirubin in a solution of $0.1 M$ potassium carbonate, EDTA seemed to stabilize the spectrophotometric data. These findings were presented in more detail by Kahán *et al.* (1964*).

Recently, Michaëlsson (1961) has described a reaction between azobilirubin and divalent Cu that gives a stable complex suited for determination of bilirubin in urine (see Chapter VI).

Heirweigh and van Roy (1965*) studied the pH dependence of the diazo reaction and described a series of metal-azobilirubin complexes that all exhibited a considerable shift in the absorption curve toward longer wavelengths upon introduction of the metal. All the metal complexes were very stable. Their studies were made on solutions containing albumin. They dissolved 20 mg of bilirubin in 2 ml of $0.05 M$ NaOH and added 20 μl of this solution to 9 ml of a 0.5% solution of bovine serum albumin in $0.16 M$ NaCl. To two volumes of this solution four volumes of caffeine-sodium benzoate reagent, then 1 ml of diazo reagent, and after 10 minutes 0.4 volumes of ascorbic acid solution were added (cf. Chapter V,D,1; Nosslin's technique). The reaction was also studied with ethanol as the coupling reagent by mixing 30 ml of water and 100 ml of ethanol with 40 μl of the bilirubin albumin solution, adding 20 ml of diazo reagent, and after 30 minutes adding 8 ml of ascorbic acid solution. The metal complexes were formed by adding appropriate amounts of metal salt solution to the bilirubin-caffeine-sodium benzoate diazo reagent mixture or to the bilirubin-ethanol-diazo reagent mixture.

The pH at which the various metal complexes were formed under optimal conditions was determined. The optimal pH value varied from 5.7 to 12.5. The absorption curves were studied in the range 450–700 nm both before and after addition of metals. The absorption maximum and the E^{mM} at maximum are given for all the metals studied—Cr, Mn, Fe, Co, Ni, Cu, Zn, Cd, and Pb. For azobilirubin itself they found in caffeine-sodium benzoate solution maximum 530 nm ($E^{mM} = 25.7$) at pH 5.7, maximum 536 ($E^{mM} = 24.5$) at pH 9.44, and maximum 598 ($E^{mM} = 32.2$) at pH 12.5. The maxima of the metal complexes in caffeine-benzoate solution were usually shifted from 15 to 55 nm toward longer wavelengths, and their E^{mM} at maximum varied between 14 and 45. In an ethanol solution azobilirubin itself exhibited maximum at 530 nm for all pH's between 1.99 and 9.99 with E^{mM} varying within 1% of 30.4. The alcoholic metal complexes all exhibited a shift of maximum toward longer wavelengths varying from 50 to 88 nm, and their E^{mM} at maximum varied from 12 to 45. Some metal complexes (Zn, Cd, and Pb) exhibited higher E^{mM} than azobilirubin itself.

Summary

The diazo reaction is positive with bilirubinoids containing a central methene bridge; the color depends on pH. The reaction product, called azobilirubin, is a mixture of two isomeric dipyrrole–azo compounds. Rubins give a red color in slightly acid or neutral solutions. In strong acid and strong alkali, the color is blue or violet. When using the diazo reaction for quantitative investigations, the composition of the reagents has to be scrutinized. The so-called direct and indirect diazo reactions are briefly mentioned. The azobilirubin metal complexes are discussed; maxima and extinction constants are presented.

K. Reactions of Urobilinoids: Benzaldehyde Reaction and Zinc Fluorescence Test

Urobilinogens give a red color with *p*-dimethylaminobenzaldehyde in strong HCl solution. The reaction was discovered by Ehrlich (1901) in certain pathological urines. It was further studied by Pröscher (1901b, 1903), and Neubauer (1903) and Bauer (1905) proved that urobilinogens are responsible for the reaction. These earlier findings were discussed by K. Thomas (1907a). The reaction was studied more closely by Fischer and collaborators, who showed that all pyrroles with free H-atoms in the α-position as well as the urobilinogens give this reaction (Fischer and Orth, 1934, pp. 66–69; 1937, pp. 716–717). Among the urobilinogens, only UG-L has a free H in an α-position, and consequently the mechanism of the reaction cannot be the same in the urobilinogens as in the simple pyrroles. The color is rather labile, and its measurement has to be carried out within 5 minutes (Schwartz *et al.*, 1944, p. 601).

Treibs and Hermann (1955) found that the Ehrlich reaction of pyrroles is more complicated than formerly believed. An equilibrium mixture is formed consisting of the pyrrole compound, dimethylaminobenzaldehyde, pyrryl-dimethylamino-phenyl-methene (the Ehrlich dye), and dimethylamino-phenyl-dipyrrylmethane (colorless). This equilibrium depends on the position of the substituents in the pyrrole. Strong acids can liberate dimethylaniline from dimethylamino-phenyl-dipyrryl-methanes and thus give rise to formation of strongly colored dipyrrylmethenes; this process is irreversible. Generally only red or purple colors exhibiting absorption bands in the green region are regarded as positive reactions, but formation of colorless dipyrrylmethane compounds cause atypical colors and may thus mask a positive reaction in the case of slow-reacting pyrrole compounds with special constitutional properties.

The mechanism of the Ehrlich reaction for urobilinogen has been studied by Yamaoka *et al.* (1956b). According to them, the reaction proceeds as follows: first *p*-dimethylaminobenzaldehyde forms a carbinol base with bridge b of urobilinogen; then a *p*-quinone ring forms on dehydration of the side chains of the benzene ring, and finally the bridge b is dehydrogenated. Thus a methine bridge forms from the methene bridge. The compound thus obtained has a bilene-type chromophore which is supplemented by the auxochrome group of the quinoid. Thus, the color is shifted toward higher wavelengths. This explains the red color (see Fig. 28). Yamaoka *et al.* showed that this reaction is inhibited by traces of formaldehyde which block the central methene bridge.

The benzaldehyde reaction is not specific for urobilinogens. Pyrrol compounds with free α-positions present in biological fluids, such as the porphyrin precursor porphobilinogen (PBG), also give the reaction. Phylloerythrinogen, a chlorophyll derivative, also reacts positively. This compound appears in feces and urine after ingestion of large amounts of vegetables. Finally, some bilirubinoids which occur in lower animals give a positive benzaldehyde reaction, for example, aplysiopurpurin (Schreiber, 1932). Porphobilinogen appears only in patients with acute porphyria, mostly during attacks. This compound was first studied by Waldenström (1937) and Waldenström and Vahlquist (1939). They showed that PBG, contrary to urobilinogens (UG), is insoluble in acetic acid ether.

PBG can easily be separated from UG when urine is extracted with acetic acid ether before the reaction is executed. Colored reaction products of UG are soluble in $CHCl_3$, whereas those of PBG are insoluble in $CHCl_3$ (Sachs, 1931; C. J. Watson and Schwartz, 1941). Color developed with UG can be considerably enhanced by addition of saturated sodium acetate. This is true only to a lesser degree with the reaction products of PBG (Schwartz, 1953). Absorption bands of the two compound classes are somewhat different. Both have bands at 560–565 nm. The PBG reaction has a weak band at 520–525 nm, which is missing for the UG reaction (Schwartz, 1953). Recently, Rimington *et al.* (1956) studied the PBG reaction in detail.

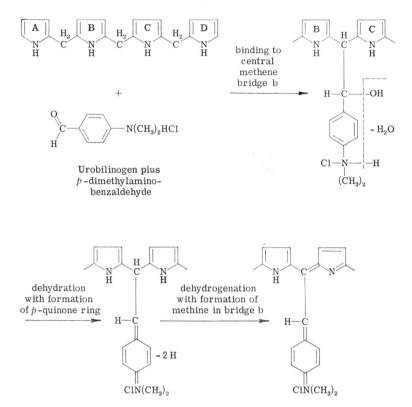

binding to
central
methene
bridge b

Urobilinogen plus
p-dimethylamino-
benzaldehyde

dehydration
with formation
of *p*-quinone ring

dehydrogenation
with formation of
methine in bridge b

FIG. 28. Benzaldehyde reaction (Ehrlich reaction) of urobilinogens.

Phylloerythrinogen as a source of error in urobilinogen determination was studied by Baumgärtel (1948b; 1950b, p. 72). This compound cannot be separated from UG by extraction methods, but its negative fluorescence test permits distinction from the urobilinoids. Furthermore, phylloerythrinogen yields a colored compound very similar to mesobiliviolin on treatment with $FeCl_3$ and boiling concentrated HCl. This compound gives green solutions in dilute NaOH, whereas mesobiliviolin is violet under the same conditions. Brugsch (1950) investigated pigments which form in the digestive tract during chlorophyll degradation. Perrin (1958) described a method for quantitative phylloerythrin determination.

The *green reaction* sometimes noted in urine with benzaldehyde reagent is due to bilirubin. Biliverdin is obtained from bilirubin under the action of the HNO_2 which forms when the strongly acid reagent is added to urines containing nitrites (A. Müller, 1938).

Other substances such as indoles and tryptophan also give color reactions with Ehrlich's reagent; the two mentioned turn red (Thomas, 1907a,b), scatol becomes blue (Herter, 1906), and urea turns yellow (Grossmann, 1912); sulfonamides and p-aminosalicylic acid also give a color reaction (Watanabe, 1959). See also Naumann (1936a) and Royer (1943, pp. 14–15).

If the benzaldehyde reaction is carried out by addition of the reagent to the urine without previous extraction, the color reactions of all the substances mentioned badly disturb the reaction of the urobilinogens present and often completely mask it. If the reaction is carried out after extraction with ether or petrol ether after acidification with glacial acetic acid, the disturbing substances are removed with the exception of phylloerythrinogen (Terwen, 1925; C. J. Watson, 1936b; Schwartz *et al.*, 1944; Watanabe, 1959).

Heilmeyer (1931b), Heilmeyer and Krebs (1931), and Schwartz *et al.* (1944) studied the absorption spectrum of the Ehrlich reaction of UG; its maximum was 557 nm. From the data of Heilmeyer, $E_{1\,cm}^{1\%} = 1083$ at maximum can be calculated ($1083 = 1:100$ A; $A =$ absorption constant). Similar values were obtained by Schwartz *et al.* with the Evelyn photoelectric colorimeter at 565 nm. These investigators found identical values for UG-I and UG-L. Sakurai (1959a,b) investigated the spectral absorption of the benzaldehyde reaction of UG-I and UG-L. Both exhibited maxima at 490 and 560 nm at pH 4.2 and at 490–492 and 558 nm at pH 4.0. If the pH increased above 4.2, the maxima shifted to 506–510 and 554–556 nm. In methanol, the maxima were 490 and 550 at pH 5.4, and no differences were found on moderate changes of pH. In acid methanol, the 490 maximum was shifted toward longer wavelengths and the maxima of UG-I and UG-L became separated 1–3 nm from each other. The 490 maximum disappeared after addition of antioxidants and is due to urobilins formed by the oxidative effect of Ehrlich's reagent on the UG. Only the 560 maximum is due to the UG-benzaldehyde compounds. UG-I dimethyl ester exhibited a postitive Ehrlich reaction with maxima at 488 and 550 nm at pH 3.8.

Henry *et al.* (1961) studied the benzaldehyde reaction of various crystalline urobilin preparations after reduction with alkaline Fe (OH)$_2$ with Terwen's method (1925). The purest preparations showed maxima at 562 nm with $E_{1\,cm}^{1\%} = 1180$–1370, an average of 1250, calculated for free urobilinogen. The extinctions became significantly increased on addition of ascorbic acid (10 mg per ml of reduced filtrate). They recommended 1.8 mg phenolsulfonphthalein (analytic quality) dissolved in 1000 ml 0.05 M NaOH as a suitable standard. This standard exhibits a maximum at 562 nm with an absorbancy varying between 0.306 and 0.353 for various commercial preparations of the acid form.

Whereas urobilinogens give a positive benzaldehyde reaction, this reaction is negative for urobilins. The situation is reversed with the *zinc fluorescence test*. Only the Zn salts of urobilins give the characteristic green fluorescence in alcohol solutions. This test is usually called the Schlesinger test. However, it would be more justifiable to call it the Jaffe-Schlesinger test, since Jaffe described it first (see Section E, this chapter). The reaction is positive with all bilirubinoids with the following chromophore group: . . . —CH_2—[. . . —CH= . . .]—CH_2— . . . , i.e., bilenes-*b* (see Section I, this chapter). This includes U-ɪ, U-ʟ, and U-ᴅ. Violins with configuration [. . . =CH— . . .]—CH_2— . . . —CH_2— . . . have Zn complexes exhibiting red fluorescence. The green fluorescence of the mesobilifuscin chromoproteid myobilin is of another nature; it is given by the compound itself and not by its Zn salt (cf. Section F, this chapter). Urobilinogens, rubins, and verdins give a negative Zn fluorescence test, but the Zn salts of many decomposition products of pyrrole compounds give green fluorescence. Thus, the reaction is not specific for urobilins (Piloty *et al.*, 1914).

Riva (1896) first investigated this reaction with purified substances and introduced Zn acetate as a reagent. This proved to be better than the $ZnCl_2$ used by Roman and Delluc (1900). The fluorescence spectra were studied by Dhéré and Roche (1931a,b). Dhéré (1934, figure p. 1009) prepared photograms of the fluorescence bands.

With light of wavelength 365 nm (Wood's light), acid solutions of the Zn salts of U-ɪ showed fluorescence bands at 637, 601, 551, and 521 nm with material prepared by H. Fischer. The first band gave the weakest fluorescence, the last band the strongest. A rather impure U-ʟ sample showed only two bands at 638 and 520 nm. In a mesobiliviolin sample, prepared by Fischer, the fluorescence bands were 641, 592, 555, and 516 nm, i.e., in the vicinity of the U-ɪ bands. However, no quantitative data have been given. Contrary to urobilins, Zn salts of phylloerythrins give red fluorescence. With this method they can easily be differentiated. Porphyrins give a red fluorescence under these conditions.

A number of compounds such as amino acids, proteins, and flavines show fluorescence themselves. Thus, the Zn fluorescence test can only be used after careful extraction and purification of biological materials.

The benzaldehyde reaction and the Zn fluorescence test can be used for the quantitative determination of the so-called "total urobilinoid," i.e., the sum of all types of U and UG compounds, including the types ɪ, ʟ, and ᴅ. When the benzaldehyde reaction is used, U must be reduced to UG. With the Zn fluorescence test, however, UG has to be oxidized to U. Thus, for accurate determinations the respective conversions should be carried out quantitatively. It is also advisable to check the specificity of the reaction. Extremely careful work is mandatory.

Reduction of U to UG can be carried out with ferrous ammonium sulfate in strongly alkaline solution (Terwen, 1925), or with $FeSO_4$ in alkaline solution (C. J. Watson, 1931). According to Watson (1936c), Naumann (1936a,c), and Royer (1943, p. 12), this reduction is accompanied by considerable losses. However, the studies of Schwartz *et al.* (1944) showed only moderate losses by use of pure UG-ɪ and UG-ʟ —3.6% in urine and 7.7% in stool. On the other hand, Henry *et al.* (1964) found a recovery of only 50–80% for urobilin-ɪ added to urine, whereas the recovery for pure solutions of urobilin-ɪ was about 90%. They found a 490 nm peak in the reduced urine, pointing to incomplete reduction. It is, however, to be emphasized that urobilinoids of type ɪ are much less stable than those of type ʟ and that the latter constitute most of the native urinary urobilinoid. Therefore, the findings of Henry *et al.* are of limited analytical relevance. They proposed to add 200 mg ascorbic acid and 100 mg potassium borohydride to every 20 ml of reduced alkaline urinary filtrate (supernatant) in order to complete the reduction in the Terwen procedure. Further, they adjusted pH to 7–8 and waited several minutes before extraction.

Oxidation of UG to U is usually accomplished by the addition of a few drops of tincture of iodine. This was studied in detail by Heilmeyer and Krebs (1931), who showed that no single well definable compound forms. The fluorescence of Zn salts of the oxidation products was very labile. C. J. Watson (1936c, 1938) could show that during oxidation of UG-ɪ considerable amounts of mesobiliviolin are formed. However, most of the natural UG belongs to type ʟ. Thus, according to Royer (1943, pp. 25–26), this source of error can be ignored.

The question of specificity has already been mentioned; it is by no means an absolute one. The benzaldehyde test is specific if it is carried out after extraction with glacial acetic acid and ether or petrol ether. Readings should be made after addition of saturated sodium acetate solution. In quantitative work, it is necessary to add ascorbic acid to counteract the oxidation of UG to U by the reagent. The Zn fluorescence test will confirm the results by addition of iodine to the extract (see Baumgärtel, 1949a), but it is less suitable for quantitative work.

The precision of the methods depends on instrumentation. The benzaldehyde test is usually more precise than the Zn fluorescence test because the commonly used methods for the latter are quite primitive. It is conceivable that more accurate fluorometers will permit better results. In principle, one prefers to measure the extinction at a well-defined spectral maximum if possible. This is especially true for extracts with a number of impurities (for example, urine and stool extracts). Royer (1943, p. 22) reported that 0.0128 µg urobilin per milliliter can be detected with the Zn fluorescence test. This concentration is too low for quantitative determination by absorption spectrophotometry because it corresponds to an extinction ($E_{1\,cm}$) of only ca. 0.001 in the benzaldehyde test (see above; $E_{1\,cm}^{1\%}$ = ca. 1000). Thus, the Zn fluorescence test will be useful when concentrations become too low for the benzaldehyde reaction. Quantitative measurements at such low concentrations, however, are always liable to errors.

More specific and more quantitative fluorescence measurements will be possible when use is made of spectrophotofluorometers with double monochromators (Bartholomew *et al.*, 1957; Duggan *et al.*, 1957) which allow precise definition of both the exciting and the emitted light. These improved instruments have not yet been used for urobilin research.

Summary

The benzaldehyde test for urobilinogens and the zinc fluorescence test for urobilins are discussed. Specificity, accuracy, suitability for quantitative analysis, and limitations are considered. The following technique can be recommended: reduction of urobilins to urobilinogens with $FeSO_4$ in alkaline solution, addition of ascorbic acid and potassium borohydride to the extract to enhance reduction, adjustment of pH to 7–8 and waiting several minutes, extraction with petroleum ether and glacial acetic acid, extraction from this solution with the benzaldehyde reagent, and reading after addition of saturated sodium acetate solution (for details see Chapter VI,C,1). Methods based on oxidation of urobilinogens to urobilins and measurement of the fluorescence of their Zn salts are less accurate and specific. Accuracy is low because of losses during oxidation. Fluorescence measurements in impure solutions have more sources of error than the spectrophotometry of colored solutions. The Zn fluorescence test is 10–100 times more sensitive than the benzaldehyde test. Thus, the former method is preferable when small amounts of material are available. However, the Zn fluorescence methods in use today allow only semiquantitative determinations.

L. Column Chromatography of Bile Pigments

Only in recent years has chromatographic adsorption analysis been used to a large extent for the study of bile pigments. The method is extremely valuable for accurate analysis if enough material is available.

It is significant to discuss the adsorptive capacities of the carrier substances. Aluminum oxide is a commercial product which always has to be standardized according to the Brockmann technique. Commercial preparations of Al_2O_3 adsorb very strongly. For the separation of porphyrin esters, a weaker preparation with Brockmann activity grade

3, 4, or 5 is preferred. Thus, it could become necessary to weaken the commercial product by wetting and redrying (cf. T. Williams, 1953).

Chromatography can be applied to free pigments or to their esters. Thus, an Al_2O_3 column is applicable for purification of $CHCl_3$ solutions of bilirubin (Sakamoto, 1956a). Esterification may be carried out with 5% sulfuric acid in absolute methanol overnight. After addition of water and neutralization with saturated sodium acetate, the ester is extracted with $CHCl_3$. After washing, drying, and vacuum concentration, the $CHCl_3$ solution is ready for chromatography. The $CHCl_3$ has to be washed and dried prior to usage. Commercial $CHCl_3$ contains a certain amount of alcohol that can lead to considerable acceleration in the development of chromatographic columns. Furthermore, one has to bear in mind that many bile pigments are very sensitive to oxidation. When bilirubin is treated with methanol–sulfuric acid, oxidation to biliverdin takes place.

Siedel (1935) was the first to use chromatography for separation of bile pigments. He adsorbed a solution of mesobiliviolin and mesobili-rhodin in ether: $CHCl_3$ (1:1) on a talc column. Two zones formed, an upper containing mesobilirhodin (red), and a lower containing meso-biliviolin (violet).

Siedel (1939) chromatographed esters on Al_2O_3 columns. After concentrating the extracts to dryness, he esterified with methanol-HCl and extracted the esters with $CHCl_3$. The solution of bile pigment esters in $CHCl_3$ was chromatographed on Al_2O_3 columns, which were developed with the same solvent. With this method Stich and Stärk (1953) isolated the following zones from icteric urine: mesobilifuscin forming a dark brown zone on the top of the column, next a brownish-yellow zone corresponding to urobilin-L, then a violet zone of mesobilirhodin plus meso-biliviolin, and finally a red one representing porphyrins.

Tixier (1945) used a similar technique to isolate biliverdin from corals and the egg shells of emus. He chromatographed esterified bile pigments dissolved in a $CHCl_3$:ether (1:1) mixture on Al_2O_3, and developed with $CHCl_3$. Biliverdin ester passed the column, whereas bilirubin was adsorbed. The same results were obtained in a mixture of one part of ethyl acetate to four parts of ether.

Later, Stich and Stärk (1953) separated bile pigment esters from normal and pathological urines. They used $CHCl_3$ solutions and Al_2O_3 columns and developed with $CHCl_3$, methanol, glacial acetic acid, and HCl. They were able to separate various fuscins with this method (see Section F, this chapter).

To purify bilirubin, M. Jirsa (personal communication, 1958) successfully chromatographed it in chlorobenzene solution on Al_2O_3, but

Tvaroha and Jirsa (1960) recommended silica gel, and Fog employed anhydrous Na_2SO_4 for this purpose.

MgO, which is successfully used in separation of porphyrin esters, has not been employed for the separation of bile pigments.

Pearson and Watson (1963*) used a packed chromatography column of powderized cane sugar to *separate mesobilirubin and bilirubin*. The $CHCl_3$ solution of the pigments was mixed with a surplus of petrol ether which precipitates most of the bilirubin, and the precipitate was collected on a paper filter and washed with petrol ether to redissolve precipitated mesobilirubin. The sugar columns were saturated with petrol ether, and the solution was applied. The columns were developed first with petrol ether, then with petrol ether—$CHCl_3$ mixtures with increasing $CHCl_3$ concentrations, and finally with $CHCl_3$ (washed, dried, alcohol-free). The column was dried and the zones cut out and eluated separately. The eluated pigments were then identified by paper chromatography.

Sakamoto *et al.* (1957a,b) and Yahata (1959) used *ion exchange chromatography* (resins of Amberlite type) for separations of bile pigments.

Partition chromatography on columns has been used by several investigators. Sakamoto (1956a,b,c,d,e) separated bile pigments extracted from bile with $CHCl_3$ on columns of Al_2O_3, silica gel, and cellulose powder. Stationary phases were benzene, chloroform, or water. $CHCl_3$, $CHCl_3$–methanol, $CHCl_3$–ethyl acetate, $CHCl_3$–acetone, petrol ether–methanol, and others were used as mobile phases. The main purpose of these investigations was the separation of bile into fractions of "direct bilirubin" (cf. Chapter V,F). Other Japanese investigators used similar methods, but unfortunately their findings have been published in Japanese with only brief summaries in English (Ekuni, 1952a,b). Ekuni (1952a) reported separation of azobilirubins from serum; he obtained two layers on an Al_2O_3 column. Billing *et al.* (1957) and Jirsa *et al.* (1958) separated azo pigments of direct and indirect bilirubin with partition chromatography.

Pittera and Cassia (1962) and Cassia and Pittera (1962) separated the components of azobilirubin by means of partition chromatography on Al_2O_3 columns with a solvent mixture of n-butanol, methyl ethyl ketone, and $1.5 M$ glycine buffer of pH 2 (cf. Section J, this chapter).

Reversed phase distribution chromatography—introduced by Howard and Martin (1950)—was employed by P. G. Cole and Lathe (1953), P. G. Cole *et al.* (1954), and Billing (1955a,b) for separation of serum bilirubin. They succeeded in separating three fractions (see Chapter V,F). They used alcoholic extracts of serum which were deep-frozen and lyophilized. Six grams of silicone-treated kieselguhr were employed,

3 ml stationary nonpolar phase, 17 ml mobile polar phase, and glass tubes of 16 mm inside diameter. The solvent system was a mixture of $CCl_4, CHCl_3$, methanol, n-butanol, acetone, ammonium sulfate, and dilute phosphate buffer (pH 6). Billing (1955a,b) employed a butanol: water:phosphate buffer system (0.005 M, pH 6) using a 50:45:5 ratio.

Pittera and Cassia (1962*) performed reverse phase partition chromatography with $CHCl_3$ extracts of bilirubin from normal and icteric sera on columns of siliconated silica gel. Noir *et al.* (1965*) and Garay *et al.* (1965*) separated biliverdin and its conjugates by means of reverse phase partition chromatography on siliconated kieselguhr with methanol extracts of human and animal biles.

Thin layer chromatography was employed by Segura and Vidal-Sèvilla (1964) to identify bile pigments extracted from serum incubated with trypsin by means of propanol. A 250 μm layer of polyamide was used as adsorbent, and a mixture of propanol, pyridine, and water as solvent. The chromoplates were sprayed with a solution of diazotized p-nitroaniline, and the spots were examined in UV light.

Gaidano *et al.* (1964*) employed thin layer chromatography on silica gel for the fractionation of concentrated diazotized extracts from ethanol-treated serum.

Tenhunen (1965a*) employed thin layer chromatography in the study of free and conjugated bile pigments in bile. Kieselgehl G (Merck, Darmstadt) in 0.25 mm layers was used, and the solvent system was n-butanol-acetone-propionic acid-water, 7:4:3:3 (v/v/v/v). For the azo pigments the solvent system was methyl ethyl ketone-propionic acid-water, 20:5:5 (v/v/v).

M. Paper Chromatography and Paper Electrophoresis of Bile Pigments

Mendioroz *et al.* (1951) were the first to use paper chromatographic methods in the study of bile pigments. They found that the chromatographic behavior of bilirubin depends on the nature of the organic solvent employed. Thus, bilirubin migrates with the solvent front in $CHCl_3$. However, it stays on the starting point in ethanol-$CHCl_3$ mixtures which contain more than 50% alcohol. If the $CHCl_3$ content is higher than 50%, two fractions are obtained: one migrating with the solvent, the other remaining on the starting point. The more $CHCl_3$ used in the solvent, the stronger the fraction which migrates with the front will become. B. A. Mendioroz (personal communication, 1957) believed that this behavior of bilirubin can be explained by its resonance structures (cf. Section A, this chapter). Later Charbonnier *et al.* (1954) examined bilirubin of icteric serum with the same method.

Kehl and Stich (1952) and Stich *et al.* (1953) developed an ascending paper chromatographic technique for separation of bile pigments based on the following solvent systems: 2,4-lutidine and water; 76% methanol, 20% water, and 4% concentrated ammonia; 40% water, 50% acetone, and 10% concentrated ammonia. Schleicher & Schull paper 2043 b was used for the lutidine system, paper 1705 for the others. The pigments were dissolved in $CHCl_3$ and applied to the paper. The lutidine chromatography was carried out at 15°, the others at 20° for 12 hours. With these techniques bilirubin was easily separated from urobilins. The separation of U-I and U-L was less satisfactory.

Gohr *et al.* (1956) and Gohr (1957) further developed this method, using ascending as well as descending techniques on Schleicher & Schüll paper 2043 b. As solvent, they employed $CHCl_3$ and a mixture of propanol and redistilled water (7:3). Bilirubinoids with a central methene bridge (for example, bilirubin) migrated with $CHCl_3$ but did not do so with propanol-water. Compounds with a central methine bridge (for example, urobilin-I) showed opposite behavior. Urobilin-I and -L could not be separated in this manner.

It is important to bear in mind that the migration of bile pigments greatly depends on their ionization and on whether or not they are esterified. So far as the central bridge (bridge b) is concerned, the esters and free acids behave similarly. The alkali salts (anions) behave just in the opposite manner. To avoid structure-dependent solubility differences, the use of glacial acetic acid–$CHCl_3$ extracts is suggested.

Another difficulty is caused by the instability of bile pigments toward air oxidation (especially at alkaline pH). Thus, it is necessary to work quickly and, if possible, under a nitrogen atmosphere. The free acids are the most stable.

According to Gohr *et al.* (1956), *round-filter chromatography* is the best technique for studies of reaction products of the Gmelin reaction. Using Schleicher & Schüll paper 2043 b, they employed a solvent composed of 0.5 ml benzene, 1.8 ml $CHCl_3$, and 0.5 ml methanol. During development, the temperature was kept at 18°. The pigments were applied as spots in the center of the paper and the sheets were placed between two glass plates. The cover plate had a hole for solvent addition. A capillary filled with the solvent and having a drop rate of 10–12 drops per minute touched the paper through the hole. It was possible to isolate the products of the Gmelin reaction in this way. Closely adjacent, distinctly colored rings were obtained. The R_f values were: bilirubin, 0.93; biliverdin, 0.55; bilipurpurin, 0.64; and choletelin, 0.76.

Gohr *et al.* (1956) also investigated the mesobiliviolin reaction with the paper chromatographic technique. The solution was acidified with glacial acetic acid and extracted with $CHCl_3$. After evaporating the

$CHCl_3$, the residue was dissolved in alcohol. The mesobiliviolin reaction was carried out as usual with HCl and a trace of $FeCl_3$. The reaction products were extracted with $CHCl_3$ and the extract subjected to round-filter paper chromatography. The solvent mixture was 0.5 ml cyclohexane, 1.8 ml $CHCl_3$, and 0.1 ml methanol. The pigments were made visible by spraying with alcoholic Zn acetate and irradiation with UV light. In this way, U-L showed green fluorescence while U-I (after transformation to mesobiliviolin) exhibited red fluorescence. U-I and U-L could themselves be separated in a mixture containing 0.02 ml methyl ethyl ketone, 1.8 ml $CHCl_3$, and 0.3 ml methanol. However, the R_f values were very close together.

Beckmann (1954) reported a paper chromatographic separation method for U-I and U-L that is based on the mesobiliviolin reaction and employs a mixture of pyridine: $1 N$ NaOH:water (1:3:6) as solvent. However, Stich (1957), in using this method, could not completely separate the two isomers.

Sakurai (1959a,b) separated the Ehrlich reaction products of UG-I and UG-L. With a methanol:butanol saturated with $NH_3:H_2O$ mixture (76:4:20) the R_f of the former was 0.64, that of the latter 0.81. Methanol:butanol:28% aqueous NH_3 (2:2:1) gave quite similar results with a fixing phase of glacial acetic acid. U-I and U-L could be separated by the same solvent systems.

Jirásek and Jirsa (1960) and Messmer and Dengler (1962) elaborated paper chromatographic methods for separation of the reaction products of the mesobiliviolin reaction of U-I and U-L.

Royer et al. (1964) described a method for paper chromatographic separation of U-I, U-L, and U-D. Bile, urine, or feces were extracted and the extracts subjected to oxidation with $FeCl_3$ or iodine. Two solvent systems were used. I, consisting of methanol:butanol:ammonia (1:3:2), was run for 3 hours and gave the following R_f values: U-D, 0.87; U-L, 0.80; U-I, 0.58. II, consisting of octanol:ethyl acetate (1:1), was run for 5 hours in an atmosphere saturated with ammonia, and gave the R_f values: U-D, 0.92; U-L, 0.44; U-I, 0.02. Solvent I is only useful when U-D is not present.

Lozzio et al. (1964a,b) used the following solvent systems to separate bile pigments extracted from bile: (1) methanol:butanol:amyl alcohol:water (6:1:1:1) for 7 hours; (2) ethanol:butanol:water (3:1:1.5) for 14 hours; (3) methanol:water (2:1) following the method of Royer and Noir (1962). They employed Whatman No. 3 paper.

Several investigators used paper chromatographic methods for separation of "direct" and "indirect" bilirubin. Polonovski and Bourrillon (1952c) and Lins (1954) subjected extracts of icteric sera and bile to paper chromatography using Whatman No. 1 paper and, as solvents, butanol—acetic acid, phenol–water, 70–90% ethanol, 70% acetone, 50–80% methanol, or methanol:acetone:water (3:5:20). Kawai (1953) used methanol and ethanol and found that "indirect" bilirubin remained on the starting line, whereas "direct" pigment has an R_f value of ca. 0.75. Similarly, he succeeded in the separation of the azo pigments formed from direct and indirect serum bilirubin by means of a propanol–water system. The R_f of the direct reacting pigment was 0.55, that of the indirect 0.65. Sato (1955a,b) separated direct and indirect reacting bilirubin in bile in a n-propanol:water (2:1) mixture. Indirect bilirubin did not migrate, while the R_f of direct bilirubin was 0.60–0.65.

Gries *et al.* (1954) used ascending chromatography on Schleicher & Schüll paper 2043 b. The 30 × 30 cm sheets were *developed in complete darkness*. Solvents were $CHCl_3$ or an aqueous buffer solution of pH 4–12. For chromatography in aqueous solutions, the substances were applied after being dissolved in 0.1 N NaOH. Duration was 3 hours at 18° (thermostat). Indirect bilirubin migrated with the solvent front in $CHCl_3$, direct bilirubin remained on the starting line. Direct bilirubin migrated in aqueous solution at every pH value. Indirect bilirubin remained at the starting line in acid and neutral solutions, whereas it migrated at alkaline pH values.

Schmid (1956a,b, 1957a,b) and Heikel *et al.* (1957) reported separations of the azobilirubins of direct and indirect bilirubin from serum, bile, and urine using ascending paper chromatography. Schmid used a solvent system of methyl ethyl ketone:n-propanol:water (75:25:30). The azo pigments from direct bilirubin, fresh bile, and icteric urine had R_f values of 0.25–0.30. Azo pigments obtained from crystalline bilirubin, indirect-reacting serum bilirubin, and heated bile showed R_f values of 0.45–0.50. Heikel *et al.* used siliconized paper and butanol, aqueous citrate buffer, or ethyl acetate–pyridine–water as solvents. Pittera and Cassia (1963) studied the azo pigments of serum bilirubin and found a third component besides the pigments A and B. This was not detected before, because only alcohol-precipitated serum had been studied (cf. Chapter V,F).

Vegas (1963) separated the azo pigments of bilirubin glucuronide, bilirubin sulfate, and the alkali-stable fraction of natural conjugated bilirubin by chromatography on carboxymethylcellulose *cation-exchange paper* (Whatman CM 50) with a solvent system of n-butanol:pyridine: 1 N ammonia (2:1:2; v/v/v), pH 11.9 at room temperature. Clear-cut separation of the three conjugates was achieved.

Kaneda (1963a*) separated the azo pigments of bilirubin, mesobilirubin and bilirubin dimethyl ester by paper chromatography. He tried about 40 solvent systems and found that the best separation was achieved with the following systems: n-propanol-acetic acid-water (4:1:5), n-propanol-water (7:3), methyl ethyl ketone-n-propanol-water (15:5:6), and n-butanol saturated with water to which 10% citric acid was added. Using these four systems distinct separations were obtained.

Heringová *et al.* (1964b[*]) separated the azobilirubin pigments A and B by means of ascending paper chromatography on Whatman No. 3 paper using a system consisting of three volumes of water-saturated butanol and two volumes of acetic acid. Twenty volumes of this mixture were diluted with three volumes of H_2O. The duration of the run was 6 hours. The conjugated azo pigment yielded an R_f value of 0.53–0.64, the nonconjugated 0.69–0.80.

Manganelli and Scotti (1964[*]) described an ingenious paper chromatographic technique for the resolution of azobilirubin from serum. One milliliter of serum and 2 ml of 94% ethanol were mixed and centrifuged for 15 minutes. To 2 ml of the turbid supernatant 1 ml of diazo reagent was added. After 45 minutes the solution was applied to a broad paper strip which narrowed rapidly into a strip ca. one-third as wide as the other end. Ascending chromatography was run for 24 hours with the strip placed vertically with the narrow end upward in a nitrogen atmosphere saturated with the solvent system which consisted of butanol-acetic acid-water (8:2:10). With this method three distinct narrow bands could be separated from normal sera.

Noir *et al.* (1965[*]) separated biliverdin, its monoglucuronide, and its diglucuronide, bilirubin and its monoglucuronide and diglucuronide by means of ascending paper chromatography on Whatman No. 3 paper overnight (14–16 hours) with a solvent system of butanol-ethanol-water (3:1:1.5). The R_f values of the pigments were 0.88, 0.31, 0.42, 0.0, 0.38, and 0.56, respectively.

Ichikawa (1956a,b,c) compared crystalline bilirubin with $CHCl_3$ extracts of bile. When the chromatogram was developed with $CHCl_3$, crystalline bilirubin migrated with the solvent front. Bilirubin of bile, however, separated into a stationary and a moving fraction. The substances behaved inversely during separation with water or with phosphate buffer of pH 7. In this case the crystalline bilirubin remained on the starting line, whereas the entire amount of bile bilirubin migrated with the solvent front. Biliverdin did not show any mobility in alcohol, $CHCl_3$, or water. However, it migrated in methanol:glacial acetic acid (4:1).

Sakamoto (1956d,e) performed paper chromatography of crystalline bilirubin and bilirubin fractions from bile using the following solvents: water, ammonia, glacial acetic acid, methanol, ethanol, n-propanol, n-butanol, butyl acetate, phenol, lutidine, and collidine. Bilirubin showed a definitive tailing in most solvents. In phenol-containing solvents, two spots were formed, corresponding to the findings of Charbonnier and Mendioroz (cf. above).

Pearson and Watson (1963*) separated bilirubin and mesobilirubin from concentrated bile extracts by ascending chromatography on Whatman No. 1 paper. A 2-hour run was performed in a system of petrol ether $CHCl_3$ (60:10) in a vertical tank saturated in advance with the solvent system. This gave R_f values of 0.6–0.7 for mesobilirubin and 0.2–0.3 for bilirubin. The paper was dried and developed with saturated alcoholic Zn acetate followed by treatment with 0.1% iodine in 95% alcohol. In this way the mesobilirubin was oxidized to give an intense red fluorescence in UV light.

Clarke (1965*) used ascending paper chromatography with an isopropanol-0.10 M sodium bicarbonate (7:3) solvent system to control the purity of bilirubin and biliverdin preparations. The method can also be used with azobilirubin. Clarke points out that *impurities have a marked influence upon the migration of bilirubin and its derivatives,* a fact which accounts for the difficulty in performing resolutions of bile pigments without preliminary purification.

Paper electrophoresis has been employed by a number of investigators. Verschure and Hoefsmit (1956) used Whatman No. 1 paper, 0.06 M barbiturate buffer at pH 8.6, 7.5 volts/cm, and 2 hours. Bile was applied directly on the paper in the form of a thin band. The strip was sprayed with freshly prepared diazo reagent without HCl (10 ml 96% ethanol, 10 ml 0.1% sulfanilic acid in water, and 0.6 ml 0.5% aqueous $NaNO_2$ solution) after the run. Two definite bilirubin bands appeared with fistular bile. Ichikawa (1956a,b) carried out electrophoresis in an acid medium. Biliverdin did not migrate in buffers of pH 2–5. A cathodic directed movement was observed in 30% acetic acid with 27 volts/cm in 5 hours.

Childs (1955) and Klatskin and Bungards (1956) made electrophoretic experiments with direct and indirect serum bilirubin (see Chapter V,B,2). Talafant (1961) separated bilirubin and its conjugates in a pH 6.1 buffer system of glacial acetic acid:pyridine:water (5:70: 925).

Kahán (1958, 1961, p. 21–29) studied the electrophoretic behavior of urobilins and their Zn complexes. By means of continuous paper electrophoresis, somewhat larger amounts of urobilinoids were isolated. At pH 9.5, U-4 migrates fastest, followed by U-ɪ and U-ʟ. Urobilinogens are partly oxidized during electrophoresis. Electrophoresis of U-ɪ at pH 7.2 gave rise to formation of mesobiliviolin. Mesobiliviolin and mesobilirhodin could not be separated electrophoretically.

Berezin and Antunes (1962) performed electrophoresis of azobilirubin from serum with indirect diazo reaction (Malloy-Evelyn's technique). Barbiturate buffer of pH 8.6, ionic strength 0.05 and high voltage electrophoresis for 4 hours were used. There was a sharp distinction between a band of yellow nondiazotized bilirubin migrating with the albumin and a bluish diazo pigment migrating with the γ-globulin.

Lozzio *et al.* (1963a,b) separated urobilins-D, -I, and -L by paper electrophoresis in a pyridine–acetate buffer of pH 6.1 at 14 volts/cm for 3 hours. U-D migrated toward the cathode, U-L and U-I toward the anode.

N. New Bile Pigments: Aureobilin, "405"-Pigment, and Phytobilin

The group of B. A. Mendioroz (personal communication, 1966) found evidence of two new forms of bile pigments, particularly in human urines. The "405"-pigment is nondialyzable (remains in the interior of the cellophane bag on dialysis), exhibits an absorption peak in the 405 nm region and one at 290 nm with an extinction ratio $E^{290}/E^{405} =$ 8.4, gives the Gmelin reaction and the direct diazo reaction, is bound to protidic compounds, and gives various carbohydrate reactions (carbazol, naphthoresorcinol, and tryptophan-perchloric acid).

Aureobilin is dialyzable and its absorption curve has a continually ascending slope from 700 to 290 nm, an inflection at 260 nm; and a new ascending slope toward 210 nm. The 290 nm peak was found to be due to a loosely attached peptidic fraction, with molecular weight of ca. 3000. Its beautiful golden color gave rise to the name. About 80% of its absorption in the visible range is between 400 and 490 nm. It gave the direct diazo reaction with an egg-yolk orange-reddish color without visible absorption maximum and UV maximum at 377 nm. It became wine red on addition of HCl. The direct pentdyopent reaction was positive (maximum 525 nm) and the same was the case with the Gmelin reaction which showed initial violet color passing through red, dark brown, orange, and yellow stages.

Aureobilin is precipitated by phosphotungstic acid, forms nonfluorescent zinc salts, and gives the above-mentioned carbohydrate reactions.

Both the 405-pigment and aureobilin were found in all normal and pathological human urines (cf. Fig. 28a), in bile and meconium, and in strongly icteric sera. They could be dissolved in $CHCl_3$, ethanol, or water. Often, the concentration in the urine was increased during the course of viral hepatitis.

Aureobilin is adsorbed on short columns (2.5 cm) of Al_2O_3 from ethanolic solutions and eluated again with distilled H_2O. Aureobilin is eluated first from such columns, closely followed and sometimes overlapped by urobilinoids. Electrophoretic separation (Whatman No. 1

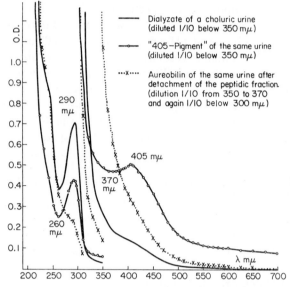

FIG. 28a. Absorption curves of "405"-pigment and aureobilin. From B. A. Mendioroz (personal communication, 1966). Measurements taken on a Beckman DU Spectrophotometer.

paper) showed the 405-pigment located near the β-globulins in sera from patients with severe hepatocellular damage. Chromatographic separation on Sephadex G25 of concentrated urine showed four colored fractions on elution with 0.15 M NaCl; aureobilin constituted the second of these fractions. On reverse phase partition chromatography on siliconated Hyflo Super Cel with the solvent system CHCl₃-methanol-water (50:30:20) aureobilin constituted the more polar fraction.

Both 405-pigment and aureobilin are ubiquitous pigments; they are probably related to the somewhat ill-defined urochrome B (cf. this chapter, Section G). Several authors have observed similar pigments without realizing their wide distribution and importance. Mendioroz regards them as products of hemoglobin catabolism and does not contemplate the possibility that they can also be formed as by-products of heme synthesis in bone marrow and liver.

A highly interesting recent observation is that the prosthetic group of the important growth-regulating *plant chromoprotein phytochrome* is a bile pigment (cf. Hendricks and Borthwick, 1965*; Butler *et al.*, 1965*; Siegelman and Hendricks, 1965*; Siegelman *et al.*, 1966*). The purified chromoproteid was denatured with trichloroacetic acid and washed with methanol, after which the chromophore was split off by refluxing with methanol containing 1% ascorbic acid. Cleavage could also be effected by refluxing with $CHCl_3$ after addition of a small volume of concentrated HCl. After hydrolysis the chromophore was transferred to $CHCl_3$, washed with 1.5 M HCl, and concentrated. The yield was about 10 μg of chromophore per kilogram of seedlings or only 10^{-8} of the initial weight!

Phytochrome and the algal chromoproteid phycocyanin had very similar R_f values in several different thin layer chromatographic systems and their Zn complexes were both nonfluorescent. It was clearly demonstrated that the chromophore of both pigments must contain two carboxyl groups—most likely two propionic acid side chains—as determined by thin layer chromatography after partial esterification.

It was concluded (Siegelman and Hendricks, 1965*; Siegelman *et al.*, 1966*) that the phytochrome chromophore is a *bilitriene closely related to the phycobilins*. It therefore seems appropriate to call this new bile pigment which forms part of a plant chromoproteid of great physiological importance *phytobilin* in analogy with the algal phycobilins forming part of the chromoproteids phycocyanin and phycoerythrin.

Additional Readings

Section C

Brodersen, R. (1966). Dimerisation of bilirubin anion in aqueous solution. *Acta Chem. Scand.* **20**, 2895–2896.

Section E

Watson, C. J., Moscowitz, A., Lightner, D., Krueger, W. C., and Weimer, M. (1966). The isolation of crystalline *i*-urobilinogen (mesobilirubinogen) from feces. Comparison with crystalline *d*-urobilinogen (H_{44}) and separation of natural *i*-urobilin into optically active components. *J. Biol. Chem.* **241**, 5037–5043.

Section H

von Dobeneck, H., and Schmierle, F. (1967). Methylen-pyrrolone. *Chem. Ber.* **100**, 647–653.

Section N

Hendricks, S. B., and Siegelman, H. W. (1967). Phytochrome and photoperiodism in plants. *In* "Comprehensive Biochemistry" (M. Florkin and E. H. Stotz, eds.), Vol. 27, pp. 211–235. Elsevier, Amsterdam.

CHAPTER II

Formation and Fate of Bile Pigments in the Body

This chapter presents a general survey on the metabolism of bile pigments. Details and quantitative aspects are discussed.

A. Different Origins of Bile Pigments

Until recently it was a common belief that all bile pigments are decomposition products of the hemoglobin of circulating mature erythrocytes.

Whipple (1922a,b) expressed the opinion that these pigments originate from a pigment complex in the body and food. This theory could not easily be rejected (see Paschkis, 1933, p. 694). Florentin (1924, p. 122 et seq.) succeeded in detecting bile pigments in degenerated nuclei of mesenchymal cells, but this histological demonstration was technically unreliable.

Virchow (1847), who found "hematoidin" crystals in blood extravasates, suggested that bile pigments are derivatives of hemoglobin. Prior to Virchow's observations, it was believed that bile pigments are formed in the liver. In the older literature the relationship between bilirubin and hematoidin was often discussed (see Asvadourova, 1913, p. 163). Fischer and Reindel (1923) finally proved that these two substances are identical (see also Fischer and Niemann, 1923; Rich and Bumstead, 1925a).

After the structure of heme and bile pigments became known, it seemed obvious that heme was the mother substance of these pigments. The possibility that they might be formed independently from common precursors was rejected until Rittenberg and collaborators, in the United States during the years 1945–1952, and, at the same time, a British group drew attention to it by isotope experiments.

These isotope studies were aimed at the biosynthesis of heme. The findings of these investigators are discussed in numerous publications (see Gray, 1953; Rimington, 1952, 1955; Eriksen, 1955; there are good surveys of the problem in most modern textbooks of biochemistry).

Porphyrins, together with proteins and nucleotides, are the most important substances of life. They are built from the simplest units of intermediary protein and carbohydrate metabolism, i.e., from glycine and components of the citric acid cycle of carbohydrate metabolism, mainly from pyruvic acid and acetate. By corresponding reactions of these substances, precursors of porphyrins form: α-amino-β-keto-adipic acid (succinylglycine); δ-aminolevulinic acid (δ-ALA), and porpho-bilinogen (PBG). Four molecules of PBG compound combine to form uroporphyrinogen (with eight carboxyl groups). Step-by-step decarboxy-lation of uroporphyrinogen yields protoporphyrin with two carboxyl groups. This then combines with iron to form heme.

This normal route is changed under abnormal conditions of synthesis (porphyria). Thus, large amounts of free porphyrins or their precursors, or both, are excreted in the urine and bile. They can also accumulate in various tissues.

The biosynthesis was studied by experiments using N^{15}-labeled glycine. These were carried out *in vitro* by incubation of nucleated erythrocytes with N^{15}-glycine, and by feeding this substance to living animals and persons (normal and sick). It was thus possible to follow the pyrrole nitrogen from the time of its entrance into the protoporphyrin of heme until its excretion as stercobilin in the stool. By means of a similar technique, it was possible to study incorporation of nitrogen into various porphyrins and the corresponding precursors in cases of por-phyria. Similarly, by feeding C^{14}-labeled glycine, pyruvic acid, or acetate, it was feasible to study the origin and fate of the various C-atoms of the pyrrole ring and the side chains. The C^{14} was incorporated at various sites in the molecule. Thus, the origin of various C and N atoms in heme, porphyrin, and bile pigments was mapped out in detail. Only a brief summary of the principal findings of these important investi-gations can be given here.

For further details, the reader should refer to the above-mentioned surveys, and to the following publications by American groups: Bloch and Rittenberg (1945a,b), Shemin and Rittenberg (1945a,b, 1946a,b), Altman *et al.* (1948), London *et al.* (1949, 1950a,b), Grinstein *et al.* (1949a,b, 1950), Radin *et al.* (1950a,b), Lowry and Hawkinson (1950), London and West (1950), Wittenberg and Shemin (1949, 1950a,b), Shemin and Wittenberg (1951a,b), Shemin and Kumin (1952).

In addition, the following British works should be consulted: Gray *et al.* (1949, 1950a,b), Muir and Neuberger (1949, 1950), Gray and Neuberger (1949, 1950), Neuberger *et al.* (1950), Rimington (1951).

In experiments in humans, a certain amount of labeled substance is administered during a short period (for example, 48 hours). Administration rate could be 1 g per hour, with no feeding between 0 and 3 hours. For example, 12 g labeled glycine, containing, say, 31 atom% excess of N^{15}, may be administered in this way. The N^{15} content of hemoglobin and of urobilin-L isolated from the stool is then determined every 4 days. In porphyria patients the porphyrin of urine and stool is isolated in crystalline form, and its N^{15} content determined.

By use of this technique, certain characteristic curves were obtained (see Fig. 29).

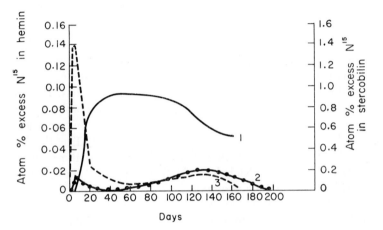

Fig. 29. Synthesis and excretion of porphyrins and bile pigments. On the ordinate, the atom% excess of N^{15} in hemin isolated from the blood (left) and stercobilin isolated from the feces (right) is plotted. The abscissa gives the days elapsed since the beginning of the experiment, at which time the patient ingested 12 g glycine with ca. 31 atom% excess of N^{15}. Curve 1 represents the atom% excess found in blood of normal subjects. Curve 2 represents the atom% excess found in stool stercobilin from normal subjects. Curve 3 represents the atom% excess found in stool stercobilin in congenital porphyria. The curve is a simplified summary of data of the literature.

Figure 29 shows a set of curves constructed from data of British workers (Gray and Neuberger, 1949, 1950; Gray *et al.*, 1950a,b). After N^{15}-labeled glycine was administered, the N^{15} content of heme increased sharply for the first 3–4 weeks, then remained on a constant level for about 3 months, and finally slowly decreased to the normal level. The curve contradicts the opinion that, similar to other proteins in the body, hemoglobin is   constantly resynthesized and decomposed. The findings can be explained as follows: hemoglobin is synthesized in the erythro-blasts of the bone marrow and deposited in red corpuscles. It remains there, unchanged until the erythrocytes decompose (about 120 days).

Statistical investigations proved that after a life span of 110–130 days 50% of the erythrocytes are destroyed.

The curve for bile pigment formation is markedly different from that for heme. It was obtained by isolating U-L from the stool in crystalline condition after N^{15}-glycine has been administered and determining its content of N^{15}. The curve shows two peaks. The first peak corresponds with the second 4-day period of stool investigation. The second one, however, appears after about 130 days. This again corresponds with the life span of erythrocytes which were formed after glycine was administered. The curve suggests *three sources* of U-L. The bulk, which under normal conditions accounts for about 70% and corresponds with the second peak, originates from destroyed mature circulating erythrocytes. Second in importance is the source indicated by the first peak and cannot originate from out-dated erythrocytes. This amount corresponds to about 10–15% of the total U-L excretion in normal persons. However, in patients with congenital porphyria it increases considerably as shown in Fig. 29, curve 3. Thus, the first increase of stercobilin excretion must somehow be a consequence of porphyrin synthesis. The third source corresponds to the low plateau between the first and the second peak.

Recently, Gray and Nicholson (1963) extended the studies to a patient with erythropoietic protoporphyria, a form of porphyria recently discovered. The first peak of N^{15}-stercobilin from stool after feeding N^{15}-glycine corresponded to more than 50% of the labeled stercobilin excreted during the entire period. The N^{15} incorporation in fecal stercobilin, coproporphyrin, and protoporphyrin was highest during the first 7 days after the glycine administration. The highest atom excess % was found in the coproporphyrin (2.8%), followed by that in protoporphyrin (1.8%), and finally, in stercobilin (0.5%). The N^{15}-protoporphyrin of the erythrocytes exhibited no peak, but a smooth increase. The authors discuss the origin of the first peak of bile pigments and believe that all the first peak bile pigment is not necessarily formed in the bone marrow; a part of it is most likely synthesized in the liver.

The origin of this "first peak" is not quite clear. The following hypotheses have been proposed: (1) destruction of erythrocytes just before or just after their entrance into the circulation, i.e., "infant mortality" among the erythrocytes (Gray et al., 1950a,b); (2) catabolism of myoglobin, catalase, and cytochromes; (3) degradation of a fraction of heme not utilized for hemoglobin synthesis; (4) direct synthesis of bile pigment from porphyrin precursors without passing through the porphyrin ring; (5) expulsion of some hemoglobin together with the nucleus of the erythroblasts during their maturing process; (6) formation of stercobilin from glycine by bacterial action in the intestinal canal;

(7) formation of "first peak" bile pigment in the liver. This possibility was recently proposed by Gray and Nicholson (1963) (cf. above) who believe that at least part of the first peak bile pigment is formed in the liver, a view supported by Gray *et al.* (1964*). Also Berendson *et al.* (1964*) pointed out that part of the first peak bilirubin may originate from sources unrelated to erythropoiesis and hemoglobin synthesis, as, for example, the heme synthesis of the liver. The same question was discussed by C. J. Watson (1965*).

Possibility (6) has finally been excluded after the experiments of Israels *et al.* (1963a,b), who administered labeled glycine-2-C^{14} intravenously and determined the C^{14} content of bilirubin isolated from bile. Hypothesis (5) was proposed by Bessis *et al.* (1961), who demonstrated in electron microscopic studies that a certain amount of hemoglobin-containing protoplasm was expelled from erythroblasts together with the nucleus. That this is sufficient to explain the "first peak" from a quantitative point of view is, however, not likely. Hypothesis (2) is unlikely because the degradation of myoglobin, cytochromes, and catalase is a continuous process (cf. below).

C. J. Watson (1965*, 1966*) supported hypothesis (5) because he found large amounts of uroporphyrin in the nuclei of the erythroblasts in patients with congenital porphyria where the first peak of bile pigment is known to be considerably increased.

Possibility (1) has been generally regarded as the most likely one (London *et al.*, 1949, 1950a,b; Gray *et al.*, 1949, 1950a,b), while hypotheses (3) and (4) have up to the present been regarded as unlikely possibilities. It should, however, be emphasized that the "erythrocyte infant mortality" concept which forms the basis of hypothesis (1) has never been directly demonstrated. In contrast, evidence apparently supporting hypothesis (4) has been published by Israels *et al.* (1963a). These investigators administered glycine-2-C^{14} intravenously to dogs and a single human patient with complete external bile fistula. Crystalline bilirubin was isolated from the fistula bile and its radioactivity was measured. Further, hemin was prepared from both the circulating blood and the bone marrow for study of the radioactivity.

In these studies, rapid variations in the production of heme and bile pigments can be followed considerably more exactly than in earlier experiments where the labeled glycine was administered orally or by intestinal tube and the bile pigments were isolated as stercobilin which is formed from bilirubin by bacterial action in the large intestine, i.e., after a considerable delay.

Israels *et al.* (1963a) found that the first peak accounted for 5–16% of the total bilirubin output in normal dogs and 16% in the human patient.

In dogs where the erythropoiesis was stimulated by bleeding, the percentage decreased to 3.5–5%; if the erythropoiesis was depressed with busulfan, it increased to 25–37%, and if erythropoiesis was severely depressed with total body irradiation the first peak accounted for 76–100% of the total bile pigment output. The observations clearly showed that the first peak bilirubin varies independently of the erythropoiesis, a finding not in agreement with hypotheses (1) and (5), but not contradictory to (4) and (7).

Israels et al. (1963a) found that C^{14} had already appeared in the bile bilirubin within 4–8 hours after the glycine injection in both the dogs and the human, whereas little or no radioactivity was demonstrable in the heme of the blood or the marrow at this point of time. In one dog subjected to total body irradiation with 700 r and surviving 6 days after the i.v. administration of C^{14}-glycine, no radioactivity was demonstrable in the hemin, but it appeared in the bilirubin after 4 hours.

In a later paper, Israels et al. (1963b) studied bilirubin isolated from the plasma and hemin isolated from the erythrocytes of humans after i.v. injection of glycine-2-C^{14} and a labeled porphyrin precursor, δ-aminolevulinic acid-4-C^{14} (δ-ALA). After injection of glycine, two peaks of radioactivity appeared in the bilirubin isolated from the plasma; the first could be traced after only 3 hours and reached its maximum after 24 hours, whereas the second began after about 48 hours and reached a maximum on the fourth day after injection. This result was found with three human subjects. After injecetion of δ-ALA, radioactive bilirubin had already appeared 30 minutes after the injection, reached a maximum after 90 minutes, and then decreased without appearance of a second peak. Further, ALA was found to be a much poorer heme precursor than glycine. A similar very early appearing bilirubin radioactivity was found in the dog (Israels et al., 1963a) which exhibited complete absence of erythropoiesis after total body irradiation.

Important animal experimentation dealing with first peak bilirubin have recently been published. Schwartz et al. (1964*) injected C^{14}-glycine, C^{14}-ALA, or C^{14}-protoporphyrin into dogs with bile fistula and followed the incorporation of C^{14} into bile bilirubin, hemoglobin, and nonhemoglobin hemes of various tissues including the liver at intervals for 1 week or longer. The daily excretion of C^{14}-bilirubin was correlated with the total C^{14}-protoporphyrin in the same glycine-treated dog during successive periods of varying erythropoietic activity (stimulation by repeated bleeding, inhibition by repeated transfusion) and daily values for erythropoietic and nonerythropoietic components were calculated. The nonerythropoietic component was found to be limited essentially to the first 48 hours after glycine administration, whereas the erythropoietic component was much more prolonged. In the normal dog approximately two-thirds of the total heme synthesis was of erythropoietic origin. Following administration of C^{14}-ALA and C^{14}-protoporphyrin ca. 20% of the total radioactivity was incorporated into bile bilirubin and over 99% of this bilirubin was nonhematopoietic. The nonhemoglobin hemes of various tissues were isolated in partially purified form from other dogs, and liver hemes alone contained somewhat more C^{14} at 3 to 83 hours than would be necessary to account for all the C^{14}-bilirubin excreted with the bile subsequent to the time of tissue analyses in dogs comparatively injected. Since the disappearance of C^{14} from liver hemes also closely paralleled the excretion of C^{14}-bilirubin during the same time intervals, it was concluded that a major part of the hemes in the liver and other tissues are intermediates in the synthesis of bilirubin and constitute the nonerythropoietic component.

Robinson *et al.* (1965a*) performed similar experiments in rats using congenitally icteric Gunn rats in which the bilirubin pool and turnover rate could be measured by isotopic methods, thus permitting long-term investigation of animals with normal and pathological erythropoiesis. Production of C^{14}-bilirubin from C^{14}-glycine, C^{14}-ALA, and C^{14}-hemin was computed electronically from the specific activity of pigment in the serum. With C^{14}-glycine ca. 85% of the total bile pigment originated from the breakdown of mature circulating erythrocytes and took place between 42 and 82 days after the C^{14}-injection. A first peak of C^{14}-bilirubin appeared during the first 4 hours with maximum at 1–2 hours and was independent of erythropoiesis. The kinetics of the first peak corresponded to the formation of labeled pigment by isolated perfused livers and was considered to be of hepatic origin. Following this early hepatic peak the C^{14}-bilirubin decreased asymptotically for ca. 60 hours. This delayed early phase was increased by erythropoietic stimuli and marrow depression. It varied parallel to the bile pigment production from mature circulating erythrocytes and was considered to be of erythropoietic origin. With C^{14}-ALA the first (hepatic) peak was strikingly increased whereas the two hematopoietic phases were both much reduced compared to the values observed with C^{14}-glycine. Thus ALA is a preferential precursor of liver porphyrin and heme; the process of production of ALA is unrelated to that of erythropoietic porphyrin and heme. C^{14}-Hemin was an efficient precursor of bilirubin formation and therefore may be a metabolic intermediate in hepatic bilirubin production. In iron deficiency there was an abnormal increase in early C^{14}-bilirubin, which was proportionally related to ineffective erythropoiesis.

Experiments on isolated perfused rat livers were reported by Robinson *et al.* (1965b*) who administered glycine-2-C^{14} or ALA-4-C^{14} in the perfusion fluid and isolated C^{14}-bilirubin from the bile. As no C^{14}-hemoglobin was present in the perfusion fluid, this is a definite proof of hepatic bilirubin synthesis. Garay et al. (1966a[*]) extended experiments with liver perfusion to the livers of rats with congenital hemolytic jaundice (Gunn rats) as well as normal rats, using ALA-C^{14} in the perfusion fluid. They found incorporation of C^{14} into partially purified hepatic nonhemoglobin hemes, suggesting that these compounds are intermediates in the formation of bilirubin in the liver. Finally, the early nonerythropoietic fraction of bile pigments was discussed in three papers at the Bilirubin Metabolism Symposium (held in London, July 1966) by Israels, Schwartz, and Robinson.

Recently L. Eales (personal communication, 1965) found clinical evidence strongly supporting the hypothesis (7), i.e., that the most early appearing fraction of bile pigment is not a product of the bone marrow heme synthesis, but is of hepatic origin. He gave labeled delta-aminolevulinic acid to human subjects with South African hepatic porphyria and found a very high percentage of label in the most early appearing fractions of these patients. The publication of these important observations must be looked forward to with great interest.

The "first peak" of bile pigment formation thus consists of two components; (1) an early one, appearing during the first 24 hours and disappearing within 48 hours, which is independent of hemoglobin synthesis in the bone marrow and takes place in the liver; and (2) a later and quantitatively more important one, beginning after about 24 hours and reaching its maximum in about 48 hours, which is connected with hemoglobin formation and probably due to degradation of heme or hemoglobin in the marrow itself.

Whether a direct synthesis or a "shunt" mechanism for bile pigments exists—i.e., synthesis from porphyrin precursors without passing through the porphyrin ring—is a difficult question to answer. With (1949) proposed this mechanism as the basis for some forms of jaundice and Israels et al. (1963b) believed that they demonstrated the existence of a shunt mechanism for bilirubin synthesis. As it became clear that the initial bile pigment peak is of hepatic origin the observations of Israels et al. (1963b) cannot however be regarded as proof of the existence of a shunt mechanism. This point was discussed by C. J. Watson (1965[*]) who could not find binding evidence for a primary shunt mechanism for bilirubin synthesis. On the other hand Garay et al. (1966[*]) could not exclude a direct pathway of bile pigment formation from porphyrins or other pyrroles prior to the formation of heme. Finally Gray expressed the belief that direct bilirubin synthesis from porphyrin precursors does not take place (Bouchier and Billing, 1967, pp. 44–45).

The third, least conspicuous source of U-L corresponds to the area between the two peaks. The small but steady amount of N^{15}-urobilin-L in stool indicates that it is formed after the synthesis of heme, but before the destruction of erythrocytes has started. As Fig. 29 shows, this source is more important in congenital porphyria than in normal persons. It is attributed to the destruction of heme from myoglobin, cytochrome, and catalase. Contrary to heme formed simultaneously in erythrocytes, this heme is constantly decomposed. It constitutes part of the general protein pool of the body, is not built into erythrocytes, and does not exhibit a half-life of about 130 days.

As explained later in this chapter, the formation of dipyrrole bile pigments as by-products of porphyrin synthesis seems to play a role under normal conditions and is even more apparent during porphyria when the first peak has a much greater significance than the later excretion.

The problem of origin of bile pigments which are formed during porphyrin synthesis has not been finally solved. Very few experiments have been conducted on normal persons, and even fewer in cases with porphyria. Lowry *et al.* (1952) published interesting studies on a case of hepatic porphyria in which large amounts of protoporphyrin were excreted in the stool. In spite of increased porphyrin synthesis, the curve obtained for N^{15}-urobilin-L isolated from the stool was the same as for normal persons. It was concluded that the excreted porphyrins were formed in the liver, and that a number of pyrrole reservoirs exist which differ only in their turnover rate. This was later substantiated by Gray and Scott (1958, 1959). They also found that the first "hematopoietic" stercobilin peak increases considerably after venesection, i.e., the first increase is in fact connected with hemoglobin formation.

Another interesting case of chronic porphyria was followed by Gray *et al.* (1948). In this case, increased porphyrin excretion developed with intermittent jaundice. Unfortunately no isotope studies were carried out. These would be especially interesting because of the combination of porphyria and jaundice. Aldrich *et al.* (1951) and Grinstein *et al.* (1951) described cases of congenital porphyria with simultaneous severe hemolytic anemia, in which the serum bilirubin was only 1 mg per 100 ml.

Watson-James and Abbot (1958) fed N^{15}-labeled glycine to patients with various forms of anemia and determined N^{15}-urobilin-L in their stool. Among these cases of anemia were vitamin B_{12}-resistant megaloblastic forms, hypo- and aplastic anemias, and a few myeloid leucoses. Although the disturbances of erythropoiesis had various causes, the first peak was considerably increased in all these cases. Thus, increase in the first peak seems to be a nonspecific indication of disturbed hematopoiesis. On the other hand, Medal *et al.* (1958) found no increase in the first peak during the regeneration phase of iron deficiency anemia although, in these cases, enhanced excretion was anticipated because of increased hematopoiesis.

The presence of a high first peak in patients with hematological disorders has been called "ineffective erythropoiesis" (Giblett *et al.*, 1956; Finch, 1959; Haurani and Tocantins, 1961). A disproportionally low reticulocyte count in the peripheral blood despite marked erythroid hyperplasia of the bone marrow is regarded as characteristic of this condition, which occurs regularly in thalassemia, refractory normoblastic anemia, megaloblastic anemia, and certain myeloproliferative disorders. In so-called thalassemia minor (known as Rieti-Greppi-Micheli-Syndrome in the Italian literature), the first peak is so pronounced that it gives rise to a pronounced jaundice in presence of a minimum of hemolysis (Robinson *et al.*, 1962).

Grinstein *et al.* (1960*) studied a patient with thalassemia major after oral administration of 100 μC of glycine-2-C^{14} and found that the radioactivity of the fecal stercobilin appeared extremely rapidly, reaching a maximum on the third day.

C. J. Watson (1963, p. 8) pointed out that the first peak—which he calls somewhat misleadingly, the "hematopoietic peak"—and the second one due to erythrocyte destruction may be impossible to separate in certain hematological cases. This is unquestionably correct if one works with oral glycine administration and urobilin isolation, but if the technique of Israels *et al.* (1963b) is adopted—i.e., i.v. glycine administration and bilirubin isolation—separation of the two peaks would presumably be much clearer.

Berendson *et al.* (1964*) found that ineffective erythropoiesis with high first peak fecal stercobilin occurs in several forms of anemia, such as pernicious anemia in relapse, thalassemia, the anemia of erythropoietic porphyria, sideroblastic anemia, and refractory normoblastic anemia. In these anemias a well-marked high first peak is demonstrable contrary to chronic hemolytic anemias where the strongly increased second peak and the moderately increased first peak exhibit a tendency to coalesce into one single broad peak.

Berendson *et al.* studied a patient with manifest jaundice due to ineffective erythropoiesis and proposed the term, *dyserythropoietic jaundice* for jaundice due to accumulation of first peak bilirubin (nonconjugated). The patient was subjected to oral loading with N^{15}-glycine, and the N^{15}-content of isolated fecal stercobilin and mesobilifuscin as well as erythrocyte protoporphyrin was studied. Besides the high first peak of stercobilin they also found a peak of labeled fecal mesobilifuscin, and this occurred 24 hours before the stercobilin peak. Berendson *et al.* interpret this finding as pointing to an increased production of pyrrole heme precursors, possibly at a stage between porphobilinogen and uroporphyrinogen in the biosynthetic pathway.

Robinson and Schmid (1964*) used the term *ELP* (*early labeling pigments*) for the first peak bile pigments and pointed out that this fraction may account for as much as 40–80% of the total bile pigment excretion in ineffective erythropoiesis, and the main part of this is of hematopoietic origin, i.e., a by-product of erythroblastic heme synthesis. The mechanism may differ from one patient to the other.

Altman and Russel (1964*) studied the incorporation of radioactivity into protoporphyrin and globin of erythrocytes after intraperitoneal injection of glycine-2-C^{14}, δ-aminolevulinic acid-2,3-C^{14}, and porphobilinogen-3,5-C^{14} in mice. Both normal mice and mice with severely genotypically determined macrocytic anemia were studied (genotypes ww, $W^v w$, and $W^v W^v$). The appearance of radioactivity was determined in protoporphyrin and globin isolated from the erythrocytes. In the homozygotic congenitally anemic mice radioactivity was not demonstrable in the protoporphyrin before 14 days after the injection of glycine and δ-aminolevulinic acid, whereas it was clearly distinguishable in the normal mice after 2 days. Unfortunately the radioactivity of bile pigment was not studied in the mice. It would be highly interesting to find out whether the failing synthesis of erythrocyte protoporphyrin in the anemic mice during the first 14 days is accompanied by an increased synthesis of stercobilin or fecal porphyrin or mesobilifuscin.

Goldberg (1965*) pointed out that so-called sideroblastic anemias, which he prefers to call *dyshematopoietic anemias,* are closely related to ineffective erythropoiesis (cf. above) and that there is considerable resemblance between these anemias and the *hepatic porphyrias.* Both groups of diseases are of multifactorial pathogenesis and in both the path of heme synthesis is deranged—in the former in the erythroblasts of the bone marrow, in the latter in the liver.

C. J. Watson (1965*) introduced the so-called P/U ratio, i.e., maximum early labeling of circulating hemoglobin protoporphyrin divided by that of the fecal urobilinogen after administration of N^{15}- or C^{14}-glycine, as a measure of the erythropoietic effectiveness in different hematological states. Watson collected data from the literature and found the normal P/U ratio to lie between 0.75 and 1.40. In hemolytic anemias the values were between 0.61 and 1.40, i.e., normal. In congenital erythropoietic porphyria it was 0.19–0.33 in cases with and without hemolytic anemia. In pernicious anemia it was 0.08–0.25, in dyserythropoietic jaundice 0.08, in primary shunt hyperbilirubinemia 0.08–0.12, in thalassemia minor 0.20, and in thalassemia major 0.17.

A highly interesting observation on bile pigment synthesis in the *newborn infant* was reported by Vest *et al.* (1965*) who administered 800 mg N^{15}-glycine with an isotope content of 95% i.v. over an 8-hour period to two normal infants, 2 and 6 days old and weighing 3300–3600 g. Crystalline hemin was isolated from samples of venous blood and stools collected for 4–5 days each week for bile pigment preparation. The feces of one infant contained only bilirubin throughout the experimental period, the feces of the other contained some stercobilin toward the close of the experiment. The first peak of fecal bile pigment was remarkably high in both infants reaching a maximum 3–4 days after the glycine injection. Vest *et al.* calculated that at least 21–25% of the total bile pigment excreted was contained in the first peak, i.e., that the first peak of bile pigment excretion is about twice as high in the newborn as in the adult. In this connection it is of interest that With (1949, p. 336) wrote that "a synthetic bilirubin hyperproduction may be active in the newborn," and later (With, 1954, p. 224) that "the possibility of a synthetic bilirubin production does not seem unlikely, but this can only be tested in experiments with glycine-N^{15} in newborn."

A great number of isotope experiments have to be executed before the question of the origin of bile pigments which form during porphyrin synthesis (the peak in Fig. 29) can be answered. Although these investigations are expensive and time-consuming, they are unavoidable. A greater variety of animal species also have to be subjected to experimentation; only men, dogs, and rats have been studied up to this time. Fistula bile and serum of hepatectomized animals should be included in these investigations. It would be interesting to follow not only tetrapyrrole bile pigments but also dipyrrole compounds.

Summary

Bile pigments are synthesized *in vivo*: (a) as by-products of synthesis of heme in the liver; (b) from heme or porphyrin in the bone marrow by degradation before reaching the circulation; (c) from continuous low-grade production from cytochromes, myoglobin, and catalase; and (d) from degradation of the hemoglobin of circulating erythrocytes.

The so-called first peak bile pigment—"shunt bilirubin" or "hematopoietic peak"—is now known to consist of two phases, an initial extramedullary phase with a maximum appearing a few hours after the injection of the label and disappearing within 48 hours, and a second medullary phase appearing after about 24 hours with a maximum after about 48 hours that is associated with the heme synthesis in the erythroblasts. The second phase has a duration of a few days. Then a long, low plateau follows due to the continuous degradation of myoglobin, cytochromes, and catalase, and finally the third peak appears which is due to disintegration of hemoglobin in mature, circulating erythrocytes.

The relative importance of these four fractions varies with the circumstances, the first two fractions being relatively small in the normal adult, higher in the normal newborn, and especially high in certain pathological conditions (porphyrias, dyshematopoietic anemias). The study of the behavior of the various fractions in different pathological conditions is in progress, but much work remains to be done. Also their variation in *different animal species* must be studied to elucidate the problem of bile pigment formation from a biological point of view. It would be of special interest to study the Canadian ground squirrel *Sciurus niger* exhibiting "physiological porphyria" and the recently discovered *antarctic ice fishes* which are completely devoid of hemoglobin; therein all bile pigment present must be of nonerythropoietic origin (cf. Ruud, 1965*).

B. Formation of Bile Pigments from Hemoglobin and Related Compounds

Hemoglobin is an iron complex of protoporphyrin bound to the protein globin. The nature of the heme-binding group of globin has been much discussed. The discussion was summarized by Keilin (1960). Four possibilities exist: (1) binding to the imidazole group of the histidine of the globin; (2) binding to the COOH groups of aspartic and glutamic acids; (3) binding to the sulfhydryl group of cysteine; and (4) that heme is not bound to any specific group of globin, but that the globin molecule fits very closely to that of heme, enabling the van der Waal's forces alone to hold the two molecules firmly together. The most widely held hypothesis is (1), the imidazole binding to histidine, but important properties of hemoglobin are best explained by the other possibilities for which the imidazole binding can hardly be the whole explanation. It is probable that the amino acid chain of globin, once it is synthesized and provided with a heme group, will coil around the heme and take up a position which is the only one satisfying the stereochemical requirements of its amino acid sequence. This explains why the denaturation of hemoglobin is reversible to a certain degree.

The following steps have to be considered to account for the formation of bilirubin from hemoglobin:

1. Separation of globin
2. Splitting off of iron
3. Opening of the protoporphyrin ring

The sequence of these processes can be different, and this has stimulated numerous discussions and disputes.

According to the classic opinion (Nencki and Sieber, 1884, 1888; Nencki and Zaleski, 1900, 1901), it was thought that globin is first split off, then the iron separated, and finally the porphyrin ring is opened. This theory was based primarily on experiments with dogs with bile fistula (Brugsch and Yoshimoto, 1911; Brugsch and Kawashima, 1911). In spite of poor experimental evidence, this hypothesis was accepted for many years (see Eppinger, 1920; F. C. Mann *et al.*, 1926a; Lepehne, 1930), although it was contradicted by Schottmüller (1914) and Schumm (1916). These authors investigated rare cases of hematin jaundice, a condition where hematin concentrates in plasma without an increase of the serum bilirubin level. Later, this condition was closely investigated by H. Schmidt (1929), Hijmans van den Bergh and Kamerling (1934), and C. J. Watson (1938). Based on experiments in which hemoglobin and hematin were intravenously injected, Bingold (1923, 1930, 1932) and Duesberg (1934, 1938) questioned the role of hematin as the precursor of bilirubin. They viewed hematin formation as a *cul de sac* of hemoglobin degradation. Thorough surveys on older studies have been presented by Watson (1938, pp. 2461 to 2464) and by Lemberg and Legge (1949, pp. 453 and 503 ff.).

The formation of bile pigment from hematin has, however, now been demonstrated *in vitro* (London, 1950) and *in vivo* (Kench *et al.*, 1950*), but was studied more closely by Snyder and Schmid (1965*) who injected C^{14}-hematin into rats with external bile fistula and found that it was converted to bilirubin with an efficiency similar to that observed with a comparable amount of hemoglobin itself by Ostrow *et al.* (1962). The injected C^{14}-hematin was converted to C^{14}-bilirubin with an efficiency of 50–70%. The rate of disappearance of C^{14}-hematin from the plasma varied depending on whether the pigment was bound to human or murine serum albumin; it is bound considerably firmer to the former than to the latter. C^{14}-Hematin was not absorbed from the intestine to any significant degree.

We are indebted to Lemberg and his collaborators for the modern view on these problems, and Lemberg (1956) has published a detailed summary of his opinions.

To understand the mechanisms involved, it is important to remember that hemoglobin decomposition is favored by biochemical conditions in the organism. Hemoglobin is only stable inside the erythrocytes (see Lemberg and Legge, 1949, p. 508; Mills, 1957; Mills and Randall, 1958). It is also important to know that bilirubin is bound to a protein. The latter, like globin, belongs to the albumins, and therefore many investigators assumed that it is globin itself. Today we know that this protein is different from globin (see Chapter V,B,2). Discussion of so-called "green hemins" is also necessary. The first pigments of this sort have been obtained from pyridine hemochromes, in which pyridine replaces the protein in the hemoglobin molecule.

Fischer and Lindner (1926) studied the first green hemins, and later Warburg and Negelein (1930) introduced the term "green hemin." To obtain the pigments they oxidized hemoglobin in the presence of liver or yeast. Karrer *et al.* (1933) prepared green hemins by oxidoreduction with ascorbic acid. Lemberg (1935) transformed green hemins into biliverdin esters with hydrochloric acid–methanol.

Oxidoreductions play a significant role *in vitro* and probably also *in vivo* during formation of these compounds. This means simultaneous oxidation with molecular O_2 and reduction with a reducing agent. Hydrogen peroxide is formed under these conditions (Fischer and Libowitzky, 1938). In this way the porphyrin ring which is connected to active iron can be opened (Kench, 1954). Among the varied redox agents, ascorbic acid was used preferentially, since it is known that it is present in corresponding concentrations under physiological conditions.

By corresponding oxidoreductions, no bile pigment is formed from free porphyrin. However, its formation is possible from hemoglobin, methemoglobin, methemalbumin, myoglobin, horse liver catalase, and horseradish catalase. The only hemoprotein which does not yield bile pigment under these conditions is cytochrome c (Kench, 1954).

C. J. Watson *et al.* (1941) demonstrated in *in vivo* experiments in dogs that protoporphyrin itself does not form bile pigments. Bénard *et al.* (1948) showed the same to be true for hematoporphyrin. London *et al.* (1951) showed that dogs injected intravenously with N^{15}-protoporphyrin excreted small amounts of N^{15}-stercobilin in stool. This can be explained by hemoglobin formation from the injected porphyrin in liver and marrow, since part of such hemoglobin is rapidly decomposed (first peak, Fig. 29). Consequently, these experiments do not disprove the numerous *in vitro* experiments, which show that free porphyrins cannot be decomposed by oxidoreduction (Kench, 1954).

The foregoing evidence indicates that iron is necessary for bile pigment formation. The form of iron (ferrous or ferric) and its binding on protein are of a lesser significance.

Although the detailed mechanism of bile pigment formation from hemoproteins is much disputed and is very complicated, extensive information has been obtained.

To simplify matters, Fischer and Libowitzky (1938) and Libowitzky (1940b) studied coproheme-I. In contrast to natural heme (protoheme IX), this compound is symmetrical and saturated in all side chains. By oxidoreduction they obtained coproglaucobilin in about 10% yield. Lemberg *et al.* (1937a,b, 1938a,b), subjected pyridine–protoheme IX–hemocrome to oxidoreduction with ascorbic acid and obtained a green hemochrome called verdohemochromogen. Independently, Edlbacher and von Segesser (1937a,b) performed similar experiments.

Investigations on the green hemoglobins proper (those containing native globin) were carried out by Barkan and Schales (1937, 1938), who used hydrogen peroxide in the presence of cyanide and obtained a green hemoglobin called pseudohemoglobin. Shortly afterward, Lemberg *et al.* (1939) subjected hemoglobin to oxidoreduction with ascorbic acid and arrived at a green hemoglobin called choleglobin; on treatment with glacial acetic acid and ethyl acetate, it yielded biliverdin.

Numerous investigations have since been carried out. The nomenclature of green hemoglobins and hemochromes is confusing. Lemberg (1956) worked out a summary which is presented in Table IA, somewhat modified.

Kiese and Kacske (1942) proposed a simplified nomenclature. They called Fe^{3+}-containing green hemoglobins verdiglobins, and those containing Fe^{++}, verdoglobins. They named the prosthetic group verde. This nomenclature was, however, rejected by Lemberg and Legge (1949, p. 453).

Most green hemoglobins are prepared under nonphysiological conditions. Ascorbic acid and glutathione are the main reducing agents which are active under physiological conditions. Under certain abnormal circumstances, sulfhemoglobin can also be formed *in vivo*.

The individual stages of physiological degradation of the protoporphyrin ring were described by Lemberg (1956). They are shown, somewhat modified, in Fig. 30.

The group within the triangular frame in Fig. 30 attains the intermediate stages shown in Fig. 31.

Initially, the ring consists of 20 C-atoms (16 in the pyrrole rings and 4 in the methine groups). On substitution with oxygen in the α-methine group, the original ring is converted to one with 19 C-atoms; this is then finally opened. The bile pigment so formed has three methine groups, i.e., it is a bilatriene. Thus, the first pigment is biliverdin and not bilirubin. The iron remains bound to the porphyrin ring during this decomposition. As previously mentioned, iron is necessary for the

TABLE IA
GREEN HEMOGLOBINS

Name	Mode of formation[a]	References
Choleglobin (Verdoglobin A)	HbO_2 + ascorbic acid	Lemberg *et al.* (1939, 1941a,b); Legge and Lemberg (1941)
Pseudohemoglobin (Verdoglobin CN)	HbO_2 + HCN + H_2O_2 or HbO_2 + KCN + H_2O_2	Barkan and Schales (1937) Lemberg *et al.* (1941a); Holden (1946); Liébecq (1947); Kiese (1947a,b,c); G. Kikuchi *et al.* (1954)
Cruoralbin	HbO_2 + HCN + $Na_2S_2O_4$ + O_2	Holden (1943, 1945); Callaghan (1949)
Sulfhemoglobin (Verdoglobin S)	HbO_2 + H_2S	Lemberg *et al.* (1942); Kiese (1948)
Verdoglobin Ph	HbO_2 + phenylhydrazine	Lemberg and Legge (1942); Kiese (1947a,b,c)
Verdoglobin NO_2	Hi + $NaNO_2$ + H_2O_2	Kiese (1947a,b,c); Holden (1947a,b)
Not named	Hb or Hi + $Na_2S_2O_4$ + H_2O_2	Kaziro *et al.* (1953, 1955), Dalziel and O'Brien (1954a)
Not named	Hb or Hi + H_2O_2	Lemberg *et al.* (1941b); George and Irvine (1952); Dalziel and O'Brien (1954b)
Not named	HbO_2 + $Na_2S_2O_4$	Legge and Roughton (1950)
Ferriverdoglobin NO_2 (Verdoglobin III)	Hi + $NaNO_2$ + H_2O_2	Scheler (1964); Scheler *et al.* (1964*)

[a] Hb, reduced hemoglobin; HbO_2, oxyhemoglobin; Hi, hemiglobin (methemoglobin)

ring opening. Nevertheless, this bond gets looser as decomposition progresses, i.e., it becomes "easily detectable" or "labile" iron.

Choleglobin played an important role in the ensuing discussions. Lemberg *et al.* (1941a,b) studied choleglobin formation and its decomposition to bile pigments *in vitro*. Lemberg *et al.* (1941a,b) showed

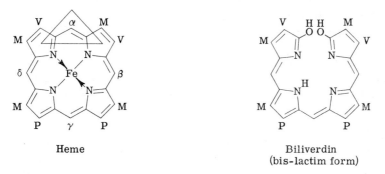

Heme

Biliverdin
(bis-lactim form)

FIG. 30. Stages in the physiological degradation of the protoporphyrin ring.

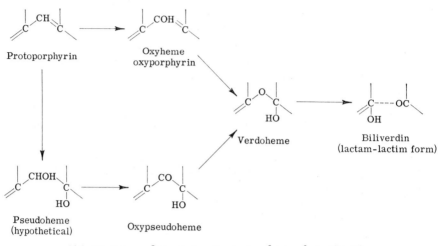

FIG. 31. Intermediate stages. See text and triangle in Fig. 30.

that iron in choleglobin is loosely bound, and compared it with the labile iron of Barkan and Schales (1937, 1938). It was found that this iron fraction increased during choleglobin formation. According to Lemberg *et al.* (1941b,c), hemoglobin of normal blood contains about 1% choleglobin. Lemberg and Legge (1942) could demonstrate biliverdin formation in normal erythrocytes. During experimental hemolysis, the production of this intracorpuscular biliverdin increased. Although Lemberg and Legge (1949) insisted on their opinions, Gardicas *et al.* (1948, 1950) doubted their findings. According to these authors, the small amounts of choleglobin which occur in normal hemoglobin are artifacts.

That choleglobin is formed from hemoglobin *in vivo* was demonstrated by Kikuchi and Rokugo (1961*) who found excretion of choleglobin in the urine of rabbits 30 minutes after i.v. infusion of hemoglobin (destromatized rabbit erythrocytes). The urine exhibited a distinct maximum at 618 nm in addition to the protohemochrome peak in the region 500–600 nm, and the 618 nm peak was shifted to 630 nm on treatment of the sample with CO.

Engel (1940) carried out the first quantitative investigation on hemoglobin decomposition. In his *in vitro* experiments, only 10% of the heme yielded bile pigments. However, Lemberg *et al.* (1941b,c) found that it yielded 20% in short-time experiments. In experiments run over longer periods, they demonstrated 50% conversion of hemoglobin in "total choleheme"; 70% of this pigment yielded biliverdin.

Easily separable iron has recently been studied by the Japanese school (Kawaguchi, 1957a,b,c). Kawaguchi injected Fe^{55}-labeled hemoglobin i.v. to rabbits. He found it questionable whether all the easily separable iron formed in the erythrocytes was due to production of choleglobin. The liver was the main site of hemoglobin breakdown. He also injected $Fe^{55}Cl_3$ and studied the nonheme iron of the erythrocytes. Takemura (1959a,b) transfused rabbits with three different categories of Fe^{59}-labeled erythrocytes (immature, mature, and old cells) and studied the distribution of the radioactivity in the organs of the animals.

Since H_2O_2 plays an important role during the formation of green hemoglobins, catalase degradation is involved. M. Engel (1940) showed that the formation of green hemoglobin is considerably retarded by catalase. This was substantiated by Foulkes and Lemberg (1949), who detected a factor in erythrocyte stroma that protects hemoglobin against the effect of catalase and stimultaneously inhibits the destruction of catalase. Mills (1957) showed that erythrocytes contain an enzyme that catalyzes the oxidation of reduced glutathione by hydrogen peroxide and thus protects hemoglobin against degradation. This glutathione peroxidase was found to be more effective for protection of hemoglobin than catalase. Mills and Randall (1958) found that reduction of the glucose level of erythrocytes is followed by a marked decrease of their protective mechanism against hemoglobin degradation, whereas this mechanism was enhanced if glucose-6-phosphate, 6-phosphogluconate, or ribose-5-phosphate, nicotinamide-adenine dinucleotide phosphate (NADP), and oxidized glutathione were added to erythrocyte homogenates.

Kiese (1942, 1947a,b,c) and Kiese and Seipelt (1943) developed methods for determination of green hemoglobin in blood and organ extracts. They followed its formation and excretion using various hemolytic poisons. Verdoglobin-containing erythrocytes normally disappear within 3 days from the circulating blood; after splenectomy, this process takes twice as long.

Investigations of the chemical structure of green hemes and hemoglobins is a complicated and disputed chapter.

Stier (1942a,b,c) succeeded in reducing green hemin esters to porphyrin esters and concluded that the porphyrin ring in green hemin esters must be intact. In his experiments he used both symmetrical coprohemes and asymmetrical meso- and protohemes. He found that green hemins are formed more easily from the latter substances than from coprohemes. It was assumed that the first stage of hemoglobin oxidation is the transformation of the α-methine bridge into =COH— with simultaneous oxidation of Fe^{++} to Fe^{3+}. Transformation of =COH— follows (see Siedel, 1943b, p. 187; 1944, p. 31). Like Lemberg et al. (1941c), Stier found bilipurpurins as well as biliverdin. Kiese (1947c) was able to show that the prosthetic group of verdoglobin NO_2 is identical to the spirographisheme which occurs in lower animals. Verdoglobin NO_2 was obtained from hemoglobin by NO_2 poisoning. The prosthetic group contains a formyl group in lieu of one of the two vinyl groups in protoporphyrin. Kiese (1948) could also demonstrate that sulfhemoglobin contains a closed porphyrin ring. This fact was confirmed by Bénard *et al.* (1946).

In contrast, Lemberg assumed that instead of α-methine bridges in green hemin there is an oxygen bridge (—O—). He based this assumption on the fact that verdohemochrome can be transformed into mono-azohemochrome, which contains an =N— bridge (Lemberg and Legge, 1949, p. 464–468).

Recently, the Japanese school has published studies on the formation of verdohemochromes.

Kikkawa (1959a,b) studied the intermediate products during formation of bile pigments from pyridine hematin and from hemoglobin by means of Fe^{59}-labeled compounds and column chromatography. Four zones appeared in the chromatograms, all of which contained biliverdin in the column from hemoglobin. Katami (1959a,b) performed spectrophotometric studies on a green hemin formed in the system pyridine–hemin–hydrazine–O_2 and its combining with proteins. The hydrazine system was found to differ substantially from the ascorbic acid–O_2 system. The verdoheme formed combined with globin and albumin to stable compounds. Yamabuki (1959a) studied the coupled oxidation of protoheme-dimethyl ester with *l*-ascorbic acid and O_2. The verdohemochrome formation was only slightly decreased because of the esterification of the carboxyl groups. The same writer (1959b) compared the progress of the coupled oxidation of pyridine-hematin with *l*-ascorbic acid and O_2 in chloroform solution, benzene solution, acetone solution, and aqueous solution. The course of the reaction was essentially the same in the nonpolar and polar solvent systems. With increasing amounts of water in the reaction system, increasing quantities of ascorbic acid were required.

All these structure studies were carried out on green hemes and hemochromes. To decide the question, experiments should be carried out on green hemoglobins. This problem, however, is extremely difficult, since their prosthetic group is very labile. In green hemoglobins the prosthetic group is both considerably more labile and much more firmly bound to the protein than in ordinary hemoglobin. In addition, it is very difficult to obtain green hemoglobins pure (Lemberg and Legge, 1949, p. 456). Important investigations have been carried out on these compounds by Liébecq and collaborators between 1943 and 1948; their work was summed up by Liébecq (1946, 1948). He found that pseudohemoglobin and choleglobin yield monoazohemochrome on ammonia treatment, while sulfhemoglobin is converted into hemochrome by alkali reduction. This is explained by the fact that sulfhemoglobin contains a —CS— bridge in lieu of the α-methine bridge (Liébecq, 1947; Liébecq *et al.*, 1947). This fact also seems to substantiate the concept of an oxygen bridge in pseudohemoglobin and choleglobin (see Lemberg and Legge, 1949, p. 455).

The Japanese school has performed a series of studies on hemoglobin breakdown and bile pigment formation.

Araki (1956a,b) found two different forms of choleglobin on treatment of hemoglobin with ascorbic acid and O_2, choleglobin a in the supernatant and choleglobin b in the precipitate formed during the process. Biliverdin was extracted from both with glacial acetic acid, but in much smaller yield from choleglobin b than from a. The amount of nitrogen present in choleglobin b decreased during the process of formation, and in the end it was less than 1% of that present in choleglobin a. Simultaneously, the amount of iron present in choleglobin a decreased and the easily separable iron increased. Maga (1956a,b,c) studied the compounds formed during coupled oxidation with ascorbic acid from hemoglobin, pyridine-hematin, and histidine-hematin; he employed column chromatography on silica gel. In all three cases six different zones appeared on the columns, and the relative magnitude of these colored zones changed during the progress of the reaction. Shimizu (1956a,b) performed studies with antihemoglobin sera and found that globin is rapidly denatured during the degradation process, and before the heme is broken down. Takeda (1959a,b) investigated the formation of pseudohemoglobin (system: HbO_2–KCN–H_2O_2) and compared it with choleglobin formation (HbO_2–ascorbic acid–O_2) using a recording spectrophotometer. He found the two processes to be closely similar.

Holden and Lynikas (1961) found that the formation of green pigments from oxyhemoglobin by coupled oxidation with ascorbic acid was accelerated by fluorides, ammonium chloride, amines, and other organic nitrogenous substances. If ascorbic acid was replaced by cyanide and sodium bithionite, fluorides inhibited the green pigment formation while it is accelerated by the N-containing compounds.

Mills (1962) studied the hemoglobin breakdown in rat liver slices and homogenates and showed that it depends on coupled oxidation with enzymatically generated hydrogen peroxide together with ascorbic acid and other reducing compounds, and that purine compounds such as nicotinamide-adenine dinucleotide (NAD) and its phosphate (NADP) play an essential role in the generation of the hydrogen peroxide required for the degradation process.

Vecchio *et al.* (1963a,b,c) studied the formation of choleglobin in hemolyzates from erythrocytes from newborns severely deficient in glucose-6-phosphate dehydrogenase (G-6-PD). The choleglobin formation was markedly increased in the G-6-PD deficient hemolyzates as compared with the normal ones, and addition of G-6-PD to the deficient hemolyzates normalized their choleglobin formation. If optimal concentrations of reduced glutathione were obtained by addition of this substance, the difference between the normal and the deficient hemolyzates also disappeared. If optimal concentrations of nicotinamide adenine dinucleotide phosphate (NADP) ($10^{-4} M$) were secured, the choleglobin formation of the deficient hemolyzates also became normal, but NAD did not have this effect.

Scheler *et al.* (1964*) described a method of intracorpuscular preparation of *metverdoglobin NO$_2$* and subjected this pigment to close study, especially its sedimentation constants and spectral properties. It exhibited a visible maximum at 607 nm ($E_{1\,\mathrm{cm}}^{\mathrm{m}M} = 11.5$) and a Soret maximum at 403 nm ($E_{1\,\mathrm{cm}}^{\mathrm{m}M} = 120$). The prosthetic group was found to be a H_2O-complex exhibiting a characteristic change of absorption spectrum on deprivation of water. The absorption was pH dependent.

Like methemoglobin verdoglobin NO$_2$ forms numerous complexes with anions such as $HCOO^-$, SCN^-, NO_2^-, and CN^-. The magnetic properties and ionization of the pigment were studied. Scheler *et al.* do not believe that the formation of metverdoglobin NO$_2$ from hemoglobin can be due to a conversion of protohemin into spirographishemin as proposed by Kiese (1947c). Their findings indicate a largely intact iron-porphyrin nucleus in metverdoglobin NO$_2$.

It is assumed that the first decomposition product which forms during the degradation of natural hemoglobin is an addition product of hemoglobin and hydrogen peroxide (Lemberg and Purdon, 1949). Keilin (1952) was able to isolate the corresponding urohematin compound (Lemberg, 1956). However, to date no addition product of protohematin and hydrogen peroxide has been isolated.

The cleavage of hemoglobin is accompanied by increase in optical density in the spectral range 630–700 nm. Simultaneously, the density decreases in the ultraviolet (Soret band). This phenomenon is known in protein-free systems (verdohemochrome) and for hemoglobin itself (Kench, 1954). In addition, Kaziro *et al.* (1955) were able to demonstrate the existence of another compound which had an absorption maximum at 760 nm. This compound formed during *in vitro* oxidoreduction of hemoglobin, myoglobin, and pyridine–hemochrome. The experiments simulated physiological conditions. In order to distinguish this compound from choleglobin, pseudohemoglobin, and cruoralbin (which have absorption bands at 624–630 nm), the authors called this green hemoglobin with absorption band at 760 nm "verdohemoglobin." However, Lemberg (1956) assumed that the band at 760–770 nm was caused by biliverdin–iron hemochromes and globins.

Takaki (1959a,b) studied the breakdown of hemoglobin in erythrocyte hemolyzates with changing concentrations of ascorbic acid and O_2 tension. With a low concentration of ascorbic acid, a compound with an absorption maximum of 630 nm formed. With rising concentrations of ascorbic acid, methemoglobin appeared and became the only reaction product if the reaction was acid and the solution aerated. In alkaline solution, a substance with a maximum at 670 nm formed.

Further, it should be mentioned that Nakadoi (1956a,b) found that the so-called *Heinz bodies* of erythrocytes are connected with the action of molecular oxygen and ascorbic acid on erythrocytes. He believes that *l*-ascorbic acid penetrates the erythrocyte membrane and produces Heinz bodies in the erythrocytes during its own oxidation.

It should also be mentioned that, according to Sjöstrand (1952a,b,c), the C-atom of the α-methine bridge of protoporphyrin is liberated as CO. On the basis of this CO formation, Engstedt (1957) developed a method of measuring hemoglobin degradation.

According to Lemberg (1956), the natural route of hemoglobin breakdown goes through choleglobin. The latter has a modified porphyrin ring with 19 C-atoms (the twentieth C-atom is replaced by an O-atom). Under physiological conditions hematin does not play a role as an intermediate. Lemberg did not overlook the fact that Kench (1954) succeeded in transforming hematin into bile pigments by oxidoreduction with ascorbic acid *in vitro;* nevertheless, he assumed that oxygen pressure and ascorbic acid concentration were too high to be regarded as physiological in these experiments. On the other hand, Kench (1954) maintains that there is no chemical reason why free hematin or other of the hemin derivatives investigated (including methemalbumin and metmyoglobin) could not be similarly decomposed if exposed to the cells of the reticulo-endothelial system.

Hematin is known to be a product of pathological hemoglobin degradation in certain hemolytic conditions (malaria, pernicious anemia, absorption of larger amounts of blood extravasates, and chronic liver insufficiency). Hematin only rarely reaches higher concentration levels (for example during hematin jaundice, see above). For these reasons Lemberg (1956) doubts that hematin is a normal "intermediate" during bile pigment formation. If hematin is added to serum it immediately reacts with serum albumin, and stable methemalbumin is formed (Fairley, 1939, 1941; Bénard *et al.*, 1948; Keilin, 1944; Rosenfeld and Surgenor, 1950). Methemalbumin, together with methemoglobin is observed during gas gangrene septicemia and certain poisonings (sulfonamides, pamaquine) (Bingold, 1923, 1930, 1932; Schumm, 1932). It is closely related to the so-called "malarial pigment" (Anderson and Morrison, 1942; Morrison and Anderson, 1942; Lemberg and Legge, 1949, p. 574).

Bingold (1934) thought that free hematin circulates in blood; this opinion was refuted by Fairley (1939, 1941). The role of methemalbumin as a possible intermediate during bile pigment formation was studied by Nakamishi (1956a,b). He observed that without species difference, one mole of hematin is always linked to two moles of serum albumin in humans, dogs, and rabbits. Methemalbumin formation, however, was pH dependent, with the optimum reached at pH 7.1. Nakamishi (1956a,b) could also show that methemalbumin formation is not immediate, but that it takes about 20 minutes at 37°. Formation can be influenced by molecular oxygen and by catalase. No hematin was bound to the serum globulins.

Shimomura (1959a) studied the formation of methemalbumin in man, rabbit, dog, and cow with spectrophotometric methods. At pH 7.2 maxima of 403, 500, 540, and 623 nm appeared without significant species differences. The formation of methemalbumin on incubation of alkaline hematin solutions with serum albumin at pH 7.2 and 37° required 25 minutes. The molar ratio of 2 albumin to 1 hematin was found optimal. Nakamishi (1956a,b) arrived at similar results in studies on men, dogs, and rabbits.

The fact that hematin does not occur under physiological conditions cannot be used as a serious objection to its possible role as intermediate. Kench *et al.* (1950) and Kench (1954) could demonstrate that methemalbumin (ferric hemalbumin) yields a considerable amount of bile pigments in *in vitro* experiments, and this was confirmed by Shimomura (1959b). However, the conclusions obtained on the basis of *in vitro* experiments cannot be applied to explain *in vivo* conditions without reservations. The presence of enzymes bound to certain cells can basically change conditions. Furthermore, it is by no means certain that hemoglobin degradation always proceeds *in vivo* as postulated by Lemberg (1956). It is possible that in various parts of the reticuloendothelial system (RES), not to mention the liver parenchyma itself, small differences in enzyme systems exist, and correspondingly various degradation routes could operate.

London (1950) demonstrated that after injection of N^{15}-hematin, N^{15}-stercobilin appeared in stool. Within 9 days, an amount appeared which corresponded to 18% of injected material. This indicated that hematin can be converted into bile pigments *in vivo* as well. Lemberg (1956), however, maintains that this process is slow and incomplete.

The role of the protein part of the molecule (globin) is an important but difficult question. According to earlier literature, only hemoglobin itself (and never hematin) can form bile pigments *in vivo* (Gitter and Heilmeyer, 1931; Duesberg, 1934, 1938; Morrison *et al.*, 1940; W. A. D. Anderson *et al.*, 1942; Gilligan *et al.*, 1941). This, however, was doubted by Pass *et al.* (1945), who could show by experiments on humans that urobilin excretion increased after intravenous injections of hematin. However, this increase was much smaller than that observed after hemoglobin injection. The quantities of hematin and hemoglobin used in these experiments contained the equivalent amount of heme.

On the other hand, Bénard *et al.* (1948) demonstrated that a fast and pronounced increase of bile bilirubin occurs after intravenous injection of hematin in dogs with bile fistula. Lemberg and Legge (1949, p. 575), however, could not find any increase in bile pigment formation after mesohematin injection in rabbits.

The experiments of Snyder and Schmid (1965*) with injection of C^{14}-hematin to bile fistula rats showed equally rapid and efficient formation of C^{14}-bilirubin from hematin and hemoglobin, i.e., the ferriprotoporphyrin ring can readily be cleaved without being attached to native or adulterated globin.

Continued *in vitro* decomposition of hemoglobin results in progressive denaturation of globin. This is equally true for choleglobin and for the remaining hemoglobin. The further denaturation progresses, the more strongly the prosthetic groups become linked to the protein. This occurs because the SH-groups of cystein in globin are condensed during progressive denaturation.

Holden (1946, 1947a) assumed that compounds which produce green hemoglobins by oxidoreduction processes (for example, cyanides, nitrites, etc.) cause small changes in the globin molecule. These he called "perturbations." The perturbations are caused by a shift of the prosthetic group to another site within the globin molecule. In opposition to this, Lemberg (1956) contends that because of the close connection between the protein structure and the electron configuration of iron, even a small change in protein structure can profoundly affect the reactivity between heme and oxygen or peroxide. An example of such a small change is the disrupting or rearrangement of hydrogen bonds of globin in the vicinity of heme ("heme bound groups").

It is necessary to distinguish between "perturbance" and denaturation. During denaturation, further oxidation of heme is inhibited. This explains why most of the reactions which lead to the formation of green hemoglobin are incomplete and always leave some protoheme unchanged (Lemberg, 1956). Yamamoto (1956a,b) studied the effect of perturbators on the formation of verdohemoglobin and verdohemochromes.

One can see that the problems of bile pigment formation during hemoglobin degradation are awaiting a final solution. Although Lemberg's arguments are substantiated by pertinent evidence, there is no proof that his theories are correct; especially since his degradation mechanism is proposed to be the only possible one which can take place in the body. Until further experimental material becomes available, final evaluation seems to be impossible.

Nevertheless, it can be stated that the classic hypothesis is incorrect in its original form. The first degradation step is oxidation of intact hemoglobin (containing globin and ferrous iron) by the addition of hydrogen peroxide. Later, choleglobin is formed which contains easily detachable iron. These processes are, at least *in vitro*, important routes of degradation. On the other hand, one cannot as yet decide whether this route is the only one or the most important one. Other processes in which globin is initially split off could be of equal significance. However, today it is a fact that, contrary to the classic theory, porphyrin iron cannot be split off before the ring is opened.

Similarly, it is certain that biliverdin is the first intermediate. Thus, Nishikawa (1959b) found that biliverdin administered subcutaneously was rapidly transformed to bilirubin in histomicrospectrophotometric studies in mice. The electronic basis for the peculiar properties of biliverdin as the primary breakdown product of hemoglobin has recently been made clear by Pullman and Perault (1959). They calculated the energy levels by means of the molecular orbital method (L.C.A.O. approximation). Protoporphyrin was found to be at one time a good donor and acceptor of electrons, a property forming the basis of its biological functioning, cf. the oxidoreduction taking place during its degradation. The α-bridge at which its ring is broken was found to be the most electron rich of its four $=CH-$ bridges. The opening of its ring is accompanied by a drastic redistribution of the electronic levels, and biliverdin has the unique property that its lowest empty molecular orbital is a bonding one ($K = 0.021$), a fact that explains its unusual electron acceptor properties. Reduction takes place in its central $=CH-$ bridge and to a much lesser degree in the two side bridges because of the central bridge being more deficient in electrons than the side bridges. Reduction of the central bridge is accompanied by a decrease of resonance energy of only 1 kcal/mole, whereas reduction in a side bridge gives a decrease of 8 kcal/mole. The degradation of protoporphyrin through bile pigments is unique in that it consists of a series of hydrogenations as compared with the degradation of other biological compounds such as, the purines and pyrimidines of nucleic acids which are degraded through a series of hydrolyses and oxidations. Both bilirubin and urobilin contain conjugated dipyrryl systems capable of further reduction but, in contrast to biliverdin, their lowest empty molecular orbitals are unbonding.

The *in vivo* conversion of biliverdin to bilirubin in the rat was studied by Royer *et al.* (1962*) and Garay *et al.* (1964a*). Two groups of rats were studied, a control group in which saline was administered intraperitoneally and an experimental group where 2 mg of biliverdin was given dissolved in the saline. The common duct was severed, ligated, and cannulated, and the concentration of biliverdin and bilirubin determined in the bile and serum of the rats using the methods described by the authors. A well-marked increase in the bilirubin concentration in both bile and serum was found in the rats given biliverdin as compared to the controls.

Goldstein and Lester (1964*) injected radiochemically pure C^{14}-biliverdin into rats with external biliary drainage in a single dose equivalent to one-sixth to one-fourth of their estimated daily pigment production. Of the injected radioactivity 54–95% was rapidly excreted in the bile as conjugated C^{14}-bilirubin, beginning 30 minutes after the injection and continuing for 20 hours. Only 1% of the radioactivity appeared in the urine. In one experiment a significant part of the radioactivity was excreted in the bile as nonidentifiable degradation products, but otherwise the major part appeared as conjugated bilirubin. These results are consistent with the view that biliverdin is the primary degradation product of hemoglobin and an intermediate in formation of bilirubin.

Rokugo (1962*) injected hemolyzates of washed erythrocyte concentrates (oxyhemoglobin), methemoglobin, and metmyoglobin i.v. to male rabbits and determined their excretion of hemoglobin derivatives and bile pigments in urine using spectrophotometric methods. After oxyhemoglobin infusion massive urinary excretion of hemoglobin and choleglobin and lesser excretion of biliverdin was found in the urine, and small amounts of choleglobin were found in the serum. No verdohemoglobin was found. When methemoglobin was infused the occurrence of choleglobin was delayed and small amounts of verdohemoglobin were excreted. *In vitro* incubation of oxyhemoglobin under conditions imitating the *in vivo* ones resulted in insignificant choleglobin formation; the choleglobin formed must be due to *in vivo* factors. Rokugo believes that the *in vivo* degradation of hemoglobin follows the system with ascorbic acid proposed by Lemberg.

Singleton and Lester (1965*) studied the enzymatic activity catalyzing the reduction of biliverdin to bilirubin by reduced NAD or NADP. They obtained a 15-fold increase in concentration in the supernatant of guinea pig liver homogenate. The enzyme that was responsible they named *biliverdin reductase*. The enzymatic activity was studied in various organs and tissues and found to be higher in the liver than in the spleen. They observed that more than one equivalent of NADH was apparently oxidized during the reduction of one equivalent of biliverdin for which it was concluded that reduction of the vinyl groups of bilirubin may also take place simultaneously to a certain extent as well as the reduction of the b-bridge, i.e., the possibility of formation of dihydrobilirubin or even mesobilirubin besides bilirubin is possible.

The importance of biliverdin as the primary product during bile pigment formation was stressed by Akagi (1960a,b) in perfusion experiments with rabbit livers *in vitro* as well as *in vivo*. If hemoglobin or verdohemochromes were added to the blood or perfusion fluid, biliverdin appeared in the bile together with bilirubin. If biliverdin itself was added, the majority was excreted unchanged with the bile *in vivo*, whereas a substantial part appeared as bilirubin in the bile in perfusion experiments with isolated livers. If the liver parenchyma was poisoned or the RES blocked, only minor changes took place, from which it was concluded that the parenchymal cells and the stellate cells play about equal parts in bile pigment formation. It was found that hydrogenation of biliverdin to bilirubin also took place in the bile ducts after excretion.

The *enzymes* responsible for the degradation of heme compounds were studied by H. Nakajima (1958, 1959, 1963), Nakajima *et al.* (1961a,b,c, 1963), and Yamaguchi *et al.* (1961). They prepared an enzyme which converts hemin to verdohemochrome in the presence of pyridine in the form of an active cell-free preparation from bovine liver. During its action the   density at 656 nm—corresponding to one of the specific absorption bands of verdohemochrome— increased proportional to the time of incubation. The pH optimum of the enzyme was 8.6 and it was completely inactivated on heating to 80° for 5 minutes. As cofactors, NADP and Fe^{++} were required. The enzyme activity was studied in various tissues and found to be high in the liver and kidney and very low in the spleen and bone marrow. Fractionation of liver homogenate by means of differential centrifugation with Schneider's method was performed by Yamaguchi *et al.* (1961); the enzyme activity was found in the supernatant fraction. The enzyme preparations were concentrated by means of ammonium sulfate fractionation and column chromatography with hydroxyl apatite and diethylaminoethyl (DEAE) cellulose. The activity of the crude preparation was increased 14-fold in this way.

Among the heme compounds occurring *in vivo*, only the hemoglobin–haptoglobin complex was degraded to a significant degree by the pyridine–hemochrome degrading enzyme. The relative yield of the enzyme was 1.2 μmoles for pyridine–hemochrome, 0.98 μmole for hemoglobin–haptoglobin, 0.16 μmole for hemiglobin, 0.10 μmole for hemoglobin and zero for free alkaline hematin. The enzyme was extremely unstable in the presence of oxygen and at pH below 7.4. Its action was inhibited by metal-binding agents and SH inhibitors (α,α'-dipyridyl, EDTA, KCN, KCNS, NaN$_3$, iodoacetate).

The name *heme α-methenyl oxygenase* was proposed for the enzyme (Takemura, 1962a,b,c). An accelerator for the enzyme was demonstrated by Takemura (1962a), who found from differential centrifugation that the enzyme activity of the supernatant fraction increased about 50% after incubation with the nuclear fraction. The activator was a low-molecular compound, stable toward heat, pH changes, and oxygen. It could be extracted from the nuclear fraction with various solvents and concentrated by means of ion exchange chromatography and charcoal adsorption. The most purified preparation gave a positive ninhydrin reaction, but exhibited no maximum in the visible and ultraviolet regions (Takemura, 1962b). Catalase did not inhibit the activity of the activated enzyme. The short lag period in formation of the 656 nm substance, which was observed with partially purified heme α-methenyl oxygenase, was completely eliminated by addition of activator to the assay mixture. The action of the enzyme apparently consists of conversion of the ferric state of the substance to an activated ferrous state followed by cleavage of the porphyrin ring at the α-methine bridge (Takemura, 1962c).

O. Nakajima (1962a) studied the conversion of hemoglobin–haptoglobin by tissue homogenates. The enzyme activity was found to be high in the liver and kidney and low in the spleen, and on differential centrifugation it was located in the supernatant fraction. The initial velocity of degradation was greater if the hemoglobin was bound to haptoglobin 2-2 than if it was bound to haptoglobins 2-1 or 1-1. O. Nakajima (1962b) showed that the hemoglobin–haptoglobin degrading enzyme apparently acts entirely differently from chemical degradation by means of peroxide, since no demonstrable change of activity was observed in the presence of excess catalase. The enzyme was inhibited by metal chelating agents and sulfhydryl inhibitors.

Yamaoka and Nakajima (1962) isolated the final reaction product of the action of heme α-methenyl oxygenase on pyridine–hemichrome, the so-called 656 nm substance. An experiment was carried out with a mixture of 80 μmoles of pyridine–hemochromogen, NADP, Fe^{++}, 50 mmoles of tris buffer of pH 7.4, and 800 mg of enzyme concentrate (ammonium sulfate fraction), and an isocitric dehydrogenase system as a NADP-generating system. At a final volume of 100 ml the mixture was incubated anaerobically in a 500 ml flask at 37° with gentle mechanical shaking. The final product was extracted from the reaction mixture with $CHCl_3$ and crystallized as green prisms. It was purified and shown to be a single substance by means of paper partition and silicic acid column chromatography. It showed absorption bands at 397, 495, 530, and 657 nm in $CHCl_3$. It formed a semicarbazone with 2,4-dinitrophenyl-hydrazone and gave Schiff's reaction and other aldehyde reactions. The infrared absorption spectrum suggested the existence of both carbonyl and formyl groups in the molecule. Acid hydrolysis released iron and formaldehyde concomitantly under formation of biliverdin; consequently the 656 nm compound is believed to be a direct precursor of biliverdin. The formulas in Fig. 32 were proposed for the pathway of degradation (H. Nakajima, 1963).

The results of Nakajima and collaborators were collected and presented in detail by H. Nakajima et al. (1963) and H. Nakajima (1963) in two papers which appeared in the Journal of Biological Chemistry. Kuma (1966a*,b*) studied the enzymatic conversion of fetal hemoglobin by heme α-methenyl oxygenase.

Other recent investigators have arrived at results not in agreement with those of H. Nakajima and collaborators. Kench and Varma (1962) found that splenic pulp from a patient suffering from hemolytic anemia markedly enhanced the production of bile pigment precursors, and a part of the increased yield arose from the action of a heat labile component. Normal human splenic tissue was ineffective. Neonatal tissues containing endothelial cells (liver, spleen, bone marrow) were also enzymically active, about one third of the gain being abolished by heating.

Kench et al. (1963) complexed human fetal Hb with human haptoglobin from pooled sera and incubated with human liver homogenate in the presence of oxygen and ascorbic acid at pH 7.3 (0.1 M phosphate buffer). The reaction products were fractionated by passing through a column of dextran gel (Sephadex G100) and the fractions subjected to spectrophotometric reading at 630, 542 and 260 mm.

The same investigators compared free human Hb with Hb-haptoglobin complex as sources of biliverdin. They found heat-labile components in fetal human liver—prepared according to Nakajima and associates—which gave rise to increased absorption at 630 nm. This increased absorption at 630 nm was greatly enhanced by addition of ascorbic acid and reduced NADP. In general Hb-haptoglobin was a slightly better source of biliverdin than free Hb, but in no experiment the authors succeeded in increasing the yield of biliverdin above that obtained with ascorbic acid and free Hb. In a series of experiments using a variety of combinations of substrate, enzyme preparations and

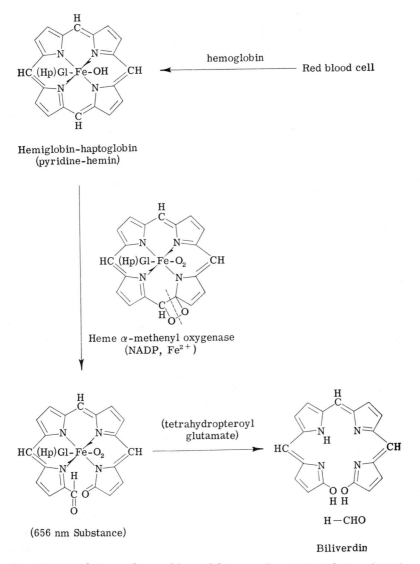

FIG. 32. Degradation pathway of hemoglobin according to H. Nakajima (1963).

cofactors, they were in no instance able to reproduce yields of the order found by Nakajima and associates (i.e., close to 50% of the Hb appearing as bile pigment). Also Schmid (1963b) mentioned in a discussion, that he had been unable to reproduce Nakajima's results.

Kench *et al.* (1963) were unable to explain the discrepancy between Nakajima and associates results and their own, but they stress that

Petryka *et al.* (1962) found that the biliverdin formed *in vitro* on coupled oxidation of pyridine hemochromogen with ascorbic acid is a random mixture of biliverdins-IXα,β,γ, and δ while, on the other hand, the biliverdin formed *in vivo* consists only of the IX,α isomer.

Consequently the ultimate test of any enzyme preparation must be that the biliverdin formed by its action on heme compounds *in vitro* is really the IX,α compound, and before this has been shown to be the case with the purified enzyme preparations of Nakajima and collaborators, these enzyme preparations cannot be regarded as those active *in vivo*.

The role of dipyrrole pigments is an interesting problem (compare Netoušek, 1956). Some authors regard bilifuscin as an important degradation product of hemoglobin (Engel, 1940; Siedel *et al.*, 1948). However, it is of no importance, according to *in vitro* experiments of Lemberg *et al.* (1939, 1941a,b) and Lemberg and Legge (1942). The only bile pigments occurring in substantial yields were biliverdin and purpurin (violin, according to the terminology of Lemberg and Legge, 1949). On the other hand, Ekuni (1952a,b) subjected hemoglobin to extended degradation experiments by oxidoreduction, using ascorbic acid, and found bilifuscin using chromatography. He believed that choleglobin is transformed into a brown pigment and that bilifuscin is formed via bilirubin and biliviolin. His extremely interesting publication, however, appeared in Japanese, and only a very poor English summary was published. As mentioned in Chapter I,G, dipyrrole bile pigments seem to be primary by-products of pyrrole synthesis in the organism. They seem to be connected only secondarily with hemoglobin degradation. Nevertheless, deviations can occur under various circumstances. At the present time our knowledge in this interesting area is very incomplete.

An important fact is that the formation of bilirubin from hemoglobin is a very fast process. This was demonstrated in a number of experiments in which dogs were injected intravenously with hemolyzed blood or hemoglobin solutions. Thus, Whipple and Hooper (1913a) observed bilirubinuria 1–1½ hours after injection. Cantarow *et al.* (1948b) established a definite increase of bilirubin concentration in bile even after 1 hour. Gilligan *et al.* (1941) observed a significant increase of serum bilirubin in humans, 6–8 hours after intravenous injections of 5–15 g hemoglobin. Komori and Iwao (1928) detected bile pigments in dog spleens after 2–4 hours in perfusion experiments using hemolyzed blood. Nishimaru (1931) was able to detect biliverdin after 20 minutes of perfusion in experiments with hemoglobin solutions in bull frog livers, if perfusion was effected through the hepatic artery. However, if perfusion was carried out by way of the portal vein the bile remained colorless throughout the experiment (1½ hours).

Ostrow *et al.* (1962) injected red cells or hemoglobin solutions labeled with C^{14} and either Fe^{59} or Cr^{51} i.v. to rats with external bile fistula. Urinary losses of pigment were prevented or minimized by the use of small amounts of Hb or by nephrectomy. The bile was collected and the bilirubin isolated in crystalline condition and its radioactivity measured. The clearance of the injected labeled erythrocytes or hemoglobin from the circulation was determined by the Fe^{59} or Cr^{51} content of the blood. Labeled bilirubin appeared in the bile within 30–50 minutes after the injection of Hb or erythrocytes, reached its maximum concentration in 2–3 hours, and disappeared completely within 24 hours after the injection. A delay was found between the sequestration of hemoglobin and the appearance of labeled bilirubin, apparently due to the time required for the conversion of heme to bilirubin. While hemoglobin degradation could be demonstrated within a few minutes after the injection, bilirubin was demonstrable only after 30–50 minutes. The time required for clearance of half the labeled heme $(t_{1/2})$ was 13–52 minutes, whereas the bilirubin $t_{1/2}$—the time elapsing until 50% of the total excreted amount of bilirubin had been reached—was 185–260 minutes. Intravenously injected bilirubin-C^{14} was almost completely recovered in the bile.

Finally, the degradation of other hemochrome proteins should be mentioned. This process differs from that of hemoglobin degradation.

Kench (1954) established that cytochrome c is the single hemochrome protein which is not subject to oxidative degradation by oxido-reduction with ascorbic acid. This finding does not exclude the possibility of bile pigment formation from cytochrome c through enzyme action. Nevertheless, this compound cannot be considered as a likely precursor of bile pigments. In contrast, all other hemochrome proteins, including myoglobin and catalase, should be considered as possible sources of bile pigment. According to Neuberger *et al.* (1950), 10–15% of fecal stercobilin between the first and second "peak" (see Section A, this chapter) most likely originates from this source. It was assumed that myoglobin leads to a primary increase of fuscin (Meldolesi *et al.*, 1939; Siedel and Möller, 1940; Stefanutti, 1940; Stefanutti *et al.*, 1940). This opinion, however, could hardly be defended after Siedel *et al.* (1947) and Perkoff and Tyler (1950) found equally high concentrations of these substances in stool of normal individuals and in muscular dystrophy patients. Another fact indicating identical degradation products of myoglobin and hemoglobin is the formation of the usual tetrapyrrole bile pigments from metmyoglobin as demonstrated *in vitro* by Kench (1954). The amount obtained was about eleven times as high as that obtained when oxyhemoglobin was used as substrate. During the process, similarly to choleglobin, a cholemyoglobin was formed.

Summary

The formation of bile pigments from hemoglobin is a complicated process and has caused numerous discussions. According to the classic theory, the globin is first split off, the separation of iron follows, and finally the porphyrin ring is opened. Contrary to this and according to Lemberg (1956), the α-methine bridge of protoporphyrin is first oxidized *in situ* by addition of hydrogen peroxide. During this process the protoporphyrin remains linked to the globin. By this oxidation choleglobin is formed, containing an oxygen bridge in lieu of the α-methine bridge. During biliverdin formation the iron and protein is split off from choleglobin. Biliverdin is then converted into bilirubin. Whereas Lemberg maintains that this is the only route of degradation *in vivo*, other authors assume that other routes are also possible, and that under certain conditions the splitting off of globin could be the first step. However, there is general agreement that iron is necessary for the opening of the porphyrin ring, and that biliverdin is the first bile pigment to be formed. The complicated problems of green hemochromes and hemes are explained and it is emphasized that final assessment of current theories is impossible at the present time.

The theoretical calculations of the energy levels of the compounds, especially of biliverdin, presented by Pullman and Perault (1959) are discussed.

The important studies of Nakajima and collaborators (from 1958 to 1963) on the enzymatic breakdown of heme compounds are discussed. According to them, the principal route of hemoglobin breakdown *in vivo* is initiated by formation of the hemoglobin–haptoglobin complex which is broken down by the enzyme heme α-methenyl oxygenase under formation of a substance absorbing at 656 nm. This 656 nm substance has a prosthetic group which is opened at the α-bridge, contains a formyl group there, and is still bound to haptoglobin, globin, and iron. Other investigators have, however, not yet been able to confirm the observations of Nakajima and his collaborators.

The possible role of dipyrrole bile pigments and hemoglobin of different hemoproteins are discussed.

C. Site of Formation of Bile Pigments

The problem of the site of bile pigment formation gave rise to numerous discussions. For detailed surveys of the earlier literature consult Bock (1924), Lewin (1928), Lepehne (1930), and F. Stern (1930). Later surveys have been published by C. J. Watson (see 1938,

p. 2459), Lemberg and Legge (see 1949, pp. 538 and 540), and Baumgärtel (see 1950b, p. 131).

Originally bile pigments were considered as secretion products of liver. Virchow (1847) pointed out their close relation to blood pigments. The question, however, remained open whether they are formed from hemoglobin in the liver or somewhere else. In order to decide this problem, experimental hepatectomy was carried out. Minkowski and Naunyn (1886) did not observe jaundice or hyperbilirubinemia in hepatectomized ducks and geese. The animals survived hepatectomy for 20 hours. The same results were obtained even when hemolytic poisons were administered simultaneously. Similarly, neither hepatecto-mized frogs (J. Müller, 1844; Kunde, 1850; Moleschott, 1852; H. Stern, 1885) nor toads (Cabello Ruz, 1943a) developed hyperbilirubinemia. However, this finding is only of limited significance since frogs with complete bile duct obstruction showed no hyperbilirubinemia (J. Müller, 1844; Leyden, 1866; H. Stern, 1885).

McNee (1913, 1914), a pupil of Aschoff, was the first to question the primary role of liver for bile pigment formation. He believed that hemoglobin degradation as well as bile pigment formation is localized in the reticuloendothelial system which was discovered at about the same time (cf. Aschoff, 1924). According to McNee (1914), the reason hepatectomized ducks and geese showed no hyperbilirubinemia can be explained by the short experimental periods used, i.e., the experimental animals did not survive long enough. Minkowsi and Naunyn (1886) and Löwitt (1889) had observed an accumulation of degrading hemo-globin and biliverdin in the Kupffer cells of animals treated with hemo-lytic poisons. However, they did not recognize the significance of these observations. Later, Auld (1896) detected degraded hemoglobin as well as biliverdin in Kupffer cells and in spleen. From these findings he concluded that the bile pigments are formed in the spleen but excreted by the liver. Because $HgCl_2$ was used for tissue fixation in these investi-gations, the bile pigment found in the experiments was biliverdin. $HgCl_2$ oxidized bilirubin to biliverdin. From a chemical standpoint (Section B, this chapter), biliverdin has to be considered as the first bile pigment formed. However, conversion into bilirubin proceeds rapidly in the organism. Langhans (1870) found bilirubin and biliverdin simultaneously in guinea pigs, rabbits, and pigeons after subcutaneous injections of blood.

The histological investigations of Aschoff (1922, 1928, 1932) support the view that the RES is the principal site of formation of bile pigments. Lepehne (1917, 1921c, 1930) was able to demonstrate hyperplasia of Kupffer star cells in splenectomized rats [according to Aschoff (1928): "spleen substitute"]. Lauda (1925, 1928), however, attributed this to

Bartonella infection. This explanation was rejected by Lepehne (1930). The fact is, that after splenectomy Kupffer cells tend to hypertrophy, but not the parenchymal cells of the liver.

The experiments of F. C. Mann (1921, 1925) and Mann *et al.* (1924, 1925, 1926a,b) carried out in hepatectomized dogs, brought the final proof for extrahepatic bilirubin formation. Before these experiments are discussed in detail, it should be emphasized that hepatectomy not only influences the mechanism of bile pigment formation, but also changes profoundly many other metabolic processes. Thus it is known that, after hepatectomy, hemoglobin degradation as well as pyrrole synthesis proceeds differently. Certainly the bile pigment formation from other sources than hemoglobin of mature circulating erythrocytes will also be affected. Thus, the appearance of "xanthorubin" in serum of hepatectomized dogs (see below) indicates enhanced formation of dipyrrole bile pigments. These questions should be more closely investigated by feeding labeled glycine to hepatectomized animals.

The investigations of Mann are continuations of experiments with the so-called Eck fistula, i.e., artificial anastomosis between the portal and inferior caval veins with simultaneous ligature of the former. This operation was introduced by the Baltic surgeon von Eck (1877) for treatment of portal thrombosis, and was used for experimental studies by Hahn *et al.* (1893; see also Bernheim *et al.*, 1910). This operation has assumed an important position in experimental surgery. The portal vein is closed between the liver and the anastomosis, so that portal blood is completely withdrawn from the liver. In so-called reversed Eck fistula, the vena cava inferior is ligated central to the anastomosis, but peripheral to the inlet of the hepatic vein, while the portal vein is patent. In this sort of fistula all the blood of the inferior caval vein is forced to pass the liver (Gebhardt, 1939a,b). A short survey of liver changes occurring after application of Eck's fistula, is given by Baumgärtel (1950b, p. 183). Recently, Bollman (1961) reveiwed the interesting perspectives of the Eck fistula in liver pathology. Castro *et al.* (1963) compared liver function and liver histology in dogs with Eck's fistula and found that the morphological changes in the liver cells were relatively slight compared with the marked clinical evidence of liver failure found in the dogs.

Whipple and Hooper (1913b) attempted unsuccessfully to completely eliminate the liver from the circulation by ligature of the hepatic artery in dogs with Eck's fistula (see Rich, 1924). Mann (1921) proposed hepatectomy in two stages; first a collateral circulation was established and then the liver was removed. The ensuing hypoglycemia was compensated by glucose injections. The dogs survived 6–20 hours. During this time they developed a moderate hyperbilirubinemia. Bilirubinuria appeared in the sixth hour. Serum bilirubin concentration fluctuated considerably during the observation period, but was constantly below 0.6 mg/100 ml (method of Hijmans van den Bergh, 1918). Injections of hemolyzed blood, given 6–7 hours after operation, led to a steep increase of serum bilirubin (up to 3 mg/100 ml).

The experiments of Mann and his associates (from 1921 to 1926) were repeated and extended by Rich (1923, 1925a,b; see also Rich and Bumstead, 1925a,b,c), Makino (1924), Melchoir et al. (1925), F. Rosenthal et al. (1926), Rosenthal (1928), Enderlen et al. (1927), Taniguschi (1928), Fiessinger and Gajdos (1932), Fiessinger et al. (1932), and Markowitz et al. (1933). All these authors used dogs in their experiments. Maddock and Svedberg (1938) and Svedberg et al. (1938) used rabbits and monkeys; Meehan (1954) and Forti (1958) employed rats. All these animals reacted similarly to dogs.

According to Rosenthal et al. and Enderlen et al., the yellow color of plasma of hepatectomized dogs is only partly caused by bilirubin, and partly to an unknown substance, xanthorubin, which was present besides bilirubin. Xanthorubin was not isolated. However, it is known that it is easily soluble in chloroform, has a high photosensitivity, and reacts negatively in the diazo and Gmelin reactions.

Melchior et al. (1925); Rosenthal et al. (1926), and Enderlen et al. (1927) found that the serum bilirubin concentration of hepatectomized dogs is much lower than that of dogs with complete bile duct obstruction or with toluenediamine icterus. These facts indicate that the liver is the principal site of bile pigment formation. Fiessinger et al. (1932) and Markowitz et al. (1933) who carried out hepatectomy of dogs in one session, could show that not more than one fifth of the total bilirubin formation was of extrahepatic origin. When hepatectomized animals were poisoned with toluenediamine or phenylhydrazine, the same light hyperbilirubinuria developed as was experienced with hepatectomized but nonpoisoned animals. However, injection of hemolytic blood led to a considerable increase in serum bilirubin. Serum bilirubin concentration in hepatectomized animals reached only 20–50% of that of normal dogs subjected to the same experimental conditions (Fiessinger et al., 1932).

These experiments on hepatectomized mammals demonstrated that, although a considerable proportion of bile pigment is produced outside the liver, its production takes place preponderantly within the liver. However these experiments cannot provide a basis for deciding whether hepatic bilirubin originates in the parenchymal cells or the Kupffer cells—the RES of the liver. In order to clear up this point, experiments on blocking of the RES were carried out.

For this purpose obstructive jaundice (occlusion of the common bile duct) was employed simultaneously with blocking of the RES by poisoning (Lepehne, 1917; F. Rosenthal and Melchior, 1922; Rosenthal, 1928;

Stern, 1930; Held, 1933a,b). Sometimes, blocking the RES resulted in absence of icterus, but in other cases intensive jaundice occurred despite the blocking. These contradictory findings are attributed to incomplete blocking. When blockage was effected with high doses of thorium dioxide (Tsunoo and Nakamura, 1931; Gottlieb, 1934a,b,c), deposits of pigments in RES cells were completely inhibited for 8–12 days. Within a week bilirubin excretion decreased to practically nil. After this time the values gradually returned to normal. The experiments of Gottlieb (1934b) strongly supported the opinion that under normal conditions RES is the most important site of bile pigment formation in dogs. On the other hand, Yamaoka *et al.* (1952a,b,c,d) showed with experiments on rabbits that the parenchymal liver cells play an equally significant role. They assumed that hemoglobin is initially taken up by the phagocytes of the RES and then converted into green hemoglobin by the parenchymal cells of liver. Finally, green hemoglobin is split by RES and bile pigments are formed. It has to be emphasized, however, that hemoglobin degradation is a process which can occur without specific cell activity (cf. Section B, this chapter). Therefore, the route of hemoglobin degradation as described by Yamaoka *et al.* (1952a,b,c,d) cannot be the only possibility.

Important observations were reported by Dumont *et al.* (1962), who analyzed both the bilirubin content of the thoracic duct lymph and the serum bilirubin in dogs with experimental biliary obstruction before and after blocking the RES with Thorothrast. This is a much more sensitive guide to bilirubin production than studies of the serum bilirubin alone. It was found that the lymph bilirubin concentration increased four- to eight-fold within 3 hours of biliary obstruction, and that this rise was prevented for at least 5 hours by injection of Thorotrast in doses of 1 ml/kg in the femoral artery. If the Thorotrast was injected 2 hours after the biliary obstruction, the increase of the bilirubin in the lymph and blood was converted to a decrease for several hours. The authors regarded it as likely that the Thorotrast effect on bilirubin formation results from some metabolic process rather than from mere blockade of RES cell surfaces.

Further, Murray (1963a*,b*) blockaded the RES and showed that this phenomenon is not quite as simple as formerly believed. He showed that blockade with one colloidal material toward tracer doses of another is primarily dependent on close similarity of the surface properties of the two colloids. Thus blockade experiments with artificial colloids can hardly bring relevant information concerning the function of the RES under physiological hemoglobin degradation. Koenig *et al.* (1965*) arrived at similar conclusions.

In this connection also the experiments of Snyder and Schmid (1965*) with injections of C^{14}-hematin i.v. to rats with external bile fistula are important. They followed the accumulation of radioactivity in the blood and bile at ½- to 4-hour intervals for 24 hours and further determined the radioactivity of the exsanguinated organs at autopsy. The rate of disappearance of plasma C^{14}-heme varied according to the type of albumin to which it was bound, being considerably faster with murine than with human albumin. Formation of C^{14}-bilirubin was found to take place only in the liver; no radioactivity was demonstrated in the other organs.

The location of the transformation of biliverdin into bilirubin was studied by Garay et al. (1964a*) who concluded that it takes place in the liver only. Their evidence is, however, not completely convincing. They studied 20 hepatectomized rats subjected to intraperitoneal injection of biliverdin (1.5 mg); 20 others served as controls. The urine was collected and a blood sample taken (heart puncture) two hours after the biliverdin injection. Blood and urine concentrations of biliverdin and bilirubin were determined at the beginning and the close of the experiment. The hepatectomized control rats showed serum bilirubin concentration of 319 ± 84 μg/100 ml, whereas the biliverdin-loaded hepatectomized rats showed 480 ± 254, a difference which is not statistically significant. But this means only that with the limited number of animals employed a difference was not firmly established. The somewhat higher mean in the biliverdin-loaded hepatectomized rats points toward a certain extrahepatic conversion of biliverdin to bilirubin which might be proved by means of a larger experimental series.

Also studies on the developing liver can contribute to solve the question of whether parenchymal cells or Kupffer cells or both are responsible for hepatic bilirubin formation. Thus Armstrong (1964*) studied the accumulation of injected dyes in the embryonic liver of the amphibian Amblystoma punctatum. He found that the sulfonated dyes indigo carmine, patent blue V, and azofuchsin G all accumulate in the liver cells of the embryo at development stages before Kupffer cells are present. Although the behavior of hemoglobin and bilirubin was not studied the findings suggest that presence of Kupffer cells is not necessary for uptake of bilirubin by the liver.

Finally it is important to bear in mind that opinions on the scope of the term "RES" are still much at variance. There is a gap between optic-microscopic and electron microscopic observations which is difficult to fill because both the form and the fine structure of RES cells is subject to change under the smallest stimulation, for which they exhibit an almost incomprehensible mutability (Akazaki, 1962).

It is also worthwhile to remember the closing comments in an introductory paper at a conference on the RES and its function: "Great care must be observed in interpretation of the data presented when making generalizations on structure and function of the RES as a unit system" (Bailiff, 1960*). This author also emphasized the difficulty in selecting suitable colloids for blocking experiments.

Histological observations can also shed some light on the possible site of bile pigment formation. However, the value of these findings is limited because bile pigments, although occurring in considerable quantities, are not always detectable by histological methods (Lepehne, 1930, p. 319). The role of RES is emphasized because, under conditions of hemolysis, the cells as a rule contain green or yellow degradation products of hemoglobin. Only recently satisfactory methods for histological demonstration of bilirubin have been introduced (Raia, 1965*; cf. also Chapter IX).

In connection with this question, clinical observations during acute yellow liver atrophy are of particular significance. According to post mortem findings (Bergstrand, 1930; Eppinger, 1937; Lucké and Mallory, 1946; Jimenez-Diaz *et al.*, 1948) Kupffer cells are relatively unharmed, whereas parenchymal cells show extensive necrosis. Nevertheless, severe icterus is present, indicating that a considerable part of bile pigment formation must take place outside the parenchymal cells.

Observations on metastasizing primary liver carcinoma, which contained hepatic cells without Kupffer cells, gave indications that bile pigment is formed in parenchymal cells. Bilirubin could be detected in such metastases (Lubarsch, 1921). But these findings are also explained by assuming that bilirubin is absorbed from the blood circulation by the carcinoma cells (Aschoff, 1922).

Fischler (1916, 1925) regarded the parenchymal cells as the principal site of bile pigment formation. His opinion was shared by Heinrichsdorff (1924), whereas F. Rosenthal (1928) could not decide the relative role of Kupffer cells and liver cells. Surveys of older literature have been given by Florentin (1924), Lepehne (1930), and F. Stern (1930). Florentin's opinion was that parenchymal cells have a purely excretory role. Contrary to this, Lepehne proposed a "dualistic theory," according to which a certain portion of the bilirubin, which is excreted with the bile, is formed in the parenchymal cells proper. This opinion was adopted by Klemperer (1933). Observations of Kodama (1925) seemed to corroborate this contention. He found that, after hemolytic poisoning, iron granules became visible in the liver cells. C. J. Watson (1938, p. 2481) questioned the dualistic theory. He was of the opinion that it is difficult to see how such profoundly different cell types as Kupffer cells and parenchymal cells can simultaneously degrade hemoglobin and bile pigments. However, this criticism is not in agreement with the concept of Lemberg that hemoglobin degradation and bile pigment formation can occur everywhere in the organism except in erythrocytes (see Section B, this chapter).

The observations of Wigglesworth (1943) show, at least in lower animals, that both mesenchymal and epithelial cells are capable of producing bile pigments. This author demonstrated bile pigment formation from digested blood in the intestinal canal as well as in the pericardium of blood-sucking arthropods. Further, microscopical studies have shown that the contact between Kupffer cells and the parenchymal cells of the liver is so intimate that differentiation of their functions by histological methods is extremely difficult (De Robertis, 1939; Jórg, 1941). This concept is strongly supported by the investigation of Knisely *et al.* (1948) (see Chapter IV,C,2), who claimed that Kupffer cells are identical with the endothelium of liver sinusoids. Radioautography furnishes a possible method of differentiating between functions of Kupffer cells and parenchymal cells, and was used by Krebs and Brauer (1949) in their studies with bromsulphalein.

Kosaka (1959a,b) injected Fe^{59}-labeled hemoglobin i.v. into rabbits and subjected their organs to autoradiography. The radioactivity accumulated in the middle zone of the liver lobules as early as 5 minutes after the administration. The stellate cells of Kupffer showed radioactivity much later–30 minutes to 4 hours after the injection. The accumulation of radioactivity in the liver cells proceeded unchanged after blockade of the RES but decreased markedly after $CHCl_3$ poisoning. The radioactivity of the stellate cells was only insignificantly influenced by $CHCl_3$ poisoning. It was concluded that the parenchymal liver cells are the main site of hemoglobin degradation in the rabbit and that the part played by the RES follows after choleglobin has been formed.

The hypothesis of Kirkovic and Russew (1927), according to which the bilirubin of the bile is formed in the liver and that of the blood outside the liver, is without experimental support.

Riggi and di Luzia (1962) employed the preparation zymosan—from *Saccharomyces cerevisiae*—which is known to enhance the functional activity of RES cells. They studied the bromsulphalein (BSP) clearance and the removal rate of i.v. injected colloidal carbon in rats treated with zymosan and in control animals. The mean removal rate ($t\frac{1}{2}$) for colloidal carbon was 0.81 minutes in the zymosan rats and 5.87 in the controls, whereas the BSP clearance in the two groups exhibited no significant difference. Further, the average liver weight of the two groups of rats was closely similar, whereas the average weights of the lung and spleen of the zymosan rats were increased by 82 and

245%, respectively, when compared with the control rats. As it is known that BSP is to be handled by the liver in a way closely similar to bilirubin, these observations support the views that RES function and the activity of the liver parenchyma are widely separated functions.

Lozzio *et al.* (1964*) studied the effect of hyperactivity of the RES. They administered p-dimethylaminoazobenzene to normal and splenectomized rats; this was followed by a considerable hyperplasia of the RES and a corresponding hyperfunction resulting in excretion of increased amounts of bile bilirubin and fecal urobinoid as well as a progressive diminishing erythrocyte lifetime as determined by means of Cr^{51} labeling. The radioactivity of the liver and spleen was 2–4 times as high in the rats treated with p-diaminoazobenzene after erythrocyte labeling with Cr^{51} than in the normal control rats. The hyperactivity of the RES in these rats was, however, not accompanied by intravascular hemolysis.

After the recent studies of the Japanese school (Kosaka, 1959a,b; Akagi, 1960a,b), there can be no doubt that the liver is by far the most important site of bile pigment formation and that its parenchymal cells play at least an equally important role in this process as its RES—the stellate cells of Kupffer. Further, the recent demonstrations of "hepatic peak" bilirubin (this Chapter, Section A) definitely proves the formation of bilirubin in the liver cells.

Although the liver is the principal site of bile pigment formation, the *spleen* does play a certain role in this process. Lepehne (1930) attributes an inferior role to the spleen. However, it is a clinical fact that therapeutic splenectomy is beneficial in hemolytic disease and that the spleen has a certain significance as a "cemetery" for damaged erythrocytes. The role played by the spleen during these processes was studied by various investigators.

Schindeler (1870, p. 25) found that the bile of dogs is darker before splenectomy than it is after this operation. Ernst (1925), Ernst and Szappanyos (1922, 1925), Ernst and Förster (1925a,b), Ernst and Hallay (1930), and Komori and Iwao (1928) could detect bile pigments when hemoglobin was added to the perfusion liquid of isolated spleens. Bieling and Isaac (1922) reported jaundice after hemolysis in splenectomized animals, thus showing that only a part of the bile pigments can be formed in the spleen. Nevertheless, they emphasized the significance of the spleen by noticing its increased volume (four times above normal) during hemolytic conditions. In humans a higher bilirubin concentration was found in splenic vein than in splenic artery (Hijmans van den Bergh, 1918; Katznelson, 1920; Greppi, 1937). Buchanan and MacGregor (1964*) studied the hemoglobin destruction in the spleen of mice by means of the "chemical splenectomy" introduced by Stewart

(1960). A 30% colloidal solution of ethyl palmitate was injected i.v. for the "chemical splenectomy" and the red cell survival was studied with the Cr^{51}-technique. A marked prolongation of the longevity of the red cells resulted compared to normal mice, the mean Cr^{51} half-life being 51 and 400 minutes respectively.

Under certain conditions the *kidneys* also play a role in hemoglobin degradation. During hemoglobinuria the iron of hemoglobin is eliminated as hemosiderin and hemosiderinuria develops. It is, however, not known if bile pigments are formed from hemoglobin under conditions like these (Crosby, 1955). In experiments with C^{14}-hematin in rats Snyder and Schmid (1965*) found no detectable C^{14}-activity in the renal tissue and urine which is an indication that the kidneys are not involved in the breakdown of hematin.

By comparing bilirubin concentration in arterial and venous blood, the functions of various organs in bile pigments production was studied. It was found that, besides the liver, the spleen and the *bone marrow* play the most important role (F. C. Mann et al., 1925, 1926a,b; Ernst and Szappanyos, 1925).

Kawaguchi (1957b) injected Fe^{55}-labeled hemoglobin in varying doses i.v. into rabbits and studied the radioactivity of the organs. Eight hours after the injection of a dose of 0.01 g/kg body weight, 50% of the injected radioactivity appeared in the liver, 0.5% in the spleen, and 14% in the bone marrow. If the RES was blocked the radioactivity of the liver was significantly reduced, while the kidneys showed substantial radioactivity. After poisoning with CCl_4 the radioactivity of the liver was less than after blockage of the RES. The role of the liver as the main site of bile pigment formation was also underlined by studies on dogs with cannulation of the thoracic duct (H. Yamamoto, 1958; cf. Chapter IV,C,3). Takemura (1959a,b) found that, following injection of radioactive hemoglobin, the radioactivity per unit weight was higher in the spleen than in the liver and bone marrow although the role of the spleen in hemoglobin degradation is less than that of the two other organs; the radioactivity accumulating in the kidneys was insignificant.

The finding of H. Nakajima (1958, 1963; cf. above) that the concentration of heme-degrading enzyme is high in the liver and kidney and very low in the spleen and bone marrow also underlines the importance of the liver as a site of hemoglobin breakdown.

Keene and Jandl (1965*) studied the relative role of various organs in the conversion of hemoglobin to bile pigment in rats by i.v. injection of Fe^{59}-labeled hemoglobin. The rats were subjected to different treatments blocking or stimulating the RES before the hemoglobin injection and were sacrificed 30 minutes after the injection. Measurement of the radioactivity of the organs showed that the hemoglobin was retained principally in the liver (71%), while the marrow retained 22% and the spleen only 7%. Haptoglobin binding had no effect on the relative distribution of the hemoglobin. Its only role seemed to be to prevent loss of hemoglobin through the kidneys.

Investigations on the formation of bile pigments in *tissue cultures* showed contradictory results. After the addition of erythrocytes to mesenchymal cell cultures, Rich (1924) observed a diffuse green coloration and the formation of bilirubin microcrystals. With ecto- or entodermal cell cultures he was not able to observe such phenomena. Doljanski and Koch (1933a,b,c) found, however, the same bile pigment formation in tissue cultures and cell-free media. Thus, they assumed that humoral bilirubin formation without cell participation must be an important factor. Furthermore, they could detect xanthorubin in their tissue cultures but not in cell-free media, and so regarded xanthorubin production as a fundamental characteristic of all living cells. F. Stern (1930) studied liver cell cultures of chicken embryos. After hemolyzed chicken blood was added to such cultures, the Gmelin reaction became positive within 24 hours; after 5–7 days, it returned to negative. No bile pigments were detectable in cultures of mesenchymal liver cells or of spleen tissue.

The formation of bile pigments in blood extravasates and streaming blood (*plasmatic bile pigment formation*) could often be demonstrated. Langhans (1870) succeeded in detecting bile pigments histologically in phagocytes of guinea pigs, rabbits, and pigeons 2–3 days after subcutaneous injection of blood. Von Recklinghausen (1889) reported on bile pigment formation in sterile frog blood. Leupold (1914), however, found that this occurs only in the presence of tissue cells. In contrast, Florentin (1924, p. 114) described intravascular bile pigment formation without cell intervention in the liver and spleen of amphibia, reptiles, and birds. Rich (1924) observed the formation of bilirubin in preserved blood, which he attributed to phagocytosis of erythrocytes by leucocytes. Czike (1929) and M. Engel (1937) reported bilirubin formation in sterile preserved blood after 24 hours incubation at 37°. The process could not be followed further, because hemoglobin which was liberated during hemolysis destroyed the bilirubin by oxidation.

Nishikawa (1959a) studied bilirubin formation in the tissues of mice after subcutaneous injection of human blood. He employed histomicrospectrophotometry and concluded that the degradation of hemoglobin to bilirubin was quite similar to the processes known from the *in vitro* investigations.

Bilirubin formation in *spinal fluid* presents a particular problem.

According to Froin (1914), the presence of cells is necessary for this process. Leschke (1921a,b) succeeded, however, in preparing bilirubin by the addition of erythrocytes to cell-free liquor.

Icterus produced experimentally by *toluenediamine poisoning* has played a significant role in the discussion of the site of bile pigment formation. Nevertheless, the findings have not contributed to a definite solution of these problems. Detailed surveys of the earlier literature were compiled by Eppinger (1920) and Lepehne (1930). Toluenediamine (diaminotoluene) was introduced by Stadelmann (1881), who could show that this compound led to the degeneration of the liver parenchyma in dogs. Later, Auld (1896) reported that it does not cause jaundice in rabbits. Gottlieb (1934b) observed a strong hemolytic effect in rats with this compound. Joannovics (1904) and Joannovics and Pick (1910) found that splenectomy significantly increased tolerance to toluenediamine in dogs. From this, they concluded that the spleen plays a significant role in the action of this poison. Perfusion experiments on spleens by Strisower and Goldschmidt (1916) confirmed this. According to Wolff (1934) and Bollman (1935), the course of toluenediamine icterus in dogs is considerably more severe than other forms of experimental icterus. Therefore, they concluded that both liver damage and increased bile pigment formation must take place. Contrary to this, McGowan (1936) found that the maximum of icterus was already reached before any destruction of blood was detectable. The important investigations of Hiyeda (1925, 1927) and Itoh (1931, 1932) will be discussed in Chapter IV,E,4. Hench (1938, p. 477), who studied the effect of toluenediamine in humans, observed a definite hemolytic anemia (erythrocytes, 1.5 million per μliter) and a moderate icterus (6.3 mg bilirubin per 100 ml serum) after peroral administration.

Summary

Although the majority of bile pigments are produced in the liver, hepatectomy experiments show that extrahepatic formation, at least in mammals, is also possible. It is difficult to decide what role is played by the cells of RES (Kupffer cells) and liver parenchyma. It is important to bear in mind that bile pigment formation from hemoglobin is not restricted to active cellular activity but also proceeds in circulating blood and blood extravasates. Although a large amount of experimental material was compiled by histological investigations, perfusion experiments, studies on tissue cultures, and experimental toluenediamine poisoning, the question as to the site of formation of these pigments has not been solved. Studies by the Japanese school (Kawaguchi, 1957b; Takemura, 1959a,b) with hemoglobin labeled with radioactive iron have shown that the liver is the main site of hemoglobin degradation and that its parenchymal cells play a role in this process which is at least of equal importance to the role of its RES (the stellate cells of Kupffer). The bone marrow is next in importance after the liver, and after it the spleen which is of limited importance in spite of the fact that it demonstrates the highest radioactivity per unit of weight. The role of the kidneys is insignificant under normal conditions. Studies with radio-Hb in hepatectomized animals have not been performed. The location of the formation site of dipyrrole bile pigments from hemoglobin has not been studied.

D. Fate of Bile Pigments in the Body; Formation and Metabolism of Urobilinoids

It is generally assumed that all the bile pigments formed in the organism are excreted with the bile. However, if experimental findings obtained in horses and cattle are considered, this assumption cannot be adopted *a priori.* It is known that the horse excretes only a minimum amount of bile pigments with bile, has a high serum bilirubin level, and under normal conditions does not have any urine bilirubin (Bierthen, 1906; see also Chapter III,B,3). This can only mean that in horses, under normal conditions, bile pigments are not excreted in the form of tetrapyrrole pigments, but that a further degradation to similar compounds occurs. C. E. Cornelius (personal communication, 1961) began a thorough study of bile pigment metabolism in the horse. He collected 100 ml bile from one horse and found 4.2 mg bilirubin per 100 ml. In another he found 30.5 mg per 100 ml. But technical problems are considerable because the horse has no gallbladder. The results of his investigations are being awaited with considerable interest. However, simultaneous studies should be made using labeled bile pigments.

According to the studies of Garner (1953), the destruction of bilirubin in cattle is equally interesting. In normal serum only traces of bile pigments are detectable. Whereas in these animals hemolysis leads to icterus with serum bilirubin concentrations of 7–8 mg per 100 ml, lesions of liver parenchyma or bile duct obstruction cause only insignificant bilirubinemia. Surely, this phenomenon is puzzling. It would seem that stable bilirubin originating from hemolysis and giving an indirect reaction is excreted, whereas the labile bilirubin found in the blood during hepatic and obstructive icterus and giving a direct diazo reaction is degraded in the organism.

Gilbertsen and C. J. Watson (1962) described a cause of refractory anemia with an abnormal pathway of bilirubin metabolism. Tube-fed bilirubin glucuronide and i.v. injected free bilirubin were largely unaccounted for as urobilinogen, mesobilifuscin or bilirubin in the excreta, and no evidence of faulty conjugation of bilirubin or hydrolysis of the conjugates was demonstrated. Mesobilifuscin was apparently not a major conversion product of bilirubin. R. Williams and Billing (1961) suggested that the depression of the jaundice in hepatitis and in the biliary obstruction which follows administration of steroids is due to increased bilirubin destruction.

The action of steroids was also studied by Sereni *et al.* (1964a*,b*) who perfused bilirubin into isolated rat liver preparations and found that hydrocortisone caused a marked inhibition of the excretion of bilirubin with the bile. These experiments were, however, only 150 minutes in duration and the ultimate fate of the bilirubin was not studied.

The observations of Schmid and Hammaker (1962) and Schmid (1963a) are of special interest in this respect. They studied a 4½-year-old boy with congenital nonhemolytic jaundice (Crigler-Najjar's syndrome) with serum bilirubin 25.9 mg per 100 ml; after injection of C^{14}-bilirubin (8.26 mg, 4.3 μc) they found a bilirubin turnover of 60 mg per 24 hours in spite of the fact that the patient excreted only negligible amounts of bilirubin with the bile because of his defective conjugation mechanism. How did this patient dispose of 60 mg bilirubin daily? It was found that 89% of the label was recovered in the excreta. Of this, 82% was recovered from the stool, with the major fraction consisting of metabolites other than bilirubin, urobilinogen, and mesobilifuscin. In the urine, only 7% of the label appeared, most of it as water-soluble metabolites of bilirubin exhibiting neither positive diazo reaction nor the spectral absorption of bilirubin. Thus most of the bilirubin was removed by way of the intestinal tract, although the bile contained practically no bilirubin. They found a total miscible bilirubin pool of 568 mg, a half life ($t_{1/2}$) of 156 hours, and a daily turnover of 60 mg bilirubin. For Gunn rats they found a pool of 4.32 mg, a $t_{1/2}$ of 55 hours, and a turnover rate of 1.30 mg (cf. below).

Gray and Nicholson (1963) reported similar studies on a 6½-year-old boy with Crigler-Najjar's syndrome with serum bilirubin 15 mg per 100 ml, injecting 0.8 μc bilirubin-C^{14}. Their studies were not quite complete because of difficulties in getting material from the patient. They found pool size of 1400 mg, $t_{1/2}$ 80 hours, and turnover rate 290 mg per 24 hours; i.e., figures more in agreement with those of Schmid (1963a) for Gunn rats than with Schmid's figures for the boy. More studies in this line are required to evaluate the range of individual variation.

Schmid and Hammaker (1963) performed similar investigations in 5 Gunn rats with external biliary fistula and collected of bile, urine, and feces separately in special metabolic cages. The bile here contained 51%

of the label, the stool 43.3%, and the urine 5.7%. Free bilirubin accounted for less than 6%, and conjugated bilirubin for less than 3% of the total biliary radioactivity. Bile from a Gunn rat containing the labeled excretory products was re-injected i.v. to a normal rat. The bile of this rat collected over 18 hours contained less than 6% of the re-injected radioactivity. If bile from a normal labeled rat was injected i.v. to a normal rat, virtually all the radioactivity appeared in the bile. Thus, approximately 50% of the bilirubin is eliminated by way of the bile in the form of nonidentifiable lower metabolites even in Gunn rats with absence of the conjugation mechanism of the liver.

The 43.3% of the radioactivity recovered from the feces of the Gunn rats (with bile deviation) contained at least 60% of the label in the form of nonconjugated bilirubin. Because of the breakdown of pigment in feces, it was impossible to decide the exact proportion of the remaining 40% of the label which was originally present as bilirubin. The experiment conclusively demonstrated that nonconjugated bilirubin can pass directly from the circulation into the lumen of the gut.

While these observations demonstrate beyond doubt that nonconjugated bilirubin can reach the gut in mammals, it is nevertheless certain that virtually all the bilirubin of mammalian bile is conjugated. In lower vertebrates this is, however, not the case. Thus Arias (1963b) found that 5–15% of the bilirubin of fresh bile from the dogfish (*Squalus acanthias*) is unconjugated. He studied the bilirubin excretion mechanism in the dogfish by cannulating the common bile duct, infusing unconjugated or conjugated bilirubin, and determining the concentration of free and conjugated bilirubin in the bile. The experiments suggested that the dogfish can transfer free and conjugated bilirubin from liver cells to bile by different mechanisms, each of which has its own transport maximum. Mammals apparently lack the mechanism for transferring unconjugated bilirubin from liver cells to bile, but it has to be emphasized that only a limited number of mammals have been studied.

Cabello Ruz (1943a) injected bilirubin intravenously into dogs and toads. He used one series of hepatectomized toads and a second consisting of toads in which the bile duct and both ureters were ligated. In the first series, the bilirubin concentration was 8.8 mg per 100 ml of serum, in the second 1.25 mg per 100 ml. This finding indicates a destruction of bilirubin in the liver. Further, 100 mg bilirubin was intravenously injected in normal and hepatectomized dogs. The bilirubin concentration immediately after injection was 10 mg per 100 ml, and after 2 hours it had sunk to 1 mg per 100 ml in the normal animals. Corresponding values in hepatectomized animals were 10 mg per 100 ml and 5–6 mg per 100 ml, respectively. This indicates that the liver eliminated only about half of the serum bilirubin. Since, in this case, the ureters were not ligated, a certain amount of serum bilirubin could have been excreted by the kidneys. Cabello Ruz also carried out perfusion experiments with livers and eviscerated rear quarters of toads using bilirubin in Ringer's solution. He found a decrease of 20–45% of bilirubin in liver and 30–70% of biliverdin. The concentration decrease was only 10% in his perfusion experiments with rear quarters.

Destruction of bilirubin in tissue cultures was studied by Dubin *et al.* (1965*) who added sterile solutions of albumin-bound unconjugated bilirubin to cultures of chick embryo macrophages and examined their bilirubin after 48 hours at 37° and 4°. The bilirubin concentration was measured using a modified Malloy-Evelyn method and the conjugated bilirubin expressed as the 1-minute direct reaction. Bilirubin concentrations up to 25 mg/100 ml in the culture medium were achieved without difficulty. With higher concentrations bilirubin crystals appeared on the coverslips. In the medium without added cell culture no significant drop in the bilirubin concentration took place in 48 hours at 4°C, while a drop of 10% in concentration was measured at 37°. In cell cultures a drop in bilirubin concentration of 10–15% occurred within 1 minute after addition of the culture both at 4° and 37°, indicating that the macrophages adsorb bilirubin very quickly. The drop in bilirubin concentration after 48 hours at 37° was, however, of the same magnitude as in the cell-free culture media. Thus the macrophages do not apparently metabolize bilirubin. The direct reaction remained negative; therefore, it was concluded that the macrophages do not conjugate bilirubin.

The question of possible destruction of bile pigments in organisms before their excretion has thus generated only moderate interest. On the other hand, the fate of these substances after their entry into the intestine (together with the bile) has been thoroughly investigated.

Until recently it was assumed that the stool of normal adults does not contain bilirubin or biliverdin. These substances would be found only in stool of infants and in adults during violent diarrhea or during hemolytic icterus (Chapter VIII,B,2). In general, these materials are converted to urobilinoids during their travels through the intestinal tract. This was very elegantly shown by A. Schmidt (1895) with the help of $HgCl_2$. With this reaction the content of the small intestine is colored green, whereas that of the large intestine becomes red. This observation led to the assumption that conversion into urobilinoids can only occur on the distal side of the cecum (Chapter VIII,B,2).

Contrary to this, C. J. Watson (personal communication, 1958) was able to detect 5–20 mg of bilirubin and biliverdin per day in normal human stool. Furthermore, he succeeded in isolating bilirubin in crystalline form from the same material.

Clarification of the problem of eventual absorption of bilirubin and biliverdin through the small intestine turned out to be extremely difficult. One should actually assume that substances of such low molecular weight can be easily absorbed. This, however, becomes rather questionable in the light of observations of Bungenberg de Jong (1937, Chapter VII), who was able to show that these substances do not pass through collodion membranes in $CHCl_3$ or in aqueous alkali solutions. This is also indicated by the experiments of Larson and C. J. Watson (1949), who found that similarly low molecular weight coproporphyrins are not absorbed in humans and in dogs. Findings of earlier authors on intestinal absorption were quite contradictory (see With, 1954, 1960). Recently, Lester *et al.* (1961) administered C^{14}-labeled bilirubin orally or by intestinal tube to rats with external bile fistula and found that substantial amounts of both free and conjugated bilirubin were absorbed from the upper, middle, and lower part of the small intestine. Re-excretion of the labeled bilirubin began within 30 minutes after the feeding and continued for 2 days, and 20–30% of the radioactivity could be recovered from the bile. Thus a substantial enterohepatic circulation of bilirubin took place.

According to Lester and Schmid (1962) and Schmid and Hammaker (1962), nonconjugated bilirubin is both absorbed from the intestine and excreted into the intestinal content for which a labile pool of nonconjugated bilirubin exists in the gut, freely exchanging with the bilirubin pool of the plasma.

Observations of Lester and Schmid (1963*) on rats with congenital unconjugated hyperbilirubinemia (Gunn rats) showed that conjugated bilirubin is not absorbed as such but is deconjugated before absorption. After peroral administration of conjugated bilirubin to Gunn rats no conjugated bilirubin appeared in the bile as would have been expected if bilirubin was absorbed in the conjugated form. It thus seems as if conjugation is severed before absorption from the intestine and that water-soluble conjugated bilirubin is not absorbed unchanged.

In this connection it is also of interest that Beck (1964*) found no evidence of entry of bilirubin into the blood stream after introduction of large amounts of conjugated bilirubin intraduodenally.

Schmid and Hammaker (1962) found that *unconjugated bilirubin is excreted into the lumen of the gut* in rats with unconjugated hyperbilirubinemia. Experiments with injection of C^{14}-bilirubin show that 60% of the C^{14} in the feces was present as bilirubin. In Gunn rats with biliary fistula the amount of fecal urobilin was the same as in Gunn rats without biliary fistula, but in normal rats with bile fistula the fecal urobilinoid gradually disappeared.

Künzer *et al.* (1965*, 1966*) demonstrated the passage of unconjugated bilirubin from the blood to the lumen of the gut in man by studying 17 newborns with jaundice and congenital biliary atresia or atresia of the gut. The color of the intestinal contents was used as an indicator of the presence of bile pigments. In all cases with atresia of the bile passages or duodenum the gut contents were colored by bile pigments; whereas in cases with atresia of the jejunum, ileum, or colon no visible color was found. This indicates that the passage of the unconjugated bilirubin from the blood to the intestinal lumen takes place principally or exclusively in the most proximal part of the small intestine.

Similar studies in man were reported by Gilbertsen et al. (1962). They administered N^{15}-bilirubin in alkaline aqueous solution through a duodenal tube to a patient with external bile fistula, crystallized the bile bilirubin, and subjected it to isotope analysis before and after the administration of the labeled bilirubin. They found that the labeled bilirubin appeared rapidly in the bile, reached maximal concentration within the first 18 hours, and subsequently declined rapidly, although it was still present in a low, but significantly elevated percentage, 48 hours after the administration. Only nonconjugated bilirubin was given.

Lester and Schmid (1963a) infused C^{14}-labeled unconjugated and conjugated bilirubin into the duodenum of two patients with external biliary drainage and studied the radioactivity of the bilirubin isolated from the bile. In a boy with Crigler-Najjar's syndrome they isolated the bilirubin from the blood serum 24 hours after instillation of labeled unconjugated and conjugated bilirubin in the duodenum and determined the radioactivity. As found previously in rats, unconjugated bilirubin was readily absorbed, whereas conjugated bilirubin was not absorbed intact. The authors stressed that this prevents appreciable enterohepatic circulation of bilirubin.

Brodersen and Hermann (1963) found that the fecal bilirubin of the newborn is mainly unconjugated, a fact due to the presence of large amounts of β-glucuronidase in the intestine of the newborn. Therefore intestinal absorption of unconjugated bilirubin can be a contributing factor in icterus neonatorum.

Cameron et al. (1965*) studied the fate of bilirubin in isolated intestinal loops with bilirubin-C^{14}. Ileocolic-gastrointestinal loops were formed on five mongrel dogs weighing 8.6–12.2 kg and the loops were anastomosed end to side with the gallbladder. The proximal part of the small intestine was anastomosed end to end with the distal end of the colon resulting in an artificial ileocolic shunt and rapid intestinal passage. The upper end of the distal part of the ileum was anastomosed end to end with the fundus of the gallbladder and the free end of the proximal part of the colon was anastomosed end to side with the distal part of the ileum. In this way a closed intestinal loop in contact with the gallbladder was formed. Finally the common bile duct was divided.

The animals were injected in the femoral vein with bilirubin-C^{14}

(1×10^6–7×10^6 counts per minute) dissolved in dog serum and blood samples were taken after 7, 15, 30, 45, 60, and 120 minutes as well as after 4 and 8 hours from the contralateral femoral vein. The urine and feces were collected for 4–14 days after which the animals were sacrificed. The liver was studied and the intestinal contents analyzed for urobilinoids, bilirubin, and pentdyopents. In one dog urobilin was isolated. In two dogs the anaerobic intestinal flora from the intestinal loop was studied and no significant deviations from the normal intestinal flora could be demonstrated.

The dogs recovered uneventfully after the operation but gradually lost weight and their feces were grossly acholic. Two dogs developed moderate hyperbilirubinemia after the operation. The fecal urobilinoids of all five animals fell from a preoperative level of ca. 30 mg/24 hours to a postoperative one of ca. 2.5 mg/24 hours. Fecal bilirubin and pentdyopent was low throughout the experiment. The histological picture of the liver at autopsy showed nothing abnormal in the 4 dogs, but the fifth showed slight periportal lymphocyte infiltration and fibrosis.

The radioactivity of the serum followed a logarithmic curve—a very steep rise followed by a decline that was initially rapid but soon slowed down and reached background level by 6–8 hours. Very little radioactivity appeared in the urine and only 1% in the feces. In the contents of the intestinal loop there was more urobilinogen than bilirubin pointing to a rapid conversion of bilirubin to urobilinogen. There was significant degradation to nonidentifiable radioactive compounds in the intestinal loop as radioactive substances occurred in the polar, water-soluble fraction, and the total amount of bilirubin plus urobilinogen in the loop contents did not nearly reach the amount of bile pigment theoretically anticipated in the loop.

Further Heringová *et al.* (1964c*) studied the disappearance of nonradioactive bilirubin from the intestinal lumen of male rats using the classic method of Verzár (1936*). In the proximal part of the small gut only 10% of the bilirubin administered remained after 30 minutes, in the middle part 25%, and in the distal part 45.5%. Thus bilirubin absorption showed a proximodistal gradient in the small intestine.

In this connection it should be mentioned that Snyder and Schmid (1965*) found no absorption of hematin from rat intestine in experiments with C^{14}-hematin. Thus hematin does not seem to be absorbed from the small intestine contrary to bilirubin and urobilinogen.

Thus, absorption of bilirubin from the small intestine and its reexcretion in the bile is an established fact in both man and the rat. Studies in other species are urgently required.

According to modern views (cf. Wilson, 1962*) the intestinal mucosa is—like the cellular membranes generally and contrary to endothelial membranes and the erythrocyte membrane—passed only by nonpolar lipo-soluble compounds and not by water and polar substances. According to this concept unconjugated bilirubin which is nonpolar should pass the intestinal mucosa, whereas water-soluble bilirubin diglucuronide should not, especially since this molecule is considerably larger than unconjugated bilirubin (molecular weights 925 and 584 respectively). On the other hand it is known that conjugated bilirubin readily passes from the blood into the bile; therefore it must be assumed that both bilirubin and its diglucuronide pass through the membranes of the liver cells. Further, it has to be remembered that Harboe pointed out that the solubility of bilirubin is not simply a question of polarity and nonpolarity (cf. Chapter I,C), and therefore the passage of bilirubin and its conjugates through membranes cannot be treated as a simple question of polarity.

Another important aspect of the fate of bilirubin is its handling by the *placenta*. This is of special interest because the fetal liver lacks a functioning apparatus for bilirubin conjugation. Schenker *et al.* (1962, 1964*) studied this in the guinea pig. In a pregnant female shortly before term the cystic duct was ligated and external bile fistula established, after which a fetus was delivered by caesarean section into a saline bath at 37° and its vitelline vessels occluded. Then bilirubin-C^{14} was injected into the umbilical vein. Under these experimental conditions both the fetal and the maternal circulation kept functioning for several hours. Maternal bile was collected in 15-minute periods for 2 hours, and crystalline bilirubin was isolated for isotope analysis. At the end of the experiment the radioactivity of the fetal organs and body fluids was studied.

If nonconjugated bilirubin-C^{14} was injected, it was completely cleared from the fetal circulation within 2 hours, 66% appearing into the maternal bile where excretion began 15 minutes after the injection into the umbilical vein. If conjugated bilirubin was injected to the fetus, the elimination was much slower, only 0.8–5.7% of the injected material being recovered from the maternal bile. Fetal bile and intestinal contents exhibited very low radioactivity when both free and conjugated bilirubin were injected, a fact suggesting that the fetal liver is unable to effect the coupling of bilirubin and also cannot excrete conjugated bilirubin. The placental elimination of nonconjugated bilirubin constitutes a highly effective mechanism.

Grodsky *et al.* (1963) performed similar experiments in rats with bilirubin-H^3. They injected physiological amounts of bilirubin into the jugular vein of 19–21 day old fetal rats and studied the distribution of radioactivity in fetal and maternal tissues after 2 hours. Only 1–4% of the total radioactivity appeared in the maternal bile, and less than 2.5% of it was present in the maternal serum and the maternal liver. As much as 93–98% of the total radioactivity was retained in the fetal tissues with the following distribution: carcass 27%, serum 21%, liver 10%, intestine 2.5%. Significant radioactivity was also found in the lungs, brain, kidneys, and stomach, and traces in the heart, placenta, umbilical vein, and spleen. Based on rate of bilirubin excretion and synthesis in adult rats, the fetal bilirubin synthesis would be 2.5–10 times as high as the placental bilirubin transfer. The low level of bilirubin found in the fetal circulation suggests that the bilirubin production rate in the fetal rat is lower than in the adult, or that the bilirubin destruction rate in the fetal rat is higher than in the adult.

The results of the studies by Schenker *et al.* in guinea pigs are quite different from those of Grodsky *et al.* in rats. This may be due to marked species differences. Repetition and extension of the experiments are highly desirable as well as similar experiments in other species.

The placenta of rodents shows, however, important differences from the human placenta, and therefore studies in primates are necessary. Lester *et al.* (1963*) studied bilirubin transfer across the placenta of rhesus monkeys using C^{14}-bilirubin with a radioactivity high enough to work with fetal serum bilirubin concentrations close to normal. The fetuses were close to term and were left *in utero* during the experiments. A fetal limb was made accessible by an incision through the uterine wall and the i.v. bilirubin injection was given into the limb. The maternal bile was collected and its bilirubin prepared in crystalline condition. The experimental technique is very difficult and in seven experiments only two fetuses survived for more than 2 hours, 6 and 2½ hours respectively. In both these experiments maternal C^{14}-bilirubin began to appear in the bile during the first hour and subsequently its appearance proceeded at an accelerated rate. The initial delay before its appearance corresponds well to mixing in the fetus, placental transfer, and maternal excretion. In the 6-hour experiment 19% of the injected radioactivity appeared in the maternal bile and in the 2½-hour experiment 8%. The excretion rate in the 6-hour experiment was 30 μg per hour, a figure of the same order as the calculated bilirubin production of the fetus. After the experiments the fetuses were subjected to analysis. Small quantities of radioactivity appeared in the fetal liver, kidney, and spleen, but always in a concentration less than that of the plasma. The fetal gallbladder contained small amounts of viscid bile (bilirubin 50 mg/100 ml). At the end of the experiments no fetal hemoglobin was demonstrable in the maternal serum, a fact demonstrating that the C^{14}-bilirubin of the maternal bile cannot be due to transplacental blood transfer. The maternal bile contained labeled bilirubin derivatives in addition to C^{14}-bilirubin, a finding pointing toward a secondary pathway of fetal bilirubin elimination, i.e., after degradation to nonidentifiable compounds.

Lester *et al.* (1963*) found no significant transfer of conjugated bilirubin through the monkey placenta.

The question of bile pigment *absorption through the walls of serous cavities* has also been studied. It has been proved that no jaundice develops in humans or in animals when bile is excreted into the free abdominal cavity. Such a condition is known as biliary peritonitis, cholascos, or as bile ascites (Eppinger, 1937, p. 221). Absence of icterus is explained by assuming that either no absorption occurs, or that the liver is able to keep pace with absorption. A possible uptake of bilirubin solutions through the peritoneum has not been studied.

Royer (1938a,b) has demonstrated bilirubin absorption through the wall of the gall bladder. Ostrow (1963) studied the absorption of labeled unconjugated and conjugated bilirubin from the isolated gallbladder in the guinea pig and found that the gall bladder epithelium, like the intestinal epithelium, preferentially reabsorbed unconjugated bilirubin.

Maly (1871) first suggested that *urobilinogen* is formed from bilirubin in the intestine; later, this hypothesis was generally accepted on the basis of the famous experiments of F. von Müller (1892). Fischler (1906) found that the stool of dogs with bile fistula did not contain urobilinoids if the animals were prevented from licking the bile, but that it reappeared when bile intake was permitted. This was confirmed by Steensma (1918, p. 54). Von Müller administered pig bile to a patient with complete bile duct obstruction, after which the initially absent urobilin reappeared in urine. Later investigators repeated these experiments with pig bile from which the urobilinoids were extracted, but could not detect urobilinuria (Fromholdt and Nersessoff, 1912a,b; Weltmann, 1923; Walzel and Weltmann, 1924). Thus, the classic observations of Von Müller did not furnish evidence, although his conclusions, which are based on these observations were correct.

It soon became clear that the formation of urobilinoids occurs in the *large intestine*. With the help of the $HgCl_2$ reaction, A. Schmidt (1895) recognized this fact. Macfadyen *et al.* (1891, p. 323) came to the same conclusions. Quioc (1909, pp. 30 and 60) reported similar results in children, but here the $HgCl_2$ reaction was also red in terminal ileum, 5–6 cm above the cecum. The results of Meinel (1903), who found urobilin in gastric juice, are questionable because the substance could only be detected by fluorescence test.

The *formation of urobilinoids after oral bilirubin administration* has been studied by various investigators. Significant fluctuations were found in excreted bilirubin (compare With, 1954, p. 70). Most recent results have shown that the form in which bilirubin is administered is very important for these fluctuations. Different results were obtained with free and conjugated bilirubin. In three cases of complete bile duct obstruction, after oral administration of crystalline bilirubin-N^{15} Gilbertsen et al. (1957) retraced only about 5% of the N^{15} in the urobilinogen and found no mesobilifuscin-N^{15} in the stool. When unpurified bilirubin-N^{15} glucuronide was given to normal persons, 100% of the N^{15} appeared in the urobilinogen. C. J. Watson (personal communication, 1958) established that after oral administration of crystalline bilirubin the fecal urobilinogen increase was only 10%. However, this value was about 100% when bilirubin glucuronide was administered. This is only true for normal bile flow; in cases of restricted bile flow these percentages are considerably lower. C. J. Watson et al. (1958) carried out in vitro experiments with broth cultures of fecal bacteria to which they added bilirubin. They compared urobilin formation after introduction of free (crystalline) bilirubin and crude bilirubin glucuronide concentrate (direct bilirubin). It was established that the amount of urobilinogen formed from bilirubin glucuronide was double that obtained from free bilirubin. Thus, for example, 62 mg of crystalline bilirubin yielded 14 mg urobilin, whereas the same amount of bilirubin glucuronide yielded 21 mg of urobilinogen. The proportion of UG-D, -I, and -L fluctuated and no tendency could be detected.

Formation of urobilinoids in the intestine is, at least during initial stages, a *bacterial process*. Kämmerer and Miller (1922a,b, 1923), who incubated colloidal bilirubin solutions in horse serum with human stool emulsions, could demonstrate urobilinogen formation. Also mesobilirubin was converted to UG, but this was not achieved with biliverdin. Pure cultures of *Escherichia coli* and sterile filtrates of stool did not produce urobilinogen. UG formation could not be inhibited by heating stool emulsions before incubation for 2 hours at 60–70°. It was therefore concluded that spore-forming organisms must play a role in these processes, and that aerobic as well as anaerobic organisms participate in the reactions. The active anaerobic organism is according to Baumgärtel *B. putrificus verrucosus* (cf. below), in modern terminology *Clostridium putrificum*.

Continuing these experiments, Baumgärtel (1943a; 1950b, pp. 113–130; Baumgärtel and Zahn, 1951) found that urobilinogen formation requires the presence of the oxidoreduction system, cysteine–cystine. The first step in this process is the conversion of food cystine into cysteine by the anaerobic *B. verrucosus* in the large intestine. In the next step, under the influence of a dehydrogenase which is liberated from dead coli bacillis, bilirubin is reduced. This dehydrogenase acts throughout the whole colon. Bilirubin thereby functions as hydrogen acceptor and is converted to stercobilinogen (tetrahydromesobilane; UG-L), and not into urobilinogen IX (UG-I). The conversion of other hydrogen acceptors is similar to that of bilirubin, e.g., cholesterol to coprosterol, cholic acid to deoxycholic acid, and chlorophyll to phylloerythrinogen (Baumgärtel, 1943b, 1947d, 1948b; 1950b, pp. 122–128). In numerous *in vitro* experiments UG-L was always detected, while UG-I was never obtained. At the same time, the oxidation of stercobilinogen to stercobilin was demonstrated, and the substance was obtained in crystalline form (Baumgärtel, 1947a). Furthermore, it was found that colidehydrogenase converts bilirubin, mesobilirubin, and dihydrobilirubin into UG-L, whereas biliverdin and mesobiliverdin cannot be reduced in this manner. Coprobilirubin is also subject to this reaction, but not coprobiliverdin (Baumgärtel, 1943b, 1945; 1950b, p. 216; 1958b). The findings of Baumgärtel were generally confirmed by W. C. Meyer (1944, 1947a,b).

In these well-conducted *in vitro* experiments, Baumgärtel has shown an important process of active urobilinogen formation in the intestines. But without having real experimental proof, he advanced the hypothesis that this is the only possible route of urobilinogen formation and that UG-I could never be formed by bacterial activity in the intestines. This opinion was contrary to Watson's interesting, but not entirely clear, preliminary observations. According to Watson and his group (see C. J. Watson and Schwartz, 1942; Schwartz and Watson, 1942; Schwartz *et al.*, 1942; C. J. Watson *et al.*, 1942), UG-I is the primary product in the conversion of bilirubin. Thus, under normal conditions UG-I is converted to UG-L, whereas under certain pathological circumstances it is transformed into UG-D. For the formation of UG-L, various factors of stool and of bile are necessary, but to form UG-D, only bile factors are needed. Watson's group did not exclude the possibility that bilirubin could be reduced directly to UG-L and UG-D.

These contradictory theories of urobilinogen formation from bilirubin led to numerous discussions. Recent experiments by C. J. Watson *et al.* (1954) and Lowry *et al.* (1954) showed clearly that Baumgärtel's theory (1943a,c, 1944, 1950b) can no longer be maintained. Their observations on intestinal urobilinogen formation, in patients treated with *broad spectrum antibiotics,* are of special interest here. This therapy led to changes in the bacterial flora of the intestines, and to the formation of UG-D as the principal urobilinogen compound.

Such findings were reported by Sborov and Watson (1949), Robbins (1951), Sborov *et al.* (1951), and C. J. Watson *et al.* (1954). When tetracycline derivatives are administered orally, urobilinogens disappear from stool, urine, and bile within a few days. At the same time the bacterial flora of the large intestine changes profoundly (*E. coli* and clostridia are destroyed). When urobilinogens disappear from stool, bilirubin appears instead. A few days after discontinuing the tetracycline treatment, UG-D appears as the prevailing urobilinogen. A possible reason for this is that after cessation of antibiotic treatment atypical coliform organisms emerge. UG-D disappears gradually and is replaced by UG-L. In certain cases of extended tetracycline therapy, UG-D can become the dominant urobilinoid of stool. When UG-D is present, the Ehrlich reaction is much more intense in aqueous stool extract than after extraction with petrol ether. This discrepancy is characteristic of UG-D, but contrary to UG-L and UG-I because UG-D is considerably less soluble in petrol ether than UG-L and UG-I.

Lowry *et al.* (1954) showed that UG-I can be converted to UG-L (stercobilin) by the action of fecal bacteria. They incubated N^{15}-labeled UG-I (mesobilirubinogen) with bacterial cultures from stools and isolated crystalline stercobilin-N^{15}. Similar experiments were carried out *in vivo* by feeding N^{15}-UG-I and isolating a marked excess of crystalline UG-L from stool. These findings could also be substantiated by clinical observations (C. J. Watson, 1959).

Mitsuda (1959a,b) found that *E. coli* alone could reduce biliverdin to bilirubin but could not reduce the vinyl of the side chains.

As a consequence of these results, our present knowledge of urobilinogen formation in the intestines can be summarized as follows: Only bilirubin and the other rubins will be converted. Verdins will not be affected. This process commences and proceeds in the large intestine. Only under pathological circumstances, in which the bacterial flora of the colon ascend into the small intestine or bile ducts, will urobilinogen formation occur in these organs. A series of various bacteria participate herein, i.e., coliform organisms and also anaerobic forms. The degradation, which was investigated *in vitro* by Baumgärtel (1943a), probably plays an important role under normal conditions, perhaps a dominant one. However, it is doubtless not the only possible route. C. J. Watson *et al.* (1954) and Lowry *et al.* (1954) showed that UG-I and UG-D can occur as intermediate stages during UG-L formation. UG-L is the principal urobilinogen under normal conditions. It is not known whether UG-I and UG-D are normal transition stages, but there is no doubt that they can occur in stool. Thus, Fischer and Libowitzky (1939) isolated UG-I from stool. C. J. Watson *et al.* (1958) added purified urobilinogens to broth cultures of fecal bacteria and established that added UG-D was converted to UG-I and UG-L. UG-I was transformed into UG-L. This is in complete agreement with the amount of hydrogen contained in these compounds; thus UG-D contains a vinyl group, whereas UG-I possesses an ethyl group, and UG-L is saturated with hydrogen.

Detailed investigations of urobilinogen formation in the intestines with special consideration of intermediate products would, in fact, be extremely difficult. Many different bacteria, living as well as dead, participate in this process and a great number of various enzyme systems may interact. Experiments with isolated strains of bacteria in many different combinations would be necessary. However, results obtained in this manner are hardly of any clinical or pathological significance.

C. J. Watson (personal communication, 1958) succeeded in isolating small amounts of mesobilirubin, dihydromesobilirubin, and UG-D from normal stool. He characterized these materials by chromatography. In the cecum he found a higher concentration of UG-D. It should be mentioned that K.-H. Brandt (1957), in his thorough treatise, completely shares Watson's concepts on fecal urobilinogenesis.

The *reduction of bilirubin in the small intestine* was studied by Matsui (1959a,b,c) who aspirated contents from different places in the jejunum with the Miller-Abbot double tube. He studied the bacterial flora of the samples and their content of bilirubinoids by means of chromatographic technique. In normal subjects the bilirubinoids found were most often dihydrobilirubin, mesobilirubin, and dihydromesobilirubin. *E. coli* was never encountered in healthy subjects but was occasionally found in patients with various diseases. In only 11 of 55 cases was a positive Ehrlich reaction found, in the jejunum once, and six times in the ileum. The urobilinogen was UG-I except in one case where both UG-I and UG-L were found. UG-D was never encountered. Also, Bungenberg de Jong (1959) found small amounts of UG in the lower ileum, although much less than in the large intestine (5–15 mg per 100 g of intestinal content as against 100–500 mg per 100 g).

Lester (1964*) pointed out that formation of urobilinogens in the small intestine is a real possibility because in many digestive diseases the proximal region of the intestine is invaded by the bacterial flora of the colon. This bacterial invasion of the proximal jejunum was already demonstrated by Martini *et al.* (1957*) and has recently been emphasized by Thaysen (1966*). In such cases urobilinogen can be absorbed to a considerable degree, and this phenomenon unquestionably plays a significant role in the pathogenesis of urobilinuria. It is quite possible that urobilinuria can occur without liver anomaly in such cases, but this has not been subjected to closer study.

Whether *"extraenteral" formation of urobilinogen* takes place besides the demonstrated enteral one, gave rise to numerous and extended discussions. This question is even today not completely solved. Some early investigators assumed that urobilinogen was formed in the kidneys (Leube, 1888; Herscher, 1902; Gilbert and Herscher, 1902), while others thought that it was formed in the liver (Hayem, 1889; Tissier, 1889; Fischler, 1906; Doyon et al., 1908). Clarens (1903) assumed that uro-bilinogen can be formed from hemoglobin, in all tissues. The older literature was summarized by Lemaire (1905, pp. 141–190) and Carrié (1913, pp. 92–105). They came to the conclusion that, besides intestinal urobilinogen formation, extraintestinal formation also exists. In contrast, the newer literature presents a peculiar national divergency of opinions on the question of extraenteral urobilinogen formation. Whereas the French always assumed such an extraenteral process, the Anglo-Saxon literature vigorously rejected the idea. German opinion up to the time of Halbach (1938) also refused to accept the possibility of extraenteral formation. The French opinion is expressed by Widal and Abrami (1928), whereas the Anglo-Saxon interpretation is spelled out by C. J. Watson (1938). Swedish investigators assumed an intermediate role in this dispute (Salén and Enocksson, 1927). This position is also shared by South American authors, e.g., Royer (1943).

The theory of exclusively intestinal urobilinogen formation originated with the experiments of von Müller (1892) and was extended by Hildebrandt (1906, 1909a,b, 1910), who developed his theory on the basis of clinical observations. The theory of exclusively enteral formation was supported by experiments of McMaster and Elman (1926), who stated categorically that there is no evidence for the assumption that urobilinogen compounds are ever formed by parenchymal activity of the liver. They admitted to only one possibility of extraintestinal urobilin formation, i.e., by bacteria in infected bile ducts. McMaster and Elman's concept was vigorously contradicted by Fischler (1906, 1916, 1925) and by Fischler and Ottensooser (1925). These authors reached their con-clusions through experiments carried out on dogs with bile fistula. They found urobilinuria after certain poisonings, and after hypoglycemic shock. These observations were made in experiments in which entry of bile into intestines was prevented. Nevertheless, Elman and McMaster (1925a) and McMaster and Elman (1926) believed that the findings of Fischler were due to bacterially infected bile ducts. Gebhardt (1939a,b) repeated Fischler's experiments under conditions which excluded any possibility of infection of bile ducts, and demonstrated that McMaster and Elman's (1925a,b, 1926, 1927) assumption must be erroneous.

This contradiction between the experiments of McMaster and Elman on the one hand and those of Fischler and Gebhardt on the other, is difficult to explain. Nevertheless, various clinical and experimental observations seem to indicate that, at least under conditions of hemolysis, extraintestinal urobilin formation can occur. Hanssen (1909, p. 1179) reported marked urobilinuria which occurred a few hours after hemolysis. This finding could not be explained by intestinal urobilinogenesis, because bilirubin could not be formed by hemolysis and reach the intestine and be converted into urobilinogen there during this short period of observation. Similar observations were reported by Jones and Jones (1922), Winternitz (1923), Halbach (1938), and Stich (1948). However, E. Meyer and Emmerich (1909) did not succeed in detecting bilirubinuria sooner than 12 hours after attacks of paroxysmal hemoglobinuria. Similarly, hemolysis experiments in animals showed that at the time the bilirubin concentration increased, urobilinoids appeared in urine and in bile (see Fischler, 1906: dogs; Beijers, 1923, Chapter II: calves; Oshima, 1931c: rabbits).

The experiments of Billi *et al.* (1933) on eviscerated dogs and cats are of particular value to the problem of extraenteral formation of urobilinoids. The entire intestine was removed from the Vater's papilla down to the anus. The animals survived the operation for 3 weeks. Blood circulation through the liver was considerably diminished, and a bile stasis with jaundice developed. Under these conditions the physiological urobilinuria disappeared within about 48 hours after the operation. However, about 9 days later, a moderate urobilinuria appeared with simultaneous decrease in urine bilirubin. The urobilinuria was attributed to bacterial processes in the duodenal stump, which remained after the operation. As a rule, urobilinogen could be detected in the stomach of these animals. Intravenous hemoglobin administration did not lead to increased urobilinuria. Billi and Heilmeyer considered these findings a confirmation of exclusive enterogenic urobilinogen formation. Nevertheless, Baumgärtel (1950b, p. 121) maintained that the urobilinogen produced in the bile of these animals is enzymatically formed UG-I and not UG-L, which is produced by bacterial activity. Although no bacteriological studies were carried out in these experiments, the fact that Billi and Heilmeyer detected indicanuria in their animals clearly indicates that bacterial processes did occur. These experiments with complete removal of intestines are of considerable interest and should be repeated using modern technique. It would be desirable to extend the survival time by complete parenteral feeding, to prevent or suppress infections by the use of antibiotics, to examine bacteriologically the contents of stomach and duodenal stump, to extend experiments to various animal species, and, last but not least, to isolate the urobilinoids in the crystalline state using the method developed by Watson and his school (see C. J. Watson *et al.*, 1953; Lowry *et al.*, 1956; C. J. Watson and Lowry, 1956).

Another pertinent point in the discussion of extraintestinal urobilinogen formation is the situation prevailing in the newborn organism. Here the intestinal tract is still sterile; the characteristics which are responsible for urobilinogen formation appear only gradually. Bile pigments from the bile are not yet reduced, and the stool contains bilirubin as well as biliverdin (see Chapter VIII,B,2). It should further be mentioned that Royer (1929b) found that urobilinoids can pass the placenta, i.e., urobilinoids which were injected intravenously into mothers were demonstrable in the liver of the fetus. His experiments, however, did not meet the requirements of modern investigations and should be repeated with reliable analytical technique.

The question of extraenteral formation could be studied in *germfree animals;* this technique is now available. Such experiments have been carried out by Gustafsson and Lanke (1960). In 25 germfree rats, urobilinoids were absent from the stool and urine, but they were present in all of 14 normal rats in quantities of 2.1–5.0 μmoles per 24 hours. In both groups, bilirubin was found in the stool—2.9–7.8 μmoles per 24 hours in the germfree as against 0.9–2.7 in the normal controls. When the germfree rats were fed a fecal suspension from normal ones, urobilinoids appeared in their feces in 2–3 days and reached the normal level on the third day. In three experiments germfree rats were fed fecal content heated to 80° for 5 minutes. One of these rats became strongly urobilin positive and from its feces a *Clostridium-like organism* (G 62) was isolated. If cultures of G 62 were fed to germfree rats, they became urobilin positive in 2–3 days. Simultaneous feeding with G 62 and *E. coli* (G 14) gave, however, a significantly higher fecal urobilinogen level, the same as in normal rats. A number of bacteria were studied in feeding experiments with germfree rats and found to give no urobilinogen formation: *Clostridium Welchii* alone and in combination with *E. coli* of rat origin (G 14) or *E. coli* of human origin; *Clostridium sporogens; Lactobacillus acidophilus; Proteus vulgaris; Bacillus subtilis; Mucor.* There was no attempt to fractionate the urobilinogen in UG-ı, UG-ʟ, and UG-ᴅ. The *Clostridium* strain G 62 was subsequently studied by C. J. Watson *et al.* (1962) who found that it reduced mesobilirubin to UG-ı and UG-ʟ, while UG-ᴅ was not formed; this is in contrast to what is seen with human fecal flora.

The presence of urobilin in individuals with complete bile duct obstruction is important to the question of extraintestinal formation of urobilin bodies. If urobilinoids were exclusively formed in intestines, urine should be completely free from urobilin during bile duct obstruction. The same would be true for bile fistula whereby the entire bile passes through the fistula, and does not enter the intestine. In these cases the individual cannot utilize its own bile. Traces of urobilinoid in urine or stool during complete absence of bile from the intestine would be proof for the existence of extraenteral urobilinogen formation. Unfortunately, the problems involved here are much more complicated. C. J. Watson (1937b, 1940) pointed out that during complete bile duct obstruction small amounts of bilirubin could enter the intestine. Complete bile duct closure is, as a rule, accompanied by high hyperbilirubinemia, and often by insufficient blood coagulation, causing continuous microscopic bleeding of the intestinal mucosa. These small amounts of bilirubin are converted to urobilinogens by intestinal bacteria. After absorption, these urobilinogens may appear in the urine. Thus, C. J. Watson (1940, 1942a,b) was able to detect small amounts of urobilinoids during complete bile duct obstruction in human stool (see Chapter VIII,C,2). McMaster and Elman (1926, p. 772) also found small amounts of urobilin in the stool of their dogs during complete bile duct closure. Baumgärtel (1947c; 1950b, p. 180) and Stich (1957) assumed that the urobilinogen which is formed during bile obstruction and during bile fistula is extraintestinal UG-ɪ, and not UG-ʟ which is produced in the intestines. The evidence presented by them, however, is unsatisfactory. C. J. Watson (1956a,b,c, 1957) and K.-H. Brandt (1957) presented a series of facts which are not in agreement with their assumption. Gebhardt (1939a,b) and Baumgärtel (1950b, p. 180) studied the urobilinogens in stool of animals with complete bile fistula. However, no significant proof for extraintestinal urobilinogen formation was obtained from these findings.

A particular form of extraintestinal urobilinogen formation is the one observed in *hematomas,* hemorrhagic exudates, and transudates. This phenomenon is related to urobilinogen formation after *intravasal hemolysis.* Various clinical observations are recorded for urobilinuria occurring under these conditions (Kunkel, 1880; Dick, 1884). In addition, experimental investigations were reported concerning urobilinuria which develops after large blood effusions and hemorrhagic exudates (Tsuchiya, 1910; Kühl, 1924a,b; Wester, 1912a, p. 828). The urobilinuria which developed in these cases was comparatively mild. Investigations on fecal urobilinoid excretion after subcutaneous blood injections were carried out by ten Bokkel Huinink (1941). He found a surprisingly high increase in fecal urobilinoids. However, his control experiments did not establish the fluctuation limits of spontaneous excretion of fecal urobilinoids with sufficient reliability; therefore his studies cannot be used as proof for extraintestinal urobilin formation.

Baumgärtel (1949c; 1950b, pp. 109 and 130) assumes that extraintestinal urobilin formation occurs regularly, and that the urobilin formed is UG-ɪ. On the contrary, UG-ʟ is formed in the intestines only.

However, as mentioned above, this concept (i.e., that urobilinogen formed in the intestines is always UG-L) cannot be accepted. According to Baumgärtel (1950b) UG-I is produced extraintestinally by the action of an enzyme present in the cells of the RES. Such extraintestinal UG-I formation can take place in bile ducts, as well as in liver or other tissues. However, this hypothesis is insufficiently supported by experimentation. The final proof for the existence of extraintestinal urobilinoid formation has yet to be obtained. On the basis of available material, at least under normal conditions, evidence is pointing to predominantly enteral formation. Nevertheless, important clinical and experimental indications are available to show that under certain conditions (excessive hemolysis) extraintestinal formation is possible. Further studies are necessary to unravel the role played by UG-I, -L, and -D. Such investigations must include the injection of N^{15}-labeled hemoglobin, the isolation of urobilinoids formed at various time intervals after the injection (to find out whether this time factor contradicts the idea of intestinal formation), and finally the identification of urobilinoids formed. In this connection it should be mentioned that C. J. Watson and Weimer (1959) studied the excretion of UG-I, -L, and -D, carrying out extensive observations on 68 patients. They came to the conclusion that all three were always of intestinal origin.

A hypothesis which played a certain role in this area is the theory of *enterohepatic circulation of urobilin*. It was introduced by Hildebrandt (1906, 1909a,b, 1910; see above) and gained wide acceptance (Paschkis, 1933; C. J. Watson, 1938; Royer, 1943). Nevertheless, this hypothesis is rather doubtful. According to this theory, one part of the urobilinogen —formed in the intestine—is absorbed and reaches the liver through the portal vein. The larger part of this urobilinogen will again be excreted with the bile. A smaller part, however, reaches the general circulation and eventually the kidneys, where it will be excreted with the urine. This small part is presumably absorbed via the hemorrhoidal plexus, the blood of which goes directly into the caval system and thus bypasses the liver. When the liver function is disturbed, more urobilinogen than normal is offered to the kidneys. This explains the urobilinuria during liver diseases. Bilirubin can be present in human serum in relatively high concentrations without being excreted with the urine. Conversely, urobilinogen appears in urine at extremely low serum urobilinogen levels, i.e., the kidney threshold for urobilinogen is close to nil.

For the existence of enterohepatic circulation, absorption of urobilinogens from the intestinal canal is a necessary requirement. That this actually takes place has been demonstrated by Fischer and Libowitzky (1939). These investigators administered 0.4 g of a crude urobilinogen preparation (containing about 90% of UG-L) orally to individuals whose stool was marked with a dyestuff. Two hours after administration, urobilinogen appeared in urine. Excretion maximum was reached after 6 hours; after this time the amount decreased slowly. It was significant that excess urobilinogen disappeared from the urine only after the fourth day, although the dyestuff which was administered simultaneously with the urobilinogen in order to color the contents of the intestinal tract had been eliminated after 18 hours. Such retarded excretion in the urine can only be explained by assuming absorption by the intestines and excretion with the bile. It is known that after oral administration not only UG-L, as in this experiment, but also UG-I is excreted with urine (Fischer and Meyer-Betz, 1911). Nevertheless, the experiments of Fischer and Libowitzky do not correspond to conditions found in nature. The urobilinogen administered by these workers reached the small intestine, whereas in nature it is formed in the large intestine. These facts weaken the theory of enterohepatic circulation of urobilinogen. Garner (1955) maintains the existence of enterohepatic circulation of stercobilinogen because he found considerable stercobilin excretion in the bile of cattle. This is not the case in humans.

The investigations by McMaster and Elman (1925a,b) using dogs with bile fistula indicate that a part of the urobilinogen absorbed from the intestine is excreted as bilirubin. Thus, prior to excretion, urobilinogen had first to be converted into bilirubin in the liver. With this possibility, however, the whole question becomes even more complicated. To accept the idea of such conversion with certainty, experiments with labeled urobilinogens must be carried out. However, such investigations have not been reported yet. A number of investigations did not succeed in bringing experimental evidence for the formation of bilirubin from urobilinogen (Felix and Moebus, 1935; J. D. Mann and Koler, 1951; Noro, 1951). To this comes the recently demonstrated enterohepatic circulation of a substantial amount of the bilirubin of the bile (cf. above).

Lester and Schmid (1965*) who administered C^{14}-UG-I into the intestine of rats were unable to demonstrate C^{14}-bilirubin in their bile.

It has been proved that urobilinogens are absorbed from the small intestine (Fischer and Meyer-Betz, 1911). However, Fromholdt (1907, 1911) doubts that urobilin itself is absorbed. Although this different behavior is certainly peculiar, it cannot be rejected *a priori*. Experiments with labeled urobilin would be of great interest. Royer (1932b) demonstrated urobilinuria after administration of urobilins in isolated intestinal loops.

The absorption of saline solutions of crystalline stercobilin from isolated loops of jejunum was studied by Kahán (1961) in dogs. She found a rapid absorption beginning in a few minutes and culminating after 15 minutes. The absorption was followed by fluorimetric measuring of the urobilin in the plasma of the venous intestinal blood. Binding of stercobilin to the intestinal mucoproteins was demonstrated. In the bloodplasma, the urobilin was bound to β-globulin and heparin. Part of the injected stercobilin was excreted in the urine as chromogen. Thus, both urobilinogens and urobilins are absorbed from the small intestine.

The *absorption of urobilinogens from the large intestine* has been investigated, but still remains an open question (compare With, 1954, p. 81). As pointed out by Gray (1961a p. 35), this question cannot be answered finally before studies with labeled urobilinogens are available. The results of Royer's (1932b) experiments, which were carried out in dogs with intestinal fistula and on isolated intestinal loops, are stimulating. After the administration of stercobilin in dilute alkali solutions into isolated loops of the large and small intestines, he demonstrated equally high degrees of urobilinuria. In addition, after enema with UG-I in two persons, With (1954, p. 82) detected the same substance in the urine. Bungenberg de Jong (1959) reported several observations supporting an absorption of UG from the large intestine but admitted that absolute proof is difficult because destruction of UG takes place during the passage through the large intestine. In one experiment, a substantially lower UG concentration was found in the rectal content than in that of the middle colon. More convincing is his observation of pronounced urobilinuria following enemas in a patient with colostomia.

Recently, Lester and Schmid (1964) studied enterohepatic circulation of urobilinoid in the rat employing C^{14}-UG-I, prepared from bilirubin-C^{14} with sodium amalgam. The labeled chromogen was radiochemically pure and more than 90% of radioactivity migrated with the Ehrlich-positive material on thin layer chromatography with silica gel. Injection of C^{14}-UG-I dissolved in plasma to rats with bile fistula resulted in excretion of 80–90% of radioactivity with bile, with less than 10% appearing in urine. Intestinal absorption was studied by administration of C^{14}-UG-I dissolved in aqueous taurocholate to anesthetized rats with bile fistula and with a plastic perianal receptacle. The C^{14}-UG-I was administered through a duodenal tube or injected directly into the terminal ileum. Bile and urine were collected at regular intervals. Isotopes appeared invariably in bile within 30 minutes after duodenal installation, and the excretion continued for 24–48 hours. About 50% of injected radioactivity appeared in bile, less than 5% in urine. A major part reappeared in bile as C^{14}-UG-I. Installation in the ileum resulted in slower absorption, only 10–20% of injected radioactivity reappearing in bile. These experiments are interesting, but do not solve the problem of enterohepatic circulation of urobilinoids because they do not include experiments where the C^{14}-UG-I is injected into the large intestine. As pointed out above, urobilinoids are normally formed only in the large intestine in significant amounts, and will therefore not reach the small intestine. Experiments with radioactive UG given into various parts of the large intestine—and not only UG-I but also and especially UG-L— are required for final elucidation of the problem of enterohepatic circulation of urobilinoids. For this purpose studies in several species including man are also required.

Lester and Schmid (1965*) extended these observations. Normal rats as well as rats with congenital unconjugated hyperbilirubinemia (Gunn rats) were studied. The rats were injected with labeled UG-I or fed by duodenal tube with rat bile containing labeled UG-I. In addition, normal rats with moderate hepatic parenchymal damage following CCl_4 injections and rats with experimental biliary obstructions were studied. Radioassay was performed on bile and urine and the UG concentration was determined after extraction and reaction with benzaldehyde. The radioactivity of the extracts was determined, and thin-layer chromatography was performed on the benzaldehyde reaction products. To investigate the eventual transformation of urobilinogen into bilirubin, bilirubin was isolated from the bile of the rats and its radioactivity was studied. The dose of UG-I administered was of the same order of magnitude as the animal's own bile pigment production per day.

After intraduodenal administration the rats with parenchymal damage excreted 70% of the radioactivity in the bile and both these rats and the rats with biliary occlusion showed a radioactivity in the urine which did not exceed that found in the normal control rats.

It was found that Gunn rats excrete urobilinogen in the bile in the same way the normal rats do, and it is unlikely that UG is conjugated with glucuronic acid in the liver, a finding of importance in considering the question of an enterohepatic circulation of urobilinogen.

No support was found in these experiments for the idea that UG-I is transformed into bilirubin by the liver, regardless of the way C^{14}-UG-I was administered.

Lester *et al.* (1965*) studied the absorption of urobilinogen in six human subjects using C^{14}-UG-I. Four patients with external biliary drainage and two subjects with intact biliary tree were studied, one of the latter was normal, the other suffered from an early portal cirrhosis. They received 20–35 mg of labeled UG with a duodenal tube. In the subjects in which a bile drain was used, radioactivity appeared in the bile during the first 2 hours and continued at a rapid rate for 6 hours.

In two subjects where the UG was injected into the duodenum 47–

56% of the label appeared in the bile, and in two where UG was injected into the terminal ileum only 12–30% appeared in the bile. In the normal control subject 4% of the label appeared in the urine, whereas the corresponding figure for the cirrhotic patient was 10%.

As urobilinogens are normally formed first in the colon and the absorption of urobilinogens injected into the terminal ileum is rather low, then enterohepatic circulation of urobilinogens can only play a minor role under normal conditions. Only if the bacterial flora of the colon invades the small intestine can larger amounts of urobilinoid be absorbed (cf. above).

Baumgärtel (1949a; 1950b, p. 98 et seq.), who could only detect UG-ɪ but never UG-ʟ in the bile, did not believe in enterohepatic circulation of urobilinogens. His findings, however, do not agree with experiments in which, after intravenous stercobilin injections, the U-ʟ appeared in the bile (Oshima, 1932a,b; C. J. Watson, 1936c). Baumgärtel (1949a; 1950b, p. 136) assumed that only UG-ɪ and not UG-ʟ can be absorbed from the part of the large intestine which belongs to the drainage area of the portal vein. He further believed that UG-ʟ can be absorbed from the part of the large intestine which is drained by the hemorrhoidal plexus. He explained physiological urobilinuria by assuming that UG-ʟ, which is absorbed by the hemorrhoidal plexus, escapes the passage through the liver and is excreted with urine. Fischler (1916, 1925) and Gebhardt (1939a,b), found that in dogs with Eck's fistula only moderate urobilinuria develops; this speaks against absorption of UG-ʟ by the portal vein. In the case of Eck's fistula, a significant urobilinuria should appear, since here the portal blood does not pass through the liver (Baumgärtel, 1950b, p. 185). However, Royer (1932b) found urobilinuria in three individuals with high colostomy, i.e., after interruption of the supply of the hemorrhoidal plexus. This observation does not agree with Baumgärtel's hypothesis. A special theory of urobilinogen formation from bilirubin originates from ten Bokkel Huinink (1941, 1942). He assumed that direct-reacting (conjugated) bilirubin is converted into urobilinogen in the intestines, whereas indirect-reacting (free) bilirubin is transformed to copronigrin. Bungenberg de Jong (1942) demonstrated that this hypothesis was wrong.

The fate of *urobilinogens introduced into the circulation* has been studied by various investigators. It was established that the liver eliminates the major part, while a smaller part is excreted by the kidneys (see Lester and Schmid, 1964; cf. above). When urobilin solutions were administered to hepatectomized frogs, the animals developed urobilinuria, while control animals were not affected (Lesieurs *et al.*, 1908). Royer (1943, pp. 68 and 152) injected urobilinogen into the portal vein of dogs and subsequently determined the urobilinogen concentration in the portal vein and in hepatic veins. He found that the urobilin concentration in the portal vein of normal livers was five times that in the hepatic. However, after poisoning with chloroform, no more concentration differences were found. In studies on the behavior of urobilin-containing blood plasma, which was incubated with normal liver brei *in vitro,* all urobilin disappeared. However, this disappearance was considerably less when livers of chloroform-poisoned dogs were used (Royer, 1928b,c,d). Felix and Moebus (1935) conducted similar experiments using acceptable techniques with pig liver brei under controlled conditions of pH, and demonstrated a slowly progressing disappearance of UG-I; the optimum velocity of this process was at pH 7.1. Oxygen accelerated the process, nitrogen stopped it completely. No bilirubin formation from urobilinogen was demonstrated.

The *excretion of parenterally administered urobilin* in the bile and urine has been studied by a number of authors. After intravenous injection of 50 mg U-L, C. J. Watson (1938, p. 2524) reported a strong positive benzaldehyde reaction in duodenal juice of normal individuals. With (1954, p. 85) obtained the same results during his studies on human fistula bile, after injections of 20 mg UG-I. Oshima (1932a), who injected U-I in the portal vein of rabbits, retraced almost the entire amount of injected as UG-L in the bile. J. D. Mann and Koler (1951) administered 0.5 mg UG-I per 100 g body weight to rats intravenously, intramuscularly, subcutaneously, or orally. Subsequently, they collected the urine and the bile of these animals through polyethylene tubes introduced into the common bile duct and bladder. After parenteral injections, about 70% of the urobilinogen was detected in the bile, whereas only 10% was recovered after oral administration. The excretion in bile developed rapidly after injection, reached its maximum about 1 hour later, and was completed within 5 hours. Simultaneous bilirubin determinations after urobilinogen administration showed no changes. This finding speaks against a conversion of urobilinogens into bilirubin in liver. It is remarkable that urobilins administered appeared as urobilinogen in the bile.

Oshima (1932a) and C. J. Watson (1936c), who injected U-L into rabbits and humans intravenously, detected UG-L in the urine of both species. Small amounts of unchanged U-L, however, were also found (Watson). Experiments conducted in nephrectomized rabbits, in perfused kidneys, and with kidney pulp, revealed that the conversion of urobilins into chromogens takes place in the kidneys. Oshima (1932b,c) and J. D. Mann and Koler (1951), in their experiments with rats, came to the conclusion (see above) that 5–25% of injected UG-I is excreted in the urine, whereas 50–75% becomes detectable in the bile. Watson (1936c, 1938) arrived at the same conclusions in experiments in humans.

The pathogenesis of *urobilinuria,* which develops after parenchymal liver damage, is not completely clarified. It is usually attributed to decreased liver function. The liver is unable to remove all the urobilinogens absorbed from the large intestine. Consequently, larger amounts of urobilinogen are transported to the kidneys. However, this theory was rejected by Baumgärtel (1949a, 1950b) and Stich (1946a), who assumed that urobilinogens excreted in cases of liver damage are of extraintestinal origin. According to clinical observations, it is well known that urobilinuria is a sensitive symptom for parenchymal liver damage (see Chapter VI,C,2). Most clinical observations can be explained without assuming extraintestinal urobilinogen formation. The mild urobilinuria of dogs with Eck's fistula (Fischler, 1916, 1925; Gebhardt, 1939a,b) can have two different causes: (a) the blood from the intestines by-passes the liver; (b) damage of the liver parenchyma caused by circulation disturbances Gebhardt, 1939a,b).

Finally, the theories of Noro (1951) deserve consideration. Unfortunately, these interesting studies are published in Japanese only, with a bad English summary. According to Noro, urine urobilinogen is a mixture of the acid urobilinogen, its ester, and its alkali salts. These fractions can be extracted with acetic acid–ether, whereas only the dibasic acid can be extracted with chloroform. The salts and esters go into the chloroform only after hydrolysis. In normal individuals, urobilinogen esters prevail; in liver damage the dibasic acid is predominately present. In contrast to this, the amount of alkali salts excreted is always small. This is the case in humans as well as in rabbits. Whereas in most cases UG-L is predominant, UG-I prevails in certain liver diseases and during paroxysmal hemoglobinuria (Noro, 1951).

Incubation of liver slices with bilirubin or biliverdin results in urobilinogen formation. This reduction is attributed to the reticuloendothelial cells. Urobilinogen formed in this manner consists mainly of UG-L. This finding contradicts the theory of Baumgärtel (1943c, 1950b). according to which UG-I is the only urobilinoid formed extraintestinally. Noro, however, found that in the case of liver damage UG-I is produced predominantly. According to Noro, UG-L prevails in the bile of rabbits. He could not demonstrate bilirubin formation form urobilinogen.

The fate of mesobiliviolin introduced into the organism was investigated by Lozzio *et al.* (1964a,b). These authors prepared mesobiliviolin hydrochloride from urobilin from human feces. Aqueous alkaline solutions of the pigment were prepared and purified by chromatography and subsequently administered intravenously intraperitoneally, or intraintestinally to rats. The common bile duct of the rats was cannulated and the bile collected in the dark in three 2-hour samples after the administration of mesobiliviolin. Control experiments with rats receiving only the alkaline solvent without mesobiliviolin were carried out. Doses between 0.38 and 1.1 mg per 250 g rat were employed. The bile samples were analyzed for bilirubin and for mesobiliviolin with a chromatographic technique. After the administration of mesobiliviolin—both as injection and via the intestinal lumen—the bile bilirubin increased signficantly. It was calculated that about 25% of the injected mesobiliviolin appeared in the bile bilirubin. Only a small part of the injected mesobiliviolin appeared unchanged in the bile.

Summary

1. Bilirubin is formed mainly in the liver, but also in other tissues, mainly the reticuloendothelial system, from mature circulating erythrocytes. Such bilirubin consists partly of free bilirubin, partly of pigment I (monoglucuronide); pigment II (diglucuronide), according to prevailing views, is formed only in the parenchymal liver cells (see Fig. 33). In several pathological conditions—ineffective erythropoiesis in blood diseases, shunt hyperbilirubinemia, perhaps other forms of jaundice— bilirubin from the "first peak," which is directly produced in the bone marrow or in the liver, perhaps without passing the porphyrin ring, is an important source of bile pigment. If the conjugation system of the liver is impaired, bilirubin is broken down and appears as unidentifiable metabolites in the bile. If the conjugation system of the liver is operating, bilirubin is excreted as glucuronide, and to some degree as sulfate in the bile, the main product being pigment II (bilirubin diglucuronide).

The bilirubin formed extrahepatically—from hemolysis or from "first peak"—reaches the liver (if not formed there) via the hepatic artery and the portal vein. Apparently that entering the liver through the hepatic artery is eliminated more efficiently than that entering through the portal vein. Extrahepatic bilirubin represents, so far as is known, about 25% of total bilirubin, the remainder being formed in the liver itself, by both the Kupffer cells and the hepatocytes.

2. Bilirubin reaches the intestine through the bile ducts in the form of conjugates, mainly pigment II (bilirubin diglucuronide). In the adult human, about 200 mg of bilirubin is transported daily in this manner. Both conjugated bilirubin and, more easily, free bilirubin are absorbed from the small intestine. On the other hand, nonconjugated bilirubin is excreted directly from the circulation into the intestine. This creates an intestinal pool of bilirubin freely exchanging with the bilirubin pool of the plasma. If the conjugation mechanism of the liver

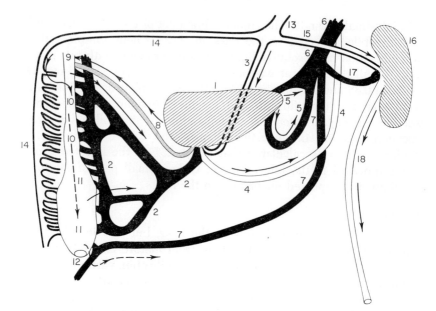

FIG. 33. Schematic diagram. (1) Liver, (2) portal vein and tributaries, (3) hepatic artery, (4) liver lymphatics and thoracic duct, (5) hepatic veins, (6) inferior caval vein, (7) hemorrhoidal veins, (8) common bile duct, (9) duodenum, (10) small intestine, (11) large intestine, (12) anus, (13) aorta, (14) mesenteric artery and branches, (15) renal artery, (16) kidney, (17) renal vein, (18) ureter.

$1 \leftarrow 3 \leftarrow 13$	Nonconjugated bilirubin (and urobilinogen) from general circulation to liver
$9 \leftarrow 8 \leftarrow 1$	Conjugated bilirubin from liver to bile and duodenum
$10 \longrightarrow 2$	Nonconjugated bilirubin and conjugated bilirubin from lumen of small intestine to portal vein
$10 \longleftarrow 14$	Nonconjugated bilirubin from arteries to lumen of small intestine
$11 \longrightarrow 2$	Urobilinogens from large intestine to portal vein
$11 \dashrightarrow 7$	Urobilinogens via hemorrhoidal plexus to caval vein (hypothetical)
$10 \dashrightarrow 11$	Bilirubin changed to urobilinogens (with considerable loss) during passage through intestine
$1 \rightarrow 4 \rightarrow 6$	Conjugated bilirubin via liver lymph to caval vein (in biliary obstruction and hepatocellular damage)
$1 \rightarrow 5 \rightarrow 6$	Conjugated bilirubin directly to hepatic vein (in biliary obstruction and hepatocellular damage)
$15 \rightarrow 16 \rightarrow 18$	Bilirubin and urobilinogen from blood via kidney to urine

is deficient, this is particularly important, and the same is the case in biliary obstruction. It seems most likely that only nonconjugated liposoluble bilirubin can pass the intestinal mucosa and that bilirubin conjugates are absorbed only to a limited degree, most likely only after deconjugation.

3. When the bilirubin reaches the large intestine, most of it is trans-

formed into urobilinogens, mostly urobilinogen-L, by bacterial reduction. Minor amounts of bilirubin escape destruction and are excreted as bilirubin. Normally this appears only traces, but in rapid passage of the bowel contents (diarrhea) and high bilirubin excretion (hemolytic jaundice), feces may contain substantial amounts of bilirubin. If no bilirubin reaches the intestine (bile duct obstruction, bile fistula, cessation of bile excretion during hepatitis), no urobilinogens are formed except if bilirubin reaches the intestine with the blood (intestinal hemorrhage). That no urobilinogen is formed during these circumstances is a well-known fact and seems to show conclusively that it is only nonconjugated bilirubin which can be excreted from the circulation into the intestine. This cannot be the case with conjugated bilirubin, for if this were true, urobilin must occur in complete biliary occlusion.

If the intestinal flora is destroyed or absent (newborns, animals kept under sterile conditions, patients treated with antibiotics), no urobilinoids are formed in the intestine and bilirubin is excreted with the feces. A substantial destruction of bilirubin to unidentifiable metabolites does, however, take place during the passage of the intestinal canal, and the same is true with the urobilinogens. Small amounts of urobilinogens are presumably absorbed from the large intestine, possibly not only into the portal circulation, but also into the hemorrhoidal plexus which drains into the caval vein, and in this way they by-pass the liver. This may be an explanation of normal urobilinuria.

Urobilinoids do not contribute significantly to the color of the stool under normal conditions, while bilirubin and biliverdin do so in newborns and infants on milk diets. Fecal color is mainly due to dipyrrole bile pigments and pigments formed in the intestine by bacterial action.

4. Urobilinogens reaching the liver are destroyed there. Only minor amounts appear in the bile. If enterohepatic circulation of urobilinoids exists, it is of minor importance. If the liver function is impaired even slightly, some urobilinoid escapes destruction in the liver, and pathological urobilinuria occurs. Convincing evidence of extraintestinal production of urobilinoids has never been produced, although some observations are rather suggestive. On the other hand, the existence of extraintestinal production of urobilinoids cannot be positively excluded.

5. Small amounts of bilirubin are excreted with normal urine, mainly as nonconjugated bilirubin. In gross bilirubinuria, conjugated bilirubin is excreted, but in man the urinary bilirubin concentration is most often significantly lower than the serum bilirubin concentration. In the dog, the opposite is the case. The excretion of bilirubin with the urine is poorly understood and exhibits pronounced species variation. As a rule, gross bilirubinuria develops only if hyperbilirubinemia due to conjugated

bilirubin is present, but exceptions to this rule occur regularly in dogs and occasionally also in man.

Pathological urobilinuria develops in man after small impairments of the liver function. Normally, 0–4 mg urobilinogen per 24 hours is excreted in humans. Pathological urobilinuria may reach 50 mg per 24 hours or more and occurs both in hepatocellular lesions and bile duct obstruction.

Urobilinuria may also be due to the invasion of the bacterial flora of the large intestine into the small intestine. Such invasion is known to occur in a variety of digestive diseases and is followed by urobilinogen formation in the small intestine from which urobilinogens are readily absorbed.

The normal color of the urine is not due to urobilinogens or bile pigments, but presumably to dipyrrole pigments mostly formed as by-products of porphyrin synthesis.

Additional Readings

Section A

Barret, P. V. D., Mullins, F. X., and Berlin, N. I. (1966). Studies on the biosynthetic production of bilirubin-C^{14}: An improved method utilizing δ-aminolevulinic acid-4-C^{14} in dogs. *J. Lab. Clin. Med.* **68**, 905–912.

Robinson, S. H., Tsong, M., Brown, B. W., and Schmid, R. (1966). The sources of bile pigment in the rat: studies of the "early labeled" fraction. *J. Clin. Invest.* **45**, 1569–1586.

Section B

Gajdos, A. (1966). Recent findings on the normal and pathological biosynthesis of bile pigments (in French). *Presse Med.* **74**, 2155–2160.

Nakajima, O., and Gray, C. H. (1967). Studies on haem α-methenyl oxygenase. Isomeric structure of formylbiliverdin, a possible precursor of biliverdin. *Biochem. J.* **104**, 20–22.

Section D

Lester, R., Klein, P. D., and Matusen, A. M. (1966). A comparison between the biliary excretion of bilirubin and urobilinogen in normal and Gunn rats. *J. Clin. Invest.* **45**, 1839–1845.

CHAPTER III

Amount of Bile Pigment Formed in the Body

A. Introduction

Students of the metabolism of bile pigments, as well as hematologists, are interested in the question of the amount of bile pigments produced. Quantitative determination of this amount is, however, difficult. Without having real evidence, it was assumed that the formation is essentially constant in various individuals. The opinion was that the only circumstances which could have an effect on the formation of bile pigments were variations in the hemoglobin destruction.

Whipple and Hooper (1913a) questioned this assumption of largely constant production of bile pigments. They found a much milder icterus in dogs with Eck's fistula and subsequent bile obstruction, than in normal dogs. No changes in blood degradation were connected with Eck's fistula. Unfortunately, these interesting experiments were not repeated. Later, With (1946b, 1954) pointed out that variations in the total amount of tetrapyrrole bile pigments excreted, independent of blood degradation, are to be expected, since the amount of dipyrrole bile pigments formed during heme degradation can vary.

At the same time the significance of dipyrrole pigments as degradation products of heme was recognized by other investigators (see C. J. Watson, 1956a,b,c; Netoušek, 1956). As already emphasized (Chapter I,G), it is difficult to distinguish how much dipyrrole pigment is produced as a by-product of heme synthesis and how much is formed during hemoglobin degradation. Observations on hemolytic anemia connected with fuscinuria (Chapter VI,D) indicate, however, that large amounts of dipyrrole pigments may originate from hemoglobin degradation.

Another moment of uncertainty is the "first peak" or "shunt bilirubin," part of which is formed in the liver (cf. Chapter II,A). In certain anemias this can constitute a significant part of the bile pigment production.

Further, degradation of bile pigments to nonidentifiable diazo-negative compounds in the organism, prior to excretion, is now known to occur regularly and has to be taken into account (cf. Chapter II,D).

163

For these reasons the classic theories of bilirubin formation and their relation to blood degradation and to icterus deserve revision.

B. Basic Theories

The study of *survival time of erythrocytes* has progressed considerably in the last two decades. Using various methods of investigation, it has been established that the average life-span of erythrocytes in normal humans is about 120 days.

Hawkins and Whipple (1938) were the first investigators who found this period of erythrocyte longevity. Hemolysis experiments in dogs with biliary-renal fistula indicated a life-span for erythrocytes of 112–133 days. Later studies based on differential agglutination experiments with human erythrocytes yielded figures of the same order of magnitude (Callender *et al.*, 1945, 1946). Similar results have been obtained by various other investigators. The following criteria were applied in these studies: maturation of reticulocytes *in vivo* (R. Berlin, 1950); labeling of erythrocytes with sulfhemoglobin (Jope, 1946a,b); labeling of erythrocytes with glycine-N^{15} (Shemin and Rittenberg, 1945); labeling of erythrocytes with radioactive chromium (Donohue *et al.*, 1955; Brante, 1956a); tracing of endogenic CO-hemoglobin formation (Engstedt, 1957); and transfusion of A_1-red cells to O-recipients and tracing by means of differential hemolysis with a powerful anti-A_1 serum, which hemolyzes the recipient cells, after which the degree of hemolysis is measured by hemoglobinometry (Mayer and d'Amáro, 1964*).

Several authors have studied erythrocyte longevity in blood disease. London *et al.* (1949) conducted experiments on the life-span of erythrocytes in humans, using N^{15}-labeled glycine. His findings showed a normal life-span during polycythemia vera, whereas a definite shortening was observed during pernicious anemia. N. I. Berlin *et al.* (1954), who carried out similar experiments with glycine-N^{15} found a life-span of 70–100 days in most cases of chronic leukemia. One case with marked anemia showed a life-span of only 18 days. Finally, Hallberg (1955), with a method based on spontaneous CO-hemoglobin formation, found that in pernicious anemia erythrocytes of various stages of maturation and of different life-span are present. In addition, Brante (1956b) studied the life-span of erythrocytes in patients with various types of anemia using the radio-chromium method.

Recently, Lewis and Gershow (1961) gave a rather complicated formula for calculation of erythrocyte life-span from bilirubin clearance rate after intravenous loading with bilirubin. This formula is based on several assumptions which cannot be taken for granted beforehand, but it gives reasonable figures for the longevity of erythrocytes.

The reviews by Singer (1945), Lemberg and Legge (1949, p. 508), Neuberger (1951), and Hallberg (1955) should be consulted on questions about survival time of erythrocytes in humans.

The many data on erythrocyte survival are not too easy to interpret. Some investigators give the life-span, whereas others using radioactive labels prefer to express their results as "half-time" ($t_{1/2}$). Bergner (1965*) discussed the theoretical basis of these expressions, pointing out that although much work has been devoted to experimental technique the theoretical analysis of the data has been comparatively neglected. The use of "half-time" ($t_{1/2}$) has thus not been given any general physico-chemical significance and half time is used simply as an analogy with radioactive decay. This analogy is, however, misleading and the concept "life-span" is preferable. On the other hand it is almost impossible to determine the life-span distribution over a population of red cells from their survival curve alone. Theoretical considerations indicate that a more satisfactory concept is the "death probability of a cell."

In order to employ the experimental data as efficiently as possible a more sophisticated approach than the relatively primitive $t_{1/2}$ is necessary. Distinction has to be made between life-span distribution function and death-probability function; the former gives the probability that a newborn cell will die at a certain age, while the latter, referring to a randomly chosen cell, gives the probability that a cell of a given age will die within the time unit. Of these two concepts that of the death probability is the more basic.

The discussion of Bergner is important because it deals with the theoretical basis not only for erythrocyte survival but also for turnover of molecules, e.g., various proteins and bilirubin. Also, for molecules there is a life-span distribution and a death-rate probability, and the present $t_{1/2}$ concept can only be regarded as a primitive method.

Similar investigations in various animals also exist. B. A. Harrison *et al.* (1951) determined the following survival times with radioactive iron: 110 days in dogs, 50 days in rabbits, and 25 days in mice. Neuberger (1951), who conducted experiments with C^{14}- and N^{15}-labeled glycine, established a life-span of 50 days in rabbits. Bush *et al.* (1955) determined an average survival time of 62 days with glycine-C^{14} in growing pigs. However, in pigs two different ways of erythrocyte degradation were detected: one part of the cells was degraded at random times, whereas the other part was destroyed after a lifetime of about 85 days. On the basis of these findings, it becomes probable that species differences exist. With the radiochromium method, Marvin and Lucy (1957) observed a life-span of 21 days for pigeons and ducks, and 32 days for rabbits. Van Putten (1958) determined 60 days for rats and 40 days for mice, with the radiophosphorus technique. Cornelius *et al.* (1959, 1960a,b) studied the erythrocyte survival time in ungulates of the families *Bovidae* and *Cervidae* as well as in horses; he employed intravenous injection of glycine-2-C^{14}. Half survival time was 95 days in a mule deer (*Oedocoileus hermionus*) and 80 days in a springbok antelope. An audad sheep exhibited two separate erythrocyte populations with half times of 65 and 175 days. Two horses had median survival times of 140 and 150 days. Kaneko *et al.* (1961b) studied four domestic sheep and a bighorn sheep with glycine-2-C^{14} and found median survival times of 64, 94, 118, and 130 days in the domestic and 147 days in the bighorn sheep. Later, Kaneko *et al.* (1961a) determined the survival time in experimental molybdenosis of two sheep and found two erythrocyte populations with median survival times of 20–28 and 80–85 days, respectively. Kaneko and Cornelius (1962) studied the erythrocyte survival time of adult goats with glycine-2-C^{14} and found median times of 160 and 165 days in two Himalayan tahr goats and 125 days in a domestic goat. Cornelius and Kaneko (1962) studied the erythrocyte life-span in the guanaco—which exhibits elliptical erythrocytes such as those found in camels—and found a median time of 225 days in two animals. Edmondson and Wyburn (1963) determined the erythrocyte life-span in mice, rats, and guinea pigs with diisopropylfluorophosphate and found 42, 65, and 79 days, respectively.

Lewis and Gershow (1961) recently used a formula for calculation of the erythrocyte life-span derived from the bilirubin clearance rate after intravenous bilirubin tolerance tests. This formula is interesting but is based on several assumptions which cannot be taken for granted. (See discussion in Chapter V,10,b.) They found a mean life-span of 53 days in rabbits. Engstedt *et al.* (1964) claimed that this method is valuable in patients with hemolytic disease.

Crosby (1955), on the basis of modern theories of erythrocyte longevity, developed an equation that expresses the relationship between the amount of hemoglobin circulating in blood (M), the amount of hemoglobin formed within unit time ($P =$ production), and the average life-span of erythrocytes (L): $M = P \times L$. The formula is correct if it is assumed that all hemoglobin formed reaches the circulation, and that there is an equilibrium between the formation and destruction of hemoglobin.

Crosby distinguishes between:

1. *Hemolytic diseases:* all conditions with decreased life-span of erythrocytes, which can occur without anemia and without icterus.

2. *Hemolytic anemias:* in these cases, the life-span is decreased

to such an extent that the bone marrow can no longer compensate for the loss of red cells.

3. *Hemolytic icterus:* in which bilirubin formation is larger than the normal excretion capacity of liver; consequently, hyperbilirubinemia develops.

The bone marrow is capable of increasing erythrocyte production to such an extent that, in spite of shortened erythrocyte survival, a normal hemoglobin level can be maintained. However, when the life-span of red blood corpuscules falls below the critical limit of 25 days, the compensatory hyperplasia of bone marrow cannot keep pace with cell destruction any longer, and anemia develops (Crosby and Akeroyd, 1952).

The capacity of the organism for converting hemoglobin to bilirubin was studied by Crosby (1958) by infusion of increasing amounts of Hb into healthy subjects and measuring the serum Hb and bilirubin. He found a maximum capacity of 45–50 g of Hb per day corresponding to formation of about 1.5 g of bilirubin.

Substituting into the above formula the average value for circulating hemoglobin $M = 750$ g, and $L = 120$ days, one obtains 6.25 g for P, which is the measure for average daily hemoglobin production. This is based on an assumed body weight of 70 kg. In other words, about 90 mg hemoglobin is produced per kilogram body weight per day. A small difference depending on sex exists. Thus $L = 120$ days in men, whereas $L = 109$ days in women (London *et al.*, 1949). No figures for children have been published. Only approximate values can be calculated from the formula.

In a patient with hemolytic anemia, with $M = 500$ g hemoglobin and $L = 12$ days, P is 41.66 g or 600 mg/kg. This is equivalent to 6–7 times the normal production. It is not certain whether the formula is valid under pathological conditions, for instance, in the case of pernicious anemia, when various erythrocyte types with different life-spans are formed (Hallberg, 1955).

On the assumption that all heme is converted to bile pigment, the amount of bile pigment formed from a given amount of hemoglobin can be calculated as follows: 1 g hemoglobin contains 3.4 mg iron (Fe = 55.85). The molecular weight of heme ($C_{34}H_{32}N_4O_4Fe$) is 616, that of protoporphyrin ($C_{34}H_{34}N_4O_4$) is 562, that of bilirubin is 584, that of urobilinogen-I is 592, and that of urobilinogen-L (stercobilinogen) is 596. Thus, 1 g hemoglobin corresponds to 3.4 mg iron $= 3.4 \times (616/55.85) =$ 37.4 mg heme, which in turn corresponds to 34.2 mg protoporphyrin, 35.5 mg bilirubin, 36.0 mg urobilinogen-I, and 36.3 mg urobilinogen-L. Consequently, 100 mg urobilinogen-L is equivalent to 2.75 g hemoglobin.

Thus, normal hemoglobin formation of $P = 6.25$ corresponds to the formation of 222 mg bilirubin and the excretion of 226 mg UG-L. However, only that part of the bile pigment production which corresponds to hemoglobin degradation of mature circulating erythrocytes is considered here. The amount of stercobilin (UG-L) which corresponds to the "first peak" is not included here (Fig. 29, Chapter II,A). The quantity of bile pigment which corresponds to the "first peak" or "early appearing urobilinogen" of Crosby (1958) is 10–20% of the daily urobilinogen output in the feces of normal persons. Thus, the bilirubin and stercobilin values should be correspondingly corrected; i.e., in a 70 kg adult person the theoretical daily bilirubin production would be 244–266 mg, and the urobilinogen excretion would be 249–271 mg. When these values are calculated for a patient with hemolytic anemia and maximal bone marrow hyperplasia, one obtains a value of 1475 mg for bilirubin and 1510 mg for UG-L based on the former example in which $L = 12$ days and $P = 41.66$ g hemoglobin. After correction for early appearing urobilinogen, the corresponding values are 1620–1770 mg bilirubin and 1660–1810 mg UG-L if, under conditions of extreme bone marrow hyperplasia, the per cent of early appearing urobilinogen is the same as that found under normal conditions; however, this is unlikely. As pointed out above the maximum capacity of the organism is about 50 g Hb and 1.5 g bilirubin. But here the bilirubin of the "first peak" is not included.

Calculation of the bile pigment produced by hemoglobin breakdown in the normal dog was given by Cameron *et al.* (1963*). For a 12-kg dog the blood volume is assumed to be 900 ml, the hemoglobin concentration 15% w/v, and the daily red cell destruction rate 1/120, i.e., the daily hemoglobin decay is $9/8 = 1.125$ g. According to Cameron *et al.* this corresponds to ca. 38 mg bilirubin, but this is not correct. According to the figures given above 1 g hemoglobin corresponds to 35.5 mg bilirubin and consequently 1.125 g hemoglobin correspond to ca. 40 mg.

C. Methods for Determination of Bile Pigment Formation

If one excludes investigations with labeled atoms, only one way to measure bile pigment formation remains, i.e., to measure the amount of excreted pigments directly. One assumes that no degradation of bile pigments occurs until excretion is completed. However, as we emphasized before (Chapter II,D), this assumption cannot be accepted *a priori*. Consequently, calculations which are based on determination of bile pigment excretion can only yield lower limit values.

The most straightforward method of determination is to collect the total amount of bile excreted in 24 hours and determine its pigment content. A more indirect method is to collect the stool and determine its urobilinoid content. When using this method, one assumes that the conversion of bile pigments into urobilinoids in the intestines is a quantitative process, and that it takes place without degradation and absorption. This assumption is not correct (Chapter II,D). That fecal urobilinoid excretion has limited significance as a measure of bile pigment formation was especially emphasized by Bungenberg de Jong (1951, 1959) and by Baldini and Pietrantonj (1957). In addition, this question becomes more complicated by the formation of mesobiliviolin (Reinert, 1948) and of fuscins (Siedel *et al.*, 1948; C. J. Watson, 1956a,b; Netoušek, 1956). Consequently, determination of fecal urobilinoids results at best in lower limit values. C. J. Watson (1965*) came to the conclusion that in man under normal conditions the fecal urobilinogen found is 20–40% below that calculated from Hb-destruction.

A third method is to determine fecal urobilinoids as well as urine bilirubin and urine urobilinoids in cases of jaundice. Under the assumption that during the observation period the bile pigment content in blood, in tissue fluids, and in tissues remains constant, the sum of excreted bilirubin and urobilinoids yields values in the lower range of bilirubin production. In cases of complete bile duct obstruction, errors introduced by absorption and destruction in the intestines can be neglected.

D. Bilirubin Formation as Measured by Bilirubin Excretion in Bile

A thorough discussion on bilirubin excretion with the bile is presented in Chapter VII. Only some facts should be mentioned here. Eppinger (1920) found 300–370 mg bilirubin per 24 hours in the bile in two patients with complete bile fistula, but in good general condition. However, his spectrophotometric method presumably included other yellow substances present besides bilirubin. With (1945d), using modern analytical methods, found 50–400 mg (in most cases 50–250 mg) bilirubin per day in the bile of patients with temporary partial bile fistula.

Bilirubin determinations in stool of infants, where the bilirubin of the bile is not converted to urobilinogens, is discussed later (Chapter VIII, B,2). Excretion during the first week of life is around 10 mg per day. Assuming 3 kg for infant and 60 kg for adult body weight (most of With's patients were women), the average excretion of 10 mg per day for newborns corresponds to 3.3 mg per kg weight, and that of 50–250 mg for adults will be equivalent to an excretion of 0.83–4.2 mg per kg weight.

A number of investigators have reported studies on dogs with bile fistula. In these experiments sufficiently exact analytical methods we~° employed. Rous *et al.* (1923), Sribhishaj *et al.* (1931), Held (19 Gebhardt (1939a,b), and Cantarow *et al.* (1948a) found values (mg, 4-6 mg, 7.4 mg, 8.4 mg, and 0.46–6.90 mg per kg body wei hours, respectively. These values are of the same order of magnitude as those found in humans (0.83–4.2 mg per kg; see above). In Ottenberg's (1943, p. 943) review, the figures 5–8 mg per kg per day are given for bilirubin formation for both humans and experimental animals.

It is, however, to be emphasized that only recently the difficult problems of experimental collection of bile under strictly physiological conditions have been solved satisfactorily (cf. Chapter VII,B,3). Studies combining satisfactory physiological bile collection and reliable analytical technique are scarce both in man and in animals.

Ostrow et al. (1962) studied bilirubin excretion in rats with external bile fistula. Sensitized erythrocytes were injected or hemoglobin solution labeled with both C^{14} and Fe^{59} or Cr^{51} was administered intravenously. When erythrocytes or relatively large doses of Hb were injected, only 63–80% of the C^{14} given could be recovered from the bile, whereas small doses of hemoglobin gave complete recovery of the C^{14} in the bile if they did not exceed the binding capacity of the plasma haptoglobin. This observation is interesting because H. Nakajima (1963) found that hemoglobin–haptoglobin is the appropriate substrate of heme-degrading enzyme (cf. Chapter II,B). Ostrow et al. found that the bilirubin production, as determined from the bilirubin output with the bile, is lower than that calculated from the hemoglobin breakdown. C. J. Watson (1963) found that the daily bilirubin excretion with the bile in adult humans is, on the average, about 70 mg higher than the 24-hour excretion of urobilinoid plus bilirubin with feces. This discrepancy cannot be due to fuscin formation from bilirubin because the average daily fuscin output in the feces of normal adult man is only about 10 mg.

E. Bilirubin Formation Measured by Excretion of Fecal Urobilinoids

Existing literature on fecal urobilinoid excretion as a measure of degradation rate of blood is quite extensive. It was carefully reviewed by Paschkis (1933) and C. J. Watson (1938). However, as mentioned above, it is of only limited interest, since the amount of fecal urobilinoids represents only a lower limit of bile pigment destruction and hemoglobin degradation. A thorough discussion on fecal excretion of urobilinoids is given in Chapter VIII,C,2. It should be mentioned that this problem has only been investigated in detail on humans and no acceptable figures from animal experiments have been reported.

Whereas normal excretion in adult humans is around 50–250 mg per day, amounts up to 3000 mg per day were observed in hemolytic diseases. London et al. (1949) showed that fecal urobilinoid excretion cannot be used without reservation as a measure for hemoglobin formation. They administered N^{15}-labeled glycine to patients with polycythemia vera and studied the synthesis of heme and the urobilin-L excretion. They found that the synthesis of heme is significantly higher than could be expected from calculations based on urobilin excretion. They pointed out the pitfalls of drawing conclusions about the magnitude of heme synthesis from fecal urobilinoid excretion by patients with blood dyscrasias. Baldini and Pietrantonj (1957) reached similar conclusions.

Little is known about urobilinoids in children. Apart from conditions in infants who excrete bilirubin instead of urobilinoids, the situation in children should be the same as it is for adults. Contrary to this expectation, it was found that urobilinoid excretion in stool is surprisingly low until the age of 12 years (Chapter VIII,C,3).

In seven normal dogs weighing 12 kg Cameron *et al.* (1963*) found the fecal urobilinoid varying between 15.8 and 55.9 mg/24 hours (average 32).

Cameron *et al.* (1966b*) found a fecal urobilinogen excretion of 1.4–6.5 mg/24 hours (0.37–6.5 mg per kg and 24 hours) in five normal rhesus monkeys.

F. Studies on Bilirubin Formation in Jaundiced Patients

The serum bilirubin level is consistently high in patients with complete bile duct obstruction. Thus, one can assume with some justification that bile pigment concentration in tissues and tissue fluids is also constant, although it is impossible to prove this assumption. As Ottenberg (1943, p. 943) clearly demonstrated, there is also the possibility of bile pigment destruction in the organism (Chapters II,D and IV,D,4).

Ottenberg writes, "What happens to the excess of bilirubin in prolonged obstructive jaundice when most of the bilirubin cannot escape from the body, is a mystery. Only a small part of the amount formed daily is accounted for by urinary excretion and deposit in the tissues and intestinal excretion. Either the hemoglobin must be disposed of by some other mechanism, or the body must have some other ways of destroying the excess of bilirubin."

For this reason the excretion of bile pigments in icterus patients represents only the lower range of bilirubin formation.

As Deenstra's observation (1950, p. 691 and Table XI) indicates, considerable amounts of bile pigments can escape determination if only urinary excretion is measured. Urine and serum concentration have to be determined simultaneously. Serum bilirubin may increase from 4 to 30.5 mg/100 ml within 24 hours, which corresponds to a production of 600 mg bilirubin.

Determination of bile pigment excretion in cases of icterus have been reported by Posthuma (1931, pp. 60–75), With (1946b), and Deenstra (1950).

Posthuma studied five cases. Urinary excretion during one observation period of one of his patients was 17–92 (average 48) mg per day and 34–142 (average 85) mg per day during another period. Corresponding values in the other cases were 77–250 (150), 72–182 (118), 62–202 (123), and 100–282 (212) mg per day. In a patient with cirrhosis of the liver, average excretion during one observation period was as follows: 164 mg per day of bilirubin in urine, 18.5 mg per day of urine urobilinoids, and 36.6 mg per day of fecal urobilinoids. On a later occasion the values were 150, 13.5, and 7.3 mg per day (see Posthuma, 1931, pp. 103–104).

With studied nine icteric patients, five of them having complete biliary obstruction. All patients were in good general condition. Hemoglobin values were between 90 and 105%. Bilirubin excretion with the urine of these five patients was only 20–50 mg per day. These values were significantly below the fecal excretion of healthy subjects (50–250 mg) and lower than those reported by Posthuma. This discrepancy can be due to different analytical methods.

Such low excretion levels during extended obstructive icterus can indicate that bilirubin formation is in fact decreased in such cases. However, it can also be explained by bilirubin destruction. Both mechanisms can occur simultaneously and neither of them can be rejected as improbable. It is conceivable that under certain conditions, when bilirubin cannot be eliminated and its concentration increases in the organism, hemoglobin degradation will take place via dipyrrole pigments. This route is also favored by kinetic considerations, i.e., a reversible chemical process is usually inhibited by its own end products.

In one of With's patients, bilirubin excretion in the urine was 125–150 mg per day, i.e., of about the same order as the normal excretion of fecal urobilinoids. However, this patient represented a unique case, because he had a urine bilirubin concentration that corresponded to 25–50% of the serum bilirubin. In three cases of hepatitis, the values for bilirubin + urobilinoid fluctuated, but they generally increased with the appearance of urobilinoids. It was remarkable that during the later course of the hepatitis, bilirubin + urobilinoid excretion was significantly higher than it was for bilirubin alone during the initial phases of the disease when no urobilinoids were excreted. This can be explained by differences in bilirubin formation, destruction of bilirubin, or both.

Deenstra (1950) studied bilirubin excretion in urine in four cases of bile duct obstruction, and in nine patients with hepatitis. Bilirubin excretion fluctuated considerably, depending on the stage of acute hepatitis even at constant serum bilirubin levels. In cases of long lasting jaundice it showed a decreasing tendency. During markedly icteric periods, values of 20–200 mg per day (average 50) were found; but they rarely excreted 100 mg. Thus, his values are twice as high as those found by With.

Cameron *et al.* (1963*) studied the excretion of bilirubin with the urine of three dogs with biliary obstruction and found excretions of 25–76 mg/24 hours (average 40.7), whereas the fecal urobilinoid of seven normal dogs was 15.8–55.9 mg/24 hours (average 32) and the bilirubin excretion calculated from the hemoglobin breakdown was 38 mg/24 hours. The actual value found for excretion is thus in much better agreement with the theoretical value expected for the dog than is the case in man. This finding points toward the fact that the destruction of bilirubin to nonidentifiable compounds plays a greater role in man than in the dog.

G. Bilirubin Level of Serum and Bile Pigment Formation

In cases of complete bile stasis the magnitude of serum bilirubin level depends on (1) bilirubin production, (2) the capability of the organism to destroy bilirubin, and (3) the ability of the kidneys to eliminate bilirubin.

The ability of the kidneys to eliminate bilirubin is low. The daily excretion of adult humans is rarely above 50 mg. During the same time 50–250 mg urobilinoids are excreted in the stool. Consequently, the amount of bilirubin produced is more important for the serum bilirubin concentration than its excretion in the urine. C. J. Watson's (1937b, 1940) assumption that the fluctuation of the serum bilirubin level in biliary obstruction is due to differences of urine excretion must be wrong. It is a general rule that the more intense the bilirubinuria, the higher the serum bilirubin level. This observation contradicts Watson's statement.

When bilirubin production varies in patients with complete bile duct obstruction, these variations must appear in the same manner in serum bilirubin level fluctuations. Such fluctuations were demonstrated by Watson (1937b, 1940), who in such cases observed icterus indexes of 59–192. With (1946b) found serum bilirubin of 10–40 mg/100 ml in his five cases of complete obstruction. Assuming that degradation in tissues remains constant, these fluctuations can only be attributed to varying bilirubin production, since secretion in urine is only of minor significance.

Watson (1937b, 1940) attributed these fluctuations to changes in blood degradation. This, however, cannot be accepted on the basis of known facts. One could as well assume that fluctuations in the amount of hemoglobin which will be converted to bilirubin, or which will be transformed into dipyrrole pigments, could play a role. This question was treated in a later work by C. J. Watson (1956a,b,c). He discussed the U-Mbf ratio, i.e., the ratio between fecal urobilinogen and mesobilifuscin concentrations.

This ratio is about 10:1 and it is quite constant under normal conditions. Under pathological conditions it can fluctuate considerably; for example, from 1:1 during certain hemolytic diseases to 50:1 in cholecystocolonic fistulas. The determination of the U-Mbf ratio is rather difficult and not very accurate; the different degrees of polymerization of fuscins render exact determination impossible. In spite of this fact, further studies of this sort are unavoidable if one wants to get to the core of this problem.

Thus, the generally accepted assumption that obstructive icterus caused by neoplasma has higher and more constant serum bilirubin than types of other pathogenesis loses some of its theoretical basis. Nevertheless, it seems even now that fluctuations in neoplastic obstructive icterus are less preponderant than those observed in other types of obstructive and in hepatocellular jaundice. The fluctuations occurring in hepatitis are excellently demonstrated by Deenstra's (1950) Case XI. In this case serum bilirubin increased from 4 to 30.5 mg/100 ml within 24 hours.

It is significant that cases of complete bile duct obstruction exist without hyperbilirubinemia, as observed by Hanot (1895) and later described by Judd and Lyons (1923), Bernhard (1930), Thyman (1950, Case I), and Sacrez et al. (1946). The case published by Sacrez involved a child without intrahepatic bile ducts. In the majority of cases icterus sets in with the onset of obstruction, but disappears slowly in spite of continued complete obstruction. Another important observation is that acute yellow liver atrophy, i.e., almost complete destruction of liver parenchyma, can occur without simultaneous hyperbilirubinemia. Such cases were described by Bergstrand (1930), Eppinger (1937, p. 310), Lucké and Mallory (1946), and Jimenez-Diaz et al. (1948).

Although lack of hyperbilirubinemia in complete obstruction and in acute yellow atrophy is rare, the possibility that this can happen has great theoretical significance. The cause is either extraordinarily low bilirubin formation, or high bilirubin destruction in the tissues, or a combination of these two factors. The same is true in certain cases of incomplete bile duct obstructions, in which one observes diminishing icterus and constantly low urobilinoid excretion in stool (Steigmann and Dyniewicz, 1943b). Thyman's case of complete obstruction is of particular interest, since in the commencing stages of the disease hyperbilirubinemia prevailed. It disappeared gradually only to reappear later.

Crosby (1955) made a calculation on the clearance of bilirubin from the blood plasma. He employed the equation: $M = P \times L$ where M stands for total bilirubin present in blood plasma, L is the average time during which a molecule of bilirubin remains in the plasma, and P is the amount of bilirubin which enters into the plasma during unit time. If the plasma volume is 3,000 ml, and the bilirubin concentration is 0.5 mg/

100 ml, M equals 15 mg. Assuming a bilirubin production of 250 mg daily, one obtains 0.06 days for L, i.e., about 110 minutes. This means that under normal conditions a bilirubin molecule, on the average, remains in the circulation for about 1½ hours. However, this calculation is meaningful only when one assumes that all bilirubin formed reaches the general circulation, but this is probably not the case because a considerable part of the bilirubin is produced in liver and excreted with the bile without entering the general circulation. Thus P is considerably lower than assumed in the calculation above, and L correspondingly is higher.

H. Correlation of Blood Degradation with Bile Pigment Formation

As mentioned above, the concept of a closer correlation between the amount of degraded hemoglobin and the amount of bile pigment formed, can no longer be maintained. It is true that under certain conditions there is a close correlation between these two factors, but under pathological conditions one should not depend on it. In conditions where so-called "ineffective erythropoiesis" is active (cf. Chapter II,A) bile pigment production significantly exceeds the degradation of hemoglobin from mature circulating erythrocytes.

Experimental studies on this question were conducted by injecting hemolyzed blood intravenously into dogs with bile fistula. Here McMaster *et al.* (1923b) found increased bilirubin excretion with the bile, corresponding to 25–50% of injected hemoglobin. Sribhishaj *et al.* (1931) and Hawkins and Johnson (1939) observed, in carefully controlled experiments, an extremely high excretion, i.e., 75–100% of injected hemoglobin. Cruz *et al.* (1942) and Laudicella (1948) observed bilirubin excretions of 67–109% (average 88%) and 100% of administered hemoglobin.

Fecal urobilinoid excretion was for a long time regarded as a measure of blood destruction. Based on indices calculated from this (e.g., the relation between fecal urobilinoid excretion and the amount of circulating Hb so-called *"Blutmauserungsindex," "*Hemolytic Index," *"Indice de logorio"*), far-reaching conclusions were drawn (Sonnenfeld, 1924; Lichtenstein and Terwen, 1925; Belonogowa, 1928, 1931; Heilmeyer, 1931c; Heilmeyer and Oetzel, 1931; Paschkis, 1933; Josephs, 1934; Miller *et al.*, 1942; Monasterio and Lattanzi, 1947; Lattanzi, 1948c,d,e,f).

Miller *et al.* found an index of 11.1–20.8 mg in normal men for the ratio fecal urobilinoid/24 hours/100 g circulating hemoglobin. In patients with anemia or a smaller body surface (children) the index was considerably higher. They considered this an extremely sensitive indicator for increased blood destruction. However, Royer (1943, pp. 138–142) and Singer (1945) were already cognizant of the pitfalls which arise when fecal urobilin excretion data are used as a measure for blood destruction.

C. J. Watson (1956a,b,c) agreed with their criticism which is underlined by his studies on the so-called U-Mbf ratio.

As mentioned before (Section B, this chapter), the average daily hemoglobin degradation in adult man is about 6.25 g. Since 1 g of hemoglobin corresponds to 36.3 mg urobilinogen-L, 227 mg urobilinoid will be formed during daily hemoglobin degradation (assuming heme is quantitatively converted). The actual fecal excretion in normal men is 50–250 mg per day (Section D, this chapter). This means that, although in some individuals almost 100% of the theoretical amount of bile pigments is produced from hemoglobin, in the majority of cases these values are lower (20% and upward).

Recent determinations of excretion of bilirubin with the bile by means of radioactive label have disclosed that only 63–80% of degraded hemoglobin appears as bilirubin in the bile if the plasma hemoglobin exceeds the binding capacity of plasma haptoglobin (Section D, this chapter).

Summary†

Determination of the bile pigment production is difficult because substantial amounts of bile pigment can arise from sources other than hemoglobin, because hemoglobin can be degraded to dipyrrole bile pigments, and because bilirubin can be destroyed, i.e., degraded to nonidentifiable compounds. Under normal conditions most of the bile pigment is formed from hemoglobin, only 10–20% arising from other sources (mostly "first peak bilirubin"). Figures for bile pigment production based on determination of bilirubin output in bile in normal human subjects with bile fistula are 60–80% lower than figures determined from hemoglobin degradation in experiments with labeled Hb. Bile pigment production as determined from fecal urobilin excretion is on the average about 70 mg lower than figures derived from bile bilirubin excretion. According to modern studies on erythrocyte longevity about 6.25 g of Hb are degraded daily, corresponding to ca. 225 mg bile pigment, but the normal range of fecal 24-hour output of urobilinoids is only 50–250 mg.

In the dog the bile pigment excretion with feces and urine shows a much better agreement with theoretical values for hemoglobin breakdown than the data obtained for man. Consequently, degradation of hemoglobin or bilirubin or both to nonidentifiable compounds probably plays a considerably more important role in man than in the dog.

Further, destruction of bile pigments in tissues is possible. False conclusions can be reached if bile pigment excretion data are used as a measure for hemoglobin destruction under pathological conditions.

† For Additional Readings see p. 743.

CHAPTER IV

Jaundice

Jaundice, or icterus, is characterized by yellow discoloration of the skin, mucous membranes, and numerous organs, and is caused by retention of bile pigments. Hyperbilirubinemia always accompanies jaundice. Increased serum bilirubin level without simultaneous yellow discoloration is called latent jaundice. The discoloration of skin during icterus is usually pure yellow, but it can develop a more greenish or black-brown shade (Horsters, 1939).

To what extent bilirubin is responsible for the discoloration during icterus is not known. Its degradation products or other yellow pigments could just as easily play a role (see Chapter V,C,3). According to all probabilities, bilirubin is the principal pigment in "yellow jaundice," whereas in "green jaundice," biliverdin is also present. Other degradation products and pigments besides bilirubin and biliverdin are responsible for "black jaundice." The last two forms of icterus are only observed during long-lasting jaundice. Ishimitsu (1959a) studied the oxidation-reduction potential of the skin with intracutaneous injections of various redox indicators and found that the color of icteric skin depends on its reduction potential.

Whereas the blood plasma is pure yellow in most icterus cases, during a long illness it can assume a greenish discoloration because of the appearance of small amounts of biliverdin (Larson *et al.*, 1947). Nevertheless, even in this case bilirubin is the preponderant pigment, although considerable amounts of other yellow colored substances can be present (see Chapter V,M).

Not all vertebrates are capable of developing icterus. Fish have not been studied until now; amphibians (frogs) develop icterus after hepatectomy or after complete bile duct obstruction (Chapter II,C). In reptiles (small turtles) icterus follows hemolytic poisoning (AsH_3) (Valentini, 1888). All birds and mammals which have been investigated to date are capable of developing jaundice. However, significant differences exist. For instance, in cattle, icterus can be induced by hemolysis, but does not occur after bile obstruction or after parenchymal liver damage (Garner, 1953). In the following sections, problems involving bile pigments and jaundice will be examined.

A. Plasma Threshold

By threshold value is meant the lowest bilirubin level of plasma (or serum) which leads to icterus. This is 1.5–2.5 mg/100 ml in adults, and 8–9 mg/100 ml in newborn infants. This remarkable difference (With, 1943e; Larsen and With, 1943; Salmon and Richman, 1943), shown in Fig. 34, has not been satisfactorily explained until now. To answer this question pertinent animal experiments would be necessary.

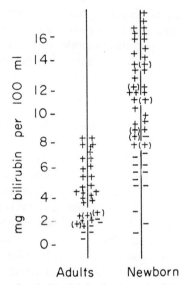

Adults   Newborn

Fɪɢ. 34. The plasma threshold of bilirubin in 34 adults and 45 newborns. Symbols: + manifest jaundice, (+) questionable jaundice, − no jaundice.

B. Origin and Site of Coloration

At first glance, the genesis of discoloration seems to be simple, but on closer consideration it becomes complicated. The first problem which needs clarification is whether the blood or the tissues is responsible for the color.

The red color of blood is about ten times as intensive as the color of plasma even during the gravest cases of icterus. The normal color of blood corresponds to 15 g hemoglobin/100 ml. One g hemoglobin corresponds to 37.4 mg heme (cf. Chapter III,B) and 15 g to $15 \times 37.4 = 560$ mg heme/100 ml. The color of maximally icteric plasma corresponds to 60 mg bilirubin/100 ml. This indicates that the plasma cannot be responsible for the yellow coloration of icteric tissues. This conclusion is substantiated by the observation that icteric skin does not lose its yellow color under glass spatula pressure.

According to results of With (unpublished experiments, 1945), bilirubin cannot be present in significant amounts in tissue fluids during icterus. He intracutaneously injected diazo reagent a few hours after death in a severe case of obstructive icterus. Although alcohol was injected before the diazo mixture, no color change took place at the site of injection. Consequently, the yellow color of icteric tissue is caused by its own bile pigment content. Blood and tissue fluid play no significant role.

The problem of how the bile pigments reach the tissue is more difficult than is generally assumed. According to the classic theory (Eppinger, 1937, p. 97; Baumgärtel, 1950b, p. 227), the pigments diffuse from the blood into the tissue fluid. This simple explanation, however, does not suffice because the bilirubin of the blood plasma is firmly bound to albumin and therefore cannot pass the capillary membrane. In order to penetrate into the tissues bilirubin can either pass through abnormally permeable capillaries bound to albumin, or it can pass through normal capillaries as molecular bilirubin dissolved in water. This molecular bilirubin must be derived from the bilirubin–albumin complex by dissociation (see Chapter V,A). An important point is the solubility of molecular bilirubin in aqueous solutions with pH and ionic strength of blood plasma. Overbeek *et al.* (1955b) found that unconjugated bilirubin is extremely heavily soluble in water, but Burnstine and Schmid (1962) found that it is reasonably soluble in electrolyte solutions of physiological pH and ionic strength; at pH 7.4 and ionic strength 0.15, about 5 mg/100 ml is soluble. If the bilirubin is conjugated, the solubility presents no difficulty for the passage of bilirubin from the plasma to the tissues.

That unconjugated bilirubin can pass from the tissues to the plasma has been well established by means of clinical observation on the so-called rebound phenomenon during exchange transfusion for jaundice in the newborn (cf. Chapter IX). According to these observations this passage must be a fairly rapid process. The distribution of unconjugated bilirubin between blood plasma and interstitial fluid was studied by Schmid and Hammaker (1963) in one patient (Crigler-Najjar syndrome) and 8 rats (Gunn rats) with a defective bilirubin conjugation mechanism. They employed tracer technique with bilirubin-C^{14} and found about equal distribution (1/1) between plasma and interstitial fluid in the human, where the bilirubin–albumin linkage is strong, and a plasma/interstitial fluid ratio of about 1/5 in the rat where the bilirubin-albumin linkage is weak.

If bilirubin accumulates in the plasma the concentration of bilirubin–albumin increases. This increase must be due to complexes of albumin and either unconjugated or conjugated bilirubin or a mixture of both.

With a rising concentration of these complexes a certain dissociation must take place, resulting in a rising concentration of molecular bilirubin in the plasma. Some of this will pass the capillary membrane with the plasma filtrate which, according to the theory of Starling (1909), continually filters through the membrane of the arterial part of the capillaries where the hydrostatic pressure is higher than the colloidal osmotic pressure. In this way bilirubin reaches the intercellular fluid, and here it is bound to colloids in a dissociable compound such as bilirubin–albumin. This binding results in a fall in the concentration of molecular bilirubin in the tissue fluid, and as a consequence the gradient for molecular bilirubin from the plasma to the tissues is maintained. Bilirubin will continue to pass from the plasma to the tissues until an equilibrium is reached between the degree of dissociation of the bilirubin–albumin of the plasma and the colloidal bilirubin complexes of the tissues. When the serum bilirubin decreases, this equilibrium is disturbed and bilirubin will move from the tissues to the plasma. This equilibrium is dynamic and depends both on the elimination of bilirubin from the plasma (via bile, and to some degree urine) and on destruction of bilirubin in the organism, a factor known to play a not negligible role (cf. Section D,4, this chapter).

Surveys of modern views on Starling's theory are presented by Chinard (1962*) and Asscher and Jones (1965*). According to the latter, electron microscope observations show that capillary endothelia can be subdivided into nonfenestrated and fenestrated groups. In the former type adjacent endothelial cells lie very close, only separated by narrow tortuous channels about 100 Å wide. In the latter, however, endothelial fenestrae measuring 300–600 Å are present and may be intra- or extracellular. The intracellular fenestrae are possibly not present under normal conditions, but are phenomena developing during abnormal states such as anoxia. Nonfenestrated capillary endothelia are found in muscle, myocardium, lung, and the nervous system, whereas fenestrated endothelia occur in the glomerular and tubular capillaries of the kidneys, the intestinal mucosa, as well as in the suprarenal glands. In the sinusoids of the liver the fenestrae are particularly wide, measuring several thousand Ångstroms.

Although the passage of molecular bilirubin through the capillary membrane is by far the most important pathogenetic factor in jaundice, some passage of the bilirubin–albumin complex must also take place because peripheral lymph is known to contain some protein (Drinker, 1945) and visceral lymph is protein-rich (Brinkhouse and Walker, 1941; McCarrel *et al.*, 1941; Kühn and Hildebrand, 1951). It has been shown that tissue fluids always contain a small amount of protein. Consequently, when bilirubin is present in the plasma the tissue fluids must contain bilirubin, though on a low level, because bilirubin is strongly bound to serum albumin, the protein fraction with lowest molecular weight (see Chapter V,B). Stead and Warren (1944), who studied extracellular fluids of skin in men, found that the protein content, which is below 0.25% under normal conditions, reaches 1% when the venous pressure is increased to about 30 mm Hg. Courtice (1946) detected 1.4–1.5% protein in the lymph of extremities of normal dogs. Mayerson and Wassermann (1950), who intravenously injected labeled serum albumin in dogs, retraced it in the lymph after about 10–20 minutes.

Normally, blood plasma contains about 8% protein with about 60% albumin; the protein content of the normal lymph of human skin is less than 0.25%. Thus, the albumin concentration of lymph can only be 1/20 of that of plasma; a similar assumption can be made for the maximum bilirubin concentration.

The bile pigment content of lymph, tissue fluids, transudates, and exudates is discussed in Chapter IX. It would be interesting to conduct direct measurements in the lymph of skin, collected according to the method of Stead and Warren (1944). Observations on discoloration of wheals after intradermal histamine injections (O. Klein, 1931; Cameron, 1943) merely show that bilirubin passes through capillaries damaged by histamine, but tell nothing of the bilirubin content of normal skin lymph.

F. Rosenthal (1930) and Gassmann (1930) studied the color of various tissues during jaundice. They extracted the skin with alcohol or acetone and determined the bilirubin content in the extracts. In icterus, not more than 4 weeks old, the color was restricted to certain "bilirubinophil" tissues (skin, conjunctiva, mucous membranes of the digestive tract, pleura, peritoneum, intima of blood vessels) which other "bilirubinophobe" tissues (cornea, cartilage, nervous tissue) did not show discoloration. However, when jaundice continued over longer periods, all organs became more or less colored.

During short term icterus, spleen and pancreas extracts were always free of bilirubin. Extracts from liver, kidneys, and adrenals contained small amounts of bilirubin; all other organs including body fat contained only traces of bile pigment. The exceptions were skin and other "bilirubinophil" tissues. Even though bilirubin cannot quantitatively be extracted with these methods, the analysis shows beyond doubt that bilirubin occurs in some organs in significantly higher concentrations than in others.

Daddi (1933) described a histological staining method which allowed detection of bilirubin in tissues. He used a 1/1000 to 1/5000 solution of the potassium salt of iso-*p*-nitrodiazobenzene in 5% formaldehyde and added a few drops of 20% sulfuric acid for stabilization. Tissues were stained without prior fixation for one to several hours at room temperature. Bilirubin appeared in diffuse areas or as granules of reddish color. Icteric skin became deep pink. Normal liver did not take the stain, but icteric liver assumed a strong pink shade and often contained colored intracellular granules. Daddi did not mention any special staining of elastic fibers. His method was not used by later investigators, but it seems to deserve further study. Recently, Raia (1965*; cf. also Chapter IX) introduced a more satisfactory method for histological staining of bilirubin.

The different affinity of various organs toward bilirubin raises the question of *partial or regional jaundice,* i.e., a jaundice which affects only a part of the skin surface. Such cases were published by F. Umber and Rosenberg (1928) and Martini (1957). Here bilirubin concentration in fluid from cantharidine blisters was the same for normal and for icteric skin regions. Danzig (1953) reported that icteric patients with vitiligo did not show color on depigmented skin areas.

Rosenthal (1930) emphasized the important role of *elastin* in the color of icteric tissues. Bilirubinophil tissues (for example, sclera, skin, and intima of vessels) are rich in elastin. Ligamentum nuchae, which is especially rich in elastic fibers, is stained intensively during icterus. Rosenthal studied the affinity of elastin for bilirubin *in vitro,* by adding alcoholic bilirubin solutions. Whereas elastin was stained a deep yellow, collagen did not take color under the same conditions. A similar observation *in vivo* was reported by Kiener and Engel (1887). They injected bilirubin solutions subcutaneously and observed the coloration of elastic fibers of connective tissues.

Elastin seems to play the same role in binding bilirubin in tissues as serum albumin plays in blood. The tissue fluid contains only a small amount of bilirubin. It fulfills only a transport function by moving it from blood into the tissues.

Ishimatsu (1959b) has studied the staining of collagenic and elastic fibers in tissues with solutions of free and esterified bilirubin and biliverdin at varying pH. The staining was strongest with esterified bilirubin and at pH near 7. He found no special affinity toward elastin, but on the contrary a stronger binding to collagen. He presents, however, only a short summary in English. After his observations renewed studies of the binding to collagen and elastin are required.

Icterography (yellow dermographism) presents an interesting phenomenon in patients with latent jaundice. The phenomenon consists of icteric color of spontaneous or artificial urticarial wheals. It has been observed in hyperbilirubinemia caused by hepatitis, bile duct obstruction, and icterus neonatorum (Strasburger, 1918; Schürer, 1922; Jadassohn,

1923; Derbes and Engelhardt, 1943). O. Klein (1931) injected 0.1 ml histamine solution and observed yellow color spread at the periphery of the wheals 1–2 minutes later. The color spread gradually all over the wheals, but their centers remained colorless. Maximum color was reached after 12–30 minutes, and started to fade after 1–1½ hours. Yellow coloration was visible at and above a serum bilirubin concentration of 1 mg/ 100 ml. When the test was carried out during manifest jaundice, coloration of wheals was always stronger than that af neighboring skin; this observation showed that bilirubin concentration in plasma must have been higher than that in tissues.

According to Adlersberg and Perutz (1932), other substances which increase capillary permeability can replace histamine (e.g., morphine). These authors investigated the coloration of wheals after intravenous injection of dyestuffs (e.g., congo red), and found that the dye entered into the wheals. Feuereisen and Klein (1932) observed brown colored wheals in patients with methemoglobinemia.

Icterus does not develop immediately after the serum bilirubin level exceeds threshold value, but after a *latency period* of several days. This had been observed in humans by Frerichs as early as 1858. Quincke (1884) reported a latency period of 2–3 days in dogs. In one of his patients it was less than 24 hours. Meulengracht (1925) showed that short term hyperbilirubinemia does not induce icterus. After repeated large intravenous bilirubin injections, Thompson and Wyatt (1938) and Hench (1938) observed a latency period of 2–7 days in humans. Snapp et al. (1944) arrived at the same results in dogs. After experimental bile duct occlusion Edlund (1948) reported a latency period of 2 days in rats. According to Berman et al. (1941) the latency period is shortened after intravenous injection of bile salts (6 g sodium dehydrocholate injected hourly into dogs).

The observations on the latency period agree with the theory that bilirubin must pass through tissue fluids to reach the tissues. However, the tissues presumably absorb only small amounts. Sufficient bilirubin must first be bound to elastin in order to cause a manifest yellow coloration.

The so-called *"urobilinicterus"* (C. Gerhardt, 1878; Kunkel, 1880) and the *"Ictère hémaphéique"* (Dreyfus-Brisac, 1878) are only of historic interest. At this time it was erroneously assumed that during these conditions yellow coloration of skin is caused by urobilin (Lanzkron, 1888; Tissier, 1889, pp. 64–71; Baumgärtel, 1950b, pp. 101–103).

Summary

Coloration of tissues is responsible for the yellow color in jaundice. The elastin content of tissues is important. Various tissues exhibit largely different affinities for bilirubin. Bilirubin concentration of blood plasma seems to be regularly higher than that of tissues. Questions of partial (regional) jaundice, icterography (yellow dermography), and latency period are discussed. The relative role of elastin and collagen in binding tissue bilirubin urgently requires renewed studies with modern methods.

C. Pathogenesis of Jaundice and Its Various Forms

1. THE BASIS OF OLD AND NEW CLASSIFICATIONS

Jaundice can be classified according to clinical, anatomical, or physiological points of view. The best known classifications are those of Rolleston and McNee (1929) and Rich (1930). The former distinguish three forms: hemolytic, hepatocellular, and obstructive icterus, whereas Rich subdivides jaundice into retention icterus and regurgitation icterus. Some confusion exists because, whereas Chabrol (1932, p. 105) used the term *"Ictère par retention"* to describe obstructive icterus as well as jaundice caused by parenchymal damage, Rich's "retention jaundice" means hemolytic icterus. Thorek (1939), from a purely anatomic standpoint, coined the terms "prehepatic," "intrahepatic," and "posthepatic" jaundice, depending on whether the location of the damage causing the icterus is before bile pigment entry in the liver, after entry in the liver, or after passage through the liver.

A schematic survey of types of jaundice is presented in Fig. 35.

The classifications of Rolleston and McNee and of Rich need revision for a number of reasons. First, they assume that bile pigments are formed solely from degradation products of mature circulating erythrocytes, which is obviously incorrect. Second, they ignore the important role played by the liver lymph, as emphasized by With (1944d, 1947, 1949). Furthermore, they take it for granted that bile pigment excretion is a function of parenchymal cells, and not—as Andrews (1955) has pointed out—possibly also a function of epithelial cells of the small bile ducts. Last but not least, they place a special emphasis on the direct diazo reaction by Hijmans van den Bergh (1918) (see Chapter V,H), a phenomenon which has proved much more complex than they assumed.

Since jaundice always occurs after hyperbilirubinemia, it must be induced by increased bilirubin formation, decreased bilirubin excretion, lowered bilirubin degradation, or a combination of these factors. Increased production is not necessarily the same as hemolysis, as already emphasized (Chapter II,A). The importance of variations in bilirubin degradation are more difficult to evaluate.

As already mentioned above (Chapter II,D), bilirubin destruction is important in horses and in cattle, and is also surely effective in humans.

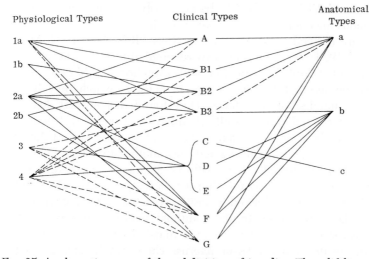

Physiological Types   Clinical Types   Anatomical Types

Fig. 35. A schematic survey of the subdivisions of jaundice. The solid lines denote established relations; the broken lines, possible relations.

Physiological types. (1) Increased bilirubin production: (1a) from hemoglobin of mature circulating erythrocytes; (1b) So-called "shunt-bilirubin" which is now known to consist of an early hepatic and a later erythropoietic component. (2) Retention of bile pigment: (2a) without defective bilirubin conjugation; (2b) with defective bilirubin conjugation. (3) Lymphogenic origin, either by secretion from blood into lymph (parapedesis) or by regurgitation from bile to lymph. (4) Decreased destruction of bilirubin to unidentifiable diazo-negative compounds.

Anatomical types. (a) Prehepatic, (b) hepatic, (c) posthepatic.

Clinical types. (A) Hemolytic jaundice. (B) Jaundice due to hyperproduction of bilirubin from causes other than hemolysis: (B1) hereditary forms with unconjugated bilirubin (Gilbert, Crigler-Najjar, etc.); (B2) nonhereditary forms with unconjugated bilirubin (ineffective erythropoiesis); (B3) hereditary forms with conjugated bilirubin (Rotor-Stransky, Dubin-Johnson, etc.). (C) Jaundice due to extrahepatic obstruction of bile ducts. (D) hepatocellular (parenchymal) jaundice. (E) Hepatocanalicular (cholangiolitic, cholestatic) jaundice; so called "intrahepatic cholestasis" or merely "cholestasis." (F) Neonatal jaundice including physiological jaundice, jaundice of prematures, and hemolytic disease of newborns. (G) Cardiac jaundice.

Garner (1953) found that in cattle only hemolysis induces marked hyperbilirubinemia. After bile duct obstruction or severe parenchymal damage only minor hyperbilirubinemia can be detected. These findings can only be explained by assuming the destruction of conjugated bilirubin in the body, whereas free bilirubin (in hemolytic icterus) appears to be more stable. The fact that frogs do not develop icterus after bile duct obstruction (Leyden, 1866; H. Stern, 1885) can also be explained by the concept of bile pigment destruction. Destruction of bilirubin to unidentifiable compounds is a concept gaining in importance. It was recently discussed by Gray and Nicholson (1963) based on observations on humans given intravenous injections of radioactive bilirubin.

We are obliged to McMaster and Rous (1921) and F. C. Mann and Bollman (1926) for important experimental studies on the relative significance of bilirubin formation and excretion. McMaster and Rous studied the serum bilirubin content in dogs, in which they ligated an increasing number of bile ducts. They found that normal dogs do not develop icterus unless 95% of all bile ducts of liver are obstructed. However, only eight dogs were used in these experiments; two of the animals had 95% of their bile ducts ligated and another two 83%. Four animals were used as controls. In those with 83% ligation, a negative diazo reaction was found in the serum after 10 days. One of the dogs with 95% ligature of bile ducts showed a positive reaction after 2 days, the other after 11 days. In a footnote, these authors mention a dog with 100% bile duct obstruction that had a negative diazo reaction even after 9 days, and did not develop any tissue icterus. These experiments are not sufficient, and should be repeated with more animals and with a number of different species using modern analytic technique and surgery including double ligature and resection of bile ducts. According to Rous and Larimore (1920b) icterus develops in rabbits when 75% of all bile ducts are ligated.

Schalm (1951) and Schalm et al. (1952) conducted similar experiments on rabbits and pigs. It was found that 65–75% restriction of bile excretion is compatible with life and does not lead to icterus. The few, and technically insufficient, experiments of McMaster and Rous cannot be regarded as a basis for a theory on jaundice.

Recent observations of jaundice in humans after obstruction of one hepatic duct point to differences between man and dogs and rodents. Mistilis and Schiff (1963) reported a patient with complete obstruction of the left hepatic duct and partial occlusion of the right by carcinoma. The serum bilirubin (total) was 34.0 mg/100 ml. In an operation the carcinoma was completely removed from the right duct which became patent, but could not be removed from the left which remained closed. The serum bilirubin dropped to 9.6 mg/100 ml after the operation, but began to rise again and reached 19.4 mg/100 ml in 6 weeks. Then left hepatic lobectomy was performed. Complete occlusion of the left hepatic ducts but no metastases were disclosed. After this operation the serum bilirubin dropped to normal values. The authors suggested the explanation that the human liver is incapable of excreting conjugated bilirubin which reaches the general circulation through lymph and blood, but this suggestion can hardly be correct (cf. this chapter, Section C,4). Tiesenga et al. (1964) reported a case of fibrous obstruction of the right hepatic duct due to inflammation secondary to cholelithiasis. In this case marked jaundice (13 mg bilirubin/100 ml) was present. After operative restoration of the lumen of the hepatic duct, the jaundice promptly subsided and was absent on reexamination of the patient 3 months later.

Obstruction of one hepatic duct in sheep was studied by Leaver and Cristie (1965*) who investigated sheep weighing 25–35 kg. Nine sheep were subjected to ligation of the hepatic duct to the ventral lobe, while nine others had both the hepatic duct and the corresponding hepatic artery ligated. One sheep in each group was killed after 3 days, one after 7 days, the remaining at 7-day intervals, and the ninth after 56 days. Autopsy and histological examination of the liver were carried out, but no bile pigment analyses were made. Jaundice did not develop in any of the sheep. The animals subjected to ligation of the hepatic duct only exhibited a slight degeneration of the ventral lobe of the liver, the hepatic duct being only slightly dilated. Histological examination showed slight edema of the connective tissue, infiltration by small round cells, slight dilatation of the bile ductules, and slight proliferation of the ductular epithelium. These findings were uniformly distributed over the whole of the ventral liver lobe. The maximum changes occurred 1 week after the occlusion of the hepatic duct and the findings subsided in 3 weeks. Ligation of both the hepatic duct and artery was followed by severe inflammatory and degenerative alterations ending in progressive atrophy and fibrosis. These changes were not uniformly distributed, but patchy.

These observations show that in man obstruction of one of the two hepatic ducts is followed by marked jaundice, contrary to the observations in dogs, rabbits, and pigs quoted above. The susceptibility of various species to partial obstruction of the bile duct system thus apparently shows considerable variation. Experimental observations on this question in more species seem required, and it would be especially interesting to study the hypothesis put forward by Mistilis and Schiff (1963), that the liver might be unable to excrete conjugated bilirubin reaching it with the blood.

F. C. Mann and Bollman (1926, p. 684) showed that even when 70% of the liver was removed in dogs, circulation in the rest of this organ did not stop. After surgery a rapid regeneration of liver tissue followed so that after 3 weeks most of the removed part has been regenerated. A similar regenerative ability was maintained when the bile ducts were ligated in a liver segment. In this case, the part which was drained by the ligated ducts became atrophic, but the rest of the segment showed hypertrophy (Schalm, 1951; Schalm et al., 1952). For this reason, only mild and transitory hyperbilirubinemia can be excepted after partial liver removal or partial bile duct obstruction. This temporary hyperbilirubinemia has also been observed by F. C. Mann and Bollman (1926, pp. 689–690). In addition, they demonstrated that partially hepatectomized dogs developed a much more pronounced and longer lasting hyperbilirubinemia if they had an Eck's fistula because then the compensatory liver hypertrophy was strongly retarded.

Therefore, it is amazing that Bollman and Mann (1936, p. 458) reported later that 80% reduction of liver tissue did not give any bile pigment retention. They believed that the temporary jaundice which developed in the first few days after surgery could be attributed to tissue injury. It hardly seems plausible that a tissue possessing such high regenerative power is functionally inactivated by this operation. From their publication it is evident that this reversal of the explanation of their own findings was influenced by McMaster and Rous' statement (1921) that a 95% restriction of the bile ducts does not lead to icterus. This statement is, however, as pointed out above, based on insufficient evidence.

Sigel et al. (1963) pointed out that the rate of reconstitution after liver resection differs from species to species. It takes 10–14 days in rats and 6–10 weeks in dogs, but reconstitution invariably takes place unless drastic alterations in the environment of the hepatic remnant exist, and under usual circumstances the total quantity of liver tissue originally present is not exceeded. The studies of Sigel et al. on dogs showed that the regeneration was slightly decreased if the excised liver tissue was implanted in another place in the same animal. Thus humoral factors from the autotransplant seem to influence the regeneration of the liver tissue.

Simpson and Finckh (1963) removed up to 96% of the liver tissue in rats. They found that the regeneration of the tissue was partly due to an increase in the number of liver units (lobuli, acini) and partly to an increase in their size. After removal of more than 66% of the liver and after repeated resections the regeneration was mainly due to an increase of the number of units, similar to the growth of the embryonic liver. Finckh and Simpson (1963) studied the regeneration of the liver after repeated resections of liver tissue in a rat suffering from liver cirrhosis of the portal type. Peculiarly enough, they found that the pattern of the liver became more normal after repeated resections and subsequent regeneration, presumably because the connective tissue bands of the cirrhotic liver were cut during the repeated resections and were not reformed.

Clerici et al. (1964*) studied rat liver regeneration after partial hepatectomy with particular regard to its dependence on the sympathetic nervous system. They found that liver regeneration is independent of the peripheral autonomous nervous system.

Verme and Campari (1965*) removed 66% of the liver (three lobes) in six rats and found only a small increase in serum bilirubin.

Mělka and Šimek (1964*) studied bilirubin excretion with the bile in 150 rats aged 3, 12, and 24 months during regeneration of the liver following partial hepatectomy. The bile was collected 30 minutes, 14 days, and 28 days after the operation. The bile bilirubin was studied both with and without bilirubin loading (i.v. injection of 0.5 mg bilirubin per 100 g body weight). The regeneration of the liver weight was more rapid in the older age group than in the younger. The excretion of endogenous bilirubin (without loading) per unit body weight showed a slow increase with age. With advancing age the fall in bile volume and bile bilirubin following hepatectomy increased, and their subsequent rise measured per gram of liver weight was lower in the older rats than in the younger. The regeneration of bile flow and bilirubin excretion without loading also became slower with advancing age. Both endogenous bilirubin excretion and excretion after loading was the same in rats of different age with the exception of a decreased excretion 14 and 28 days after hepatectomy in the 24-month-old rats.

Human liver has a similar regenerative ability after bile duct obstruction (Bax, 1956) and after necrosis of parenchyma (Kalk and Wildhirt, 1956; Kalk, 1958).

After experimental loading of the body with bilirubin (see Section D,1, this chapter) a two- or threefold increase of bilirubin production suffices to cause icterus within a week. This finding is in agreement with the results of Mann and Bollman (1926) that after 70% removal of liver tissue a temporary hyperbilirubinemia develops, but it contradicts the conclusions of McMaster and Rous (1921) that even after 95% ligation of bile ducts no hyperbilirubinemia is observed. Thus, Rich's (1930) theory of icterus, which was based on the assumption that if the bilirubin production is normal 5% of the normal amount of liver tissue suffices to prevent hyperbilirubinemia, needs reevaluation.

When increased formation of bilirubin causes jaundice, one logically talks about "*overproduction icterus*" which can be "*hemolytic*" or "*nonhemolytic*." The subdivision of jaundice into *hepatocellular* and *obstructive* icterus is a practical classification for clinical purposes but does not give a clue about the intimate pathogenetic mechanisms. One of these mechanisms is "*retention*." When hyperbilirubinemia occurs because excretory cells are damaged and their excretion capacity decreased, retention icterus develops. When the small bile ducts are affected to such an extent that bile pigments are pressed back into the lymph or blood, icterus by *stasis* or "*regurgitation icterus*" occurs. A third mechanism is based on abnormal excretion ("*parapedesis*") from blood directly into the lymph instead of from blood into bile ducts. With (1944d) coined the term *"lymphogenic jaundice"* which can occur by regurgitation as well as for other reasons (parapedesis).

To explain parenchymatous icterus, Minkowski (1892, 1904) and Pick (1894) proceeded on the assumption that active excretion of bile pigments into the lymph spaces occurs in hepatic jaundice. They called this process "parapedesis." Their theory was accepted by Ogata (1913a, pp. 275–277) and by Rosenthal and Melchior (1922). Later, it was questioned because of insufficient experimental evidence (Eppinger, 1920; Barron, 1931). The physiological and histological observations of Edlund (1948) support "parapedesis" or "nonregurgitative" lymphogenic jaundice (see Section C,5 this chapter). Recent developments of our knowledge of lymph and lymphatics (see Mayerson, 1963) point the same way. According to this there are important differences between lymphatic and capillary endothelium. Contrary to most blood capillaries, the lymphatic capillaries have endothelium exhibiting open junctions between adjacent cells, presumably because of absent or poorly developed basement membrane. This means that particles can pass through the lymphatic endothelium. For reasons not yet clear, the lymph flow is characterized by being a one-way pattern, i.e., microscopic particles and macromolecules go into the lymphatics, but do not travel in the opposite direction. In the light of these observations, it seems reasonable to conclude that macromolecules normally secreted into the bile will pass into the lymph if the normal secretion way is blocked. Finally, the development of jaundice in congenital absence of intrahepatic bile ducts, a condition where bile canaliculi are completely absent, strongly suggests the existence of parapedesis (cf. Section E,3, this chapter).

2. RECENT DEVELOPMENTS IN MICROANATOMY AND CIRCULATORY AND SECRETION PHYSIOLOGY OF THE LIVER

To understand the pathogenesis of jaundice, it is necessary to have a correct picture of the microscopic anatomy of the liver. This field is developing rapidly at present, partly because of the accumulation of electron microscope data which are quite new, difficult to evaluate, and full of pitfalls (Popper and Schaffner, 1963), but also because of recent observations by means of classic histological studies (Serrão, 1959). In the following a survey of the facts most important to the understanding of jaundice and bile pigment biology is attempted.

Gates *et al.* (1961) recently studied the cell population of the liver in man, using surgical biopsies. He found about 200×10^3 cells per milligram of human liver tissue, of which 170×10^3 were parenchymal.

Elias (1948, 1955) demonstrated the erroneousness of the conventional assumption that the liver consists of lobuli arranged around a central vein and limited by the portal triads. In addition, the liver capillaries—the so-called sinusoids—are not sinusoid in shape but cylindrical; in a contracted state they can assume a sinusoid form. Furthermore, the sinusoids are not crossed in a bridge-like fashion by Kupffer cells. The latter are formed from the endothelial syncytium which surrounds the capillaries. Contraction of capillary walls causes their star-like appearance. This concept of liver capillaries and Kupffer cells originates from *in vivo* experiments in frogs (Knisely *et al.*, 1948). This was later confirmed by Elias (1948, 1949a,b,c), using higher animals.

An important feature of the microcirculation of the mammalian liver is that the hepatic artery supplies a capillary plexus enmeshing the bile ducts in particular and draining mainly into the portal vein and to a smaller extent into the sinusoids (Julian and De Ome, 1948; Andrews *et al.*, 1949, Elias and Petty, 1953). This means that the parenchymal cells close to the bile ducts, i.e., the periportal areas, are supplied by relatively highly oxygenated blood while the remaining parts of the lobules, including the parts close to the central vein, receive blood poorer in oxygen.

The *circulation physiology* of the liver is dominated by the fact that about four-fifths of its blood supply is venous (portal vein) and only about one-fifth is arterial (hepatic artery). Consequently the liver works under low oxygen pressure, and this is especially true for the cells close to the central veins because the hepatic arterioles empty their oxygen-rich blood in the sinusoids in the peripheral parts of the liver lobules. It is therefore to be expected that enzymes catalyzing anaerobic processes are located mainly in the central part of the lobuli, whereas those catalyzing aerobic processes are found in the periphery of the lobules. This has been confirmed both for human and rat livers by quantitative histochemical studies to locate enzymes active in carbohydrate metabolism (Morrison *et al.*, 1965*).

The spaces of Disse play a considerable role in liver pathology. They are perisinusoid lymph fissures between the endothelial wall of sinusoids and the parenchymal cells. According to Knisely (1949) and Elias (1955, Fig. 4, p. 277) they are filled with lymph by the contraction of sinusoids. However, numerous investigators consider these interstices as artifacts (Grafflin and Chaney, 1953). Thus, Fellinger *et al.* (1953) did not obtain them in electron microscope studies in rats and guinea pigs. They did not appear in normal animals, either at bile stasis, or after poisoning with histamine or allyl formate. The capillary wall was closely and tightly adjacent to parenchymal cells. However, Cossel's (1959) electron microscope studies on mouse and human liver punctates finally confirmed the existence of the spaces of Disse. These investigators showed that these spaces are not always present but can be demonstrated, depending on the function of the liver.

Later, Novikoff and Essner (1960) and Hampton (1961) confirmed the existence of the spaces of Disse in electron microscope studies, and Laschi (1963) found that they consist of numerous small spaces among the many microvilli of the surface of the parenchymal liver cells. Notable discontinuities of the wall of the sinusoidal endothelium were observed. Intense pinocytosis activity was found in both the endothelial cytoplasm and the vascular surface of the hepatic cells, pointing toward active transport mechanisms in both types of cells. The spaces of Disse's are widened in several liver lesions (cf. Popper and Schaffner, 1963). Schaffner and Popper (1963) subjected liver biopsies from 63 patients with various liver lesions to electron microscopy and found a progressive transformation of the spaces of Disse in chronic liver diseases, ultimately leading to development of a basement membrane in the sinusoids which were thus transformed to ordinary capillaries. In this way the *"open circulation"* of the liver sinusoids is transformed to the *"closed circulation"* of ordinary capillaries exhibiting much lower permeability. This transformation decreases the effectiveness of hepatic circulation and aggravates hepatocellular insufficiency.

According to Elias (1948) the *liver of mammals consists of an uninterrupted cell mass arranged in plates (laminae hepatis)*. This concept of liver structure is beautifully illustrated by numerous color plates in his "Functional morphology of the liver" (Elias, 1953). The laminae hepatis are connected by cords of liver cells. The interstices between these plates are the "lacunae hepatis," which are connected through perforations in the plates, thus forming the *hepatic labyrinth*. This labyrinth and its lacunas contain capillaries, larger blood vessels, bile ducts, and lymphatic vessels of liver. Although the lobuli are artifacts, this designation is somewhat justified, i.e., certain physiological and pathological differences are known to exist between liver cells located close to the central vein, and others in the vicinity of the portal triad. Further, it has been found that there is a certain structural as well as functional variation in the liver cells according to their position in the lobule (Novikoff, 1959). Whereas in mammals these liver plates consist of only one layer of cells, two layers can be found in lower vertebrates.

Knisely *et al.* (1948) and Elias (1955) studied the microscopic liver vessels. It was found that arterial capillaries (which run from the portal triads to the lobuli) possess "sphincters," which can interrupt the arterial blood supply to various parts of the lobuli. Contractile anastomoses connecting hepatic arterioles with portal venules were found in frogs. In addition, each sinusoid had an afferent entry sphincter and an efferent exit sphincter, where it was connected with the portal and central veins, respectively. With the help of these sphincteric muscles and anastomoses, the amount of blood as well as its arterial or venous blood content, can be effectively controlled while the blood passes through the drainage area of a sinus. In this way, large amounts of blood, and also erythrocytes without plasma, can be stored in the liver and can be released when the need arises.

The *periportal tracts* (the interstices of Mall) each contain one portal venule, one hepatic arteriole, one bile duct, some lymphatic vessels, and surrounding connective tissue. The *bile canaliculi* form a polygonal network which surrounds the liver cells and liver plates. These canaliculi, although produced from two neighboring liver cells, have their own solid walls. They always form anastomotic nets and never form free terminal vessels. They enter the periportal bile ducts through extremely fine inter-lobular canals or through shorter periportal cholangioles (Hering's canals).

Knisely *et al.* (1948) found in *in vivo* experiments with frogs that the membrane which surrounds the sinusoids is contractible, and that it has three distinct permeability possibilities. During one phase it is permeable for all colloids of blood, during another phase it shows permeability only for albumin, and finally in a third phase it becomes completely imperme-able. Such changes in permeability enable the sinusoids to filter out plasma and to accumulate the erythrocytes.

Knisely *et al.* (1948) also studied the phagocytotic activity of the endothelia (Kupfer cells) surrounding the sinusoids for foreign particles including damaged erythrocytes. These particles were coated with a glasslike, translucent mass, which probably originated from blood plasma and phagocytized erythrocytes. This process occurred without formation of pseudopodia, and it appeared to involve only changes in surface tension.

Knisely *et al.*'s (1948) findings that plasma-free erythrocytes can be stored in sinusoids are interesting from the point of view of bile pigment formation from hemoglobin. When over-mature erythrocytes are coated with the mass mentioned above they are taken up and degraded by sinus-oid epithelia. Thus, it is easily understood that the predominant locus of hemoglobin degradation is the liver.

It has been questioned whether the endothelial cells of the liver sinusoids and the stellate cells of Kupffer are really identical (Carsten, 1961), but Holle (1962) maintains their identity on the basis of electron microscope studies and points out that the essential peculiarity of the liver sinusoids is the absence of any basement membrane.

All the details of liver structure are by no means completely understood. Andrews *et al.* (1949, 1956) promulgated somewhat deviating opinions concerning the microscopic anatomy of liver vessels, because he could not detect arteriovenous anastomoses within the "lobuli" of mammals.

Recently, Kolpakov (1961) pointed out that species differences play an important role in the comparative physiology of the liver circulation and that ignorance of this fact has caused much confusion. Saltwater and fresh-water mammals exhibit the most extreme examples, but terrestrial mammals also exhibit important differences. Special smooth muscle sphincter-like structures in the form of rings and spirals in the small branches of the hepatic veins are peculiar to certain genera and species of the canine family (dogs, wolves, foxes, jackals, raccoons). These sphincters can under certain conditions almost completely occlude the lumen of the vessels, and lead to pooling of large volumes of blood in the liver. Well-developed sphincters in the hepatic veins are found in dogs, martens, raccoons, bears, and badgers as well as in *Pinnipedia,* whereas such sphincters are absent in the feline family. There are no sphincters in the openings of the main hepatic veins into the *vena cava.*

Bradley (1949) conducted physiological experiments on blood circulation through the liver using heart catheters and measuring the bromsulphalein (BSP) sodium clearance. He demonstrated the following important facts: normally only one quarter of the sinusoids are open at the same time, liver circulation decreases with a change from horizontal to vertical position, and increases during fever. In 50 resting normal persons, having a body surface of 1.73 m², blood circulation through the liver was 950–1840 (average 1490) ml per minute. Grindlay *et al.* (1941) found 40–160 ml per 100 g liver tissue per minute in dogs. Lichtman (1954, Vol. I, p. 52) gave an average value of 100 ml per 100 g per minute.

Recently Neumayr (1964*) discussed the hepatic circulation in health and disease. He found the normal hepatic blood flow in man to be 1570 ml/min (±320 ml) using the bromsulphalein method and 1310 ml/min (±280 ml) using the radiogold method. He admits that the close agreement of these average values is in contrast to the unanimous experiences of all other investigators that the total liver blood flow varies over an extremely wide range of values in normal subjects and even more in patients with liver diseases.

This leads to one point which must be carefully considered in physiological studies of the pathogenesis of jaundice: the difference between *commencing* and *manifest icterus.* At the beginning of jaundice a considerable difference exists between bilirubin concentration of the blood plasma and that of the bile and liver lymph. In manifest icterus all three contain plenty of bilirubin, so that concentration differences, relatively speaking, are less pronounced (Giorgio and Luigi, 1938). Therefore, physiological studies on the genesis of jaundice must be conducted in the beginning stages of the illness.

Furthermore, it should be emphasized that when the efficiency of the bile excretion mechanism is investigated (from blood into bile or, under pathological conditions, from blood into lymph), it is incorrect to compare the bilirubin concentration of plasma in the general circulation with that of bile or liver lymph. It has not been proved that the bilirubin concentration of liver blood and that of the general blood stream are identical. Bilirubin is produced in the liver, both in Kupffer cells (endothelial cells of sinusoids), and the parenchymal cells (see Chapter II,C). The situation becomes even more complex because dyestuff excretion with the bile depends to a higher degree on the blood supply from the liver artery than on that from the portal veins (Section C,3 and 4, this chapter). Therefore, it is important to compare the bilirubin concentration of blood in liver arterioles and portal venules with that of bile and liver lymph.

Consequently, quantitative analyses directed toward the elucidation of the pathogenesis of jaundice should include blood or perfusion fluid from the liver artery, the portal vein and the liver veins, as well as from the bile and the liver lymph. Such extensive studies can presumably be conducted only on surviving liver preparations where varying quantities of bilirubin or other pigments are to be added to the perfusion fluid passed through the hepatic artery and portal vein. Such studies, although extremely desirable, have not yet been reported.

The so-called *hepatic clearance* of bilirubin and bromsulphalein (BSP) has been much discussed. The dye BSP is excreted in a manner similar to bilirubin, but not quite identically, as it is conjugated to amino acids, whereas bilirubin is conjugated to glucuronic acid and sulfate (Heikel *et al.*, 1960). The findings of Weech *et al.* (1941) on the clearance of bilirubin are widely quoted, although these investigators only performed serum bilirubin analyses with a technique of questionable accuracy and made no bile analyses. It is to be emphasized that the major part of bilirubin injected into the circulation does not appear in the bile (cf. Chapter V,J) and that most of it is probably destroyed. In rats with hereditary nonhemolytic hyperbilirubinemia (Gunn rats)—where bilirubin accumulates in the blood because of a deficient conjugation mechanism in the liver—the bilirubin clearance is greatly delayed and only an insignificant fraction of the injected bilirubin is recovered from the bile (Arias and Johnson, 1959; Arias *et al.*, 1961; Schmid *et al.*, 1958c). In small animals, the clearance of the livers is as high as about

1000 mg bilirubin per kg body weight per 24 hours (cf. Chapter V,J), whereas in man an intravenous load of 1000 mg of bilirubin daily (15 mg per kg per 24 hours) will cause jaundice in the course of about 1 week.

Recent comparative studies with the dyes indocyanine green (ICG) and BSP (Leevy, 1961; Leevy *et al.*, 1963) have greatly increased our understanding of the physiology of the liver. Given simultaneously, BSP and ICG influence hepatic extraction of each other, similar to the competition between BSP and bilirubin.

Brauer (1963a) discussed the hepatic clearance in detail, including its mathematical aspects. Another discussion of this subject is presented by Leevy (1961). Knowledge is only indirect because micropuncture data are lacking. Radioautographs after injection of labeled substances constitute an important source of information. BSP is handled by the liver in three stages. It is first transferred from blood to parenchymal cells, then it is stored in these cells, and finally it is excreted into the bile. But circumstances are complicated because part of the BSP is conjugated—a process most likely taking place mainly in the liver—and its conjugates have already appeared in the blood during the first phase when BSP is still being taken up by the parenchymal cells. Brauer (1963a, p. 160) states: "BSP disappearance curves obtained by methods which do not separate BSP proper from its conjugates can lead to grossly misleading results," and that: "Not withstanding the usefulness of physicochemical hypotheses in predicting certain aspects of the transfer of BSP to the tissue, the actual situation must be viewed as far more complex."

The hepatic clearance is also discussed by Hargreaves and Lathe (1963), who emphasize that rate of clearance cannot be equated with rate of secretion, and that BSP and bilirubin compete with one another at several stages in their transport from plasma to bile. Further, they stress the fact that bilirubin and BSP differ significantly in their excretion with the bile, because bilirubin is excreted mainly as glucuronide, whereas BSP is excreted mainly as a conjugate of glutathione although it can be excreted unchanged (Wheeler *et al.*, 1958). The studies of Leevy *et al.* (1963) comprised observations in both adult and newborn humans. Winkler (1965*) discussed the kinetics of elimination of BSP in man after single injections and continuous infusion including the proposal of a mathematical model taking into account hepatic uptake, biliary elimination, recirculation (diffusion), plasma volume, liver volume, maximal enzymatic velocity, the constant of Michaelis, and the constant of diffusion.

Techniques for rat liver perfusion had already been described by Brauer *et al.* (1951*) and Miller and Axelrod (1954*). Otto *et al.* (1958*) showed that isolated dog liver could extract bromsulphalein, produce bile, and lower the blood ammonia level from a dog with Eck's fistula. Krebs *et al.* (1964[*]) performed perfusion experiments on rat livers with BSP-S[35] and came to the conclusion that a type of nonobstructive nonhemolytic jaundice could exist due to failure of labile mechanisms which normally prevent diffusion of biliary substances into the extra-cellular space as indicated by "spontaneous" occurrence of bile in the hepatic lymph. Their experiments are described in more detail in Section D,3 of this chapter. Sereni *et al.* (1964a[*]) described an improved technique for perfusion of the isolated rat liver. Eiseman (1965[*]) perfused an isolated pig liver, washed free from blood, with blood from a patient with hepatic coma with the result that the patient temporarily recovered from the coma.

The maximal bilirubin clearance of the perfused isolated rat liver was determined in 50 experiments by Sereni *et al.* (1964b[*]). The livers were loaded four times with the addition of 2.5 mg or 10 mg after 30-minute intervals (the duration of the experiment was 150 minutes). The bilirubin concentration of the bile increased somewhat after the 2.5 mg doses (maximum 800 μg/100 ml) and increased considerably more after the 10 mg doses (maximum 5000 μg/100 ml). The bilirubin excretion per 30-minute interval was below 20 μg without loading, 1500 μg with four 2.5 mg doses, and 3000 μg with four 10 mg doses. The figures are in good agreement with those found by Weinbren and Billing (1956) for the maximal bilirubin excretion capacity of the liver of the rat: 66 μg/minute or 1980 μg/30 minutes.

Grafflin and Bagley (1952), Hanzon (1952), Edlund and Hanzon (1953), Grafflin and Chaney (1953), and Grafflin and Corddry (1953) studied the anatomy and function of liver *in vivo* using fluorescence microscopy after injection of *fluorescing materials* that are excreted with the bile. They confirmed Elias' (1948) concept of the microscopic anatomy of liver. In amphibia, as well as in mammals, a direct contact between bile canaliculi and the sinusoidal walls was demonstrated. This offers the possibility of direct entry from blood into bile capillaries without passage through liver cells.

Hanzon (1952) conducted similar *in vivo* experiments in rats with uranin (sodium salt of fluorescein). The results of his experiments were, however, questioned by Grafflin and Chaney (1953) and by Grafflin and Corddry (1953). Hanzon studied living rats under normal and pathological conditions. Besides fluorescence experiments, he employed chemical methods to determine the uranin and bilirubin in bile. He emphasized a number of similarities between the excretion of these two compounds, but found that uranin diffuses faster than bilirubin (Hanzon, p. 148 et seq.). This difference is significant because it could mean that uranin is not bound to albumin, as is bilirubin. As long as this problem is not solved, the behavior of uranin cannot be considered comparable to that of bilirubin. Hanzon also studied the effect of ultraviolet radiation, oxygen deficiency, and bile stasis on rat liver *in vivo*. In his regurgitation experiments he observed direct passage from the bile capillaries into the blood stream. This process took place regularly, shortly before maximum pressure was reached. The average pressure was about 12–13 mm Hg in the ductus choledochus. This bile regurgitation, contrary to that described by Rich (1930) from bile to lymph capillaries, took place from the bile to the blood of the sinusoids. Hanzon does not thoroughly discuss the role of lymph; he could not observe a transfer of uranin in the lymphatic system. One cannot decide how the lymph affects the behavior of uranin during bile stasis, because in Hanzon's experiments on rats, the thoracic duct and ductus choledochus were not simultaneously closed.

Contrary to Hanzon, Grafflin and Chaney (1953) never found any sign of uranin regurgitation in their fluorescence studies in living mice. Even during protracted bile obstruction, up to 2 months, they could not detect dilatation of bile capillaries. This again is in opposition to Hanzon, who found in his rats a general widening of bile capillaries during bile regurgitation. Grafflin and Chaney explained Hanzon's findings as the results of intensive ultraviolet radiation, which he used in his experiments. When liver parenchyma which has already been damaged by bile stasis is exposed to the after effects of radiation, it is quite possible that the lesions described by Hanzon would develop. The lesions could not be due to bile stasis alone. Grafflin and Chaney rejected Hanzon's published fluorescence photomicrographs as "absolutely unconvincing," and regarded the diameter of bile capillaries in Hanzon's photographs as normal. Furthermore, Grafflin and Corddry (1953) point out that employing high intensity radiation, as used by Hanzon, in living or freshly killed animals is unacceptable in any case. Such high energy irradiation can cause artifacts under certain conditions. Consequently, only very limited conclusions can be reached from these fluorescence studies. The results surely cannot support the concept that the widening of bile canals during bile stasis results in regurgitation into blood or lymphatics.

Recent *electron microscope* studies (Novikoff and Essner, 1960; Hampton, 1961) have also failed to disclose regurgitation from bile to blood or lymph. Hampton speaks of an active energy-consuming process transporting the bile constituents through the hepatic cells to the Disse's spaces.

Regular studies on the physiology of biliary excretion have recently been performed by Morris (1956, 1960), who investigated the correlation between blood circulation, oxygen supply, and bile flow. He unfortunately did not study the bile pigment content of the blood and bile. Studies of this sort, including bile pigment analyses under various pathological conditions, would be of considerable value.

Other recent developments concerning microanatomy and secretion physiology are discussed in Section C,4.

3. Role of Lymph in the Pathogenesis of Jaundice

Seen from a *theoretical* point of view the lymph must play an important part in the pathogenesis of jaundice. This is evident after electron microscope studies have revealed open junctions between the endothelial cells of lymph capillaries, allowing free passage of macromolecules (cf. Mayerson, 1963). It may be added that the lymph is also being recognized as a major pathogenetic factor in hepatic cirrhosis (Dumont and Mulholland, 1962). It is important to keep in mind that liver lymph has almost the same composition as blood plasma (Brinkhouse and Walker, 1941; McCarrel et al., 1941; Kühn and Hildebrand, 1951). Thus, it could be said that liver cells are practically bathed in blood plasma. However, according to the investigations of Friedman et al. (1956), this is not exactly correct. They demonstrated that although the lymph proteins have the same composition as plasma, their concentration is inversely proportional to the volume of the lymph flow, and that the protein concentration of liver lymph averages only two thirds that of plasma. Whereas the average lymph flow in rats is 1.5 ml in 12 hours, it increases to 5 ml during bile stasis. The maximum pressure of lymph in this case is about 26 cm water. Bilirubin and cholic acid of lymph were determined, but these substances could only be detected during bile stasis. Under these conditions the lymph assumed a character which, at least partly, reflected the activity of parenchymal liver cells. When albumin enters the liver lymph, bilirubin bound to serum albumin necessarily has to follow. In this way, bilirubin concentration levels of liver lymph, however, only reaches that of blood plasma. When higher concentrations are detected, the participation of special energy-consuming mechanisms must be assumed.

Morris (1956) studied the exchange of proteins between blood plasma and liver lymph in the cat by means of I^{131}-tagged albumin. In the course of 3–4 hours, the albumin-I^{131} in the liver lymph reached 90% of the level in the blood plasma. He found that the interstitial fluid of the liver constituted 3% of the weight of the organ and that its protein pool was 154 mg per 100 g of liver. If the hepatic veins were ligated (an operation resulting in an increase of the portal venous pressure to 10–12 cm of water), the flow of liver lymph increased tenfold. Under these conditions equilibrium between the albumin-I^{131} in plasma and lymph was reached after 1 hour. The liver lymph was found to contribute 30% of the lymph flow of the thoracic duct in the anesthetized cat and 40% of its protein.

Later, Courtice *et al.* (1962) and Woolley and Courtice (1962) reported similar studies in rabbits. They determined the lymph:plasma ratio of different proteins and found 91.6% for albumin, 69.2% for lipoprotein of density 1.063–1.200, 43.4% for lipoprotein of density 1.019–1.063, and 32.8% for lipoprotein of density below 1.019; i.e., they found that passage of macromolecules into the liver lymph is related to their size. Further, they found by means of serum proteins labeled with I^{131} that only minor amounts of protein just synthesized by the liver cells can be reaching the lymph.

On the basis of available data on the extent of blood circulation through liver, and the amount of circulating lymph, certain calculations can be made.

The amount of blood entering the liver is 40–160 ml per 100 g per minute in dogs (Section C,2, this chapter). According to Cain *et al.* (1947), the lymph flow through the liver is 0.3–5.8 (average 2.26) ml per 10 minutes in normal dogs weighing 12–26 kg. Assuming that liver weight is about $\frac{1}{40}$ of body weight, one obtains 300–650 g for the liver weight and from 120–480 to 260–1040 ml per minute (or from 1200–4800 to 2600–10,400 ml per 10 minutes) for the amount of blood. Corresponding lymph production averages 2–3 ml. However, Andrews (1955) and Andrews *et al.* (1956) showed that BSP, which is excreted similarly to bilirubin, is more readily eliminated through the hepatic artery than through the portal vein. The amount of blood flowing through the former is about one fifth of the total blood supply of the liver. Thus, to calculate bilirubin clearance one has to use about one fifth of the blood volume above. Assuming that during bile stasis all the blood bilirubin goes into the lymphatics, a concentration shift of from $\frac{2.5}{240} - \frac{2.5}{960}$ to $\frac{2.5}{520} - \frac{2.5}{2080}$ (10-minute volumes) or from $\frac{1}{100} - \frac{1}{400}$ to $\frac{1}{210} - \frac{1}{1830}$ has to take place from plasma to lymph. Assuming further, that these values are also true for humans having a normal serum bilirubin concentration of about 0.5 mg per 100 ml, one obtains bilirubin concentrations of 50–400 mg per 100 ml in the liver lymph during beginning bile duct obstruction.

The role of liver lymph is thoroughly discussed in a recent review by Brauer (1963a), who writes (p. 142): "The liver must contain a rather extensive vascular region separated from the liver substance with tenuous walls, almost freely permeable to the largest plasma protein molecules. Under such circumstances, the effective osmotic pressure exerted on the vessel walls by the plasma colloids should be very small, and ultrafiltration which could lead to concentration of plasma proteins within the stream of blood as this progressed along its vascular pathway should be well-nigh absent. Since this, however, is a major factor limiting fluid loss from the blood to the extravascular spaces in other tissues, fluid balance in the hepatic parenchyma ought to be exceedingly labile." Thus, in rat experiments an increase of the hilus pressure of only 2 cm H_2O above the pressure of the hepatic veins results in formation of protein-rich exudation of the liver surface. Brauer (1963a, pp. 146–147) suggests the following theory: "Liver lymph formation involves two sites. The first of these would appear to be the sinusoidal portion of the hepatic vascular tree, where a very large area of endothelium with demonstrably large pores surrounds the blood stream, and where one would expect the formation of a large volume of lymph, differing from the blood primarily in the absence (in the normal liver at least) of erythrocytes and of the greater part of the leucocytes elements. This primary lymph for the most part would have to move countercurrent to the blood stream to enter the lymphatic vessels within the Glisson sheath. Here it passes through the peribiliary plexus, the second important site of lymph formation. The principal role of this plexus in the normal liver should be sought in the opportunity it affords for secondary modification of the liver lymph composition by exchange of soluble components between bile, lymph and blood." Brauer (1963a, p. 146) regards the liver as a system of cells and other structural elements suspended in a complex of three moving fluid phases: the endovascular blood, moving rapidly (1.5 ml per gram of tissue per minute) and occupying 15% of the volume of the normal liver; the bile, moving slowly (0.0015 ml per gram per minute) and occupying at most 2% of the liver volume; and the lymph moving yet more slowly (0.0005 ml per gram per minute).

Extensive *experimental* material exists demonstrating the role of liver lymph during pathogenesis of jaundice, and this includes earlier observations, as well as some experiments obtained by means of modern methods.

Saunders (1803) and Tiedemann and Gmelin (1826) observed widened dark yellow lymph vessels of the liver during bile stasis. Later, bilirubin was detected in the lymph of the thoracic duct 15–30 minutes after the ductus choledochus was ligated (Wertheimer and Lepage, 1897, 1898, 1899; Barron and Bumstead, 1928). The time of bilirubin appearance in lymph was dependent on the dilatative capacity of the biliary tract. To establish identical conditions, the cystic duct has to be ligated (McMaster and Rous, 1921; Mayo and Greene, 1929). After simple ligature of the ductus choledochus, Afanassiew (1883) detected icterus in dogs 4 days later. Jaundice developed after 24 hours when the bile ducts were obliterated with wax injected simultaneously with the ligature.

When the lymph of the thoracic duct is drained during bile duct occlusion, icterus develops several hours later, as compared to normal lymph flow conditions (Fleischl, 1874; Kunkel, 1875; D. Gerhardt, 1897; Wertheimer and Lepage, 1897, 1898, 1899; Whipple and King, 1911). Mayo and Greene (1929) produced icterus at normal flow conditions of lymph after 45 minutes, whereas it developed only after 5 hours when the lymph of the thoracic duct had been drained. All these observations were made on dogs in which the thoracic duct can easily be isolated; this is more difficult in rabbits, but Giorgio and Luigi (1938) succeeded in carrying out similar experiments and observed bilirubin in the large lymphatic vessel, 16 hours after ligature. When the lymph was drained, bilirubin appeared in blood only 8 hours later. After 26 hours, the bilirubin concentration was the same in blood and lymph, and icterus developed after 24–30 hours.

Harley (1892, 1893) simultaneously ligated the ductus choledochus and thoracic duct. He found no icterus after 17 days, but it is possible that the ligatures were insufficient or that lymphatic anastomoses formed; these should, however, have been detected at autopsy. This is difficult to understand, since other authors found hyperbilirubinemia after bile duct closure even when the entire lymph of the thoracic duct was drained off. The difference was only that hyperbilirubinemia developed later than under normal conditions. Shafiroff et al. (1942) carried out similar experiments on 23 dogs in which, the gallbladder had been removed at the same time as ligature was carried out. They ligated only the ductus choledochus in seven control animals and in seven others only the thoracic duct. Only 5 of the 23 dogs with double ligature did not develop collateral lymphatic circulation. Two hours later bilirubin was detected in the blood of these animals. Bilirubin concentration reached 7 mg per 100 ml after 65 hours. At this time, the concentrations in the lymph and urine were the same.

In their experiments on dogs Hoffman et al. (1960) determined the bilirubin in the liver lymphatics and the blood serum after occlusion of the common bile duct. They determined both bilirubin and its conjugates by chromatographic methods. Their experiments are described in more detail in Chapter V,G. They found a rapid increase of bilirubin in both the liver lymph and the blood serum during the first 72 hours after the occlusion. At first the diglucuronide of bilirubin dominated, but later the monoglucuronide.

Dumont et al. (1961) concluded, on the basis of experiments with dogs and studies of the thoracic duct lymph in patients with obstructive jaundice, that the elevated serum bilirubin is due solely to bilirubin reaching the circulation through the lymph. Dumont et al. (1962) found, in dogs with cannulated thoracic ducts and cystic duct that within 3 hours of the biliary obstruction the level of the lymph bilirubin had already increased four- to 8-fold.

Alican and Hardy (1962) performed both short-term and more extended experiments on the lymph and blood bilirubin in cholecystectomized dogs with biliary occlusion. In seven dogs the lymph from the thoracic duct was diverted to the outside, and samples of arterial blood and thoracic duct lymph were taken every 6 hours for 24 hours. Two of the dogs were followed for 48 hours. In 13 dogs thoracic duct lymph and blood were studied simultaneously at various intervals during the first to the seventeenth day after the biliary occlusion. In these animals the lymph was not diverted to the outside. The bilirubin determinations were performed with the Malloy-Evelyn method (1937) without chromatographic fractionation; therefore, only limited conclusions regarding bilirubin and its conjugates can be drawn. Alican and Hardy (1962) speak of conjugated and unconjugated bilirubin, but their findings can also be explained by variations in the relation between bilirubin monoglucuronide and diglucuronide; in the light of the chromatographic investigations of Hoffman *et al.* (1960), the latter explanation is the more likely one.

Alican and Hardy found that the thoracic duct lymph bilirubin began to increase during the first hours after the occlusion; after 6 hours the mean value for direct bilirubin was 5.37 and for total bilirubin 6.63 mg per 100 ml. After 24 and 48 hours, the serum bilirubin was higher than the lymph bilirubin even with continuous diversion of the lymph. This is interpreted by the authors as evidence of a mechanism of direct transport of bilirubin from the liver cells to the blood plasma. This, however, cannot be regarded as a conclusive proof; liver lymphatics not emptying into the thoracic duct will probably go into action in biliary occlusion of more than a few hours' duration if the lymph from the thoracic duct is diverted to the outside, (as in Alican and Hardy's short-term experiments) because the diversion of the thoracic duct lymph constitutes a significant loss of protein.

In the dogs studied after the first day, the thoracic duct lymph bilirubin was somewhat lower than the serum bilirubin. In two dogs the liver lymphatics were cannulated, and bilirubin analyses were performed in liver lymph, thoracic duct lymph, and serum. One of the dogs was studied on the seventh day and showed total bilirubin of 2.85 mg (direct bilirubin 2.10) mg per 100 ml in the thoracic duct lymph, 4.44 (3.30) mg per 100 ml in the liver lymph, and 3.30 (2.80) mg per 100 ml in the blood serum. The other, studied on the seventeenth day of the occlusion, showed 2.18 (1.62), 3.04 (2.30), and 4.15 (3.30) mg per 100 ml, respectively. The highest bilirubin concentrations were found in both serum and thoracic duct lymph on the fourth to seventh day of the occlusion. After the first week, rather constant values of 4–5 mg per 100 ml in the blood serum and 3–4 mg per 100 ml in the thoracic duct lymph were found. Alican and Hardy regarded these findings as evidence of a mechanism of leakage of "direct bilirubin" from the liver cells to the blood independent of the lymph. The findings can, however be explained by retention and secretion into the lymph by means of so-called parapedesis (cf. Section C,1 and D,3, this chapter) and the observations of Hoffman *et al.* (1960; cf. also Chapter V,G). These authors found that bilirubin monoglucuronide dominates in the serum of dogs with biliary obstruction after a few weeks and that the same is the case in the serum or hepatectomized dogs. If one assumes that the parapedesis excretion mechanism into the lymph is less effective than the normal excretion into the bile, and that consequently some retention of bile pigment in the serum develops, then it is not difficult to understand that, in protracted biliary occlusion, serum bilirubin reaches values higher than thoracic duct bilirubin, and even higher than the liver lymph bilirubin.

The studies of Krebs *et al.* (1964*) on isolated perfused rat liver during continuous infusion with labeled bromsulphalein (BSP-S[35]) are of interest here. Samples of hepatic lymph showed two types of response. The first was characterized by lymph BSP concentrations below those in the perfusion fluid (plasma) and by a chromatographic distribution of BSP and its conjugates in the lymph different from that found in both plasma and bile. The second type of response showed lymph BSP grossly higher than in the plasma with identical chromatographic patterns in lymph and bile. The second type was found when the bile flow was deliberately stopped, but it could also be seen when bile was apparently flowing freely. The findings indicate that the lymph (extracellular fluid) compartment of the liver is physiologically independent of the bile duct system and that an important part of its contents arises from the hepatic parenchyma rather than from the blood plasma. A large part of the BSP in the lymph of the second type presumably arises from hepatic cells, i.e., BSP which has been diverted or lost from the main pathway of biliary excretion. But this finding is actually similar to the effects denoted by the old term "parapedesis" (cf. above).

Tisdale *et al.* (1959) published observations on humans supporting the role of the lymph. In his experiments, human volunteers received large amounts of bilirubin intravenously, and the amount of total and direct serum bilirubin was determined and plotted. Although only free bilirubin and not the conjugated form was administered, 13% of the serum bilirubin increase corresponded to conjugated bilirubin. Contrary to these findings in normal individuals, corresponding results on persons with liver cirrhosis gave 32%. Furthermore the author established that the peak of the curve representing direct (conjugated) bilirubin was reached $\frac{1}{2}$ to 1 hour later than the peak of total bilirubin. This delay can be explained by the assumption that, when the organism is overloaded with bilirubin, a certain amount of conjugated bilirubin is excreted in the lymph; the bulk, however, passes through the bile.

Bilirubin, which is excreted into the lymph, needs a certain time to reach the general circulation. In experiments with dogs performed by Shafiroff *et al.* (1939), in which the ductus choledochus was ligated, bilirubin appeared in the lymph of the thoracic duct 15 minutes after ligature. This seems to be in agreement with the $\frac{1}{2}$ to 1 hour delay in the human tolerance experiments. Surprisingly. Tisdale *et al.* (1959) considered this function of the lymph only as a secondary possibility. They interpreted their findings on the basis of regurgitation, although they did not offer any valid proof for this assumption. On the contrary, they were forced to admit that the lymph could play a role in the outcome of their findings.

The recent studies of Harth and Waldeck (1964; see also Section C,5 this chapter) show that "regurgitated bile" reaches the lymph not only at elevated bile pressure, but already at relatively low and normal bile pressure. At increasing bile pressure, however leakage into the blood stream also takes place. This is in good agreement with the observations of Shafiroff *et al.* (1939) in dogs, according to which bilirubin appears in the lymph as early as 15 minutes after the occlusion, but in the blood only after 2 hours.

Recently, anatomical studies on the lymphatic system of the liver were published. Comparini (1964*) studied the lymphatic vessels of the liver in 20 human subjects ranging from newborn to elderly persons and found three separate systems—the portal system following the branches of the portal vein, the subcapsular system forming a superficial rete just under the capsule and a rete profunda lying deeper, and a hepatic system following the branches of the hepatic vein that was much less developed than the other two systems. The liver lymphatics of the dog and the cat were studied by Comparini *et al.* (1965a*,b*). The same three systems were found, but in the dog the hepatic system was well developed. Grau and Meyer-Lemppenau (1965*) studied the liver lymphatics in calves, pigs, dogs, cats, and rats by means of dye injection techniques and found lymphatics in the portal tracts, in the interlobular connective tissue, and under the capsule, but never intralobulary.

4. Theories of Secretion in Bile Formation

The appearance of bilirubin in the liver lymph during bile stasis is based either on a filtration or diffusion, or it is caused by cell activity. To solve this problem, the knowledge of the mechanism of bile formation is necessary. According to customarily accepted theories, bile is formed by the parenchymal liver cells by an active process. However, Pavel (1943a,b) and Andrews (1955) have proposed two theories which are in contradiction to this hypothesis. Pavel believes that filtration and re-absorption mechanisms prevail similar to urine production. Contrary to this, Andrews assumes that epithelial cells of the smallest bile ducts, and not parenchymal liver cells, are responsible for bile formation.

Pavel's theory is supported by histological observations on various forms of icterus (Pavel and Velciu, 1951). However, it is difficult to accept this theory, because the liver possesses only low pressure capillaries and no high pressure capillaries comparable to the glomeruli of the kidney, and no bile acids are detectable in normal serum. Furthermore, Brauer *et al.* (1954) showed in experiments with rats that bile production is connected with an active, energy-consuming mechanism, which cannot be exclusively a filtration or reabsorption process. Finally, Hargreaves and Lathe (1963) and Wheeler (1963), on the basis of thorough physiological studies, draw attention to the fact that the secretory function of the liver exhibits a remarkable degree of autonomy with respect to hepatic blood supply and innervation, and must therefore depend, for the most part, upon chemical processes acting on the boundaries of the bile canaliculi and the duct system.

On the other hand, it has to be admitted that although the sinusoids are low-pressure capillaries in contrast to the high-pressure glomerular capillaries of the kidney, the effective colloidal osmotic pressure counter-acting the ultrafiltration from sinusoids to perisinusoidal spaces is very low because of the high permeability of the sinusoidal walls to proteins. Another question of importance concerns the fact that the hydrostatic pressure must be much higher in the sinusoids of the periportal region where the hepatic arterioles empty than in the central parts of the lobuli close to the hepatic venules. Ultrafiltration must therefore be expected to take place mostly in the periportal part of the lobuli, and perhaps in the opposite direction in the central parts of the lobuli. The state of contraction of the hepatic arterioles must play a dominant part in any ultrafiltration in the liver.

Pavel and Campeanu (1965*) maintain that bile is formed by filtration-reabsorption but they state simultaneously that today the process of transcapillary ultrafiltration cannot be looked upon as a merely passive process. Active intervention of the endothelial cells can be expected. They regard conjugation of bilirubin as a surface phenome-non taking place between adjacent surfaces of liver cells while the ultrafiltrate of the plasma is filtered between parenchymal liver cells from sinusoids to bile capillaries. This view is, however, contradicted by some recent observations. Maggiore *et al.* (1963a*,b*) found that considerable storage of bilirubin—both conjugated and unconjugated—took place in the exsanguinated rat liver after bilirubin loading, and Brown *et al.* (1964*) found that 50% of the injected tritiated bilirubin was present in the cell sap of the liver cells 5 minutes after the injection, which indicates that bilirubin enters the liver cells in bulk.

Andrews' hypothesis needs serious consideration. He is correct when he states: "It has been assumed for centuries that parenchymal cells secrete bile, and the assumption appears to have remained unchallenged and unproven." It is quite possible that bile is secreted by the cuboidal epithelia of small bile ducts, and the function of parenchymal cells remains limited to liver metabolism. And it is just as possible that both parenchymal cells and cubic epithelial cells of bile ducts are capable of production. Andrews bases his assumption on the vascular supply of liver lobuli. It is well known that the liver artery primarily supplies the small bile ducts and that the parenchymal cells obtain blood from the portal vein. Andrews *et al.* (1956) demonstrated that 2 to $2\frac{1}{2}$ times more BSP was extracted from surviving liver preparations after infusion into the liver artery than by infusion through the portal vein. The experiments of Shafiroff *et al.* (1944) in dogs seem to lend some support to Andrews' theory. In these experiments the presence of bilirubin was determined in the lymph after ligature of the bile ducts and during various changes of liver circulation. Ligation of the liver artery did not lead to changes in bilirubin concentration of lymph. However, enhanced circulation due to denerving of the liver artery rapidly increased bilirubin concentration in the lymph. When, by applying Eck's fistula, the hepatic artery was ligated at the same time, bilirubin concentration of lymph decreased. The highest lymph bilirubin values were obtained after partial ligature of liver veins. Gebhardt's experiments (1939a,b,) on bilirubin excretion in dogs with Eck's fistula and reversed Eck's fistula seem to support the theory of Andrews. Gebhardt found that only bilirubin which reaches the liver through the hepatic artery can be detected in the bile.

Experimental evidence for secretory activity of the biliary ductules was provided by Goldfarb *et al.* (1963). They found that in rats poisoned by various drugs, the ductular cells added an electrolyte-containing solution to the bile. They provide, however, no evidence of bilirubin excretion by the ductules in these experiments.

Fluorescence studies of Grafflin and Chaney (1953) with uranin also shed some light on Andrews' hypothesis. Bile capillaries were rendered excellently visible with uranin. It was found that at least the excretion of uranin, and probably all other bile components, must occur in the bile capillaries, which might be due to liver cell activity. This does not directly support Andrews' theory, but, on the other hand, does not disprove it either. It could be that both liver cells themselves and cuboidal epithelial cells of bile ducts are capable of bile formation. Possibly these different cells are responsible for the production of different bile components.

Elias (1955, p. 270) pointed out the barely understandable fact that bile components can be transported from sinusoids directly into superficial bile capillaries without passing through the liver cells, a transport which would have to overcome a large concentration gradient. A possible explanation for this seemingly contradictory phenomenon is that the walls of bile capillaries are not merely passive border membranes but are, in reality, a part of the liver cytoplasm. This phenomenon could be observed with fluorescent dyestuffs as well as with indigo carmine.

The electron microscopic study of intrahepatic biliary ductules performed by Sternlieb (1965[*]) are of interest in view of Andrew's hypothesis. Present concepts concerning the ultrastructure of human bile ductules are sketchy compared to those of the ultrastructure of the bile canaliculi. Sternlieb studied transverse, oblique, and longitudinal sections of bile ductules from liver biopsies of two patients with Wilson's disease but without impairment of the liver.

They recorded the following findings: The epithelial cells of the ductules were roughly fusiform with intricate outlines and elongated ovoid nuclei; the cytoplasm was mainly distributed toward the cell poles. Varying numbers of microvilli projected from the luminal aspects of cells; pinocytosis proceeded also on the basal part of the cells. Intercellular gaps containing projections of membranes or microvilli apparently formed parts of the intracellular draining systems; segmented narrowings of the ductular lumina because of intraluminal bulging of nuclei were visible. Sternlieb believes that his findings indicate that metabolically the ductules do not represent passive channels—a view in agreement with Andrew's theory.

Andrew's hypothesis also gets some support from studies by Wood (1965[*]) on the development of the liver in rat embryos using electron microscopy. He found that before developing ducts are recognizable there is a widespread distribution of tubular ductules throughout the liver parenchyma. Wood believes that the hepatic tubular epithelium originates from a generalized reorientation of hepatic cells at a particular stage of development.

Ashworth and Sanders (1960) studied the anatomic pathway of bile formation by means of electron microscopy. The sinusoidal endothelium formed a very incomplete lining over the liver cells. It was interrupted by comparatively large spaces (pores) up to 20,000 Å in diameter through which ready communication of the sinusoidal lumen and the Disse spaces was possible. The contents of the latter were similar to those of the sinusoids except for the absence of erythrocytes, leukocytes, and platelets. Contrary to expectation no signs of phagocytosis were found in the endothelial cells. They interpreted their findings as supporting the concept that an energy-consuming mechanism of the cell membrane plays an important role in bile formation and they found considerable similarity between the mechanisms of uptake by hepatic cells and the intestinal absorption of lipids.

The bile canaliculi were formed solely by the membranes of the hepatic cells from which extend numerous microvilli. It was assumed that conjugated bilirubin, BSP, and other specific constituents appearing in the bile in concentrated form pass from the hepatic cell cytoplasm into the bile canaliculi. The delay in appearance of bilirubin and BSP in bile after their introduction into the blood, as compared with the more rapid appearance of diffusible compounds, e.g., lithium salts, is readily understood in light of these observations as incorporation into the hepatic cell; conjugation and transit would all be expected to require a certain time period.

Ashworth and Sanders think that a *passive mechanism* based on ultra-filtration is also active in the formation of bile *besides the energy-consuming* passage through the liver cells. Such a mechanism is necessary to explain the presence of electrolytes in the bile in the same concentrations as in blood plasma. They believe that this ultrafiltration takes place through the 100 Å wide intercellular spaces between adjacent liver cells. The bile canaliculi themselves did not approach the sinusoids or Disse spaces closely; however, there were narrow but distinct intercellular channels connecting bile canaliculi with Disse spaces. These channels are amply wide to permit flow of water and solutes of small molecular size, but too narrow to let albumin pass. There was no evidence that the lining endothelium or Kupffer cells functioned as intermediate carriers of bilirubin. The transfer of bilirubin from the liver cells to the bile canaliculi could not be seen in the electron microscope. Similarly, fluid transport across epithelia through long intercellular channels was demonstrated in the gallbladder by Diamond and Tormey (1966*).

Important studies on the secretion physiology of bile excretion have been published by Morris (1956, 1960) but he did not perform bilirubin analyses.

Recently Hargreaves and Lathe (1963) and Wheeler (1963) discussed bile secretion. The former proposed the term choleplilic for all substances—endogenous and exogenous—concentrated in the bile. It appears probable that bile formation involves two simultaneous processes, the formation of a fluid similar to deproteinized plasma and the secretion of cholephilic substances into this fluid. Bile formation does not depend on the hydrostatic pressure perfusing the liver, but on the energy provided by chemical mechanisms. The secretion of organic anions—such as bile salts—seems to be the primary event in bile formation. The cholephilic substances compete with one another at several stages in their transport from plasma to bile.

Important observations related to the problem of bile formation have also been made based on the *microchemical study of hepatic cells.* Brown *et al.* (1964*) investigated the subcellular fractions of liver and bile in rats at intervals of 2, 5, 15, and 30 minutes after i.v. injection of bilirubin-H[3]. The liver was homogenized and fractionated by ultracentrifugation, and separated into well-defined particulate fractions consisting of nuclei, mitochondria, cell surface membranes, microsomes, and lysosomes. The different fractions were subjected to a determination of bilirubin, radioactivity, and enzymes. The fraction containing the nuclei contained 2–7% of the bilirubin, the mitochondrial fraction 5–14%, the lysosomes 2–10%, the microsomes 9–20%, and the supernatant cell sap 46–86%. The distribution of bilirubin among the fractions was relatively independent of the phases of bilirubin uptake and secretion.

Brown *et al.* emphasized that bilirubin dissociates from albumin during hepatic uptake. More than 40% of the bilirubin-H[3] was concentrated intracellularly in the liver within 5 minutes after the injection, although only 10% of the injected radioactive albumin was retained in the liver. Furthermore, the subcellular distribution of bilirubin at any time was grossly different from that of albumin, the bulk of the bilirubin being present in the cell sap while that of the albumin was confined to the microsomal fraction. It was concluded that the rapid intracellular concentration of bilirubin is due to an initial dissociation of the bilirubin-albumin complex at the cell surface after which the free bilirubin quickly passes through the cell membrane.

The observations of Odell (1965) that the distribution of bilirubin between mitochondria isolated from liver homogenates and albumin varied with pH is of little biological relevance because albumin only enters liver cells in small quantities (cf. above).

The dissociation of bilirubin and albumin during bile formation was also discussed by Lathe (1965*) who pointed out that the intracellular albumin pool of the rat liver is only about 0.1% of that of the serum; therefore the entire albumin pool of the liver would be exchanged every 30 seconds if the bilirubin should enter the liver cells bound to albumin.

As this is clearly impossible, the dissociation of the bilirubin-albumin bond must take place before bilirubin enters the liver cell.

On the other hand small amounts of serum albumin really were demonstrated in human bile by Rosenthal *et al.* (1965*) with radioactive albumin. A point of considerable interest is the difference in the handling by the liver of free and conjugated bilirubin, but this question has only been subjected to a few experimental studies. Based on observations of a patient with partial biliary obstruction Mistilis and Schiff (1963) suggested that the human liver is incapable of excreting conjugated bilirubin reaching it with the blood (cf. Section C,1 in this chapter). As pointed out in Chapter II, Section D nonpolar, free, unconjugated bilirubin (molecular weight 584) readily passes the mucosa of the small intestine, whereas polar, conjugated water-soluble bilirubin (molecular weight 925) does not. It is to be expected that the behavior of these molecules toward the lipid membrane of the liver cells is similar. Experimental studies on this problem were conducted by Maggiore *et al.* (1963b*). Preparations of free and conjugated bilirubin were infused i.v. into rats; at first a dose of 2 mg/100 g body weight was infused rapidly and subsequently the infusion was continued at a rate of 1 mg every 3 minutes for 45 minutes. The bile was collected during three 15-minute periods and at the end of the experiment the rat was sacrificed and the bilirubin content of its blood and liver determined. The rate of bilirubin excretion with the bile (T_m) was determined for both free and conjugated bilirubin in 12 rats. For conjugated bilirubin it was 47.8 ± 1.9 μg/min/100 g body weight; for free bilirubin it was 54.0 ± 1.80 μg/min/100 g. The total serum bilirubin concentration was 43.3 mg/100 ml 35 minutes after the injection of 6.1 mg conjugated bilirubin per 100 g body weight, but only 17.7 mg/100 ml after injection of the corresponding amount of free bilirubin (5.7 mg/100 g). If the total bilirubin present in the body was calculated as the difference between the quantity infused and that excreted with the bile the quotient total body bilirubin/total serum bilirubin concentration was 0.06 for conjugated as against 4.91 for free bilirubin. There were 15 rats in each group in these experiments. Direct measurement of the amount of bilirubin present in the liver at autopsy showed that 24% of the total body bilirubin was stored in the liver in the rats infused with free bilirubin and only 10% was stored there in those infused with conjugated bilirubin (from bile). Experiments with rats having a deficient capacity for bilirubin conjugation (Gunn rats) showed similar results indicating that the capacity of the liver for storing bilirubin must be independent of its capacity for conjugating it with glucuronic acid.

The experiments of Maggiore *et al.* show that the capacity of the rat to store conjugated bilirubin is clearly inferior to its capacity to store free bilirubin. Further experiments to clarify this question are required in a number of species.

Summary

The excretion of bilirubin with the bile consists of various steps. The first is the uptake of bilirubin by the liver cells which is associated with the dissolution of the bilirubin-albumin bond. The second is the passing of the bilirubin molecule through the membrane of the liver cell and the conjugation of bilirubin within the cell. The third is the passage of bilirubin glucuronide into the bile capillaries. Besides the energy-consuming secretion by the liver cells, ultrafiltration of water and solutes through spaces between adjacent liver cells also plays a part in bile formation, which explains its water and electrolyte content.

Conjugated bilirubin is handled by the liver in a decidedly different manner than free bilirubin, but experimental studies are few. Bromsulphalein is handled by the liver by mechanisms similar to those for bilirubin (cf. Goresky, 1965*).

5. ROLE OF RUPTURES AND REGURGITATION

The mechanism which, after obstruction of the biliary tract, transports bilirubin into the liver lymph must be very efficient because only a short time elapses between bile duct obstruction and the appearance of bilirubin in lymph vessels of the liver. According to Cain *et al.* (1947), bilirubin appears immediately after the ductus choledochus and the cystic duct have been ligated. Appearance of bile acid in the lymph also indicates active lymph-directed excretion (Gonzales-Oddone, 1946). Friedman *et al.* (1956) found a maximum pressure of 26 cm water for liver lymph excretion and also for bile excretion in rats. This fact indicates an active excretion process. They remark that in biliary obstruction hepatic lymph assumes a character specifically reflecting, in part at least, hepatic parenchymal cell activity. However, this fact is not necessarily a consequence of secretion into the lymph; it could take place because of a rupture in the biliary tract or by regurgitation. In my opinion, the immediate appearance of bilirubin in lymphatic vessels of liver is the strongest argument against regurgitation having a major role. However, there has been much discussion for and against regurgitation.

Eppinger (1903) was the first to detect the rupture of bile capillaries after long extended bile duct obstruction in humans. However, rupture never occurred in recent experimental bile stasis (Sterling, 1911; Ogata, 1913a, pp. 264–265; Barron and Bumstead, 1928; Scheunert, 1931; Edlund, 1948; Grafflin and Chaney, 1953). Hanzon (1952) was the only one who could detect it, but his findings were criticized by Grafflin and Chaney (1953) who interpreted these ruptures as the result of cell degeneration caused by intensive ultraviolet radiation. Therefore, it can hardly be maintained that rupture of bile canaliculi causes the appearance of bilirubin in liver lymph in the early stages of bile duct closure. Furthermore, regurgitation, as observed by Hanzon, caused backflow into the blood stream and not into the lymph. Eppinger (1937, pp. 100 and 114) admitted that ruptures cannot play a significant role during the pathogenesis of jaundice. Nevertheless, they have assumed a rather important role in the literature, because Rich (1930) considered regurgitation, caused by such ruptures, important for the pathogenesis of both obstructive and hepatocellular icterus. The opening of bile capillaries by necrosis of parenchymal cells was considered especially important in hepatocellular icterus (Hiyeda, 1925, 1927; Rich, 1930).

Thus histological observations do not support the assumption of regurgitation, although Rouiller (1956) described direct connections between the bile capillaries and the spaces of Disse in the rat liver. These connections were more pronounced in bile stasis than normally.

Electron microscope studies have also failed to support the rupture hypothesis. Novikoff and Essner (1960, p. 122), who worked with rats and humans, thus writes: "If, as seems the case, direct continuity between canaliculi and the spaces of Disse is not common in obstructive jaundice then movement of bile into the blood (regurgitation) would probably involve intracellular transport." Hampton (1961), who studied obstructive jaundice in mice, also found that active energy-consuming transport from the bile into the spaces of Disse across the parenchymal cells must be the mechanism underlying obstructive jaundice. It is curious that both authors believe that the substances of the bile must first be secreted into the bile and from there cross the hepatic cells once more and go into the lymph spaces. As the hydrostatic pressure in the bile duct system most likely is too high for the parenchymal cells to work against, it seems more likely that the secretion into the bile is diverted into a secondary pathway directly into the lymph spaces—in this way the theory of transport twice through the same cell in two directions would be unnecessary.

Finally, Steiner and Carruthers (1962) performed electron microscope studies of the liver of rabbits and rats with experimental extrahepatic biliary obstruction. They found an obvious dilatation of the bile capillaries with edema of the microvilli, whereas ruptures were not reported. The preductules (canals of Hering), where the hypothetical ruptures are often presumed to take place, showed less evidence of dilatation than the bile capillaries proper.

On the other hand, physiological experiments on rats and dogs concerned with the relationship between pressure in the biliary tract and bile flow showed that backflow of bile can take place. This has been attributed to ruptures in bile ducts (Brauer et al., 1954). Shafiroff et al. (1944) observed a similar backflow in dogs. They investigated the relationship between the magnitude of bile backflow ("bile take-up") and pressure prevailing in bile ducts. A constant pressure of 30 cm water in the biliary tract was maintained. They found that the volume of backflow varied between 4 and 28 ml, depending on the changes occurring in liver circulation. The smallest backflow (4.2 ml) was observed during partial ligation of liver veins, when the amount of lymph and the bilirubin concentration reached their maximum. These findings do not support the assumption that backflow occurs because of ruptures in bile ducts, followed by seepage of bile into the lymph fissures. However, it is compatible with a backflow into the blood vessels.

Investigations on the enzyme content of bile and chromatographic determination of bilirubin glucuronides in icteric serum fail to support the concept of regurgitation. Linde (1958) pointed out that glutamic oxalic acid transamidase (GOT) and glutamic pyruvic acid transaminase, as well as lactic acid dehydrogenase (all enzymes originating from parenchymal liver cells), were considerably increased in the serum of patients with regurgitation icterus. These enzymes are usually present only in very low concentrations in the bile. Furthermore, M. Dunn et al. (1958) investigated the concentration of GOT in serum and bile of dogs after intravenous GOT injections. They found that after large amounts of GOT were injected, the GOT concentration of bile remained unchanged, but that of serum increased 50- to 100-fold. These findings indicate enzyme excretion into the lymph or blood. Billing (1955a,b) finally found that 80% of bile bilirubin is present as diglucuronide. However, in cases of regurgitation icterus, icteric serum contained a lower percentage of this conjugate (cf. Chapter V,H). Diglucuronide was the main pigment of icteric serum in rats with experimental obstructive icterus.

Edlund's (1948) investigations on rats support the hypothesis of active excretion into the lymphatic system during bile stasis. He showed that, under normal conditions, secreting granula of liver cells are oriented toward the bile capillaries. However, during bile duct obstruction orientation is directed toward the lymph fissures.

Shafiroff et al. (1939) conducted experimental studies on the dynamics of bile secretion in dogs. These investigations are of considerable interest for pathogenesis of jaundice. In these experiments the ductus choledochus was put under a known constant pressure and the lymph was drained from the thoracic duct. The bilirubin concentration was determined in the blood plasma and lymph. The cystic duct was ligated and up to 75 cm of water pressure was applied in all 28 experiments. At pressures lower than 25 cm water neither blood nor lymph contained bilirubin. At pressures of 30 cm water bilirubin appeared in the lymph of all dogs, but appeared in the blood in only half the animals. At pressures above 40 cm water, bilirubin was detected in the blood and the lymph of all experimental animals. Bilirubin appeared in the lymph of the thoracic duct 15 minutes after applying the pressure, but it was detected in blood only after 2 hours. Similar results were published by Gonzales-Oddone (1946).

Important experiments on the relation between pressure and volume of the biliary tree in the rat and the "bile intake" have recently been published. Barber-Riley (1963a) developed a method of measuring the capacity of biliary tree in rats based on injection of dyes (BSP and others) rapidly excreted into the bile and determination of their concentration in the bile and the bile volume at different times after the injection. From the curves thus obtained and the "dead space" of the instruments employed, the capacity of the biliary system could be calculated. This method was used by Barber-Riley (1963b) in the study of the rat biliary tree during short periods of obstruction of the common bile duct. It was found that the capacitance of the biliary tree increased with increasing back pressure, that the secretion rate was not reduced by back pressure, and that leakage of bile from the biliary tree ("bile intake") was absent (or constant) until the back pressure reached 75% of the maximum excretory pressure. The original contents of the biliary tract were removed exponentially during obstruction. To judge from the pressure–volume curves, the rate of bile excretion declined to zero as the maximum pressure was approached, but this apparent decline could equally be due to increased rate of reabsorption of biliary contents. That the latter explanation is the correct one was supported by the findings. When the marker dye was injected after the maximum pressure had been reached and a further ca. 10 minutes allowed to elapse before release of the biliary obstruction, about nine tenths of the tree which had previously been distended with clear bile was found to contain dye-stained bile. The clear bile is progressively replaced by stained bile from above downward during continued biliary obstruction. This points to a process of secretion going on in the peripheral twigs of the biliary tree in biliary obstruction while reabsorption takes place at a lower level.

Similar studies in rats with a somewhat different technique were carried out by Waldeck and Harth (1963) and Harth and Waldeck (1964). The former studied the bile intake in rats with biliary obstruction of shorter and longer duration. The bile pressure and bile flow were measured. The flow was higher after removal of the obstruction; the maximal pressure was constant during the first 6 days, after which it decreased; the capacitance of the tree increased with the duration of the obstruction; and the leakage of bile (bile intake) after increasing the pressure became higher the longer the duration of the obstruction. Harth and Waldeck (1964) demonstrated that backflow of bile takes place not only when the bile pressure is increased, but also under normal circumstances. They used rats cooled to 12–15° in which the bile secretion is abolished and the pressure in the biliary tree is equal to the intrahepatic pressure. The bile tract of such rats was subjected to pressures below the maximal secretory pressure of freshly operated rats (21 cm water) and it was found that backflow began already at pressures a little above the intra-hepatic pressure (ca. 10 cm water). With increasing pressure the bile intake augmented, at first slowly, later more rapidly. At normal pressure values the backflow was already significant. The resistance against back-flow was relatively high at pressures below 15 cm water, but at pressures above 17 cm water the resistance became very low. This observation points to a normal leakage mechanism in the bile tract of the rat, opening at pressures of 17 cm water. In the opinion of Harth and Waldeck, backflow of bile takes place to both the lymph and blood in rats with biliary obstruction. Possibly the increased leakage at 17 cm water can be explained by beginning backflow to the blood, while it takes place only to the lymph at lower pressures.

Waldeck and Harth (1965*) and Harth and Waldeck (1965*) extended their former experiments and included dogs in addition to rats. The bile flow and backflow were correlated with the hydrostatic pressure in the common bile duct. The maximal bile pressure is not an expression of the upper limit of the secretion pressure of the active cells, but is only the pressure at which the bile secretion and the backflow of bile reaches equilibrium. The bile secretion per kilogram of body weight in the rat is at least 10–15 times greater than in the dog, and consequently the two species show important differences. In the rat backflow takes place both to the blood and the bile. In the dog backflow of bile was already demonstrated at pressures below the maximal pressure in the biliary system, and this backflow was already larger than the basic rate of bile secretion at pressures in the middle range. The maximal hydrostatic bile pressure could only be reached in the dog if the bile secretion was increased by the action of choleretic substances.

Christoffersson et al. (1965*) believe that regurgitation of bilirubin occurs although they found that cytoplasmatic enzymes directly leak into the lymph and blood in biliary occlusion in rabbits. This view can hardly be maintained after the observations of Krebs et al. (1964*) on the secretion of BSP-S[35] directly into liver lymph.

In the light of these recent observations the occurrence of ruptures of the bile canaliculi can hardly be maintained, and the divergences concerning "regurgitation" and "parapedesis" lose their importance. If backflow of bile into the lymph also takes place in other species at normal bile pressure and into the blood at elevated bile pressure within the physiological range, then both "regurgitation" and "parapedesis" are normal physiological processes. The most correct terminology is therefore to speak of "lymphogenic-regurgitational jaundice."

6. HEPATOCANALICULAR JAUNDICE (INTRAHEPATIC CHOLESTASIS)

C. J. Watson and Hoffbauer (1946, 1947) coined the term "cholangiolitic jaundice" to describe icterus caused by enhanced permeability of cholangioles (cf. Martini and Dölle, 1958). Since that time, this form of icterus has played an increasingly important role. Andrews (1955) preferred to call this condition "hepatocanalicular jaundice." According to his assumption, the cuboidal epithelial cells of microscopic bile ducts are the sites of bile formation. Later, Popper and Schaffner (1957) introduced the term "intrahepatic cholestasis" for this form of jaundice. This term, or simply "cholestasis" has since been widely used in the literature, although it is highly questionable whether stasis is really the main causative factor.

If the cuboidal cells are really responsible for bile production, icterus can be explained by a process which is localized exclusively in these epithelial cells, and no parenchymal cells would participate in this process. Andrews' main argument is that cases of jaundice exist in which lesions are exclusively inside the cuboidal epithelial cells. During hepatic icterus, when more or less severe changes in parenchymal cells occur, the cuboidal cells of bile ducts also change. According to Andrews, these lesions, and not those occurring in the parenchyma, are responsible for icterus. During "acute yellow atrophy" of the liver which consists of an almost complete necrosis of parenchyma, icterus is often intense. This result would be surprising if parenchymal cells alone were responsible for bile secretion. However, accepting Andrews' theory, this can easily be explained because the epithelial cells of bile ducts are attacked far less than the parenchymal cells themselves in acute liver atrophy; the cholangioles even proliferate to replace the necrotic liver cells.

Concerning the term "intrahepatic cholestasis" the recent experiments of Albot and his collaborators on rats are of interest (Housset *et al.*, 1962*, 1965*; Barbé, 1963*; Nepveux *et al.*, 1965*; Albot *et al.*, 1965a*, b*). They studied rats with total and partial *choleperitoneum* produced experimentally by dividing the common bile duct or the right hepatic duct and allowing the bile from the end of the duct to flow freely into the peritoneal cavity. In partial choleperitoneum the bile from the left hepatic duct reaches the intestine through the common bile duct. In both these experimental states there is a free flow of bile, and any pathological alteration found in the liver cannot be due to cholestasis. The alterations occurring must be due to the toxic action of bile absorbed from the peritoneal cavity. The rats were severely affected by total choleperitoneum rarely surviving for 48 hours, but those with partial choleperitoneum survived and their livers were subjected to study after 28, 60, and 80 hours. Both histological, electron microscopic, and enzymological methods were employed. The micrographs showed a *remarkable similarity with so-called intrahepatic cholestasis in man.* The bile canaliculi and ductules were dilated and rarified and sometimes exhibited swollen microvilli. An increase of alkaline phosphatases in the blood was also found, and its maximum did not coincide with the culmination of the necrosis of liver cells, but seemed to coincide with the peak of the hypertrophy of the Golgi apparatus which was observed as a characteristic feature.

The findings of these authors strongly suggest that the histological picture referred to as "intrahepatic cholestasis"—or merely "cholestasis" —in human pathology can be caused by factors other than bile stasis, e.g., intoxication of the liver with bile constituents entering the parenchyma as a result of various pathological conditions (cf. also Sections C,4 and C,5).

7. Icterus Due to Specific Poisons: Icterogenin, Steroids, Sporidesmin

A theoretically important form of jaundice is that caused by certain plant poisons. Icterogenin, a pentacyclic triterpene acid of the South African plant *Lippia Rehmanni* (Pears) plays a prominent role. Quin (1933) began the investigations of jaundice due to plant poisons with his study of combined icterus and photosensitivity in South African domestic sheep. This syndrome is known under the name "Geeldikkop" from Dutch *geel* = yellow, *dik* = thick, and *kop* = head. During poisoning with *Lippia*, the bile of sheep became water clear and a certain, although not complete, inhibition of bile excretion occurred. Simultaneously, jaundice and severe photosensitivity developed which were due to retention of plant porphyrins absorbed from the intestines. These porphyrins are excreted with the bile in the normal animal. In poisoned sheep, however, porphyrin excretion and bile pigment excretion are stopped. Inhibition of bile pigment excretion developed 24 hours after poisoning and reached its maximum in 2 days. After this period icterus subsided and the color of bile gradually reappeared. Within 8–9 days conditions returned to normal. However, the remarkable fact was that examination of liver did not reveal any sign of bile duct closure or parenchymal damage. Later studies with electron microscopy have, however, revealed changes in cytomembranes and lysosomes without liver cell necrosis.

Since this report, a number of more or less similar substances have been studied. All of them were plant poisons, and they all caused jaundice and severe photosensitivity in sheep. Riemerschmied and Quin (1941) showed that *Lantana camara* which, as does *Lippia,* belongs to the family of *Verbenaceae,* causes the same effect in sheep. After Rimington and co-workers (1937) obtained icterogenin in crystalline form, D. H. R. Barton and de Mayo (1954) established the structure of this compound. Similarly, Barton *et al.* (1954) determined the structure of the active principle of *Lantana.*

In an extensive series of publications, Clare and associates (summarized by Clare, 1955) described similar diseases in New Zealand sheep. Pathological changes were present in the liver of his animals. It is very interesting that these conditions found in New Zealand sheep are hereditary and independent of plant poisonings (Hancock, 1950; Jamieson and Swan, 1952). This indicates that the animals suffer from some sort of enzyme deficiency. Finally, Ender (1955) reported a similar disease found in Norway, which is caused by the plant *Narthecium ossifragum.* In this form of disease, as in icterogenin poisoning, the liver damage seems to be purely functional. Unfortunately, the lymph was not studied in these sheep; therefore, it is impossible to decide whether a retention icterus was present, or lymphogenic jaundice took place. Retention icterus is associated with unimpaired excretion of liver; during lymphogenic jaundice, a reversed excretion mechanism operates (bilirubin is excreted into the lymph instead of the bile). Pure retention, however, is unlikely, since the serum of the sheep gave a dirct diazo reaction. Experiments which would contribute to the elucidation of the problem would be valuable, not only in case of sheep treated with icterogenin, but even more so for New Zealand sheep which show congenital liver dysfunction (cf. With, 1957a).

Attempts to produce icterogenin jaundice in small laboratory animals were unsuccessful at first. The writer administered 200 g *Lippia* leaves to rabbits weighing 2 kg without observing icterus or bilirubinemia. C. Rimington (personal communication, 1960) found icterus only occasionally in rats after icterogenin injections. According to R. Schmid (personal communication, 1960), Enslin experienced similar difficulties in Pretoria. Rimington (personal communication, 1960) found that oral icterogenin administration leads to jaundice only when the poison is given in alcoholic solution or in fine aqueous emulsions. Since 1960 extensive studies of Rimington's group (see J. M. M. Brown *et al.*, 1963a,b; Heikel *et al.*, 1960) have been published. Heikel *et al.* (1960) succeeded in producing icterogenin jaundice in rabbits by introducing icterogenin in powder form in the peritoneal cavity. The icteric rabbits were subjected to detailed studies. The icterogenin doses employed were 100–200 mg per kg body weight. Jaundice developed in a few hours after the operation and reached its maximum in 16–18 hours, after which it decreased gradually. Simultaneously, the bile volume decreased and reached one tenth of the preoperative figure in 16–24 hours, at which point the bile was practically devoid of color. In spite of these conspicuous chemical and physiological alterations, no histological changes could be demonstrated. The amount of bilirubin and coproporphyrin in the bile decreased parallel to the bile volume and returned to normal levels simultaneously with the bile volume in about a week if the animal survived. Studies on the lymph flow from the liver and the bilirubin content of the liver lymph of the rabbits are not reported. Loading experiments with bilirubin, BSP, coproporphyrin, and phylloerythrin were carried out in icteric as well as in normal rabbits. The BSP excretion was practically abolished during the first 2 days of the poisoning, whereas excretion of bilirubin, coproporphyrin, and phylloerythrin was much inhibited, but to a lesser degree. The investigators conclude that icterogenin has a very profound effect on bile excretion because it inhibits the excretion of bilirubin which is conjugated with glucuronic acid and sulfate, of BSP which is conjugated with amino acids, and of coproporphyrin and phyloerythrin which are excreted in unconjugated condition. An inhibition of a single or a few biochemical mechanisms cannot explain all these findings; more fundamental aspects of cell physiology must be impaired, e.g., the permeability.

In one of the rabbits with icterogenin jaundice, the pigments of the blood plasma were subjected to inverse phase partition chromatography according to the Billings method (Heikel *et al.*, 1960, p. 69). Here 41% of the bilirubin present was recovered as free bilirubin, 42% as the monoglucuronide, and 7% as the diglucuronide. This finding points toward retention playing a considerable role in the pathogenesis of icterogenin jaundice in the rabbit.

Agarawala *et al.* (1962*) produced experimental poisoning with *Lantana camara* in sheep and cattle in India and confirmed the South African observations. The serum bilirubin rose to 10.7 mg/100 ml in cattle and 8.2 mg/100 ml in sheep. The animals lost their appetite 3 days after feeding with *Lantana* began; focal, edema and eczema developed in both cattle and sheep; and the bulls succumbed in 32–67 days, the sheep in 11–31 days.

J. M. M. Brown (1963) isolated 22β-angeloyloxyoleanic acid in pure form from *Lippia,* and the same substance was synthesized by Anderson *et al.* (1961). This compound is the most potent icterogenic agent known at present. It is active in doses of 5 mg per kg body weight when given intraperitoneally; the corresponding figure for icterogenin is 80 mg per kg. It is remarkable that only the β-equatorial stereoisomer compounds exhibit icterogenic activity, whereas the corresponding α-axial isomers are inactive.

Rimington's group is engaged in studies on the relation between chemical structure of pentacyclic triterpenes and their icterogenic activity. Their first publication on this question (J. M. M. Brown *et al.,* 1963a,b) deals with certain structural variations in triterpenes of the oleanane and 24-noroleanane series. They recorded 16 compounds including four new icterogenic agents: 22β-angeloyloxyoleanic acid; 22β-angeloyloxyhedragolic acid; 22β-angeloyloxy-24-oxooleanic acid; and 22β-angeloyloxy-24-hydroxyoleanoic acid. The first two compounds are extremely active, their potency far surpassing that of icterogenin itself (22β-angeloyl-24-hydroxy-2-oxoolean-12-en-28-oic acid; cf. Fig. 36). The activity of these acids appears to be based upon the presence of a β-equatorially orientated OH-group at C-3 or an OH at C-24 and a 22β-angeloyl side chain on the triterpene molecule. Stereoisomer specificity is shown with respect to icterogenicity by these compounds since the epimers of two of them carrying α-axially orientated OH at C-3 have been shown to be devoid of icterogenic effect. Removal of the angelic acid side chain, substitution of the OH groups, or replacement of the OH with a ketone function, is followed by loss of activity.

J. M. M. Brown (1963) presented a detailed study of the biochemical lesions and the chemical pathology of all stages of the natural syndromes in South African sheep, geeldikkop and enzootic icterus. Geeldikkop in its typical form is characterized by the sudden onset of a severe photosensitization, extremely severe parenchymal jaundice, and nephrosis. Enzootic icterus is distinguished by an explosive hemolytic crisis, marked retention jaundice, hemoglobinemia, and acute nephritis. The basic metabolic disturbances in geeldikkop are believed to be a simultaneous failure of the hepatic and renal excretion of bilirubin, phylloerythrin, BSP, and copper. In both diseases erythrocyte methemoglobin reductase is deficient, leading to explosive hemolytic crisis in enzootic icterus and to low-grade intravascular hemolysis in geeldikkop. Both conditions are precipitated by severe nonspecific forms of stress. High levels of selenium in the tissues possibly play a predisposing role. Triterpene-induced jaundice is similar to natural geeldikkop, but the kidneys are not affected here, as they are in the natural disease. Serum bilirubin is highly elevated in sheep affected by geeldikkop, reaching as high figures as 40 mg per

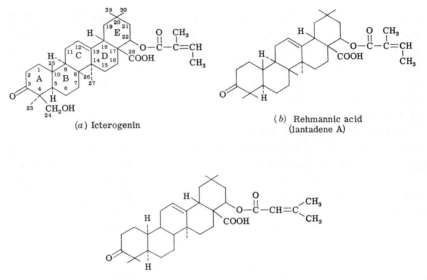

(a) Icterogenin

(b) Rehmannic acid (lantadene A)

(c) Lantadene B

FIG. 36. Structures of (a) icterogenin, (b) rehmannic acid (lantadene A), and (c) lantadene B according to J. M. M. Brown et al. (1963a,b).

100 ml (total bilirubin). About two thirds of the bilirubin present in the plasma is conjugated, and ca. about one third is free. These observations seem to demonstrate that icterogenin jaundice is partly a retention jaundice, but mainly a lymphogenic–regurgitational jaundice.

Done et al. (1960*) described the morbid anatomy, histopathology, and chemical pathology of a large sampling of affected sheep. They found a wide range in severity of disease within a flock. Many of the pathological alterations of the liver were obviously due to biliary obstruction and in three cases "white bile" was found.

Recently, Arias (1963a) pointed out that certain C-17 alkylated anabolic steroids are icterogenic in man, especially 17-ethyl-19-nortestosterone, which has a structure resembling that of icterogenin (see Fig. 37).

Administration of large doses of this steroid to humans is regularly associated with hyperbilirubinemia and BSP retention without liver cell necrosis. These symptoms are reversible and related to the dosage of the steroid. Arias infused free and conjugated bilirubin intravenously to Wistar rats and Gunn rats and studied their bile and serum bilirubin before and after treatment with icterogenin and various steroids. Unfortunately, study of the lymph was not included. Cortisone and testosterone were without effect, but C-17 alkylated anabolic steroids and icterogenin

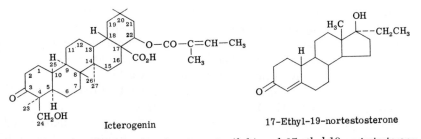

Fɪɢ. 37. Structural formulas of icterogenin (left) and 17-ethyl-19-nortestosterone (right) according to Arias (1963a).

caused a significant reduction in the bilirubin excretion. The reduced bilirubin excretion was the same after infusion of unconjugated bilirubin to Gunn rats having defective conjugating mechanisms, and Arias concluded that neither icterogenin nor steroids affect the properties of the liver cells for bilirubin conjugation. Histological studies of the liver of the rats revealed no abnormality, but cytochemical (enzymatic) and electron microscope studies disclosed unquestionable alterations after both icterogenin and C-17 alkylated anabolic steroids.

Study of the serum bilirubin in patients with steroid jaundice showed 6–24 mg per 100 ml (total bilirubin) with 75–83% conjugated bilirubin. Arias believes that the main anomaly in icterogenin and steroid jaundice is a defect in the capacity of the liver cells to transport conjugated bilirubin to the bile. It would be of considerable interest to study the bilirubin of the liver lymph in these conditions to disclose to what extent the jaundice is due to lymphogenism and to what extent to back-secretion to the blood plasma. The connection between steroid jaundice and pregnancy jaundice is discussed in Chapter V,L.

Finally, the poison *sporidesmin* is of principal interest. MacFarlane *et al.* (1959) described a form of jaundice in sheep in New Zealand caused by a chemical cholangitis due to poisoning by hay contaminated with the fungus *Pithomyces chartarum* Ellis (formerly *Sporodesmium bakeri Sydow*), which forms the substance sporidesmin (Synge and White, 1959). Sporidesmin causes inflammation of bile ducts with diameter less than 0.2 mm, while the parenchymal liver cells are not affected. Cholangitis with secondary fibrosis and intrahepatic occlusion follows. As in icterogenin jaundice, photosensitivity accompanies the condition in sheep. A closer study of this form of jaundice could possibly clarify the problems of hepatocanalicular jaundice in man.

Mortimer *et al.* (1962) found that hepatic cell injury precedes the biliary obstruction. They studied the early lesions in experimental sporidesmin intoxication in sheep and rabbits and found evidence of parenchymal cell damage. Changes in the liver lipids could be demonstrated as early as during the first 4 days after the poisoning, and the serum bilirubin showed an increase that reached a maximum of 8–9 mg per 100 ml after about 10 days. The GOT began to increase after about a week and increased steadily during the subsequent 2 weeks.

Sporidesmin was isolated by Synge and White (1959). It has the empirical formula $C_{18}H_{22}O_6N_3S_2Cl$, but its structural formula is yet unknown. A single intraperitoneal injection of 1–5 mg per kg body weight produced a multitude of lesions in female rats (Rimington et al., 1962; Slater et al., 1964). Rats were more resistant than guinea pigs and rabbits, and male rats were more resistant than female ones. Sporidesmin intoxication of the rat differed markedly from that of the sheep. In the rat, lung damage, proteinuria, and hypoproteinemia were dominant, and lesions of the liver and biliary tract played only a second role.

Russel (1962) described a method for the detection of sporidesmin in pasture extracts.

Peters (1963) confirmed the results of Mortimer et al. (1962) and pointed out that the disturbance of hepatic triglyceride metabolism following sporidesmin poisoning resembles the effect of other hepatotoxins. Slater and Griffiths (1963) injected sporidesmin intraperitoneally to rats with cannulated common bile duct and measured the bile flow. The injection was followed by a rapid decrease in bile flow. No bile was obtained between the 18th and 30th hour, but flow was normal again on the third day. Thus the action of sporidesmin is similar to that of icterogenin.

Mortimer and his group subsequently published a series of papers on experimental sporidesmin poisoning in sheep. Mortimer and Taylor (1962*) administered purified sporidesmin orally or parenterally to 117 sheep. Mild liver lesions without photosensitization followed a dose of 0.3 mg/kg, but a 0.5 mg/kg dose gave severe liver lesions and photosensitization in two-thirds of the animals, and 1 mg/kg dose resulted in photosensitization in 83% of the animals and a high mortality. The toxic range of sporidesmin was remarkably narrow. "White bile" was frequently found. The clinical picture was biphasic, beginning with an acute phase of a few days' duration with reduced food intake, diarrhea, and dehydration. After 6 days the condition of the animals improved, but from the 10th day photosensitization began to develop. Done et al. (1962*) reported on the serum chemistry of sheep with sporidesmin poisoning, estimating the serum bilirubin with Malloy and Evelyn's (1937) method. The serum bilirubin reached 3–4 mg/100 ml in sheep receiving 0.5 mg sporidesmin per kilogram and 1–2 mg/100 ml in sheep receiving 0.3 mg/kg. Even after 3 mg/kg the serum bilirubin increase remained moderate. Mortimer (1962*) studied the bromsulphalein clearing rate and the blood coagulation in the sporidesmin-poisoned sheep and made a thorough study of the development of their liver lesions (Mortimer, 1963*). During the first 2–4 days after the intoxication, acute, but largely reversible, degenerations of the parenchymal cells were found. At the same time marked pericholangiolitic inflammatory exudation, necrotizing cholecystitis, and cholangitis were apparent. Granulative repair of these lesions had begun and usually resulted in partial stenosis and obliteration of the large- and medium-sized bile ducts with scar tissue. From the 10th day onward biliary obstruction was manifest, and photosensitization developed simultaneously. Besides the liver lesions a unique range of vascular lesions and necrotizing inflammation in the urinary bladder and ureters as well as mild kidney lesions occurred.

Peters and Smith (1964*) studied the composition of liver lipids and the chemical effect of early sporidesmin poisoning and interpreted the early effects of the poisoning on the sheep liver as a malfunction of a hepatic triglyceride-producing mechanism.

The structure of sporidesmin has been studied by Fridrichsons and Mathieson (1962), Hodges et al. (1963), and Ronaldson et al. (1963). The latter give the formula $C_{18}H_{20(22)}ClN_3O_6S_2$, and for sporidesmin-B— another toxic metabolite of the fungus Pithomyces chartarum—the formula $C_{18}H_{20}ClN_3O_5S_2$, i.e., sporidesmin is hydroxysporidesmin-B. Both substances contain two methoxyl, two N-methyl, and a hydroxyl group. Hodges and Taylor (1964*) synthesized a possible biogenic precursor of sporidesmin.

Summary

The classification of jaundice is discussed and the following basic pathogenetic mechanisms are recognized: (1) increased production (overproduction, hemolytic and nonhemolytic), (2) retention, and (3) lymphogenic–regurgitational genesis to which comes (4) decreased destruction of bilirubin in the body. The problem of icterus caused by secretion into the lymph or back-secretion into the blood plasma is discussed. According to recent studies the backflow or back-secretion of bile to the lymph takes place at normal bile pressures, and to the blood at elevated but physiological pressures. Therefore, lymphogenic and regurgitational jaundice cannot be distinguished, and the term lymphogenic–regurgitational jaundice is preferred. The theory of bile secretion, as recently advanced by Andrews, is discussed. According to this theory, bile is secreted by the cuboidal epithelial cells of small bile ducts. A number of facts seem to support this hypothesis which requires serious consideration. However, the experimental material available is as yet insufficient to permit a final decision. Furthermore, icterus caused by icterogenin in sheep and rabbits is discussed. This remarkable form of icterus is inducted by a complete cessation of bilirubin excretion in the bile, although a limited excretion of white bile continues. The liver damage is functional. Jaundice due to steroids and to the poison sporidesmin is also discussed. Newer conceptions of the anatomy of the liver, its blood circulation, the physiology of liver lymph, and the dynamics of bile production are discussed in connection with the pathogenesis of jaundice. The requirements for reliable physiological studies on the pathogenesis of jaundice are difficult to meet.

Ruptures of bile canaliculi, regurgitation of bile into blood, and parapedetic secretion into lymphatics are discussed as pathogenetic mechanisms in jaundice. According to recent studies, ruptures of bile canaliculi are not a pathogenetic factor. Physiological studies in rats indicate that there is no contradiction between regurgitation to the blood and parapedetic secretion into the lymph, both processes being normal physiological mechanisms in the rat. A basic feature of all recent physiological studies is their emphasis on the important role played by the lymph in the pathogenesis of jaundice, a point not yet sufficiently understood by all clinical investigators.

D. Four Basic Pathogenetic Mechanisms of Jaundice

All forms of icterus can be caused by one or more of four mechanisms: (1) increased production of bile pigments; (2) their retention; (3) lymphatic involvement ("lymphogenism-regurgitation"); or (4) decreased destruction of bilirubin in the body (cf. Chapter, II,C). The mechanisms operating in each type of jaundice are varying. In the majority of cases, two or more of these mechanisms act simultaneously.

1. First Mechanism: Jaundice Caused by Increased Bilirubin Formation

As previously mentioned, icterus due to increased bilirubin production can be hemolytic or nonhemolytic in nature. In the nonhemolytic form the pathological increase of bilirubin formation is from other sources than destruction of mature circulating erythrocytes. Israels et al. (1959) reported four cases of familial hyperbilirubinemia, which they considered nonhemolytic. They called such primary overproduction "shunt" hyperbilirubinemia.

What role such nonhemolytic bilirubin formation plays in human pathology can only be decided with certainty by administering labeled glycine and determining either labeled stercobilin in stool or labeled bilirubin in bile. In a patient with overproduction icterus, when the amount of labeled stercobilin which appears about 1 week after feeding, i.e., during the "first peak" (cf. Fig. 29 Chapter II,A), is larger than the second peak, a nonhemolytic mechanism of bile pigment formation is indicated. However, such experiments are difficult to perform and only few are available at present (cf. Chapter II,A). Recently two different nonhemolytic bile pigment sources have been distinguished: erythropoietic and hepatic; but their mutual role is not known at present (cf. Chapter II,A).

According to determinations of erythrocyte longevity, slightly increased hemolysis is operative in many blood diseases (cf. Chapter III). Pitcher and Williams (1963) studied red cell survival in various liver diseases including infective hepatitis, portal cirrhosis, obstructive jaundice, and congenital hyperbilirubinemia (Gilbert's disease) and found decreased half-life in 34 of 41 patients, including two cases of congenital hyperbilirubinemia. Thus hemolysis can also be a contributory factor in hepatic jaundice. Thus Berendson *et al.* (1964*) made a detailed study of a patient first believed to have hemolytic anemia; however, it was found that the great excess of bilirubin being formed and excreted as urobilinogen was not derived from the hemoglobin of mature circulating erythrocytes, but was related to a dyshematopoiesis and disturbed hemoglobin synthesis in the bone marrow. They proposed the term *"dyshematopoietic jaundice"* for this form of jaundice characterized by unconjugated hyperbilirubinemia and great excess of fecal urobilinogen. Labeling with N^{15}-glycine revealed that these excesses were mainly due to "first peak bilirubin." The bone marrow exhibited normoblastic hyperplasia, considerable phagocytosis of red cells and normoblasts, and marked hemosiderosis, but siderocytes were relatively rare in the peripheral blood. A basic anomaly in the hemoglobin synthesis in the normoblast was considered due to hemoglobin or heme produced in excess and conversion of these pigments to bilirubin in the normoblasts, and perhaps also after excretion into the blood. There was no evidence of hemolysis in the ordinary sense. The extent to which this anomaly was due to intramedullary destruction of young red cells or to a basic hemoglobin synthesis anomaly in the normoblasts could not be determined. Hepatic bile pigment formation directly from porphyrin precursors was regarded as unlikely, but could not be excluded.

Vest *et al.* (1965*) demonstrated by administering N^{15}-glycine to two newborns that excess production of "first peak bile pigment" is a factor of importance in the genesis of icterus neonatorum.

According to Rich (1930), icterus develops during normal liver function only when bilirubin production increases 20-fold higher than normal.

It has been pointed out above that this concept is only supported by insufficient experimental evidence. In fact, a threefold increase of normal bilirubin production suffices to induce icterus within a week, if the liver function is normal.

A particular form of icterus can be produced by artificial overloading with high doses of intravenously administered bilirubin. With these conditions, interesting experiments in humans have been described that indicate a dose of 500–1000 mg bilirubin per 24 hours suffices to produce icterus (see also Chapter V,J). Normal bilirubin production is 200–300 mg per 24 hours in humans (see Chapter III,B). Consequently, icterus results from a charge of bilirubin which is about double that normally produced, i.e., jaundice occurs when bilirubin production is increased threefold. These results are the same as those calculated from the available data in hepatectomized dogs and dogs with bile duct obstruction (see Section C,1, this chapter).

It has recently been disclosed that hormones have a profound influence on the development of loading jaundice. Thus, Lazard and Sobotka (1962) found that intravenous injection of bilirubin in dose of 48 mg per kg body weight to normal adult rats was not followed by jaundice, whereas such injections in hypophysectomized rats resulted in severe general jaundice affecting even the brain. Further studies on the role of hormones in the pathogenesis of jaundice seem indicated.

2. SECOND MECHANISM: BILIRUBIN RETENTION

Liver cell damage with diminished bilirubin excretion causes icterus if the decrease of excretion activity is so high that normal bilirubin formation can no longer be compensated. This is the entity of retention icterus; it is, however, a "pure" retention jaundice only as long as no simultaneous excretion into the liver lymphatics and no regurgitation of bile take place. In experiments of Mann and Bollman (1926), temporary hyperbilirubinemia developed in partially hepatectomized dogs (about 70% of liver removed). This finding indicates that a 70% reduction of excretory capacity is necessary to cause icterus during normal bilirubin production. Rich's (1930) theory (Section C,1, this chapter), which assumed that a 95% reduction is necessary, cannot be true.

It should be emphasized that a moderate reduction of the excretory capacity of the liver, about one third of the normal value, will only cause icterus if it lasts 3 days or more. This was demonstrated by experiments with artificial bilirubin loading (see Chapter V,J).

The role of retention in the pathogenesis of jaundice is not sufficiently known. In icterogenin icterus it plays a role; however, the part played by lymphogenism–regurgitation is unknown (see Section C,7, this chapter). The same is true for congenital hereditary jaundice of Southdown sheep (Hancock, 1950), for hereditary nonhemolytic jaundice of rats (Malloy and Loewenstein, 1940; Gunn, 1944), and for various forms of constitutional nonhemolytic hyperbilirubinemia in humans (see Section E,2, this chapter; Chapter V,K). If Andrew's (1955) hypothesis of bile excretion is correct, retention could possibly be an important factor during pathogenesis of so-called cholangiolitic or hepatocanalicular jaundice. In such a case retention can occur without parenchymal cell damage, when the function of the cuboidal cells of small bile ducts is restricted.

In some of the experiments of Shafiroff et al. (1939) and Alican and Hardy, (1962); see Section C,3, this chapter), a pure retention icterus developed during bile stasis when the lymph of the thoracic duct was drained off simultaneously.

Pure retention icterus of short duration can hardly lead to high hyperbilirubinemia. However, when this condition extends over longer periods, serum bilirubin concentration easily reaches 12 mg per 100 ml. This was shown by bilirubin loading experiments (see Chapter V,J). It has been claimed that truly severe isterus can probably never originate from pure retention alone (Rich, 1930; Itoh, 1932). However, this opinion can hardly be accepted.

3. Third Mechanism: Lymphogenic-Regurgitational Jaundice

The important role of the lymph in the pathogenesis of jaundice has already been discussed (Section C,3, this chapter), along with concepts of "regurgitation" and "parapedesis." Here a few additional contributions to this discussion are presented.

An argument in favor of parapedesis is *congenital absence of intrahepatic bile ducts* (see Section E,3, this chapter). This condition, which is compatible with life for several years, is accompanied by jaundice. And this jaundice must be due to either retention or parapedesis or both because of the absence of the intrahepatic bile duct system. That a secretion of bile constituents really takes place is shown by the pruritus and xanthomatosis which accompanies the condition, and when bile salts and cholesterol reach the plasma by secretory mechanisms it can be looked upon as an established fact that bilirubin must do the same. The role of the lymph in this form of jaundice has not been studied. It would be important to find out whether parapedetic secretory processes substituting normal bile excretion take place into the lymph (lymphogenism) or the blood (regurgitation) or into both.

Experiments such as those of Arias (1963a) with icterogenin and steroid jaundice in rats would give important contributions to the relative role of the lymphatic component and the back-excretion to the blood plasma of conjugated bilirubin. According to Arias (1963a) the substances in question inhibit the capacity of the liver to excrete conjugated bilirubin into the bile. Repetition of such experiments with collection of the liver lymph and extension to other species would be of considerable interest.

Regurgitation by the rupture of small bile ducts has been much discussed in this connection (Section C,5, this chapter). It was pointed out above that there is only slight evidence for such ruptures. However, regurgitation can also be caused by necrosis of parenchymal cells and by anastomosis of bile ducts with lymph fissures. According to the classic theory based on bile production as a function of parenchymal cells, bile could seep into lymphatic vessels. According to Andrews' (1955) theory, i.e., bile production by the cuboidal epithelial cells of the smallest bile ducts, this possibility hardly exists because necrosis of bile ducts does not occur even during severe liver damage. If this theory is correct, the lymphogenic mechanism of hepatic icterus is not a passive regurgitation. According to recent studies of Barber-Riley (1963a,b,), Waldeck and Harth (1963) and Harth and Waldeck (1964)—cf. Section C,5, this chapter—bile constituents go into the lymph at normal bile pressures and into the blood at elevated physiological pressures. It is therefore most correct to speak of lymphogenic–regurgitational jaundice.

Experimental evidence for the assumption of lymphogenesis during occlusion icterus is plentiful, but is scarce for hepatic icterus. E. Fleischl and A. Kunkel (cited in Hiyeda, 1927) and Itoh (1931) showed that toluenediamine icterus developed considerably later, and was much less distinct when the lymph of the thoracic duct was drained off than when it was not. Repetition of these experiments in other forms of parenchymal damage and experiments of longer duration would be of interest. To approximate physiological conditions in these experiments, the fluid and protein loss caused by the lymphflow should be compensated.

H. Yamamoto (1958) has studied the bilirubin content of the lymph of the thoracic duct in dogs after injection of hemoglobin into the mesenteric or femoral veins. Experiments were performed with normal dogs as well as with dogs poisoned with CCl_4 and dogs with blocked reticuloendothelial systems (RES). In the *normal dogs the Hb injections* gave rise to *substantial increase of bilirubin of the lymph,* whereas the corresponding increase was considerably less in the poisoned animals and those with RES block. These experiments show that if the liver cells or the RES is impaired, the excretion of bilirubin after Hb loading is decreased. The cause of this is presumably decreased bilirubin formation.

In most forms of hepatic icterus, lymphogenic–regurgitational mechanisms exist besides the retention mechanism. The lymphogenic mechanism may be due to the normal excretion route of bile, with blood to bile being shunted into another route, blood to lymph. This process is called "parapedesis" (see Section C,1, this chapter). It is not unlikely that inflammation and degeneration of liver cells, or cuboidal cells of bile ducts, lead to parapedesis. If caused by increased pressure in the biliary tract, parapedesis can also be due to changes in cells. Similarly, it might occur in immature liver cells of newborns and thus be partially responsible for icterus neonatorum. Last but not least, parapedesis can be caused by nervous reflexes. This last possibility was established by the observation that during simple laparotomy in dogs the lymphatic system of the liver may turn yellow (Volwiler, 1950, personal communication). This explains, perhaps, why types of long lasting functional jaundice can often be healed by laparotomy (Pavel, 1956, 1957; Pavel and Campeanu, 1957a,b; Pavel and Velciu, 1957).

Recently such distinguished workers as R. W. Brauer and J. L. Bollman have supported the concept of lymphogenism (Krebs *et al.*, 1964*). They performed continuous i.v. infusion of labeled bromsulphalein (BSP-S[35]) at a rate of 4 mg per hour on isolated perfused rat livers as well as on livers from whole rats and collected bile and lymph samples at 15- to 45-minute intervals. In their experiments with perfused livers blood samples were taken freely, whereas in the experiments with whole animals blood samples were taken 2–2.5 hours after the start of the infusion and at the end of the experiment. Two different types of response were encountered with respect to lymph BSP; the first was characterized by lower concentrations of BSP in lymph than in blood plasma, the second by grossly higher concentrations in lymph than in blood plasma. Chromatographic separation of the various fractions of BSP metabolites excreted disclosed that the pattern of such fractions was identical in bile and lymph from the second type of response, whereas lymph from the first type exhibited a BSP pattern different from both blood plasma and bile. The second type was obtained whenever bile flow was deliberately arrested, but could also be observed when bile was flowing freely. The chromatographic BSP pattern of lymph of the first type suggests that part of the BSP of hepatic lymph normally arises from the hepatic cells, rather than from either blood plasma or bile. Because the BSP molecule is of moderate size and is albumin bound in plasma for the most part, the properties of BSP closely resemble those of bilirubin. Krebs *et al.* conclude that the lymph compartment of the liver is physically independent of the bile duct system and that an important part of its contents arises from the hepatic parenchyma rather than from the blood plasma. Further they point out that the existing mechanism preventing diffusion of bile into the hepatic lymph space is easily damaged, and this fact points to the presence of a mechanism for causing nonhemolytic nonobstructive jaundice. Such a jaundice could be produced by pathological conditions causing failure of the apparently labile mechanisms which normally prevent diffusion of bile components into the lymph and leading to a return of conjugated bilirubin in the blood.

The suggestion of this important group of workers covers as closely as possible what Minkowski (1892*, 1904), Pick (1894a,b), and Ogata (1913a) called "parapedesis" and what the author of this monograph called lymphogenic jaundice 20 years ago (With, 1944d, 1947, 1949).

In this respect the experiments of Christoffersson et al. (1965*) on rabbits with biliary occlusion are of interest. They found that the enzyme increase in serum cannot be mainly a "regurgitation," but that an altered permeability of the hepatic cell membrane must be active with direct leakage of cytoplasmic enzymes into lymph and blood. Nevertheless, they do not discard the notion of regurgitation of bilirubin.

It is peculiar that most authors associate jaundice with regurgitation rather than with a lymphatic transport mechanism, and this in spite of all the evidence supporting the last alternative. Thus, Tisdale et al. (1959) prefer to explain their results using the regurgitation concept, although they have to admit that lymphogenic mechanisms can play a role (see Section C,3, this chapter). They talk about "regurgitation through the lymph," a term which is hard to understand. In reality, the observations of Tisdale et al. support the concept of a lymphogenic mechanism (Section C,3).

4. FOURTH MECHANISM: DECREASED BILIRUBIN DESTRUCTION

As mentioned above, decreased bilirubin destruction may be a pathogenetic factor in jaundice (Chapter II,D), although it can never alone cause icterus. Variations in bilirubin destruction are known to play a significant role in cattle, and this factor is also active in man. Recently, R. Williams and Billing (1961) suggested that the decrease in serum bilirubin after steroid therapy in hepatitis and biliary obstruction is due to decreased bilirubin destruction. That this mechanism must also be operative in congenital atresia of the intrahepatic bile ducts is seen from the case of Cotton (1960) where the serum bilirubin decreased to normal values.

Schmid and Hammaker (1963) studied one human and eight rats with defective bilirubin conjugation mechanism (Crigler-Najjar syndrome; Gunn rats) by means of tracer technique (bilirubin-C^{14}) and found that a significant fraction of the bilirubin was excreted as polar diazo-negative compounds.

Gray and Nicholson (1963) discussed the role of breakdown of bilirubin to diazo-negative compounds and concluded that "unidentifiable pathways" are important mechanisms in bilirubin elimination, at least in congenital hyperbilirubinemias.

Lester *et al.* (1963*) pointed out that catabolism of bilirubin may be a secondary means of bilirubin elimination in the fetus. Murano (1964*) studied the influence of large parenteral doses of prednisolone (10–20 mg daily for 10–20 days) in icteric newborn and found a pronounced decrease of the conjugated serum bilirubin; the free serum bilirubin was not influenced. He suggested that this may be due to diversion toward unknown supplementary metabolic pathways.

An interesting question is the *relative rate of destruction of free and conjugated bilirubin* in different organs and in different animal species. Maggiore *et al.* (1963a*,b*) unfortunately did not discuss the amount of bilirubin destroyed in rats loaded with free or conjugated bilirubin, but they found that the proportion of the bilirubin stored in the liver which was present in the conjugated state after loading with free bilirubin decreased with increasing bilirubin load. From their Fig. 3 it can be calculated that if 0.7 mg free bilirubin was given approximately 60% of the liver bilirubin was present as conjugate, but if the bilirubin load was 2.5 mg only about 35% of the liver bilirubin was conjugated. Whether this is associated with an increased rate of destruction after the higher doses is, however, not known. Experimental studies concerning this question are required.

Summary

The four basic pathogenetic mechanisms of icterus are discussed. They are: increased bilirubin production, retention, lymphogenic–regurgitational origin, and decreased destruction in the body. Their relative significance and their participation in clinical jaundice types are examined. It is questionable whether regurgitation through ruptured bile canaliculi really exists. The lymphogenic mechanism seems to be caused by a reversion of bile excretion to the lymph instead of to the bile, so-called parapedesis. That parapedesis really exists is supported by the jaundice in subjects with congenital absence of intrahepatic bile ducts (cf. Section E,3, this chapter). This mechanism seems to occur together with retention during biliary stasis, and during parenchymal liver damage.

According to recent physiological investigations (cf. Section C,5, this chapter), "backflow" or "back-excretion" of bile into the lymphatics is a normal phenomenon proceeding parallel to bile secretion, and backflow into the blood takes place if the pressure of the bile reaches a certain value which is below the maximum secretory pressure. If these studies are confirmed and extended to other species than the rat, both

"lymphogenesis" (parapedesis) and "regurgitation" are normal secretory
mechanisms. The term lymphogenetic–regurgitational seems therefore
to be the most correct from a physiological point of view.

In many cases lymphogenic–regurgitational mechanisms will be active
simultaneously with retention. This will be the case in parenchymal,
obstructive, and hepatocanalicular jaundice and possibly also in icterus
neonatorum. This is illustrated in the schematic survey given in Fig. 35,
Section C,1, of this chapter. The role of hormonal influences in the pathogenesis of jaundice, especially the hypophysis, is pointed out.

E. The Seven Clinical Forms of Jaundice

All known types of jaundice, human, animal, or experimental, can be
classified into one of seven forms: hemolytic, familial (hereditary, nonhemolytic), obstructive, parenchymal (hepatocellular), hepatocanalicular
(cholangiolitic, intrahepatic cholestasis), neonatal, and cardiac. The
pathogenesis of these types will be discussed below and is illustrated in
the schematic survey in Fig. 35, Section C,1, of this chapter. The role of
bilirubin glucuronides (direct bilirubin) will be discussed in Chapter
V,H.

1. HEMOLYTIC JAUNDICE

This is production jaundice due to excess formation of bilirubin from
the hemoglobin of mature circulating erythrocytes. Rich (1930) and C. J.
Watson (1937b) assumed that diminished liver function is required to
induce hemolytic icterus. They made this assumption on the basis of the
erroneous concept that twenty times the normal bilirubin production
is necessary to produce icterus under the condition of normal liver function. However, it is known that a threefold overproduction of bilirubin
suffices to produce jaundice (Section C,2, this chapter). Thus, hemolysis
itself is fully sufficient to cause icterus, since it is capable of reducing
the life-span of erythrocytes to a tenth or even less of the normal life-
span (Chapter III,B). However, decreased liver function can also develop as a complication caused by anemia, and can contribute to the total
effect. This is seldom of great clinical significance, since jaundice is
generally marked when hemolysis is accompanied by only mild anemia.
On the contrary, during severe anemia, icterus is usually not very distinct,
because of the loss of hemoglobin through renal excretion in cases of
severe hemolysis.

A peculiar form of physiological hemolytic anemia has recently been
discovered in the hedgehog during its prehibernation period by Eliassen
(1961) of the zoological laboratory of Bergen. During this period the
hedgehog reduces its blood volume and a substantial part of the erythro-

cytes are destroyed. This is accompanied by a marked splenomegaly, hyperbilirubinemia, and bilirubinuria. This phenomenon is interesting and similar studies in other hibernating species are required.

2. NONHEMOLYTIC JAUNDICE (FAMILIAL OR HEREDITARY NONHEMOLYTIC JAUNDICE; DYSHEMATOPOIETIC OR DYSERYTHROPOIETIC JAUNDICE)

The term familial or hereditary nonhemolytic jaundice covers several more or less well-defined conditions, most of them due to "Enzymopathias" (inborn errors of metabolism). The most well-known form is due to absence of the enzyme responsible for the formation of bilirubin glucuronide in the liver, and it is known in both man and the rat (Malloy and Loewenstein, 1940; Gunn, 1944); such rats are known as Gunn rats. In children with this form of icterus, kernicterus may develop (Crigler and Najjar, 1952; Childs and Najjar, 1956). Nonconjugated bilirubin dominates in the plasma, and bilirubinuria is absent. For a more detailed discussion, see Chapter V,K.

Israels et al. (1959) described a closely similar form of hereditary hyperbilirubinemia which they called shunt hyperbilirubinemia, because the surplus of bilirubin was not due to hemolysis but to bilirubin from sources other than mature circulating erythrocytes. Israels et al. (1963a) found that this form of hyperbilirubinemia is due to increase of the "first-peak bilirubin" (cf. Chapter II,A).

Familial nonhemolytic hyperbilirubinemias with conjugated, direct-reacting bilirubin in the blood and bilirubinuria are also known. Such conditions were first described by Rotor et al. (1948) and Stransky (1950, 1955) in the Philippines and later by Dubin and Johnson (1954) in the United States. The latter found an unidentified lipofuscin-like pigment in the liver cells of their patients. This form of jaundice is known as the Dubin-Johnson syndrome or chronic idiopathic jaundice (Sprinz and Nelson, 1954; John and Knudtson, 1956; N. L. Brown and Shnitka, 1956; Dubin, 1958).

The hereditary liver dysfunction of New Zealand Southdown sheep, which is accompanied by photosensitivity (Hancock, 1950), also belongs in this category.

Dyshematopoietic or dyserythropoietic jaundice is seen in certain patients with ineffective erythropoiesis—increase of "first peak" bile pigment (cf. Berendson et al., 1964*, and Chapter II,A). How much of the bile pigment is of erythropoietic (hepatic) origin is not known.

3. OBSTRUCTIVE JAUNDICE

One is inclined to believe that if the pressure in the duct of a gland exceeds the maximum secretion pressure of which the gland is capable, the secretion will stop until the hydrostatic pressure in the duct system falls below the critical level. This view, however, is not correct. Bile formation proceeds at pressures above the maximal secretory pressure and is balanced by backflow (see Section C,5, this chapter). Biliary obstruction is followed by a rise in pressure in the bile duct system which continues until equilibrium is reached between the secretory pressure and the backflow.

The pressure attained in the biliary tract after ligature of the common bile duct was found to be 146–147 mm water in dogs and 163 mm water in rabbits (Heidenhain, 1868), 250–350 mm water in dogs and in cats (Mitchell and Stifel, 1916), and 186–412 (average 285) mm water in dogs (Shafiroff *et al.*, 1942). Excretion pressure under normal conditions was 42–114 (average 104) mm water in the common bile duct of dogs (Shafiroff *et al.*, 1942), and 260 mm in the lymphatic vessels of the liver of rats (Friedman *et al.*, 1956).

The excretion pressure of the human liver is 230–375 mm water according to Wiechel's (1963) studies of the intraductal bile pressure in patients with "white bile" due to complete biliary obstructions with abolished gallbladder function.

Wiechel (1963) recorded the pressure in the intrahepatic veins and bile ducts during percutaneous transhepatic cholangiography in surgical patients with jaundice. The venous pressure was measured in 37 patients and varied between 65 and 200 mm water (mean 115) in five cases with free bile duct system, between 85 and 160 (mean 117) in ten with gall stones in the bile ducts, between 80 and 275 (157) in 11 patients with neoplastic bile duct occlusion, and 145 mm water in one with benign bile duct stricture. Thus, biliary occlusion of longer duration was followed by a significant increase of the venous pressure. The intraductal pressure was determined in 42 patients. In eight with free bile passages, it was 80–195 (mean 119) mm water; in 12 with gall stone of the bile ducts, 113–290 (207); in one with benign stricture, 330; in 14 with neoplastic obstruction, 155–357 (254); and in one with cysts of the liver, 500 mm water. Simultaneous recording of the venous and the intraductal pressures was performed in 23 cases. In nine without obvious biliary obstruction, the venous pressure was 65–150 (mean 117) mm water and the intraductal pressure was 70–130 (99) mm water, while the corresponding figures in 17 patients with obvious biliary obstruction were 80–275 (138) and 170–380 (246) mm water, respectively. Thus, there is a significantly higher pressure in the intrahepatic veins than in the bile ducts under normal conditions, whereas the intraductal pressure surpasses the venous pressure by about 100 mm water in bile duct obstruction.

Edlund's experiments with rats emphasized the role of excretion by the glands of larger bile canals (Edlund, 1948, p. 59). He found that bile formation stopped 15 minutes after ligature. However, a small pressure increase occurred, caused by the excretion by mucous glands of larger bile canals. This agrees with the observation of Brauer *et al.* (1954), who investigated the relation existing between bile pressure and perfusion pressure in surviving rat liver preparations. These observations speak against the assumption of regurgitation as an explanation for the pathogenesis of obstructive icterus: if a pressure high enough to stop bile excretion is reached within 15 minutes, no more bile can enter into the bile ducts after this time if the pressure is maintained. However, various authors reported definite experimental evidence that the entry of bile components into the lymph continues for several hours after ligature. This stream certainly cannot come from the bile which was formed before ligature, not even when ruptures occurred in the bile duct system, because the pressure in the bile ducts remain high according to Edlund. Consequently, excretion which takes place there must be into the lymph. The same phenomenon can be observed with partial closure of the ductus choledochus. But here it is less pronounced than with complete obstruction because of the slow pressure increase in the biliary tract and the lower final pressure (Edlund, 1948, p. 40). In the light of the backflow concept (cf. above) it cannot be maintained that bile secretion stops when maximum pressure is reached.

Hanzon's (1952) fluorescence microscope investigations on rats with bile stasis showed normal excretion processes 20 minutes after maximum pressure was reached. However, a later seepage from bile capillaries into the blood (and not into the lymph) was noticed. According to Grafflin and Chaney (1953), this seepage is an artifact, which was caused by the strong ultraviolet radiation used by Hanzon to activate fluorescence.

Partial obstruction of the biliary tract has not been sufficiently studied. When one of the hepatic ducts is ligated, icterus does not develop in humans, dogs, or pigs (McMaster and Rous, 1921; Eppinger, 1937, p. 112; Rich, 1930; Schalm, 1951; Schalm *et al.*, 1952). According to Lopez Garcia *et al.* (1943), partial obstruction causes jaundice in rabbits, but this could not be substantiated by Schalm *et al.* (1952). Recent clinical observations on obstruction of one hepatic duct showed, however, definite jaundice (cf. Section C,1, this chapter). Extensive experimental studies in several species are required before the problems of partial biliary obstruction are satisfactorily understood. In such studies both unconjugated and conjugated bilirubin have to be taken into account, as well as varying degrees of obstruction, from 0–100% of the biliary tree.

Bile duct obstruction of one part of normal liver leads to fast atrophy in this area with compensatory hypertrophy of other parts (Schalm,

1951; Schalm *et al.*, 1952). This regenerative ability can disappear under pathological conditions. Thus, obstruction of small bile ducts may be an important cause for jaundice in these cases. This so-called *intrahepatic biliary obstruction* plays an important role in the literature. Its development has been attributed to inflammatory edema, proliferation of connective tissue, or accumulation of mucus or thrombi of concentrated bile in small bile ducts ("bile thrombi"). Such phenomena are regularly observed during hepatitis. In the normal state of the parenchyma no icterus is induced by such processes. However, when hepatitis causes diminished excretion capacity, the closure of numerous small bile ducts can very well be instrumental in producing icterus. In other words, intrahepatic biliary obstruction can play a significant role in the pathogenesis of parenchymatous icterus.

G. R. Cameron and Oakley (1932) and Edlund (1948) carried out important experimental studies on obstructive icterus with rats. If animal species which have a gallbladder are used in such experiments, not only the common bile duct but also the cystic duct has to be ligated. Otherwise, the gallbladder can function as a reservoir, and can significantly retard the results of obturation. Similarly, the simple ligature of a duct is insufficient to prevent recanalization; resection has to be performed. Great care has to be taken not to damage the vessels. Furthermore, accessory bile ducts must be ligated and resected. Finally, after sacrificing the experimental animal, it is necessary to check the success of the operation by autopsy.

Since rats do not have a gallbladder, they are especially suited for these studies. According to Edlund, during the first hours after ligature a definite distension of the biliary system occurs. The small bile ducts were also moderately dilated, but no jaundice occurred. After 24 hours the total diameter of the biliary tract practically had not changed, and the skin did not yet show signs of icterus. However, the urine was already discolored. At the same time, degenerative changes in liver cells and isolated necrosis in peripheral areas of the lobuli became visible. When the rats were killed after 48 hours' obstruction, Edlund observed cutaneous icterus, stronger degenerative and necrotic changes of liver cells, and further dilatation of the bile ducts. This dilatation turned out to be progressive. After 8 days the ductus choledochus was ten times wider than normal. Beginning on the fourth day a proliferation of connective tissue and of small bile ducts in periportal areas could be observed. With the duration of obturation, this process became more and more marked and led to increasingly changed liver structure. The necrosis of liver cells increased to the eighth day, after which regression was observed. Twelve days after ligature, only slight necrosis was detectable. After 12 days the bile capillaries were extremely dilated, and connections between bile ducts and lymph capillaries became visible. Thirty-six days after ligature the choledochus reached the size of a walnut. It ruptured frequently, causing a fatal peritonitis. It is important to note that during this process periportal tracts and neighboring parts of the lobuli are affected, whereas areas around the central vein remain relatively unharmed.

Edlund delegates a major role to the secretion of mucus glands of larger bile ducts. Actual bile excretion was believed to stop during the first hour after closure, and no pressure increase or widening of bile ducts takes place in the next 24 hours. After this time, continuing function of the mucus glands of the bile ducts changes this picture and the pressure increases gradually and steadily. A proliferation of small bile ducts and connective tissue commences as a response to mounting pressure. This process is the characteristic feature of extended bile duct obstruction. One of Cameron and Oakley's rats survived such an obstruction for 338 days.

The observations of Edlund are important because they demonstrate that the pressure in the bile duct system gradually increases and never falls during occlusion. Further, he found that the critical hydrostatic pressure is reached early in the occlusion. The later increase he ascribed to the secretion of the mucus glands. The conclusion of Edlund, that the bile secretion stops when a certain critical pressure is reached, is contradicted by recent physiological experiments in rats by Barber-Riley (1963a,b), Waldeck and Harth (1963), and Harth and Waldeck (1964) (cf. Section C,5, this chapter). According to them, bile formation and backflow of bile proceed parallel at normal as well as at elevated pressures. The secretion is believed to take place in the small, peripheral bile ductules, the absorption of fluid in the more central parts of the biliary tree. Further studies of this type on other species than the rat are highly desirable.

Edlund's explanation of his findings is based on the assumption that secretion from the mucous glands of the larger bile ducts continues after bile secretion has stopped. In light of recent studies (Cohen, 1964*) on the common bile duct epithelium in rats Edlund's basic assumption appear doubtful. Cohen found that the so-called glands of the common bile duct in rats are really not glands but renewal areas of the duct epithelium—just like the "glands" in the epithelium of the gut.

The fine structure of the proliferating bile ductules and the vascular tree of the liver in extrahepatic biliary occlusion in rats was investigated by means of electron microscopy by Carruthers and Steiner (1961) and Steiner et al. (1962a,b). The proliferating bile ductules constitute the primary histological feature of biliary obstruction in rats, but the vascular bed is also affected. The proliferating ductules are surrounded by vascular granulation tissue containing blood capillaries, lymph capillaries, and sinusoids. The majority of the sinusoids and capillaries of the liver maintain their normal morphology after ligation of the common bile duct in the rat, but focal areas are found where they are profoundly altered. The involved areas, seen only rarely, are confined to regions immediately surrounding newly proliferated ductules, and to adjacent peripheral zones of lobules. Small capillaries are more likely to be severely altered than larger ones. These changes in the vessels were seen throughout the whole period 1–39 days after the obstruction. Necrosis of the liver cells were observed in the same areas where the vascular alterations occurred and commenced to develop immediately after the obstruction. In the areas of vascular alteration, the parenchymal cells show degenerative changes and some of them become permeable to colloid particles of HgS administered through the common bile duct. The cause of these vascular alterations is still uncertain.

The bile duct proliferation in obstructive jaundice has also been studied in parabiotic rats to decide whether humoral influences are active. Moore et al. (1942*) found less bile duct proliferation, less hepatic cell necrosis, and less serum bilirubin in an obstructed parabiotic rat joined to a normal partner than in single rats with biliary occlusion. Zeckwer (1949*) found that such parabiotic rats lived longer than single obstructed rats. Heimann et al. (1963) studied single and parabiotic obstructed rats using H^3-thymidine and autoradiography of liver cells to detect and to quantitate the nuclear synthesis of DNA. Common duct obstruction in a rat joined to a normal partner resulted in less liver cell degeneration and necrosis, less liver cell proliferation, and less serum bilirubin elevation than in single obstructed rats. The nonoperated partner showed slightly elevated serum bilirubin and no change in hepatic cell mitosis. Heimann et al. concluded that liver cell proliferation following obstruction is due to damage to liver cells by mechanical factors, together with the effects of retention of bile components, and this effect is not transmitted to the parabiotic partner.

The origin and fate of proliferated bile ductules were studied by Rubin (1964*) who employed rats in which various hepatic cell types were labeled with tritiated thymidine with the thought that transfer of the autoradiographic label from one cell type to another would be evidence of transformation. It was found that ductules produced by chronic hepatic injury (synthetic diet with ethionine for 49 days) did not derive from parenchymal cells, mesenchymal cells, or bile duct epithelial cells, but represented a distinct cell type probably originating from preexisting ductules. On the other hand the proliferated tubules produced by bile duct ligation do not originate from preexisting tubules, but rather are outgrowths of bile duct epithelium. The cells of proliferated ductules disappear by necrosis and are not transformed into other cell types.

No detailed experiments have been conducted with animals other than rats, but species differences surely exist. It should be pointed out that Grafflin and Chaney (1953) did not observe dilatation of bile capillaries during bile duct obstruction lasting for a period of 2 months in mice. Considering Edlund's findings with rats, this observation is surprising. Up to the present time, the following animals have been studied: dogs, cats, rabbits, guinea pigs, rats, sheep, chicken, geese, pigeons, and frogs (see Cameron and Oakley, 1932). The experiments of Grafflin and Chaney on mice and those of Lopez Garcia *et al.* (1943) on pigs and monkeys can also be included in this list.

Cameron and Oakley (1932), Lopez Garcia *et al.* (1943), and Edlund (1948, p. 28) thoroughly discussed the different reactions of various animal species during bile duct obstruction. After obstruction of bile ducts, no icterus develops in frogs (Leyden, 1866; H. Stern, 1885). Although the reason for this has not yet been investigated, it is plausible that destruction of bile pigments is more important than their excretion in frogs (see Section D,4, this chapter). Susceptibility to cholangitis is an important factor in pigs. Most animal species tolerate bile duct obstruction badly. As a rule, rabbits, dogs, cats, rats, and pigs die within a few weeks; the greatest resistance is shown by humans and monkeys. The degree of bile duct proliferation is different in different species and most marked in rats (Lopez Garcia *et al.*, 1943).

Cameron and Oakley point out the tendency for *recanalization of bile ducts*. Thus, in 5 of 120 rats recanalization occurred in spite of double ligature and resection. Brodie (1823) early reported such recanalizations. Recanalization was studied by Trams and Symeonides (1957), Kraus and Beltram (1959), and Wright and Braithewaite (1962), who found recanalization of the common bile duct as early as 14 days after occlusion in rats. The latter demonstrated that this phenomenon is brought about by enlargement of preformed biliary canaliculi which course along the walls of the portal vein and its tributaries.

Obstructive jaundice in the rhesus monkey was studied by J. L. Cameron *et al.* (1966b[*]) using C^{14}-bilirubin on five monkeys weighing 2.9–4.5 kg. The common bile duct was subjected to double ligation and resection, and the cystic duct was ligated. The bilirubin in the serum and the bilirubin and urobilinogen in the bile and urine were observed until a steady state with relatively constant serum bilirubin was reached in 3–9 weeks. Unfortunately the serum bilirubin was measured using the Malloy-Evelyn method. The average serum bilirubin varied between

10.8 and 18.3 mg/100 ml (mean 15.5). Thus the increase of the serum
bilirubin during biliary occlusion in the rhesus monkey and the average
concentration observed is much like that found in man and much higher
than that in dogs and rats. After the steady state had been reached
radioactive bilirubin was injected and its fate in the organism was followed. It was found that about 80% of the radioactivity was excreted
with the urine and that most of the urine radioactivity was due to
bilirubin.

Important observations on proliferation of fine bile ducts in 55 patients
subjected to liver biopsy and experimental studies on rabbits have
been presented in a Portuguese monograph (Serrão, 1959). Some rabbits
were given CCl_4 subcutaneously, while others received whole bile, ethionine, and α-naphthylisothiocyanate (ANITC) perorally. Some were
subjected to ligature of the common bile duct. Elias' idea (1948) of a
"connective space" surrounding the vessels (arterial, venous, lymphatic),
bile ducts, and connective tissue is of the highest importance in understanding hepatic pathology. The hyperplastic bile ductules frequently
observed in hepatic lesions arise from biliary ductules in periportal areas
and not from liver cells undergoing necrosis. Necrosis of liver cells is
accompanied by proliferation of the bile ducts and enlargements of the
connective space. Pure hypertrophy of bile ductules without alteration
of parenchymal liver cells is achieved by administration of ANITC. This
poison, introduced by Mazzanti and Lopez (1952) in rats, acted as a
specific agent for ductular proliferation in rabbits. Connective tissue
increase in the centrilobular zone is not accompanied by ductular hyperplasia. Periportal necrosis due to ethionine caused connective tissue proliferation and ductular hyperplasia. Ox bile did not produce cirrhosis in
rabbits. The property of ANITC to cause bile ductule proliferation was
confirmed by Ungar *et al.* (1962) in studies with rats.

Necrosis of parenchyma and proliferation of bile ducts are most
marked in rats, guinea pigs, and pigeons, i.e., in those animals which
produce considerable amounts of bile. However, it is interesting to note
that, in animals with moderate bile flow, bile pressure is regularly higher.
Thus, for example, 300 mm water pressure was found in dogs and cats,
but in rabbits and guinea pigs only 140–191 mm water. According to
Hiyeda (1925), rabbits produce about seven times as much bile as dogs.
Rabbits develop hyperbilirubinemia after obstruction faster than dogs.
Hiyeda assumed that the icterus is a consequence of ruptures of so-called
ampullas, which are the connections between bile capillaries and small
ducts; they are supposed to be weaker in rabbits than in dogs. On the
other hand, Ogata (1913a, pp. 275–277) did not detect any ruptures of
bile ducts in the early stages of bile duct obstruction; the occurrence of
such ruptures is questionable (cf. Section C,5).

Recently, Aronsen (1962) published a thorough study of the liver function during biliary obstruction in the dog. Unfortunately, he omitted studies of the lymph and of the pressure in the bile ducts. The average serum bilirubin level reached was 9 mg per 100 ml (maximum 15 mg per 100 ml) 6–12 days after occlusion. After this, the serum bilirubin decreased slightly. The serum bilirubin reached normal values 1–2 weeks after the removal of the obstruction.

J. L. Cameron et al. (1963*) subjected 12 dogs to ligation and division of the common bile duct and simultaneous cholecystectomy and observed three different patterns of jaundice. Three of the dogs showed a rise in the serum bilirubin to ca. 15 mg/100 ml during the first 14 days followed by a fall to a plateau of 4–8 mg/100 ml. In three others the serum bilirubin slowly increased to a 4–8 mg/100 ml plateau within 2 weeks; no peak was observed. Finally one dog exhibited a continuous rise of serum bilirubin reaching 31 mg/100 ml in 14 days after which it died; here no plateau was observed. Gliedman et al. (1963*) also studied experimental biliary occlusion in the dog and found a wide range of serum bilirubin concentrations, the mean value being about 12 mg/100 ml; their experiments did not, however, include cholecystectomy.

Leaver and Cristie (1965*) published a detailed account of the pathological changes following obstruction of the common bile duct and the hepatic duct in sheep; also the effect of simultaneous closure of the hepatic artery and the bile duct was studied. It was found that the maximal proliferation of bile ductules was brought about by simultaneous closure of the bile duct and the hepatic artery. Thus the violent proliferation of bile ductules often associated with biliary occlusion is most likely only partly caused by the obstruction itself, but to a certain degree it is caused by ischemia of the parenchyma secondary to the occlusion. In sporidesmin poisoning this proliferation of the bile ductules also occurs (cf. Section C,7, this chapter).

Acute obstructive cholangitis exists as a clinical syndrome in man (Ostermiller et al., 1965*). Another cause of obstruction of the common bile duct is dysfunction and other disturbances of the sphincter of its duodenal orifice (sphincter Oddi) at the ampulla of Vater. An experimental study of disturbances of the function of sphincter Oddi in rats has recently been published by Das (1965*).

A form of jaundice of special interest is congenital biliary atresia, which has attracted much attention recently (cf. Lancet, 1963a; Stowens, 1963; Sterling and Lowenburg, 1963). The defects in the biliary tree vary greatly in these patients, but about 15% of the cases exhibit complete absence of bile ducts of all sizes and of all structures composed of bile duct epithelia (Stowens, 1963). Such cases of congenital atresia of intrahepatic bile ducts were described by Ahrens et al. (1951), Sass-Kortsak et al. (1956), and Haas and Dobbs (1958), and the condition is occasionally compatible with survival for several years. The patient of Cotton (1960) thus reached the age of 7 years. In this patient the serum bilirubin during one period was as low as 0.8 mg per 100 ml, a fact pointing to destruction of bilirubin to nonidentifiable compounds. Sterling and Lowenburg (1963) inserted tubes of silver or plastic, connecting the liver and the stomach, to function as artificial bile passages; in this way a certain amount of bile constituents reached the intestinal canal after the operation. Studies on the content of bile constituents of the lymph from the liver or the thoracic duct have never been performed in such patients, although they would be of considerable interest. From recent physiological studies on reabsorption of bile from the biliary tree at different pressures (Barber-Riley, 1963a,b; Waldeck and Harth, 1963; Harth and Waldeck, 1964; cf. above), it is to be expected that bile constituents will occur in the lymph when they cannot go into the bile, and that this takes place at normal pressures, whereas "regurgitation" to the blood only takes place at elevated pressures.

The causes of bile duct obstruction vary considerably. The most important factors in human pathology are bile stones and neoplasmas of the pancreas head or the ampulla of Vater. Functional dyskinesias can also be effective (Lichtman, 1949). Baumgärtel (1950b, pp. 160–176) discussed the functional significance of extrahepatic bile ducts of various animal species.

4. Hepatocellular Jaundice

In hepatocellular jaundice, also known as parenchymatous icterus, the damage is located in the liver cells. It can consist of slight degeneration or of more severe alterations culminating in liver cell necrosis. If the main damage is located at the smallest bile canals and the liver cells look relatively normal, the jaundice is called hepatocanalicular jaundice (cf. Section E,5, this chapter). If necrosis is present, regurgitation of the contents of bile capillaries into lymph can take place. However, it is questionable whether such regurgitation is significant for the pathogenesis of icterus (see Section C,5, this chapter). Physiological experiments have not yet unequivocally demonstrated the role of such regurgitation.

Retention and lymphogenism–regurgitation are the basic mechanisms of parenchymatous icterus. In addition, so-called intrahepatic obstructions (see Section E,3, this chapter) are of significance in some cases. Since during obstruction icterus, retention and lymphogenism–regurgitation also constitute the basic pathogenetic processes, no essential difference between the two forms of icterus can be visualized.

Even light hepatitis can be accompanied by *necrosis of parenchymal* cells (Iversen and Roholm, 1939; Roholm et al., 1942; Axenfeld and Brass, 1942; Dible et al., 1943; Kalk, 1947). Lucké (1944a,b) emphasized the role of intrahepatic bile duct obstruction. Kühn (1947a,b, 1948), who examined 213 biopsies in 172 cases of virus hepatitis, assumed that necrosis of liver cells does not play an important role in the pathogenesis of jaundice, at least not in the initial stages of hepatitis. He concluded, therefore, that retention is the principal pathogenetic mechanism. However, he overlooked the possibility that, owing to hepatitis, active excretion of bile components into lymph might occur. Liver cell necrosis was also described as a side symptom by "allergic cholangiolitis" in chlorpromazine icterus (Zelman, 1959).

The so-called "serous inflammation" of Eppinger and Rössle (see Eppinger, 1937; Lichtman, 1949; Baumgärtel, 1950b) can hardly play a role during hepatitis (Kühn, 1947a,b, 1948). It is probably either an artifact or a normally occurring phenomenon (Kühn and Hildebrand, 1951).

A question of importance is to what extent the Kupffer cells, the RES of the liver, are affected in parenchymal jaundice. The electron microscope observations of Miyai et al. (1963) in viral hepatitis in mice clearly demonstrated that the Kupffer cells are involved to the same degree, and even earlier, than the parenchymal liver cells in this condition. Therefore, one might expect that the formation of bilirubin from aged circulating erythrocytes may be decreased in certain forms of parenchymal jaundice.

Experimental studies on hepatocellular icterus are much rarer than those on obstructive icterus. Most of the studies have been carried out on animals with toluenediamine icterus (see Chapter II,C). Toluenediamine was introduced as a liver poison by Stadelmann (1881, 1882, 1887). Its effects have since been studied in detail by Afanassiew (1883), Hiyeda (1927), Yuasa (1928), Eitel (1928), Itoh (1931), H. J. Wolff (1934), and McGowan (1935). After toluenediamine poisoning, icterus develops in dogs; cats develop hemoglobinuria as well as icterus; but no icterus is induced in rabbits (Afanassiew, 1883; F. Rosenthal and Meier, 1921). The poison becomes effective only after activation by the spleen (Itoh, 1932). Afanassiew (1883) found yellow discoloration of lymphatic vessels even before jaundice developed. Hiyeda (1927) and Yuasa (1928) underlined the *lymphogenic character of toluenediamine jaundice*. Bollman (1935) showed that toluenediamine poisoning leads to the highest known values of hyperbilirubinemia in dogs. Hench (1938) described one case of toluenediamine icterus in humans. Other poisons besides the classic liver poisons (phosphorus and $CHCl_3$) which have been employed to produce experimental icterus are phenylhydrazine (Itoh, 1932), allyl formate, and pyrrole compounds (Popper, 1937). However, the majority of experiments designed to study parenchymatous icterus have been performed with toluenediamine. C. J. Watson (1963) recently renewed the study of experimental toluenediamine jaundice in dogs and found that it is accompanied by pronounced urobilinuria which disappears if the bile is diverted from the intestine by means of a biliary-renal fistula.

The proliferation of bile ductules following CCl$_4$, ethionine, and α-naphthylisothiocyanate (ANiTC) poisoning was discussed above (Section E,4, this chapter). Rüttner *et al.* (1964*) studied ANiTC jaundice in rats and regarded it as a model of toxic hepatosis. A single dose of 20 mg was given to rats weighing 100–500 g and the concentration of serum bilirubin was followed. In the rats weighing 500 g the rise in serum bilirubin began after 12 hours and reached a maximum (below 2.5 mg/100 ml) in 48–72 hours, but in rats weighing 100–200 g the increase began after 6 hours and reached a maximum (up to 5 mg/100 ml) in 24 hours. Using electron microscopy and histological studies lesions of the membranes of the parenchymal cells were established.

Verme and Campari (1965*) studied experimental parenchymal jaundice in rats induced by BeSO$_4$, dibutyldichloride, and deficiency in vitamin E and proteins. They studied the serum bilirubin with particular reference to the distribution between free and conjugated bilirubin and found that the capacity of the liver for conjugating bilirubin was to a considerable degree independent of the histologically demonstrable lesions. This is not a surprise because they could also demonstrate that operative removal of as much as three-fourths of the normal rat liver parenchyma only caused small changes in the excretion and conjugation of bilirubin.

Another observation pointing to the importance of the lymph in the pathogenesis of parenchymal jaundice is that of Bagenstoss (1957), who found a marked increase in number and size of the lymphatics of the hilus of the liver in chronic liver inflammation.

The importance of humoral factors in parenchymal jaundice was studied in parabiotic rats by Heimann *et al.* (1963). Pairs consisting of one normal rat and one with bile duct obstruction were used. The rats were given tritiated thymidine to trace the liver cell proliferation (nucleic acid synthesis). The degeneration and necrosis of liver cells and the proliferation of new cells was less in rats in parabiosis with a normal partner than in single rats with bile duct obstruction.

Jaundice due to specific poisons is discussed in Section C,7, this chapter, and jaundice due to drugs in Section E,5, this chapter.

Minkowski (1904) was the first to assume that *parapedesis* is the mechanism of parenchymatous icterus, i.e., the excretion in liver lymph instead of in bile (see Section C,1, this chapter). Eppinger (1920) rejected this assumption because of lack of experimental evidence. Minkowski's theory was revived by With (1944d, 1947, 1949) and Baum-gärtel (1947b, 1948a, 1949d, 1950b, pp. 15, 31, 204, and 220). The latter author proposed an interesting theory on the relationship between glyco-genolysis and parapedesis but it is not yet supported by experiments.

Various authors investigated the *site of the lesions* which occur during the different forms of parenchymatous icterus, i.e., the central, inter-mediate, or peripheral part of the lobule. Varela Fuentes (1943) differ-entiated between two major groups of parenchymatous icterus depending on the site of changes in the lobuli: "ictericias per hepatosis" accompanied by centrilobular changes, and "ictericias peri-hepatociticas" in which damage occurs principally in the peripheral part of the lobuli and in the periportal tissue. As a rule, the lesions are more or less diffusely dis-tributed in the first type, while they are focal in the second type. Bioptic examination during virus hepatitis showed that, during its first stages, changes mainly affect the periphery of the lobuli and the periportal tracts (see Kühn, 1947a,b). In more severe cases, however, necrosis in the lobular center prevails. Nevertheless, cases were described in which lesions were concentrated in the intermediate zone of the lobulus, for example in septic peritonitis (Ogata, 1913b) and yellow fever (da Rocha-Lima, 1912). Wallach and Popper (1950) and Ellenberg and Osserman (1951) distinguished two kinds of centrilobular changes. The first is caused by toxic effect and shows all the symptoms of an acute necrosis, whereas the other form caused by stasis produces atrophy without signs of acute necrosis. According to these authors, anoxemia caused by circu-latory disturbances plays an important role here. Centrilobular necrosis was observed during extended shock. Ellenberg and Osserman attributed central necrosis caused by $CHCl_3$ and CCl_4 poisoning to ischemia of the lobular center. Brody (1963) found that parenchymal necrosis after CCl_4 is markedly reduced by prior administration of adrenergic blocking agents or by high spinal transsection. This was confirmed by Clerici et al. (1964*). Foord and Lawrence (1965*) studied CCl_4 poisoning in sheep by feeding single doses of 1 or 2 ml orally once a week for 12 weeks. The animals were followed using liver biopsies and were finally subjected to autopsy. Although marked centrilobular necrosis developed, the serum bilirubin concentration remained in the normal range.

Hübner (1965*) studied the ultrastructural changes in the mouse liver after oral and intrasplenic administration of CCl_4 as well as after immersing liver tissue in CCl_4. He concluded that the lesions were due to the disintegration of the cell membranes by the liposolvent action of CCl_4.

It is important to remember that secondary parenchymal liver lesions will accompany any form of biliary obstruction, a fact early pointed out by Charcot and Gombault (1876). The mechanism of this liver cell necrosis secondary to biliary obstruction was recently studied by Hou *et al.* (1962) in rats. They suggested that the cause is alteration of the permeability of the liver cells due to anoxia which leads to diffusion of cytotoxic bile components (bilirubin, bile salts) into the liver cells. The old mechanical explanation, i.e., leakage of bile from the bile canaliculi into the tissue spaces, is not satisfactory, partly because ruptures of the canaliculi or ampulla of Hering have never been directly proved, and partly because experiments have shown that bile does not inhibit the respiration of liver slices *in vitro*. It is only in cell-free liver homogenates that bile gives a depression of the respiration.

It is highly important to bear in mind that biliary obstruction is rapidly followed by parenchymal cell necrosis and, *vice versa*, that inflammation of the liver parenchyma is followed by intrahepatic bile duct occlusion. This fact makes it practically impossible to make a clear-cut separation of parenchymal jaundice and occlusive jaundice. This difficulty in distinguishing between occlusive and parenchymal jaundice is further underlined by recent studies concerning the involvement of the biliary tracts in acute hepatitis (Sotgiu, 1965*). In systematic studies of the sediment of bile from duodenal draining, in chemical and electrophoretic studies of bile, as well as in duodenal biopsies, Sotgiu found that the large bile ducts and the duodenal mucosa are frequently involved in acute hepatitis and that this involvement can in certain cases contribute materially to the persistence of jaundice. He subdivides acute hepatitis into a strictly hepatic type and a hepatoangiobiliary type. In the latter "intrahepatic cholestasis" is a regular feature. The observations of Sotgiu revive to a certain extent Virchow's (1865*) 100-year-old "mucous plug" theory. Pavel and Pieptea (1966*) arrived at similar conclusions.

5. Hepatocanalicular Jaundice (Cholangiolitic Jaundice; Intrahepatic Cholestasis) and Jaundice Induced by Drugs and Food

C. J. Watson and Hoffbauer (1946, 1947) described a form of icterus the pathological substrate of which was damage of small bile ducts without demonstrable involvement of parenchymal cells. They called this type of icterus "cholangiolitic jaundice." They thought that it was caused by increased permeability of bile canaliculi. During this condition histologically detectable bile thrombi were observed, which were thought to cause cholestasis and penetration of bile through the wall of the affected canaliculi into the lymph and blood. This explanation may be correct, but it is hard to believe that the relatively slight changes observed in the cuboidal cells of the ductules in this form of jaundice suffice to explain the icterus. If Andrews' theory (1955) of bile formation is correct, this form of jaundice can be explained more easily; according to this theory, the small bile ducts, which represent the main site of damage in this form of jaundice, are responsible for the production of bile.

Popper and Szanto (1956) and Popper et al. (1963) used the term "intrahepatic cholestasis" as a synonym for "cholangiolitis," meaning "accumulation of bile in the liver with absence of extrahepatic biliary obstruction"; this terminology is of questionable merit because the role of the bile accumulations observed, for the pathogenesis of the jaundice, has never been proved. The term "intrahepatic cholestasis," and more recently the abbreviation "cholestasis," has, however, been widely accepted and is presumably impossible to get rid of. Here the term hepatocanalicular jaundice, introduced by Andrews, is preferred as being more correct.

Schaffner and Popper (1959) and Reichel et al. (1960) performed electron microscope studies of the liver in this condition and found a type of disturbance of the microvilli of the liver cells peculiar to this condition and absent in most cases of hepatocellular jaundice as well as in the Dubin-Johnson syndrome (cf. Section E,2, this chapter). Schaffner and Kniffen (1963), with the electron microscope, found changes in the bile secretion apparatus of the hepatocytes involving microvilli, vacuoles, and lysosomes.

Dubin et al. (1960) studied an epidemic of virus hepatitis and found that 40% of the cases presented the histological picture of hepatocanalicular jaundice. Pavel and Campeanu (1962) proposed to limit the use of the term intrahepatic cholestasis to acute syndromes caused by viral infections or drugs. But so defined, it would lose its original meaning as a special histological picture seen in some forms of jaundice. Schaffner and Kniffen (1963) proposed to broaden the definition of intrahepatic cholestasis to include ultrastructural changes in the bile-secreting apparatus provoked by certain hepatotoxic drugs.

Sotgiu (1965*) found that intrahepatic cholestasis occurs regularly in acute hepatitis and that this disease does not affect the liver cells exclusively, but also the bile tubules, as well as the larger bile ducts, and even the duodenum. In some types of acute hepatitis, called strictly hepatic, the lesions of the parenchymal cells dominate, whereas in the hepatoangiobiliary type the small and larger bile ducts are also affected.

Albot et al. (1965a*,b*) demonstrated in experiments with total and partial choleperitoneum in rats that so-called intrahepatic cholestasis can be due to intoxication with bile components in the absence of stasis (cf. Section C,6, this chapter). Therefore the term "cholestasis" is certainly not appropriate and "hepatocanalicular jaundice" is more fitting.

It should be kept in mind that hepatocanalicular jaundice is a *product of the era of liver biopsies.* It cannot be recognized as a special form of jaundice different from perenchymal jaundice without liver biopsy. This histological picture is found both in jaundice due to drugs and in hepatitic icterus, and a sharp distinction between hepatocanalicular and hepatocellular jaundice is impossible. It seems doubtful whether it is of much practical interest to distinguish between these two histological types of jaundice. With the material of Shorter *et al.* (1959) in mind, the clinical value of this distinction seems questionable.

Congenital absence of intrahepatic bile ducts (see Section E,3, this chapter) and icterogenin jaundice (see Section C,7, this chapter) are forms of jaundice which, like hepatocanalicular jaundice, exhibit no histologically demonstrable changes of parenchymal cells. The histological pictures of these conditions are, however, different from that of hepatocanalicular jaundice.

Hepatocanalicular jaundice is seen after administration of a number of drugs. Some drugs showing severe hepatotoxicity, like CCl_4 and $CHCl_3$, produce parenchymal jaundice with necroses, but a number of drugs giving rise to jaundice produce milder lesions of the liver parenchyma, among them icterogenin and other specific liver poisons. The jaundice following administration of chlorpromazine has been widely discussed in the literature. Mostly this drug gives rise to hepatocanalicular jaundice but, according to Zelman (1959), necrosis of parenchymal cells can always be demonstrated in chlorpromazine jaundice if the histological preparations are carefully studied.

Jaundice following administration of *drugs* is a complicated problem which has recently attracted much attention. Popper and Schaffner (1959b) and Popper *et al.* (1963) classified it in four groups: (1) Zonal hepatocellular alteration, mainly necrosis of liver cells. Example: CCl_4 poisoning. (2) Predominantly hepatocanalicular manifestations. Example: chlorpromazine jaundice. (3) Hepatitis picture, resembling virus hepatitis. (4) An unclassified group associated with primary toxic manifestations in other organs. In this connection the studies of Brody (1963) are important because he found that the action of CCl_4 on the liver parenchyma is highly dependent on the sympathetic nervous system. In rats the necrosis and lipid accumulation in the liver following CCl_4 poisioning is markedly reduced by prior administration of adrenergic blocking agents or high spinal transsection.

In the discussion of association between drugs and jaundice, it is important to remember that parenteral administration of drugs always carries a certain risk of *inoculation hepatitis.* Only if this can be ruled out, can the drug be held responsible. Most cases of arsphenamine jaundice were unquestionably inoculation hepatitis (cf. Genner, 1936; Hanger and Gutman, 1940).

The most important drug-induced jaundice today is *chlorpromazine* jaundice; here, inoculation jaundice can be ruled out because the drug is most often given perorally. Numerous publications have appeared since the condition was first recognized in 1954 (cf. de Voret *et al.*, 1956; Burlina, 1956; Werther and Korelitz, 1957; Sandring, 1957; Hollister, 1957; Hammerberg, 1958; Nørredam, 1962; Ruttner *et al.*, 1962). A. A. Stein and Wright (1956) described post mortem findings in patients who died from intercurrent illness during chlorpromazine jaundice. The jaundice cannot be due to direct hepatotoxic effects of chlorpromazine because it is not seen in all patients but only in a small percentage, varying between 0.2 and 5% in different materials according to Nørredam (1962). The total dose of chlorpromazine taken by the patients before the jaundice appears varies between 10 and 5700 mg (average 1200 mg). Similarly, the period from the beginning of chlorpromazine medication to the appearance of jaundice varies (2–95 days). Chlorpromazine jaundice is most often harmless, but fatal cases have been reported (Boardman, 1954; A. A. Stein and Wright, 1956; Peitersen, 1959; Ranek, 1964), and progression to a chronic condition has also been reported (Jespersen, 1959; Read *et al.*, 1961; Nørredam, 1963; Ranek, 1964). In Jespersen's case, liver cirrhosis developed, but in Ranek's, cirrhosis was not found at autopsy after 18 months' jaundice.

The condition usually begins with a prodromal stage of a few days' duration with fever, malaise, and often abdominal complaints before the jaundice develops. The jaundice is mostly moderate or slight, and anicteric cases have been described. The pathogenesis is doubtful. Most authors assume an allergic reaction, but activation of a latent "Enzymopathy" present in the affected minority of patients also has to be considered. Bollman's (1958) observation that bilirubin monoglucuronide is prevailing in chlorpromazine jaundice indicates hepatocellular damage.

Besides chlorpromazine, a number of *other drugs* and poisons are icterogenic. The classical hepatotoxins such as phosphorus, CCl_4, and $CHCl_3$ have been mentioned above, and special poisons like toluenediamine (Section C,4), icterogenin, and sporidesmin (Section C,7, this chapter) have been discussed separately. Among others, certain steroids giving rise to icterus of the chlorpromazine type have attracted special attention. Jaundice after methyltestosterone was described by S. C. Werner *et al.* (1950), Westlake (1956), Kaplan (1956), H. C. Johnson and Doenges (1956), Sherlock (1956), Martini and Dölle (1958), and Hoffbauer (1959). Icterus following administration of norethandrolone (Nilevar) was described by Dunning (1958). Arias (1963a) recently pointed out that large doses of certain C-17 alkylated anabolic steroids regularly give rise to hepatocanalicular jaundice in man and called attention to the structural similarity between these compounds and icterogenic triterpenoids of the icterogenin type (cf. Section C,7, this chapter). This question was reviewed by Gordan *et al.* (1965*).

Jaundice due to arsphenamine and cinchophen (Atophan) was much discussed 20–30 years ago (Genner, 1936; Hanger and Gutman, 1940). Most cases were due to inoculation hepatitis, but some cases were caused by drug reaction. It was, however, difficult to distinguish between the two conditions then because liver biopsy was first introduced by Iversen and Roholm (1939).

The number of drugs occasionally giving rise to jaundice is steadily increasing. They have been reviewed by Zimmerman (1963). The psychopharmacological agents iproniazid (Popper, 1958) and Catron (Dominguez *et al.*, 1962) are of special importance because they give icterus of the hepatocellular type with a fatality of more than 10%. Certain antibiotics have been claimed to provoke hepatocanalicular icterus (M. M. Robinson, 1961, 1962a,b; Havens, 1962), and the same is true for antidiabetics (chlorpropamide; Reichel *et al.*, 1960). Recently the widely used anesthetic fluothane (halothane), closely related to $CHCl_3$, has been claimed to be icterogenic in some cases (cf. *Lancet*, 1963c; Chadwick and Jennings, 1964; Galvin, 1964), but the causal relation between jaundice and fluothane is highly questionable because of the very low frequency of this type of jaundice, about one case among a million anesthesias (Kristoffersen, 1964). Long-continued treatment with large doses of nicotinic acid has also been claimed to be a cause of hepatocanalicular jaundice (Rivin, 1959).

A new group of liver poisons has recently been discovered, the *Senecio alkaloids*. Men as well as domestic animals are susceptible to these alkaloids derived from pyrrolizidine and occurring in plants of the genus *Senecio* (compositae). Several alkaloids with varying toxicity are known. They cause hemorrhagic necrosis of the liver cells with secondary block of the central veins leading to liver engorgment and ascites (Chiari's syndrome, veno-occlusive disease) and later to cirrhosis. The literature is reviewed by Hill (1960), Markson (1960), and Schoental (1960). Senecosis—as this poisoning is called—however, has not been used in the study of the metabolism of bile pigments.

Another poison producing hepatocellular damage is ethionine (Hoffman *et al.*, 1960), which acts as antagonist for the essential amino acid, methionine. If 15 mg per kg per 24 hours is administered *per os* to dogs, a hyperbilirubinemia of 3–4 mg per 100 ml develops.

Yet another group of substances causing toxic hepatitis has recently been discovered; they were first observed in turkeys in England (Stevens *et al.*, 1960) fed with Brazilian groundnut meal. The toxic factor is formed during the storage of the meal under humid conditions by certain strains of *Aspergillus flavus* (Wooldridge, 1962). Outbreaks of groundnut hepatitis have also been reported in pigs (Loosmore and Harding, 1961), and in cattle a liver lesion indistinguishable from senecosis has been seen as a result of this poisoning (Loosmore and Markson, 1961). The toxic factor is now known as *aflatoxin* (cf. Lancet, 1964).

Nosslin (1963) described jaundice due to unconjugated bilirubin after administration of male fern extract (*Dryopteris filix mas*) commonly used against tapeworm infestation. Of 14 patients treated with this extract, all exhibited an increased serum bilirubin (maximum value 0.6–6.6 mg per 100 ml), but only one patient developed visible jaundice. Retention of BSP accompanied the hyperbilirubinemia, but other signs of hepatocellular damage were absent. Nosslin and Morgan (1965*) studied the hepatotoxic action on rabbits of 19 different purified substances from male fern. Four compounds having certain structural details in common caused BSP retention; one of them, flavospidic acid, was studied in detail. Intravenous injection of 0.02 mmole/kg body weight gave an immediate retention of BSP, bilirubin, and rose bengal lasting several hours.

Davidson (1963) discussed the *hepatotoxicity of food* in man and animals. Some members of the flowering plant genuses *Senecio, Srotolaria, Heliotropium*, and *lupinus* may cause liver lesions in man and animals. Forgacs (1962) discussed the role of fungus toxins as hepatotoxins (*Mycotoxicoses*).

Smetana (1963) thoroughly discussed the histopathology of drug-induced liver disease. The possibility of latent anicteric forms of drug-induced liver lesion was stressed by Kalk and Ulbricht (1963). It is important to bear in mind that the histological picture of hepatocanalicular jaundice (intrahepatic cholestasis) is far from specific to drug-induced jaundice; in some epidemics of viral hepatitis, it is found in ca. 40% of the cases (Dubin *et al.*, 1960).

The pathogenesis of drug-induced jaundice is largely unknown. Its biochemical aspects were recently discussed by Billing *et al.* (1963), who reported experimental studies on the cholecystographic medium, bunamiodyl (orabilix)—used orally—which induces mild hyperbilirubinemia that disappears within 48 hours in most patients. This and other cholecystographic media such as iodopanoic acid, are excreted as ester glucuronides like bilirubin, and the jaundice induced by them is due to interference in the hepatic uptake of unconjugated bilirubin caused by competition with the icterogenic substance (cf. also Hargreaves and Lathe, 1963).

The literature on drug-induced jaundice is expanding rapidly. Cases of icterus due to intrahepatic cholestasis after steroids had been administered orally as contraceptives were reported by Cullberg et al. (1965*), Larsson-Cohn and Stenram (1965*), Lundbergh (1966*) (18 cases, 1964–1965), and Nermark and Thulin (1966*) (7 cases).

Increases in serum concentration of various enzymes after peroral uses of steroid contraceptives were reported by Brohult and Westgren (1965*). The question of halothane jaundice was discussed in detail by Mushin et al. (1964*) who could not decide whether it was due to a specific toxic effect, an allergic reaction, or activation of a latent error in metabolism. Cyclopropane was also mentioned as a cause of hepatosis (Bennike and Hagelsten, 1964*). Certain contrast media for cholecystography—Telepaque, biligrafin, bunamiodyl (orabilix)—were found to induce jaundice (Bolt et al., 1961*; Billing et al., 1965*). The latter investigators administered the three mentioned substances as well as the antibiotic novobiocin to rats and found that these substances interfered with the secretion of bilirubin from liver microsomes and that novobiocin inhibited the hepatic uptake of bilirubin. These substances appear to induce jaundice by competing with bilirubin for the transport mechanism of the liver cells. Collens and Dobkin (1965*) reported cholestatic jaundice after oral use of antidiabetic sulfonyl ureas (chlorpropamide and tolbutamide) and Ward (1965*) described "cholestasis" after administration of tanderil (oxyphenylbutazone). Einhorn and Davidsohn (1964*) observed jaundice in a leukemic patient treated with the cytotoxic drug mercaptopurine. Here the jaundice was associated with hepatic necroses in addition to the "cholestasis." The sensitivity of the liver toward this drug exhibits wide individual variations.

Hepatic reactions to drugs were reviewed for the Council on Drugs by Tumen et al. (1965*). These reactions are characterized by their lack of uniformity as well as their rarity. Both the clinical and pathological picture as well as the pathogenesis vary considerably, and causal relationships between the jaundice and the drug in question is often difficult to prove. The question is also discussed in an editorial in the J. Am. Med. Assoc. [191, 149 (1965)] where it is pointed out that future studies should be directed toward possible immunological drug reactions as well as toward genetically determined variations in drug metabolism. Schaffner (1965*) discussed the diagnosis of drug-induced hepatic damage and distinguished four types; only the first is associated with jaundice. Hargreaves (1965*) discussed the influence of hepatotoxic drugs on bilirubin metabolism and pointed out that the intrahepatic cholestasis induced by phenothiazines is often associated with extrahepatic manifestations, whereas that induced by C-17α alkyl-substituted steroids has no extrahepatic manifestations. He emphasized that it is an oversimplification to describe chlorpromazine jaundice as purely cholestatic, since about one-half the patients have significant parenchymal liver lesions. Hargreaves studied the action of phenothiazines and steroids on the formation of glucuronides of bilirubin and o-aminophenol *in vitro* with rat liver slices and rabbit liver homogenates, as well as the action of phenothiazines on the bile secretion of rats. The experiments gave no simple answer to the question of why drugs cause "cholestasis." The action of drugs on bilirubin metabolism proved to be complex.

6. ICTERUS NEONATORUM

The hyperbilirubinemia of newborn mammals increases significantly during the first week after birth, and falls to normal values after several weeks. Similar hyperbilirubinemia at birth has also been described in birds (W. Koch, 1928). The pathogenesis of such hyperbilirubinemia which often leads to jaundice is discussed elsewhere in detail (Chapter V,I,2). It should be emphasized that besides the physiological icterus neonatorum, several pathological forms are known, e.g., congenital absence of the intrahepatic bile ducts (Section E,4, this chapter), hemolytic icterus neonatorum gravis, and congenital hepatitis (Chapter V,I,2). Vest *et al.* (1965*) showed in experiments with N^{15}-glycine that "shunt bilirubin" plays an important pathogenetic role in icterus neonatorum.

7. CARDIAC JAUNDICE

This form of jaundice is found in some cases of cardiac insufficiency. Its pathogenesis is not fully clear. Oertel (1906, 1910) found histological lesions localized in the centrilobular parts of the parenchyma. In severe cases, rather extended necrosis of the lobular center can occur. Eppinger (1920) assumed that the sudden onset of jaundice during heart attacks is due to additional bilirubin production from blood of pulmonary infarctions. However, Rich and Resnik (1926) showed convincingly that the amount of bilirubin formed in this way was too insignificant to produce jaundice. According to Meakins (1927), cardiac jaundice is caused by hemolysis and intrahepatic bile duct closures. Rich (1930) was of the opinion that it was induced by a combination of retention due to chronic hypoxia and of increased blood destruction. Consequently, in every case of chronic heart insufficiency hyperbilirubinemia should develop. Ottenberg (1932) assumed that the following four factors are active: increased bilirubin production, decreased liver function due to anoxia, centrilobular atrophy of liver cells, and diminished liver circulation. Similar assumptions were advanced by Kugel and Lichtman (1937) and by Eppinger (1937). Kugel and Lichtman emphasized that cardiac jaundice is often seen in diseases of the mitral valve. They thought that severe cardiac icterus is a result of cirrhosis caused by the cardiac condition. However, Chavez et al, (1943) were able to establish a parallel between the serum bilirubin and the clinical condition of the patient; they found the highest bilirubin values in rheumatic heart disease.

Wallach and Popper (1950) could detect only a central atrophy of the lobuli in uncomplicated heart disease, but acute central necrosis of liver lobuli occurred in extensive heart or lung infarction. Hanger (1950) pointed out that lymph production is increased during cardiac stasis. He assumed that this is essential for the pathogenesis of cardiac icterus. Baumgärtel (1950b, p. 246) was able to detect the just-described changes in liver of patients with obstruction limited to the portal circulation. However, these findings have not yet been confirmed by other authors.

Sherlock (1951) bioptically examined the liver in 50 cases of cardiac icterus, from which 28 cases were autopsied. She pointed out that the usual autopsy specimens are unsuitable for the study of more delicate liver changes because of cadaverosis. In most of the cases she could detect centrilobular necrosis, which in more severe cases involved the peripheral zone as well. Furthermore, an initial increase of reticular fibers and later proliferation of connective tissue were observed in the lobular center, which in protracted cases caused cardiac cirrhosis. The structural changes exhibited a parallelism to the degree and duration of the heart disease. Clinically manifest jaundice was rare, except by mitral stenosis and tricuspid insufficiency. However, a latent increase of the serum bilirubin level was generally observed. The average serum bilirubin concentration was higher in patients with severe liver cell necrosis and with pulmonary infarction than in patients with milder disease. Whereas in general serum bilirubin concentration was only moderately increased, there was one particular case in which a value of 22 mg per 100 ml was found.

Evans et al. (1952) determined serum bilirubin in 53 patients with severe heart disease and found over 1 mg per 100 ml in 25%. They explained their low values by the fact that they did not examine patients with lung infarctions. Schalm and Hoogenboom (1952) determined serum bilirubin in 30 cardiac patients, and found increased levels in all severe cases, irrespective of the nature of the illness. The highest value was 7.2 "units," about 3 mg per 100 ml. High values were found by mitral stenosis, but lung infarctions did not show significantly increased concentration. The determination of serum bilirubin level was considered a sensitive and reliable test in the evaluation of severity of heart failure.

Chodos et al (1964) studied the red cell survival in 11 patients with congestive heart failure by means of red cells tagged with radiochromium.

The survival time was normal in 8, slightly decreased in 2, and definitely decreased in 1 patient. In 6 of the patients fecal urobilinogen was studied and found to be within the normal range. Thus hemolysis can play only a minor role in the pathogenesis of cardiac jaundice.

Summary

The seven clinical types of jaundice are briefly described. These are: hemolytic, hereditary nonhemolytic, obstructive, parenchymatous, hepatocanalicular, neonatal, and cardiac icterus. Special consideration is given to pathogenetic relationships. The attention of the reader is directed toward the recent observations of Eliassen (1961) on physiological hemolytic jaundice in the hedgehog during hibernation and toward congenital absence of the fine bile ducts, a condition supporting the pathogenetic role of parapedesis. The bile constituents in lymph from the liver and thoracic duct have not been studied in such patients, although this would be highly interesting. The lack of basic knowledge concerning partial biliary obstruction is also pointed out. So-called "intrahepatic cholestasis" is discussed, and the problems of jaundice induced by drugs and food are briefly outlined.

Additional Readings

Section C,2

Abei, T., and Iber, F. L. (1967). Kinetics of bilirubin-C^{14} distribution in the dog with bile duct ligation. In "Bilirubin Metabolism" (I. A. D. Bouchier and B. H. Billing, eds.), pp. 217–224. Blackwell, Oxford.
Andrews, W. H. H. (1965). Hepatic circulation with special reference to the relationship of the bile duct and the lymphatic system. In "The Biliary System. A Symposium of the NATO Advanced Study Institute" (W. Taylor, ed.), pp. 79–87. Blackwell, Oxford.
Billing, B. H., Ali, M. A. H., and Cartter, M. (1967). Bilirubin-C^{14} metabolism in the bile duct ligated rat. In "Bilirubin Metabolism" (I. A. D. Bouchier and B. H. Billing, eds.), pp. 225–230. Blackwell, Oxford.
Grodsky, G. (1967). Studies in the uptake and intrahepatic transport of bilirubin-H^3. In "Bilirubin Metabolism" (I. A. D. Bouchier and B. H. Billing, eds.), pp. 159–169. Blackwell, Oxford.
Hargreaves, T., and Price, V. (1966). The uptake of conjugated bilirubin by rat liver. Biochem. Pharmacol. 15, 657–667.
Reeves, J. T., Leathers, J. E., and Boatright, C. (1966). Microradiography of the rabbit's hepatic microcirculation. The similarity of the hepatic portal and pulmonary arterial circulations. Anat. Record 154, 103–107.
Schmid, R. (1967). The role of protein interaction in the tissue uptake of bilirubin. In "Bilirubin Metabolism" (I. A. D. Bouchier and B. H. Billing, eds.), pp. 147–158. Blackwell, Oxford.
Ternberg, J. L., and Butcher, H. R. (1965). Blood-flow relation between hepatic artery and portal vein. Science 150, 1030–1031.

Section C,3

Dumont, A. E., and Witte, M. H. (1966). Contracting patterns of thoracic duct lymph formation in hepatic cirrhosis. Surg. Gynecol. Obstet. 122, 524–528.
Magnenat, P. (1964). The lymph system of the liver. Spectrum Intern. (Pfizer) 10, 49–52.

Section C,4

Bernstein, L. H., Ezzer, J. B., Gartner, L., and Arias, I. M. (1966). Hepatic intracellular distribution of tritium-labeled unconjugated and conjugated bilirubin in normal and Gunn rats. J. Clin. Invest. 45, 1194–1201.
Grodsky, G. See reference quoted above in Section C,2.

Section C,5

Barber-Riley, G. (1965). Measurement of the capacity of the biliary tree. In "The Biliary System. A Symposium of the NATO Advanced Study Institute" (W. Taylor, ed.), pp. 89–97. Blackwell, Oxford.

Section D,1

Gartner, L. M. (1967). The hormonal regulation of hepatic bilirubin excretion. In "Bilirubin Metabolism" (I. A. D. Bouchier and B. H. Billing, eds.), pp. 175–182. Blackwell, Oxford.

Section E,3

Abei, T., and Iber, F. L. See reference quoted in Section C,2.
Billing, B. H., Ali, M. A. M., and Cartter, M. See reference quoted in Section C,2.
Powell, L. W. (1967). Haemolysis and bilirubin production in obstructive jaundice. In "Bilirubin Metabolism" (I. A. D. Bouchier and B. H. Billing, eds.), pp. 65–71. Blackwell, Oxford.
Ritchie, H. D. (1967). Secretion into the biliary tree during obstruction. In "Bilirubin Metabolism" (I. A. D. Bouchier and B. H. Billing, eds.), pp. 213–215. Blackwell, Oxford.

Section E,4

Ashworth, C. T., Werner, D. J., Glass, M. D., and Arnold, N. J. (1965). Spectrum of fine structural changes in hepatocellular injury due to thioacetamine. Am. J. Pathol. 47, 917–951.
Ghoshal, A. K., and Recknagel, R. O. (1965). On the mechanism of carbon tetrachloride hepatotoxicity: Coincidence of loss of glucose-6-phosphate activity with peroxidation of microsomal lipid. Life Sci. 4, 2195–2209.

Section E,5

Breinstrup, H., and Søgaard-Andersen, J. (1966). Cholestasis intrahepatica after treatment with griseofulvin (in Danish). Ugeskrift. Laeger 128, 145–147.
Christensen, M. S., Askrog, V. F., Olsen, T. S., Kemp, E., and Tygstrup, N. (1966). Liver function, histology, and cytochemistry in man following halothane and cyclopropane anaesthesia. Acta Med. Scand. 180, 29–41.
deLorimer, A. A., Gordan, G. S., Rolland, C. L., and Carbone, J. V. (1965). Methyltestosterone, related steroids and liver function. Arch. Intern. Med. 116, 289–294.
Eisalo, A., and Räsänen, J. (1965). Jaundice during administration of an oral contraceptive. Ann. Med. Internae Fenniae 54, 47–49.
Goldstein, M. J., and Rothenberg, A. J. (1966). Jaundice in a patient receiving acetohexamide. New Engl. J. Med. 275, 97–99.
Hargreaves, T. (1966). An anti-viral drug (M and B 7714) and bilirubin conjugation. Nature 210, 639.
Heikel, T. A. J. (1967). Effect of steroid drugs on biliary secretion: Intrahepatic cholestasis. Biochem. J. 193, 63P–63P.
Klein, N. C., and Jeffries, G. H. (1966). Hepatotoxicity after methoxyflurane administration. J. Am. Med. Assoc. 197, 1037–1039.
Orellana-Alcade, J. M., and Dominguez, J. P. (1966). Jaundice and oral contraceptive drugs. Lancet II, 1278–1280.
Popper, H., Rubin, E., Gardiol, D., Schaffner, F., and Paronetto, F. (1965). Drug-induced liver disease. A penalty for progress. Arch. Intern. Med. 115, 128–136.
Stoll, B. A., Andrews, J. T., and Motteram, R. (1966). Liver damage from oral contraceptives. Brit. Med. J. I, 960–961.
Subcommittee of the National Halothane Study of the Committee on Anaesthesia, National Academy of Sciences–National Research Council (1966). Summary of the national halothane study. J. Am. Med. Assoc. 197, 775–788.

Section E,7

Kisfalvi, I., and Fonyodi, L. (1965). Occurrence of hyperbilirubinemia in heart failure (in Hungarian). Orv. Hetilap 106, 1021–1023; abstracted in Excerpta Med., Sect. VI, 20, 535 (1966).

CHAPTER V

Bile Pigments of Blood

A. Introduction

Bile pigments are found in the blood of several animal species even under normal circumstances, but are observed only under pathological conditions in other species. The bile pigment of blood is almost exclusively bilirubin, although traces of biliverdin, and urobilinogens can be found occasionally. Similarly, dipyrryle bile pigments are sometimes found. Creniflavine and cyclopterine, bile pigments of chromoproteid character, which were detected in certain fishes (*Labridae* and *Cyclopteridae*), present a special case of bile pigments in blood (Fontaine, 1941).

When speaking of bile pigment in blood, one tacitly assumes that it is bile pigment in plasma or serum which is meant. Recently D. Watson (1962b) has, however, pointed out that this view is wrong. He was able to extract considerable amounts of bilirubin from washed erythrocytes from icteric blood from a human newborn by means of mixing the erythrocytes with a 3% solution of pure human albumin in physiological saline and gently shaking. After separation of the albumin solution it contained definite amounts of bilirubin. Further, incubation of normal human erythrocytes with icteric human serum resulted in a decrease of the serum bilirubin for every time the serum was incubated with fresh erythrocytes. This phenomenon may play an important role in the pathogenesis of jaundice, especially because Watson found that it is influenced by various drugs.

The phenomenon was further studied by Oski and Naiman (1963), who expected a certain binding of unconjugated bilirubin, which is non-polar, to the red cell membrane because it contains appreciable amounts of lipid. They found that erythrocytes are capable of binding limited amounts of free bilirubin. If 100 ml erythrocytes were added to 100 ml of serum containing unconjugated bilirubin, a reduction in bilirubin concentration of ca. 3 mg per 100 ml resulted. This was, however, not the case if erythrocytes coated with antibody—giving positive direct Coombs, test—were employed. Such sensitized erythrocytes did not bind

259

bilirubin. The capacity to bind free bilirubin was limited to nonsensitized erythrocytes. The binding ability appears to be a physicochemical property of the cell membrane since it occurs almost instantly, the stroma retains the ability to adsorb bilirubin, and inert latex particles exhibited no adsorption. Stroma from nonsensitized erythrocytes adsorbed 0.014 mg per ml stroma, whereas stroma from sensitized erythrocytes did not adsorb bilirubin. The bilirubin-binding protein albumin competes effectively with the erythrocyte membrane for bilirubin binding and is able to extract bilirubin bound to its lipid structures.

In their experiments, Oski and Naiman corrected for the fall in bilirubin concentration due to dilution from saline trapped among the washed erythrocytes by means of the formula: Amount of bilirubin reduction expected from dilution alone is equal to $B_i \times V_{sal} / (V_{ser} + V_{sal})$, where V_{sal} = saline volume (volume of red cell mixture added — volume of packed cells), V_{ser} = serum volume, and B_i = initial serum bilirubin concentration of red cell serum mixture.

Schettini and Meloni (1964[*]) compared the ability of red cells from five Sardinian infants with glucose-6-phosphate dehydrogenase deficiency and erythrocytes from six normal infants to adsorb unconjugated bilirubin from serum and found no difference.

Kaufmann and Blondheim (1966[*]) confirmed the ability of erythrocytes to bind unconjugated bilirubin present in serum already at physiological serum bilirubin levels and found a steep increase in their bilirubin binding capacity at serum bilirubin concentrations exceeding 33 mg/100 ml, i.e., corresponding to a bilirubin/albumin molar ratio exceeding 1.

The presence of bilirubin was shown in early investigations in normal horse serum (Hammarsten, 1878) and human serum (Gilbert *et al.*, 1903b). Hijmans van den Bergh and Snapper (1913) introduced Ehrlich's (1883) diazo reaction into clinical chemistry and thereby started modern investigations of serum bilirubin. Since this time a huge amount of literature has been accumulated, mainly because the question of direct and indirect diazo reaction created a great deal of confusion. These terms were introduced by Hijmans van den Bergh and Müller (1916), who observed that serum in hemolytic icterus reacted with the diazo reagent only after the addition of alcohol (indirect reaction), whereas this reaction took place without adding alcohol in serum of patients with obstructive icterus (direct reaction). This dissimilarity was considered to be extremely important. Although the significance of these reactions was mainly hypothetical, a whole series of various icterus theories were based on it. Only a few authors retained a critical attitude toward the significance of the direct diazo reaction, among them G. A. Harrison (1930, 1937, 1947), who stated (1947, p. 241): "Until more is known of the chemistry of bilirubin and of its diazo reaction in particular, it would be wise to set on one side theories developed from findings by van den Bergh's test." However, during the last few years our knowledge of this phenomenon has increased considerably, and a final evaluation and understanding of the direct diazo reaction is now in sight.

B. Bilirubin and Serum Proteins

As Overbeek *et al.* (1955b) have demonstrated, bilirubin is insoluble in water at the pH of serum. These authors measured the solubility of bilirubin in aqueous solutions, using potentiometric titration with glass electrode at various pH levels. Simultaneously, control titrations were performed in the absence of oxygen and carbon dioxide, and the reaction constants were determined. The solubility of bilirubin in the form of acid was 5×10^{-11} mole per liter or 0.03 μg per liter. It was considerably higher in its mono- or divalent ions. Absolute solubility of bilirubin (ions as well as acid) was 2×10^{-6} mole per liter at pH $= 7$, and 2×10^{-4} mole per liter at pH $= 8$.

Recent studies by Burnstine and Schmid (1962) have demonstrated that free bilirubin is considerably more soluble in protein-free extracellular fluids than formerly believed. The studies of Overbeek *et al.* (1955b) were carried out at considerably lower ionic strength than that found in extracellular fluid. Burnstine and Schmid found that as much as 5 mg bilirubin can be dissolved in 100 ml protein-free extracellular fluid at pH 7.4 and ionic strength 0.15. The solubility decreases rapidly, however, on slight reduction of pH.

Bungenberg de Jong (1937, 1943) found that precipitation of bilirubin from aqueous solutions starts at pH $= 6.2$, and reaches the maximum at pH $= 4$. With (1945a,c) observed flocculation already at pH $= 7$–7.5.

If serum is added to bilirubin solutions, the color immediately changes slightly but markedly. After this, the solution can be further diluted indefinitely with saline without precipitation, in contradistinction to aqueous bilirubin solutions. This fact indicates impressively the bond formation, which occurs between bilirubin and serum proteins. The various methods which serve the elucidation of the nature of this bond will be discussed below.

It is to be emphasized that the binding of bilirubin to serum albumin varies considerably from species to species (Ostrow and Schmid, 1963*; Snyder and Schmid, 1965*). Similar differences affect the binding of hematin to serum albumin. The biological significance of these differences is apparent from the finding of Snyder and Schmid that the biological half-life of hematin injected in rats is 3.7 hours with human albumin as ligand, but only 1.5 hours with murine albumin as ligand.

R. Schmid *et al.* (1965*) compared the binding of bilirubin to albumin from man, rat, and guinea pig by exposing bilirubin-albumin solutions to a slurry of cholestyramine—a substance having a greater affinity toward bilirubin than albumin has—and estimating the rate of transfer of the bilirubin to the insoluble resin. With human albumin the transfer of bilirubin to the resin was considerably lower than with rat and guinea pig albumin.

In vivo, this binding of bilirubin is subjected to rapid turnover. Thus Grodsky *et al.* (1962) found that biological half-life of H^3-bilirubin injected intravenously into rats is 25–35 minutes (cf. also this chapter, Section B,12).

1. DIALYSIS AND ULTRAFILTRATION

Early dialysis and ultrafiltration studies on serum bilirubin yielded contradictory results (Hoover and Blankenhorn, 1916, 1921; Brulé *et al.*, 1922; Hijmans van den Bergh, 1918, p. 45; Leschke, 1921a; F. Rosenthal, 1924; Collinson and Fowweather, 1926; Davies and Dodds, 1927; Roberts, 1928; Weltmann and Hückel, 1928, 1929; de Castro, 1930; Dominici and Marengo, 1933a,b). Thus, some authors found that, contrary to "indirect bilirubin," only serum bilirubin which gives direct diazo reaction can be dialyzed. Others maintained that neither "direct" nor "indirect" bilirubin passes through the membrane. Furthermore, addition of bile, alcohol, or caffeine sodium benzoate renders bilirubin dialyzable, but it is not dialyzable without such additions. However, other investigators doubted these findings. Bendien and Snapper (1931, 1933) and Bennhold (1932, 1938) carried out very thorough ultrafiltration and diffusion experiments. These showed that membranes which did not permit the passage of protein were also impermeable for bilirubin. In these experiments it made no difference whether the bilirubin reacted "directly" or "indirectly." This fact was confirmed by Hartog (1935, p. 67). This author did not succeed in dialyzing aqueous alkaline bilirubin solutions through collodion membranes. Bungenberg de Jong (1937, 1943) obtained the same experimental results with collodion as well as with parchment membranes, the impermeability of which to protein was established in the most meticulous fashion. These membranes were impermeable for serum bilirubin even when bile salts or concentrated electrolytes were added to the serum. However, bilirubin from bile and bilirubin from urine readily passed through these membranes. Pure aqueous bilirubin solutions were retained, but after alcohol addition bilirubin penetrated through the membranes. However, a high alcohol concentration had to be maintained on both sides of the membrane. At 50% alcohol concentration only slight dialysis of bilirubin occurred. When the alcohol concentration was increased to 80% on both sides of the membrane, a rapid permeation took place. Azobilirubin, independently of its origin (serum, bile, or bilirubinate solutions), did not pass these membranes. The same was true for pure bilirubin solutions in chloroform.

Deenstra (1947, p. 84) repeated these experiments, and was able to confirm Bungenberg de Jong's findings in every respect. Aqueous bilirubinate solutions were not dialyzable below pH = 11, but they passed through collodion membranes in solutions of 0.1 N NaOH. According to Jendrassik and Cleghorn (1937), the addition of two parts of caffeine benzoate reagents to bilirubinate solutions led to a fast dialysis. Correspondingly, high alcohol concentrations rendered serum bilirubin as well as pure bilirubin solutions dialyzable.

Dulière and Minne (1937) and Gregory and Andersch (1937) could show that cellophane, as well as collodion membranes which were impermeable for proteins, also retained the bilirubin in all the sera studied. The authors did not succeed in dialyzing bilirubin from the gallbladder bile and icteric urine.

Westphal and Gedigk (1948) showed that serum bilirubin, as well as azobilirubin, formed by diazotation, cannot pass through cellophane membranes. This was the case for both "direct" and "indirect" reacting sera. These authors used 0.9% sodium chloride solution as diluent for dialysis experiments. When stronger salt solutions were employed (up to 6%), slight dialysis occurred after 2–3 days in some cases. In protein-free bilirubinate solutions (20 mg per 100 ml) and at pH 7–8, definite dialysis was detected after only a few hours. Talafant (1954b) demonstrated that direct as well as indirect bilirubin is strongly bound to protein. However, the pigment–protein complexes of direct bilirubin were found to be more labile to the effects of salts of bile acids than complexes of the indirect form.

Odell (1959a,b) studied sera from 20 newborn infants and artificial bilirubin sera prepared from crystalline bilirubin and bovine serum albumin. The sera were subjected to dialysis or ultrafiltration in cellulose casings with and without addition of various sulfonamides, glucuronate, or salicylate in concentrations of 2–200 mg per 100 ml. The ultrafiltrates were protein-free and colorless, but with concentrations of sulfonamides and salicylate above 5–25 mg per 100 ml, bilirubin appeared in the filtrate. D. Watson (1962a) likewise performed dialysis and ultrafiltration experiments with solutions of bilirubin-albumin and with icteric sera from newborns with and without addition of electrolytes. He found that no bilirubin passed the membrane if the ratio of bilirubin/

albumin did not exceed 1/40 (3 moles bilirubin per 1 mole albumin). Taurocholate, salicylate, and caffeine brought about passage of bilirubin, but concentrations as high as 2000 mg per 100 ml or more were required. Thus bilirubin can only leave the blood stream by diffusion or ultrafiltration under special circumstances because of its firm binding to serum albumin.

Ostrow et al. (1963) performed 24-hour dialysis experiments with bilirubin-C^{14} added to human and rat sera with varying bilirubin and albumin concentrations. The sera were diluted with nine parts of tris buffer at pH 8.6. At concentrations below 2 moles bilirubin per mole of albumin only about 2% of the radioactive label appeared in the dialysates. With higher pigment concentrations, on the other hand, approximately 40% of the label present in excess of 2 moles of bilirubin per mole of albumin passed the membrane.

The action of salts on the albumin bond found in vitro by Odell was verified in vivo by R. Schmid et al. (1965[*]) on a female rat with unconjugated hyperbilirubinemia (Gunn rat) that was injected with a tracer dose of C^{14}-bilirubin. The serum bilirubin level was followed at appropriate intervals for 2 days after which sodium salicylate was infused for 4 hours at a rate of 16 mg per hour. This caused a rapid and profound drop in the serum bilirubin—from 12 to 3 mg/100 ml—and for the following 24 hours the serum bilirubin remained low (4 mg/100 ml). Then an i.v. infusion of 500 mg salt-poor albumin was given, after which the serum bilirubin rapidly rose to 10 mg/100 ml. This effect is explained by assuming that salicylate replaces bilirubin from the binding sites of albumin after which bilirubin is able to enter the extravascular space.

Fulop et al. (1964, 1965[*]) dialyzed plasma from men and dogs with obstructive jaundice with 82–88% of the bilirubin present in the conjugated form. Plasma specimens of 5 ml each were placed in cellophane casing and dialyzed at 4°C against 5 ml buffer (0.01 M phosphate, 0.15 M NaCl; pH 7.2) in flasks covered with aluminum foil and gassed with 5% CO_2, 95% N_2. Equilibrium was attained in 24 hours with specimens from subjects with normal renal function and more slowly with specimens from subjects with renal failure. The dialyzates were faintly yellow and diazo-positive. Their bilirubin content (Malloy-Evelyn method) was 1.4–3.2% of the total bilirubin concentration of the dog sera and 0.4–2.0% of that of the human sera. The total bilirubin concentration was 3.4–11.2 mg/100 ml in the dog sera, 16.8–40.2 mg/100 ml in the human sera. The spectral curve of the dialyzates showed absorption maxima between 435 and 445 nm, whereas the bilirubin-albumin solution had 460 nm.

Lüders (1964[*]) performed dialysis experiments of 3-days duration at 4°C in darkness using cellophane bags and ultrafiltration studies of 1- to 3-hours duration using collodium membranes with a water suction pump.

The membranes were tested for protein impermeability before the experiments. Solutions of unconjugated bilirubin of an initial concentration of 40 mg/100 ml were used as inner fluid. The results varied with the composition of the fluid outside and inside the membrane. In all experiments with protein (calf serum or 5% human albumin) added to the inner fluid no bilirubin passed into the outer fluid even after 3 days of dialysis. This was the same even when the outer fluid was 0.1 M sodium carbonate. It was found that dialysis and ultrafiltration could only take place when free bilirubin was soluble in the outer fluid. Thus no passage took place if the outer fluid was acidic. With protein-free bilirubin solutions as the inner fluid passage of bilirubin was demonstrable in a few hours if 0.1 M sodium carbonate, 0.9% NaCl, and serum were used as the outer fluids. Passage of bilirubin when protein was present in the inner fluid took place only if accelerators of the diazo reaction—bile salts (decholin) or caffeine-sodium benzoate—were added to the inner fluid, i.e., substances enhancing the solubility of free bilirubin. Contrary to Odell, Lüders found no passage of bilirubin by dialysis and ultrafiltration of protein containing bilirubin solutions after addition of sulfonamides (Solu-Supronal) in concentrations up to 1 g per 100 ml.

Scholtan and Gloxhuber (1966*) found that a substantial amount of bilirubin is adsorbed in the dialysis membrane if bilirubin solutions are dialyzed against buffer solutions through cellophane membranes. Only a minor part of the bilirubin disappearing from the inner compartment reaches the buffer solution in the outer compartment.

Josephson and Furst (1966*) performed ultrafiltration experiments through cellophane membranes with a pressure of ca. 1 kg per cm^2 at 4° and 37°C. The bilirubin passed freely from protein-free buffer solutions (Clark and Lub borate buffer, pH 7.8). Unconjugated bilirubin present in native sera or added to human serum did not pass at concentrations below 30 mg/100 ml, but at 35 mg/100 ml traces of bilirubin were present in the filtrate and with 50 mg/100 ml the filtrate contained ca. 1 mg bilirubin/100 ml. If sulfa compounds were added to the serum the bilirubin passed more freely, but only if the sulfa compound concentration was 15–20 mg/100 ml or above and the bilirubin concentration was above 20 mg/100 ml.

Further investigations—including other species—with radioactive bilirubin and azobilirubin using various ionic strengths at different pH values would be of interest.

2. ELECTROPHORESIS

Bennhold (1932, 1938) was the first to study the electrophoretic behavior of serum bilirubin. He showed that bilirubin migrates with the albumin fraction in both direct and indirect reacting sera. In highly icteric serum, he could detect a small bilirubin fraction which was localized before the albumin. Pedersen and Waldenström (1937) confirmed these results. Stenhagen and Teorell (1938) found that between pH 4.12 and 8.00 the bond between serum albumin and bilirubin is stable. When nucleic acid was added to bilirubin dissolved in serum, transfer of bilirubin from serum proteins to *nucleic acid* occurred; i.e. a carrier change took place. Stenhagen and Rideal (1939) observed in investigations with the Tiselius apparatus that bilirubin migrates exclusively with the serum albumin fraction at pH = 7, but one part of bilirubin migrates before the albumin front at pH = 8.2.

Pedersen and Waldenström failed to show the presence of any bond between bilirubin and ovalbumin. Stenhagen and Rideal established in studies with monomolecular layers that the *phenolic groups of bilirubin* are bound to the primary amino groups of the protein. Since lysine has a free amino group in the ε-position, proteins poor in lysine can hardly be bound to bilirubin. This explains why ovalbumin with 3.8% lysine content cannot bind bilirubin, contrary to serum albumin (13.2% lysine). These authors also found that bilirubin penetrates monomolecular lipid layers readily.

Coolidge (1940) showed in electrophoretic experiments that the bilirubin–serum albumin bond is so strong that it is not affected even by addition of 50% alcohol. Westphal and Gedigk (1948) conducted electrophoresis on dilute icteric sera before and after addition of diazo reagent. They found that bilirubin migrates with serum albumin at pH 4.12–8.00; however, it migrates before the albumin front at pH over 8.00. One part of bilirubin migrates toward the cathode at pH 4.1–4.3, whereas the rest moves toward the anode.

Martin (1948, 1949) demonstrated that during separations in the Tiselius apparatus there is a striking agreement between the migration of serum albumin and bilirubin. Gray and Kekwick (1948) confirmed these findings. These authors did not observe differences between direct and indirect bilirubin. Westphal *et al.* (1950) studied the electrophoretic behavior of icteric and normal sera after bilirubin addition using concentrations up to 100 mg per 100 ml and demonstrated that the entire amount of bilirubin migrates with the albumin except in strongly icteric sera where a small part coincides with the α_2- and β-globulin.

Childs (1955), Tuttle (1955), Klatskin and Bungards (1956), Bourrillon (1956, 1957, 1958a,b,c), Weicker (1957), and D. Watson (1962a) carried out paper electrophoretic studies on serum bilirubin. Childs followed migrations at pH values of 8.6, 7.5, 6.0, 5.5, and 5.0. He found that direct as well as indirect reacting bilirubin migrated with albumin at pH 8.6 and 7.5. However, at pH values under 6.5 direct reacting bilirubin migrated with albumin, but indirect reacting bilirubin was only partly found in the albumin fraction. The rest migrated more slowly, tailing the albumin. Klatskin and Bungards studied the electrophoretic mobility of direct and indirect serum bilirubin at pH values between 2 and 9. They demonstrated that both forms of bilirubin migrate with albumin at pH 6–9. At pH 5 and below, the bilirubin–albumin bond was cleaved and less soluble, free bilirubin was liberated. The cleavage was complete at pH 5 for indirect bilirubin, whereas a considerable part of direct bilirubin still migrated with albumin at this pH. However, at pH 4 and below, the electrophoretic mobility of both types of bilirubin was again practically identical. Tuttle (1955) studied icteric sera of newborns. Bilirubin was bound to albumin, and to a lesser degree to β-globulin.

Bourrillon (1956, 1957, 1958a,b,c) conducted paper electrophoresis and free electrophoresis studies (Perkin-Elmer apparatus, equipped with special filters to render visible the migrating bilirubin front). He showed that in concentrations up to 20 mg bilirubin per 100 ml serum the entire amount of bilirubin was attached to albumin; but he could never observe binding on globulin. The bilirubin-containing protein fraction was purified by zone electrophoresis on starch (16–20 hours, 0°C, 800 volts) and the purity of the isolated fractions was checked by subsequent paper chromatography. In this case, too, bilirubin was found to be bound on albumin. Traces migrating with the α-globulin were considered as albumin impurities of this fraction, since it is very difficult to separate this protein completely from α-globulins.

Weicker (1957) found that direct bilirubin (bilirubin glucuronide) is bound only to serum albumin, whereas indirect bilirubin (free bilirubin) is connected to the lipoprotein component of the albumin fraction.

D. Watson (1962a) performed electrophoresis of hyperbilirubinemic sera of newborns on paper or cellulose acetate at pH 8.6 and pH 7.0. The bilirubin was completely bound to the albumin band except in excessive hyperbilirubinemia, in which case some pigment could be eluted from the α_1-globulin band. The α_2- and β-globulin fractions were bilirubin free. Darocha et al. (1962) used electrophoreses on starch gel at pH 8.5, a method giving especially high resolving power. They found that the only bilirubin-carrying fraction of human serum protein is the albumin.

It is thus an established fact that bilirubin is strongly bound to serum albumin, but it is still questionable whether a minor part is bound to α_2- and β-globulin. This problem was recently attacked by Ostrow et al. (1963) by means of C^{14}-labeled bilirubin of high specificity. In experiments with nonradioactive bilirubin, comparatively high concentrations are necessary, and this may have prevented detection of globulin fractions of high affinity but limited carrying capacity for the pigment. This error is eliminated with the use of radioactive bilirubin. Both human sera and rat sera were studied. All the sera investigated contained unconjugated bilirubin, and sera from patients with various diseases as well as newborns were incorporated as well as sera with anomalous albumin (bis-albuminemia, hypalbuminemia). The electrophoresis was performed with continuous flow technique. It was found in all instances, at pigment concentrations ranging from physiological levels to the limit of the bilirubin-binding capacity of serum, that C^{14}-bilirubin migrated *only with albumin.*

Fulop *et al.* (1965[*]) studied the electrophoretic pattern of free and conjugated bilirubin in plasma of man and dog. If only free bilirubin was present, all bilirubin migrated with the albumin both at pH 8.6 (barbital and Tris buffers) and pH 7.4 (phosphate buffer). This was the case with electrophoresis on both paper and polyvinyl chloride. Bilirubin concentrations up to 40 mg/100 ml were studied. In sera containing conjugated bilirubin (from obstructive jaundice) and having a total serum bilirubin of at least 15 mg/100 ml electrophoresis constantly disclosed a small bilirubin fraction migrating with the β-globulins. This bilirubin fraction gave typical reactions with Fouchet and diazo reagents. In dogs with obstructive jaundice the findings were similar. Thus the electrophoretic behavior of conjugated bilirubin differed significantly from that of unconjugated bilirubin.

D. Watson (1964b) (cf. this chapter, Section B,11) found that the bilirubin binding capacity of sera from adult women is substantially higher than calculated from their albumin content suggesting that other bilirubin binding substances are present in serum besides albumin. Later he (D. Watson, 1967[*]) studied the albumin binding capacity of various dyes and confirmed his earlier findings. The discrepancy between his findings and most modern electrophoresis studies he looks upon as only apparent because it is feasible that more than one bilirubin-bearing globulin fraction may migrate together with the albumin.

3. ULTRACENTRIFUGATION

Pedersen and Waldenström (1937) carried out investigations of the bilirubin–protein complex of serum with the help of the ultracentrifuge. They found that "direct" as well as "indirect" bilirubin accompanies the albumin.

Scholtan and Gloxhuber (1966[*]) used the Beckman-Spinco-Ultracentrifuge L 50 with Titan rotor 50 and subjected sera containing unconjugated or conjugated bilirubin to 40,000 rpm for 15 hours at 4°C in ultracentrifuge tubes of 11.5 ml capacity. In this way a considerable separation of the serum proteins took place.

The upper layers of the fluid in the tubes were practically protein-free and contained a small amount of bilirubin not bound to protein. Control experiments showed that protein-free solutions of conjugated and unconjugated bilirubin did not sediment during this treatment. Unconjugated bilirubin was, however, not stable in protein-free solutions during the 15-hour-long procedure in contrast to conjugated bilirubin. The centrifuge tubes were frozen immediately after centrifugation and the different protein layers as defined by refractometry were analyzed for bilirubin after thawing. The complex bilirubin–human albumin exhibited nearly the same wandering speed as pure human albumin (3.75 and 3.93 Svedberg units, respectively).

The concentration of bilirubin in the upper protein-free layer was determined and compared to the bilirubin concentration before the ultracentrifugation; both for unconjugated and conjugated bilirubin the concentration of the bilirubin in the protein-free layer was found to be about 0.6% of the total bilirubin concentration.

No significant difference between the protein binding of unconjugated bilirubin and that of conjugated bilirubin was demonstrated in the experiments. Protein binding was independent of temperatures in the range 4°–20°C. Addition of bile salts caused a partial displacement of the bilirubin from the albumin.

4. PRECIPITATION

Cristesco (1937), Coolidge (1942), Bourrillon (1952), and Polonovski and Bourrillon (1952b) found that practically the entire bilirubin amount of icteric sera can be precipitated with ammonium sulfate. They found that precipitation occurs together with the albumin fraction and only insignificant amounts with the globulins.

Dulière and Minne (1937) found that serum bilirubin precipitates quantitatively with protein on trichloroacetic acid addition. Najjar and Childs (1955) claimed that with ammonium sulfate indirect bilirubin precipitates with the globulins, direct bilirubin with the albumin; but Klatskin and Bungards (1956) found with the same technique that both direct and indirect bilirubin are precipitated with the albumin.

Cohn (1948), Martin (1948, 1949), Cohn et al. (1950), Barac (1953), and Vitelli et al. (1956) fractionated plasma protein with alcohol in the cold according to Cohn's method (1948). With this method bilirubin is found mainly in fractions I, III, and V. Cohn isolated an α_1-globulin fraction very rich in bilirubin, but its concentration is so low that it can only account for a minor amount of the serum bilirubin. Vitelli et al. (1956) found free (indirect) bilirubin especially in fractions I and III, whereas the conjugated (direct) bilirubin came mostly with fraction V. Fasoli (1949, 1950) and Fasoli and Franzini (1950) studied bilirubin contents of serum proteins by precipitation with cold methanol. They found that 37–86% of the bilirubin remained in solution after precipitation of all serum proteins. They were able to determine a relationship between indirect bilirubin content and serum proteins.

5. Increased Stability to Oxidation

Unlike pure aqueous alkaline bilirubin solutions which are rapidly oxidized to biliverdin, solutions containing serum proteins are considerably more stable.

This was first shown by Boutaric and Roy (1939) and has since been confirmed by many investigators (With, 1942a; Barac, 1946a–h; Barac and Roseman, 1946a,b,c; Barac and Gernay, 1949; D. Watson, 1962a). This protective action of serum protein indicates strong binding between it and bilirubin.

This protective action of serum albumin is also present during irradiation with X-rays, whereas ovalbumin and γ-globulin do not protect bilirubin from oxidation caused by irradiation (Barac et al., 1961a,b).

6. Changes in Spectral Absorption

It is known that interaction between proteins and organic pigments leads to changes in the absorption spectrum of the latter (see Klotz, 1946; Klotz et al., 1946). Thus, one may anticipate that the spectrum of serum bilirubin will differ from that of pure bilirubinate solutions. When serum is added to pure aqueous alkaline bilirubin solutions, a definite color change occurs (Penati and Pagliardi, 1943; With, 1945a; Bénard et al., 1949c; Hunter, 1951, p. 93). After addition of serum to bilirubin, the absorption maximum of pure solutions shifts from 420–430 nm to 450–460 nm. Very small amounts of serum suffice to cause this displacement (With, 1945a). Thus, addition of one part serum to 100 parts of bilirubin solution leads to marked displacement, and 2.5 parts cause a maximal shift. These maximal shifts are only characteristic of human serum. The corresponding value in horse serum is 470 nm. Globulins, globin, and protein degradation products do not produce changes (Bénard et al., 1949c; Bourrillon, 1952; Polonovski and Bourrillon, 1952b). These color changes are not produced by the pH changes caused by the serum addition (With, 1945a).

Barac (1951, 1953) examined in greater detail the changes in absorption spectra of bilirubin solutions after addition of serum proteins. He demonstrated that solutions whose serum albumin content corresponded to normal serum could dissolve 100 mg bilirubin per 100 ml at pH 7.4 completely. However, solutions without serum albumin already precipitated at 1 mg bilirubin per 100 ml at the same pH. When pure albumin from human or cattle serum was added to bilirubin solutions the absorption maximum changed from 4330 Å to 4600 Å. This shift was independent of the pH in the range of 7–12.

He determined by potentiometric titration that the amount of bilirubin bound to 1 mg albumin was 20 mg in humans and 21 mg in cattle. Normal human serum contains about 4% albumin. Since the molecular weight of bilirubin is 584 and that of serum albumin is about 65,000, 100 ml serum is capable of binding about 100 mg bilirubin, and about 5 moles of bilirubin are bound to 1 mole of serum albumin. Additions of fibrinogen, γ-globulin, and acid glycoprotein gave no changes in absorption. Iron-containing β-globulin shifted the maximum to 4550 Å, and a simultaneous increase in solubility of bilirubin could be observed.

Klatskin and Bungards (1956) investigated the absorption spectrum of fractions isolated by electrophoresis from icteric serum. They could detect bilirubin only in the albumin fraction. Absorption spectra of the globulin fractions corresponded to hemoglobin and not to bilirubin.

Odell (1959a,b) studied the change in spectral absorption caused by addition of salicylates, sulfonamides, and other electrolytes to icteric sera of newborns and to artificial bilirubin sera with pH 7.4. He found a decrease of absorbancy at maximum (460 nm) and a corresponding increase in absorbancy at 420 nm, the maximum of free bilirubin not bound to protein. With artificially icteric bovine sera he arrived at similar results.

Fog (1960, p. 60) studied the spectral absorption of bilirubin in serum with varying pH. The absorbancy was highest at pH 8.1. At pH 7.4 it was 9% lower than at pH 8.1. Simultaneously, a shift of the maximum toward shorter wavelengths took place—465 nm at pH 8.3 as against 460 nm at pH 7.4, for human sera with addition of free bilirubin.

D. Watson (1962a) investigated mixtures of bilirubinate solutions and pure human albumin solutions with varying bilirubin/albumin ratios and electrolyte contents. Further, mixtures of bilirubin solutions with α_2-, β-, and γ-globulin solutions were studied. No evidence for binding of bilirubin to the latter proteins was found. At pH 7.38 and temperature 32°C bilirubin—albumin solutions in 0.1 M phosphate buffer showed the absorption maximum 465–466 nm, and mesobilirubin–albumin solutions, 427–428 nm if the molar ratio of bilirubin/albumin was between 1.0 and 3.7. If this ratio increased above 3.7, the maximum shifted toward shorter wavelengths (439 for bilirubin, 407 for mesobilirubin at the molar ratio 10.0). Several hundred icteric sera from newborns all showed maxima between 455 and 460 nm except two with maxima of 461 and 469. Addition of salicylates to a concentration of 30 mg per 100 ml was followed by the appearance of a new maximum at 420 nm. Addition of bilirubin in excess to such a degree that it could not be bound by the albumin present resulted in one maximum at 440 nm rather than the two maxima of 420 and 465 nm found on addition of salicylate. This finding makes Odell's interpretation of this phenomenon open to doubt (cf. above). D. Watson emphasized that the spectral absorption maximum of bilirubin added to pure serum albumin solutions is not the same as that found for bilirubin added to blood plasma, a fact which he ascribes to interfering substances present in plasma and not to incomplete binding of bilirubin to albumin. He further claimed that oral administration of salicylates causes a quite dramatic drop of the serum bilirubin. But he does not take the spontaneous diurnal variations of serum bilirubin into account (cf. Section G, this chapter). Before it is definitely shown that his findings are not due to the action of meals and fasting, they cannot be regarded valid.

Blondheim *et al.* (1962) studied the effect of light on the absorption spectrum of jaundiced serum of the direct and indirect type as well as on pure bilirubin added to normal sera or albumin solutions. Exposure to a fluorescent daylight lamp for several hours resulted in a decrease of the absorbancy at 450–460 nm, corresponding to the maximum of bilirubin–albumin, and a corresponding increase in the absorbancy at the maximum of biliverdin at 660 nm. There was also a shift of the absorption maximum at 450 nm and an increase of the absorbancy at 420 nm— corresponding to the maximum of molecular bilirubin. If the solutions which had been exposed to light were subjected to ultrafiltration in a nitrogen atmosphere in the presence of ascorbic acid, the protein-free filtrate was definitely yellow and showed a well-marked maximum at 420 nm. These observations seem conclusive, and similar studies on the effect of addition of drugs on the diffusibility of serum bilirubin are highly desirable to verify the theory of Odell on the effect of certain drugs on the bilirubin–albumin linkage.

Novák *et al.* (1962) found in studies with incubation *in vitro* that nonesterified fatty acids displace bilirubin from its binding to serum albumin.

It is also to be emphasized that colloidal aggregation of bilirubin molecule causes a spectral displacement from 430 to 470 nm in pure solutions (Jirsa and Šponar, 1956). However, the result is a flattening of the curve together with a lowering of extinction; this is just the opposite of what can be observed after protein addition (see Fig. 15, Chapter I, Section C).

The change of the spectral absorption of bilirubin diglucuronide on addition of albumin is discussed in Section F of this chapter.

7. Molar Ratio of Bilirubin–Protein Compounds

On the basis of spectrophotometric titrations, With (1945a,c) determined that about 1 mg bilirubin is bound to 0.1 ml serum (about 5 mg albumin). Thus, 1 g serum albumin binds 200 mg bilirubin, or 1 mole protein binds 20 moles pigment. Contrary to this, Martin (1948, 1949) and Barac (1953) determined that 2–3 moles of bilirubin are bound to 1 mole of serum albumin. Bourrillon (1952) and Polonovski and Bourrillon (1952b) further studied this molar ratio, measuring the retarding effect of serum albumin on the diazo reaction. They concluded that 1 mg serum albumin binds 10 μg bilirubin. Consequently, each gram of serum albumin takes up 10 mg bilirubin corresponding to an equimolar compound.

Odell (1959a) held that 1 mole albumin binds 2 moles bilirubin, an opinion based on Martin's studies. The first mole of bilirubin bound to albumin is regarded as much more strongly bound than the second one. If bilirubin-monoalbumin is AB, bilirubin-dialbumin is AB_2, the dissociation constants are:

$$\frac{[A^{++}][B^-]}{[AB^+]} = K_1 \quad \text{and} \quad \frac{[AB^+][B^-]}{[AB_2]} = K_2$$

then

$$K_2 > 4K_1$$

If a third bilirubin molecule was to be bound to albumin, an even higher dissociation constant would be expected corresponding to a much looser attachment.

D. Watson (1962a) found in spectrophotometric studies an average molar ratio of 3.3 moles bilirubin to 1 mole albumin.

Besides the bilirubin–serum albumin bond, other bilirubin protein bonds have been studied. Pedersen and Waldenström (1937) could not detect bond formation with egg albumin. Martin (1948, 1949) found the same for human β- and γ-globulin, but some binding to α_1 and α_2-globulin. In these experiments he found that 1 g human serum albumin binds 21.1 mg bilirubin; 1 g α_1-globulin 16.4 mg bilirubin; and 1 g α_2-globulin 11.4 mg of this pigment. Based on these experiments, Klatskin and Bungards (1956) calculated that in 100 ml serum only 0.05 mg indirect reacting bilirubin can be bound to α_1-globulin. Barac (1953) assumed that about 90% of serum bilirubin was bound to albumin. Bourrillon (1958c) could not find any binding of bilirubin or globulin.

Vitelli *et al.* (1957) reported, however, two cases of jaundice where the serum bilirubin was bound exclusively to the α_2-globulin. On the other hand, D. Watson (1962a) who studied several hundred sera found only binding to albumin except in two instances with binding to albumin and α_1-globulin. He ascribed this to the special bilirubin-binding lipoprotein fraction of Cohn (1948) and Cohn et al. (1950). Darocha et al. (1962) found that bilirubin is exclusively bound to albumin.

The molar ratio bilirubin–albumin was studied with C^{14}-labeled bilirubin by Ostrow et al. (1963) in 24-hour dialysis experiments at pH 8.6 in tris buffer. They found that 1 mole of albumin binds 2 moles of unconjugated bilirubin so firmly that dialysis can virtually not take place. At higher bilirubin/albumin ratios, about 40% of the bilirubin in excess of the 2 moles/1 mole ratio became dialyzable. Thus there seems to be a firm binding of 2 moles of bilirubin per mole of albumin and a looser association of excess bilirubin.

R. Schmid et al. (1965*) found in gel filtration studies that 2 moles of bilirubin are bound to 1 mole of albumin (cf. Section B,9 of this chapter).

In their studies with ultrafiltration through cellophane membranes (cf. this chapter, Section B,1) and Sephadex filtration (Section B,9 of this chapter) Josephson and Furst (1966*) found that a 2% solution of human albumin binds 35 mg bilirubin per 100 ml corresponding to ca. 2 moles of bilirubin per mole of albumin. Their results were, however, not in agreement with the hypothesis of Odell (1959b) that the reaction of bilirubin and serum albumin follows the law of mass action. Josephson and Furst believe that bilirubin adheres completely to albumin up to the point where 2 moles of bilirubin are bound per mole of albumin and only then can bilirubin dissociate. The binding is believed not to be reversible if bilirubin is not "squeezed out" by competing molecules.

This hypothesis of Josephson and Furst (1966*) makes it quite impossible to understand the pathogenesis of jaundice due to unconjugated bilirubin. In what way can bilirubin reach the tissues when the albumin–bilirubin complex is not reversible? It is also in disagreement with the finding of Scholtan and Gloxhuber (1966*) in ultracentrifuge experiments that 0.6% of the total serum bilirubin present does not follow the albumin during ultracentrifugation.

It should be mentioned here that bilirubin can react with other colloids besides proteins. Bonds with *nucleic acids* were demonstrated by Stenhagen and Teorell (1938) (Section B,2, this chapter). Furthermore, bilirubin is equally strongly bound to "Kollidon" which is contained in the plasma substitute "Periston" (Bennhold and Schubert, 1944; Schubert, 1949). This is also true for other pigments, for example, azorubin, which is bound to serum proteins as well as to other colloids (Westphal et al., 1950).

The molar ratio of the albumin bond of bilirubin diglucuronide is discussed in Section F of this chapter.

8. The Alleged Bilirubin–Globin Bond in Serum

Since bilirubin is a derivative of heme which is linked to globin in the hemoglobin molecule, it can be expected that this bond remains preserved when heme is converted to bilirubin.

Thus, Duesberg (1934) proposed the hypothesis that bilirubin remains bound to the same globin to which its precursor heme was attached in the hemoglobin molecule, and that this globin becomes a part of the serum albumin. However, this concept was questioned by Pedersen and Waldenström (1937), because the isoelectric point of serum albumin is at about pH 4.5, whereas that of globin is around pH 7, and bilirubin migrates with serum albumin during electrophoresis. Later Fiessinger *et al.* (1941, 1942) and Polonovski *et al.* (1942) proposed the theory that serum bilirubin, which gives the indirect diazo reaction, is attached to globin, whereas "direct" bilirubin is bound to albumin. C. J. Watson (1946) accepted this theory, in spite of the serious objections of Pedersen and Waldenström. Bourrillon (1952) and Polonovski and Bourrillon (1952b) finally disproved this hypothesis by demonstrating that the concentrations of globin in sera giving the indirect diazo reaction were not higher than in sera which gave the direct reaction. They showed that if bilirubin is at all bound to globin, this bond must be much weaker than the one between serum albumin and bilirubin. The globin hypothesis was also doubted by Corà (1952) and Klatskin and Bungards (1956), who investigated globin–bilirubin mixtures with electrophoresis, could not demonstrate any complex of bilirubin and globin.

Based on these findings one can conclude with certainty that globin has nothing to do with serum bilirubin and its various types of diazo reactions.

9. Molecular Sieve Studies with Sephadex Columns; Disruption of Bilirubin–Albumin Bond with Formamide

Harboe (1965) performed molecular sieve chromatography with Sephadex G-200 on serum and disclosed that bilirubin appears in the third protein fraction with the albumin, well separated from the Hb–haptoglobin complex and the turbid matters causing errors in serum bilirubin determinations. He searched for a solvent disrupting the bilirubin–albumin bond without denaturing the protein and found that 40% formamide in water accomplished this dual purpose. Formamide is an extremely polar solvent which on addition to all turbid sera make them crystal clear. He performed runs with 1 ml serum properly mixed with formamide and buffer on Sephadex G-200 columns 50 cm × 1 cm² in dim light at 5°C in order to avoid gel formation. The flow rate was about 2

ml per hour. As eluent he used equimolar KH_2–K_2H–phosphate, ionic
strength 0.3, containing 2 g bovine albumin per liter as bilirubin-
protecting agent. The formamide concentration varied from 32 to 48%
(v/v). The eluate was collected in a time-controlled collector and the
absorbancy determined at different wavelengths, including 440 nm in
all fractions. In this way he succeeded in getting various bilirubin fractions (cf. Section F, this chapter).

R. Schmid et al. (1965*) used gel filtration through a 122 × 1.2 cm
column of Sephadex G-25 to separate albumin-bound bilirubin from the
unbound pigment. The bilirubin–albumin complex passed through the
gel rapidly, whereas the smaller molecule of unbound bilirubin remained
on the column. One milliliter of 0.0625 M phosphate buffer (pH 8)
containing 40 mg crystalline human serum albumin (molecular weight
ca. 65,000) and varying amounts of bilirubin were applied to the column.
The albumin had been pretreated by passing it through a similar Sephadex column. Elution was performed with the phosphate buffer and the
concentrations of bilirubin and albumin in the effluent were determined.
The results indicated that bilirubin applied in excess to 2 moles per mole
of albumin remained on the column, whereas with ratios of less than 2:1
virtually all pigment appeared in the effluent bound to the protein. When
bilirubin to albumin ratios were just less than 2:1, traces of unbound yellow pigment were detectable on the column, but the amounts were too
small to be detected in the effluent.

Josephson and Furst (1966*) employed Sephadex G-25M in 200 ml
columns equilibrated with borate buffer (Clark and Lub, pH 7.8). Ten
milliliters of a 20% solution of human albumin containing 22.5 mg unconjugated bilirubin was added to the column followed by elution with
borate buffer at a flow rate of 15 ml per hour. With this technique the
recovery of bilirubin was 91% and that of albumin 93%.

A broad yellow-brown band containing the bilirubin-albumin was
clearly visible and 5–6 cm higher up in the column there was a narrow
green zone, presumably biliverdin. At the top of the column a light yellow precipitate accumulated—probably impurities from the bilirubin
preparation.

10. NATURE OF THE ALBUMIN–BILIRUBIN BOND

The methyl ester of bilirubin is as strongly bound to albumin as to
bilirubin itself (Barac, 1946g), and this bond is even more stable than
that of free bilirubin (Kimura, 1953). This indicates that the bilirubin–
albumin bond does not take place on the carboxy groups of bilirubin
because these are blocked by the ester groups. Paper electrophoretic
studies on serum azobilirubin showed that the bilirubin–albumin bond

is destroyed by the diazo reaction (With, 1958b). This observation suggests that this bond possibly involves the central methylene bridge. However, this can hardly be the case since biliverdin can form similar compounds with albumin (Barac, 1946e). It has also been considered that the bond formation involves the two methine bridges of bilirubin, but vinyl and phenolic groups could also furnish possible sites for such bonds. In any case, the question of bond site cannot be regarded as solved, especially since there is no explanation for the fact that this bond is ruptured by diazotation.

Recently Grodsky *et al.* (1962) found that equilibration of bilirubin-H^3 with albumin removed the tritium from the bilirubin and concluded that the binding of bilirubin to serum albumin involves hydrogen bonding at an aliphatic group of the bilirubin molecule. This hypothesis is supported by the finding of Novák *et al.* (1962) that nonesterified fatty acids compete with bilirubin for the binding sites on serum albumin. The biological half-life of the compound bilirubin–serum albumin was 25–35 minutes in the blood of rats (Grodsky *et al.*, 1962).

Fog and Bakken (1967a*) studied the nature of the bilirubin-albumin bond by measuring of the extinction at the absorption peaks of bilirubin in pure and protein-containing solutions. They found that the extinction at the maximum of bilirubin-albumin (E_{470}) varied rapidly at about pH 12 showing a steep fall when pH increased from 11.5 to 12.5. On the contrary, aqueous protein-free bilirubin solutions exhibited a steep rise in peak extinction (E_{420}) when pH increased from 11.5 to 12.5.

If the ratio E_{450}/E_{420} was plotted against pH in the range pH 10–14 the curve for aqueous protein-free bilirubin solutions consisted of three straight lines intersecting at about 11.5 and 12.5, indicating that bilirubin ionizes in two steps. The steep decrease of the peak extinction of bilirubin-albumin (E_{470}) occurs just in the interval between these two ionizing steps, indicating that the bilirubin-albumin bond is split when the first bilirubin ion is formed. Other factors may, however, contribute to the steep change in the absorption curve of bilirubin-albumin around pH 12.

Fog and Bakken further found that the absorption curves at different pH values between pH 10.8 and 12.6 in the interval 380–480 nm showed only one common point of intersection (isobestic point)—at 410–415 nm —in the case of protein-free bilirubin solutions, but the corresponding curves for bilirubin-albumin solutions exhibited two isobestic points (at ca. 425 and 445 nm). They believed that the first of these two isobestic points must be due to release of bilirubin from the albumin complex.

An explanation of the bilirubin-albumin linkage which has to be taken into account is the possibility of steric adjustment of certain locations in the large albumin molecule to accept the much smaller molecule of bilirubin. Such steric interaction might be transformed into strong bonding by means of various hydrogen bonds between appropriate parts of bilirubin and albumin.

11. Plasma Bilirubin Binding Capacity

D. Watson (1964b) proposed a method for determination of the bilirubin binding capacity of plasma based on extraction of bilirubin from a xylene solution with a borate buffer to which the plasma was added. Two ml of borate–KCl buffer [0.05 M; pH 8.5; containing 0.5 meq ethylenediamine tetraacetate (EDTA), disodium salt per liter] are pipetted into a stoppered centrifuge tube, and 50 μliters of plasma are introduced. Then 5.0 ml of a xylene solution of bilirubin (approximately 10 mg per liter) are added and the mixture is shaken for 2 minutes, centrifuged for 2 minutes, and the extinction of the upper organic layer measured at 454 nm in 1 cm cells. The entire procedure has to be carried out protected from direct light at 15–20°C. Standards and blank are set up in which the plasma is replaced, respectively, by aqueous solutions of crystalline bovine albumin (Armour) containing 10, 20, 40, and 60 mg per ml, and by water. From the measurements of the bilirubin extracted by the albumin solution a curve is constructed (abscissa: albumin concentration; ordinate: decrease in 454 nm extinction of the organic layer), and by comparison with this curve the bilirubin binding capacity of the serum is expressed in milligrams albumin per milliliter. This bilirubin binding capacity is compared with the albumin concentration of the plasma. In normal pregnant women the bilirubin binding capacity of plasma was 47–77 (mean, 60) mg albumin per mg of plasma while the plasma albumin concentration varied between 44 and 53 (mean, 47) mg per ml. This suggests that bilirubin is bound to other vehicles than albumin. In the normal newborn the binding capacity was 37–54 (mean, 45) and the albumin concentration 35–50 (mean, 42), suggesting that albumin is the only vehicle for bilirubin in the newborn.

This determination of the bilirubin binding capacity of plasma is interesting, but further studies are needed before its theoretical and practical implications can be evaluated.

12. The Concept of the Bilirubin Pools

In recent literature the concept of bilirubin pools plays an increasing role although a regular theory of these pools has not yet been presented. A discussion therefore seems appropriate here.

Pools of bilirubin exchanging more or less freely with each other can theoretically exist in the blood plasma, the tissue fluids—including the interstitial fluid, the cerebrospinal fluid, the fluid in the serous cavities, edema fluid, and glomerular urine—various secretions and excretions, the contents of the intestine, the intercellular substance of connective tissues, and last but not least, the cells of various organs.

As bilirubin is albumin bound in blood plasma it cannot pass through the intact capillary membrane without being dissociated from albumin —with the exception of the vascular compartments of the liver and intestine where the capillary membrane is highly permeable to proteins. Therefore exchange between the plasma bilirubin-albumin pool and all the other bilirubin pools can only take place via a smaller pool of protein-free bilirubin in the plasma (cf. Chapter IV). That such a pool really exists has recently been supported experimentally through the ultracentrifuge experiments of Scholtan and Gloxhuber (1966*) who found that ca. 0.6% of plasma bilirubin (unconjugated as well as conjugated) does not sediment with the serum proteins.

Although the pools of protein-free bilirubin in plasma and interstitial fluid must be small, they are of high physiological importance because bilirubin cannot pass from the large pools of protein-bound bilirubin in the plasma and the tissues except through the protein-free bilirubin pools. It is only through them that the unconjugated bilirubin which causes newborn jaundice can reach the nerve cells and cause damage. Thanks to the observations of Burnstine and Schmid (1962) (cf. Chapter IV, Section A) we know that enough unconjugated bilirubin can actually dissolve in protein-free biological fluids to make the existence of pools of free bilirubin in plasma and tissue fluids possible. For the bilirubin conjugates which are polar it is easier to understand the existence of protein-free pools.

Really one *cannot speak of one single system of bilirubin pools;* one has to operate with a separate system of pools for unconjugated bilirubin and every form of conjugated bilirubin. Owing to the differences in solubility—and accordingly to the differences in their passage through biological membranes and their binding to macromolecules present in the plasma, the tissues, and the cells—bilirubin and the different bilirubin conjugates must be treated separately.

The problems are relatively simple in the case of unconjugated bilirubin and more complicated for the conjugates because the latter are only partially known (cf. Chapter V, Section F).

A special case is the bilirubin pool within the liver cells because unconjugated bilirubin is transformed into bilirubin conjugates here. Since it is known that bilirubin conjugates, at least pigment I (cf. this chapter, Section F), are also formed outside the liver, certain other tissues like the liver must contain transitions between pools of un-conjugated bilirubin and pools of bilirubin conjugates—a fact which makes the problem concerning the pools of bilirubin conjugates rather complicated.

Ultimately the question of bilirubin pools depends on three factors: the solubility of the bilirubin and its various conjugates in the tissue fluids, their binding to the various biological macromolecules present, and their passage through biological membranes, i.e., especially the capillary endothelia, the intestinal barrier, and the membranes of the cells of various organs.

The question of membrane permeability is important, but far from simple. Generally the capillary endothelial membrane is permeable to water, electrolytes, and polar organic substances like urea and glucose, whereas cell membranes are impermeable to these substances but permeable to nonpolar substances. There are, however, important exceptions such as the erythrocyte membrane which is permeable to water, urea and glucose.

The most commonly accepted model of the cell membrane is the so called "butter sandwich," i.e., a double layer of phospholipids with the nonpolar parts of their molecules pointing toward each other, forming the middle of the membrane while their polar groups form the outside surface closely adjacent to layers of globular proteins. This model is, however, far from perfect and cannot explain all experimental facts (cf. Sandborn et al., 1965[*]; Lee Kavanau, 1966[*]; K. S. Cole, 1966[*]). Actually every type of cell may accept or reject specific compounds depending on its reaction to these special compounds themselves (Sandborn et al., 1965[*]).

In this connection it is important to remember the binding of bilirubin to the elastin of connective tissues (cf. Chapter IV, Section A) which is of great importance in the understanding of the large tissue pools of bilirubin in jaundice. Surprisingly enough this has only been the subject of very few studies and we actually know very little about the binding of bilirubin in the tissues in jaundice. Radioactive studies would seem highly appropriate here.

Another little known observation which may be quite significant in connection with bilirubin pools is the firm binding of bilirubin to nucleic acids found by Stenhagen and Teorell (1938) (cf. this chapter, Section B,2). As this binding was found to be more firm than the bilirubin-albumin linkage it can be of importance in the formation of intracellular bilirubin pools and may be an important pathogenetic factor in kernicterus. This observation seems to be forgotten, but deserves renewed experimental study with radioactive methods.

A schematic survey of the theoretical foundation of the bilirubin pools is attempted in Fig. 37a.

After this introduction a survey of the bilirubin pools as they are treated in the literature follows below.

The bilirubin pools were first studied in congenital nonhemolytic hyperbilirubinemia in man (Crigler-Najjar syndrome) and the rat (Gunn rats); this disease represents a special case because all bilirubin present

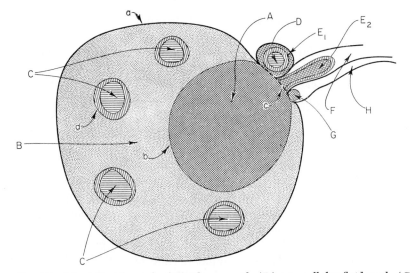

FIG. 37a. The bilirubin pools. (A) Plasma pool; (B) intercellular fluid pool; (C) pools within the cells of various organs; (D) intracellular pool of the liver; (E_1) liver lymph (interstitial fluid of liver); (E_2) intestinal lymph (interstitial fluid of intestine); (F) intestinal lumen (jejunum); (G) glomerular plasma; and (H) glomerular urine. (a) Liver capsule and other organ-limiting membranes; (b) capillary membranes tight to proteins but passable to water, ions, and polar nonelectrolytes; (c) capillary membranes partially passable to proteins; and (d) cell membranes passable to lipid substances. Macromolecular bilirubin binding contents in cells (lined area). Albumin in blood plasma, liver lymph, and intestinal lymph (darkly stippled area). Macromolecular bilirubin binding contents of intercellular substances of connective tissue (lightly stippled area).

is unconjugated. Schmid and Hammaker (1962, 1963) and Schmid (1963a) studied a 4½-year-old boy using C^{14}-bilirubin injections and found that the time curve of the radioactivity of bilirubin isolated from the blood plasma exhibited a rapid fall during the first few minutes followed by a second slower mixing phase during the subsequent 24 hours. After this—from about the 30th hour—a logarithmic decline in radioactivity followed indicating that complete equilibration between the plasma pool and the miscible body pools had taken place. On the basis of this assumption a bilirubin half-life of 156 hours and a total miscible bilirubin pool of 568 mg was calculated. The daily bilirubin turnover was found to be ca. 60 mg. In similar studies with Gunn rats a half-life of ca. 55 hours, a total miscible pool of 4.3 mg, and a daily turnover of 1.3 mg was found.

In similar studies Gray and Nicholson (1963) and Billing et al. (1964a*) found a half-life of 80 hours, a total miscible pool of 1400 mg, and a daily turnover of 290 mg in a case of Crigler-Najjar's syndrome, i.e., figures diverging considerably from those of Schmid, but in better agreement with his figures for Gunn rats (see also p. 457).

Studies on the far more complicated problems of bilirubin pools in obstructive jaundice have also been attempted.

J. L. Cameron et al. (1966a*) studied the bilirubin pool in three infants with congenital biliary atresia using C^{14}-bilirubin. The method of Malloy and Evelyn (1937) was the only analytical method employed for separation of free and conjugated bilirubin, i.e., a completely inadequate technique (cf. this chapter, Sections D–F). The C^{14}-bilirubin injected was unconjugated, and as no reliable analytical distinction between conjugated and unconjugated bilirubin was attempted the observations are of limited value. If reliable conclusions are to be drawn from such experiments, separate injections of unconjugated and conjugated bilirubin each labeled differently to enable differential analysis is necessary! The patients all exhibited a "steady state" with total serum bilirubin between 12 and 20 mg/100 ml. An early rapid decline of radioactivity was observed followed by a more gradual logarithmic decline during the subsequent 48 hours. The following parameters were calculated from the findings and the questionable basic hypotheses and analytical methods: half-life, 3.5–8.8 days (average 6.4); total miscible bilirubin pool, 353–452 mg (average 396.5 mg); plasma bilirubin pool, 40.7–70.8 mg (average 50.8 mg); daily turnover, 36.6–69.9 (average 50.1 mg); and per kilogram of body weight 4.6–11.5 mg. The labeled bilirubin had distributed itself between the extravascular and intravascular spaces in the ratio 7.2 to 1 which clearly differs from the corresponding distribution ratio of albumin (1.4 to 1).

J. L. Cameron et al. (1966b*) later studied the bilirubin pools in five rhesus monkeys with experimental biliary obstruction using the same technique. The common bile duct was subjected to double ligation and section, and the cystic duct was ligated. The C^{14}-bilirubin was injected after the serum bilirubin was stabilized. The findings were as follows: half-life, 2.8–4.6 (average 3.6 days); total miscible bilirubin pool, 67.4–145.5 (average 106.3 mg); plasma pool, 10.4–29.4 mg (average 20.2 mg); and daily turnover, 14.6–25.2 (average 20.0) mg.

Comparison of these results with those of patients with unconjugated hyperbilirubinemia exhibits no striking differences except perhaps a higher daily bilirubin turnover in the latter. But because of the uncertain theoretical and analytical foundations it is hardly appropriate to compare the figures.

Billing *et al.* (1966*) injected C^{14}-bilirubin into rats with experimental biliary obstruction and performed separate determinations of conjugated and unconjugated bilirubin with the method of Weber and Schalm (1962). Conjugated C^{14}-bilirubin appeared in the plasma within 2 minutes after injection of unconjugated C^{14}-bilirubin indicating immediate hepatic uptake of the injected bilirubin. Complete mixing was first achieved after 24 hours and the total miscible pool was seven times greater than the plasma pool. The calculated half-life was 53 hours for unconjugated bilirubin and 35 hours for conjugated bilirubin.

Separate labeling of unconjugated and conjugated bilirubin was performed by Lester and Klein (1966*) who prepared both C^{14}- and H^3-bilirubin from correspondingly labeled δ-aminolevulinic acid (ALA). In experiments on rats unconjugated H^3-bilirubin dissolved in rat serum and conjugated C^{14}-bilirubin from bile was injected i.v. simultaneously. A few experiments of this type on the excretion of unconjugated and conjugated bilirubin in rat bile were reported and showed that conjugated bilirubin is excreted somewhat more rapidly with the bile than unconjugated bilirubin. It is, however, important that a double labeling with a separate determination of unconjugated bilirubin and conjugated bilirubin (i.e., mainly the diglucuronide) is possible. This technique must be used in future studies on the bilirubin pools and bilirubin turnover rates when both bilirubin and its conjugates are involved.

The pool of unconjugated bilirubin in the lumen of the small intestine in unconjugated hyperbilirubinemia has been discussed in Chapter II, Section D. Unconjugated bilirubin passes through the wall of the jejunum rather freely in both directions. In unconjugated hyperbilirubinemia consequently there exists an intestinal pool of free bilirubin exchanging with the plasma pool. Conjugated bilirubins cannot, however, pass through the intestinal wall to any appreciable extent without previous deconjugation, and therefore any significant exchange between the plasma pool of conjugated bilirubin and the intestinal pool of conjugated bilirubin excreted with the bile cannot take place.

The passage of bilirubin—unconjugated as well as conjugated— through liver cell membrane must take place freely as seen from the experiments of Billing *et al.* (1966*) mentioned above (cf. also Chapter IV, Section C,4). The passage of bilirubin into nerve cells in kernicterus is discussed in Chapter IX, Section E. Surprisingly little work has, however, been done on the passage of bilirubin through cell membranes and on its possible binding to nucleic acids in the cells in view of the finding of Stenhagen and Teorell (1938) that bilirubin is more firmly bound to nucleic acids than to albumin.

Finally it is to be mentioned that the concept of "half-life" ($t_{1/2}$) and the mathematical model on which it is based cannot be used on biological phenomena without reservation as recently pointed out by Bergner (1965*) (cf. Chapter III, Section B).

Summary

Bilirubin is firmly bound to serum albumin. It has been discussed whether minor quantities are bound to other serum proteins, but according to most investigations serum albumin seems to be the only bilirubin bonding serum protein. One mole of albumin binds 2 moles of bilirubin tightly; further bilirubin is more loosely associated. The hypothesis that bilirubin is bound to globin in serum derived from hemoglobin is wrong. Bilirubin is probably bound to albumin by means of hydrogen bonding. Bilirubin in blood is usually regarded as identical with bilirubin in serum. Recently D. Watson (1962b) showed that not inconsiderable quantities of bilirubin are adsorbed to the erythrocyte membrane. This was later confirmed by other investigators.

The problems of bilirubin pools are discussed theoretically and the inherent serious difficulties pointed out. Really a different set of pools exist for bilirubin itself and each of its conjugates. Experimental studies on both pools of unconjugated bilirubin alone and pools of bilirubin and its conjugates are discussed, and the seriously inadequate techniques used in these studies on pools and turnover of conjugated bilirubin is pointed out. More reliable results can probably be achieved with double labeling according to the methods introduced by Lester and Klein (1966*).

C. Bilirubin Determination in Serum

Exact quantitative determination of bilirubin in serum is one of the most difficult analyses in clinical chemistry. The great variety of techniques introduced for this purpose demonstrates this (see, e.g., Reiner and Thomas, 1962; Schellong, 1963).

In serum bilirubin analysis it is important to know that bilirubin on account of its binding to protein is present in serum in a relatively stabile form. Thus, it can be kept in the refrigerator for 14 days without significant losses (Boutaric and Roy, 1939; With, 1942a). Ascorbic acid addition increases this storage time even more (Lauersen and Sauerbruch, 1936; Sauerbruch, 1937). Since bilirubin is destroyed by light, all materials containing this pigment should be worked up in dim light, and direct sunlight should be avoided (see Gigon and Noverraz, 1939, 1942).

Martinek (1966*) investigated the stability of serum bilirubin in stoppered tubes at room temperature under diffuse fluorescent light and found losses during 24 hours amounting to 5–12% in serum from newborn (20–30 mg/100 ml, unconjugated bilirubin) and 10–30% in adult icteric sera (5–17 mg/100 ml, mainly conjugated bilirubin).

Zaroda (1966*) studied the losses in icteric sera stored in a refrigerator for 17 days. A green tinge was grossly visible after 6 days. A loss of 6% was noted after 2 days' storage, 10% after 4 days, and 20% after 8–12 days if bilirubin was determined (Malloy-Evelyn method), but if bilirubin and biliverdin were measured with the oxidation method of Zaroda no demonstrable decline was demonstrated. The losses of serum bilirubin during storage in the refrigerator are thus apparently mainly due to biliverdin formation.

According to most writers the bilirubin contents of blood plasma and serum are the same (Jacobi et al., 1931; Brøchner-Mortensen, 1935; With, 1942a, 1943a)—and this is to be expected since fibrinogen does not bind bilirubin (Cohn, 1948). According to Rothe (1939), plasma has a somewhat higher bilirubin content than serum; he gives, however, no data. Unquestionably, the differences reported by Shinowara (1954) are also due to analytical errors, because bilirubin values of the processed sera were consistently low.

Recently D. Watson (1961b) claimed that oxalated or heparinized plasma contains some 4–8% more bilirubin than the corresponding serum. He presents, however, no data. Michaëlsson (1961, p. 21), on the other hand, found no difference between serum and corresponding heparinized plasma in 23 blood samples. This author likewise presents no data. A study of an appropriate series of sera and corresponding plasmas, including both strongly and slightly icteric ones and such with direct and indirect diazo reactions, and an adequate statistical treatment is therefore required before the question can be finally elucidated.

Recently Martinek (1966*) found no difference in bilirubin concentration between serum and plasma with heparin or EDTA as anticoagulants, but with potassium oxalate he found 4–8% more bilirubin in plasma than in serum.

Bilirubin standards are now regarded as necessary for accurate quantitative analyses, but they are difficult to keep because they are easily destroyed by light and oxygen. Because the commercial preparations of bilirubin may vary it is necessary to control standard preparations with respect to both the extinction at the spectral maximum and at the maximum of the diazo reaction (cf. this chapter, Sections C,4 and J).

It is further to be emphasized that standards consisting of free bilirubin are not appropriate in analysis of sera containing conjugated bilirubin (cf. this chapter, Section C,4).

Three different methods have been suggested for bilirubin determination in serum: (1) oxidation reactions, which were introduced by Gilbert *et al.* (1903a,b,c); (2) measuring the degree of the yellow color (or spectral absorption) which was proposed by Meulengracht (1918); and (3) The diazo reaction, introduced by Hijmans van den Bergh and Snapper (1913).

In addition to these methods Heilmeyer (1938) described a color reaction, in which concentrated hydrochloric acid is used to develop the color. Since it is not convenient to use concentrated HCl, this method is of no practical interest.

Recently Vella (1962) observed a brilliant green color on addition of brilliant cresyl blue or methyl blue to icteric serum. On closer study, including chromatography, electrophoresis, and absorption spectrophotometry in the region 350–750 nm, it was found that this color reaction essentially is due to blending of colors and not to a chemical reaction (see also Chapter VI,B,1).

1. OXIDATION REACTIONS

The first methods used for quantitative serum bilirubin determination were oxidation reactions originally used as qualitative tests, namely the Gmelin reaction and its modifications.

Oxidation was performed with various reagents or by boiling in air (Hammarsten, 1878; von Jaksch, 1890, 1891; Hedenius, 1894; Syballa, 1904). Bouma (1902) oxidized with ferric chloride in concentrated hydrochloric acid, after precipitation with disodium hydrophosphate and barium chloride. Gilbert *et al.* (1903a) introduced the so-called layer reaction (*reaction limite*) in serum with fuming nitric acid. When the reaction is positive, a color ring develops on the border line between serum and reagent. This process was later developed into a semiquantitative method by using graded dilution series of serum. The bilirubin concentration, which gave a barely visible ring in diffuse daylight, was estimated as 1:40,000 (2.5 mg per 100 ml). Gilbert *et al.* pointed out that Frerichs (1858) had already used the Gmelin reaction as a ring test, but called this test "Hayem's test."

The process of Gilbert *et al.* was modified by Scheel (1911), Sunde (1911), and F. Bang (1915). The last two authors used the time interval which elapsed until the color reaction appeared as a measure for bilirubin concentration. Hooper and Whipple (1916) precipitated with Na_2CO_3 and $CaCl_2$. After centrifugation of the precipitate, it was washed and dissolved in a reagent composed of 100 ml 95% alcohol, 0.4 ml concentrated HNO_3, and 2 ml concentrated HCl. The solution was left standing overnight, and the color measured against a copper sulfate standard. Fouchet (1917) introduced a solution which consisted of 25 g trichloroacetic acid, 10 ml 10% $FeCl_3$ solution, and 100 ml distilled water. With (1954, pp. 142–144) discussed early methods thoroughly.

Interest in oxidation methods for serum bilirubin determination declined sharply after 1925. However, more recently Chabrol *et al.* (1949), Houssaye (1949), and Zak *et al.* (1954) developed oxidation processes which function with accuracy. Chabrol *et al.* and Houssaye used a reagent composed of phosphoric acid and sodium nitrite. They performed the ring test either with serial serum dilutions or examined the following reaction mixture with a photometer: 0.5 ml serum + 0.45 ml concentrated phosphoric acid (density 1.61) + 0.05 ml of a 0.5% solution of sodium nitrite. They used the same sample but without sodium nitrite as a blank. With strongly icteric sera, higher serum dilutions with phosphoric acid were employed (for example, 0.2 ml serum + 0.75 ml phosphoric acid + 0.05 ml nitrite solution). Color development was followed for 2–3 minutes, until the maximum was reached. The maximum value remains constant for a while, after which the color fades. Determinations with pure bilirubin solutions showed that the curve follows Beer's law at concentrations of 0–3 mg per 100 ml. Comparisons with the diazo method of Malloy and Evelyn in sixteen sera with 0.2–40 mg bilirubin per 100 ml showed deviations up to ±5%.

Zak *et al.* (1954) used the following reagents: (1) Sulfuric acid solution: 1.0 g $FeCl_3 \cdot 6H_2O$ dissolved in 10 ml glacial acetic acid. 1 ml of this solution filled up to 100 ml with concentrated sulfuric acid. All the chemicals used has to be chemically pure. (2) Sulfuric acid, glacial acetic acid solution: 40 ml of reagent (1) diluted with glacial acetic acid to 100 ml. (3) Perchloric acid solution: the same $FeCl_3$ solution is used as with (1); 1 ml of this solution is diluted to 100 ml with 72% perchloric acid. When bilirubin was dissolved in these reagents, characteristic stable colors developed. A green color developed with reagent (2), showing a maximum at 660 nm and a minimum at 500 nm. When these green solutions were diluted with an equal volume of water, the color changed to deep blue immediately after mixing. This solution has a maximum at 640 nm and a minimum at 480 nm. These two colors were extremely stable and Beer's law was valid at a concentration range of 0–5 mg per 100 ml. A clear reddish color developed with reagent (3) which changed to deep violet when an equal volume of water was added. The compounds formed with reagent (3) seemed to be purpurins, while those formed with reagent (2) were apparently bilatrienes. The reddish color showed a maximum at 510 nm, the violet at 580 nm and a minimum at 480 nm. These colors were stable for hours; Beer's law could be applied to concentrations below 5 mg per 100 ml.

Investigations of icteric and normal sera after bilirubin additions were carried out in the following way: 1 ml serum + 3 ml water + 3 ml pure 85.4% phosphoric acid + 2 ml reagent (1) were mixed; a deep green color developed. This color complex had a maximum at 600 nm, although the maximum of protein-free bilirubin solutions treated in the same manner was at 670 nm. Furthermore, the absorption was significantly enhanced by the serum protein (albumin). This green color was stable; Beer's law was valid at serum bilirubin concentrations between 0 and 20 mg per 100 ml. When spectrophotometric determinations were performed at 600 nm, bilirubin, which was added to serum, was completely recovered. Reagents (2) and (3) were found to be useless for serum bilirubin determination, since other compounds interfered with color development (cholesterol, tryptophan, etc.).

Ferro and Ham (1963) introduced a method based on a modified Fouchet reagent consisting of $FeCl_3$ in isopropyl alcohol. The stock solution is an aqueous solution containing 7.2 g $FeCl_3 \cdot 6H_2O$ per 100 ml. A diluent, which is stable for 6 months is prepared from 90 g trichloroacetic acid (reagent grade) dissolved in isopropyl alcohol (reagent grade) and adjusted to 900 ml. To this is added 1 ml $FeCl_3$ stock solution and subsequently 100 ml ethylene glycol monomethyl ester. The procedure is as follows: 1 ml of serum (or serum dilution) is mixed with 10 ml of reagent, allowed to stand for 3–5 minutes, and then filtered to remove the protein precipitate. The filtrate is read at 660 nm with the reagent as blank. A solution of bilirubin in $CHCl_3$ is used as standard. The extinctions read were consistent with Beer's law over wide ranges. The method showed excellent reproducibility and good agreement with diazo methods of the Malloy Evelyn type. Ferro and Ham (1965*) later developed their method into a micromethod employing 50 μl, high dilutions, and usual spectrophotometer equipment.

Zaroda (1966*) proposed to oxidize bilirubin and biliverdin to a biliviolinoid substance in order to determine the total bile pigment present. They employed a reagent consisting of 5.0 g $HgNO_3$ and 2.5 ml of conc. HNO_3 in 1000 ml distilled water. Extreme care is required during the preparation of the reagent to avoid slow and incomplete oxidation. The biliviolinoid substance formed is stable and shows strong red fluorescence in UV light and an absorption peak at 613–622 nm. Six milliliters of reagent was added to 1 ml clear, unhemolyzed serum in a tube which was placed for 30 minutes on a waterbath of 37°C. The reading was taken at 620 nm against a reagent blank. A serum blank consisting of 1 ml serum and 6 ml buffer (Sørensen, pH 7.40, 0.15 M) was subtracted. Standard curves for pure bilirubin and biliverdin were constructed and they were represented by the same straight line.

Summary

Earlier investigators employed oxidation processes as more or less semiquantitative methods for serum bilirubin determinations. More recently Chabrol *et al.* (1949), Zak *et al.* (1954), Ferro and Ham (1963) and Zaroda (1966*) developed these methods into usable and reliable quantitative processes.

2. DETERMINATIONS BASED ON MEASUREMENT OF THE YELLOW COLOR (ICTERUS INDEX)

Measurement of yellow serum color can be performed easily and with sufficient accuracy. Nevertheless, other yellow compounds (hemoglobin, carotinoids, anilin dye, etc.) can cause significant errors. The customarily employed spectrophotometric determinations are reliable, but they are subject to errors because bilirubin does not have sharp absorption bands. The specificity of the method can be increased by extractions. However, quantitative extractions are difficult to perform because of the protein binding. Methods of determination of bilirubin by measurement of serum extracts (CHCl$_3$ and other solvents) are discussed in Section D,2 of this chapter.

Meulengracht (1918, 1920, 1921) diluted plasma with 0.9% sodium chloride solution until the color became identical with a standard potassium bichromate solution. He called the dilution value which was obtained "icterus index." Since this time this method has been widely used and modified by various investigators. Wang and Eastman (1936) worked it out for capillary blood determinations. To avoid errors which could arise from traces of hemoglobin, Ernst and Förster (1924) and Newburger (1937) extracted with acetone (acetone icterus index), and evaluated the filtrate colorimetrically. However, since acetone precipitates an unknown amount of serum bilirubin with the protein, the method cannot be recommended (see Wiss, 1942). With (1954, p. 145) thoroughly discussed these earlier methods.

Various writers have proposed *spectrophotometric methods*. Sheard *et al.* (1926), and Davis and Sheard (1934) developed such methods, in which a correction was introduced for traces of hemoglobin. Heilmeyer and Wappler (1928) recommended determinations with the Pulfrich photometer. To exclude errors due to hemoglobin, Dähne (1937) proposed the addition of Na$_2$S$_2$O$_4$ to the serum, which causes changes in hemoglobin absorption. Peter (1933) preferred to perform spectrophotometric determinations in alcoholic serum extracts. Henry-Cornet and Henry (1937) measured bilirubin in serum directly by means of a spectrophotometer. With (1945a,c,e, 1946a) used filter S43 of the Pulfrich photometer, whereas Waagstein (1946) used filter S47 in his measurements. Roy and Boutaric (1942) questioned the validity of Beer's law in direct spectrophotometric serum bilirubin determinations. However, Martin (1949) and Fog (1958b) showed that serum bilirubin values obey this law over a wide concentration range.

The most important sources of error in direct spectrophotometric serum bilirubin measurements are the turbidity of serum, traces of hemoglobin, carotinoids, and artificial dyes. To eliminate cloudiness, which is a serious source of error, Fog (1949, 1952, 1958b) proposed a number of suitable methods. To correct errors caused by traces of hemoglobin, Hunter (1951), Henry et al. (1953), Shinowara (1954), and Fog (1958b) worked out various methods. Carotinoid impurities are rare in humans, but the icterus index can be extremely misleading in cattle, which have high serum carotinoid levels (Garner, 1953). Artificial yellow pigments have a significance only under special conditions, for example simulated icterus of malingerers. However, such yellow sera can be quickly recognized by comparison with a diazo reaction or an oxidation test.

Fog's turbidimetric investigations are important. In his first publication (1949) he proposed a correction of data obtained with the Pulfrich photometer by the use of three different filters. Later (1952), he developed a spectrophotometric method based on an extended analysis of the problem of turbidity. The measured absorption is the sum of the absorption of the solution and its turbidity. Turbidity can be calculated from measurements performed at wavelengths where bilirubin absorption can be neglected. Measurements with various colorless turbid solutions showed that the extinction of turbidity obeys a law, which can be expressed by $E = k\lambda^{ky}$ (where E = extinction; λ = wavelength; k and y = constants). When measurements are carried out at suitable wavelengths, k and y can be calculated for colored solutions and corresponding corrections for turbidity are thus obtained. For serum bilirubin determination he performed his readings at 460, 524, and 590 nm (Fog, 1958b).

Hunter (1951) and Henry et al. (1953) proposed a correction for traces of hemoglobin. They performed measurements at 420 nm [highest maximum of oxyhemoglobin (Soret band)], and at 460 nm (maximum of serum bilirubin). The proposition of Hawk et al. (1947) to carry out measurements at 420 nm leads to errors, because at this wavelength the absorption of hemoglobin is greater than that of bilirubin. Henry et al. (1953, p. 844) proposed the following formulas:

mg bilirubin per 100 ml (corrected for hemoglobin)

$$= \frac{(E_{460} \times 0.067) - (E_{420} \times 0.0074)}{0.0514} \times 10$$

and

mg hemoglobin per 100 ml (corrected for bilirubin)

$$= \frac{(E_{420} \times 0.78) - (E_{460} \times 0.053)}{0.0514} \times 10$$

Najjar (1952) proposed another formula based on readings at 420 and 460 nm. Abelson and Boggs (1956) also reported a procedure which is based on measurements at 415 and 460 nm. Another correction method was described by Shinowara (1954) based on measurements at 450, 560, and 575 nm. However, this method is inferior to that proposed by Hunter and Henry *et al.* because the hemoglobin extinction at 575 nm is only about 1/10 that measured at the Soret maximum (415–420 nm) (Hunter, 1951). Accordingly, traces of hemoglobin can be detected much better by measurements at 420 nm than at 575 nm. In spite of this theoretical inferiority and turbidity errors inherent in Shinowara's method, he and Svenneby (1956) found good agreement between results obtained with this procedure and those obtained with the diazo method of Malloy and Evelyn. Childers and Barger (1958) proposed another method based on readings at 450 and 575 nm and a calculation formula. D. White *et al.* (1958) described an "ultra micromethod" which requires only 20–50 μliters of serum and is based on measurements at 455 and 575 nm. They pointed out that corrections for traces of hemoglobin measured at the Soret band (415–420 nm) are only accurate when all hemoglobin is present as oxyhemoglobin. Their method was modified for the Bausch and Lomb Spectronic 20 with micro cell carrier by Eichmann *et al.* (1959). Meites and Hogg (1960) added 20 volumes of $M/15$ phosphate buffer (pH 7.4) to 1 volume of serum, read at 455 and 575 nm, and calculated the bilirubin concentration from a formula. This method is subject to the same objections as that of Shinowara, although it has given good results on newborns in the hands of Meites and Hogg.

Chiamori *et al.* (1961) compared the methods of Najjar, Abelson and Boggs, and Shinowara with a method of their own based on readings at 415 and 460 nm and a calculation formula; they further included the diazo methods of Malloy and Evelyn and Fog (1958a). They found a high degree of correlation between results obtained with these techniques, although it was evident that the different calculation formulas were based on different standards.

Richterich (1963[*]) modified the method of D. White *et al.* (1958) for micro use by employing 20 μl serum to which was added 1.0 ml Tris buffer; readings were taken at 426 and 478 nm. The bilirubin concentration (mg per 100 ml) was calculated from the formula

$$c = 87E_{1\,\text{cm}}^{426} - 197E_{1\,\text{cm}}^{578}$$

Jackson (1965[*]) developed a special direct-reading "bilirubinometer" on which the difference in adsorbance at 450 and 540 nm was read. Using a micropipet 30 μl serum was added to 1 ml saline before the reading. The instrument was calibrated with pure bilirubin solutions and gave a straight line as the calibration curve. Comparison of the bilirubinometer readings with analyses with the method of D. White *et al.* (1958) read in a Zeiss spectrophotometer showed essentially identical results.

Martinek (1966[*]) placed 1 ml 0.9% NaCl in a 1-cm spectrophotometer cell, added 20 μl serum, mixed by vigorous tapping (e.g., a Vortex mixer), and took readings at 455 and 415 nm. He found that hemoglobin caused errors below 2% if it was present in concentrations below 200 mg/100 ml. In sera from newborn he found excellent agreement with diazo methods. He emphasized that each laboratory should make a check on its own instruments at the absorption peaks of bilirubin and hemoglobin. His calculation formula was

$$c(\text{mg}/100\ \text{ml}) = [E^{455} - \tfrac{1}{9}E^{415}] \times 111$$

Recently Hertz and Dybkaer (1966[*]) proposed thoroughly documented methods—one based on readings at 469, 540, and 576 nm and the other on readings at 469 and 521 nm. They found that the two-wavelength method was essentially as specific as the three-wavelength method. Their calculation formulas were as follows.

$$c(\text{mg}/100\ \text{ml}) = \frac{E_{469} - 5.1E_{540} + 4.3E_{576}}{0.85}$$

and

$$c = \frac{E_{469} - 1.25E_{521}}{0.81}$$

Although the classical determination of the *icterus index* is a primitive and not vary accurate method, it was and is widely used in clinical practice. However, newer methods which do not express concentration in empirical units but rather in milligrams per 100 ml, are gaining more and more acceptance. Because of the wide use of the icterus index, attempts have been made to transcribe these values into units of milligrams per 100 ml.

Elton (1931a) was the first to compare values obtained by the diazo method and those obtained with the icterus index. He found great scattering. Later, With (1943c) showed that the ratio of serum bilirubin/ icterus index is about 1/5 for definitely icteric sera, and with wide scattering it is about 1/10 in normal and lightly icteric sera. Young (1947a,b) found a ratio of 1/5 to 1/8 for strongly icteric sera and for others 1/7 to 1/13. Lichtman (1949, p. 227) determined a ratio of 1/5 for definitely icteric sera. With spectrophotometric determinations, Henry *et al.* (1953) determined this ratio as 1/20 to 1/100 for normal sera and 1/5 to 1/10 for icteric sera.

These figures show that the icterus index cannot be converted with any accuracy into milligrams bilirubin per 100 ml, even when the icterus index is measured by spectrophotometry. The scattering range of the serum bilirubin/icterus index ratio is considerable in icteric sera, but it is extremely wide in normal sera.

Summary

Serum bilirubin determinations which are based on measurement of the yellow color vary from simple determination of the icterus index to complicated spectrophotometric methods. Some of the latter methods include corrections for traces of hemoglobin and turbidity. Simple icterus index determination is useless for quantitative scientific purposes. Fog's (1958b) method with turbidity and hemoglobin trace corrections is recommended.

3. YELLOW COLOR OF SERUM NOT CAUSED BY BILIRUBIN (YELLOW "NON-BILIRUBIN")

As previously mentioned (Chapters III,B, and II,C), yellow colored substances different from bilirubin can occur in human blood and in urine, as well as in the serum of hepatectomized animals. Such substances are, for example, carotinoids, which are regularly present in cattle (Garner, 1953). However, carotinoids play only an insignificant role in humans in Northern Europe (With, 1945c, 1946a). Hemoglobin has greater importance, as previously discussed (Section C,2, this chapter). Other nonbilirubins also occur in blood serum.

Heilmeyer and Krebs (1930) and P. Müller and Engel (1931a,b,c,d) were the first to study yellow nonbilirubins in serum. Heilmeyer and Toop (1932) and also Penati and Pagliardi (1943) emphasized that traces of hemoglobin constitute a significant part of these nonbilirubins, and that they occur in all sera, even in those which appear to be free from hemolysis. Peter (1933) investigated the ratio E_{580}/E_{450}, where E_{580} is the extinction of the diazo reaction of alcoholic serum extracts at 580 nm and E_{450} represents the extinction of the serum itself at 450 nm.

He found an average value for sera of 1.32, whereas pure bilirubin solutions showed values of 1.44–1.47. The serum thus showed a stronger yellow coloration than could be expected from the diazo reaction. This fact indicated the presence of yellow pigments, which were different from bilirubin. Verzár *et al.* (1934), who conducted similar investigations, found that 38–94% (average 74%) of the yellow color of normal sera was caused by bilirubin. The pigment content due to carotinoids was estimated as 10%. With (1945c, 1946a) carried out comparative measurements in which he first directly measured the yellow coloration of serum (Pulfrich photometer, filter S43) and then determined the diazo reaction according to the method of Jendrassik and Gróf. The ratio E S61/E S43 was simultaneously determined for bilirubin added to serum. In this manner a quantitative estimate of nonbilirubin content in extinction units became possible. Considerable amounts of nonbilirubin were found in normal as well as in icteric sera. Lups and Meyer (1946) confirmed these findings.

Since hemoglobin is insoluble in alcohol, Lups and Francke (1947) avoided errors due to hemoglobin by alcohol extraction of serum prior to measurement. As a rule, only insignificant amounts of nonbilirubin could be detected by this method. However, this process could lead to errors, because nonbilirubins could be present in serum, which are different from hemoglobin and insoluble in alcohol. Del Bono (1949) studied the absorption spectra of 10 sera and compared them with those obtained by diazo reactions performed in suitable alcohol extracts. He found extinction values which indicated the presence of nonbilirubins in two sera. Henry *et al.* (1953, Table I) determined bilirubin based on its yellow color spectrophotometrically with hemoglobin correction, and at the same time by the diazo method of Malloy and Evelyn. They found that the spectrophotometric values were definitely higher than those determined by the diazo reaction. This was the case in practically all their normal sera (30), and in 10 of 17 icteric sera. In two cases the value determined by the diazo method was 15–16 and that obtained spectrophotometrically was 21 mg per 100 ml, after correction. Further, Fog (1958c) obtained similar results with his method, which included hemoglobin and turbidity corrections and avoided extraction procedures, thus confirming With's (1945c) results.

Fog (1958c, 1960) pointed out that the differences in the relation of yellow color/diazo reaction are probably mainly due to the more intense yellow color of conjugated (direct) bilirubin than that of the free (indirect) bilirubin.

Reiner and Thomas (1962) found identical results in newborn sera with spectrophotometric reading of the yellow color and with diazo methods, provided the sera were free from hemolysis. Otherwise the latter methods gave definitely lower values. D. Watson and Rogers (1961) found higher values with D. White *et al.*'s (1958) spectrophotometric method than with Lathe and Ruthven's (1958) diazo method in plasma from adults, but these two methods gave identical results in newborn plasma. D. Watson (1961a), however, found in three infants with hepatitis much higher bilirubin values by spectrophotometry than by diazo methods; the nonbilirubin fraction amounted to 30–45% of the total yellow color.

Summary

Yellow substances different from bilirubin, carotinoids, and hemoglobin appear regularly in normal as well as in icteric human serum. These substances frequently contribute significantly to the yellow color of serum. They are possibly related to "xanthorubin," which is present in the blood of hepatectomized dogs, and they can possibly be dipyrroles, which are formed either as by-products of hemoglobin degradation or are produced during the synthesis of porphyrins. However, we know very little about these substances. Fog (1958c, 1960) has pointed out that most of this yellow nonbilirubin may be explained by differences in the spectral absorption of free and conjugated bilirubin.

4. Serum Bilirubin Determination Based on the Diazo Reaction

The diazo reaction is the most widely used method for serum bilirubin determination. Numerous modifications of this method have been described. Hijmans van den Bergh and Snapper (1913), who introduced the method, used alcohol as an accelerator to reach a rapid quantitative reaction (see Chapter I,J). Here, however, the difficulty arises that serum proteins are precipitated with alcohol. And this removes unknown and varying amounts of bilirubin with the precipitate. Thus, numerous proposals have been made to avoid the protein precipitation step.

Use of caffeine–sodium–benzoate as a coupling reagent proved advantageous. This reagent was introduced by Enriques and Sivó (1926), but their original method was useless because of brown discoloration. The advantages of the caffeine reagent were only fully exploited after Jendrassik and Gróf (1938b) combined this reagent with a strongly alkaline buffer solution. Another way to avoid precipitation consists in diluting the serum before the addition of the alcohol. Hijmans van den Bergh (1924) proposed this device which was rediscovered by Malloy and Evelyn (1937) who read in a photoelectric colorimeter. However, the principle has the disadvantage of development of turbidity by addi-

tion of alcohol to diluted sera. Such turbidity, if not corrected, can lead
to considerable errors in sera with low bilirubin content. The large dilutions required also make this method unsuitable for sera low in bilirubin.
Nevertheless, it has been widely accepted, especially in the United States
(see Reiner, 1953). It has been pointed out on various occasions by
European investigators (With, 1943a; Deenstra, 1948a, p. 114; Dangerfield and Finlayson, 1953; Vink, 1954; Fog, 1958a) that this method is
for several purposes inferior to that of Jendrassik and Gróf. However,
this has not been generally accepted by Anglo-Saxon authors (cf. D.
Watson and Rogers, 1961), although Lins (1950, 1952) proposed to replace methanol by a caffeine reagent in the Malloy-Evelyn method.

Experiments with the diazo reaction necessarily led to many modifications in the composition of the diazo reagent, the nature of the coupling
reagent used, the pH, and the electrolyte composition of the solutions
subjected to the actual reading, as well as the dilution of the serum with
the reagents, reaction time, and reading method (colorimetric, photometric, etc.). The most important modifications are compiled in Table II.

The influence of varying the composition of single reagents will be
discussed in the following sections. Only a few special points will be
mentioned at this time.

Colorimetric standard values and empirical units were important in
earlier methods. This led to manifold discussions in the literature. With
(1954, pp. 150–153) gives a detailed survey on this subject.

Hijmans van den Bergh and Snapper (1913) used a bilirubin standard
for comparison to the diazo reaction. However, since this led to many
difficulties, artificial standards had to be introduced. Thus, they (loc. cit.)
proposed iron rhodanide [$Fe(CNS)_3$] in ether, and later (Hijmans van
den Bergh, 1918) aqueous solutions of cobalt sulfate ($CoSO_4$). Their
original standard was an azobilirubin solution which corresponded to a
bilirubin concentration of 1–250,000, i.e., 0.4 mg in 100 ml. Hijmans van
den Bergh (1918, p. 17) later quoted this value erroneously as 1–200,000
or 0.5 mg per 100 ml, ignoring the fact that $\frac{1}{4}$ of the volume of the solution was added in the form of reagents (see Hijmans van den Bergh and
Grotepass, 1934, footnote p. 1157; Bungenberg de Jong, 1937, p. 99).
This error caused some confusion in the interpretation of so-called "van
den Bergh units." They were usually referred to as 0.5 mg per 100 ml,
but in reality represented only 0.4 mg per 100 ml. However, this is not
the only source of confusion. Hijmans van den Bergh (1918) originally
used 0.5 ml serum + 1.0 ml of 96% ethanol + 0.25 ml diazo reagent, but
later (1928) he changed this to 1.0 + 2.0 + 0.25 and so decreased the
concentration of diazo reagent by 50%. Consequently the van den Bergh

units do not represent well defined units, and they should be considered as semiquantitative estimates.

It is difficult to equalize the colorimetric standards introduced by Hijmans van den Bergh with diazotized sera. Repeated attempts have been made to resolve this difficulty in various ways (Haselhorst, 1921, 1928; Adler and Meyer, 1922; McNee and Keefer, 1925; C. E. Newman, 1928; Chiray and Thiebaut, 1929; Nichols and Jackson, 1930).

However, it was not enough to modify the standard color solutions to render the Hijmans van den Bergh method reliable. The error introduced by protein precipitation was not eliminated in this way. To avoid these errors many changes of the procedure have been suggested, as may be seen in Table II. Today, most of these propositions have only historical interest and do not require a review.

Holzer and Mehner (1922) and Chabrol and Busson (1934a,b) discussed the considerable deviations which were obtained by using different analytical procedures on the same serum.

An important point which deserves attention is that azobilirubin is adsorbed to the serum protein precipitate to a certain degree. Bungenberg de Jong (1937, p. 118) could show that the entire amount of azobilirubin together with globulins precipitates on half saturation with ammonium sulfate. This fact can be utilized for precipitation of azobilirubin. However, it is not convenient since the globulin precipitate has approximately the same density as the precipitating agent. Therefore, to obtain a precipitate, very high speed centrifugation becomes necessary. Adsorption is extremely labile in this case. By addition of alcohol, azobilirubin is redissolved. It is surprising that azobilirubin can be precipitated with globulins, whereas bilirubin accompanies albumins (Section B,I, this chapter). Contrary to this, Westphal and Gedigk (1948) found, by dialysis and zone electrophoresis of diazotized sera, that azobilirubin has the same strong serum albumin binding as bilirubin itself. To elucidate this question, With (1958b) performed paper electrophoretic experiments. These studies showed that azobilirubin is not attached to any serum protein fraction. Consequently azobilirubin is not as strongly bound to serum proteins as is bilirubin. Absolutely no binding was detected at pH 8.5. Bungenberg de Jong's findings of labile absorption by globulins do not contradict this observation.

Investigations on the absorption spectrum of serum azobilirubin are similarly somewhat contradictory. For azobilirubin, prepared after additions of serum to bilirubin, With (1945b) found a higher extinction, $E_{1\,cm}^{1\%}$, than for the same bilirubin in serum-free solutions. However, Westphal and Gedigk (1949) reported the opposite. They attributed

TABLE II

The Most Important Diazo Methods for Determination of Serum Bilirubin (Total)

No.	Author	Year	Coupling reagent	Diazo reagent Composition[a]	Diazo reagent HCl normality	Diazo reagent Other reagents	Protein precipitation	Dilution[b]	Acidity during diazotization[c]	Reading	Remarks
1	Hijmans van den Bergh and Snapper	1913	Ethanol, 96%	ND[d]	ND	None	+	ca. 1/3.5	a (pH ca. 2)	Colorimetry, artificial standard (AS)	First alcohol, then centrifugation, then diazotization
2	Hijmans van den Bergh	1918	Ethanol, 96%	1 + 15 + 0.15 (conc. HCl)	ca. 0.17	None	+	ca. 1/3.5	n (pH ca. 5.3)	Colorimetry, AS	Alcohol, centrifugation, diazotization
3	Hijmans van den Bergh	1928	Ethanol, 96%	1 + 15 + 0.15 (25% HCl)	ca. 0.11	None	+	ca. 1/3.5	n (pH ca. 5.3)	Colorimetry, AS	Alcohol, centrifugation, diazotization
4	Thannhauser and Andersen	1921	Ethanol, 96%	5 + 50 + 0.10 (conc. HCl)	ca. 0.55	Sat. $(NH_4)_2SO_4$ and HCl	+	1/6	a	Colorimetry, AS	Diazotization prior to alcohol addition
5	Strausz	1923	Ethanol, 96%	ND	ND	None	+	ca. 1/3.5	n	Colorimetry, AS	
6	Enriques and Sivó	1926	Caffeine-benzoate reagent	ND	ND	None	None	5/12	n (pH ca. 5.4)	Colorimetry, AS	First method using caffeine-benzoate; often brown discoloration
7	Jendrassik and Czike	1928a	Caffeine-benzoate reagent	5 + 15 + 0.05 (conc. HCl)	ca. 0.16	Alcohol after reaction	+	1/5	n (pH ca. 5.8)	Colorimetry, AS	Diazo reagent and serum mixed prior to alcohol addition
8	Weltmann and Jost	1928b	Ethanol, 96%	5 + 50 + 0.20 (conc. HCl)	ca. 0.55	HCl	+	1/6	a	Colorimetry, AS	
9	G. Hunter	1930b	Ethanol, 96%	1 + 15 + 0.15 (conc. HCl)	ca. 0.17	None	+	1/4	n	Colorimetry, AS	
10	Heilmeyer and Krebs	1930	Caffeine-benzoate reagent	5 + 15 + 0.05 (conc. HCl)	ca. 0.17	Alcohol and HCl	None	1/5	a	Pulfrich photometer	Alcohol and HCl added after reaction
11	Hijmans van den Bergh and Grotepass	1934	Ethanol, 96%	1 + 15 + 0.15 (25% HCl)	ca. 0.11	None	+	ca. 1/4	n	Pulfrich photometer	Indirect technique
12	Laemmer and Beck	1934	Ethanol, 96%	1 + 15 + 0.15 (25% HCl)	ca. 0.11	HCl and sat. $(NH_4)_2SO_4$	+	11/96	a	Filter photometer	

298

No.	Reference	Year	Reagent	Composition	Acid	Additional reagent	Precipitation	Dilution	pH	Instrument	Remarks
13	Jendrassik and Cleghorn	1936a,b	Caffeine–benzoate reagent	5 + 15 + 0.125 (25% HCl)	ca. 0.11	None	None	1/5	n (pH ca. 6.0)	Pulfrich photometer (two filters)	No precipitation, only moderate turbidity; correction by reading at two wavelengths
14	Malloy and Evelyn	1937	Methanol	1 + 15 + 0.15 (25% HCl)	ca. 0.11	Dilution with water	None	1/25	a (pH ca. 2.1)	Photoelectric colorimeter	Moderate turbidity
15	Bungenberg de Jong	1937	KCNS	3 + 15 + 0.35 (25% HCl)	ca. 0.11	None	None	1/4	n	Colorimetry	
16	Jendrassik and Gróf	1938b	Caffeine–benzoate reagent	5 + 15 + 0.125 (25% HCl)	ca. 0.11	Alkaline buffer (Fehling II)	None	1/5	n (pH ca. 5.3)	Pulfrich photometer	Reading in alkaline solution
17	Castex et al.	1940	Caffeine–benzoate reagent	1 + 5 + 0.125	ca. 0.04	Conc. sugar solution	None	1/7	n (pH ca. 4.7)	Pulfrich photometer	Sugar as clearing reagent
18	L. D. Scott	1941	Ethanol, 31%	1 + 15 + 0.125	ca. 0.11	None	None	1/10	n (pH ca. 6.5)	Colorimetry	
19	Powell	1944	Caffeine–benzoate reagent	1 + 15 + 0.15 (conc. HCl)	ca. 0.17	None	None	1/10	n	Photoelectric colorimeter	Heating to 40°C for 5 minutes
20	E. J. King and Coxon	1950	Ethanol, 85%	1 g sulfanilic acid in 1 liter 0.25 N HCl + 0.15	0.25	Sat. $(NH_4)_2SO_4$ and buffer solution	+	1/10	n (pH ca. 4.2)	Colorimetry, AS	
21	J. Patterson et al.	1952	25% Urea in 85% ethanol	1 g sulfanilic acid in 1 liter 0.175 N HCl + 0.15	0.175	$(NH_4)_2SO_4$, sodium azide, phenol, $CHCl_3$, buffer solution	None	1/11	n (pH ca. 3.4)	Photoelectric colorimeter	Complicated and time-consuming technique
22	Lins	1950, 1952	Caffeine–benzoate reagent	1 + 15 + 0.15 (conc. HCl)	ca. 0.17	None	None	1/25	n	Pulfrich photometer	
23	Dangerfield and Finlayson	1953	Caffeine–benzoate reagent with phosphate buffer	1 + 15 + 0.15 (conc. HCl)	ca. 0.17	None	None	1/6.5	n (pH ca. 6.0)	Photoelectric colorimeter	
24	Caraway and Fanger	1955	Methanol	1 + 15 + 0.15 (conc. HCl)	ca. 0.17	None	None	10/242	n	Spectrophotometer (540 nm)	
25	Laurence and Abbot	1956	Methanol	1 + 15 + 0.15 (conc. HCl)	ca. 0.17	None	None	1/60	n (pH ca. 4.2)	Filter photometer (520 nm)	
26	Hsia et al.	1956	Caffeine–benzoate reagent	3 + 15 + 1.15 (conc. HCl)	ca. 0.17	Methanol	None	1/100	a (pH ca. 1.8)	Filter photometer (540 nm)	
27	Perryman et al.	1957	Ethanol, 85%	0.1% sulfanilic acid and 1.5% $(NH_4)_2SO_4$ in 0.25 N HCl	0.25	Sodium azide (in substance)	None	1/100	n	Filter photometer (425 nm and 530 nm)	Calculated by means of special formula

299

TABLE II *(Continued)*

No.	Author	Year	Diazo reagent				Protein precipitation	Dilution[b]	Acidity during diazotization[c]	Reading	Remarks
			Coupling reagent	Composition[a]	HCl normality	Other reagents					
28	Stoner and Weisberg	1957	Ethanol	1 + 15 + 0.15 (conc. HCl)	ca. 0.17	Conc. HCl, sat. $(NH_4)_2SO_4$	+	1/40 or 1/100	a	Spectrophotometer (580 nm)	
29	Barac	1957	Buffer solution	1.5 + 15 + 0.15 (conc. HCl)	ca. 0.17	None	None	1/5	n	Spectrophotometer (540 nm)	
30	O'Hagan *et al.*	1957	Caffeine-benzoate and urea	1 + 15 + 0.15 (Conc. HCl)	ca. 0.17	None	None	1/10	n	Photoelectric or spectrophotometric (524 nm)	Reading in alkaline solution
31	Fog	1958a	Caffeine-benzoate reagent	5 + 15 + 0.15 (conc. HCl)	ca. 0.17	None	None	1/5	a	Spectrophotometer (600 nm)	Correction for turbidity and hemoglobin
32	Lathe and Ruthven	1958	Methanol	10 + ca. 20 + 0.15	0.20	None	None	1/35	a (pH ca. 1.8)	Photoelectric colorimeter (625 nm)	No hemoglobin error
33	Brückner	1959	Antipyrine–urea–sodium acetate	10 + ca. 20 + 0.20	0.20	Phosphoric acid	None	1/3.5	a	Spekker absorptimeter (569 nm)	
34	Meites and Hogg	1959	Methanol, 50%	5 + 60 + 0.60 (conc. HCl)	ca. 0.60	None	None	1/25	a (pH ca. 1.5)	Spectrophotometer (560 nm)	
35	Brückner	1959, 1961	Antipyrine–urea–sodium acetate; or acetamine–urea–sodium acetate	10 + ca. 30 + 0.20	0.30	Phosphoric acid	None	1/5	a	Spectrophotometer (568 nm)	Diazotation for 15 minutes before addition of coupling reagent; 3 minutes later, addition of H_3PO_4
36	Nosslin	1960	Caffeine-benzoate reagent	5 + 15 + 0.15 (conc. HCl)	ca. 0.17	Alkaline buffer	None	1/5.1	a	Spectrophotometer (620 nm)	Reading in alkaline solution
37	Michaëlsson	1961	Dyphylline-sodium acetate	5 + 15 + 0.125 (conc. HCl)	ca. 0.17	Ascorbic acid	None	1/5.1	a	Spectrophotometer (600 nm)	Reading in alkaline solution; elimination of hemoglobin error

38	Rand and di Pasqua	1962	Methanol, ca. 85%	Diazotized 2,4-dichloroaniline	ca. 0.25	None	+	1/25	a	Spectrophotometer (540 nm)	Rapid and simple, but requires serum dilution 1/10
39	Boutwell	1964	Acetamide–sucrose	8.4 + 15 + 0.84	ca. 0.18	None	None	1/32 (5/32)	pH 2.7	Spectrophotometer (540 nm)	Reading in acid solution with sucrose as clearing reagent
40	Martinek	1966*	90% v/v methanol (analyt.)	10 + 15 + 0.25	ca. 0.17	None	(+)	a		Spectrophotometer (565 nm)	

[a] 1 + 15 + 0.15 means a diazo reagent containing 1 g sulfanilic acid, 15 ml HCl (concentrated or 25%) and 0.15 g sodium nitrite per 1000 ml.
[b] Volume of serum employed divided by volume of reading solution.
[c] a = acid; n = neutral or slightly acid; the pH figures are quoted from Lathe and Ruthven (1958) and D. Watson and Rogers (1961) and refer to the mixture of serum, coupling reagent, and diazo reagent.
[d] Not disclosed.

301

their 10% loss to the influence of proteins on the absorption spectra of acidic pigments. Such losses have been mentioned by Klotz (1946) and Klotz et al. (1946). This discrepancy between With's and Westphal and Gedigk's findings can be caused by a different reaction sequence. With added the serum to the bilirubin solution before the diazo reagent, whereas the other authors introduced the diazo reagents first and added the serum after completed diazotation. Another possible explanation could be that With's data, obtained with pure aqueous solutions, were low because such solutions are much more prone to oxidation than those which contain serum. However, this is not very likely, because With's extinctions were remarkably high.

Hijmans van den Bergh's (1924) suggestion to avoid protein precipitation by diluting the serum prior to alcohol addition was followed in Malloy and Evelyn's (1937) studies. However, this modification is not an ideal one because *alcohol addition always causes turbidity* and one also has to cope with the *considerable dilution.* Modifications, which employ caffeine benzoate mixture, prevent precipitation. However, this can only be achieved when no alcohol is used during the whole process (i.e., modifications where alcohol is added after the diazo reaction are not reliable), and when the diazo reaction is not conducted in strongly acid media. Acids can cause protein precipitation, whereby azobilirubin will also be precipitated. Therefore, only those diazo methods which avoid the use of alcohol or an acid medium can yield truly quantitative results. It is more advantageous to perform the measurement in strongly alkaline buffer solutions, as proposed by Jendrassik and Gróf (1938b), than to work at weakly acid reaction. The diazo reaction is stopped by strongly alkaline solution, but progresses slowly in weak acids. This can lead to moderate errors, since it is difficult to do the readings always at the same time after reagent addition.

In recent times (see Table II) improved colorimetric, photometric, and spectrophotometric methods have been described. Thus, Jendrassik and Cleghorn (1937) could recover added bilirubin with ±3% error. Much higher values were found with this method than with those using precipitation (Dirr and Sereslis, 1939). However, this method had the disadvantage of requiring two filters for the readings in order to correct for turbidity.

All methods, which use the red color of "neutral" azobilirubin for determination, have an intrinsic source of error. This is due to the presence of small amounts of hemoglobin in the serum. This error can be avoided by measuring the blue color of alkaline azobilirubin, as introduced by Jendrassik and Gróf (1938b). A detailed description of their procedure will be given below. Fog (1958a) drew special attention to this method.

Description of the Method of Jendrassik and Gróf (1938b)

Reagents:

1. 20 g caffeine and 30 g sodium benzoate are dissolved in water, 50 g sodium acetate are added, and the mixture is filled up to 400 ml with water.

2. *Diazo reagent:* to be freshly prepared from 10 ml reagent 2a and 0.25 ml 2b.

Reagent 2a: 5 g sulfanilic acid and 15 ml 25% HCl are dissolved in H_2O and diluted to 1000 ml.

Reagent 2b: 0.5 g sodium nitrite ($NaNO_2$) is dissolved in water and filled up to 100 ml.

When stored in the dark, the reagent is usable for 7 days.

3. 10 g sodium hydroxide and 35 g Seignette salt (potassium sodium tartrate) are dissolved in 100 ml water.

4. 15 ml 25% hydrochloric acid are diluted to 1000 ml with water.

Procedure:

To 1 ml serum 2 ml reagent 1 is added and carefully mixed. After this, 0.5 ml freshly prepared reagent 2 is added and mixed again. After 10 minutes standing at room temperature, 1.5 ml reagent 3 is added and carefully mixed. Reading can follow immediately or, if necessary, after hours. The final volume of the reaction mixture is 5 ml, the dilution of serum is 1:5. The blank is prepared in the same manner, except that reagent 4 is used instead of reagent 2.

Remarks:

Jendrassik and Gróf carried out the measurements in a Pulfrich photometer with filter S 61. To compensate for the slight diazo reaction given by the caffeine, a corresponding correction was suggested. However, this has no importance for clinical practice (see With, 1942a, 1943a). Measurements with simple Duboscq or Autenrieth colorimeters can be carried out in a similar manner (E. Mertens and Samlert, 1950). This method can also be employed as a micromethod using only 0.1 ml serum, without other modification of technique than micro cells for the reading. In this case the necessary quantity of reagent is one tenth of the usual amounts (With, 1942a, 1943a). Determinations can also be performed spectrophotometrically at 600 nm. Using a spectrophotometer (Hilger Uvispec) the following $E_{1\,cm}^{1\%}$ values have been obtained for various commercial bilirubin preparations which were added to serum: 990 for Hoffman–La Roche's preparation; 965 for a material of the British Drug Houses; and 890 for Merck's bilirubin (With, unpublished results, 1960). For filter S 61 of the Pulfrich photometer the corresponding extinction values were as follows: 845, 842.5, and 785. The bilirubin concentration can be calculated from these values and the dilution of serum (1:5). Fog (1958a) measured somewhat higher values for $E_{1\,cm}^{1\%}$ (600 nm) of Hoffman–La Roche bilirubin: between 1057 and 1143.

Various investigators have used Jendrassik and Gróf's method (Rothe, 1939; With, 1942a, 1943a, 1945b); Westphal and Gedigk, 1949; Fog, 1958a; Charbonnier, 1958). They found that bilirubin introduced to serum can be quantitatively recovered with ±5% error. Deenstra (1947, pp. 46–48, 1948a, p. 116) compared this procedure with that of Malloy and Evelyn. He found that the values obtained by Jendrassik and Gróf's method were somewhat higher, sometimes significantly higher, than those measured with the other technique. Lins' (1950, 1952) modification, where 1:25 dilution is used, is less suitable.

Malloy and Evelyn's (1937) method is clearly inferior to that of Jendrassik and Gróf, at least in normal and slightly icteric sera. However, because it is widely used in Anglo Saxon countries, and because it yields good results in sera with high bilirubin content, it deserves a special discussion. A significant disadvantage of this method is the high dilution employed (1:25). This means that a serum containing 1 mg bilirubin per 100 ml can give an extinction in 1 cm layer of only about 0.04 in the reaction mixture, since the $E_{1\,cm}^{1\%}$ of the diazo reaction of bilirubin is about 1000. Consequently, the method is useless in sera low in bilirubin because of the limitations of photoelectric measurements and unavoidable turbidity (With, 1943a; Deenstra, 1948a, p. 114). Moreland et al. (1950) also are against the use of high dilution of sera with low bilirubin content. Furthermore, the methanol concentration in the reaction mixture is 50%; therefore no optimum color development can take place with the diazo reagent used in this method (Deenstra, 1947, p. 48). Also, the red color of the diazo reaction is used for measurement, which can lead to errors due to the presence of traces of hemoglobin. In Jendrassik and Gróf's method this source of error is reduced. Furthermore, absolute methanol is a very difficult reagent to keep in routine laboratories, and if the methanol is not absolute, color development is not optimal (Moreland et al., 1950). Finally the absence of buffering with this method makes it very sensitive to minor variations in technique (cf. below).

The technique recommended by the American Association of Clinical Chemists is described in Reiner's handbook (1953). Sherman and Zak (1953) simplified the method by the use of tablets for the preparation of the diazo reagent. About the same values are obtained with this method in icteric sera as with Jendrassik and Gróf's technique. They are, however, usually somewhat lower (Deenstra, 1947, 1948a).

Martinek (1966*) modified the Malloy-Evelyn method by using diluted methanol (900 ml absolute, acetone-free methanol plus 100 ml distilled water) instead of pure methanol. In this way the problem of turbidity in the final reaction mixture was obviated, but this represents a compromise from the standpoint of maximal color development and final color intensity.

An interesting method was introduced by Brückner (1959), who employed a coupling reagent with antipyrine, urea, and sodium acetate and added strong phosphoric acid before reading. The dilution of the serum was only 1/3.5. The molar extinction of bilirubin was as high as 72×10^3 with this method (absorption maximum 569 nm). He claims that hemoglobin errors are avoided because oxyhemoglobin is equally converted to hematin in blank and test solutions by the strong acid. Compared to the Malloy-Evelyn method it has two advantages: low dilution factor and buffering. Especially the absence of buffering renders the Malloy-Evelyn method particularly sensitive to minor alterations in experimental conditions. Further, the strong acid gives a pronounced clearing effect in turbid, especially lipemic, sera. Brückner (1961) modified his method by introduction of minor modifications (cf. Table II). In this modification the molar extinction of bilirubin was 77×10^3 at maximum 568 nm and the dilution factor was 1/5.

Reinouts van Haga (1963) studied Brückner's claim that hemolysis does not seriously interfere with bilirubin determinations with his method. It was found to be correct with low bilirubin concentrations, but with high bilirubin concentrations definitely too low bilirubin values were found. This was demonstrated to be due to lack of a coupling reagent. Adding twice the original volume of coupling reagent reduced the loss to below 10% if 500 mg Hb per 100 ml serum was present.

Michaëlsson (1961) modified the Jendrassik-Gróf method by substitution of caffeine with dyphylline (cf. The A.M.A. publication "New and Non-official Remedies," 1956). This substance was more effective than other xanthine derivatives tried. He further found that losses due to the presence of hemoglobin, even in considerable concentration, could be avoided by adding an appropriate amount of ascorbic acid as introduced by Nosslin (1960) in the study of the direct reaction. Up to 1400 mg hemoglobin per 100 ml serum did not disturb the bilirubin determination with this technique (Michaëlsson, p. 38, Table). Later With (unpublished observations, 1962) found that hemoglobin concentrations as high as 5 g per 100 ml did not disturb the determination. As Michaëlsson's method employs a dilution factor of only 1/5.1 and includes buffering, it seems to be the best method available at present. It is given in detail below.

Michaëlsson's (1961) Modification of Jendrassik and Gróf's Method

Reagents:

1. *Dyphylline mixture:* 5 g dyphylline + 12.5 g Na–acetate, $3H_2O$ dissolved in 100 ml distilled water at 30–40°C.

2. *Diazo reagent:* 0.25 ml 0.5% (w/v) $NaNO_2$ + 10 ml sulfanilic acid solution. To be used within 30 minutes. The sulfanilic acid solution consists of 5.0 g sulfanilic acid + 15 ml conc. HCl, diluted to 1,000 ml with distilled water.

3. *Ascorbic acid solution:* 200 mg ascorbic acid dissolved in 5 ml distilled water. Renewed daily.

4. *Alkaline buffer:* 100 g NaOH + 350 g Na–K–tartrate dissolved in distilled water and made up to a volume of 1000 ml.

Procedure:

For icteric sera (or plasmas) dilute 1:10 with distilled water before the determination is carried out. Direct sunlight has to be avoided.

One ml of serum (plasma or dilution) + 2.0 ml reagent 1 + 0.5 ml reagent 2. Mix after addition of each reagent. Wait for 10 minutes. Add 0.1 ml reagent 3 and immediately afterwards 1.5 ml reagent 4. Blank is prepared as follows: 2.0 ml reagent 1 + 0.1 ml reagent 3 + 0.5 ml reagent 2 + 1.0 ml serum (plasma, dilution) + 1.5 ml reagent 4.

Reading:

At 600 nm in a 1 cm cell against the blank solution described. The bilirubin concentration is found by multiplication of the E_{1cm} by 4.30 if undiluted serum or plasma, and by 43 if dilution is used.

This method is simple and rapid and it has the advantage that it avoids the serious hemoglobin error. This has not been achieved satisfactorily with previous methods (cf. Meites and Hogg, 1959; Brückner, 1959, 1961; McGann and Carter, 1960; D. Watson, 1960) of which only those of Lathe and Ruthven (1958) and Brückner (1959, 1961) avoid the hemoglobin error to a certain degree.

The *comparative merits of diazo methods of the Malloy-Evelyn (M-E) and Jendrassik-Gróf (J-G) modifications* have been much discussed. Anglo-Saxon investigators usually prefer the M-E while workers from Scandinavia and the European continent prefer J-G methods. In this discussion it must be remembered that the $E_{1cm}^{1\%}$ of the azobilirubin of the reaction mixture from sera is about 1,000. Consequently a serum containing 1 mg bilirubin per 100 ml will give an E_{1cm} of only ca. 0.04 in the reading solution with the M-E technique which has a dilution factor of 1/25. In the J-G method employing a 1/5 dilution the corresponding E_{1cm}

is ca. 0.20. Extinctions of the order 0.04 are on the limit of accuracy, and bilirubin concentrations below ca. 5 mg per 100 ml cannot be read with reasonable accuracy with methods of the M-E type for purely physical reasons. To this is added the fact that methanol inevitably causes some turbidity, a fact recently emphasized in the penetrating study of Boutwell (1964, Table 2). Nath *et al.* (1960) writes: "Sometimes the intensity of the azo-color is so low that the difference in the readings for the test and the blank is within the rank of experimental error."

D. Watson and Rogers (1961) compared the original J-G method with modern modifications of the M-E technique. They found 5–10% higher results with Lathe and Ruthvens' M-E modification than with the J-G method for bilirubin concentrations below 5 mg per 100 ml. Michaëlsson (1961, p. 21) compared M-E with J-G in the concentration range 8–22 mg per 100 ml without finding significant differences between the two methods if 30 minutes diazotation time was employed in the M-E method. If the serum was diluted 1/31 in the M-E method, the correlation between the two methods was very good, but if a dilution factor of 1/10 was employed the scatter was considerably greater. Michaëlsson presents a statistical comparison of the two methods in the range 5–25 mg per 100 ml.

Jacobs *et al.* (1964) compared the following methods: Malloy-Evelyn (1937), Brückner (1959), Meites-Hogg (1960), Lathe-Ruthven (1958), and Nosslin (1960) on 10 different sera. If Malloy-Evelyn figures were put at 100% the other methods gave: Brückner 78–93%, Meites-Hogg 80–98%, Lathe-Ruthven 83–111%, and Nosslin 83–108% for total bilirubin. With direct bilirubin the results were widely discrepant. The authors emphasize the serious problems caused by the unavailability of reference standards for conjugated bilirubin and the confusion caused by the numerous techniques differing only in minor details. They further recognized the source of error inherent in all the M-E methods: the high dilution factor.

Present evidence warrants the conclusion that the M-E and the J-G methods give practically the same results on sera with bilirubin concentrations above 5 mg per 100 ml, whereas J-G methods and methods of the Brückner type are to be preferred for lower concentrations. To this comes the fact that M-E methods are liable to errors due to inferior quality of the methanol employed, and thus are much more vulnerable in non-specialized laboratories than J-G methods (Michaëlsson, 1961, p. 25). Moreland *et al.* (1950) early showed that the purity of the methanol is of the utmost importance in M-E methods. A newly opened bottle of absolute methanol gives a more rapid color development than one which has been used repeatedly. Further, minor variations in pH are possible in M-E methods where the reaction mixture is insufficiently buffered; the pH may vary between 2.0 and 2.5 (Michaëlsson, 1961). As Fog (1957; see also Fig. 26, Chapter I,J, this volume) found that the absorption curve of azobilirubin varies considerably in this pH range this renders the M-E method open to uncontrollable errors.

As stated by Michaëlsson (1961, p. 40): "It becomes more and more clear that the method of J-G is preferable to other methods"—a view which is particularly well founded in routine laboratories where high-quality absolute methanol is not easily obtainable. All published comparisons between M-E and J-G methods are from laboratories especially interested in bilirubin determinations. Their validity for clinical routine laboratories is questionable.

Finally the observations of Nath et al. (1960) with the M-E method under tropical conditions ought to be considered. A trial of J-G methods, especially with ascorbic acid addition, under such circumstances might yield better results.

Recently Michaëlsson et al. (1965*) made a thorough comparison between their own method (modified J-G with ascorbic acid) and the methods of Malloy-Evelyn (1937), Powell (1944), Ducci and Watson (1945), and Lathe and Ruthven (1958) with special consideration given to the effect of added hemoglobin. The coefficients of variation of these five methods were 0.9, 2.4, 6.8, 4.3, and 3.2%, respectively, with a serum containing 15 mg bilirubin per 100 ml. After addition of hemoglobin to a concentration of 100 mg/100 ml the coefficients of variation changed to 1.5, 2.3, 6.1, 2.9, and 4.2%, respectively, and the fall in the bilirubin concentration measured with the five methods was 0.1, 2.0, 2.3, 1.4, and 1.0 mg/100 ml, respectively.

With the notable exception of Moreland et al. (1950) recent Anglo-saxon writers unanimously prefer the methods of the M-E type in spite of the numerous aforementioned points in favor of the J-G methods. A recent review (Zieve, 1964*) does, however, indicate that opinion in the United States now seems to be changing on this point. Zieve writes (loc. cit., p. 77): "The most widely used method in this country is that of Malloy and Evelyn. . . . Better methods for measuring bilirubin are available. One of the best methods is that of Jendrassik and Gróf. . . ." Also Jacobs et al. (1964) recognized that methods of the M-E type cannot give accurate results at serum bilirubin levels below 2 mg/100 ml because of low extinction (high dilution), and they point out that with the method of Lathe and Ruthven a concentration as high as 7 mg/100 ml is required to give an absorbance of 0.1.

A point of decisive importance is the question of how far the azobilirubin absorbancy follows Beer's law. According to Gray and Whidborne

(1946), the absorbancy of solutions with concentrations higher than 1.6 mg bilirubin per 100 ml reaction mixture do not follow Beer's law. However, Kilchling and Kühn (1951, p. 493) could show that this is caused by too small amounts of reagent. When sufficient quantities of diazo reagent are used, Beer's law is obeyed even in very high concentrations, up to 80 mg per 100 ml serum. Similarly, Castex *et al.* (1940) could show that Beer's law is valid for concentrations expected in sera. Schalm and Schulte (1950a) found that this is the case for reaction mixtures of concentrations between 0 to 0.8 mg per 100 ml. According to F. D. White and Duncan (1952) these limits are 0–0.6 mg per 100 ml. Reiner (1953) reported that only sera with less than 3 mg bilirubin per 100 ml adhere to Beer's law when Malloy and Evelyn's method is employed. Also Barac (1957), Fog (1958a), and Lathe and Ruthven (1958) asserted the validity of Beer's law. Hogg and Meites (1959) found the law valid up to the concentration 0.60 mg per 100 ml in the reaction mixture.

Another important factor is the *calculation constants* employed. These vary with reaction conditions, but especially with the mixture prepared for reading and are also influenced by the instrument used (see further discussion in this section). Since the concentration of serum bilirubin is expressed in milligrams per 100 ml, $E_{1cm}^{1\%}$ is a suitable calculation constant. Concentrations expressed in mmoles per liter can be calculated from the former by dividing by 58.4 (the molecular weight of bilirubin is 584). Overbeek *et al.* (1955c) measured the extinction constant of purified azobilirubin. They found $E_{1cm}^{mmole} = 29.8$ at 530 nm in a mixture of 60% alcohol, 30% chloroform, and 10% water, at 0.006 mole per liter HCl concentration. Since each molecule of bilirubin yields two molecules of azobilirubin this corresponds to an $E_{1cm}^{1\%}$ value of 1020 ($E_{1cm}^{mmole} = 59.6$) for bilirubin as found by diazo reaction. According to data reported by Heilmeyer and Krebs (1930), $E_{1cm}^{1\%} = 1215$ at 580 nm can be calculated for the diazo reaction of bilirubin in a mixture consisting of about 11 parts of alcohol, 4 parts of water, 4 parts of concentrated HCl, and a trace of chloroform. With (unpublished results, 1960) found $E_{1cm}^{1\%} = 1230$ for bilirubin at the maximum 575 nm with a Hilger-Uvispec photoelectric spectrophotometer. With (1945b,d) determined the constants of various forms of diazo reactions of pure bilirubin and of serum bilirubin using the Pulfrich photometer. Spectrophotometric studies of the diazo reaction of bilirubin with and without addition of serum carried out with the method of Jendrassik and Gróf (reading in strongly alkaline solution) showed a maximum at 595–600 nm in the presence of serum and a maximum at 590–595 in the absence of serum (With, unpublished results, 1960). Measurements with bilirubinate solutions without serum are extremely cumbersome. To avoid oxidation they must be diazotized before dilution (solutions of 10 mg per 100 ml were employed). These solutions become stable immediately after serum addition. After a reaction period of 15 minutes, measurements showed $E_{1cm}^{1\%} = 760$ for solutions without serum, and $E_{1cm}^{1\%} = 1220$ for solutions containing serum (With, 1945a,c). To correct the influence of bilirubin present in normal serum a blank serum with no bilirubin was used.

An important problem is the difficulty in obtaining *adequate bilirubin standards*. Commercial bilirubin preparations vary widely in purity (cf. Chapter I,C), and bilirubin is a difficult substance to handle correctly in many clinical laboratories where the technicians are not accustomed to work with such easily oxidizable substances. Further, bilirubin in serum is a mixture of bilirubin itself and varying amounts of different conjugates in proportions only partially known. Consequently a pure preparation of unconjugated bilirubin cannot be a fully adequate standard, and the same is the case with any mixture of bilirubin and its conjugates in fixed proportions. Recently this problem has been studied by several investigators. Michaëlsson (1961, p. 13–21) emphasized the difference between preparations of varying manufacture and found that chloroform solubility of a bilirubin preparation is no adequate criterion of purity. Often the chloroform-insoluble residue showed strong diazo reaction if dissolved in alkali. Recrystallizing of bilirubin is a difficult procedure because of its sensitivity toward light and oxidation. Errors from the presence of mesobilirubin are difficult to exclude.

Rand and di Pasqua (1962) emphasized the great variability of bilirubin standards and regarded standard solutions in $CHCl_3$ as unsuitable for several reasons. They advocate standards in aqueous solutions containing albumin. "Roche's" bilirubin gave the highest extinction constants. Schellong (1963) compared values obtained on identical lyophilized serum samples in 20 different laboratories in Europe and the United States and found figures from 10.8 to 16.2 mg per 100 ml. The source of the discrepancies was found to lie in differences in the bilirubin standards employed. The fall in bilirubin content of the lyophilized samples was shown to be insignificant. Schellong compared bilirubin standards prepared from buffered solutions of purified serum albumin as used by Mather (1960) ("synthetic serum") with standards prepared with native human serum poor in bilirubin. It was found that the albumin standards were considerably less stable than the serum standards. Schellong recommended dissolving a small quantity of highly purified commercial bilirubin in alkali and immediately adding this concentrated solution to the serum—a technique actually already adopted 18 years earlier by the author (With, 1945a). In the laboratory of the writer the following method is used: 10.00 mg bilirubin is weighed off in a 35 ml beaker and dissolved in 1–2 ml of 0.1 *N* NaOH, freshly prepared with fresh redistilled water. The solution is transferred to a 100 ml measuring flask by means of fresh pooled human serum poor in bilirubin, after which the flask is filled to the mark with the serum. Then follows thorough mixing. These operations are performed in dim light; exposure to direct sunlight destroys bilirubin. Citrate plasma from outdated blood bank blood cannot be used for this purpose according to the experience in our laboratory as well as in that of D. Watson (1961a).

The Standards Committee (1963) of the College of American Pathologists recommended a uniform bilirubin standard. They tentatively accepted the molar absorptivity of $CHCl_3$ solutions of bilirubin at 453 nm and 25°C as purity criterion, recommending figures between 59,100 and 62,300. They preferred solutions of bilirubin in pooled serum as standard solutions for the assay of bilirubin in serum, and regarded artificially prepared buffered serum protein solutions as less suitable (cf. Schellong above). The Committee recommended preparing the standard from "acceptable bilirubin" by dissolving *completely* in $M/10$ Na_2CO_3 as quickly as possible (i.e., less than 5 minutes; surprisingly they do not recommend $M/10$ NaOH which dissolves 10 mg of bilirubin in a few milliliters in a few seconds. The clear solution is immediately diluted with "acceptable serum diluent," i.e., pooled serum having an absorbance of less than 0.100 at 414 nm and less than 0.040 at 460 nm at a dilution of 1:25 in 0.85% NaCl. This diluent is also used in all subsequent dilutions for calibration purposes. All manipulations are performed in dim light. The absorbance of the diluent is used to determine the fraction of the absorption of the bilirubin standard due to the serum diluent. Standard solutions prepared in this way are claimed to be stable for about 1 week at −20°C. More stable standards can be obtained by lyophilization and storing in ampules or bottles, but the shelf life of such preparations must be established. With regard to standardization of conjugated bilirubin in serum—a most intricate problem, cf. above—the Committee could not provide any recommendation. D. Watson (1964a) criticized the tendency toward rigorous standardization of serum bilirubin methods. He emphasized that proper standardization of spectrophotometers and meticulously clean utensils are more important than standard procedures.

Bilissis and Speer (1963) proposed using *N*-(1-naphthyl) ethylenediamine dihydrochloride as standard in measurements of the diazo reaction of bilirubin. A stock solution is prepared by dissolving 129 mg of the substance in distilled water to 200 ml. This solution is stable for many months when stored in a brown bottle at 4°C. A 1/20 dilution of this standard is approximately equivalent to 5 mg bilirubin per 100 ml and a 1/10 dilution is equivalent to 10 mg per 100 ml, etc. The absorption curve of these solutions covers closely that of azobilirubin in slightly acid solution (maximum ca. 530 nm). Riding and Ellis (1963) used a $CoSO_4$ standard.

Smith and Richards (1963) prepared a stable bilirubin standard by using nonicteric human serum sterilized with filtration through a Seitz filter. They weighed off 100 mg laboratory grade bilirubin (Pfannstiehl) in a beaker, dried it at 60°C for 2 hours, and cooled it in a desiccator. The dried bilirubin was dissolved in 0.2% $NaCO_3$ and transferred to a 50 ml volumetric flask. Then 15 ml ascorbic acid solution was added, followed by dilution with serum to the mark. The manipulations were performed under protection from exposure to strong light. The ascorbic acid was added to prevent oxidation, but it may also interfere with the diazo reaction, and is not necessary because serum itself has a pronounced anotioxidant effect on alkaline bilirubin solutions. T. B. Smith (personal communication, 1964) found that standard sera prepared according to the method of Smith and Richards are stable for several months if they are frozen or lyophilized immediately after preparation. In one instance the extinction only decreased from 0.205 to 0.200 after storage for a year.

Schellong (1965*) studied three different commercially available lyophilized control sera (Warner Chilcott, Dade, Hyland) with Jendrassik-Gróf's method. In the two latter preparations, prepared according to the recommendation of the Standards Committee, there was good agreement between findings and declaration, whereas the analytical values for the Warner Chilcott preparation were about 90% of the declaration values.

Meites and Traubert (1965*) recommended the use of a stock solution of bilirubin in $CHCl_3$ to standardize quantitative serum bilirubin analyses with the diazo reaction. He gives the value 70.30 ± 0.28 for the $E_{1\,cm}^{mM}$ at maximum (560 nm) in $CHCl_3$-methanol with Malloy-Evelyn's method. As a matter of principle it is, however, not suitable to standardize an analysis of an aqueous protein-containing bilirubin solution with a solution of bilirubin in $CHCl_3$ when good standard sera are available (cf. above pp. 310 and 311).

The studies of Meites and Traubert (1965*) show that commercial bilirubin standards have now reached a remarkably good quality. The five different preparations studied showed a mean value of $E_{1\,cm}^{mM}$ at 453 nm in $CHCl_3$ of 60.0 ± 0.58 and a diazo extinction of $E_{1\,cm}^{mM}$ at 560 nm of 70.3 ± 0.20 (in $CHCl_3$-methanol) and the ratio $E_{453}/E_{diazo\,560}$ was 0.858 ± 0.0061. Meites and Traubert found the mean absorptivity of bilirubin in serum-containing solutions at maximum 460 nm to be 49.1 ± 0.69, i.e., $E_{1\,cm}^{mM}$ at 460 nm was ca. 85% of that of bilirubin in $CHCl_3$. On the other hand the maximum and extinction of azobilirubin was not significantly influenced by the presence of protein.

Martinek (1966*) studied five commercial bilirubin preparations (Eastman, Fisher, Mann, Hoffmann–La Roche, and Pfanstiehl) and found the absorptivity of the diazo reaction of serum-containing solutions of these preparations at the absorption maximum ($E_{1 cm}^{mM}$ 565 nm) to be 58.6–64.3. The ratio between $E_{1 cm}^{mM}$ of the bilirubin preparations in $CHCl_3$ and their diazo extinction at 565 nm varied between 0.90 and 1.00.

Dybkaer and Hertz (1966*) described the preparation of thoroughly controlled standard solutions of bilirubin in serum by means of potassium cyanide-formamide (0.10 mole/liter). These standard sera were stable for at least 1 month.

Fog and Bakken (1967a*) described the preparation of standard solutions of purified bilirubin in serum employing a stock solution of alkaline bilirubin in pooled normal serum containing EDTA. The standard solutions were calibrated spectrophotometrically by means of potassium dicromate solutions (Fog, 1962). Absorption coefficients for bilirubin in normal human serum and calculation constants are presented for four different pH values (6.6, 7.4, 8.3, and 0.8).

To acquire the highest possible accuracy, one could add bilirubin to the serum to be analyzed and determine the increase of the diazo reaction after addition of a known amount of bilirubin. But even this laborious procedure is liable to error because bilirubin is not present as free bilirubin alone but as an unknown combination of various conjugates.

Strictly spoken, free bilirubin is to be measured against standards of free bilirubin, and conjugated bilirubin against a standard of the particular bilirubin conjugate in question. But this is not possible for several reasons. First, the composition of the mixture of bilirubin and its conjugates present is not known exactly. Second, bilirubin diglucuronide (pigment II) is the only bilirubin conjugate whose exact composition is known (cf. this chapter, Section F). Third, most of the conjugates are very labile substances. The belief that free bilirubin is a suitable standard for measurement of bilirubin conjugates is not based on chemical evidence; on the contrary existing evidence is the opposite of this assumption (Jirsa and Jirsová, 1959; cf. also Jacobs *et al.*, 1964, p. 437).

It is questionable if it is rational to use exactly calibrated bilirubin standards in quantitative determination of serum bilirubin. If thoroughly standardized spectrophotometers are used (cf. Fog, 1962) it is not necessary to employ exact bilirubin standards if the calculation constants employed are based on the purest possible bilirubin preparations. Such calculation constants are found in the literature (cf. Chapter I,C). If the formula $c = C \times e/E$ is used (where c is the concentration of the sample, C the concentration of the standard, e the extinction of the sample, E that of the standard) the standard has to be calibrated exactly. But if the calculation formula is $c = F \times e/E_{1 cm}^{mmole}$, (where c is the concentration of the sample in mmoles per liter, e the extinction of the sample in 1 cm layer, and F is the factor by which the serum is diluted to achieve the solution read) then the calculated concentration does not depend on the standard which is reduced to a running control to avoid gross errors.

Some authors tried to *replace sulfanilic acid* with other substances. Lins (1949, 1951) used sulfathiazole, sulfadiazine, sulfamethazine, and sulfamerazine as well as other substituted sulfonamides in molar concentrations equivalent to 1 g sulfanilic acid per 1,000 ml. The diazo reaction of bilirubin with some of these modified reagents gave somewhat higher extinction than with the usual reagent with sulfanilic acid, the highest value being 120% of the extinction with the usual diazo reagent. Moreland *et al.* (1950) and Kupfershtein and Roomere (1962) recommended the use of sulfanilamide instead of sulfanilic acid because it gives a more rapid color reaction. Fog *et al.* (1962) investigated the diazo reaction with 25 different primary aromatic amines. The only ones giving higher extinctions than sulfanilic acid (100%) were sulfanilamide (113%) and 2-aminoanthraquinone (103%). The absorption maximum varied from 520 to 600 nm with the reagents.

Rand and di Pasqua (1962) introduced a reagent containing 2,4-dichloroaniline. It was prepared as follows: 1 volume 1% $NaNaO_2$ is added to 50 volumes of 0.2% 2,4-dichloroaniline (Eastman #88) containing 25 ml concentrated HCl per liter. The mixture is allowed to diazotize in an ice bath for 20 minutes, after which 5 volumes of methanol is added to every volume of the mixture. The reagent is stored at $-10°C$, thawed just prior to use, and employed immediately after thawing. It is stable for 3–5 weeks if kept at $-10°C$. It contains about 85% methanol (v/v).

Three ml of this reagent is added to 2 ml of a 1:10 dilution of serum (giving a total serum dilution of 1:25) and the extinction is read at the maximum 540 nm after 5–10 minutes. The absorption obeys Beer's law. The $E_{1cm}^{1\%}$ of bilirubin bound to albumin at 540 nm is about 1,000 according to the absorption curves presented by Rand and di Pasqua. This new method is most interesting, but the high percentage of methanol must give some protein precipitation, the dilution is high (1:25), and the reagent is rather difficult to prepare and handle. The method of Rand and di Pasqua was modified to an *automated method* for serum bilirubin determination by Golub (1964).

Van den Bossche (1965*) modified the method of Boutwell for automated determination using readings at 570 nm under acid conditions. The reproducibility was good even at low concentrations, daily calibrations were unnecessary, and the hemoglobin error was low if the serum hemoglobin concentration was below 100 mg per 100 ml.

Hassan (1963*) introduced a modification of the diazo method based on the use of a solution of precipitated p-sulfobenzene diazonium sulfate in HCl. Sulfanilic acid (50 g) was dissolved in a solution of $2\,N$ KOH (225 ml) and cooled to 4°C. A 10% solution of $NaNO_2$ (200 ml) was added and the mixture added dropwise to $12\,N$ H_2SO_4 (120 ml) cooled to 0°C. The precipitated p-sulfobenzene diazonium sulfate was filtered off, washed successively with ice water, ethanol, and ether, and dried in air. Varying concentrations of the precipitated diazonium sulfate dissolved into different strengths of HCl were tried and a solution of 50 mg p-sulfobenzene diazonium sulfate in 10 ml $0.10\,N$ HCl was preferred as reagent.

The analytical procedure was as follows: 0.4 ml of reagent and 0.2 ml of serum were mixed in a 25-ml tube. After 2 minutes 4.4 ml distilled water were added. A clear pink solution resulted which was measured at 520 nm in a 1-cm cell with water as a blank. A solution of cobaltous sulfate (1.728 g in 100 ml) was used as standard. This solution was equivalent to 0.40 mg bilirubin per 100 ml.

The method of Hassan is interesting and deserves to be subjected to closer study. It employs a surplus of strong acid as coupling reagent. One would expect that this would give precipitation of serum proteins, but Hassan claims that this is only seen occasionally.

Boutwell (1964) described a method with *acetamide* as coupling reagent. The conditions of the reaction were studied in great detail. The technique finally adopted is summarized in Table II, No. 39. The reaction is carried out at pH 2.7 and the reading at pH 1.7 at maximum 570 nm. The diazo reagent employed contained more diazonium than usual. The reading is carried out within 30 minutes, and the coupling is completed in 5 minutes. Sucrose is employed to remove turbidity—as "clarifier," and the problems concerning *clarifiers* in serum bilirubin determination is discussed in some detail. The dilution is 1:32, but may be reduced to 5:32. The azobilirubin is stable at the low pH employed. Under the conditions used the E_{1cm}^{mmole} of azobilirubin was found to be 73. In certain sera from patients with myeloma, protein precipitation took place and reading was impossible.

With (1942a, 1943a), Graham (1955), Caraway and Fanger (1955), Stoner and Weisberg (1957), L. J. Johnson (1957), and Stehr and Vogt (1962) described *micromethods* for serum bilirubin (diazo methods). These determinations can be performed without difficulties if microcells and equipment suitable for the separation of the serum from capillary blood are available.

Maclay (1959*) modified Powell's (1944) method for ultramicrocuvettes and the serum-microadapter of the Coleman Junior spectrophotometer and found good agreement between the micro- and the macro-methods. Boulanger and Fierro (1964*) modified the Malloy-Evelyn method for microscale by employing 0.2 ml heparinized whole blood diluted with 2.5 ml 0.9% NaCl. They centrifuged the erythrocytes down at low speed and determined the volume per cent by microhematocrite; 0.5 ml of diazo mixture was added to 1 ml of the plasma dilution and 1 ml of absolute methanol was added. Readings were taken at 540 nm after incubating for 15 minutes at 37°C on water bath.

Ardelt and Pfleiderer (1964*) modified the Jendrassik-Gróf method for the Beckman-Spinco analytical outfit and was able to use 20–40 μl of serum. The percentage of error was $\pm$3–4%, i.e., the usual accuracy of the macromethod.

Automated serum bilirubin determination was described by Technicon Instruments Corporation (1960*) based on the Malloy-Evelyn method, by Golub (1964) based on Rand and di Pasqua's 2,4-dichloro-aniline method, and by Van den Bossche (1965*) based on Boutwell's acetanilide method.

Nath *et al.* (1960) pointed out that the temperature is important under tropical conditions where room temperature may reach 40°C. Here a NH_2 group may be replaced by OH instead of the desired —N$=$N—Cl with too low extinction as a result. Performance of the diazo reaction below 10°C gave consistently higher concentrations than performance at room temperature—e.g., 0.56–0.23, 0.27–0.09, and 2.52–1.77 with Malloy-Evelyn's method.

The *brown diazo reaction* of uremic sera and the *yellow diazo reaction* caused by urobilinogens should be mentioned. The former is caused by benzene and indoxyl derivatives and can show considerable intensity (Andrewes, 1924a,b; G. A. Harrison and Bromfield, 1928; Chrometzka, 1929b; Jendrassik and Rébay-Szabó, 1937). Using Jendrassik and Gróf's method the error caused by this source is excluded. The yellow reaction (Lopez Garcia, 1941; Castex and Lopez Garcia, 1941) has no practical importance.

The inhibiting effect of ascorbic acid on the diazo reaction of serum bilirubin was described by Sauerbruch (1937) and Lauersen and Sauerbruch (1936). Vink and Deenstra (1951) employed ascorbic acid as an inhibitor of the diazo reaction, and Nosslin (1960) studied this effect more closely. He added 0.1 ml ascorbic acid solution of varying strength to the reaction mixture in Jendrassik-Gróf's method—i.e., 0.1 ml ascorbic acid solution to 3.5 ml of the mixture of serum, caffeine reagent and diazo reagent. He found that ascorbic acid solutions containing below 50 mg per 100 ml gave no inhibition of the diazo reaction, while concentrations above 110 mg per 100 ml caused complete inhibition. This corresponds to an ascorbic acid concentration in the reaction mixture of 1.39 and 3.05 mg per 100 ml, respectively. The ascorbic acid was added to the diazo reagent immediately before it was added to the sample. It was calculated that 1 mole ascorbic acid inactivates 1.4 moles of diazonium. This inhibitory effect of ascorbic acid was also found in the Malloy-Evelyn method.

Besides the procedures described above, M. Engel's (1939) method of bilirubin determination in whole blood should be discussed. Engel treated the blood with carbon monoxide to convert oxyhemoglobin into carboxyhemoglobin (protection from oxidation by air) and hemolyzed it. As a further protection he added ascorbic acid, precipitated the hemoglobin with the proteins, and finally carried out the diazo reaction. Michaëlsson (1961) found that addition of ascorbic acid effectively counteracted the hemoglobin error in hemolyzed serum.

Finally, it should be pointed out that analytical results obtained in *normal sera* with *low bilirubin content* with the current modifications of the diazo method are, most likely, not at all specific. Thus, M. Salvini and Gonzato (1947a,b) investigated the absorption spectra of normal sera treated with Malloy and Evelyn's method and found a maximum at 530 nm in only 6 cases of 20. In the remaining 14 cases no maximum was observed. When low bilirubin contents of normal sera have to be determined with some degree of accuracy, methods requiring concentration of the bilirubin in solutions (instead of the usual dilution) must be employed. Bungenberg de Jong (1937, p. 121) reported a method consisting in addition of sodium acetate to the solutions, of absorption of azobilirubin on talcum powder, and finally elution with acid (HCl) alcohol. However, this method has not been used in serial experiments with normal sera; only Tosti (1949) used this procedure. The method of Brückner (1959) should also be of special value here.

Bungenberg de Jong's Technique

One part serum is mixed with one part of diazo reagent [1 + 30(25% HCl) + 0.15; cf. Table I] in a centrifuge tube, and one part of 60% sodium acetate solution is added to the mixture. After standing for a few minutes a teaspoon of talcum powder is added and the tube filled with water. A few drops of ether are added to the mixture, which is vigorously agitated and centrifuged. In this process the entire amount of bilirubin becomes absorbed on the talcum powder. After decanting, the talcum powder is washed with distilled water, centrifuged again, and the aqueous supernatant discarded. Subsequent elution is preferentially performed with small amounts of HCl containing alcohol under constant stirring. After centrifugation the supernatant is decanted and elution repeated until no more blue color is coming off.

By this process it is possible to concentrate small amounts of bilirubin from large amounts of serum. The method is based on the observation, of Terwen (1928) and Posthuma (1931), that talcum powder adsorbs azobilirubin. Bungenberg de Jong (1937) determined that azobilirubin is partly adsorbed by Fuller earth from acid solution, and that it is quantitatively retained by talcum powder from acid and neutral solutions but not from alkaline solutions. Kaolin does not adsorb azobilirubin at any pH value. Bilirubin itself was not adsorbed from sera with indirect reaction, and only to a limited degree from "direct reacting sera." Azobilirubin is eluted from talcum powder with alcoholic HCl, pyridine, or dilute alkali. Thus, quantitative measurements of eluates seem to be possible.

Summary

A greater number of diazo methods have been described for serum bilirubin determinations. The most important processes are compiled in Table II. A good determination must avoid precipitation of serum proteins and has to keep the dilution of the serum with the necessary reagents as low as possible. Consequently, the best method today is that of Jendrassik and Gróf (J-G) and its modifications. This method is superior to the method of Malloy and Evelyn (M-E) and its modifications for sera with low bilirubin concentration (below 5 mg per 100 ml).

In sera rich in bilirubin, the M-E and the J-G methods give identical results when carried out in specialized laboratories. The M-E methods are, however, much more sensitive to variations in the quality of reagents, especially the methanol, than the J-G methods and consequently less suitable for routine use. In addition, the serious hemolysis error is easily removed by addition of ascorbic acid in the J-G method (Michaëlsson, 1961).

An important problem is that of standardization. It is pointed out that fully adequate standards for determination of bilirubin in serum do not exist, that bilirubin solutions in chloroform are inadequate as standards, and that standardization of spectrophotometers is more important for exact determinations than are bilirubin standards.

None of the customarily used analytical determinations for low bilirubin concentrations of normal sera are acceptable. A suitable method which would permit this requires concentration of the bilirubin, instead of the usual dilution. Bungenberg de Jong suggested such a procedure, but its value has not yet been established. Experiments aimed at improving the diazotizing mixture by using compounds other than sulfanilic acid are discussed. Errors due to high room temperatures are mentioned.

5. COMPOSITION OF DIAZO REAGENT

The reaction between the components of the diazo reagent can be expressed as follows:

$$\underset{\substack{p\text{-Sulfanilic}\\ \text{acid}}}{\overset{173}{C_6H_4NH_2SO_2OH}} + \overset{36}{HCl} \rightleftharpoons \underset{\substack{p\text{-Sulfanilic acid}\\ \text{hydrochloride}}}{\overset{209 \text{ (molecular weight)}}{C_6H_4NH_2SO_2OH \cdot HCl}}$$

1.

$$\overset{69}{NaNO_2} + \overset{36}{HCl} \rightleftharpoons \overset{47}{HNO_2} + \overset{58}{NaCl}$$

2.

3. $\overset{47}{HNO_2} + \underset{\substack{p\text{-Sulfanilic acid}\\ \text{hydrochloride}}}{\overset{209}{C_6H_4NH_2SO_2OH \cdot HCl}} \rightleftharpoons \underset{\substack{p\text{-Benzenesulfonic}\\ \text{acid diazonium}\\ \text{chloride}}}{\overset{220}{C_6H_4 \Big\langle \begin{matrix} SO_2OH \\ N:NCl \end{matrix}}} + 2\,H_2O$

The diazo reagent used by Hijmans van den Bergh (1918) contained 1 g sulfanilic acid and 15 ml HCl (25%) per liter ("diazo 1" or "diazo A"). He added 0.3 ml of 0.5% sodium nitrite solution to 10 ml of the former solution, i.e., 0.15 g $NaNO_2$ per liter reagent. This combination has been abbreviated to $1 + 15 + 0.15$ in Table II, and this abbreviation will be used in the following discussion. Ehrlich's (1883) original diazo reagent had the composition $1 + 15 + 0.1$; later he (1901) used a reagent composed of $4 + 50 + 0.10$.

The *nitrite* is the most unstable of the chemicals used. It has to be stored under refrigeration, in the dark, and freshly prepared every week (see Guillaumin, 1939). Nosslin (1960, p. 60) found it possible to store in darkness up to 14 days at room temperature. Recently Martinek (1966*) claimed that the 0.5% w/w solution of $NaNO_2$ is stable at least 2 years at room temperature in an amber bottle and that the diazo mixture is perfectly usable for 24 hours if stored at room temperature, although it shows some yellowing after 7–8 hours. The importance of the nitrite concentration was emphasized by Thannhauser and Andersen (1921) who pointed out that increase in nitrite concentration gives rise to augmentation of the reaction velocity. The first systematic studies on this subject were those of Bungenberg de Jong (1937, 1943). He studied diazo reagents of the combination $1 + 15 + n$, where n varied between 0.075 and 0.9. He could show that highest reaction velocities were obtained when $n = 0.600$ to 0.525. Even when the HCl concentration varied the fastest reaction occurred at nitrite values of 0.6–0.525. "Indirect" sera were used in these studies because the rate of reaction was so fast with "direct" sera that determination of the reaction velocity became difficult. In the reagent with optimum reaction rate the molar concentrations of sulfanilic acid and nitrite are 1/173 and 0.6/69 respectively. Considering the formula given in Chapter I,J (i.e., 1 mole bilirubin reacting with 2 moles of diazonium salt) the molar bilirubin concentration corresponding to this reagent is 1:346. Since the molecular weight of bilirubin is 584, this is, 584 divided by 346 = 1.69 g bilirubin per liter. This means that with the reagent in question 169 mg bilirubin per 100 ml can be diazotized quantitatively. This amount is about 2–3 times more than the highest amount of bilirubin ever found in any icteric serum. In other words, the customarily used diazo reagents contain a large excess of diazonium molecules, provided that all diazonium reacts with bilirubin, and not with other substances present in the serum.

Bungenberg de Jong (1937, Chapter III) found that a portion of diazonium reacts with other substances than bilirubin. If diazonium would react only with bilirubin, one tenth of the normally used amount of diazo reagent would suffice to diazotize all bilirubin in weakly icteric sera. However, this amount of reagent could never start the reaction, but a positive reaction was obtained when one quarter of the usual amount was used. On the other hand, if the same reaction was carried out in protein-free aqueous bilirubin solutions, containing the same quantity of bilirubin, 1/50 of the usual amount of diazo reagent yielded a positive reaction. When the serum was treated with proteolytic enzymes, e.g., papain, prior to reaction, the amount of reagent necessary to induce a positive reaction was even larger than that required in normal serum. Thus, it seems that the free carboxy or amino groups of amino acids react with the diazonium. Profitt and Morrison (1949) arrived at similar conclusions, but their results are presented in a short preliminary note. Brodersen (1960) found that 20–50% of the diazonium molecules are bound to serum proteins prior to the reaction with bilirubin. Boutwell (1964) studied the effect of varying concentrations of diazonium by changing the volume of 0.5% $NaNO_2$ from 0.2 to 2.0 with a fixed volume of sulfanilic acid solution (10 ml 1%). Excess of $NaNO_2$ over sulfanilic acid caused a lower yield of azobilirubin. Consequently an optimal nitrite concentration is necessary. At higher or lower nitrite concentrations the rate of reaction decreases. The assumption that reaction velocity increases with increasing amounts of nitrite is erroneous.

Bungenberg de Jong also studied the role of *sulfanilic acid*. He used mixtures containing 1–4 g sulfanilic acid per liter. This compound was found to influence the reaction rate, and a certain excess is necessary, because some diazonium is attached to serum protein (see above). An excess of sulfanilic acid without corresponding amounts of nitrite retarded the reaction, and large excess led to brown and in some cases to blue discolorations. Ehrlich originally used a saturated solution of sulfanilic acid, later one with 5 g per liter, and finally 1 g per liter.

Some experiments have already been mentioned (Section C,4, this chapter) in which sulfanilic acid was replaced by sulfanilamide and other sulfonamides. The reaction rate was somewhat accelerated by some of these substitutions but no significant improvement was achieved.

Also the *hydrochloric acid* content of the reagent is important. The usual content is 15 ml concentrated or 25% HCl per liter—ca. 0.17 and 0.11 mole HCl per liter respectively. According to the formulas given in the beginning of this section 1 mole sulfanilic acid requires 1 mole HCl and 1 mole $NaNO_2$. The molar concentration of the customary $1 + 15 + 0.15$ mixture is 0.00578 (1/173) for sulfanilic acid, and 0.00217 (0.15/69) for nitrite; as each of them reacts with equimolar amounts of HCl, they bind together the sum, i.e., 0.00715 mole HCl. The molar concentration of HCl in the reagent is about 0.11 or 0.17 (with 25% or concentrated HCl, respectively), i.e., there is an excess of ca. 0.1 or 0.15 mole HCl, which corresponds to about pH 1. When serum, i.e., a buffer with pH 7.3, is added, the pH changes. Bungenberg de Jong (1937) investigated the pH for various mixtures of serum and reagent ($1 + 15 + 0.15$). He determined the following values: 1 part of serum + 2 parts of reagent, pH = 1.7; $1 + 1$, pH = 3.6; $1 + 0.5$, pH = 4.5; $1 + 0.25$, pH = 5.7; $1 + 0.125$, pH = 6.7.

Hijmans van den Bergh (1918) employed 1 part serum + 0.25 parts reagent (pH = 5.7); Lepehne (1920, 1921a, 1923) and Davies and Dodds (1927) used $1 + 0.8$ (pH = 4); Adler and Strausz (1925a,b,c,d) used $1 + 0.5$ (pH = 4.5) and $1 + 1$ (pH = 3.6). Peter (1933) used a reagent which contained more than the customary amounts of HCl: $5 + 50 + 0.25$. For pH of reaction mixtures containing caffein sodium benzoate or similar buffers, see Table II where pH determinations of the reaction mixture in several methods are given.

Various investigators studied the *influence of pH* on the course of the reaction (Collinson and Fowweather, 1926; Davies and Dodds, 1927; C. E. Newman, 1928; Weltmann and Hückel, 1928, 1929; Maeda and Morishima, 1929; Griffiths and Kaye, 1930a,b; G. Hunter, 1930b,c). We are indebted to Bungenberg de Jong (1937) for the most thorough investigations. He studied the reaction conditions of horse serum (indirect reaction) with diazo mixtures containing between 4 and 20 ml of 25% HCl per liter. The other components were present in the usual proportions, i.e., 1 and 0.15. The fastest reaction took place with 8 ml HCl, but the color was not stable. When 15–18 ml HCl were used, the reaction was somewhat slower but an intensive and stable color developed. Concentrations above 18 ml HCl led to a bluish or brownish discoloration. Fig. 38

shows his reaction curve drawn by plotting HCl concentration against the time required for the reaction of 75% of bilirubin present, as determined with a comparator.

He found different curves for sera with direct and indirect diazo reactions. Indirect reacting sera showed maximum reaction velocity with 8 ml HCl per liter, and the curve dropped precipitously on both sides of the maximum. Contrary to this, an asymptotic curve was obtained with direct reacting sera, which practically reached the abscissa after 10 minutes and the ordinate at 40 ml per liter. When the customary diazo reagent was used $(1 + 15 + 0.15)$, increase of hydrochloric acid

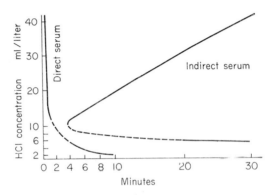

FIG. 38. Curves of the velocity of the diazo reaction of bilirubin in serum with direct and indirect diazo reactions at varying pH (varying HCl concentration of reagent). From Bungenberg de Jong (1937, p. 24).

concentration caused retardation of the reaction with indirect reacting sera, but no change occurred in direct reacting sera. Dilute NaOH additions to indirect sera showed that the reaction rate was highest between pH 4.9 and 5.5. The maximum rate was at pH 5.2. The maximum rate of reaction occurred at the same pH when only the HCl concentration was varied.

It was impossible to obtain a direct reaction by changing the pH in sera exhibiting an indirect reaction with the usual diazo reagent. The highest attained reaction velocity to convert 75% of bilirubin present was 3 minutes in an indirect reacting serum. Direct reacting sera formed azobilirubin at pH 1.7. This was not the case in indirect reacting sera. Pure protein-free bilirubinate solutions showed a negative diazo reaction at pH 2.55–2.80, and traces of a diazo reaction at pH 3.15 and at 3.70–10.2. The color changed to a brownish yellow at pH 5.2. The main difference between sera and pure solutions is that bilirubin flocculates from pure solutions at acid pH values (compare Chapter I,C).

Later, Cabello Ruz (1943c) investigated the influence of pH on the diazo reaction of direct and indirect reacting sera, as well as on normal sera to which bilirubin had been added. His reagent contained 0.1% sulfanilic acid and the HCl concentration varied from 0.015 to 6%. The pH of the solutions varied between 2.9 and 0.1. The reaction mixture consisted of 1 ml serum, 4 ml water, and 1 ml reagent. Measurements were performed in a Pulfrich photometer with filter S 53, after 30 minutes. The pH of the reaction mixtures varied between 1.5 and 7.9. The nitrite concentration was not reported, but it was probably the customary 0.15 g per liter. The reaction took its course rather independently from pH in direct reacting serum; the maximum was observed at pH 2–3, the minimum was at pH 7 (about 60% of the extinction at maximum). However, significant variations occurred in indirect reacting sera, and in sera to which bilirubin had been added. The maximum here was at pH 5.9 and the minimum at pH 1–2. Minimum extinction was only 12% of the maximum. These findings agree with those reported by Bungenberg de Jong.

Recently Lathe and Ruthven (1958) again studied the role of the composition of diazo reagent. Their reaction conditions differed, however, from those of the above investigators in that they used a much higher serum dilution. The main points of their results agree with those of Bungenberg de Jong. They emphasized that only when pH and concentration of diazotized sulfanilic acid are kept low can differences between the diazo reaction of direct and indirect bilirubin be expected. Furthermore, they established that the pH as well as the protein concentration have an influence on the absorption spectra of azobilirubin. Thus, to exclude erroneous analysis, both these factors must be known exactly. They also reported a simple procedure for simultaneous quantitative determinations of direct and indirect bilirubin in icteric newborns. Meites and Hogg (1959) also studied the influence of increased concentrations of HCl, sulfanilic acid, and nitrite on the diazo reaction. D. Watson (1961b, p. 608) doubted Bungenberg de Jong's finding that the optimal nitrite concentration with Hijmans van den Bergh's reagent (1+15+n, cf. above) is equimolar to the sulfanilic acid concentration. He arrived at this conclusion partly from theoretical reasons, partly on the basis of the observations of Lathe and Ruthven. This is, however, erroneous because one cannot compare Bungenberg de Jong's method (dilution factor 1:3.5) with Lathe and Ruthven's method (dilution factor 1:35). The difference in optimal nitrite concentration between these two methods is due to the difference in protein concentration because much more diazonium is bound by the serum proteins in the former method than in the latter (cf. above). On the other hand, it is correct that equimolar concentrations of sulfanilic acid and nitrite are only optimal in diazo methods with low dilution factors (Bungenberg de Jong's, Jendrassik-Gróf's and others) and correspondingly high protein concentration in the reaction mixture. Boutwell (1964) studied the effect of pH changes on coupling by adding HCl or NaOH to the reagent. He found—using 0.1 ml serum + 3.2 ml reagent—that the pH of the reagent giving the highest difference between direct and free bilirubin was 1.8–2.0 while pH 2.7 gave optimal coupling conditions for free bilirubin with acetamide as accelerator.

Verschure and Hoefsmit (1956) employed a peculiar diazo reagent for staining bilirubin on paper strips. This reagent consisted of 10 ml 96% alcohol, 10 ml 0.1% aqueous sulfanilic acid, and 0.6 ml 0.5% aqueous sodium nitrite solution. Reaction occurred immediately after spraying, and the red color was comparatively stable when the strips were stored in the dark after drying. This diazo reagent is remarkable because it does not contain HCl.

Summary

The customary diazo reagent, the composition of which is briefly described as 1 + 15 + 0.15, contains a considerable excess of diazonium molecules. This excess is sufficiently high to give reaction in every icteric serum. This excess of diazonium molecules is necessary because a certain amount of it is bound by proteins. To induce a positive reaction, dilute aqueous bilirubin solutions require only one tenth of the amount of reagent required by undiluted sera with the same bilirubin content. If the dilution of the serum with the reagents is of the order 1:5, the optimum nitrite concentration is equimolar with the sulfanilic acid content, i.e., it corresponds to 0.35–0.40 g per g sulfanilic acid. The rate of reaction varies with the concentration of diazonium not bound by proteins. The influence of pH is discussed. Figure 38 shows the basic differences existing between direct and indirect reacting sera.

6. ACCELERATORS (COUPLING REAGENTS) AND INHIBITORS OF THE DIAZO REACTION

As previously mentioned some sera with high bilirubin content give a positive reaction with diazo reagent without the addition of alcohol (so-called direct reaction). However, other sera produce color only in the presence of alcohol (indirect reaction). Hijmans van den Bergh and Müller (1916) discovered this phenomenon. They found that besides methanol or ethanol, other substances, such as sodium hydroxide, bile acids, citric acid, and other organic acids, exhibit the same influence on this reaction. Since this time a number of such substances (accelerators, coupling reagents) have been found, which exert a similar accelerating effect on the diazo reaction of indirect reacting sera. Examples are acetone (Lepehne, 1920) and caffeine sodium benzoate (Adler and Strausz, 1922). The activity of the latter reagent was ascribed to sodium benzoate (Weltmann and Hückel, 1929). Similarly behaving materials are sodium salicylate, urea, bile salts, digitalis (Adler and Strausz, 1925d), butyric acid, and acetoacetic acid (Kerppola and Leikola, 1931), glacial acetic acid (Kerppola and Leikola, 1931; May *et al.*, 1934), propanol (Kerppola and Leikola, 1931, Keyser and Sanders, 1953), and pyridine (Bungenberg de Jong, 1937).

These accelerators show the same influence on pure aqueous bilirubinate solutions as on sera (Hijmans van den Bergh and Muller, 1916). Bungenberg de Jong (1937) showed that all alkali salts of weak acids act as accelerators and that this effect is based on their buffering ability. Maximum reaction rates occurred at significantly higher pH values when such buffer solutions were employed than in their absence (for example at pH 5.7–7.0 with buffer, and pH 4.9–5.5 without buffer). Therefore, electrolyte concentration and pH value are of decisive importance in the diazo reaction of bilirubin. This is true for sera as well as for pure bilirubin solutions. However, the mechanism of accelerators, for example alcohols, cannot be explained with differences in pH and variations in electrolyte concentration alone, but depends on other factors too, as the alcohol concentration. Whereas 15% alcohol has practically no effect, maximum reaction velocity is obtained at 66% ethyl alcohol. The effect of alcohol is not that of converting bilirubin in direct reacting modification. The "direct" reaction induced by alcohol in the filtrate of indirect reacting serum becomes immediately indirect again when the filtrate is diluted far enough so that the alcohol concentration falls below the level of activation (Bungenberg de Jong, 1937, p. 46). To reach the maximum reaction velocity ethanol concentration must be 50% or higher (Coolidge, 1940). Methanol shows an even stronger accelerating action. However, to obtain constant maximal extinction values the methanol employed must be redistilled (Moreland *et al.*, 1950; Michaëlsson, 1961). Mendioroz (1952, 1953a,b) and Mendioroz *et al.* (1954) also reported important investigations on the effect of electrolyte buffers and alcohols on the diazo reaction. They reached essentially the same conclusions as Bungenberg de Jong.

The accelerating effect of propanol, acetone, and glacial acetic acid is of similar nature to that of ethanol and methanol. All these materials are excellent solvents for bilirubin and azobilirubin (May *et al.*, 1934). Their effect is pH independent; thus, glacial acetic acid accelerates the reaction at pH 1.5, and pyridine does the same despite a significant pH increase in the reaction mixture. Since these substances are strongly hydrophilic, it is plausible that their accelerating effect is due to this character. However, Bungenberg de Jong (1937, p. 36) did not succeed in converting the indirect diazo reaction of bilirubin into the direct form by adding an excess of strongly hydrophilic substances, e.g., phosphorus pentoxide or anhydrous sodium sulfate. The mechanism of these accelerators of the diazo reaction is based on the fact that they are good solvents for the otherwise insoluble free bilirubin.

Ichikawa (1956a) investigated the accelerating effect of caffeine on the diazo reaction of bilirubin. This author showed that caffeine converts indirect bilirubin into direct. Bilirubin is insoluble in saturated aqueous solutions of caffeine, sodium benzoate, or sodium acetate, and does not dissolve in mixtures of the last two. However, it dissolves easily in a mixture of caffeine and sodium benzoate, or in a mixture of caffeine, sodium benzoate, and sodium acetate solutions. Bilirubin and its caffeine derivatives could be separated by paper chromatography. Caffeine derivatives exhibited a certain mobility, but bilirubin remained in the starting position. These findings agree with those of Mendioroz (1952), who found that the final extinction values are reached considerably faster after addition of caffeine reagent than when alcohol was added.

Yamaoka et al. (1956b) found that alcohol, as well as caffeine, forms molecular compounds with bilirubin. This explains the mechanism of acceleration of the bilirubin reaction by caffeine, sodium benzoate, alcohol, etc. Powell (1944) added urea to the caffeine–sodium benzoate reagent in order to increase its coupling effect. Brückner (1959) employed a coupling reagent containing antipyrine, urea, and sodium acetate; he later (1961) substituted antipyrine with acetamide. The mechanism of action of these coupling reagents has not been studied in detail except for acetamide (Boutwell, 1964).

Lüders (1964*) performed systematic quantitative studies of the accelerator effect of a series of compounds on the diazo reaction in serum. He used an artificial bilirubin serum prepared from calf serum and unconjugated bilirubin, containing 20 mg/100 ml. It was found that the single components of the caffeine-sodium benzoate reagent each had accelerator effect and that the effect of caffeine alone was less pronounced than that of its mixture with the electrolytes. Further, pure caffeine solutions were difficult to use because of the instability of the reaction products and turbidity. The extinctions were read after 2, 5, 30, 60, and 120 minutes; 0.1 ml of serum plus 0.5 ml of diazo reagent plus 4.4 ml of coupling reagent were used. The extinction was read at 534 (red diazo color) and multiplied by 1000. With methanol as the coupling reagent the extinction value was 220 after 2 minutes, 245 after 5 minutes, 281 after 30 minutes, 303 after 60 minutes, and 319 after 120 minutes. Without coupling reagent (physiological saline 4.4 ml added) the extinction value after 60 minutes was only 41; with a 10% sodium citrate solution it was 213 after 60 minutes, and 252 after 120 minutes; with a 30% urea solution it was 72 after 2 minutes, and 161 after 120 minutes; with caffeine-sodium benzoate reagent it was 272 after both 2 and 30 minutes; and the same was the case with Decholin (1.0 ml 20% sodium dehydrocholate + 3.4 ml 5% albumin solution) as coupling reagent. Lüders emphasized that the action of the coupling reagents on the diazo reaction cannot be a catalysis *sensu strictorii* because the action is highly dependent on the concentration of the compounds in the reagent.

Naskalski and Szczepkowski (1963) studied the *inhibition* of the diazo reaction of bilirubin by various substances. Phenol, aniline, N-methyldianiline, pyrrole, and hydroquinone did not inhibit the coupling of bilirubin, whereas cysteine and glutathione did so.

Summary

A group of substances exert an accelerating effect on the diazo reaction of bilirubin. One group consists of alcohols (methanol, ethanol, propanol, butanol) and the other of organic solvents (acetone, glacial acetic acid, pyridine), which are all strongly hydrophilic. They act by solubilizing the free insoluble bilirubin molecules. Another group of accelerators are electrolytes, which exert their influence by affecting the pH of the reaction mixtures. However, the electrolyte concentration plays an equally significant role. Caffeine accelerates the reaction by the formation of an easily soluble bilirubin–caffeine complex if electrolytes are present. The accelerators act on indirect reacting serum bilirubin as well as on pure bilirubinate solutions.

7. Influence of Water and Salts on the Diazo Reaction

The concentration of bilirubin, as well as that of the diazonium compound, is decreased by simple dilution. Therefore, too high dilutions must be avoided because both the reaction velocity and the intensity of the reaction depend on the concentration of the reaction mixture. The basis of the effect of salts according to Adler and Strausz (1925a,b,c,d) is the lyotropic effect of ions (corresponding to their position in the Hofmeister series) which determines the degree of hydratation of serum colloids. This view has been vigorously discussed. Thus, it was assumed that "swelling," caused by hydratation would result in retardation, whereas "de-swelling" would correspond to acceleration. However, Bungenberg de Jong (1937, 1943) could not confirm the findings of Adler and Strausz. He maintained that the accelerating effect of various ions on the diazo reaction is based exclusively on their position in the lyotropic Hofmeister series, provided the pH is not influenced by the same ions. Bungenberg de Jong could show that a series of anions developed optimal accelerating action at various pH values. Thus, it was shown that salts influence the direct as well as the indirect diazo reactions of sera, but completely different results were obtained in protein-free bilirubinate solutions. These last results can easily be accounted for by the extremely low solubility of pure bilirubin at acidic pH values, which causes its precipitation by a number of ions. When bilirubinate solutions were added to egg albumin the manner of action of these ions corresponded to the Hofmeister series. Bungenberg de Jong studied the mode of action of anions as well as that of cations, and established that the accelerating effect of both is largely influenced by the hydrogen ion concentration. Thus, the reaction was stopped on addition of aluminum chloride at pH 5.7, but was accelerated at pH 3.4–4.5. Similarly, ions present in the diazo reagent (Na^+, Cl^- and NO_2^-) exert a certain accelerating action if the pH of the mixture is approximately 5.5. In a like manner, salts which are in serum can act as accelerators. This was shown by Bungenberg de Jong, who studied the reaction conditions before and after dialysis of serum. The diazo reaction was considerably retarded by dialysis. This was also the case when dialysis was discontinued at the moment when serum proteins started to precipitate. Mendioroz (1953b), who carried out very careful studies on the mode of action of salts on the diazo reaction, reached the same conclusions as Bungenberg de Jong.

Summary

Since dilution with water retards the diazo reaction, unnecessary dilution must be avoided. Anions and cations exert a considerable influence on the reaction. Ions present in serum and in the diazo reagent itself contribute equally to this influence. The particular ions show their maximum effect, acceleration or retardation, at characteristic pH values. When changes in pH are excluded, the action of ions corresponds to their respective position in Hofmeister's lyophilic series. This fact indicates that the degree of hydratation of serum colloids plays a certain role in diazo reactions.

D. Direct and Indirect Diazo Reaction

As mentioned above, Hijmans van den Bergh and Muller (1916) showed that some icteric sera reacted with the diazo reagent, whereas others did not. However, addition of alcohol induced a positive reaction also in the latter type sera. Correspondingly, sera which immediately gave a reaction were called "direct reacting," whereas the others, which became positive only after addition of alcohol, were named "indirect reacting." It is important to keep in mind that even sera with typical indirect reaction give a slightly positive reaction when they stand for half an hour or longer. Under certain conditions 24 hours are required for developing the reaction (Katznelson, 1920). The only solutions which yield a truly negative reaction are pure aqueous colloidal solutions of bilirubin in which not even addition of alcohol, acetone, or glacial acetic acid leads to a positive reaction (Varela Fuentes and Recarte, 1934b).

It was soon established that direct and indirect reacting sera differ not only as far as rate of the diazo reaction is concerned, but also in other respects. Thus, Hijmans van den Bergh (1918, p. 43) showed that proteins precipitated from "direct" icteric sera with alcohol contain more bilirubin than such proteins from indirect reacting icteric sera. Furthermore, the bilirubin of direct sera is much more sensitive to oxidation than that of indirect sera. Grunenberg (1922, 1923a,b) discovered that bilirubin of indirect sera can be much more easily extracted with chloroform than that of direct sera. In addition, a number of investigators found slight differences of absorption spectra of bilirubin (Davis and Sheard, 1937; Penati and Pagliardi, 1943) and of azobilirubin (Castex *et al.*, 1940; M. Salvini and Gonzato, 1947a,b) in direct and indirect sera.

The terms *direct* and *indirect* are not always used in a clear and well-defined manner, and in each case it is important to clarify what the various authors mean by this terminology. These terms are used correctly only when they refer to untreated sera, without any addition of accelerators. Some authors speak about direct reaction after accelerators have been added. This, however, is inaccurate because all sera become direct reacting under these conditions. To designate various degrees of reaction velocity of fresh sera with the diazo reagent, but without any addition of accelerator, the following terms have been used: "direct," "retarded," and "indirect." More complicated terms also were proposed, including "biphasic" (Feigl and Querner, 1919), "prompt direct," and "retarded direct" (Lepehne, 1920, 1921a,b); C. J. Watson (1938) proposed five reaction types. This is, however, too far fetched and unnatural. "*Total bilirubin*" includes all bilirubin present in serum which can be measured after the addition of a suitable accelerator. The term "indirect bilirubin" or "indirect diazo reaction" is sometimes used synonymously with "total bilirubin" or "total diazo reaction," but this is quite misleading. The term "indirect" only expresses the difference between "total" and "direct." The cause of various reaction rates of diazo reactions of untreated sera, i.e., the reactions called "prompt," "retarded," "biphasic," etc., is far from clear and surely varies from one serum to another.

1. THE DIRECT DIAZO REACTION AND THE REACTION VELOCITY

Hijmans van den Bergh and his direct successors distinguished between direct and indirect reactions with the naked eye. Later, with the development of photometric methods, quantitative reaction rate determinations were introduced. Deenstra (1948a) pointed out that readings of the direct reaction with the naked eye depend on both reaction rate and bilirubin concentration and that a positive direct reaction can be caused either by low concentrations of a fast reacting bilirubin or by high concentrations of a slowly reacting bilirubin. Thus, quantitative photometric measurements are necessary, and the only reasonable approach is the construction of *time curves for the diazo reaction* as introduced by Hartog (1935). He constructed time/reaction curves for sera with different types of diazo reactions by comparative colorimetric measurements, using a Dubosq colorimeter (bicolorimetry). Hartog studied 34 icteric patients. Some showed positive direct reaction with a steep increase immediately after reagent introduction (pure direct); others became positive after a latent period, and thereafter increased steeply (retarded direct); again, another group developed gradually after a certain latent period (biphasic); and finally others showed a very much retarded reaction, which increased only slowly (indirect). However, Hartog's method was not quite appropriate, since he used 1 ml serum + 7 ml of 0.9% NaCl + 2 ml diazo reagent instead of the ratio originally introduced by Hijmans van den Bergh, namely $1 + 1 + 0.5$.

In earlier studies, reaction was usually considered direct when the color became visible after 30 seconds (Hijmans van den Bergh, 1918, p. 35; Hartog, 1935, p. 69). This definition was used until photometry was introduced in 1935. From that time on, the general tendency has been to read 1 minute after reagent addition. The resulting measurements are called *"one-minute bilirubin."* However, these time limits of 30 seconds or 1 minute are entirely arbitrary and the only correct method is the construction of time curves covering the whole course of the reaction.

It is important not to add any accelerator, and to maintain the standard composition of diazo reagent (see Section C,5, this chapter) at $1 + 15 + 0.15$. The technique most widely used today for quantitative determination of the direct diazo reaction was introduced by Malloy and Evelyn (1937) and corresponds to their method for total bilirubin (Section C,4, this chapter) with the difference being that, instead of 5 ml methanol, 5 ml water are employed. Readings are performed at various intervals up to 120 minutes) in a photoelectric colorimeter. Different types of curves were obtained which resembled those obtained by Hartog. High dilutions and the unavoidable turbidity are inherent sources of error which can influence the differences between reaction mixture and control.

Several authors devised procedures for the determination of direct diazo reaction which are mainly modifications of their methods for total bilirubin determination, the main difference being that they replace the accelerator by a corresponding amount of 0.9% sodium chloride solution (Jendrassik and Cleghorn, 1937; Balzer and Schulte, 1949; Castex *et al.*, 1940, 1941). A survey is presented in Table III. Addition of other electrolytes has also been recommended, e.g., sodium acetate, but this is wrong because this reagent has a considerable accelerating action itself. Moreover, diazo reagents deviating from the classic composition (1 + 15 + 0.15) have been employed which may also influence the results.

Bungenberg de Jong (1937, 1943) applied his finding—that "direct sera" react immediately at pH 2, whereas "indirect sera" show no reaction at this pH (Fig. 38)—to the determination of the direct reaction. He used a special acid reagent for this purpose. Measurements were made 2 minutes after addition of reagent. This method is interesting and fully substantiated, although it has not yet been accepted in clinical practice.

It has been proposed that, to achieve a precise reading of the direct reaction at a definite time, the course of the reaction should be stopped at that time and subsequently read. This has been achieved by powerful oxidation (Colangiuli and Barengo, 1940), by strong alkalization (With, 1943b, 1944a), by reduction with $SnCl_2$ (Ridgway, 1959), or by strong acid (Brückner, 1959, 1961). However, such procedures are subject to uncontrollable sources of error. Deenstra (1947, 1948b) showed that errors could originate from a sharp final increase of reaction rate, before the reaction comes to standstill. Bungenberg de Jong (1937, p. 121) proposed the addition of talcum powder to the reaction mixture after a certain period, in the study of direct reaction. In this way azobilirubin would be adsorbed, while nondiazotized bilirubin remains in solution. Thus, one could discontinue the reaction at any desired time interval and corresponding curves could be constructed. Berezin and Antunes (1962) proposed to separate bilirubin and azobilirubin in the reaction mixture by means of high voltage electrophoresis, during which procedure bilirubin moves rapidly with the albumin while azobilirubin moves much more slowly. In this way a clear separation is achieved. However, they did not propose a technique suitable for clinical use.

Time-curves of the direct diazo reaction have been published by Hartog (1935), Malloy and Evelyn (1937), Gigon and Noverraz (1939), Cantarow *et al.* (1940, 1942), Lepehne (1942a), Ducci and Watson (1945), C. J. Watson (1946), Gray and Whidborne (1946), Pagliardi

TABLE III

The Direct Diazo Reaction: Quantitative Methods Based on Reaction Velocity

Author	Year	Type of reagent[a]	Other reagents	Serum dilution	pH of reaction mixture	Time (minutes)
Hartog	1935	1 + 15a + 0.15		1/10	1.8	Curve
Jendrassik-Cleghorn	1936a,b	5 + 15a + 0.125		1/5	3.5	5
Malloy-Evelyn	1937	1 + 15a + 0.15		1/25	2.0	30
Gigon-Noverraz	1939	5 + 15b + 0.20		1/1.17	5.8	Curve
Castex et al.	1940	5 + 5a + 0.125	Reaction temperature 60°C	1/7	2.5	15
Rappaport-Eichhorn	1943	1 + 15b + 1.00	Urea and buffer	1/5	4.2	
Sepulveda-Osterbergh	1943a,b	1 + 15a + 0.15		1/10	1.8	1-10
With	1943b	5 + 15a + 0.125	Na-acetate, Fehling II	1/3.5	6.4 } Reading in	5
With	1944a	5 + 15a + 0.125	Fehling II	1/3.5	3.5 } alkaline solution	5
Powell	1944	1 + 15b + 0.15		1/10	3.5	10
Ducci-Watson	1945	1 + 15b + 0.125		1/25	1.8	1 and 15
Gray-Whidborne	1946	1 + 15a + 0.15	Urea, buffer	1/9	3.5	Curve
Gray-Whidborne	1947	1 + 15a + 0.15	Buffer	1/9	3.5	Curve
Deenstra	1947	1 + 15a + 0.15		1/2	2.8	1
Balzer-Schulte	1949	5 + 15b + 0.125	Na-acetate	1/5	5.3	5
King-Coxon	1950	1 + 25b + 0.15		1/10	2.8	1
Schalm-Schulte	1950a	3 + 15b + 0.15		1/5	2.1	10

	Year					
White-Duncan	1952	$3 + 15^b + 0.50$		1/25	2.1	1 + 15
Kingsley et al.	1953	$1 + 15^b + 0.15$		1/6	1.6	1 + 15
Popper-Schaffner	1957	$1 + 15^b + 0.15$		1/6	3.2	1
Sims-Horn	1958	$1 + 15^b + 0.30$	HCl	1/5	3.6	10
Lathe-Ruthven	1958	$1 + 20^a + 0.15^{c,d}$		1/35	1.8	$\frac{1}{2}$, 1, 30, curve
Brückner	1959	$1 + 20 + 0.20$	Phosphoric acid and coupling reagent with antipyrine	1/3.5	Strongly acid	Less than $2\frac{1}{2}$ minutes
Nosslin	1960	$5 + 15^a + 0.125^{c,d}$ and others	Ascorbic acid	1/5.1	3.5, reading in alkaline solution	10
Brückner	1961	$1 + 20^a + 0.30^e$	Phosphoric acid and coupling reagent with antipyrine or acetamide	1/10	Strongly acid	5, 30, and curve
Boutwell	1964	$8.4 + 15 + 0.84$	Sucrose as clearing reagent	1/32 (5/32)	1.7	5

[a] 25% HCl.
[b] Concentrated HCl.
[c] Sulfanilic acid dissolved in 0.15 or 0.25 HCl.
[d] Sulfanilic acid dissolved in 0.2 N HCl.
[e] Sulfanilic acid dissolved in 0.3 N HCl.

and Penati (1948), Brückner (1959, 1961), Gaidano (1959), Nosslin (1960), and Brodersen (1960). Watson, however, recommended the 1 minute method of Malloy and Evelyn for practical purposes and considered this "1 minute bilirubin" an adequate expression for the direct diazo reaction. However, their conclusions have been seriously questioned on the basis of thorough analysis by Deenstra (1948a), Klatskin and Drill (1950), and Lathe and Ruthven (1958). The objections of these workers were later reviewed and discussed by the group around Watson (see Zieve et al., 1951). They admitted that readings made at any time between 1 and 1.5 minutes give equally good results. However, they persisted in their former views based on Malloy and Evelyn's technique.

Gray and Whidborne (1946) compared the method of Malloy and Evelyn with that of Rappaport and Eichhorn (1943). Their results are, however, of limited value because the latter method introduces an acidic buffer solution which can lead to acceleration of the direct reaction, as well as to retardation of the indirect reaction; this is seen from the curves of Bungenberg de Jong (cf. Fig. 38). Deenstra (1948a, p. 113) wondered why Gray and Whidborne found only such slight differences in degree of reaction between direct and indirect bilirubin. A closer study of the graphs of Gray and Whidborne (1946, p. 84, Fig. 2b, and p. 85, Fig. 3) and those of Deenstra (1948a, p. 117) show, however, great similarities although they were obtained with different techniques. It must be borne in mind that Gray and Whidborne's curves obtained on hemolytic sera show the time in hours, and not in minutes, a fact which Deenstra has apparently overlooked.

Pagliardi and Penati (1948) studied time curves on 18 direct sera over a period of 3 hours, at 22°C and at 36°C (thermostatic control). Similar curve types were obtained for both temperature levels, but the rate of reaction was faster at 36°C than at 22°C. Thus, as Adler and Strausz (1925c) pointed out, it is important to avoid major temperature variations; cf. also Nath et al. (1960).

Deenstra (1948a,b,c) maintained that a single reading is not an adequate substitute for the reaction curve of a direct diazo reaction and proposed to perform readings after 1 minute, as well as after 10 minutes, and use both data as "1 minute per cent" and "10 minute per cent."

Westphal and Gedigk (1949) carried out the reaction according to the method of Jendrassik and Gróf, and used 0.9% sodium chloride solution in place of the caffeine reagent. The pH of the reaction mixture was 3.8–4.1. They also used a 12.5% sodium acetate solution instead of the sodium chloride solution; this resulted in an increase of the pH to 5.5. They emphasized the important fact that it is difficult to obtain correct calibration curves because this requires a pure direct reacting bilirubin without admixture of indirect bilirubin or accelerators. Westphal and Gedigk tried to overcome this difficulty by studying pure bilirubinate solutions. However, this indirect method does not yield acceptable results.

Schalm and Schulte (1950b) studied time curves of the direct diazo reaction by a modification of the method of Jendrassik and Cleghorn (1936a,b). They came to the conclusion that readings made after 10 minutes (10 minute per cent) are the most important for clinical purposes. They considered the 1 minute per cent readings as unreliable, because of the fast color changes occurring during the first 2 minutes. Klatskin and Drill (1950) emphasized that, because of the high dilution, measurements by the method of Malloy and Evelyn are absolutely useless in normal sera. Corà (1954) could show that on dilution of icteric sera a more or less strong increase of direct reaction occurs. Lathe and Ruthven (1958) described a simple method for determination of direct bilirubin in icteric sera. As it uses a dilution of 1:35 it is, however, only usable in strongly icteric sera. Riding and Ellis (1963) described another simple modification of Malloy and Evelyn's test. They employed 0.1 ml serum and 3.0 ml reaction mixture, i.e., a dilution at 1:30.

Brückner (1959, 1961) interrupted the diazo reaction with strong phosphoric acid after which the coupling reagent was added before reading. According to his own comparisons (Brückner, 1961, Table III) this method gives consistently higher figures for the direct reaction than the Malloy-Evelyn method. This discrepancy may be due to a rapid increase in the diazo reaction immediately after the addition of the acid similar to what Deenstra (1947, 1948b) found after addition of strong alkali.

Gaidano (1959) studied the time curve of the direct diazo reaction in 11 sera from patients with occlusive and hepatocellular jaundice. He followed the extinctions at 435 and 565 nm for several hours and calculated the velocity constants for the disappearance of the bilirubin (435 nm) as well as for the formation of the azo compounds (565 nm). Both these processes exhibited a very rapid initial phase with identical velocity constant 5.544. The disappearance of bilirubin showed three phases: (1) initial phase ($k = 5.544$) accounting for ca. 60% of the bilirubin; (2) intermediate phase ($k = 0.968$) accounting for ca. 15% of the bilirubin; (3) final slow phase ($k = 0.095$) accounting for the remaining 25%. The formation of the azo pigments exhibited two phases only: (1) initial rapid phase ($k = 5.544$) accounting for ca. 80% of the pigment formed; and (2) slow final phase ($k = 0.238$) accounting for the remaining 20%. Brodersen (1960)—cf. below—performed similar studies.

Nosslin (1960) has published extensive experimental and clinical studies on the direct and indirect diazo reaction of serum bilirubin, of which only a brief survey can be given here. Readers interested in these problems will find much valuable information in his book. Nosslin used ascorbic acid in his investigations of the direct diazo reaction. Ascorbic acid gives noncoupling compounds with diazonium; 1 mole ascorbic acid inactivates somewhat more than 1 mole of diazonium. Thus, it is possible to stop the diazo reaction at any desired time by introducing an excess of ascorbic acid, and to determine the amount of azobilirubin formed prior to ascorbic acid addition. In this manner, a time curve of the diazo reaction can be constructed, based on a series of data obtained by interrupting the reaction at various time intervals. Nosslin's technique corresponds almost completely to the method of Jendrassik and Gróf (see Section C,5, this chapter). He measured the direct reaction after 10 minutes and thus accepted the criticism advanced for the "1 minute" bilirubin and for Malloy and Evelyn's method (see Section C,5, this chapter). His reagents are exactly the same as these described earlier (Section C,5, this chapter), with the addition of a freshly prepared 4% ascorbic acid solution (200 mg acid dissolved in 5 ml distilled water). Sera, with more than 5 mg bilirubin per 100 ml, are diluted before analysis. For total bilirubin determinations Nosslin added 2.1 ml caffeine reagent and then 0.5 ml freshly prepared diazo mixture to 1 ml serum (serum dilution) and mixed thoroughly. After 10 minutes 1.5 ml Fehling II solution was added and the color determined spectrophotometrically at 620 nm, against water as blank. The technique of the direct reaction followed the same method except for the addition of 2 ml water instead of the 2.1 ml caffeine reagent. After exactly 10 minutes 0.1 ml ascorbic acid was added and thoroughly mixed, and the Fehling II solution was added. For direct reaction measurements the serum blank was prepared with diazo I, instead of the diazo mixture in the same manner. A reagent blank was superfluous.

Besides this standard procedure Nosslin studied the direct reaction at other pH values and at higher diazonium concentrations: (1) direct reaction at pH 1.8 and with a diazo reagent with 35 ml concentrated HCl instead of the commonly used 15 ml. (2) direct reaction at pH 2.0 by using 2.0 ml 0.05 N HCl instead of the commonly used 2.0 ml distilled water. (3) diazo reaction by using diazo reagent with 0.30 ml 0.5% $NaNO_2$ instead of 0.25 ml. Moreover, Nosslin investigated the influence of pH. He published reaction curves in the pH range of 1.5 to 8.0, the widest pH range yet studied. His method is better than earlier ones as it minimizes turbidity. He found that the pH curves of the direct reaction (expressed in per cent of total bilirubin) were the same in normal sera to which free bilirubin was added, in native icteric sera with negative direct reaction, and in normal sera. The maximum of the direct diazo reaction was at about pH 5.5. Contrary to this icteric sera with positive direct reaction showed curves with two more or less marked maxima at about pH 2.0 and about 5.5. In some cases the maximum at pH 2.0 dominated, in others that at pH 5.5 did so, according to the relative ratio of conjugated and unconjugated bilirubin present in the sera. Bilirubin not bound to protein reacted at pH 2.0, whereas that bound to protein reacted at 5.5. It was demonstrated that the percentage of direct bilirubin varied considerably with the extent of serum dilution; this should be considered when various sera are compared.

Nosslin compared the methods described by various authors and tabulated these numerous investigations. His own method gives values close to that of Malloy-Evelyn. He compared his own method and the "1 minute bilirubin" of Ducci and Watson (1945). As expected, considerably higher values were obtained with Nosslin's method. He emphasized that the terminology "direct bilirubin" and "indirect bilirubin" has no chemical significance, since unconjugated bilirubin also participates in the direct diazo reaction.

Michaëlsson *et al.* (1965*) modified Nosslin's method by adding dyphylline mixture instead of distilled water after the ascorbic acid and called this modification "Jendrassik-Gróf-Nosslin-Michaëlsson."

Brodersen (1960; cf. Chapter I,J) came to quite similar results. He found that the reaction velocity varied with the dilution of the serum. The velocity constant did not change at low serum concentrations, but it increased when larger amounts of serum were used. This phenomenon was attributed to the presence of serum proteins. To exclude individual serum differences, mixtures of 0.6 ml serum and 4.9 ml reaction mixture were employed. Six "direct sera," 5 "indirect" icteric sera, and 5 normal sera were studied. It was established that azobilirubin formation proceeds in *two or three simultaneous reactions,* i.e., in phases I, II, and III. At constant diazonium concentrations each step seems to follow a first order equation. In "indirect" sera the predominant portion of azobilirubin was formed in phase III, and only a small amount appeared in phase I. In contrast, in "direct" sera the larger part of azobilirubin was formed in phases I and II, whereas only insignificant color developed in phase III. Normal sera reacted in phases I and III. Pure bilirubin dissolved in serum reacted in two phases, as was also described by Overbeek *et al.* (1955c) for bilirubin solutions in alcohol–chloroform–water mixtures. Indirect bilirubin of icteric sera did not react according to this pattern. Side reactions prevented a considerable amount of bilirubin from forming azobilirubin. This was especially observed if dilute diazo reagent (0.1 mmole per liter) was used. Phases I and II were attributed to conjugated bilirubin, phase III was attributed to the free compound. Brodersen's experiments show that the diazo reaction as it is used in routine clinical practice can help to differentiate between sera containing mainly conjugated bilirubin and sera containing mostly free bilirubin. However, the reaction cannot be used for accurate determination of the concentration of these two bilirubin forms.

Boutwell (1964) employed a concentrated diazo reagent (cf. Table III, final entry) and used sucrose as clarifier. The coupling was carried out at pH 1.7. He read after 5 minutes at 570 nm after addition of concentrated HCl. Both the reaction of conjugated bilirubin and the rapid reaction of free bilirubin were completed in 4 minutes.

Jacobs et al. (1964) admitted the inherent inaccuracy of all methods proposed for quantitative determination of direct (conjugated) bilirubin, the different techniques giving widely discrepant results. They were inclined to ascribe this to the unavailability of reference standards of conjugated bilirubin. Equally important, however, is that bilirubin in serum consists of a mixture of free bilirubin with a varying mixture of several only partially known conjugates (cf. Section F, this chapter). Consequently it is impossible to get an adequate reference standard suitable for all sera. See also G. W. Stevenson et al. (1964), and Section D,2, this chapter.

Summary

Various methods for the determination of a direct diazo reaction are discussed. Meticulous accuracy of technique is mandatory for quantitative determinations; however, the addition of accelerators and unnecessary dilution must be avoided. When comparisons are desired between direct diazo reaction and total bilirubin, the same dilutions as for determination of the "total diazo reaction" must be maintained. The composition of diazo reagent as well as the pH of the reaction mixture is of decisive importance. Errors can also be caused by temperature fluctuations.

For a true characterization of the direct reaction the time reaction curve is required. Measurements performed at a single time interval (1 minute and 10 minute reactions) have been proposed and are used widely. However, these single measurements yield only rough approximations. The "1 minute bilirubin" is especially subject to considerable sources of error.

2. Extractability of Serum Bilirubin with Solvents. Analytical Methods Based on Solvent Extraction

Grunenberg (1922, 1923a,b) discovered that bilirubin can be extracted almost completely, with chloroform, from the sera of patients with hemolytic icterus. However, in direct reacting sera only a small part of bilirubin can be extracted in this way. When sera were alkalinized with 0.1 N NaOH, bilirubin became inextractable with chloroform. Later investigators confirmed Grunenberg's observations. It was found that serum bilirubin with indirect diazo reaction was CHCl$_3$ extractable, whereas serum bilirubin with direct reaction was not (Andrewes, 1924a; Collinson and Fowweather, 1926; C. E. Newman, 1928; Roberts, 1928; G. Hunter, 1930b,c; Kerppola and Leikola, 1931, 1932; Kerppola, 1936, 1942).

De Castro (1929a,b), Varela and Esculies (1931), and Varela *et al.* (1931b, 1934) reported quantitative methods for the determination of CHCl$_3$ extractable bilirubin. Varela *et al.* (1934) discussed the various quantitative methods. Bárdos (1936) as well as Varela Fuentes *et al.* (1944) proposed adding 12% sodium sulfate solution, which was found to make 80% of indirect bilirubin extractable (1 ml serum + 2 ml sodium sulfate solution + 3 ml CHCl$_3$). Other modifications of the process have been introduced by Heilbrun and Hubbard (1940), Polonovski *et al.* (1942), Lopez Garcia and Zelasco (1942), Sepulveda and Osterberg (1943a,b), and Maclay and Osterberg (1944).

Hijmans van den Bergh (1918, p. 34) had already investigated the possibility of extracting bile bilirubin with CHCl$_3$ and found a considerable part of the bilirubin of fresh human bile to be extractable. This was confirmed by Weltmann and Hückel (1928, 1929) and seemed to indicate that CHCl$_3$ extractability and indirect diazo reaction of bilirubin cannot be identical, since the bile bilirubin shows a direct diazo reaction. However, it must be remembered that under certain conditions bile can contain considerable amounts of indirect reacting bilirubin besides the direct modification. Varela Fuentes *et al.* (1944) found no CHCl$_3$ extractable bilirubin in duodenal contents. Bungenberg de Jong (1937, p. 117) pointed out that bilirubin of icteric sera in hemolytic disease cannot be completely extracted with CHCl$_3$. Therefore, not all indirect reacting bilirubin is extractable with CHCl$_3$. Later (1942) he could not demonstrate any relation between the type of diazo reaction and the CHCl$_3$ extractability of the bilirubin of icteric urine.

Ducci and Watson (1945) did not succeed in establishing a close relationship between the indirect diazo reaction (method by Malloy and Evelyn) and CHCl$_3$ extractable bilirubin (method by Sepulveda and Osterberg). These authors determined total as well as direct bilirubin, and calculated the indirect as the difference.

Lopez Garcia and Zelasco (1942), Zelasco and Lopez Garcia (1944), and Lopez Garcia (1943, pp. 87–110) found that CHCl$_3$ extractability of serum bilirubin is affected by serum lipid. Gastaldo and Testoni

(1947a,b) and Gastaldo *et al.* (1947) studied the chloroform extract-ability of bilirubin on fresh bile from the gallbladder of dogs and found that extractability is dependent on pH. No bilirubin was extracted at strongly alkaline reaction, but partial bilirubin extraction took place at the pH of serum (about 7.5). After storage the extractable bilirubin fraction increased considerably. This phenomenon was detectable after 6 hours of storage. After addition of 6% hydrogen peroxide solution a similar increase in extractability of bilirubin could be observed. This suggests that oxidation enhances extractability. Investigations of icteric sera showed similar results. M. Salvini and Feruglio (1949) confirmed that $CHCl_3$ extractability of bile bilirubin is strongly pH dependent. No extraction took place at pH above 7 and the extraction was complete at pH 5.

Mendioroz *et al.* (1951) found that benzene or toluene extraction yielded the same results as $CHCl_3$ extraction. They attempted to separate the $CHCl_3$ extractable fraction in bile from the nonextractable one by paper chromatography. These experiments could not be extended to serum, since alcohol was one of the solvents employed. Bourrillon (1952) showed that bilirubin can be completely extracted from pure bilirubinate solutions with $CHCl_3$. The same result was obtained when the solutions contained serum globulins or globin. However, extraction did not occur if serum albumin was present.

Mendioroz *et al.* (1953) arrived at the conclusion that "indirect bili-rubin," calculated as the difference between total and direct bilirubin, is an artifact. On the contrary, indirect bilirubin, determined by $CHCl_3$ extraction, is a true bilirubin fraction of physiological significance. This conclusion agrees with most of the recent investigations (see Section G, this chapter). Mendioroz *et al.* (1954) investigated the effect of ethanol, methanol, and sodium and ammonium sulfates on $CHCl_3$ extractability of serum bilirubin. They found that addition of these materials con-siderably increases chloroform extractability. Mendioroz (1957) studied the $CHCl_3$ extractable serum bilirubin in ca. 200 normal adults and ca. 300 jaundiced patients and concluded that the diagnostic value of such determinations is limited. Varela Fuentes and Mendioroz (1959) found two $CHCl_3$ extractable bilirubin fractions—one giving indirect diazo reaction and with absorption maximum 450–455 nm, and another giving direct diazo reaction and showing a maximum of 412 nm; the latter was identical with the ether extractable bilirubin occurring in sera from patients with neoplastic obstructive jaundice.

Brodersen and Vind (1963a) studied the extraction of bilirubin from serum in relation to pH. They found that $CHCl_3$ for analysis and $CHCl_3$ for anesthesia were equally suitable and that the process of purification was important to the stability of bilirubin. If the $CHCl_3$ was washed very carefully to remove traces of ethanol, which exhibit a stabilizing effect on $CHCl_3$, the bilirubin was completely destroyed within a few minutes. The best method for pretreatment of the $CHCl_3$ was to wash once with an equal volume of a 10% aqueous sodium thiosulfate solution (analytical quality) at 2–4°C under incandescent light, to discard the first few milliliters of the $CHCl_3$ from the separatory funnel to avoid contamination with thiosulfate, and to use the $CHCl_3$ within 2 hours. Bilirubin dissolved in $CHCl_3$ purified in this way showed no changes in absorption after several days at 2°C in darkness.

Serum was buffered prior to extraction by adding 0.3 M postassium phosphate (pH 7.9) containing 6% ascorbic acid. After this, pH was adjusted by addition of HCl or KOH. Extraction with $CHCl_3$ was carried out in glass stoppered centrifuge tubes by shaking by hand for 2 minutes and centrifuging at 3,000 g for 10 minutes in a cold room. In this way a clear $CHCl_3$ phase was usually obtained, but in some cases 10,000 g was required. To get a clear aqueous phase 20,000 g for 30 minutes was required. A considerable amount of protein collected between the two layers. The pH of the upper phase was controlled with a glass electrode, the disc of protein removed, and the lower phase ($CHCl_3$) subjected to reading in a Bausch and Lomb spectronic recording spectrophotometer in the range 350–600 nm. This procedure took 1–2 minutes. The sera employed were blood bank sera and contained no $CHCl_3$ extractable carotenoids. The absorption curve of the $CHCl_3$ extracts ordinarily exhibited exactly the same shape as a bilirubin curve in the range 650–390 nm, but below 390 nm a slight deviation was found, presumably caused by a substance other than bilirubin. Irradiation of the serum was carried out in a layer of 1 ml with an incandescent bulb at a distance of 6 cm for 2 hours under occasional mixing. The temperature was about 30°C.

The pH extraction curve of bilirubin solutions without serum showed the same figures at all pH levels between 8 and 4, but at pH above 8 the extracted amount rapidly declined to reach zero at pH ca. 10.5; at pH ca. 9.7 50% of the bilirubin present was extracted. The curve is in agreement with what is to be expected with a nonpolar acid. With normal human serum the alkaline branch of the curve (above pH 8) was parallel to the curve of the serum-free solution, but displaced about 0.5 pH unit toward the acid side. The extraction exhibited a maximum at pH 7.8–8.2 and decreased at lower pH to reach a plateau at pH 6 and lower. The height of this plateau relative to the maximum extraction varied from serum to serum, ranging from 24 to 56% in the 8 sera studied. Bilirubin added to serum behaved in a way similar to native serum bilirubin.

Extraction at pH below 4 resulted in $CHCl_3$ extracts exhibiting spectral curves differing from that for bilirubin, the more the lower the pH. At pH 1–2 the absorption maximum at 455 nm disappeared and was replaced by one at 393 nm. Whether this maximum was due to a transformation product of bilirubin or an unrelated substance from serum was not found out.

Irradiation of serum was followed by a decrease in extracted bilirubin to ca. 35%, but the pH curve was the same as for nonirradiated serum. To study the eventual losses due to protein precipitation, urea was added to serum to the concentration of 7 M prior to extraction. This greatly decreased the protein precipitate, but the extracted amount of bilirubin was not significantly affected, which shows that only minor amounts of bilirubin can be bound to the protein precipitate. Adding salicylic acid (20 mg per 100 ml of serum) prior to $CHCl_3$ extraction caused a displacement of the alkaline branch of the curve of 0.5 pH units toward the alkaline side, i.e., the alkaline branch of the serum became identical with that of an aqueous bilirubin solution. The extraction curve at pH below 8 was, however, unchanged.

Later Brodersen and Vind (1963b) developed a specific method for quantitative determination of unconjugated bilirubin and mesobilirubin based on $CHCl_3$ extraction in the cold at pH 8 after addition of ascorbic acid and salicylic acid. This method is time consuming and consequently not suitable for routine work. The technique is as follows:

The serum is diluted to a concentration not above 3 mg per 100 ml (50 μM per liter) before analysis. One ml of serum is mixed with 1 ml of the following buffer solution: K_2HPO_4 2.7 g, ascorbic acid 3 g, salicylic acid 20 mg, dissolved in H_2O in a 50 ml flask; pH adjusted to 8.15 ± 0.05 with 2 N KOH; then diluted to 50 ml. To 2 ml of the serum-buffer mixture 2 ml petrol ether are added for extraction of the carotenoid. After vigorous shaking and centrifugation the upper layer is discarded, the last drops being removed by means of a strip of siliconized Whatman No. 4 filter paper. In this way a small mucoid interphase is removed too. Then follows extraction with 2 ml $CHCl_3$ by vigorous shaking for 2 minutes followed by centrifugation. The $CHCl_3$ has to be freshly washed with 10% sodium thiosulfate. All extractions and centrifugations are carried out at 4°C under incandescent light. The centrifuged $CHCl_3$ extract is subjected to spectrophotometric reading in a 1 cm cell in the range 390–650 nm, sufficient readings being taken to construct an absorption curve. The curve is compared to transparent sheets of standard curves of bilirubin and mesobilirubin to determine the proportion of the two pigments present. Approximate values for the concentration of the two pigments can be calculated by means of the following two formulas: $B = -4.63 \times E_{444} + 23.8 \times E_{468}$; $M = 22.3 \times E_{444} - 23.8 \times E_{468}$. B is the bilirubin concentration, M the mesobilirubin concentration in the CHCl$_3$ extract in μmoles per liter, E the 1 cm extinctions at the respective wavelengths.

Biliverdin is not extracted from serum with CHCl$_3$ at pH 8. Conjugates of bilirubin are not extracted with CHCl$_3$, but some alkali-labile conjugates may cause error if the extraction is not performed rapidly after the addition of the buffer. The method is highly reproducible, having a coefficient of variation of 4% (2.7% if the petrol ether extraction of carotenoids is omitted). The recovery of added bilirubin and mesobilirubin is 90–100% (95–100% if petrol ether extraction is omitted). Without addition of salicylate and ascorbic acid the recovery is considerably lower (50–90%). Hemoglobin does not interfere with the determination. Strongly hemolyzed samples gave the same results as samples without hemolysis.

Several investigators tried to separate bilirubin and its conjugates by solvent extraction methods.

Schachter (1959) reported a method for quantitative determination of mono- and diglucuronides. According to this process the azo pigments, formed by diazotation, were extracted with *n*-butanol, and subsequently separated into pigments A and B by simple phase separation in *n*-butanol–CHCl$_3$–2 M acetate buffer (pH 3). McGill *et al.* (1962) found good agreement between this method and chromatographic methods. Jardin *et al.* (1963) found that the method was of problematic value because of lack of sensitivity and reproducibility. Because of the uncertainty of the nature of pigment I, the theoretical basis of the method is questionable because it depends on the assumption that pigment I is bilirubin monoglucuronide (cf. Section F, this chapter).

A simple fractionation method based on extraction of buffered serum with ethyl acetate and butanol was described by Eberlein (1960). The principle of this method is that when serum is diluted with a pH 5 phosphate buffer unconjugated bilirubin is quantitatively extracted by ethyl acetate. When the aqueous phase is reextracted with butanol pigment I ("monoglucuronide") is believed to go into the butanol layer.

This method of Eberlein has been widely used, especially by pediatricians, both in the United States and abroad (cf. Blacklidge, 1963[*]), but it has also been subject to criticism. Thus Tisdale and Welch (1962) found that it was technically simple but it had poor reproducibility and it had poor correlation with other methods; they regarded it as a semiquantitative method. Ibbot and O'Brien (1964[*]) pointed out that it is sensitive to small temperature changes and that turbidity is often present in the final solutions. The extraction with butanol was inefficient if special precautions were not taken, and further much pigment was retained on the protein precipitate. If these sources of error were taken into account much lower concentrations of "monoglucuronide" were found than with the original method. Control of the fractions with reverse phase chromatography disclosed a similar composition of the ethyl acetate and butanol fractions, and consequently it is not possible to determine monoglucuronide with the method of Eberlein. Finally it was found that the spectrum of heme pigments was changed during the extraction procedures for which the correction factors are inaccurate. Ibbot and O'Brien concluded that neither the original method nor their own improved modification is satisfactory for quantitation of free and conjugated bilirubin and that conclusions concerning monoglucuronide concentrations based on this method are invalid.

Romano (1965*) summarized numerous Italian publications based on the method of Eberlein. He doubted the validity of absolute values for bilirubin and its conjugates found with this method, but believed that the results were sufficiently accurate to guide the pediatrician concerning the question of exchange transfusion in icteric newborn.

Weber and Schalm (1962) introduced a simple method for quantitative separation and determination of free and conjugated bilirubin in serum, based on extraction and phase separation with a mixture of ethyl acetate, lactic acid, and $CHCl_3$. The serum was separated from a 10 ml sample of fresh venous blood which was centrifuged after standing for 30 minutes at room temperature protected from light. In a centrifuge tube 1.62 ml of a previously prepared solution of a 5:8 v/v mixture of ethyl acetate and lactic acid (85–95%) is placed, 0.25 ml of serum added, and subsequently, after mixing, 0.50 ml $CHCl_3$. Immediately afterward 0.03 ml of a concentrated diazo reagent is added. This reagent has to be freshly prepared twice daily from a stock solution containing 4 g sulfanilic acid in 60 ml 38% HCl diluted to 1000 ml with water. To 10 ml of this solution 0.30 ml of a 0.2% $NaNO_2$ solution is added. If more than 0.25 ml of serum is examined all the reagents are changed in proportion. After the diazo reagent has been added and mixing has taken place, the solution is centrifuged. This divides the solution into two clear layers, an upper one containing the conjugated bilirubin and a lower one containing the free bilirubin. From the color of these two layers a rapid semiquantitative estimation of free and conjugated bilirubin can be made. Quantitative determination of conjugated bilirubin may be obtained by reading the extinction of the upper layer at 470 nm. In normal sera this extinction was always below 0.02. The free bilirubin was determined by transferring 0.70 ml of the lower layer to another tube and adding 0.50 ml of methanol and 0.10 ml of the diazo reagent. After mixing and standing for 60 minutes in darkness at room temperature, a reading at 555 nm was carried out.

Weber and Schalm claimed that conjugated bilirubin can be detected visually from contrations of 0.15 mg/100 ml and upward. They did not try to concentrate the small amounts of conjugated bilirubin present in normal serum as did Royer and Noir (1962). Their method is interesting and may be of value in clinical practice, but it is a relatively complicated and time-consuming procedure.

G. W. Stevenson et al. (1964) introduced a micromethod for fractional determination of free and conjugated bilirubin based on addition of 2 ml 10% (v/v) acetic acid in ethylene glycol to 0.1 ml serum. After mixing and centrifugation to remove air bubbles, readings were performed at 450 and 420 nm with a blank containing 0.1 ml H_2O instead of serum. $E_{450}–E_{520}$ was used as a measure in order to eliminate hemoglobin errors and turbidity. If the absorbancy exceeds 1.0 the process was repeated after dilution. Then the mixture was cooled in an ice bath for 1 minute (to avoid turbidity) and 3 ml $CHCl_3$ added. The layers were equilibrated by repeatedly inverting or gently shaking for 3 minutes, followed by brief centrifugation. The absorbancy of the $CHCl_3$ layer was read using a reagent blank as reference. The method was standardized with pure bilirubin preparations. High levels of carotene give errors with this technique. It was found that 84% of free bilirubin in serum was extracted in the $CHCl_3$ with this method. Comparison with diazo methods (Malloy-Evelyn) showed good agreement for total bilirubin, but the diazo method gave consistently lower figures for conjugated bilirubin. Stevenson et al. conclude: "The course of the diazo reaction has never been satisfactorily elucidated and the discrepancy between the results of the two methods cannot therefore be resolved with certainty."

Girard and Paolaggi (1965*) and Girard et al. (1965*) introduced methyl-isobutylketone in the presence of $BaCl_2$ for extraction of bilirubin. They added 4 drops of a saturated solution of $BaCl_2$ (98 g per 100 ml at 0°C) and 4 ml of methyl-isobutylketone (analytical) to 1 ml of serum, agitated the solution energetically for 2 minutes, and centrifuged it for 3–4 minutes at 4000 rpm. Readings were taken in 1-cm cells at 460 nm and the results compared with a standard curve obtained by measuring a series of solutions of free bilirubin. These solutions were prepared by dissolving 25 mg bilirubin in 2 ml 0.10 N NaOH, adding distilled water to 50 ml, and diluting with pooled bilirubin-poor serum. The calibration curve was linear. The barium ion was found to be indispensable for the passage of bilirubin into the organic phase. Girard and Paolaggi determined free bilirubin with this extraction method and total bilirubin with the Jendrassik-Gróf method. They cautiously speak of "methyl-isobutylketone extractable bilirubin" because its identity with free bilirubin has not yet been sufficiently established. Their technique is simple, rapid, sensitive, and reproducible.

Summary

Chloroform extractable bilirubin and the difference between "total" and "direct" bilirubin show a certain parallelism. However, these two bilirubin fractions cannot be identical. $CHCl_3$ extractability is pH dependent and is affected by serum lipids. The $CHCl_3$ soluble bilirubin fraction is possibly physiologically significant, whereas indirect bilirubin as determined as total bilirubin minus direct bilirubin is an artifact. Benzene and toluene exhibit the same behavior toward bilirubin as $CHCl_3$. The determination of $CHCl_3$ extractable serum bilirubin is time consuming and of limited clinical interest. The pH–$CHCl_3$ extraction curve was recently studied by Brodersen and Vind (1963a,b) who also gave a specific and quantitative determination of bilirubin and mesobilirubin based on $CHCl_3$ extraction.

Analytical methods for bilirubin and its conjugates in serum based on extraction procedures are critically reviewed.

3. ETHER EXTRACTABLE SERUM BILIRUBIN

Varela *et al.* (1931a) observed that certain "indirect" icteric sera contained an ether extractable bilirubin fraction which remained after the complete chloroform extraction. Varela Fuentes and Viana (1933a,b, 1935b) and Famulari (1934a,b), investigated this phenomenon more thoroughly. The former described a quantitative method for determination of the ether soluble fraction. They showed that a large amount of ether extractable bilirubin is characteristic for neoplastic occlusion of the bile ducts. Franchi Pade and Graña (1941) confirmed this observation. These authors extracted the serum to completion with chloroform before the extraction with ether. Allesandro and Indovina (1935) suggested a test based on ether extraction, without prior chloroform extraction. Mutolo (1948) found this test positive in 95% of patients with neoplastic jaundice, but negative in patients with jaundice from other causes. Ninger and Továrek (1951) rejected this procedure as having no diagnostic value because they could not show any relationship between the ether test and the etiology of jaundice. Kühn and Beck (1955) found that neoplastic obstruction can be assumed with great probability when more than 7% of the total bilirubin is ether soluble. However, they observed some cases of non-neoplastic icterus, having values between 7 and 10%. Talafant (1956a) found that ether extractable bilirubin consists of extremely alkali-labile bilirubin esters and other very labile bilirubin derivatives.

K. Beck and Kühn (1956) found that ether soluble bilirubin is always bound to serum albumin and exceptionally to β-globulin. It was considerably more difficult to adsorp it to active carbon than was the case with free bilirubin. The spectral maximum of native ether soluble bilirubin was 415 nm with an inflection at 470 nm, whereas that of free bilirubin added to serum was 445 nm when extracted in ether. The ether extractability was found to depend on pH. Aqueous solutions of pure bilirubin were extractable with ether at pH below 8.8 and could be completely extracted at pH 5. Icteric sera exhibited some ether extractability at pH 7.5; the extractability increased with decreasing pH to pH 6, but fell at lower pH. Sera with ether extractable bilirubin showed, on the contrary, already significant extractability at pH about 9, and the extractable fraction became constant at pH 7.4, the physiological pH of serum. At pH below 7.4 part of the other bilirubin fractions began to appear in the ether extracts too. If ether solutions of bilirubin were extracted with aqueous buffers, free bilirubin and bilirubin from ordinary icteric sera passed into the aqueous phase if pH was above 6, but native ether extractable bilirubin did not pass into the aqueous phase at pH between 6 and 9, only at pH above 9. The ether soluble pigment is labile toward oxidation, which transforms it to biliverdin. Addition of acetone to its ether solutions causes crystallization of yellow needles—contrary to ether solutions of free bilirubin which form a brown amorphous precipitate under similar conditions. Beck and Kühn concluded that ether extractable bilirubin cannot be bilirubin itself, but must be a pigment closely related to bilirubin.

Stiefel (1959) studied 94 patients with chronic occlusive jaundice and 54 with hepatitis and found that a negative ether test excluded malignant biliary obstruction. Jordans (1959) recommended extraction of 1 ml serum with 2 ml ether in a test tube. If the ether becomes yellow the test is positive, if not it is negative. This simple test was found valuable in the differentiation between neoplastic and non-neoplastic occlusive jaundice. Charbonnier and Poungouras (1959) presented detailed studies of the ether extractable bilirubin. While only traces of pure bilirubin are soluble in ether, a certain quantity becomes ether soluble if the bilirubin is first dissolved in chloroform and the chloroform is subsequently evaporated: secondary ether solubility. Two kinds of ether extractable bilirubin occur in serum: (1) secondary ether extractable bilirubin which can only be extracted after previous extraction with chloroform, and (2) primary ether extractable bilirubin which is characteristic of sera from patients with malignant biliary occlusion. The latter pigment showed an absorption maximum at 410–420 nm with an inflection at 450–460 nm. On paper chromatography it was separated into two fractions. The diazotation product of the pigment could be separated in a major spot corresponding to pigment B, and a minor one corresponding to pigment A. Varela Fuentes and Mendioroz (1959) found two $CHCl_3$ extractable bilirubin fractions, an indirect one with maximum 450–455 nm and a direct one with maximum 412 nm. The latter was found to be identical with ether extractable bilirubin. G. A. Mertens and Croal (1960) performed spectrophotometric readings of the ether extracts of serum of 112 icteric patients. A defiintely positive and a definitely negative ether test were valuable in the diagnosis or exclusion of malignant obstruction. The maximum of the ether solution was found at 430 nm while other authors found 410–420 nm (cf. above).

Talafant and Appelt (1966*) found that ether-soluble bilirubin is characterized by its inability to pass into alkaline solutions. They purified primarily ether-extractable bilirubin from sera of patients with neoplastic biliary occlusion by removing the majority of the lipids from the ethereal extracts by precipitation with three volumes of acetone. In this way the ether-soluble bilirubin precipitated, while lecithins remained in solution. Some phospholipids were precipitated together with the ether-soluble bilirubin. The precipitate was redissolved in ether and reprecipitated with acetone to achieve further purification. By addition of water and ethanol (0.2 volumes of each) to ethereal solutions of the purified pigment it passed easily into the aqueous ethanolic phase. This transfer was pH dependent, and after this extraction the pigment had lost its ether extractability and behaved like bilirubin diglucuronide. Hydrolysis of purified ether-extractable bilirubin with 1 N NaOH resulted in formation of bilirubin.

To test the possibility of a binding of one of the carboxyl groups of bilirubin in the form of a lactone or ester, ammonolysis in methanol was tried to obtain glucuronamide, but paper chromatography disclosed no glucuronamide spot. It was found that the ether extractable bilirubin was not a lecithin complex because this pigment could be separated from lecithins by acetone precipitation. Bilirubin could be extracted with ether from solutions of bilirubin glucuronide with ether, but the pigment could be extracted with alkalies from these solutions contrary to the case with ethereal solutions of primarily ether-extractable bilirubin. It is likely that phospholipids play a role in ether-extractable bilirubin because they are precipitated together with this pigment. At present there is, however, no decisive evidence of the nature of the linkages which cause the loss of the acidic properties of the strongly anionic bilirubin glucuronides and transform them to ether-extractable bilirubin.

Summary

Certain sera contain a fraction of bile pigment which is ether extractable. This pigment is closely related but not identical to bilirubin. Bilirubin added to serum as well as bilirubin present in most icteric sera is not ether extractable, but if it is extracted with chloroform it becomes secondarily ether soluble. Primarily ether soluble bilirubin is a special pigment which is most often found in patients with occlusive jaundice due to malignancy. A simple ether extraction of icteric serum seems to be of value in the diagnosis of neoplastic biliary occlusion.

4. Adsorption of Bilirubin on Precipitated Serum Proteins

Hijmans van den Bergh (1918, p. 143) observed that bilirubin is precipitated with the protein from direct reacting sera; however, this is not the case in indirect reacting ones. Wiemer (1926), who thoroughly studied this phenomenon, introduced the "bilirubin index," which expresses the amount (%) of total bilirubin remaining in solution after alcohol precipitation. This index was low in cases of obstructive icterus, and increased rapidly after removing the obstruction. Weltmann and Jost (1928) determined that 30–50% of serum bilirubin was bound to the precipitate during obstructive icterus. They preferred to use the term "adsorption value," meaning 100 minus the "bilirubin index." Fiessinger *et al.* (1929) and Fiessinger and Walter (1931, 1934) spoke about "bilirubin *de retour*," i.e., bilirubin which streamed back into the blood from icteric tissues during disappearing jaundice; and "bilirubin *d'aller*," i.e., bilirubin which migrated into tissues at the initial stages of jaundice. Jourdain (1932) investigated the relationship between these two types of bilirubin and the differences between direct reaction and precipitation with proteins. Bilirubin *d'aller* was assumed to be responsible for the direct reaction and it was thought to precipitate with the proteins. Hartog (1935) studied the adsorption of bilirubin on protein precipitates. He could never detect any precipitation of indirect bilirubin, not even in hemolytic icterus with 15 bilirubin units (ca. 7 mg per 100 ml). Sera which showed adsorption values above 90% always exhibited direct reaction. Hartog substantiated his results with 13 curves, showing the adsorption values and total bilirubin values during various forms of jaundice.

Bungenberg de Jong (1937, pp. 52–53) demonstrated that pH also plays a role, since indirect reacting bilirubin could also be adsorbed on the precipitate when acid was added. However, without addition of acid no bilirubin was precipitated from pure indirect reacting sera. Gigon and Noverraz (1939, 1942) precipitated serum with acetone and showed that indirect reacting sera and sera with added bilirubin solution gave considerably higher bilirubin yields on extraction than direct reacting sera and sera to which bile was added. These workers used the expression "retention index," i.e., the ratio of adsorbed bilirubin to total bilirubin, which averaged 0.78 for direct reacting sera, and 0.37 for indirect reacting ones. Wiss (1942) investigated the alcohol and acetone precipitates of serum bilirubin. He pointed out that these precipitates should be worked up in the dark in order to avoid destruction of very labile solutions. He called the ratio of absorbed bilirubin/extracted bilirubin the "retention index." He was able to determine linear relations between albumin concentration and this index in mixtures of dilute serum and bile. The retention index was not affected by storage of serum or changes in pH within physiological limits. A retention index above 1 was found only in cases of hepatitis and obstruction. All other cases including hemolytic icterus showed indices under 1.

If one sets t for total bilirubin and a for adsorbed bilirubin, the bilirubin remaining in solution is equal to $t - a$. Thus, the various indices can be defined as follows:

$$\text{Wiemer's "bilirubin index": } 100(t - a)/t$$
$$\text{Weltmann and Jost's "adsorption value": } 100a/t$$
$$\text{Gigon and Novarraz's "retention index": } a/t$$
$$\text{Wiss' "retention index": } a/(t - a)$$

These indices have only a limited practical value and their determination is considerably more difficult than that of the reaction velocity.

Direct reaction and magnitude of adsorption on protein precipitates show different behavior during disappearing jaundice. The former decreases during hepatitis, while adsorption increases with considerable regularity (Hartog, 1935). Finally, Deenstra (1948b) and Corà (1952) could show that direct reaction and protein adsorption of bilirubin are different processes which proceed independently during jaundice in many patients. Weicker (1957) pointed out that differences observed during hepatitis in the type of diazo reaction and adsorption on protein precipitates can be related to changes in the composition of serum proteins. It is important to note that free bilirubin is bound to albumin, and conjugated partly to protein–lipid complexes. Dialysis experiments with serum bilirubin indicate that protein binding of direct serum bilirubin is significantly less stable than that of the indirect (Talafant, 1954b). As a consequence of this difference in adsorption of bilirubin on serum protein precipitates, "the acetone icterus index" and the "aqueous icterus index" (i.e., classic icterus index) are equal during hemolytic icterus, while the acetone index is lower than the aqueous index in other jaundice types.

Summary

The amount of bilirubin adsorbed on protein precipitated by alcohol or acetone is much lower in hemolytic icterus than in other forms of jaundice. On the basis of this observation a series of indices have been introduced; however, these have limited significance. Bilirubin adsorption on protein precipitates and direct reaction cannot be closely related since they vary independently in many cases of jaundice.

5. SENSITIVITY OF SERUM BILIRUBIN TO OXYGEN AND LIGHT

Hijmans van den Bergh (1918, p. 43) observed that bilirubin of direct reacting sera is significantly more sensitive toward oxygen than indirect reacting bilirubin. Thus, sera from cases of obstructive jaundice rapidly developed a green discoloration; sometimes they even showed a greenish hue at the moment the blood was taken from the patient. Davies and Dodds (1927) reported similar observations. Andrewes (1924a) found that icteric sera with direct reaction are more sensitive to oxidation with FeCl$_3$ than are indirect reacting sera. Hartog (1935, p. 96) confirmed these observations by quantitative experiments with NaNO$_2$ oxidation. He plotted oxidation time curves for serum bilirubin, and found that bilirubin was completely destroyed within 20–30 minutes in direct reacting sera. However, only 10–20% decomposition occurred in indirect reacting sera.

Morishima (1930) found that the oxidation rate increased with increasing pH, but the addition of egg albumin depressed oxidation. For the determination of the oxidation rate of serum bilirubin Chabrol *et al.* (1949) recommended quantitative photometric measurements. They employed a phosphoric acid–nitrite reagent as oxidizing agent. They concluded that this "oxidoreaction relative" agrees with the amount of direct bilirubin determined by Malloy and Evelyn's method. Kühn and Beck (1951) also conducted quantitative photometric investigations on oxidation rates of serum bilirubin. They exposed the serum to light and to oxygen. Subsequently, they determined the amount of bilirubin in 6-hour intervals until a constant reading was obtained. The time which was necessary to obtain constant bilirubin extinction was called "oxidation time." The oxidation time increased with increasing serum bilirubin content, and decreased with increasing direct reaction. A longer oxidation time was more often found in hepatitis than during obstructive icterus.

Cremer *et al.* (1957) studied the light sensitivity of bilirubin. They found that indirect (free) bilirubin (from sera of newborns) is extremely sensitive to light and that this is the case under normal conditions as well as under a nitrogen atmosphere. Free bilirubin was three times as sensitive to light as conjugated bilirubin. Thus, analysis of newborn sera should not be performed in direct sunlight.

Blondheim and Kaufmann (1965*) exposed solutions of unconjugated bilirubin in albumin to light and found an increase in their direct diazo reaction. With weak light this was the only effect noted, but with intense light there was a destruction of bilirubin too. They believe that illumination causes subtle changes in the bilirubin molecule, making it more polar. Attempts to separate the direct-reaction pigment formed by illumination were unsuccessful.

Summary

Free (indirect) bilirubin is significantly more stable toward oxidation than conjugated (direct) bilirubin (see Table IV). This property has been used for quantitative determinations of direct bilirubin. Usually, measurements showed good agreement with determinations based on reaction velocity. Conjugated bilirubin is about three times as stable toward light as is free bilirubin. It is important to avoid direct sunlight during analysis of sera from newborn.

6. ABSORPTION SPECTRA OF DIRECT AND INDIRECT BILIRUBIN

A number of investigators maintained that the absorption spectra of bilirubin and azobilirubin are identical in sera with direct diazo reaction and indirect reacting sera (Heilmeyer and Krebs, 1930; P. Müller and Engel, 1931b; Peter, 1933; Hijmans van den Bergh and Grotepass, 1934). However, other workers detected slight differences. Davis and Sheard (1937) found an absorption maximum for direct sera at 440–455 nm, and for indirect reacting sera at 458–460 nm. However, these authors investigated only nine sera. Penati and Pagliardi (1943) found a maximum at 445–458 nm in 18 direct reacting sera, and 460–465 nm for indirect reacting ones. Pagliardi and Penati (1949) investigated the diazo reaction in seven direct sera. They found a maximum at 570 nm, besides the principal maximum in some of the sera. M. Salvini and Gonzato (1947a,b) determined the absorption curves of the diazo reaction for indirect sera and pure bilirubinate solutions and found identical curves with maxima at 530 nm. Frequently, a second maximum could be observed. This was caused by unchanged bilirubin. In direct reacting sera the curve was flatter and showed no maximum at 530 nm. However, the authors did not report details of their experimental technique. It should be mentioned that Castex *et al.* (1940, graph 9) obtained a curve which closely resembles that of Salvini and Gonzato in a direct reacting serum with 4.6 mg per 100 ml total bilirubin. However, they found the typical curve with a maximum at 530 nm in a serum with 50 mg per 100 ml.

Charbonnier et al. (1954) found the absorption maximum of indirect bilirubin at 450–460 nm in $CHCl_3$ (i.e., extracts of pure bilirubin from hemolytic and normal sera). Contrary to this, direct $CHCl_3$ insoluble bilirubin (i.e., direct bilirubin split off by alcohol) and ether extractable bilirubin showed a maximum at 414–422 nm. P. G. Cole et al. (1954) studied the spectral absorption of the chromatographic fractions (Section F, this chapter) and found a maximum at 450 nm for the free bilirubin fraction, 452 nm for pigment I, and 448 for pigment II if dissolved in equal volumes of butanol and phosphate buffer of pH 6. Pigment II also showed a secondary maximum in the region 250–300 nm which was absent in the other two. Yamaoka et al. (1956b) found the maximum of $CHCl_3$ soluble indirect bilirubin at 450 nm, and that for methanol and water-soluble direct bilirubin (salt or ester) at 415–420 nm. Vitelli et al. (1956) found that serum proteins, fractionated according to Cohn (1948), exhibited two maxima at 420 and 460 nm in icteric sera. Fractions I and II showed the maximum at 460 nm, whereas fraction V absorbed mainly at 420 nm. Pagliardi and Gaidano (1956) investigated the absorption spectra of serum fractions obtained by reverse phase chromatography. They found two maxima at 415–420 nm and at 450–455 nm for all fractions in the visible range. The ratio of extinction peaks varied in both polar fractions; however, it was always within certain limits. This was not the case in the nonpolar fraction. However, the differences between the three fractions were too small to permit differentiation.

Bourrillon (1957) found a maximum at 460 nm for bilirubin isolated by electrophoresis of indirect sera. Similarly, he determined a maximum at 450–455 nm for direct sera. Later, the same author (Bourrillon, 1958a,b) determined two maxima, one at 410–420 nm, the other at 450–460 nm, for plasma bilirubin. The maximum was found mainly at 460 nm in hemolytic icterus and in normal sera to which bilirubin had been added. Icteric direct reacting sera to which bile was added showed, besides the major maximum at 450 nm, a second maximum at 420 nm. However, the latter maximum could no longer be detected in fractions purified by electrophoresis. The 420 maximum was not detectable in the bile, but it appeared when bile was added to serum. Thus, the phenomenon can surely not be attributed to traces of hemoglobin. Bourrillon explained this phenomenon by dissociation of bilirubin containing macromolecules in the bile. Fog (1958c) suggested that the difference in the ratio of yellow color to diazo color existing between various icteric sera could be explained by differences in their content of free bilirubin and bilirubin conjugates. Hyvarinen et al. (1958) claimed that free bilirubin has a maximum at 455 nm in serum while bilirubin glucuronides have a maximum at 422 nm.

Pagliardi and Gaidano (1959) discovered a slowly developing absorption at 380–400 nm in the diazo reaction of certain icteric sera, mainly from patients with hepatocellular jaundice. This *short wavelength band* was most often absent in patients with obstructive jaundice. The phenomenon was studied more closely by Gaidano and Pagliardi (1959) in 24 icteric patients. Only perfectly fresh sera were employed. The diazo reaction was performed after dilution of the serum with phosphate buffer pH 8, 1/6 *M*. The pigment was extracted after deproteinization and the extract was purified by chromatography on Al_2O_3. The columns were washed with acetone, benzene, and ether after which the pigment was eluated with equal parts of propanol and phosphate buffer. The purified extract was subjected to diazo reaction and spectrophotometric study in the region 380–600 nm. The band at 380–400 nm developed slowly and reached maximum intensity after 6 hours. The ratio between the intensity of the visible diazo color and the short wavelength band (E 565/380) was between 1.5 and 2.5 in most cases of obstructive jaundice but was significantly lower (0.4 to 0.8) in the majority of patients with hepatocellular icterus. The increase in the absorption at 380 nm during the 6 hours varied from 1.5–198% of the intial extinction. In neoplastic jaundice it was usually below 30%, in hepatocellular icterus above 45%. If pigment extracts from icteric sera were added to normal sera the reaction type did not change. Gaidano and Gravario (1959) studied the diagnostic value of the short wavelength slowly developing band of the diazo reaction in 64 cases of jaundice and found that all the patients with occlusive jaundice exhibited figures below 50% while the hepatocellular cases exhibited values above 50%, with a few exceptions.

Jirsa and Jirsová (1959) studied the azo pigment of conjugated bilirubin using synthetic taurobilirubin instead of the natural glucuronic acid conjugates. Measurements were carried out with purified azobilirubin and azotaurobilirubin in aqueous solution at varying pH, in methanol, in albumin solutions, and in diluted serum. Azobilirubin and azotaurobilirubin behaved indentically at different pH levels, the maximum being 560 nm in acid, 510–520 nm in neutral, and 570–580 nm in alkaline solution. The spectral curves of the two pigments differed, however, as azobilirubin showed an increase in extinction with rising pH with maximum at pH 8, while azotaurobilirubin exhibited constant extinction between pH 4 and 9. Methanol shifted the maximum of azobilirubin to shorter wavelengths accompanied by an extinction increase while azotaurobilirubin showed the same maximum in aqueous and methanolic solutions. The two pigments behaved identically in albumin and serum solutions, but here methanol caused considerable increase in extinction without shift of the maximum. The maximum extinction was considerably higher for azobilirubin than for azotaurobilirubin; even though twice the amount of taurobilirubin was used in the preparation of azotaurobilirubin, its extinction was lower than that found for azobilirubin. This finding is important with regard to the calculation of serum bilirubin concentrations from diazo extinctions—for serum is a more or less ill defined mixture of free bilirubin and various conjugates. Further, determinations of direct bilirubin are subject to error, if azo pigment in serum mixtures without alcohol is compared to a standard containing alcohol, e.g., a total bilirubin estimation based on an extinction in alcoholic medium. As extinctions are higher in solutions containing alcohol than in alcohol free ones, this error will give too low values for the direct bilirubin.

The studies of Jirsa and Jirsová are important, in spite of the fact that they were performed with synthetic conjugates, as they present a strong case for the view that all quantitative determinations of the direct diazo reaction with methods in general use are subject to serious systematic errors.

Chiamori et al. (1961) could not find a serum bilirubin fraction with a maximum at 410–420 nm and believed that the absorption of direct and indirect bilirubin in serum are identical.

Fog (1960) presented strong evidence for a significant difference between the spectral absorption curve of free bilirubin and its conjugates He controlled his technique painstakingly, fixing the pH with appropriate buffers and subjecting his spectrophotometers to rigid standardization. He proved his point directly by the study of isolated direct pigment and indirectly by the difference in spectra between sera before and after diazotization. He isolated conjugated bilirubin from serum by adding ca. 5 mg EDTA (ethylenediamine tetraacetate) to 2 ml serum with prompt direct diazo reaction and subsequently adding 0.35 ml of a standard ammonium acetate solution and 5 ml ethanol. After mixing and standing in the dark for 1 hour centrifugation was carried out. Then followed chromatographic fractionation on Whatman I filter paper, previously treated by dipping in EDTA solution (5 meq per liter) and subsequent drying. This paper is dipped into the clear supernatant from the above centrifugation until the fluid is completely absorbed. Then the paper is dried and placed between two glass plates with one free end dipping into the chromatographic solvent, the other placed in air current. The chromatographic solvent consists of either $CHCI_3$ or a mixture of one volume of EDTA (5 meq per liter) and two volumes of methanol. With the former solvent the free bilirubin, with the latter, the conjugated is carried to the paper front. Eluation follows, with a 1.3% sodium bicarbonate solution (pH 7.5).

To the eluate 0.1–0.5 ml normal bilirubin-free serum was added and spectrophotometric readings performed, with a mixture of sodium bicarbonate and normal serum as blank. The use of EDTA was necessary to prevent the oxidation of the bilirubin to biliverdin; this oxidation is catalyzed by traces of metals which are inactivated by EDTA.

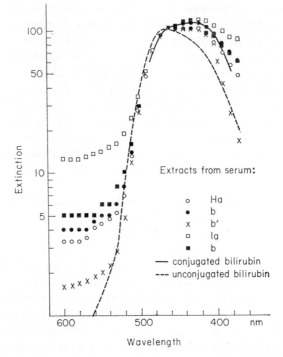

FIG. 39. Typical absorption curves of free and conjugated bilirubin in serum. The points marked "a" correspond to nonpolar fractions isolated with CHCl₃ as chromatographic solvent, those marked "b" to polar fractions isolated with EDTA–methanol as solvent. The letters H and I designate two different normal sera employed in the experiments. From Fog (1960, Fig. VII,5).

As seen from Fig. 39 the absorption curve of free bilirubin exhibited a sharper and more rounded maximum at 460 nm, while conjugated bilirubin showed a broader and blunter maximum, like a small plateau, at 420–460 nm. The elevation of the curve at 500–600 nm is due to turbidity.

Moreover, Fog (1960) also attacked the problem in a more indirect way, i.e., by determining the spectral absorption curve before and after elimination of the conjugated bilirubin. The absorption of the latter was thus found by subtraction. He achieved the removal of conjugated bilirubin without affecting the unconjugated bilirubin by means of diazotation without addition of a coupling reagent and subsequent oxidative destruction of the azo pigments formed by means of sodium hydrosulfite. In another series of experiments, the conjugates were destroyed by addition of strongly alkaline buffers. The experiments were rather complicated, involving a series of control readings and various reagent blanks. In one blank, addition of 0.1 ml of a 0.2 M sodium azide solution was used to suppress the diazo reaction. In Fig. 40 examples of the absorption curves for various mixtures of conjugated and free bilirubin, obtained in this way, are shown.

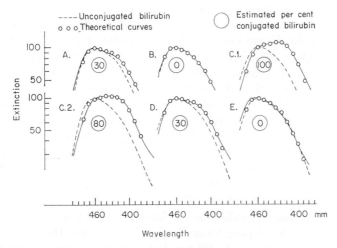

FIG. 40. Spectral absorption curves of bilirubin in various icteric sera obtained by difference measurements before and after removal of the conjugated bilirubin from serum. From Fog (1960, Fig. VIII,3).

In Fig. 40 B and E, the theoretical absorption curve corresponds to the unconjugated bilirubin curve of Fig. 39, i.e., the serum contains practically exclusively free bilirubin. In C.1. the theoretical curve corresponds to pure conjugated bilirubin; in the remaining examples the curve corresponds to mixtures of the two pigments. The indirect differential method gave curves closely similar to that obtained by Fog on direct preparative isolation of the free and conjugated bilirubin. The absorption curve of the concentrate of bilirubin diglucuronide prepared by Lucassen (1961*) is presented in Fig. 41a (p. 372).

It is important to remember that even free (unconjugated) bilirubin gives a certain diazo reaction without accelerators when dissolved in serum. This was emphasized by Tisdale *et al.* (1959) and Blondheim and Kaufmann (1965*) who found that its direct reaction, read after 1 minute, included about 3% of the total bilirubin.

Pagliardi and Gaidano (1965*) continued their studies on the UV absorption of azobilirubin taking readings at 5 nm intervals in the region 250–600 nm. Serum was diluted with phosphate buffer 0.016 M, pH 8, diazo reagent was added, and readings were taken immediately and after 8, 15, 60, and 120 minutes. They further purified the bilirubin by extraction with butanol from acid solution, washing of the extract several times, extracting the butanol solution with 0.03 M NaOH, and finally adjusting to pH 8 with 0.03 N HCl before reading. They diazotized the purified extracts as well as pure bilirubin with ethanol as coupling reagent and extracted the azo pigment with butanol. Azopigments A and B were isolated from diazotized sera—normal and icteric—with reverse-phase chromatography. In diazotized sera they found the maximum 560–565 nm and a secondary maximum at 435–455 nm due to unchanged bilirubin besides an UV maximum at 340 nm ascribed to the diazo reaction and considerably higher than the visible maxima (ratio ca. 50/18). In certain sera from patients with hepatocellular jaundice—but not in sera from those with occlusive jaundice—a third diazo maximum was found at 400 nm. At wavelengths below 340 nm a rapidly increasing end absorption and no characteristic findings were found. Azobilirubin prepared from pure bilirubin showed maxima at 560 and 340 nm and the bilirubin itself showed maxima 435–455 and 280 nm. The pure azobilirubin had no absorption peak at 400 nm. The azopigments from purified bilirubin from hepatocellular jaundice sera exhibited an intense absorption band at 380–400 nm developing immediately after diazotization. Normal sera showed no maximum at 400–405 nm, but if purified pigment from hepatocellular jaundice sera was added a maximum at 400 nm appeared. The 400 nm diazo maximum and its increase during the first 2 hours after diazotization were employed in the differential diagnosis between hepatocellular and occlusive jaundice.

Pittera and Cassia (1964*) subjected bilirubin extracted from sera with CHCl$_3$, as well as free bilirubin, to inverse-phase column chromatography on a gel of siliconated silica. In this way two pigments, called I and II, were isolated from normal and icteric sera, both giving indirect diazo reaction. Bilirubin I was eluted from the gel column with n-butanol, had spectral maximum at 450 nm, and represented the bulk of normal serum bilirubin. Bilirubin II was retained on the column and exhibited two maxima—410–420 and 440–450 nm, the former being the higher. Azobilirubin prepared from CHCl$_3$-extractable bilirubin behaved similarly, separating into two fractions. Further subdivisions of bilirubin I by means of paper chromatography resulted in two fractions, A and B; A had maximum at 450 nm, B at 420–430 nm. The ratio between fractions A and B varied with domination of A in normal sera and hemolytic jaundice sera.

Maggiore and Giovannetti (1965*) isolated three conjugates from bile by means of paper chromatography: Fraction 1 consisting of pigment II (diglucuronide) and exhibiting maximum at 450 nm in aqueous solution, fraction 2 consisting of pigment I with maximum 420 nm, and fraction 3 consisting of an alkali-labile conjugate with glucuronic acid and another unknown ligand and exhibiting maximum at 435 nm in aqueous solution.

Summary

Studies on the spectral absorption of free and conjugated bilirubin and their azo pigments have lead to controversial results, but recent well-controlled investigations have made it clear that there are significant differences between the absorption curves of free bilirubin and its conjugates as well as between the corresponding azo pigments. These differences are sufficiently marked to render open to doubt the possibility of exact quantitative determination of free and conjugated bilirubin in serum.

E. Chemical Basis of the Direct and Indirect Diazo Reaction

Since the discovery of the direct diazo reaction by Hijmans van den Bergh and Müller (1916), the nature of various types of diazo reaction has been a much studied but very elusive biochemical problem (see Ferrari, 1934; Zabel, 1949). Some assumed that the direct and indirect reactions are caused by two closely related forms of bilirubin; others thought that the phenomenon occurs because of the binding of bilirubin to different substances; and still others believed that the real cause was not associated with the bilirubin itself but with its surroundings, i.e., variation in the amount of accelerators or retarders, or differences in the colloids of the serum. Finally, a few authors assumed that the main cause is variation in total bilirubin concentration. However, P. G. Cole and Lathe (1953) succeeded in isolating direct and indirect bilirubin as different fractions from serum by distribution chromatography. Thus, it became clear that polar water-soluble bilirubin derivatives are responsible for the direct reaction, and nonpolar insoluble free bilirubin causes the indirect reaction. As previously mentioned, both types are rather strongly bound to serum albumin and this binding makes possible the presence of nonpolar water-insoluble bilirubin in serum. It is believed that polar bilirubin derivatives, which cause the direct reaction, occur mainly as glucuronic acid esters in human serum and in bile (Billing and Lathe,

TABLE IV

PROPERTIES OF DIRECT (CONJUGATED) AND INDIRECT (FREE) BILIRUBIN

Property	Direct bilirubin	Indirect bilirubin
Chemical nature	Conjugated bilirubin, mainly bilirubin diglucuronide	Free, unconjugated bilirubin
Solubility	Polar; water soluble over wide pH range	Nonpolar; water soluble only at pH above 8, except when bound to protein
Diazo reaction		
With coupling reagent	Prompt	Prompt
Without coupling reagent	Prompt	Indirect
pH dependence of diazo reaction	Fastest diazo reaction at low pH (below 1); extinction reached in 1 hour independent of pH	Fastest diazo reaction at pH 6–7; extinction reached in 1 hour highest at pH 6–7; reaction very slight at pH 4.5 and below
State in serum	Strongly bound to serum albumin at natural pH. Migrates on electrophoresis at pH 7 and higher with indirect bilirubin, but separates from it at lower pH	Strongly bound to serum albumin at natural pH. Migrates on electrophoresis at pH 7 and higher with direct bilirubin, but separates from albumin and direct bilirubin at low pH values
$CHCl_3$ extractability	Not extractable from serum with $CHCl_3$	Extractable from serum with $CHCl_3$
Precipitation with alcohol	Precipitates practically quantitatively on addition of alcohol to serum	Only partially precipitated on addition of alcohol to serum; loose binding to protein precipitate
Oxidation stability	Relatively labile; easily converted to biliverdin	Relatively stable
Light sensitivity	Relatively low light sensitivity	Highly light sensitive
Occurrence	Icteric sera of all types of jaundice except hemolytic, neonatal, and some cases of familial nonhemolytic; bile and icteric urine	Icteric sera of hemolytic jaundice, neonatal icterus, and some types of familial nonhemolytic hyperbilirubinemia
Biological properties	Excreted with bile and urine; formed from bilirubin by liver cells and excreted into bile or liver lymph Harmless excretion product	Not excreted with bile or urine or only in insignificant quantities. Formed all over the organism, but mainly in RES and liver. Exhibits cytotoxic properties. Especially harmful for brain of infants and presumed to be the main cause of kernicterus

1956; Schmid, 1956a,b; Talafant, 1956b), and this explains without difficulty most of the well-known characteristics of direct and indirect bilirubin.

Lucassen (1961*) presented a thorough study of the reaction kinetics of the diazo reaction of both bilirubin and purified bilirubin diglucuronide. He found that azobilirubin is decomposed by excess diazo reagent and that this is counteracted by the presence of caffeine which explains the advantage of the Jendrassik-Gróf caffeine reagent. *The behavior of the diazo reaction was found to be so complicated* that a fractionate *quantitative determination of bilirubin and its conjugates based on its reaction course is practically impossible.*

Lathe (1956) proposed replacing the expressions "direct" and "indirect" bilirubin with "conjugated bilirubin" and "bilirubin." However, Jordan (1956) pointed out that the old terminology is so widely accepted that attempts to change it would lead to confusion rather than to simplification of the question.

The extremely extensive literature of earlier theories which try to explain direct and indirect diazo reactions is outside the scope of this treatise and will not be discussed here. A full treatment of earlier work is found in the writer's first monograph on bile pigments (With, 1954, pp. 186–200).

F. Recent Studies on the Chemistry of Free and Conjugated Bilirubin

Newer investigations which promised final clarification of the problem of direct diazo reaction started with the work of Kosaka (published in Japanese in 1950 and 1951) and Yamaoka and Kosaka (1951; English review by Yamaoka *et al.*, 1956b). It was demonstrated that indirect bilirubin is a free acid, whereas direct bilirubin is an ester or a salt of this acid.

Polar water-soluble direct bilirubin was converted to nonpolar chloroform-extractable indirect bilirubin when serum, bile, or urine which contained direct bilirubin was saponified with methanol–potassium carbonate. Since 1951 Japanese investigators have published a series of important studies. Yamamoto (1951) found biliverdin occurring in two forms in the bile of rabbits, i.e., a free, chloroform soluble and an esterified water soluble form. Ekuni (1952a,b) subjected azobilirubin from alcoholic serum extracts to chromatography on Al_2O_3 columns. This author observed separation into two fractions, which he assumed was due to a methyl and an ethyl ester. Kimura (1953), who prepared the dimethyl ester of crystalline bilirubin, could show that this ester gives a direct reaction when dissolved in organic solvents or in serum. This ester could no longer be extracted from serum solutions with chloroform. It was found that this ester is more strongly adsorbed to the alcoholic protein precipitate than free bilirubin. However, Jirsa and Šponar (1955) found that the bilirubin dimethyl ester is insoluble in water and gives a negative direct diazo reaction in colloidal solution. Kawai (1953) and Sato (1955a,b) developed paper chromatographic processes for the separation of direct and indirect bilirubin and corresponding azobilirubin derivatives. However, these publications appeared only in Japanese with an inadequate English summary.

Sakamoto (1956a,b,c,d) continued and extended these investigations. Fortunately, his studies were published in good English, and contained the necessary details. Yamaoka et al. (1956b) summarized his results. Chloroform extracted cystic bile of dogs was the source of the bile pigments used in these investigations. The extracts which were centrifuged and filtered contained the entire amount of direct and indirect bilirubin of bile. Sakamoto (1956a) described the separation of indirect bilirubin. According to this process, the extract in $CHCl_3$ was adsorbed on a silica gel column and developed with a mixture of 20 parts of $CHCl_3$ and 3 parts of methanol. Three zones were obtained; the first, which contained indirect bilirubin, was collected after it had passed through the column. A half-crystalline powder was obtained on vacuum evaporation. Direct bilirubin remained on the top of the column. The indirect bilirubin obtained in this manner was further fractionated on silica gel and aluminum oxide columns. It was shown that it consisted mainly of free bilirubin (acid), but it also contained some smaller fractions, comprising various degradation products.

Sakamoto (1956b) described the separation of direct bilirubin from $CHCl_3$ extracts of bile. In this process the $CHCl_3$ extract was also adsorbed on a silica gel column, but it was developed with water. Indirect bilirubin remained on the top of the column, whereas direct bilirubin formed two zones and passed through the column. The first of the zones was brown and contained esterified bilirubin, whereas the following zone was yellow and consisted of bilirubin salts. These fractions were purified by chromatography on aluminum oxide and silica gel columns and were developed with 10% and 50% aqueous n-propanol and with 0.1 N NaOH. Direct bilirubin, which was present in the form of its esters or salts, was obtained as a hygroscopic, semicrystalline powder. It was easily soluble in methanol and water, but it was insoluble in $CHCl_3$ and CCl_4. It could not be extracted with $CHCl_3$ from aqueous solutions. However, the salts and the esters (after saponification; see above) were quantitatively extracted by adding dilute HCl to the solution. The salt could not be extracted with $CHCl_3$ after saponification of the ester from aqueous solutions, and the same was true for the esters after addition of dilute HCl. The absorption maximum of the purified salt was at 420 nm in methanol solution, and that of the esters was at 415 nm. Sakamoto *et al.* (1957a,b) described the separation of bilirubin salts and esters on ion exchangers.

In a third paper, Sakamoto (1956c) studied the biliverdins obtained by oxidation of indirect bilirubin, as well as esters and salts of direct bilirubin. He found slight differences in the absorption maxima of unpurified pigments. However, these differences were not detectable when the pigments were purified by chromatography. To exclude inorganic impurities, Sakamoto (1956d) separated the salt and ester derivatives of direct bilirubin by paper chromatography. He subsequently determined the infrared absorption spectra, as well as the fluorescence spectra, of these substances and was able to show that these preparations contained considerable amounts of bile acids and bile salts, together with various benzidine and ninhydrin positive organic compounds. Also, numerous inorganic ions were present. Thus, the half-crystalline ester and salt derivatives isolated from direct bilirubin are by no means pure substances.

Ichikawa (1956b,c) studied bilirubin fractions from dried bile from the gallbladder of dogs and from icteric urine by paper electrophoresis and by paper chromatography. Whereas the esters and salts of direct bilirubin migrated with substances which could be stained with bromophenol blue (proteins), this was not true for the corresponding indirect bilirubin derivatives. However, there was no parallelism between the amount of bromophenol blue-positive substances and direct reaction. Thus, it is apparent that the direct reaction could not be caused by binding of bilirubin to these substances.

Monasterio and Giovannetti (1954, 1955) confirmed that indirect bilirubin is, in reality, free bilirubin, whereas direct bilirubin of serum, bile, and urine is composed of a special bilirubin compound. They called this substance "cholebilirubin," but could not characterize its structure.

Najjar (1951) and Najjar and Childs (1951, 1953) isolated crystalline direct and indirect bilirubin from serum. These authors used an unnecessarily complicated method and overlooked the fact that Hijmans van den Bergh (1918, pp. 20–25) had already succeeded in crystallizing direct as well as indirect bilirubin from serum. Hijmans van den Bergh's technique was much simpler than that used by Najjar and Childs. Microphotograms of crystals obtained by Hijmans van den Bergh have been published in his classic monograph. Hijmans van den Bergh also succeeded in crystallizing bilirubin from normal serum. It was difficult to obtain crystals from icteric sera with direct bilirubin reaction, because bilirubin was oxidized to biliverdin and showed green discoloration, before crystallization started.

As mentioned above, significant progress was made in the study of serum bilirubin by the introduction by P. G. Cole and Lathe (1953) of the inverse phase partition chromatography described by Howard and Martin (1950). The chromatography was performed with columns of siliconized kieselguhr, i.e., with a water repellent adsorbent. One volume serum with 0.18 volume saturated ammonium sulfate solution and 2.5 volumes ethanol was used for chromatography; after 1 hour the mixture was centrifuged. Bile was treated with 4 volumes of ethanol or with a mixture of 2 parts of ethanol and 2 parts of methanol. The extracts were stored at $-12°C$ and vacuum concentrated just before use. Glass tubes with a diameter of 18 mm containing 6 g kieselguhr were employed. The solvent system was obtained by mixing 25 volumes $CHCl_3$, 25 volumes CCl_4, 38 volumes methanol, and 12 volumes $0.025 M$ phosphate buffer solution of pH 6; a 3 ml stationary, nonpolar (bottom) phase, and a 17 ml mobile, polar (top) phase were used.

First, direct bilirubin passed through the column; indirect bilirubin migrated significantly more slowly. Pure bilirubin behaved as indirect bilirubin. Bile obtained post-mortem contained direct as well as indirect bilirubin, the former being predominant. Trypsin hydrolysis experiments on sera caused no difference in pigment distribution, indicating that the type of bilirubin is independent of the serum–protein binding. Therefore, it was concluded that distribution chromatography, in fact, separated different bilirubin compounds.

P. G. Cole et al. (1954) expanded these studies. They used the following three solvent systems:

A. The solvent system described by Cole and Lathe (see above).

B. A mixture consisting of equal parts of n-butanol and $0.005 M$ phosphate buffer (pH 6).

C. A solvent mixture of 25.9 ml acetone, 17 g ammonium sulfate, 62.5 ml $0.05 M$ phosphate buffer (pH 6), and enough $2.5 N$ NaOH to bring the pH of the mixture to 6 (about 1.7 ml).

Chromatography was performed in glass tubes of 16 mm diameter; 6 g kieselguhr and 3 ml stationary phase were employed for systems A and B, whereas only half the amount was used for solvent C.

Sometimes two bands were found in the zone of direct (polar) bilirubin when solvent A was used. However, these two bands were always eluted together. When systems B and C were used, these two bands were eluted separately, although migration of the second pigment was often erratic and exhibited tailing. The two direct bilirubins obtained in this manner were called *pigment I* (the less polar) and *pigment II* (the more polar).

Investigations of absorption spectra of the three pigments in the 250–500 nm range showed that the absorption curve of nonpolar indirect bilirubin was identical to that of pure bilirubin. Using solvent B, the maximum was found at 450 nm. The maximum for pigment I was at 452 nm and for pigment II at 448 nm in the same solvent system. Furthermore, pigment II showed a distinct peak, whereas pigment I yielded a flat curve in the range between 250 and 300 nm. Nonpolar bilirubin did not show any elevation. Both polar pigments gave the direct diazo reaction, whereas the nonpolar pigment reacted indirectly. Pigments I and II were found to be extremely labile and it was impossible to obtain them in the pure state.

Billing (1955a) described a micromethod for the separation of the three bile pigments from 1 ml icteric serum, based on chromatographic separation on kieselguhr. Reproducibility of results obtained by this method was satisfactory. Average variation between measurements of individual pigments was about 5%. Experiments performed on 27 icteric sera showed good agreement between values obtained for direct bilirubin by Malloy and Evelyn's method, and those obtained for pigments I and II by chromatography. On the other hand, determinations of 1-minute bilirubin according to Ducci and C. J. Watson (1945) could not be used as a measure for pigment II concentration.

The next step, which is significant in the characterization of these materials, was the *elucidation of structure of polar bilirubin pigments.* Billing and Lathe (1956) in England, Schmid (1956a,b) in the United States, and Talafant (1956b) in Czechoslovakia demonstrated almost at the same time that the polar pigments are glucuronic acid esters of bilirubin. Independently, Jirsa and Večerek (1956, 1958) and Jirsa *et al.* (1956, 1958) succeeded in preparing di- and monotaurobilin, the first synthetic polar bilirubin derivative obtained. Later, Billing *et al.* (1957) confirmed the glucuronide nature of pigment I and pigment II in a comprehensive publication. These authors studied the azo compound of free bilirubin (pigment A) and the azo compound of water soluble pigment II (pigment B). They could show that pigment B is a glucuronic acid derivative of pigment A. The authors were cognizant of the fact that these azo compounds represented mixtures of equal parts of very closely related materials (cf. Chapter I,J). However, these substances were not separated, since they behaved as a homogeneous substance during these studies. Pigment B was obtained by a complicated process from human hepatic bile. The glucuronic acid content of purified preparations was determined. Furthermore, the effect of β-glucuronidase and alkali was studied. Finally, the properties of pigments A and B, including absorption spectra measurements, were examined. Pigment II was identified as a diglucuronide, and pigment I as most likely being a monoglucuronide.

V. *Bile Pigments of Blood*

Pigment B was found to be the glucuronic acid ester of pigment A (azo-bilirubin). Pigment I was found to require ethanol to complete its diazo reaction.

Schmid (1957a,b) confirmed these findings by paper chromatography of bile, icteric serum, and urine. Heikel *et al.* (1957) came to the same results using paper chromatography. On the basis of these studies it is not difficult to explain the well known properties of direct and indirect bili-rubin because it is known that coupling with glucuronic acid increases water solubility of many substances.

At first glance these findings do not seem to agree with the results of the Japanese school, which determined two polar bilirubin compounds, i.e., bilirubin esters and salts. However, these polar substances were isolated

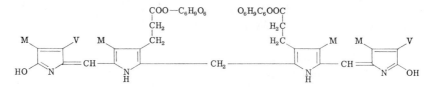

FIG. 41. Structural formula of bilirubin diglucuronide (pigment II).

only as concentrates and contained numerous impurities. Therefore, it is not unlikely that these two pigments really represent pigments I and II. Distribution chromatography of preparations obtained by the Japanese workers would be desirable. Sakamoto's (1957) studies suggest that bilirubin in the form of its salt and pigment I are identical. He could determine that this pigment becomes $CHCl_3$ soluble when $0.1\,N$ HCl is added to the aqueous phase. This cannot be explained by assuming a transformation into free bilirubin, because the diazo reaction remains direct. Sakamoto (1957) separated the ester and salt derivatives of direct bilirubin by anion exchange chromatography using various resins, and he suggested that it is not necessarily true that the entire amount of direct reacting bilirubin present is attached to glucuronic acid. Isselbacher and McCarthy (1958) and C. J. Watson (1958) proved that this assumption is correct (cf. discussion throughout this section).

Schmid (1956a,b) thought that the glucuronic acid was bound to the α- and α'-hydroxy groups of bilirubin, but later he (1957a), as well as Billing *et al.* (1957), found that bilirubin glucuronides are acylglucuro-nides, i.e., the glucuronic acid is linked to the carboxyl groups of propionic acid side chains of bilirubin, as illustrated in Fig. 41.

According to this formula, the diglucuronide contains 584 parts of bilirubin and 388 parts of glucuronic acid, which corresponds to a proportion of about 1.5:1 (T. Wegmann and Marogg, 1959). Schachter (1957) confirmed this by studying the reaction between bilirubin glucuronides and hydroxylamine. He obtained hydroxamic acids and glucuronic acid, which indicate the presence of acylglucuronides.

Studies of the content of free and conjugated bilirubin of normal human serum were carried out by Brodersen (1962) and by Royer and Noir (1962). Brodersen extracted the pigment with $CHCl_3$, coupled the extracts with diazotized sulfanilic acid in acid–alcoholic solution, determined the velocity constants and stoichiometric proportions of this process, and found them to be identical with those of pure bilirubin. In a second series of experiments he precipitated the serum with a surplus of ethanol and studied the light absorption and velocity constants of the diazo reaction of the supernatant, which were found to be similar to those of bilirubin; kinetic studies, however, suggested that the alcoholic supernatant contained a bilirubin derivative substituted in one half of the molecule. This pigment may be identical with pigment I of P. G. Cole *et al.* (1954), which is generally believed to be bilirubin monoglucuronide, or perhaps with the bilirubin–diglucuronide–bilirubin compound of Weber *et al.* (1963) (cf. below). Brodersen *et al.* (1963) confirmed that small but significant quantities of conjugated bilirubin are present in normal human sera. These authors came to the result that the bilirubin conjugate present is monosubstituted. In some of their sera this substance was present in sufficiently high concentration to allow closer study. The conjugate was found to be stable to hydrolysis with both alkali and acid, and its spectral absorption curve was similar to that obtained from the alkali-stable bilirubin conjugate of human bile.

Royer and Noir (1962) precipitated 80 ml portions of normal serum with saturated sodium sulfate and 3 volumes of ethanol. The supernatant was precipitated with $BaCl_2$, the precipitate washed with water, and the bilirubin eluated as a concentrated solution with a small volume of HCl–alcohol and stabilized by a small amount of ascorbic acid. This pigment solution was subjected to paper chromatography and shown to contain both unconjugated bilirubin and pigment II (bilirubin diglucuronide) and, in some of the 30 cases studied, minor amounts of pigment I (monoglucuronide) as well.

Weber *et al.* (1963) pointed out that the existence of bilirubin monoglucuronide is far from proved and gave several reasons for regarding pigment I as a labile equimolar complex of bilirubin and its diglucuronide. They mention that P. G. Cole *et al.* (1954), Billing *et al.* (1957), Billing and Lathe (1958), and Nosslin (1960) discussed this possibility and that no binding proof of the existence of a bilirubin monoglucuronide has been delivered. Their argumentation is convincing, and the problem must at present be considered open. The findings of Royer and Noir mentioned above support their view, as they regularly found both unconjugated bilirubin and the diglucuronide in normal serum and only occasionally minor amounts of pigment I.

Gregory (1963) also found that pigment I is a complex of unconjugated bilirubin and bilirubin diglucuronide. While Weber *et al.* found that pigment I is an equimolar complex of bilirubin and pigment II, Gregory found the ratio between these two components to vary from 0.4 to 1.7. He thought that various polymers of bilirubin and its conjugates exist, and made it clear that his findings do not exclude the existence of bilirubin monoglucuronide. Gregory's experiments were based on three partition chromatographies in succession with a slightly modified Cole-Lathe method, a very elaborate and complicated technique. By means of paper chromatography of the diazo products of the different fractions, he showed that they did not constitute quite pure pigments. He expressed the view that final clarification of the existence of bilirubin monoglucuronide must await use of isotopically labeled bilirubin and glucuronic acid and purification of the enzyme systems involved and subsequent kinetic studies.

Schoenfield and Bollman (1963) attacked the monoglucuronide problem by studying rat fistula bile, isolated rat liver, liver slices, macerates, and hepatectomized dogs; they used reverse-phase partition chromatography as well as paper chromatography. They regard the presence of pigment I in the plasma of hepatectomized dogs as a very strong argument in favor of pigment I being bilirubin monoglucuronide. In the dog pigment II is probably only formed in the liver. They believe that pigment I is a monoglucuronide and that it is formed solely in extrahepatic sites.

Jirsa and Šponar (1955) and Jirsa and Sedláček (1956) assumed that various physical forms of bilirubin were responsible for the varying diazo reactions. Monomolecular bilirubin solutions give a direct reaction, whereas increasing aggregation of bilirubin molecules leads to indirect reaction. Jirsa and Šponar (1955, 1956) and Jirsa and Sedláček (1956) investigated various solutions of bilirubin and its dimethyl ester. The effect of added colloids and surface active materials was especially examined. Alkaline bilirubin solutions flocculated on addition of saturated sodium chloride solutions, and simultaneously the diazo reaction was retarded. Similar retardation of the diazo reaction could be observed after addition of concentrated alkali solutions (e.g., Fehling II). Bilirubin can exist in acid solutions only in the presence of protective colloids such as albumin or saponine. An aqueous alkaline bilirubin solution can be kept in monomolecular form for a longer time, even after acidification to pH 5, when a strongly polar, anionic, or cationic, but neutral surface active material (e.g., Tween 85) is added. The diazo reaction of the acidified solution remains positive under such circumstances. Bilirubin dimethyl ester is insoluble in water, but it forms colloidal solutions. Monomolecular solutions, prepared by the addition of dioxan or surface active substances, give a direct diazo reaction.

Jirsa and Sedláček concluded that their experiments do not decide if a specific direct bilirubin compound exists or not. However, the aggregation state of bilirubin molecules in solution is of decisive importance, whether or not such a compound exists. This does not contradict the hypothesis that the differences of diazo reaction in sera are due primarily to the existence of bilirubin compounds of various degrees of polarity. The fact that Jirsa *et al.* (1956, 1958) prepared two bilirubin taurine compounds (mono- and ditaurobilin) and could show that these compounds, when added to serum, give diazo reaction, agrees with the role of glucuronides in the diazo reaction of icteric sera. However, the studies of Billing *et al.* (1957) on the glucuronic acid content of highly purified pigment II and pigment B preparations showed that taurine compounds can hardly play a role in the direct bilirubin reaction in human serum or in bile.

Talafant (1954a,b) first thought that pigment I is a monoester and pigment II a diester of bilirubin and deoxycholic acid. However, he could later show that this assumption was erroneous, and bilirubin in its direct reacting form is, in fact, conjugated with glucuronic acid (Talafant, 1956b,c,d, 1957). Talafant (1959b) prepared a bilirubin giving direct diazo reaction from bile by fractionation with acetone or ammonium sulfate followed by extraction with methanol and adsorption on diatomaceous earth in the presence of ammonium sulfate. The concentrate was precipitated with cinchoidine acetate and the precipitate was extracted with CHCl$_3$ at slightly alkaline reaction and further purified with ion exchange. The concentrate contained mainly bilirubin diglucuronide and about 80% diglucuronide. He used dog bile which contains mostly taurocholate which is less liable to precipitation than glycocholate. The concentrated preparation of Talafant had the property of a strong detergent—violent foaming in aqueous solution and the power to dissolve many heavily soluble compounds, e.g., free bilirubin and lead salts, as colloidal solutions. Because the method of preparation of Talafant has only been published in detail in Czech, a translation of the original text is given below.

Two volumes of acetone were added to the bile to precipitate proteins and mucoids. To the supernatant 10 volumes of acetone were added. In this way a precipitate forms which contains ca. 5% bilirubin diglucuronide. This can be stored as a powder ("acetone powder") in dry conditions without significant loss of bilirubin for several months. If liver bile is used for the preparation hydrolysis takes place to a considerable extent because it contains more bicarbonate than bladder bile. For further purification the acetone powder is used. It contains ca. 90% bile salts (taurocholates). During this procedure it is necessary to work quickly and in subdued light to avoid losses, but it is not necessary to work in a cool room. The acetone powder is dissolved in distilled water—ca. 1 g/ 6 ml—and acetic acid is added to pH 6. Then precipitation follows using chinconidine acetate (1 ml, 0.1 M) precipitating the glucuronides, and subsequently centrifugation. The precipitate is suspended in ca. 2 ml distilled water and 3 ml Tris buffer (0.5 M, pH 8) is added immediately. In this way the cinchonidine is set free, and it is now removed by extraction twice with ca. 5 ml of $CHCl_3$ (pharmocopoeia quality). The pigment is now in the aqueous phase which has to be acidified quickly to pH 6 with acetic acid and precipitated with 0.6 ml 1% Pb-acetate. The precipitate is washed with distilled water, and then with ethanol (dissolving phospholipids and remaining bile salts), and once again with water to remove the ethanol. The washed precipitate is suspended in 1 ml H_2O and treated with a cation exchanger in sodium form (Czech preparation "Katex FN," a polycondensate of phenolsulfuric and naphthalenesulfonic acid, corresponding to Amberlite IR 112, 120, or 200. An equal volume of a concentrated suspension of the ion exchanger is added. The resin is then removed by centrifugation and the supernatant evaporated *in vacuo* over P_2O_5. The dry residue is extracted with methanol and the methanolic extract is evaporated *in vacuo* in the presence of anhydrous $CaCl_2$. The residue is a dark lamellar preparation and contains ca. 80% bilirubin diglucuronide.

Another method for preparation of highly purified bilirubin diglucuronide was described by Lucassen (1961*, pp. 11–12), based on the extreme solubility of its sodium salt in water as contrasted to its much less soluble undissociated form. To 1 liter of fresh human fistula bile 100 ml 10% $Na_2S_2O_3$ were added to prevent oxidation. The temperature was kept at 5°C. While stirring, the pH was brought to 6.0 by adding a 10% oxalic acid solution dropwise. After cooled centrifugation the precipitate was discarded and 10% oxalic acid was added to the supernatant to pH 3.5. Then the mixture was centrifuged once more, and this time the supernatant was discarded. The precipitate was washed with 50 ml 0.01% oxalic acid. The residual slurry, containing ca. 20 ml of water, was ground in a porcelain dish with 200 ml of acetone. This mixture was stored for 2 hours at −15°C and then filtered. To the clear, brownish yellow filtrate, containing ca. 90% acetone, a 0.1 N NaOH solution in 96% ethanol was added under vigorous stirring. Meanwhile the apparent pH of the solution was measured with a pH meter. When the pH had changed from its initial value of approximately 5 to a value of 7.0 the addition was stopped. A flocculous precipitate had now been formed. This precipitate was quickly centrifuged, washed twice with 20 ml of water-free acetone and twice with 20 ml of water-free ether. It was dried in a vacuum dessicator over concentrated sulfuric acid and stored in darkness.

The first precipitate, which was rejected, contained unconjugated bilirubin and bile acids. The second precipitate formed between pH 6.0 and 3.5 contained bilirubin diglucuronide, proteins, bile acids, cholesterol, and lecithin. Taurine-conjugated bile acids remained in solution at pH 3.5. In the 90% acetone solution only bilirubin diglucuronide, cholesterol, and bile acids were present; lecithin and protein are insoluble in this solvent. By the final addition of NaOH the sodium salt of bilirubin diglucuronide is precipitated, while cholesterol and bile acids remain in solution. The yield of the disodium salt of bilirubin diglucuronide varied from 50 to 300 mg per liter of bile. The purity, calculated on weight basis, averaged between 80 and 90%. The impurities probably consisted mostly of water with some sodium hydroxide. The purity was not enhanced by repeating the whole process once more.

The disodium salt of bilirubin diglucuronide is a brownish-yellow powder; it is amorphous, extremely hygroscopic, and highly soluble in water. On exposure to sunlight or when left standing in moist air its color turns green, but when stored in a vacuum dessicator in darkness it remains stable for at least 1 year.

The absorption curve of bilirubin diglucuronide prepared in this way and dissolved in water (pH 7.5, ionic strength 0.133) with and without the presence of serum albumin is given in the range 350–550 nm (Lucassen, 1961*, Fig. 25, p. 44). His figure is presented here as Fig. 41a. In pure aqueous solution the absorption maximum is 460 nm with a gradual decrease until 400 nm is reached, after which a steep fall of the curve takes place toward lower wavelengths. After addition of serum albumin the maximum is displaced to ca. 420 nm with a gradual fall toward 480 nm and a deflection at ca. 450 nm.

This curve is much like the curves given by Fog for conjugated bilirubin in serum (cf. Figs. 38, 39), but the inflection of the curve is not visible in the curve of Fog; this is easy to understand because Fog did not employ a purified preparation. Lucassen found that the extinction increased both at 420 and 480 nm after the addition of albumin. This was studied more closely by addition of increasing amounts of serum albumin solution (concentration ranges from zero to 3×10^{-5} mole albumin per liter). It was found that the 420 nm extinction showed a decrease on addition of small amounts of albumin, whereas it increased gradually when the albumin concentration increased above 0.5×10^{-5} mole/liter. On the other hand the 480 nm extinction increased steeply on addition of small amounts of albumin, reaching maximum at 0.5×10^{-5} mole/liter after which it remained constant for increasing albumin concentration. This Lucassen (1961*, pp. 65–66) explains in the following way: four molecules of bilirubin diglucuronide are bound to one molecule of albumin as is the case with unconjugated bilirubin; this binding takes place between the phenolic OH-groups of the bilirubin compounds and the primary amino groups of the protein. This is reflected in the 480 nm measurements. The change in 420 nm extinction is probably due to a less

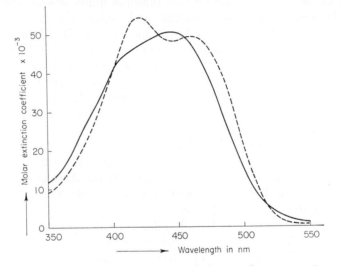

FIG. 41a. Absorption spectrum of bilirubin diglucuronide in water. Concentration, 1.4×10^{-5} mole/liter; pH 7.5; ionic strength, 0.133. Solid line: without serum albumin. Dashed line: in the presence of 2×10^{-5} mole/liter serum albumin. From Lucassen (1961*, p. 44).

strong interaction between another part of the bilirubin diglucuronide molecule and the albumin, and this interaction becomes important at rather high albumin concentrations after the 480 nm interaction has been completed. It is suggested that the glucuronic acid groups are responsible for this secondary 420 nm interaction.

Lucassen (1961*, pp. 69–70) also stressed that the chromatographic separation methods of Cole and Lathe (1963) and similar procedures are imperfect because bilirubin and especially its conjugates are precipitated on the addition of alcohol before chromatography and because the conjugates are very labile in protein-free solution.

Paper chromatographic investigations of Gries *et al.* (1954) and of Heikel *et al.* (1957) showed that direct bilirubin was stationary in chromatograms with $CHCl_3$ as solvent, whereas it migrated when acid or neutral aqueous solutions were used. Indirect bilirubin behaved in just the opposite way. Heikel *et al.* also confirmed the glucuronic acid content of direct bilirubin.

Isselbacher and McCarthy (1958, 1959) demonstrated the presence of bilirubin *conjugates with sulfuric acid*. They injected radiosulfate to rats, cats, and humans and identified radioactive bilirubin conjugates in their bile. The sulfate is bound to the phenol groups (OH-groups) of the bilirubin molecule and not to the carboxyl groups as is glucuronic acid. They demonstrated that azobilirubin prepared from bilirubin conjugates from bile contained a fraction resisting hydrolysis with β-glucuronidase. This nonglucuronidic fraction was subdivided into an alkali-stable (sulfate) and an alkali-labile (nonsulfate) subfraction. No taurine could be demonstrated after hydrolysis. Analysis of bilirubin azo pigment from 11 human T-tube bile samples showed an average glucuronidase-resistant fraction of 23.7 ± 6.4%, an average sulfate fraction of 13.7 ± 5.6%, and an average alkali-labile fraction of 15.0 ± 6.2%. The nonglucuronide–nonsulfate fraction of conjugated bilirubin may consist of amino acid conjugates.

Because glucuronic acid is bound to the COOH-groups of bilirubin and sulfate to its OH-groups, double conjugates containing both are possible. Also, conjugates with one and two sulfate groups per molecule bilirubin are possible, but these possibilities have not yet been studied. The possibility of a number of different conjugates can, however, be anticipated.

Isselbacher and McCarthy claimed to have produced bilirubin sulfate conjugates by means of enzymatic synthesis and described a method for purification and subsequent chromatographic fractionation of bilirubin azo pigments. C. J. Watson (1958) could not verify the existence of bilirubin conjugates with sulfuric acid, but Schoenfield *et al.* (1962) confirmed their occurrence in rat bile and serum from rats with obstructive and hepatocellular jaundice in experiments with radioactive-SO_4. They found that sulfate was only associated with bilirubin diglucuronide and not with monoglucuronide. The sulfate conjugation was found to depend on an intrahepatic mechanism, although extrahepatic sulfate conjugation could not be completely excluded. It was not established whether both mono- and disulfate conjugates existed and whether glucuronic acid and sulfate were bound to the same bilirubin molecule. The experiments only demonstrated that the sulfate conjugates and the diglucuronide were present in the same chromatographic fraction.

Gregory and Watson (1962b) studied serial samples of bile from 6 dogs and 6 patients with draining T-tubes after intravenous administration of 1.2 μc $S^{35}O_4$ daily for several days. They found that the azobilirubin could be freed completely from S^{35} by two-dimensional paper chromatography or extraction. A molecular relationship between alkali-stable conjugated bilirubin and direct reacting bilirubin sulfate could not be established, and it was concluded that the alkali-stable, direct reacting bilirubin fraction could not be identified with a nonglucuronide conjugate. Further, they prepared a water-soluble bilirubin sulfate compound from crystalline bilirubin dissolved in $CHCl_3$ and a solution 1:160 of concentrated H_2SO_4 in acetic anhydride and studied this compound closely. The most likely site of the conjugation was the pyrrole-N. The number of sulfate groups per bilirubin molecule was not determined. The compound was easily oxidized to biliverdin sulfonate and reduced to urobilin sulfonate.

In an addendum to their paper, Gregory and Watson discuss the findings of Schoenfield *et al.*, from whom they borrowed a bile fistula rat; they administered 100 μc $S^{35}O_4$ to this animal and confirmed that its bile contained a bilirubin sulfate in contrast to their own dogs and humans. It remains to be clarified whether there is an actual species difference or whether the amounts of $S^{35}O_4$ used in Gregory and Watson's studies were too small to permit detection.

Sommerhalder *et al.* (1962a,b) and Kuenzle *et al.* (1963a,b) studied icteric serum with a modification of the reverse phase chromatography of P. G. Cole and Lathe (1953) employing protein-containing serum dilutions instead of alcoholic extracts. In this way they regularly found four serum bilirubin fractions which they called α, β, γ, and δ. Fraction α contained the unconjugated bilirubin while the other three contained conjugates. Only the fractions α and δ occurred in normal sera. Only quite recently they published their technique—based on column partition chromatography on siliconated kieselguhr without previous protein precipitation, with separate elution of the zones after pushing the column out of the chromatographic tube (Kuenzle *et al.*, 1966a*). They added 0.1 ml saturated ammonium sulfate solution to 0.5 ml icteric (1 ml if the serum bilirubin is below 2 mg/100 ml) serum and mixed it with 0.5 ml of the mobile phase of the solvent system employed, i.e., *n*-butanol/0.05 M phosphate buffer pH 6.0/H_2O, 50/5/45 (v/v/v). Of this mixture 0.5 ml was placed on the top of a column of 4 g siliconized kieselguhr, prepared according to Cole *et al.* (1954), and subsequently the surface of the column was covered with ca. 1 ml of the mobile phase. After this a separatory funnel, serving as a reservoir for the mobile phase, was fixed to the chromatography tube with an outlet close to the level of the liquid covering the column; then the stopcock at the lower end of the chromatography tube was opened. The chromatography tube has to be wrapped with aluminum foil to protect it from light. After ca. 20 minutes the four bilirubin fractions—α, β, γ, and δ—were clearly separated on the column. The separatory funnel was removed and the liquid allowed to drain. The procedure is applicable both for jaundiced serum and for bile and urine with small modifications.

Elution of the fractions was carried out with an elution fluid prepared daily from a stock solution consisting of 1 volume 10% w/v aqueous Na-dithionite (analytical, Riedel-Hannover) and 9 volumes of 0.1 N NaOH. The stock solution was made up weekly and stored at 0°–4°C. The elution fluid was prepared by mixing 99 volumes of stock solution and one volume of an aqueous 10% w/v solution of ascorbic acid, freshly prepared from analytical ascorbic acid (Fluka, Ag, Buchs, Switzerland). The purity of the dithionite and the ascorbic acid is important as impurities may shift the absorption maximum of bilirubin toward longer wavelengths.

The kieselguhr column was gently blown out of the tube onto a flat glass plate by holding the tube almost horizontally to the surface of the plate. Then the column was cut into slices to separate the colored zones. The slices were placed in separate centrifuge tubes with 3 ml of the elution fluid, the tubes were shaken vigorously for 30–40 seconds and left standing for 1 hour in the dark in order to saponify alkali-labile bilirubin conjugates. After this the tubes were centrifuged at 1800 g for 5 minutes and the supernatants decanted and filtered by suction through small glass filter funnels, type 3G3, into separate 20-ml suction tubes wrapped with aluminum foil. The kieselguhr residues were reextracted with 3 ml eluent, recentrifuged, decanted, and filtered into the appropriate suction tubes. A third extraction was performed with 2 ml of the eluent and the suspension filtered without previous centrifugation.

The fractions β, γ, and δ are extracted in this way. Fraction α cannot be determined spectrophotometrically in the eluate because of turbidity and has to be determined as the difference between the total bilirubin—determined according to Jendrassik and Gróf (1938b)—and the sum of the three other fractions. Readings were taken at 450 nm in 2-cm cells against the eluent as a blank. It is important to carry out the spectro-photometric readings between 2½ and 3½ hours after the first admixture of the eluent to the slices of the column. The absorption maximum is really at 440 nm, but errors due to impurities were found to be reduced by reading at 450 nm. Special calibration curves for bilirubin dissolved in the eluent were employed and the absorption curves of the four fractions and that of pure bilirubin were compared in the spectral range 390–510 nm. The absorption of all the fractions was much higher than that of unconjugated bilirubin below 395 nm. According to the curves given, the absorbancy of unconjugated bilirubin falls off rapidly from below 400 nm, that of fraction α exhibits a similar but less pronounced decrease, whereas the curves of fractions β, γ, and δ show no decrease, but on the contrary an upward trend at wavelengths below 400 nm. Between 430 and 510 nm the absorption curves of free bilirubin and the four fractions showed identical maxima but different forms—γ and β being quite flat, α and δ higher but not as high as that of pure unconjugated bilirubin. Hemoglobin incubated with the eluent for 2 hours at room temperature exhibited a peak at 421 nm which showed a rapid fall toward higher wavelengths. The solutions read were found to be stable under the conditions described. The decrease in absorbancy was below 5% in 3 hours.

The reproducibility of the chromatographic determination of the fractions β, γ, and δ was from ± 3.4 to $\pm 5.8\%$ (2 SD), whereas that of fraction α, which was determined as difference, was $\pm 13.8\%$. More than 800 sera were chromatographed with the method described and only seven (from 2 patients) did not separate well.

Kuenzle et al. also fractionated bile bilirubin and found three fractions called 1, 2, and 3. The R_f values of the four serum fractions α, β, γ, and δ were 0.05, 0.29, 0.76, and 1.00, respectively, while those of the three bile fractions 1, 2, and 3 were 0.08, 0.53, and 1.00, respectively. In normal bile the three fractions were present in the following proportions: fraction 1, 5–10%; fraction 2, 10–25%; fraction 3, 65–85% of the total bile bilirubin. The same pattern was found in most pathological biles studied.

Kuenzle et al. found that their method is definitely superior to previously used methods in which at least half of the bilirubin is lost with the protein precipitate. Elution of the bilirubin fractions after diazotization was not possible because the diazo compound of fraction δ was insoluble and the azo pigments decomposed markedly during elution. It is emphasized that it is not possible to determine the amount of pigment lost during elution. This would require recovery tests with pure bilirubin conjugates, and these are not available. The losses are, however, believed to be low because the kieselguhr is virtually completely decolorized during elution.

The nature of the fractions α–δ was studied thoroughly in a subsequent publication by Kuenzle et al. (1966b[*]). Fraction α represented unconjugated bilirubin; fraction β was found to be identical with Pigment I and to represent a complex of one mole of unconjugated bilirubin and one mole of diconjugated bilirubin; fraction γ represented diconjugated bilirubin, but consisted of equal parts of alkali-labile and alkali-stable conjugates. Also fraction β contained about equal parts of alkali-labile and alkali-stable conjugates. The chemical nature of the alkali-stable and the alkali-labile subfractions was, however, not elucidated. The previously unknown fraction δ consisted of fraction β firmly adsorbed to serum albumin. Of the three fractions from bile fractions 1 and 2 corresponded to serum fraction β bound to different bile components other than protein, whereas fraction 3 corresponded to serum fraction γ (Pigment II). Fractions β and γ were dialyzable, whereas fraction δ was not.

Mathematical correlation analysis of the results of chromatographic determinations on 31 icteric sera from different patients resulted in the equation: $\beta + \delta = k[\log_e (\alpha \cdot \gamma) - c]$ where β, δ, α, and γ stand for the concentrations of the fractions, while k and c are constants. Determined for the material as a whole the value of k was 1.86, that of c —1.40; correlation analyses performed on the results of analyses on individual patients at different times showed values of k varying between 1.25 and 10.05, whereas those of c varied between 2.68 and —3.29. The correlation coefficient of the correlation equations was highly significant ($r = +0.713$).

Harboe (1965) used fractionation of serum bilirubin on Sephadex columns after addition of formamide to disrupt the bilirubin–albumin bond (cf. Section A,9, this chapter). In this way three fractions were obtained in normal and pathological human sera. In sera from newborns, 40% (v/v) formamide disrupted the bilirubin–albumin bond, but in sera from patients in the healing phase of hepatitis the bond was mainly intact at 40% formamide, but began to split with 44%. Experiments with different formamide concentrations disclosed that the stability of the bilirubin–albumin bond varies. The method of Harboe seems to be a powerful and promising tool in the study of the serum bilirubin fractions and their protein binding.

Vegas (1963) studied the chromatographic behavior of glucuronic acid and sulfate conjugates of bilirubin with ion exchange paper chromatography. Both bilirubin conjugates from serum and from human bile were studied. The paper employed was carboxymethylcellulose cation exchange paper (Whatman CM 50) pretreated with washing for 18–24 hours in the downward direction with (1) 0.1 N HCl, (2) H_2O, (3) 0.1 N NaOH, and (4) H_2O in a long chromatographic cabinet. After drying the paper at 40°C for 1 hour, ascending chromatography was carried out with n-butanol–pyridine–1 N ammonia, 2:1:2 (v/v/v), pH 11.9 at room temperature. In this way Vegas obtained clear-cut resolution of the azo pigment of synthetic bilirubin sulfate (prepared by the method of C. J. Watson, 1958) and the azo derivative of the alkali stable fraction of naturally conjugated bilirubin from the azo pigment of bilirubin diglucuronide (pigment B). No breakdown of pigment B took place during the chromatography.

Weber and Schalm (1965*) subjected the question of bilirubin sulfates to a thorough study. They point out that the evidence for the existence of this conjugate is only indirect as it has not been isolated from natural sources. Further there is no evidence of the identity of alkali-stable bilirubin conjugates and bilirubin sulfate. Weber and Schalm studied 100 ml samples of fresh human drain bile from 17 different patients. They added 150 ml 0.1 N NaOH and incubated the solution at room temperature for 30 minutes after which acidification to pH 2 with 4 ml 6 N HCl was carried out. Then extraction with 180 ml CHCl$_3$ and washing the CHCl$_3$ extract twice with 100–150 ml 0.1 N HCl followed, after which the extract was divided into two portions, one of which was submitted to purification by means of ion exchange (Amberlite IR 45/OH, CG type III). In both portions of the CHCl$_3$ extract SO$_4$ determinations were carried out by evaporation followed by hydrolysis with 12 N HCl on a boiling water bath and by precipitation with 10% BaCl$_2$. The quantitation was performed by spectrophotometric reading of the turbidity.

In all biles studied both CHCl$_3$ extracts contained considerably less SO$_4$ than predicted from their content of alkali-stable bilirubin conjugates. Consequently the alkali-stable bilirubin conjugates from human liver bile can contain only insignificant amounts of bilirubin sulfates. One of the patients studied had the drain inserted into the right hepatic duct while the left was occluded. Although in this case the right liver lobe had to excrete all the bilirubin no appreciable sulfate conjugation was found in the bile. Thus conjugation of bilirubin with sulfate does not take place to any appreciable extent even under excessive load on the conjugation mechanism.

Weber and Schalm pointed out that the presence of protein enhances the formation of alkali-stable bilirubin conjugates in bile. If serum or a serum precipitate with alcohol or acetone were added to bile or purified bilirubin diglucuronide from bile, the proportion of alkali-stable pigment increased considerably, e.g., from 20 to 40%.

Colombo and Bonomo (1965*) likewise were unable to demonstrate any sulfate in purified alkali-stable bilirubin conjugates from human icteric sera.

On the other hand Noir et al. (1966*, 1967*) found that sulfate conjugates of bilirubin play a certain role in bile. The amounts present are, however, only small. They prepared synthetic bilirubin sulfate according to C. J. Watson (1958) employing bilirubin B.D.H., laboratory grade. This was adsorbed on Al$_2$O$_3$ on a column which was subsequently washed first with a solvent to elute nonyellow pigments and then with distilled water until the eluate became neutral. The solvent consisted of the upper phase of a mixture of 200 ml distilled water, 20 ml CHCl₃, and 3 ml Liebermann-Burchard's reagent [i.e., acetic anhydride/conc. H_2SO_4 10/1 (v/v)]. To obtain adequate yields of bilirubin sulfate the procedures must be carried out at maximum speed because otherwise most of the bilirubin is transformed into verdins, violins, and fuscins by the Liebermann-Burchard reagent. These pigments are removed with the elution solvent. The subsequent washing of the column with water makes the final elution of the bilirubin sulfate easier. This elution is performed with a minimal quantity of $0.5 N$ KOH which gives a concentrated yellow-brown eluate containing the bilirubin sulfate. This is purified by paper chromatography after being placed in a band on Whatman No. 3 paper. The run is performed with butanol-ethanol-water, 3/1/1.5 (v/v/v) for 20 hours, after which the paper is dried at room temperature. The pigment now forms a well-defined yellow zone and is cut out and eluted with minimal volumes of distilled water.

Then examination for the presence of SO_4 with two-dimensional paper chromatography was carried out, the first run with butanol/ethanol/water, 3/1/1.5 (v/v/v) was followed by drying and then by hydrolysis for 3–4 hours in a paper-lined closed cylindrical glass jar (12×24 inches) containing dioxane/water/conc. HCl, 9 ml/36 ml/5 ml. The second run was subsequently performed at right angles to the first run with pyridine/ammonia/butanol, 20/40/40 (v/v/v) for 18 hours after the application of reference samples of inorganic sulfate and dehydroepiandrosterone sulfate on the paper in line with the orange-yellow spot. The sulfate spots were made visible using the method of Schneider and Lewart (1956*). The eluate was analyzed for bilirubin using the method of Jendrassik and Cleghorn (1936) and for organic sulfate using the method of Roy (1956*).

The eluate containing the purified bilirubin sulfates was adjusted to pH 4 after which equal volumes of freshly prepared diazo reagent (5 + 15 conc. HCl + 0.15; cf. Table II, footnote) were added. For determination of absorption spectra and paper chromatographic studies the azo pigment solution was evaporated *in vacuo* and then the residue was dissolved in 1 M acetic acid. The azo pigment could then be purified by ascending paper chromatography according to Schmid (1956) and eluted from the paper with butanol/water/glacial acetic acid, 5/2/3 (v/v/v).

For comparison with the synthetic bilirubin sulfate Noir *et al.* (1966*, 1967*) prepared the azo pigments from the alkali-stable fraction of conjugated bilirubin from six samples of human bile as well as from the bile of normal rats and rats injected with bilirubin sulfate, i.v. One hundred milliliters of human bile were treated with 1 volume of diazo reagent for 30 minutes at room temperature after which 1 volume of 1 M NaOH was added. After 20 minutes the azo pigment was acidified and concentrated to a small volume using the method described by Noir et al. (1965*) and subsequently dried in vacuo and dissolved in $1\,M$ acetic acid. Paper chromatography showed a distinct third azo pigment band (pigment C) in addition to the two known azo pigment bands, pigments A and B. This third azo pigment gave exactly the same R_f as the synthetic bilirubin sulfate $[R_f = 0.34$ in the chromatographic system of Schmid (1956a)].

The absorption maximum of bilirubin sulfate in neutral aqueous solution was 455 nm. In acid solution it was immediately oxidized to a green solution. Attempts to purify it on a Dowex 50 column were unsuccessful because it was strongly adsorbed on the resin. On reverse phase chromatography it behaved like pigment II. Hydrolysis of the pigment showed the presence of 2 moles of SO_4 for each mole of bilirubin and the corresponding azo pigment exhibited equimolar amounts of pigment and SO_4, i.e., findings corresponding to bilirubin disulfate. Whether the pigment is present in bile in the free form or as glucuronic acid conjugate could not be decided.

The amounts present in bile were found to be small—of the order of magnitude of a few per cent. In rat bile it could be increased to ca. 20% of the bile bilirubin after intravenous injection of bilirubin sulfate.

Noir et al. (1966*, 1967*) point out that the failure of Weber and Schalm (1965*) to detect bilirubin sulfate in bile is most likely due to destruction and inadequate extraction from the bile with $CHCl_3$ at pH 2.

Pittera and Cassia (1963) performed paper chromatography of azobilirubin from aqueous serum–diazo mixtures without alcohol with ascending technique on Whatman I paper; a solvent system of methylethyl ketone–n-propionic acid–water, 7.5:2.5:3.0 (v/v/v) was used. In this way, a third pigment (pigment C) was discovered besides pigments A and B. Pigment C remained on the start line and was missed in earlier studies in which only alcoholic serum extracts were used. The authors believe that pigment C is formed by the bilirubin fraction being most firmly bonded to the serum protein; it is probably identical with the δ-fraction of Kuenzle et al. (cf. above).

Shigeru (1958a,b) studied the influence of bile salts on the diazo reaction by evaporating equivolumetric mixtures of chloroformic bilirubin solutions (concentration 1 mg per 100 ml), and ethanolic solutions of different bile salts in various concentrations. The dry residue was water insoluble with low bile salt concentrations and increasingly soluble with rising concentrations. The solutions showed pH about 6.8 and were stable and showed a positive diazo reaction 5–15 minutes after addition of diazo reagent. The formation of bilirubin–bile salt compounds with the molar ratio of 1 bilirubin to 2,000 bile acid was assumed.

Talafant (1961) improved the electrophoretic separation of bilirubin conjugates by using a sodium acetate/acetic acid buffer of pH 6.1 containing 5 ml glacial acetic acid and 70 ml pyridine per liter. In this way the tailing of spots and the instability of the conjugates in alkaline solutions were avoided. If about 100 μg bilirubin and a paper width of 2–3 cm was used, free bilirubin and two conjugates were clearly separated. The presence of excess bile salts precludes the possibility of distinguishing between the conjugates, but the use of pyridine–acetate buffer made it possible to perform electrophoretic separation of bilirubin preparations devoid of bile salts.

Maggiore et al. (1961a,b) precipitated human bile with ammonium sulfate and extracted with butanol. The extract was precipitated with methanol and subsequently subjected to descending paper chromatography (Whatman 3 paper) for 18–24 hours with the solvent system, propanol–butanol–3% acetic acid (30:40:30 by volume). In this way three fractions were clearly separated: a bottom spot (diglucuronide), an intermediate spot (not identified), and a top spot (monoglucuronide). The pigments were eluted and their spectral curves studied in the range 350–520 nm. The diglucuronide showed a maximum at 450 nm, the monoglucuronide at 425 nm, and the unidentified conjugate at 435 nm. The quantitative relation between the three pigments was 65–85% diglucuronide, 10–20% monoglucuronide, and 5–15% unidentified conjugates. The findings are in reasonably good agreement with Fog's absorption curve for bilirubin conjugates in serum (Figs. 39, 40, 41a) which exhibits a plateau in the region 420–460 nm. Such a plateau would be expected from a mixture of pigments with maxima at 450, 435, and 425 nm.

Maggiore et al. subjected the three pigments to diazotization and studied the resulting azo pigment by means of paper chromatography. Further, the pigments were analyzed for glucuronic acid, sulfate, and amino acids. The bottom and top fractions were found to behave as bilirubin di- and monoglucuronide, respectively, while the intermediate fraction was found to be conjugated with one molecule of glucuronic acid at one of its carboxyl groups and with one molecule of an unknown substance. This substance was not sulfate and not an amino acid. Sulfate conjugates could not be demonstrated—similar to C. J. Watson's (1958) studies. But in neither of these studies was radioactive-SO_4 was employed.

Koumans and De Groote (1961) evaluated recent analytical methods for bilirubin conjugates and concluded that quantitative partition chromatographic fractionation on columns (Billing, 1955a) is very difficult and liable to errors because of precipitation of protein. Extraction methods (Schachter, 1959) are easier to handle, but give only relative quantities of mono- and diglucuronide.

Recently, Jacobs et al. (1964) compared the results of determination of "direct bilirubin" in serum with 5 different diazo methods (Malloy-Evelyn, Brückner, Hogg-Meites, Lathe-Ruthven, Nosslin) and extraction methods (acetone, ethyl acetate, $CHCl_3$) and found wide discrepancy. They pointed out that the large number of techniques differing only in minor details is confusing, and that unavailability of reference standards of bilirubin conjugates is a serious obstacle to the analytical problem. They did not, however, point to the basic cirumstance that exact quantitative determination of conjugated bilirubin is an analytical problem which is *a priori* impossible to solve because serum bilirubin is a varying mixture of only partially known conjugates with varying protein bonding. Even if pure standards of the main bilirubin conjugates were available, exact analysis would only be possible if the quantitative relation between free and conjugated bilirubin in the serum in question was known beforehand.

Schoenfield *et al.* (1964*) compared three methods of analysis of bilirubin and its conjugates—column partition chromatography and the extraction methods of Schachter and Eberlein—on jaundiced sera and found differences great enough to doubt the wisdom of additional clinical studies with existing methods.

Pittera and Cassia (1964*) *fractionated unconjugated bilirubin*—extracted from serum with $CHCl_3$ or isolated by means of reverse phase chromatography—in different fractions with varying absorption maximum employing chromatography. The columns were made from 5.5 g of siliconated silica placed in tubes of length 22–25 cm with 6-mm internal diameter. The length of the gel column was ca. 15 cm. The columns were percolated with the aqueous phase of a solvent system consisting of 50 ml *n*-butanol, 45 ml H_2O, and 5 ml phosphate buffer (0.05 M, pH 6). After the excess solvent was passed through, ca. 3 ml remained bound on the column forming the stationary phase. The flow velocity was 1 ml per 3 minutes. Extracts of 1–2 ml fresh serum with 8–10 ml $CHCl_3$ were evaporated to dryness with a small quantity of siliconated silica and subsequently placed on the top of the column after which 1–2 ml of the aqueous phase of the solvent system were poured on. Then the column was eluted with 2–5 ml of the butanol phase of the solvent system. This resulted in rapid mobilization of part of the bile pigment toward the interior portion of the column. Then more of the butanol phase (7–9 ml) was poured on the top of the column resulting in elution of a second mobile fraction while a stationary phase was retained. Azobilirubin prepared from $CHCl_3$ extracts of bilirubin from serum behaved similarly, separating into two fractions. Further subdivision of the two fractions, called bilirubin I and II, was achieved by means of ascending paper chromatography with the solvent system methylethyl ketone/*n*-propionic acid/H_2O, 7.5/2.5/3.0, which resulted in separation of bilirubin I into two fractions, A and B, A remaining stationary, B moving with the front. The spectral absorption maximum of bilirubin I and II as well as of fractions A and B showed small, but significant differences, and the proportion of these pigments in sera from various type of jaundice showed marked differences. The composition of the bilirubin I and II and fractions A and B and their relation to the known bilirubin conjugates are not known.

Gaidano *et al.* (1964*) fractionated azobilirubin from ethanol extracts of sera or bile as well as from commercial bilirubin preparations by means of thin layer chromatography on silica gel (0.3 mm layer) with the solvent system *n*-propionic acid/methylethyl ketone/H_2O, 25/75/30. They found two bands with R_f ca. 0.50 and 0.35. The 0.50 band contained the bulk of the azobilirubin from commercial bilirubin preparations, the 0.35 band the bulk of the azobilirubin from bile extracts. In sera from adults the 0.35 pigment contained ca. 50–65% of the total bilirubin. In sera from patients with hepatocellular jaundice a third band with R_f 0.20 was present which was barely demonstrable in sera from obstructive jaundice. In a case of neoplastic occlusion, on the other hand, a pigment with R_f 0.62 was present. The spectral maxima of the isolated fractions were 530 nm for the 0.50 and 0.35 fractions, 400 nm for the 0.20 fraction, and 490–500 nm for the 0.62 fraction.

Manganelli and Scotti (1964*) fractionated azobilirubin from 30 normal sera by means of a special paper chromatographic method (cf. Chapter I, Section M) and clearly distinguished between one main band and two secondary bands. The composition of these bands was not studied.

Colombo and Bonomo (1965*) studied the alkali-stable fraction of conjugated serum bilirubin with reverse phase partition chromatography. The alkali-stable fraction was found to be proportional to the total serum bilirubin; it included ca. 22% of the concentration of total bilirubin. Purified extracts of pigment II were hydrolyzed much more rapidly (ca. 85% being split within 30 minutes) by alkali than pigment present in the sera. They determined the ratio of bilirubin to bilirubin diglucuronide in the alkali-stable fraction and found that the molar ratio of glucuronic acid to bilirubin was ca. 1.80, i.e., close to that of the diglucuronide. No sulfate was demonstrable.

Maggiore and Giovannetti (1965*) isolated three fractions of conjugated bilirubin from 11 samples of bile or duodenal juice by means of paper chromatography with the solvent system *n*-propanol/*n*-butanol/3% acetic acid, 30/40/30 (v/v) during 20 hours. The first fraction contained about 73%, the second ca. 10%, the third ca. 17% of the pigment; their spectral absorption maxima in H_2O were 450, 435, and 425 nm, respectively. The velocity of their diazo reaction varied, that of fraction 1 reaching maximum in 1 minute, that of fraction 2 in 4 minutes, and that of fraction 3 in 8 minutes. The diazo products of the three fractions were also subjected to paper chromatography. Fraction 1 gave only one fraction by this method, corresponding to pigment B, whereby it was concluded that fraction 1 is bilirubin diglucuronide. Fraction 3 yielded equal quantities of pigment A and pigment B so that it was regarded as being bilirubin monoglucuronide. Fraction 2 gave two diazo products, pigment B and one differing from both pigments A and B. This third azo pigment was not influenced by β-glucuronidase and was alkali-labile, but contained neither sulfate nor amino acids. It was also present in cat bile, but not in rat bile.

Controversial problems include the alkali-stable conjugates and the composition of pigment I. These questions have not yet been solved satisfactorily in spite of intensive research. Recent studies on bilirubin conjugates have, on the contrary, made the problems increasingly complex. Further investigations with both chromatographic and extraction methods including careful comparison of the many methods introduced are necessary before final evaluation of existing evidence is possible.

An attempt to correlate the findings of Japanese and Western investigators on bilirubin and its glucuronides was made in a brief review by Kondo (1964*). Fractionation with Japanese chromatographic methods showed that pigment I was a mixture of free bilirubin and salt-type and ester-type bilirubin, whereas pigment II consisted mainly of ester-type bilirubin.

The important question of whether pigment I is bilirubin monoglucuronide or a mixture of bilirubin and bilirubin diglucuronide is discussed in Section G of this chapter. Finally it is to be emphasized that factors other than solubility may be active in causing the differences in diazo reaction velocity between bilirubin and its conjugates—e.g., intramolecular H-bonding (cf. Fog and Jellum, 1963).

Summary

Since 1950 it has become increasingly clear that direct and indirect bilirubin represent at least two different molecular compounds: the first being polar (water soluble) and the latter nonpolar (chloroform soluble). Today it is assumed that, at least in humans, direct bilirubin is a mixture of several conjugates of which bilirubin monoglucuronide (pigment I) and bilirubin diglucuronide (pigment II) are the most important. The glucuronic acid is linked to the carboxylic groups of bilirubin. Japanese researchers (see Yamaoka and Kosaka, 1951; Yamaoka *et al.*, 1956a,b;

Sakamoto, 1956a,b,c,d,e) described ester and salt derivatives of bilirubin, the exact constitution of which is not yet known. These substances could not be obtained in pure form.

In addition to glucuronides (alkali-labile) other conjugates, both alkali-stable and alkali-labile have also been found. Numerous different pigments have been prepared in purified condition by various investigators, most often by using partition chromatographic methods on the pigments themselves or their azo derivatives. The composition of these conjugates is, however, not known. Sulfuric acid conjugates (bilirubin sulfate) form a certain amount of the alkali-stable fraction, but usually only a few per cent of the total conjugated bilirubin of the bile according to present evidence.

Besides the conjugates of bilirubin, other factors also play a role in the direct reaction. Among these factors, the physical form of bilirubin molecules in solution is of decisive importance. Monomolecular solutions give direct reaction. Solutions in which the molecules are in a higher aggregation state show a retardation of the diazo reaction, depending on the magnitude of these aggregates. This does not contradict the fact that natural "direct bilirubin" is a mixture of molecular conjugates.

Various other conjugates are also found, both alkali-stable and alkali-labile. Among them, sulfate conjugates are interesting because conjugation here takes place at the phenolic groups of bilirubin and not at its carboxyl groups. Also amino acids are believed to form natural conjugates with bilirubin. The role of these nonglucuronidic bilirubin conjugates is, however, insufficiently known.

It should be borne in mind that values for "direct bilirubin" obtained by measurements of the reaction rate do not necessarily yield the same results as determinations based on other characteristics of bilirubin and its conjugates (i.e., chloroform solubility or adsorption on protein precipitates), on chromatographic separation of bilirubin and its conjugates (Billing, 1955a), or on separation by means of extraction procedures (Schachter, 1959). The so-called 1-minute-bilirubin does not represent the diglucuronide concentration (Billing, 1955a). Weber *et al.* (1963) and Gregory (1963) pointed out that the evidence of the existence of bilirubin monoglucuronide in biological products is doubtful and that pigment I is more likely a labile equimolecular complex of bilirubin and its diglucuronide; but Schoenfield and Bollman (1963) strongly argued that pigment I must be bilirubin monoglucuronide.

It was demonstrated by Brodersen (1962) and Royer and Noir (1962) that normal human serum contains small amounts of conjugated bilirubin besides free bilirubin.

Synthetic bilirubin conjugates were prepared by Jirsa *et al.* (1956,

1958) from taurine and by Gregory and Watson (1962b) from sulfate. Talafant (1959a,b) and Lucassen (1961*) prepared highly purified concentrates of bilirubin diglucuronide from bile. The questions of the bilirubin conjugates are very complicated. Important research is still bringing new data. The Sephadex–formamide method of Harboe (1965) seems especially promising.

G. Biological Significance of Bilirubin Glucuronides and the Direct Diazo Reaction

Hijmans van den Bergh (1918, pp. 108–109) advanced the hypothesis that indirect reacting serum bilirubin of hemolytic jaundice ("dynamic icterus") has not passed through liver cells, whereas direct reacting bilirubin streams back from bile to blood during "mechanical jaundice" after having passed the liver cells. According to earlier terminology, mechanical jaundice described jaundice caused by obstruction, as well as hepatocellular jaundice. One of the principal observations which led to this theory was the direct reaction of bile bilirubin. In the following discussion, this is called the "liver passage hypothesis."

Even though Hijmans van den Bergh still had some doubts about this hypothesis of bilirubin becoming "direct" by passing the liver cells, later investigators viewed it as a fact (Lepehne, 1920; McNee, 1922; C. J. Watson, 1946, p. 103 et seq.). A number of special nomenclatures were coined based on this assumption. French investigators spoke about *"bilirubine franche"* (direct) and *"bilirubine dissimulée"* (indirect). They even subdivided the latter in *"bilirubine hématique"* which did not pass through liver cells, and *"bilirubine de retour"* which was deposited in tissues during disappearing jaundice (Fiessinger *et al.*, 1929; Fiessinger, 1934). Aschoff (1928, 1932) introduced the terms "bilirubin II" and "bilirubin I," and Jenke (1931) spoke about "cholerubin" and "hemorubin," depending on whether bilirubin had or had not passed through liver cells.

The *liver passage hypothesis* offers a simple and elegant explanation of the elementary observations of the direct and indirect diazo reactions. Only a few authors doubted this hypthesis, emphasizing that it was not backed by sufficient evidence. They pointed out that thorough study has brought up various points which the passage theory could not explain (F. C. Mann and Bollman, 1926; Harrison, 1937, p. 246; H. B. Stein, 1941; Cantarow *et al.*, 1942; Pavel, 1943a,b; With, 1944a; Cantarow and Trumper, 1945, p. 441; Jimenez-Diaz *et al.*, 1948; Kühn, 1950). Latest developments, but especially the fact that the direct diazo reaction is due to bilirubin conjugates while the indirect reaction is due to free bilirubin, have shown that the liver passage theory is at least partially correct. However, it must be emphasized that this theory greatly over-simplifies the problem. Numerous facts have been reported which cannot be explained by this widely accepted simple theory.

One fact which the hypothesis cannot explain is that not all *bilirubin of the bile reacts directly, but that considerable amounts can show indirect reaction* (see P. G. Cole and Lathe, 1953; Sakamoto, 1956a,b,c). Hoffman *et al.* (1960) reported that 15–30% of direct bile bilirubin consists of pigment I (monoglucuronide). Also, the observation that under certain conditions the entire amount of canine bile reacts indirectly is not in agreement with this theory (Gebhardt, 1939a,b; Deenstra, 1947, pp. 99–106).

Further, Arias (1963b) found that as much as 5–15% of the bilirubin in freshly obtained dogfish bile is unconjugated. By intravenous injection of unconjugated and conjugated bilirubin to dogfish with cannulated common bile ducts, it was found that both pigments were transferred to bile by mechanisms having transport maxima. In mammals the ability to transfer unconjugated bilirubin from liver cells to bile is apparently lacking; at least it is the rule in the species studied up to the present.

In this connection it should also be mentioned that Mistilis and Schiff (1963) studied a case of jaundice due to obstruction of one hepatic duct in a human (cf. Chapter IV,E,3) and pointed to the possibility that the jaundice in this case could be due to limitation in the ability of the human liver to transport conjugated bilirubin from blood to bile. Our knowledge of the handling of bilirubin conjugates by the liver is actually extremely limited. Only a few species have been studied. Experimental work with more species and purified preparations of various bilirubin conjugates is desirable.

Another fact which is hardly compatible with the liver passage theory is the observation that in severe cases of *acute yellow liver atrophy* (extremely severe and extended necrosis of the liver parenchyma) the diazo reaction of the serum is prompt direct (Castex and Lopez Garcia, 1940a; H. B. Stein, 1941; Pavel, 1943a,b; C. J. Watson, 1946, p. 108, Table 2; Jimenez-Diaz *et al.*, 1948). The explanation for this phenomenon is not simple; the direct reaction could be induced by the action of enzymes of necrotic liver cells; it is also possible that a sufficient number of liver cells are still functioning so that conjugation of a certain quantity of bilirubin still occurs.

A further series of observations difficult to explain by means of the liver passage hypothesis is the behavior of the diazo reaction during *experimental hepatectomy*. F. C. Mann *et al.* (1924, p. 398) and F. C. Mann and Bollman (1926, p. 689) found that the diazo reaction of serum is initially indirect after complete hepatectomy in dogs, and later becomes biphasic.

They concluded that this sufficiently proves that the mechanism of the direct and indirect Hijmans van den Bergh reactions is not simple. Therefore, it is surprising that Bollman and Mann (1932), without advancing new experimental material, expressed completely opposite views. In further studies on hepatectomized dogs and rats, Bollman and Mendez (1955) initially detected an indirect reaction which gradually became delayed, but never really direct. Partition chromatographic investigation of serum showed the presence of two pigments. The dominating pigment was CHCl$_3$ soluble and exhibited a gradually accelerating indirect reaction.

Bollman (1958) found small amounts of diglucuronide and correspondingly greater amounts of monoglucuronide in experimental jaundice after carbon tetrachloride poisoning. Billing's (1955b) findings are also of interest in this respect. She infused rats intravenously with large amounts of bilirubin, exceeding the excretion capacity of the liver. The animals, whose common bile duct was catheterized, retained pigment I in the blood and excreted pigment II with the bile. Royer (1943, pp. 156–157) demonstrated that the serum of partially hepatectomized rats reacted directly.

Hoffman et al. (1960) and Schoenfield et al. (1961) both found that bilirubin monoglucuronide most often constituted over 50% of the total bilirubin of the serum of hepatectomized dogs and rats. Schalm et al. (1962a) reported similar findings for hepatectomized rabbits as well as for rabbits without both liver and kidneys. It is thus an established fact that conjugation of bilirubin takes place to a considerable extent outside the liver and that the kidneys cannot play a major role in this extrahepatic conjugation of bilirubin and glucuronic acid. Alican and Hardy (1962) studied the bilirubin in the lymph and blood plasma of dogs with biliary obstruction and found elevation of both the indirect and the direct diazo reactions. The direct reaction was often higher in the serum than in simultaneous samples of thoracic duct lymph and liver lymph.

That other factors besides the condition of liver cells, such as the diet, may play a role was shown by Bonetti and Verme (1960) in rat experiments. Liver necrosis was produced by vitamin E-deficient diet, and the bilirubin conjugates were determined with Schachter's solvent partition method. One group of rats developed jaundice when they reached the weight of 176 g (group I), another first at a weight of 199 g (group II). Although the two groups exhibited the same histological liver picture, the serum bilirubin was much lower in group I than in group II. Fractionation of the bilirubin was only possible in the strongly icteric group II where 50% of the pigment was identified as monoglucuronide. If rats fed a vitamin E-deficient diet with 5% casein were subjected to ligature of the common bile duct, their serum bilirubin contained 40–60% mono-glucuronide on the second–third day. In rats on a normal diet the corresponding figures were 20–30%.

Schoenfield and Bollman (1963) studied rat fistula bile, isolated rat liver, liver slices incubated with bilirubin, and hepatectomized dogs. Bilirubin fractionation was carried out with reverse phase chromatography according to Cole and Lathe and with paper chromatography according to Schmid's method. The evidence favored the theory that pigment I is really bilirubin monoglucuronide and that it is formed solely in extrahepatic sites. In the dog, pigment II—the diglucuronide—was formed only within the liver.

Yet another series of observations difficult to explain by means of the liver passage theory is the *development of the indirect diazo reaction before the direct* one in the serum of dogs and rabbits with *experimental obstruction of the bile ducts* (Lepehne, 1921b; Retzlaff, 1923a,b; Kodama, 1925; Davies and Dodds, 1927; Barron and Bumstead, 1928; Griffiths and Kaye, 1930a). Indirect or biphasic reaction can be observed in dogs for a few hours and in rabbits for 24 hours or more. This is difficult to reconcile with the theory of liver passage because it was shown (Shafiroff *et al.*, 1939; Chapter IV,C,3) that bilirubin, responsible for the initial hyperbilirubinemia, is furnished by the liver lymph during obstructive jaundice. Contrary to this, bilirubin retention is insignificant and develops only later.

Schalm and Schulte (1953a) questioned the value of earlier observations because they were obtained with rather primitive analytical methods, and the cystic duct had not been closed. These authors performed some experiments on rabbits in which the ductus choledochus, as well as the cystic duct, had been ligated. They determined the total bilirubin and direct bilirubin (10 minute bilirubin). In examining the data presented, it can be seen (Table III, p. 1018) that the first increase of total bilirubin is due to indirect bilirubin. The latter shows a significant increase within the first 75 minutes. During the same time direct bilirubin did not show significant increase. The direct reaction started to increase after 2 hours, but accounted for only 15% of the total bilirubin at that time. After this period direct bilirubin continued to increase, while the accumulation of indirect bilirubin stopped.

Further facts which are difficult to explain by the liver passage theory are certain observations made on the direct reaction in serum after *intravenous injections of pure bilirubin solutions*. Cabello Ruz (1943a) studied the serum bilirubin level of normal and hepatectomized dogs before and 10–120 minutes after intravenous infusions of 100–200 mg of bilirubin. The total serum bilirubin was 12–14 mg/100 ml after 10 minutes, and 1.1–1.5 mg after 120 minutes in normal dogs. Corresponding values were 11–20 mg and 5–6 mg per 100 ml in hepatectomized animals. Direct bilirubin determined by the method of Malloy and Evelyn was 50–60% in normal animals and 18–21% in hepatectomized ones. Thus, it can be seen that 50–60% of injected indirect bilirubin is converted into direct bilirubin within 2 hours in normal dogs. Although this amount is somewhat depressed in hepatectomized animals, conversion still occurs. Cabello Ruz (1943b) studied bilirubin transport through surviving toad liver in perfusion studies by adding bilirubin to the perfusion fluid. Similar experiments were performed on eviscerated hind quarters of toads. A 37% increase of direct reaction was observed in the liver experiments when 2–3 mg bilirubin per 100 ml perfusion fluid was used. The increase was only 10% in eviscerated preparations.

Snapp et al. (1944, 1947) showed that intravenous injections of aqueous alkaline bilirubinate solutions induced hyperbilirubinemia with indirect reaction in dogs. However, hyperbilirubinemia with direct reaction occurred when normal dog plasma was mixed with the bilirubin solution and a sufficient amount of alkali was added to make this mixture direct reacting before injection. Kühn et al. (1954) found that intravenous administration of aqueous alkaline bilirubin solutions always caused hyperbilirubinemia of the indirect type in humans and in animals. Increase of direct diazo reaction, gradually advancing and reaching its maximum 2 hours after injection, was observed in rabbits and guinea pigs poisoned with CCl_4 and in one patient with cirrhosis of the liver. Schalm et al. (1962b) found a well marked increase in the conjugated bilirubin in serum in three humans after intravenous loading with 100 mg bilirubin. In one of the patients 29% of the serum bilirubin consisted of diglucuronide 1 hour after the loading. Schalm and Weber (1964) found significant quantities of conjugated bilirubin in the blood after massive bilirubin loading in men and rabbits as well as in severe hemolytic anemia. The percentage of conjugated bilirubin reached as high as 50% of total bilirubin in some of these cases.

Jimenez-Diaz et al. (1948) determined total and direct bilirubin contents of arterial and venous blood of various organs in dogs with experimental bile duct closure. The authors concluded that present assumptions concerning the direct and indirect bilirubin need thorough revision. Montanari and Bracaloni's earlier (1931b) experiments of a similar nature also showed completely irregular variations; however, this could be attributed to the inadequate analytical technique employed.

Tenhunen and Torsti (1959) recently showed that liver and kidneys as well as intestinal mucous membranes are capable of coupling bilirubin with glucuronic acid. These experiments were performed *in vitro* with surviving tissue slices of rats. This observation also indicates that the classic theory of liver passage can no longer be accepted.

The observations of Bollman and his group (see Hoffman *et al.*, 1960) are particularly important. Bile, serum, and urine of dogs and rats, as well as those of patients, were investigated by reverse phase chromatography by the method of Cole *et al.* (1954). In four samples of human gallbladder bile, about 70–85% of the total bile pigment content, consisted of pigment II (diglucuronide), whereas the rest was pigment I (monoglucuronide). This gallbladder bile was obtained by surgery. Similar results were obtained in the fistula bile of seven dogs and four rats. Free bilirubin was found in small amounts in some rats, but was completely absent in dogs and in the patients. However, small amounts of free bilirubin also appeared regularly in the bile of dogs or rats when the biliary bilirubin content was increased four- to sixfold by intravenous injections of hemoglobin or bilirubin.

Monoglucuronide was the predominating pigment in the serum of 14 *hepatectomized* dogs; free bilirubin was present in only one case. Monoglucuronide was eliminated with the urine. The same pigment distribution was found in two hepatectomized and bilaterally nephrectomized dogs. Thus, it can be concluded that in the dog the kidneys cannot be held responsible for extrahepatic bilirubin conjugation. In addition, ten hepatectomized rats were studied, three completely eviscerated and five bilaterally nephrectomized. Four of these rats were given intravenous bilirubin infusions. Both mono- and diglucuronide were detectable in the serum of all rats with intact kidneys. Diglucuronide was absent in nephrectomized rats. Free bilirubin predominated in all animals with the exception of one case. Postoperative bilirubin injections did not significantly alter this pigment distribution in the serum of dogs and rats.

Experimental obstructive icterus was obtained by ligation of the common bile duct and simultaneous cholecystectomy in 22 dogs. In some of the animals the lymphatic vessels of the liver were drained. Within the first 72 hours after ligature a rapid increase of direct reacting pigment was observed in lymph and blood; diglucuronide made up 56–84% of the total bilirubin. This predominance of the diglucuronide lasted for 3–5 weeks. *Later*, however, monoglucuronide prevailed and made up 56–68% of the total bilirubin. Experimental hepatocellular icterus was produced in two dogs by ethionine feeding (15 mg per kg per day) and in two others by CCl_4 administration (1 ml per kg per day). Monoglucuronide predominated in the serum of all four animals (57–69% of total bilirubin; the average maximum reached was 3.34 mg bilirubin per 100 ml). Chromatographic separation of the pigments of the bile gave normal pictures in all four dogs.

Schoenfield *et al.* (1961) isolated pigment I chromatographically from icteric serum of hepatectomized dogs and identified it as bilirubin monoglucuronide. With this, direct experimental evidence of extrahepatic bilirubin conjugation has been delivered.

The role of sulfate conjugates has been studied by Bollman's group (see Schoenfield *et al.*, 1962). Whole animals and isolated livers were studied. Both rats with bile duct obstruction (double ligation and cutting) and rats with hepatocellular damage ($CHCl_3$ poisoning) were investigated. Biliary obstruction of 24 hours duration (acute) and more chronic occlusion (6–10 days) were included in the experiments. After administration of 100 μg of $S^{35}O_4$ the conjugates were fractionated by means of partition chromatography (P. G. Cole *et al.*, 1954) and the phases thus obtained were subjected to further separation. For this purpose diazotation was carried out and the azo pigments were fractionated by phase separation according to Schachter (1959) followed by paper chromatography. Bile from normal rats contained 10–20% mono- and 80–90% diglucuronide, and this ratio remained unchanged after chloroform poisoning. In serum from rats with acute biliary obstruction there was 20–40% mono- and 60–70% diglucuronide, whereas the corresponding figures for chronic obstruction and hepatocellular damage were 50–70% and 20–50%, respectively. The monoglucuronide fraction was free from radioactive SO_4 but the diglucuronide fraction contained significant amounts of radioactivity. The radioactive subfraction was resistant toward β-glucuronidase and exhibited increase after $CHCl_3$ poisoning. The percentage of the diglucuronide fraction bound to sulfate was essentially the same in bile from normal rats and perfused rat liver preparations and in serum from rats with acute obstruction. In chronic obstruction and hepatocellular damage this percentage increased considerably. Bilirubin monoglucuronide was absent from the bile from isolated rat livers.

Schalm *et al.* (1962a) and Weber *et al.* (1963) doubted the existence of a bilirubin monoglucuronide and thought that pigment I is more likely a labile equimolecular complex of bilirubin and its diglucuronide. Gregory (1963) came to a similar conclusion. If this is correct, the occurrence of pigment I in hepatectomized animals implies that formation of bilirubin diglucuronide takes place outside the liver, and that the classical "liver passage hypothesis" is completely misleading and many current views must be modified. Gregory (1963) is aware of this implication. Schoenfield and Bollman (1963) strongly doubt that pigment I is not a monoglucuronide and believe that at least in the dog and rat bilirubin diglucuronide is only formed in the liver. Intensified studies on the nature of pigment I and the site of formation of different bilirubin conjugates are required.

Lathe (1965*) discussed the composition of pigment I and drew attention to the observation of Weber *et al.* (1963) that a pigment with chromatographic behavior like pigment I can be prepared by alkaline hydrolysis of bilirubin diglucuronide or by addition of bilirubin to a solution of the diglucuronide in serum. This suggests that either the acyl glucuronide group can migrate or that pigment I is a complex of bilirubin and its diglucuronide. If the first possibility can be rejected two questions remain: What is the behavior of the true monoglucuronide? What is the basis of complex formation between bilirubin and its diglucuronide?

According to C. J. Watson *et al.* (1958), conjugated bilirubin is more easily reduced to urobilinogen than to free bilirubin by the intestinal flora. However, the reason for this is not completely clear. It is possible that solubility differences are responsible for this finding.

The occurrence of bilirubin conjugates *varies with the species.* Heikel *et al.* (1960) found that about 50% of bile bilirubin is found as monoglucuronide in the rabbit, the other half as diglucuronide. This is a much higher percentage of monoglucuronide than found in man and the dog. Also in serum from icteric rabbits the monoglucuronide dominates, and in case of icterogenin jaundice 41% of the serum bilirubin was unconjugated bilirubin. In the horse the conjugation of bilirubin seems to be quite variable. In normal horses Cornelius *et al.* (1960b) found 0.2–6.2 (average 2.7) mg total bilirubin and 0–0.4 (0.1) mg conjugated (1-minute) bilirubin per 100 ml of serum. In four horses with verified hepatocellular damage and total bilirubin between 6 and 13 mg per 100 ml, the 1 minute bilirubin was below 1 mg per 100 ml. Later C. E. Cornelius (personal communication, 1961) observed a horse with hepatocellular jaundice where as much as 40% of the total serum bilirubin was conjugated. Other species have not yet been subjected to studies in this respect, but such investigations would be important to elucidate the biological role of the bilirubin conjugates.

Billing *et al.* (1963) studied hepatic transport of bilirubin in the rat and the distribution of bilirubin and its conjugates in the body of the rat after i.v. loading with free and conjugated bilirubin. Whereas 90% of the bilirubin of the blood was unconjugated after infusion of free bilirubin, 40–60% of the hepatic bilirubin was conjugated under these circumstances; the higher the infused doses of bilirubin, the lower was the percentage of conjugation of the liver bilirubin. The excretion capacity of the rat liver was quite similar for free and conjugated bilirubin, the T_m being ca. 50 μg/minute/100 g body weight. The ratio between the total amount of bilirubin present in the body and the serum bilirubin concentration was, however, twice as high after infusion of conjugated bilirubin as after infusion of free bilirubin, pointing toward a more effective elimination of the latter.

Recently strong support has accumulated for the theory that free (indirect) *bilirubin is toxic* to tissue cells (especially nerve cells), as well as to bacterial enzymes. On the contrary, conjugated (direct) bilirubin seems to be completely harmless. In plants Deysson and Charbonnier (1953) found that bilirubin cancels the toxic effect of sodium cholate on the meristem cells of the onion (*Allium cepa* L.) in concentrations of 4 mg per 100 ml. Day (1954) demonstrated, in *in vitro* experiments, that the respiration of brain tissue is retarded by free bilirubin. Zetterström and Ernster (1956) found, *in vitro,* that free bilirubin in concentrations higher than 3×10^{-4} moles paralyzes phosphorylation processes of tissue respiration by rat liver mitochondria. Hermann (1957) and Baumgärtel (1958b) demonstrated that free bilirubin, but not the glucuronides, inactivates the bacterial enzyme streptolysine. Furthermore, Baumgärtel found that free bilirubin completely suppresses methylene blue reduction by *Escherichia coli,* as well as tryptophan oxidation by *Bacillus subtilis.* Conjugated bilirubin was absolutely inactive. This author also found that bilirubin concentrations lower than about 2.5 mg per 100 ml (4.3×10^{5} moles per liter or 0.043 μmoles per ml) stimulated respiration rate of *B. subtilis* as measured in the Warburg apparatus, but higher concentrations caused definite retardation.

Labbe *et al.* (1959) found that bilirubin concentrations of 0.23 to 1.4 μmoles per ml inhibit *in vitro* synthesis of heme from iron and protoporphyrin catalyzed by soluble enzyme preparations from rat liver, and heme synthesis in rat liver homogenates. Rozdilsky (1961a,b) and Rozdilsky and Olszewski (1961) found that free bilirubin is responsible for both neural lesions and lesions of the gastrointestinal canal in experimental animals. Further, Bernstein and Landing (1962) observed necrotic lesions in the gastrointestinal tract, spleen, renal medulla, adrenals, testes, respiratory tract, mucous glands, and bone marrow of newborn infants with kernicterus. They studied 69 newborns with kernicterus, among whom 44 were prematures, and a further 50 newborns without kernicterus, among whom 30 were prematures. The necrotic lesions in the organs were considerably more pronounced in the patients with kernicterus than in the control group, and the authors concluded that the necroses were more likely caused by the hyperbilirubinemia than by asphyxia or infection.

Biesold *et al.* (1962) studied the effect of unconjugated bilirubin in concentrations occurring in the brain in kernicterus, on the respiration of rat brain homogenates *in vitro.* They employed bilirubin concentrations between 60 and 80 μmoles (3.6 and 4.8 mg per 100 ml) in brain homogenates with succinate, pyruvate–fumarate, or α-ketoglutarate and found inhibitions of respiration of 48, 58, and 68%, respectively. Bilirubin concentrations as low as between 10 and 20 μmoles (0.6–1.2 mg per 100 ml) caused demonstrable inhibition of the respiration of the rat brain homogenates. There was no difference between homogenates of brain of newborn rats and adult rats. Preparations of brain mitochondria showed respiratory inhibition in the same range of bilirubin concentration as the brain homogenates, but somewhat more marked. Bilirubin concentrations in the range 60–80 μmoles also uncoupled oxidative phosphorylation as well as respiration.

Behrman and Hibbard (1964) studied the influence of increased unconjugated serum bilirubin on the oxygen uptake of the peritoneum in newborn Rhesus monkeys by means of polarography. They employed fine platinum oxygen electrodes placed between loops of bowel. Serum bilirubin was elevated by infusion of a 200 mg/100 ml solution of bilirubin in saline-sodium carbonate. The bilirubin dose was 2–4 mg per kg body weight, and serum bilirubin concentrations of 30–40 mg per 100 ml were reached. The duration of the experiments was between 3.5 and 10 hours. When serum bilirubin exceeded 30 mg per 100 ml, the peritoneal concentration of molecular oxygen decreased gradually and stabilized itself on a lower level—30–50% of the initial level—in about 1 hour.

The effect of bilirubin on animal cells in tissue culture was investigated by Kikuchi (1961*) and Dubin et al. (1965*). Kikuchi worked with bilirubin concentrations ranging from 0.1 to 3.0 mg/100 ml culture medium (1.7–52 μmoles per liter). He found a slight inhibitory effect on rat ascites hepatoma cell cultures, but no effect on HeLa cells, fibroblasts, and monkey kidney cells. Dubin et al. added serum albumin to the cultures and used much higher bilirubin concentrations, up to 25 mg/100 ml (430 μmoles per liter). They found no adverse effects on macrophage cultures after 48 hours of incubation. If 30 mg bilirubin per 100 ml (515 μmoles per liter) was used, the macrophages were however, killed.

Several investigators have studied the *biosynthesis of bilirubin glucuronic acid esters*, including uridine diphosphoglucuronic acid transferase (UDP-transferase), the enzyme responsible for the transfer of glucuronic acid from uridine diphosphoglucuronic acid (UDPGA) to various acceptors. This enzyme system consists of the heat stable coenzyme, UDPGA and the heat sensitive enzyme UDP-transferase, also called UDP-transglucuronylase or bilirubin-glucuronyl-transferase. The enzyme system is attached to liver microsomes, but also occurs in the kidneys and gastrointestinal mucosa in smaller concentrations. It not only catalyzes glucuronic acid coupling of bilirubin, but also the formation of glucuronides of other substances, such as *o*-aminophenol. The formation of glucuronide proceeds according to the equation: uridine diphosphoglucuronic acid (UDPGA) + acceptor → glucuronide–conjugate + uridine diphosphate (UDP). Glucuronic acid is formed by oxidation of glucose contained in the uridine coenzyme (UDPG → UDPGA). Schematic representation of the process involved is given in Fig. 42.

Grodsky and Carbone (1957) showed in rat liver homogenates that uridine diphosphoglucuronic acid (UDPGA) activates the coupling of bilirubin to glucuronic acid, but this process is inhibited by borneol. The pigment so produced is split by β-glucuronidase. Besides the liver, the

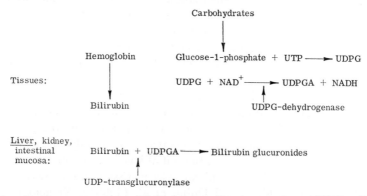

Fig. 42. Enzymatic routes of bilirubin coupling in organisms. UDPG = Uridine diphosphoglucose; UTP = uridine triphosphate; UDPGA = uridine diphosphoglucuronic acid; UDP = transglucuronylase is also called bilirubin-glucuronyl-transferase or UDP-transferase; NAD$^+$ = nicotinamide adenine dinucleotide; NADH = reduced nicotinamide adenine dinucleotide.

kidneys were also capable of coupling. Schmid *et al.* (1957a), Lins (1957), and Arias and London (1957) confirmed these findings in similar experiments. Arias and London (1957), Lathe and Walker (1957a,b, 1958a,b) as well as Schmid *et al.* (1958a) found that the UDPGA-transferase system of the liver shows a considerably decreased activity in newborns, and in patients and rats with congenital, nonhemolytic jaundice with indirect diazo reaction. Recently Tenhunen and Torsti (1959) showed that the intestinal mucous membrane can also couple bilirubin with glucuronic acid. This was confirmed by I. H. Stevenson and Dutton (1962).

Lathe and Walker (1958b) demonstrated that serum from infants and from pregnant women definitely inhibits coupling of bilirubin by rat liver homogenates *in vitro*. Similar observations were made for the coupling of various steroids. Also, serum of older children with nonhemolytic jaundice and indirect hyperbilirubinemia (Crigler-Najjar syndrome) showed similar characteristics (Peterson and Schmid, 1957). Dutton and Greig (1957) and Dutton (1958a,b) investigated the UDPGA- transferase system of various organs in guinea pigs, rabbits, mice, and rats. Using menthol and o-aminophenol as substrates, fetal liver of these animals, as well as human fetus, showed low values at the age of 3–4 months. Stevenson and Dutton (1962) found that bilirubin and o-aminophenol are coupled with glucuronic acid by the same enzyme system. Robinson and Williams' (1958) investigations on cats indicate that the UDPGA-transferase system does not seem to play the same role in all mammal species. Talafant and Továrek (1959a,b) studied the influence of various factors on the degree of bilirubin conjugation by liver homogenates *in vitro*.

Driscoll *et al.* (1959) demonstrated by means of intravenous injection of C^{14} labeled compounds into bile fistula dogs that glucose is several hundred times more effective as precursor of bilirubin glucuronide than glucuronic acid itself. This supports the view that UDPG and not glucuronic acid is the direct precursor of the bilirubin–glucuronides. Vest and Streiff (1959) studied the conjugation of the acetanilide metabolite N-acetyl-p-aminophenol in newborn and found it to be incomplete just as that of bilirubin. Both these conjugation deficiencies were ascribed to the deficient UDPGA-transferase system of the newborn liver.

Isselbacher (1961) and van Leusden *et al.* (1962) have shown that one has to distinguish between three *different glucuronyl transferase systems:* (1) forming ester glucosides, (2) forming O-glucosides, and (3) forming N-glucosides. In Gunn rats where bilirubin glucuronide formation is deficient, the p-nitrophenyl glucuronide formation was found to be normal in liver microsome preparations.

The question whether bilirubin monoglucuronide is an intermediate step in the formation of diglucuronide by the liver is discussed by Billing (1961a,b), who believed that this is the case, but admits that the evidence is incomplete.

Arias (1963a) studied the role of glucuronide formation for the transport of various compounds from the intestinal lumen to the blood using normal and UDP-transferase deficient rats (Gunn rats). They found that in Gunn rats all preparations of intestinal mucosa as well as inverted intestinal sacs had a markedly reduced ability to form glucuronides. This supports the view that the biosynthesis of glucuronides in the intestinal mucosa is similar to that in the liver.

Dutton (1963) compared glucuronide synthesis in the developing mammalian and avian liver and found that the chick embryo liver resembles the adult mammal liver in this respect rather than the liver of the mammalian fetus. UDP-transferase is formed early in the development of the liver of the chick embryo, whereas it is deficient in the new-born guinea pig and mouse. This finding underlines once more the importance of species differences in bile pigment metabolism.

Dutton (1964*) discussed the specificity of UDP-glucuronyl trans-ferases and found striking differences in rate, order of appearance during fetal development, and activity toward different substrates (o-amino-phenol, p-nitrophenol, phenolphthalein, 4-methyl umbelliferone, biliru-bin) in different species (rat, mouse, guinea pig, rabbit, cat, man). These observations are most simply explained by the assumption of multiple UDP-glucuronyltransferases—from species to species as well as within any one species.

The possibility of *hormonal influences* on bilirubin conjugation be-comes actual after Lazard and Sobotka's (1962) experiments in normal and hypophysectomized rats after intravenous loading with unconjugated bilirubin (48 mg per kg body weight). While normal rats did not develop jaundice, hypophysectomized ones became severely jaundiced, including jaundice of the brain. Similar experiments in other species including investigations of the conjugation state of the serum bilirubin are necessary.

In studies on rats with fresh biliary obstruction Sommerhalder et al. (1962a,b), using a modified reverse phase chromatography without protein precipitation, found dominance of their γ-fraction over their β-fraction. Fulop et al. (1964) found that a small fraction of the conjugated bilirubin in the plasma of humans and dogs with obstructive jaundice is dialyzable, and they believe that this fraction is the source of the urinary bilirubin in jaundice (cf. Section B,1, this chapter, and Chapter VI,A,4).

Various substances—among them a number of steroids—inhibit con-jugation of bilirubin with glucuronic acid in the liver (Lathe and Walker, 1958b; Holton and Lathe, 1963*; Bevan et al., 1965*). This was demon-strated in experiments *in vitro* with liver slices. On the other hand Careddu et al. (1965*) found that the conjugation of bilirubin in the liver of the rabbit and the rat was enhanced by certain drugs (barbitu-rates, Coramin).

Important criticism of the generally used technique of quantitative estimation of bilirubin conjugates formed during *in vitro* experiments with liver slices or liver homogenates was put forward by Boerth et al. (1965*), who studied a variety of methods based on the direct diazo reaction. The figures for bilirubin conjugates in liver homogenates ob-tained by reliable technique by Boerth et al. were much lower than those found with the original methods published by most investigators study-ing liver homogenates. Boerth et al. further found that control flasks incubated without tissue can form "direct bilirubin" and that the protein content, pH, and turbidity of the extracts of the incubated tissue are important factors neglected by many investigators. The techniques of different authors vary considerably, some working under nitrogen to prevent oxidation of the labile conjugates, while most investigators incubate in the air. Boerth *et al.* warn against the use of diazo methods in protein-rich extracts of tissue systems and stress the necessity for better assay procedures to measure *in vitro* bilirubin conjugation. *Many data on in vitro conjugation of bilirubin are open to doubt.*

A specific method for microdetermination of bilirubin glucuronides and bilirubin glucuronyltransferase in liver tissue was described by Metge *et al.* (1964*). They diazotized with S^{35}-sulfanilic acid, performed paper chromatography, and subjected the strips to radioautography. In this way a more reliable method for the demonstration of formation of bilirubin glucuronides *in vitro* should be possible.

Brodersen (1965*) put forward an interesting hypothesis concerning bilirubin conjugation. The classical biological explanation is detoxication because unconjugated bilirubin is toxic, whereas conjugated is not. Brodersen introduces the point of view of biochemical energetics. Because of the tight binding of bilirubin to albumin the free energy of circulating bilirubin is low and chemical energy has to be put into the system to make excretion possible. This is done by the process of conjugation which utilizes energy from ATP for synthesis of the conjugate bond and brings the free energy of bilirubin back to a level where excretion is possible. The process of conjugation can thus be looked upon as one of active excretion. The presence of albumin makes it possible for the organism to transport large amounts of bilirubin without surpassing dangerous levels of unbound bilirubin. Albumin is a detoxifying agent, and the advent of albumin during evolution of animal species has been necessary for the evolution of a highly developed central nervous system.

This theory of Brodersen is supported by the finding of Schmid *et al.* (1965*) that the binding of bilirubin to human albumin is much stronger than to albumin from various rodent species (cf. Section B in this chapter). It would be interesting to study the strength of the bilirubin-albumin bond in a greater variety of species. An argument against the theory is the existence of other mechanisms of bilirubin elimination rather than excretion as conjugated bilirubin (cf. Chapter IV, Section D,4).

Summary

Hijmans van den Bergh introduced the liver passage theory of bilirubin. With the exception of a few sceptical notes, this theory was generally accepted. According to this hypothesis indirect bilirubin, produced in the reticuloendothelial system, is converted into direct bilirubin during its passage through the liver. Correspondingly, the diazo reaction of serum is indirect during hemolytic icterus, but becomes direct during obstructive or hepatocellular icterus when bile regurgitation occurs.

This theory is simple and attractive, for which it has been widely accepted. However, more critical examination of the available experimental and clinical evidence reveals facts difficult to explain. Recent discoveries on the role of free and conjugated bilirubin in the direct and indirect diazo reaction lends some support to the theory. Nevertheless, it is apparent that the theory in its present form greatly oversimplifies the problems involved.

Recently the existence of a bilirubin monoglucuronide has been doubted, and pigment I regarded as a labile equimolecular bilirubin–diglucuronide–bilirubin complex. If this is correct the classical liver-passing hypothesis is completely misleading and many current views on bilirubin metabolism will have to be modified. Current views on the role of the liver in bilirubin conjugation need revision. Circumstances are certainly much more complicated than most investigators are inclined to believe.

Recent investigations on the uridine diphosphoglucuronic acid-transferase system of the liver, kidney and gastrointestinal mucosa, and the enzymes which catalyze the coupling of bilirubin to glucuronic acid are discussed and represented schematically. The UDP-bilirubin-transferase is not identical with the enzyme system responsible for p-nitrophenol conjugation.

Furthermore, the toxicity of free (indirect) bilirubin for tissue cells (especially nerve cells) and its inactivating effect on bacterial enzymes are mentioned. Conjugated (direct) bilirubin is nontoxic.

H. Clinical Value of Direct Diazo Reaction and Fractional Determination of Unconjugated and Conjugated Bilirubin

The direct diazo reaction is used all over the world in clinical practice. Only Scandinavia, and especially Denmark, where this reaction has never got foothold, are exceptions. The method for icterus index determination introduced by the Danish investigator, Meulengracht (1918), was found to be completely satisfactory for clinical purposes—the only exception being jaundice in the newborn—and there was no need to use Hijmans van den Bergh's method.

The qualitative direct reaction is negative during hemolytic icterus, during certain forms of familial nonhemolytic hyperbilirubinemia, and during icterus neonatorum. Contrary to this, it is positive in occlusive, hepatocanalicular, and hepatocellular jaundice and the Dubin-Johnson syndrome.

McNee and Keefer (1925) state: "The qualitative reaction may enable a positive diagnosis of obstructive or hemolytic jaundice to be made. As, however, in the commonest type of jaundice (the toxic and infective group) no information of any diagnostic or prognostic value is given to the clinician." Barchi (1926), Mogena (1929), Elton (1935), and Colangiuli and Barengo (1940) expressed similar opinions. E. Schiff and Eliasberg (1922) as well as Hollos (1929) reported cases of obstructive icterus with negative direct reaction, but considered them rare exceptions.

Nowadays some investigators maintain that quantitative determination of the direct reaction has a certain clinical value; however, this contention is refuted by others.

Even sera with negative qualitative direct reaction show a certain "direct percentage" in quantitative studies (Cantarow *et al.*, 1940, 1942; Lepehne, 1942a; Cantarow and Trumper, 1945, pp. 410 and 442). For normal individuals, for hemolytic icterus, and for pernicious anemia, the following "direct percentages" were reported: 0–75%, 3–14%, and 44–67%, respectively. C. J. Watson (1956b) determined the following values for "1-minute bilirubin": normal persons, 10–20%; hemolytic icterus and heriditary nonhemolytic hyperbilirubinemia, below 10%; declining hepatitis and liver cirrhosis, 40–50%; yellow liver atrophy and neoplastic obstructive jaundice, 60–70%. Pollock (1945, 1951) and C. J. Watson (1946) found that " direct percentages" were enhanced before increase of total bilirubin during the preicteric stage of hepatitis. Verniory (1946) found a direct percentage of 14–55% in normal persons, 20% in hemolytic jaundice, 35–75% in obstructive icterus, and 55–75% in hepatocellular jaundice. C. J. Watson (1956b) emphasized the clinical significance of "1-minute bilirubin" and considered increased "1-minute bilirubin" with normal total bilirubin important, in spite of the fact that his method of serum bilirubin determination has been severely criticized (see Section D,1, this chapter). Zieve *et al.* (1951) pointed out that Watson did not consider numerical values of "1-minute bilirubin" significant when total bilirubin was normal. He only regarded increased 1-minute percentage as a sign of liver insufficiency or disease of the bile duct system. Direct percentage below 20% he considered characteristic for hemolytic icterus. Similar values were only obtained during icterus neonatorum and during some forms of nonhemolytic, hereditary hyperbilirubinemia. Values of 45–80% are characteristic for obstructive icterus and for hepatic jaundice; however, there were numerous cases of hepatitis which showed lower values.

In this connection it is to be emphasized that the technique of Malloy and Evelyn employed by Watson's group operates with high serum dilutions and uses methanol as the coupling reagent. This renders results with bilirubin concentration in or close to the normal range liable to serious error, partly because the extinctions read are very low, and partly because of inevitable, although minor, turbidity from interaction of methanol and serum proteins. Therefore, purely technical considerations render the clinical value of "1-minute bilirubin" highly questionable.

Deenstra (1948a) found considerable variations in 1-minute bilirubin percentage from day to day. He, therefore, proposed to measure this percentage at least twice consecutively. He obtained values under 20% for hemolytic icterus, whereas 40% and often higher values were found for hepatitis and bilary obstruction. As a rule, 1-minute bilirubin varied parallel to total bilirubin, with the exception that it increased with decreasing serum bilirubin during disappearing jaundice. Based on extensive clinical evidence Schaffner *et al.* (1949, 1950) stated that 1-minute bilirubin is worthless in differential diagnosis of hepatitis, cirrhosis, and bile duct closure. Values under 15% were found in hemolytic icterus. According to Schaffner *et al.*, the only value of this test in clinical diagnosis is the exclusion of hemolytic icterus and that consistently high values during fading jaundice indicate a persistent pathological process. Ducci and Roeschmann (1949) came to the same conclusion as Watson regarding the value of 1-minute bilirubin determination. Like him, they considered it of some value in individuals with normal total serum bilirubin.

Lattanzi (1948a), who measured the direct reaction after 2 hours, found it worthless in the differential diagnosis between obstructive jaundice and hepatitis. Franzini and Arnoletti (1950) who measured the direct reaction by the method of Jendrassik and Cleghorn (1936a,b) after 5 and 10 minutes, reached the same conclusions. Kilchling and Kühn (1950), Klatskin and Drill (1950), as well as Profitt and Morrison (1951), confirmed that quantitative measurements of direct diazo reaction are of little clinical value. On the other hand, Schalm's group (see Schalm and Schulte, 1950a,b, 1953a,b; Schalm and Hoogenboom, 1952; Schalm *et al.*, 1952; Schalm, 1953a,b) think that the clinical value for determination of direct reaction, by the method of Jendrassik and Cleghorn after 10 minutes, is not insignificant. They found that determination of direct bilirubin is a useful measure for heart failure during cardiac insufficiency. However, examinations of their tables reveals that total bilirubin determination would yield similar good results in this regard. They determined that even after normalization of the total bilirubin content, during disappearing hepatitis, direct reaction can increase. However, the opposite could also be observed. The determination of direct reaction was diagnostically valuable in cases of bile stone attack which proceeded without jaundice. Thus, the amount of direct bilirubin increased without a simultaneous increase of total bilirubin in a number of cases. Furthermore, the direct reaction achieved diagnostic significance for the detection of hemolytic and hereditary, nonhemolytic jaundice in which the 10-minute bilirubin percentage rate was practically always lower than 20%.

Billing (1955b) studied fourteen cases of obstructive icterus and three hepatitis cases. This author found a definite prevalence (38–62% of total bilirubin) of pigment I (monoglucuronide). Corresponding values for pigment II (diglucuronide) were 15–35%, and 18–39% for free bilirubin. Pagliardi and Gaidano (1956) and Baikie (1957) obtained similar results. The latter author found 40–60% monoglucuronide, 15–30% diglucuronide, and 20–40% bilirubin in these types of jaundice. He pointed out the wide variation range. Bollman (1958) usually found a higher percentage rate of pigment II during biliary obstruction than during hepatitis. However, according to Billing and Lathe (1958) and Schachter (1959), this is only so in very early stages of jaundice. Bollman (1958) also observed a predominance of pigment I during chlorpromazine jaundice. Mendioroz (1957) subjected the clinical material from the clinic of Varela-Fuentes at Montevideo to statistical studies; these included ca. 200 normals and ca. 300 jaundiced subjects. The diazo reaction was determined by Malloy-Evelyn's method. She concluded that the direct diazo reaction is clinically useless with adult patients. The mean "direct percentage" was 68 ± 11% in parenchymal jaundice and 74 ± 7.7% in bilary obstruction. This was, however, without clinical value because of the broad zone of overlapping.

Schachter (1959) assigned only limited clinical interest to the quantitative determination of mono- and diglucuronides, in spite of the fact that high diglucuronide concentrations were observed chiefly during obstructive icterus, and increased amounts of monoglucuronide mainly appeared during hepatic jaundice. Tisdale *et al.* (1959) investigated blood plasma of various forms of jaundice for conjugated bilirubin. The authors studied 21 cases of fetal erythroblastosis and 25 cases of hemolytic anemia of various types in adults. Increased 1-minute bilirubin was detected in 77% of the cases. The "direct percentage" was, as a rule, below 15% when complicating liver damage was absent. The 1-minute bilirubin was rarely higher than 1.2 mg/100 ml in uncomplicated hemolytic diseases and the "1-minute percentage" rarely above 20%. The major part of the serum bilirubin consisted of water soluble bilirubin conjugates (monoglucuronide), even in hemolytic icterus.

Witmanns *et al.* (1961) investigated the 10-minute bilirubin and found it to be of a certain clinical value. Gaidano and Gravario (1959) studied the ultraviolet absorption of the diazo reaction of serum bilirubin at 380 nm after 10, 60, 120, and 360 minutes and found the percentage increase of this absorption to be definitely higher in hepatocellular jaundice than in biliary occlusion.

Bollman's group (see Hoffman et al., 1960) studied a clinical material with chromatographic separation of the serum bilirubin fractions. The serum of 147 icteric patients, with total bilirubin content higher than 3 mg/100 ml, was examined. Diagnosis was confirmed either by surgery of by biopsy; 91 of the patients suffered from extrahepatic obstruction. Among these, pigment II dominated in 80. Among 29 patients with acute or subacute hepatitis and 27 with liver cirrhosis, pigment I dominated in 47, and amounted to more than 50% of the total bilirubin. Chromatography of the pigments of the bile showed normal conditions in 12 patients with hepatic jaundice. Eight patients with chlorpromazine jaundice were examined. Pigment II dominated in 4 of them and pigment I in the others. Free bilirubin was the only pigment detectable in the serum of 8 patients with constitutional liver dysfunction. Surprisingly, however, the composition of pigments of the bile was normal, and the fecal urobilinogen was also within normal limits in these eight cases. Free bilirubin was the only detectable pigment in the serum and bile of two homozygote Gunn rats with congenital jaundice. In three animals, chromatographic examination did not show any changes in the composition of serum bilirubin after bile duct ligature.

Pigment II dominated during acute and subacute bile duct obstruction. During chronic obstructions, however, pigment II gradually disappeared until finally pigment I dominated. This phenomenon could be explained by anomalous metabolism of the damaged parenchymal cells.

It is noteworthy that only a small portion of the patients with hepatocellular jaundice showed above 50% pigment II. On the other hand, more than 50% of the total bilirubin consisted of diglucuronides in the majority of patients with obstructive icterus. Pigment II content between 40% and 60% was found in both obstructive and hepatocellular jaundice. Values below 40% were only found in hepatocellular jaundice, and levels higher than 60% only in obstructive icterus. These findings indicate that under certain circumstances chromatographic serum examinations could be diagnostically valuable. However, results obtained during experimental acute and chronic obstructive icterus in dogs do not support the diagnostic value. Moreover, chromatographic tests are technically cumbersome and without clinical value according to Nosslin (1960) and Koumans and De Groote (1961).

Nosslin (1960) presented an exhaustive discussion of the clinical value of the direct diazo reaction. The impressive diagrams in his publication are divided by lines into three zones: a normal zone, a positive zone showing the values obtained in fresh cases of acute hepatitis and in bile duct obstruction, and an intermediate biphasic zone. His graphs show both data obtained by his own method, and data obtained by Malloy and Evelyn's method. Findings at various serum dilutions are also recorded. On the basis of these results Nosslin concluded that the direct reaction is worthless in the differentiation between acute parenchymal liver damage and extrahepatic obstruction. This is also true for repeated determinations. It was shown that continuing positive reaction after the jaundice disappeared had no prognostic value in acute hepatitis. Similarly, routine determinations of the direct reaction have no practical value in newborn infants.

Nevertheless, Nosslin did not completely deny the practical clinical value of the direct reaction. With serum bilirubin concentrations over 5 mg/100 ml the value of the direct reaction is questionable, but with normal serum bilirubin and light hyperbilirubinemia it may be of value. In such cases a negative direct reaction limits the differential diagnosis to the following possibilities:

(1) Overproduction jaundice, caused either by hemolysis of circulating erythrocytes or by parahematic bilirubin production.

(2) Intoxication by certain drugs, certain forms of posthepatic hyperbilirubinemia, and quiescent liver cirrhosis.

(3) Neonatal jaundice, the Crigler-Najjar syndrome, and certain forms of hereditary, nonhemolytic jaundice (defective conjugation).

When the reaction is positive, diagnosis is limited to extrahepatic bile duct obstruction, acute parenchymal damage and "intrahepatic cholestasis." Only very limited clinical conclusions can be derived when a biphasic reaction pattern is found. The majority of the chronic hepatocellular diseases fall into this group.

Tisdale and Welch (1962) found that separate determination of bilirubin and its glucuronides with Eberlein's simplified solvent partition method was of little diagnostic or prognostic value. McGill *et al.* (1962) studied 53 jaundiced patients with Schachter's solvent partition method and found it of limited clinical value. Obstructive jaundice tends to produce a proportionally higher elevation of pigment II than of pigment I, and after relief of obstruction pigment II is cleared faster than pigment I. Kupershtein and Roomere (1962) reported studies from the Soviet Union. They used a modification of Jendrassik-Gróf's method, with sulfanilamide instead of sulfanilic acid, in children with infectious hepatitis. In general both the direct and the indirect bilirubin were elevated, but the values for the indirect showed the best correlation with the severity of the disease. Jardin *et al.* (1963) studied 47 jaundiced patients with Schachter's solvent partition method and Schmid's paper chromatographic method. Evaluation was difficult because of lack of sensitivity and repro-ducibility, but despite overlapping the percentage of pigment B was found to be higher in patients with posthepatic jaundice than in cases with hepatic or prehepatic icterus. The determination was of some value in the differential diagnosis of jaundice. Galambos (1963) stated, in dis-cussing the paper of Jardin *et al.*: "In the large majority of patients, the proportion of the elevated direct and indirect reacting serum bilirubin is of no help whatever . . . ", and expressed the belief that this disap-pointing result is due to the complicated pathogenesis of jaundice, especially the role of the lymph.

Schalm and Weber (1964) reported 3 cases of hemolytic jaundice with high quantities of conjugated serum bilirubin. Their case 1, suffering from autoimmune hemolytic anemia, had total serum bili-rubin 2.6 mg/100 ml and conjugated serum bilirubin 1.0 mg/100 ml. Case 2 suffered from AsH_3 poisoning and had total bilirubin 25 mg/100 ml; conjugated bilirubin was demonstrable on reverse phase partition chromatography on columns (P. G. Cole *et al.*'s method, 1954) during the first 3 days after poisoning. This patient recovered. Their case 3 was a fatal case of AsH_3 poisoning showing similar results as case B; here autopsy, including histological examination, showed normal liver. Further, these authors subjected both humans and rabbits to massive loading with unconjugated bilirubin intravenously and found that con-siderable quantities of conjugated bilirubin were present in the serum after the loading (cf. Section J, this chapter). Schalm and Weber empha-sized that appearance of conjugated bilirubin in the blood is a regular symptom of gross overloading of the organism with unconjugated bili-rubin, due either to artificial loading or to gross hemolysis, and that its appearance is quite independent of liver insufficiency.

The clinical value of the Sephadex-formamide method of Harboe (1965)—cf. Sections A and F, this chapter—remains to be decided. Pre-liminary studies showed differences in the mutual relation of his three bilirubin fractions in hepatitis, cirrhosis, and neoplastic occlusion.

Sommerhalder *et al.* (1962a,b) and Kuenzle *et al.* (1963a,b, 1964a,b) claimed that partition chromatography of serum bilirubin without previous protein precipitation yields results of clinical importance. They found that their γ-fraction is larger than their β-fraction in beginning occlusive jaundice. In hepatitis they found their α-fraction to dominate during the initial phase, their β-fraction during the middle phase, and their δ-fraction during the healing phase. In hemolytic disease their β-fraction dominated. Predominance of their β-fraction over all pigments associated with a low δ-fraction indicated severe liver damage.

A number of authors consider determination of the indirect bilirubin by means of chloroform extraction clinically significant (Varela Fuentes and Viana, 1935a; Fiessinger and Bardós, 1936; Heilbrun and Hubbard, 1940; Lopez Garcia, 1943, p. 87 et seq). The chloroform soluble bilirubin was 50–80% of total bilirubin during hemolytic icterus, 15–25% during obstructive jaundice, and 15–60% during hepatitis. Concentrations around 60% were determined during cardiac jaundice. Mendioroz (1957) concluded, based on a large body of clinical material, that the chloroform soluble bilirubin is of little practical value. Osipov (1962), working from the Soviet Union with the method of Varela Fuentes, found that an increase in the indirect fraction in hepatitis indicates severe inflammation of the liver and grave prognosis.

Finally, it should be mentioned that certain investigators have used determinations of glucuronic acid and β-glucuronidase in serum and urine in the clinical study of jaundice.

T. Wegmann and Marogg (1959) proposed to differenciate between biliary obstruction and hepatocellular jaundice by determining the serum bilirubin and glucuronic acid concentration after hydrolysis. The ratio of glucuronic acid/bilirubin should be high for obstructive icterus, whereas for hepatic icterus it should be low. Wegmann and Marogg consider this test superior to all differential diagnostic tests known to this time. K. Beck and Kühn (1959) and Beck and Kiani (1960) found impaired glucuronide formation in nonhemolytic functional hyperbilirubinemia, and K. and E. Beck (1960) found a decreased glucuronide excretion in hemolytic jaundice. K. Beck et al. (1962) found that the excretion of glucuronic acid with the urine after loading with menthol was decreased in 14 patients with hemolytic jaundice of varying genesis. After splenectomy the glucuronic acid excretion increased, but did not reach the normal level. Vest and Fritz (1961) demonstrated that the glucuronide formation is depressed in the acute phase of hepatitis and recovers during the later stages of this disease. Goldbarg et al. (1959) studied the β-glucuronidase of serum, urine, and tissues in health and disease and found that most patients with increased serum-glucuronidase activity exhibited evidence of liver dysfunction. Finally it should be mentioned that Yokoe (1957) had already earlier studied the behavior of glucuronic acid in liver diseases in a comprehensive paper which is, however, unfortunately only published in Japanese with a brief English summary.

The most recent investigations comprise one group of investigators continuing the use of current analytical techniques on clinical material and trying to attach clinical significance to their results, as well as another group of authors with a critical attitude toward these methods of fractionate determination of bilirubin and its conjugates; they regard these methods as too unreliable to yield information of clinical value.

McGill *et al.* (1962*) compared fractionation of serum bilirubin with Schachter's method by chromatographic determination on 53 patients with different forms of jaundice. Their most remarkable finding was the complete absence of diglucuronide during subsiding hepatitis. Their figures for pigment I were 10–15% higher with Schachter's method than with chromatography. They conclude (McGill *et al.*, 1962*, p. 264): "Despite improved understanding of the chemistry of bilirubin, the kinetics of the van den Bergh method remains complex and obscure. Variations of pH, reagent strength, length of diazotization and particularly protein binding make separation of conjugated and unconjugated bilirubin by any modification of the van den Bergh method impossible. There is no precise method by which the relative amounts of Pigment A derived from unconjugated bilirubin and from Pigment I can be determined. In particular, the reactivity of conjugated bilirubin will vary from sample to sample and the amount of Pigment I which couples without alcohol is not known."

Pittera and Cassia (1964*) separated two fractions of free bilirubin called "bilirubin I" and "bilirubin II" by means of partition chromatography of $CHCl_3$ extracts of jaundiced sera. The fraction bilirubin I was further separated into two fractions, A and B, by means of paper chromatography. They found that fraction A dominated in normal sera, as well as in sera from patients with hemolytic and hepatocellular jaundice, whereas bilirubin II and fraction B were present in about equal amounts in obstructive jaundice sera. These interesting observations are somewhat difficult to bring into agreement with current concepts.

Schoenfield *et al.* (1964*) compared the results of column partition chromatography and the extraction methods of Schachter and Eberlein with Malloy-Evelyn's diazo test (direct reaction after 5 minutes) in a study of 75 sera from 26 patients with proved extrahepatic biliary occlusion and 75 sera from 20 patients with histologically verified hepatocellular jaundice. They found a certain parallelism between the "5-minute bilirubin" and the three other methods, which, however, did not give identical results and clearly did not measure the same bilirubin fractions. No significant correlation was found among the results of any of the three partition methods and either the presence of biliary occlusion or hepatocellular damage or the results of standard liver function tests. The major problems in this area are concerned with methods and the variable pathological processes responsible for jaundice. Clinical interpretation is at present hindered by insufficient understanding of basic phenomena pertaining to bile pigments, particularly regarding structure and the significance of pigment I. The advisability of additional chemical studies based on existing methods and concepts is questioned.

Ibbot and O'Brien (1964*) studied the technique of Eberlein's extraction method in detail, improved the method, and investigated the sera of 35 premature and 73 full term infants during the first 10 days of life. They further performed reverse phase chromatography on extracts of the same sera for comparison. They concluded that neither the original nor the improved Eberlein method was reliable—especially regarding pigment I determinations. They found mean values for monoglucuronide of only 0.3 mg/100 ml and total bilirubin of 14.8 mg/100 ml with their improved Eberlein method. They regard all previous conclusions on the significance of the monoglucuronide in jaundice of the newborn based on Eberlein's method as invalid.

Zieve (1964*) admitted the superiority of Jendrassik-Gróf's method over Malloy-Evelyn methods, but found, nevertheless, that the frequency distribution curves for total and direct bilirubin in normal subjects and in various categories of jaundice were surprisingly similar in materials based on these two types of diazo methods. This was well documented by comparison of his own curves with those of Nosslin (1960). In spite of his admission that the J-G type of method is superior, he continued to recommend the 1-minute modification of the M-E technique.

Osipov (1964*) studied material from 138 patients from Leningrad with epidemic hepatitis, 21 with obstructive jaundice, 38 with cholecystitis, and 14 with hemolytic jaundice as well as 60 normal subjects, employing Eberlein's method. In epidemic hepatitis bilirubin conjugates dominated—in about half the cases monoglucuronide was the main pigment at the height of the disease. In obstructive jaundice the diglucuronide dominated.

Pagliardi and Gaidano (1965*) studied the ultraviolet absorption of the diazo reaction of sera after extraction with butanol and reextraction with 0.03 N NaOH and found (after adjustment to pH 8) a maximum at 380–400 nm which was only seen in cases of hepatocellular jaundice and not in normal subjects or cases of occlusive jaundice.

Colombo and Bonomo (1965*) subjected extracts of sera from icteric patients to inverse phase chromatography, purified the fractions of pigments I and II and studied the alkali lability of the conjugates. They could not demonstrate any difference between sera from patients with hepatocellular and occlusive jaundice.

Verme and Campari (1965*) produced experimental liver damage in rats by various methods—$BeSO_4$, dibutylenedichloride, vitamin E deficiency, and protein deficiency—and subjected other rats to experimental bile duct occlusion and partial liver resection. They performed fractionate bilirubin determinations on the sera of the rats using Schachter's method. They found that the capacity of the liver for bilirubin conjugation was widely independent of the presence of histologically demonstrable liver damage and that resection of as much as three-fourths of the liver resulted only in a small decrease of the conjugation capacity as measured by Schachter's method.

Lathe (1965*) expressed the opinion that the obscure state of the pigment I problem makes the clinical use of pigment I analyses premature.

Summary

Whereas the clinical value of the direct diazo reaction is highly esteemed by some investigators, others criticize it vigorously. The value of this determination is unanimously recognized for the diagnosis of hemolytic jaundice. Its value in the diagnosis of nonhemolytic hereditary jaundice is questionable since figures of the same order of magnitude can occur during mild cases of hepatitis. Qualitative as well as quantitative determinations have similarly limited diagnostical value and this is also the case with chromatographic and other fractionate determinations of free and conjugated bilirubin. The analytical method recently introduced by Weber and Schalm (1962) for separate determination of bilirubin and conjugated bilirubin in serum may be of some value, but material to decide this does not yet exist. The same is the case with the Sephadex-formamide method of Harboe and the reverse phase chromatographic method without protein precipitation of Kuenzle *et al.* (1963a,b, 1964a,b). Finally it is mentioned that determinations of glucuronic acid and β-glucuronidase have recently been introduced in the clinical study of jaundice.

I. Normal Serum Bilirubin

The serum bilirubin varies with age and with animal species; in addition, it is influenced by various other factors such as food intake and physical exertion; finally, it even varies during the day. Since special conditions prevail in newborns and in very young organisms, it is preferable to discuss adults and infants separately.

1. Serum Bilirubin in the Adult Human and Animal

Before discussing the normal serum bilirubin level, daytime variations and day-by-day fluctuations should be considered. It has been found that the serum bilirubin varies parallel to the serum iron. Both increase during the night and decrease during the day. The highest values can be determined after fasting in the early morning hours (Laurell, 1953; Stengle and Schade 1957). An explanation of this phenomenon could be that iron and bilirubin are both degradation products of hemoglobin, and hemoglobin degradation increases during the night (Laurell, 1953).

It has long been known that the serum bilirubin is highest after fasting and that it decreases with food intake. Gilbert and Herscher (1906), as well as Saudé (1906, p. 52), had already demonstrated this fact. The serum bilirubin concentration increased 20–200% after 24 hours of fasting (E. C. Meyer and Knüpffer, 1922; E. C. Meyer and Heinelt, 1923). However, the opposite was frequently true in patients with liver diseases; accordingly, this was called "paradoxical reaction." Perkins (1927), Jacoby (1928, 1929, 1930), Montanari and Bracaloni (1931a), Beltrametti (1932), Satke and Thums (1932), and Väyrynen (1934) obtained the same results. The last two authors, however, could not confirm the paradoxical reaction described by Meyer and Heinelt.

More recently, Brøchner-Mortensen (1935), Fellinger and Pfleger (1935), Huhtala (1937), Balzer (1953), and Brüschke and Volkheimer (1956) published investigations on the influence of food intake and fasting. The highest values were found in the morning, the lowest around 4 PM, and a definitive decrease of serum bilirubin occurred after food intake. The latter effect became more marked when the initial serum bilirubin concentration was high. Neither decrease nor increase occurred during hepatitis and bile duct obstruction. Extended fasting (24–36 hours) enhanced serum bilirubin concentration 100 to 200%. Even higher values (up to 600%) were obtained when physical exertion took place in addition to fasting. A decrease due to feeding occurred after half an hour and reached its maximum within 4–6 hours. At that point serum bilirubin concentration dropped to 50% of the starting level.

According to Beutel and Heinemann (1928), Demichelis and Giacchero (1936), Stanojévić and Arandjelović (1937), and Nolli (1938), water intake causes serum bilirubin increase in normal as well as in icteric individuals. However, these findings need further confirmation.

The cause of these variations in serum bilirubin after food intake is not entirely clear. It is possible that they are due to changes in the bile excretion. It is interesting to note that bromsulphalein sodium excretion varies similarly to bilirubin excretion (Havens *et al.*, 1950).

Muscle activity is another physiological process which influences the serum bilirubin level. A 20–40% increase in serum bilirubin takes place on exercise. The peak concentration is reached after about 30 minutes of exertion. Deutsch and Hermann (1931), Schrumpf (1932a), Verzár *et al.* (1933), Väyrynen (1934), Stanojévić and Petković (1935), Meythaler and Jennemann (1936), and Huhtala (1937) studied this phenomenon. Observations in icteric patients or in animals (e.g., horses) have not been reported.

Förster and Förster (1926) and L. Schiff (1927) investigated day-by-day fluctuations. Huhtala (1937), using a reliable analytical technique, found constant values in some individuals, whereas others showed considerable variations.

Bramanti (1948a,b) summarized the contradictory opinions regarding the influence of hormones on the serum bilirubin level. It was claimed that adrenaline causes hyperbilirubinemia. An increase in serum bilirubin content was observed in normal persons after intravenous injections of 30 mg nicotinic acid. The amount of serum bilirubin increased until it reached double that of the starting level (Mattei, 1946; Feruglio and Salvini, 1947b; M. Salvini and Feruglio, 1948). Gydell (1958, 1959) could show that when serum bilirubin concentration increases, an equimolar increase in serum iron occurs; this is especially marked in cogenital hemolytic anemia. The bilirubin concentration of duodenal fluid increases after nicotinic acid injections (Rosa and Marchionini 1949, 1950). Further more, it was reported that intravenous injections of bile salts cause moderate increase of the serum bilirubin in normal individuals (Dal Co, 1950). This was substantiated by Hoenig and Hoenigová (1959) who found that Decholin injection is followed by inhibition of the excretion of bilirubin by the liver cells. Talafant (1959a) found that potassium nicotinate inhibits the conjugation of bilirubin by liver homogenates, but only slightly. In contrast, Tetrahydrofurfurol ester of nicotinic acid shows a stronger inhibiting effect. This inhibition is too slight to explain the hyperbilirubinemia following nicotinic acid injections.

Investigations of normal serum bilirubin content in *animals* are rather scarce. It is known that bilirubin is present in the bile of a great number of vertebrates (fishes, amphibia, reptiles, birds, and mammals) (Tiedemann and Gmelin, 1826, pp. 80–81). However, few observations of its presence in the blood of normal animals have been reported.

Gilbert *et al.* (1903b) found a positive Gmelin reaction in sera of chickens, canaries, pigeons, horses, and cattle. Auché (1909) found a lower serum bilirubin content in donkeys than in horses. Varela Fuentes and Munilla (1934) could not demonstrate bilirubin in sera of normal dogs, pigs, sheep, cattle, rabbits, guinea pigs, chickens, or pigeons. Similarly, Fahrak (1948) could not find bilirubin in sera of normal mice, rats, guinea pigs, ferrets, porcupines, hamsters, cats, dogs, pigs, sheep, or goats. However, bilirubin was detected in sera of normal cattle, buffalos, mules, horses, camels, sparrows, swallows, canaries, pigeons, chickens, ducks, geese, turkeys, parrots, quails, doves, and sea birds. Varela Fuentes and Munilla (1934) used the diazo reaction as a test for bilirubin; Fahrak used, in addition, the Fouchet (1917, 1918) test.

Most investigators maintain that serum of normal dogs, rats, guinea pigs, and rabbits does not contain bilirubin (see Hijmans van den Bergh and Snapper, 1913; Hijmans van den Bergh, 1918, Beijers, 1923; Heimann, 1933;

Heller, 1933; Stanojévic and Petković, 1935; Edlund, 1948; Fahrak, 1948). However, some authors could detect traces in these animals (see van de Velde, 1927, 1929; Gianini, 1929; Orten, 1936; Orten and Smith, 1936). Lopez Garcia *et al.* (1943) observed the following bilirubin concentrations in sera of normal animals: 0.35–0.50 mg/100 ml in rabbits, 0.3–0.8 mg/100 ml in pigs, 0.4–0.5 mg/100 ml in monkeys (*Cebus paraguayensis*), 0.0–0.2 mg/100 ml in dogs, and 0.15–0.20 mg/100 ml in cats. Royer *et al.* (1941) found 0.5–3.0 mg/100 ml, and Cornelius *et al.* (1960b) 0.2–6.2 (average 2.7) mg/100 ml in normal horses. The following values have been found in normal cattle (in mg/100 ml): 1.0–7.4 (Rudra, 1946), 0.5–3.0 (Ramsay, 1946), 1.1–1.2 (Beijers, *et al.*, 1950), and 0.0–1.4 (average 0.31 mg/100 ml) (Garner, 1953).

Using the method of White (1932*) Agarawala *et al.* (1962*) found 0.14–0.34 (average 0.26) mg/100 ml in normal cattle and an average of 0.34 mg/100 ml in normal sheep in India.

Sova (1964*) reviewed the literature on serum bilirubin in horses. Values between 0.20 and 8 mg/100 ml were reported for normal horses. His personal studies comprised 33 healthy horses in which he found a serum bilirubin of 0–2, average 1.33 mg/100 ml. The concentration of "indirect bilirubin" was still higher than that of "direct."

Soliman and Amrousi (1965*) studied the serum bilirubin in 348 buffaloes and 248 camels in Egypt with the Malloy-Evelyn method. In male buffaloes aged 1–2 months the range was 0.71–1.40 (average 0.99) mg/100 ml; in male buffaloes aged 1–2 years, 0.71–1.05 (0.85); in male buffaloes aged 6–10 years, 0–1.22 (0.56); and in female buffaloes over 7 years, 0–1.22 (0.69) mg/100 ml. In male camels aged 5–7 years it was 0–1.22 (0.72) mg/100 ml and in female camels aged 5–7 years, 0–1.22 (0.65) mg/100 ml. The authors also studied young sheep and cattle in which they found similar values. Medway *et al.* (1966*) found an average serum bilirubin of 0.43 mg/100 ml in three dolphins.

These values obtained in various mammals are contradictory. More studies with reliable analytical methods extended over more animal species would be most desirable. However, on the basis of available evidence it can be concluded that most vertebrates possess little bilirubin under normal conditions. Significant exceptions are humans, cattle, horses, and closely related species such as monkeys and mules. The findings in birds are even more contradictory and uncertain.

The bilirubin in *normal adult humans* has been the subject of extensive investigations. The most reliable studies have been compiled in Table V.

Brøchner-Mortensen (1935) took samples early in the morning from fasting patients. Bilirubin concentration was determined by Heilmeyer

TABLE V

SERUM BILIRUBIN OF NORMAL ADULT HUMANS

Author	Year	Total no. of subjects	0–0.09	0.1–0.19	0.2–0.29	0.3–0.39	0.4–0.49	0.5–0.59	0.6–0.69	0.7–0.79	0.8–0.89	0.9–0.99	1.0–1.09	1.1–1.19	1.2–1.29	1.3–1.39	1.4–1.49	1.5–1.59	1.6–1.69	1.7–1.79	1.8–1.89	1.9–1.99	>2.0
Brøchner-Mortensen	1935	78 persons	0	3	14	25	21	9	3	1	0	2	0	0	0	0	0	0	0	0	0	0	0
Huhtala	1937	50 men	0	0	1	6	12	5	13	4	6	3	0	0	0	0	0	0	0	0	0	0	0
		50 women	0	0	4	10	11	7	8	2	4	3	1	0	0	0	0	0	0	1	0	0	0
Vaughan and Haselwood	1938	50 men	0	0	0	2	7	10	11	5	8	1	1	2	1	1	1	0	0	1	0	0	0
		50 women	0	0	4	13	16	12	2	3	0	0	1	1	1	0	0	0	0	0	0	0	0
With	1943e	50 men	0	2	3	6	5	6	3	6	8	0	1	1	0	1	0	0	0	0	2	1	0
		50 women	0	1	3	6	4	8	7	7	6	4	1	1	2	2	1	0	0	1	1	1	0
		200 patients	0	5	18	23	22	20	24	23	17	20	7	8	3	2	1	1	0	2	1	1	2
C. J. Watson	1946	27 persons	0	0	1	3	4	7	8	2	0	1	1	0	0	2	2	1	0	0	1	0	0
Zacho and Larsen	1946a	87 patients	9	6	16	15	7	6	4	4	3	1	1	0	1	2	2	1	1	1	0	0	1
Alwall	1946	383 persons	3	26	47	78	59	60	42	31	18	6	6	3	2	1	0	0	0	0	0	0	0
Raule and Grisler	1950	205 persons	0	0	7	61	54	42	29	12	0	0	0	0	0	0	0	0	0	0	0	0	0
Zieve et al.	1951	719 persons	0	1%	2%	16%	19%	20%	16%	10%	8%	3%	2%	1%	1%			1%			0		0

Josephson and Dahlberg, 1952 — Only averages and standard deviations (σ) are given for the various groups:

	20–30	16–50	60–65	over 70
257 men	$M = 1.137\ (\sigma = 0.429)$	$0.914\ (0.457)$	$0.697\ (0.235)$	$0.788\ (0.372)$
195 women	$M = 0.973\ (\sigma = 0.262)$	$0.763\ (0.300)$		$0.766\ (0.242)$

Author	Year	Total no. of subjects	0–0.09	0.1–0.19	0.2–0.29	0.3–0.39	0.4–0.49	0.5–0.59	0.6–0.69	0.7–0.79	0.8–0.89	0.9–0.99	1.0–1.09	1.1–1.19	1.2–1.29	1.3–1.39	1.4–1.49	1.5–1.59	1.6–1.69	1.7–1.79	1.8–1.89	1.9–1.99	>2.0
Weiss	1955	1002 blood donors	0	14	30	110	140	175	142	130	86	47	42	30	14	12	8	7	2	3	4	3	3
Sen Gupta and Ganguly	1955	100 Indian students	0	10	18	20	12	10	5	2	3	0	0	0	0	0	0	0	0	0	0	0	0
O'Hagan et al.	1957	200 blood donors / 133 men	2	3	22	46	51	30	17	7	8	2	2	2	4	2	0	1	1	0	0	0	0
		67 women																					
Brückner	1959 (Fig. 5)	233 blood donors	3	38	89	43	31	11	8	0	3	1	1	3	1	0	0	0	1	0	0	0	1
Nosslin	1960 (Fig. 46)	113 blood donors	0	0	1	18	20	24	15	11	4	7	4	4	1	4	0	0	0	0	0	0	0
Witmanns et al	1961	140 normal subjects	0.2–1.0 mg/100 ml (mean 0.525)																				
Brodersen et al.	1963	61 male blood donors[a]	0.10–1.45 mg/100 ml (mean 0.40)																				
		53 female blood donors[a]	0.11–0.70 mg/100 ml (mean 0.28)																				

For men $M = 0.448\ (\sigma = 0.189)$ calculated for values $\leqq 1.0$ mg/100 ml

For women $M = 0.363\ (\sigma = 0.178)$

and Krebs' (1930) method. Huhtala (1937) also took morning blood; he used Jendrassik and Cleghorn's method. Vaughan and Haslewood (1938) employed a method including protein precipitation as described by Haslewood and King (1937). In spite of differences in the procedure their results and those of Huhtala did not vary significantly. With (1943c) employed the method of Jendrassik and Gróf and found an average of 0.71 mg/100 ml in men and 0.69 mg/100 ml in women. Besides normal persons, With examined 200 ambulatory patients, who did not suffer from either liver or bile duct diseases or from hemolytic illnesses. Average values of 0.67 mg/100 ml were obtained in these patients. The distribution curve obtained was almost identical with that published by Vaughan and Haslewood. C. J. Watson (1946, p. 107), using Malloy and Evelyn's method, determined an average of 0.57 mg/100 ml in medical students. Zacho and Larsen (1946a) employing Jendrassik and Gróf's method, examined patients with surgical diseases. They ascribed the surprisingly low values to the fact that their patients were in bed and immobilized. Alwall *et al.* (1946a) found average values of 0.56 mg/100 ml in 263 healthy men and 0.50 mg/100 ml in 120 women, with the method of Jendrassik and Gróf. The average of the total material was 0.54 mg/100 ml. Raule and Grisler (1950), working with the same method, did not find values over 0.80 mg/100 ml. Zieve *et al.* (1951) performed thorough statistical analyses of results obtained with the method of Malloy and Evelyn. Values over 1.5 mg/100 ml were regarded as definitely pathological. Josephson and Dahlberg (1952), who carried out bilirubin determinations on large numbers of healthy men and women with the help of Jendrassik and Gróf's method and did not publish distribution curves, treated their data statistically. As other investigators, they determined somewhat higher values in men than in women. In addition, they found a consistent decrease with progressing age. Their values are surprisingly high. Contrary to all other investigators, who reported an average of about 0.5 mg/100 ml, Josephson and Dahlberg found averages of 0.7–1.0 mg/100 ml. The explanation of this is not clear; possibly some error is involved. Using Jendrassik and Gróf's method, Weiss (1955) examined 1002 blood donors and presented the results in a distribution curve. The numbers in Table V are taken from this curve. This author observed high values more often than most other investigators. Sen Gupta and Ganguly (1955) reported studies on Indian university students; Malloy and Evelyn's method was used. Their results agree with those published by European and American investigators. Average values of 0.43 mg/100 ml were reported. O'Hagan *et al.* (1957) examined 200 apparently normal blood donors in Australia using the method of Powell (1944). Their results are given in Table V. Brückner (1959, Fig. 5) examined 233 blood donors with his own analytical method and presented the results as a distribution curve. From this curve the figures given in Table V are taken. His mean value was 0.349 mg/100 ml which is somewhat lower than found by most other workers. Nosslin (1960, Fig. 46) presents a distribution curve for the total serum bilirubin of 113 and the direct bilirubin of 102 blood donors determined with Jendrassik and Gróf's method. His values are included in Table V. Witmanns et al. (1961) studied 140 normal subjects with the technique of Jendrassik and Cleghorn (see Table V). Brodersen et al. (1963) determined the serum bilirubin of 114 blood donors, 61 men and 53 women. For unconjugated bilirubin they employed a $CHCl_3$ extraction method with hemoglobin correction; for total bilirubin they used Powell's method with turbidity correction according to Morton and Stubbs (1940). Their values of unconjugated bilirubin are presented in Table V. They do not give their figures for total bilirubin in a table, but present a curve giving the relation between their values of unconjugated bilirubin and total bilirubin. From their curve it is evident that there is a nearly linear correlation between total and unconjugated bilirubin in normal human sera, and that the figures of total bilirubin are only slightly, although significantly, higher than those of unconjugated bilirubin.

In addition to these authors, who published distribution curves or statistical data, the following values have been reported for normal serum bilirubin: Varela et al. (1931a) determined an average of 0.2–0.4 mg/100 ml using $CHCl_3$ extraction; Zelasco (1940) found 0.30–1.10 mg/100 ml by using the method of Castex and Lopez Garcia (1940b); Vahlquist (1941, pp. 154–158) found 0.34–1.67 mg/100 ml (average 0.82) in 38 men, and 0.34–1.62 mg/100 ml (average 0.63) in 42 women, using the method of Jendrassik and Cleghorn. The age of the subjects ranged from 20 to 30 years. Welin (1945) examined 53 healthy men and 47 healthy women with the method of Jendrassik and Czike (1928a,b). With this method, protein precipitation occurs. Average values of 0.50 mg/100 ml were obtained in men and 0.46 mg/100 ml in women. His distribution curve contains no numerical values. Cantarow and Trumper (1945, p. 435) reported 0.1–0.8 mg/100 ml as normal. Pollock (1945) gave 0.47 mg/100 ml as an average. Both authors used Malloy and Evelyn's method. Balzer and Schulte (1949) examined the bilirubin concentration of serum using Jendrassik and Cleghorn's method in 518 apparently healthy persons. He found values under 0.6 mg/100 ml in half of them. The highest value observed was 1.20 mg/100 ml. Schaffner et al. (1950) found the average to be 0.51 mg/100 ml with the method of Malloy and Evelyn.

Girard et al. (1965*; Girard and Paolaggi, 1965*) studied 100 normal sera with their methyl-isobutylketone extraction method, determining mainly unconjugated bilirubin, and found a range of 0.05–0.80 (average 0.45) mg/100 ml. Martinek (1966*) studied 30 fasting normal subjects with a modification of Malloy-Evelyn's method and found 0.2–1.2 mg/100 ml for total bilirubin and 0–0.4 mg/100 ml for "direct bilirubin." No sex difference was found.

Figure 43 (from With, 1943c) shows the asymmetrical distribution of normal serum bilirubin. Very similar curves have been obtained by Vaughan and Haslewood (1938), Welin (1945), Weiss (1955), O'Hagan *et al.* (1957), Brückner (1959), and Nosslin (1960). Weiss did not report values below 0.10 mg/100 ml, and values below 0.20 mg/100 ml were

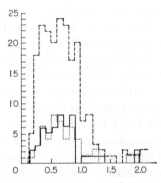

FIG. 43. Serum bilirubin level in normal adult man. Solid line represents 50 apparently healthy men; dotted line, 50 apparently healthy women; dashed line, 200 medical patients without lesion of liver or bile passages and free from hemolytic processes. Ordinate: Number of subjects studied; abscissa: Bilirubin (total) in milligrams per 100 milliliters.

relatively seldom. The curve ascends rather steeply until a peak is reached at 0.50 mg/100 ml, after which it drops sharply to 1.0 mg/100 ml. Above this value a low plateau is reached. O'Hagan *et al.* reported a very similar curve obtained by investigations of 5540 blood donors, the most extensive normal material yet assembled.

Although the average values are somewhat lower for women than for men, sex has only a slight influence on the serum bilirubin level. Similarly, age seems to have only a slight influence, in spite of Josephson and Dahlberg's (1952) findings that the values decrease somewhat with progressing age. It is difficult to be certain that all persons studied are really free from diseases. Thus, apparently healthy persons could carry latent diseases. Further, most normal materials consist mainly of young subjects for which the age distribution is erroneous. Hospitalized patients free from infections and with no liver, bile system, or blood diseases are perhaps more suitable for such investigations than apparently healthy individuals. Hospitalized persons are more thoroughly examined for possible latent diseases than are apparently healthy ones. A particularly important point is the possible presence of nonhemolytic, hereditary hyperbilirubinemia and latent or inactive hepatitis.

Alwall *et al.* (1946a) pointed out these complications. Acute latent subclinical cases of virus hepatitis could lead to serious errors, especially during hepatitis epidemics. This was confirmed by Havens *et al.* (1950). Another possible source of error is residual hyperbilirubinemia after manifest or latent virus hepatitis (Hult, 1950). Increased bilirubin concentration can continue and remain for many months, even for a few years in these cases. Inoculation hepatitis can lead to further complications. Weiss (1955) pointed out that latent hemolytic conditions or milder dyskinesia of the bile duct system should also be considered. During routine examination of persons available in a large bloodbank, Weiss discovered 150 healthy blood donors with hyperbilirubinemia (1.5–4.0 mg/100 ml) within 7 months. This latent hyperbilirubinemia was more frequently observed in men than in women. About 4% of the blood donors showed serum bilirubin concentrations higher than 1.2 mg/100 ml using the method by Jendrassik and Gróf. Of the 150 blood donors with hyperbilirubinemia 66% were men. Younger age groups were affected more frequently than older ones. Seventy-five of these blood donors were subjected to thorough clinical examination to find out the cause of hyperbilirubinemia. Sixteen showed signs of liver damage, 23 showed slightly increased blood degradation, and 7 exhibited a combination of these conditions. No abnormalities were detected in the remaining 29 persons. These latter normal individuals were perhaps variants with high physiological levels. A transitory dyskinesia of the bile duct system might also be considered. In any event it is worthless, for practical purposes, to differentiate between these possibilities. It must be concluded that even among completely healthy persons there could be a few with high serum bilirubin levels.

O'Hagan *et al.* (1957) found, among 25,000 blood donors, 11 women and 97 men with over 1.5 mg bilirubin/100 ml. On repeated analysis no increased values were found among the 11 women, whereas over 1.5 (up to 3.1) mg/100 ml was determined in 30 of the 97 men. One man was examined many times over a period of 6 years. The authors also examined 44 American marines and found 6 with values over 1.0 mg/100 ml (3.8, 2.1, 1.4, 1.3, and 1.1 mg/100 ml). No significant pathological laboratory results were detected in these 30 blood donors and 6 soldiers.

Naumann and Young (1960) determined the serum bilirubin post mortem in 34 unjaundiced male bodies at autopsy 5½ hours after death, and found a mean of 0.9 ± 0.16 mg/100 ml using the Malloy-Evelyn method, i.e., a significantly higher mean than found ante mortem in all existing materials (cf. Table V).

It is difficult to define the highest limit of normal serum bilirubin. At the present time it is reasonable to consider concentrations below 1.0 mg/100 ml as normal, between 1.0 and 1.5 mg/100 ml as questionable, but probably pathological, and concentrations over 1.5 mg/100 ml as definitely abnormal. The 1.5 mg/100 ml level is, of course, only an estimate (O'Hagan *et al.*). It is difficult to differentiate normal subjects with high bilirubin from patients with mild nonhemolytic, familial hyperbilirubinemia. However, since the latter condition is harmless, this is of little practical interest.

Although most authors attempt to characterize the highest limit of normal serum bilirubin when discussing distribution curves, this subject is by no means exhausted. Huhtala (1937) drew attention to the lower limit and assumed that it is at 0.20–0.30 mg/100 ml. He found that daily variations can be neglected in individuals with such low values. However, Zacho and Larsen (1946b) could not detect bilirubin in the serum of many bedridden surgical patients. Thus, the question of normal lower limits is still open. It should be borne in mind that, as M. Salvini and Gonzato (1947b; see also Section C,4, this chapter) emphasized, all routinely employed analytical processes yield very questionable data in the lower normal range.

Hereditary factors also have a significant influence on the serum bilirubin level. It is well known that nonhemolytic hyperbilirubinemia can be inherited in man and animals (see Section K, this chapter). Thus, it is conceivable that low or intermediate serum bilirubin concentrations are also governed by hereditary factors. This possibility, however, has not yet been investigated.

Summary

Normal serum bilirubin content shows periodic variations. These variations occur simultaneously with serum iron. The highest values are found after fasting in the early morning hours. Food intake causes a decrease in serum bilirubin concentration. Physical exertion leads to an increase in bilirubin content. The results of investigations on the influence of hormones and certain vitamins (e.g., nicotinic acid) on the bilirubin concentration are contradictory.

Investigations of normal serum bilirubin concentration in animals are scarce. Most mammals exhibit very low normal serum bilirubin concentration. The most important exceptions are horses and cattle. Systematic studies involving a greater number of mammalians and using reliable analytical techniques would be of considerable interest. In birds, the results are even more contradictory.

Numerous studies have been conducted on the normal serum bilirubin in humans. The most important results are compiled in Table V. Average values of 0.5–0.6 mg/100 ml were reported. The distribution curve is rather steep on both sides of these values (Fig. 43). Concentrations under 0.2 mg/100 ml are rare. However, a few percent of normal persons show a bilirubin concentration over 1 mg/100 ml, and sometimes 2 mg/100 ml. No fixed highest limit can be defined. For simplicity, concentrations under 1.0 mg/100 ml are considered normal, between 1.0 and 1.5 mg/100 ml questionable, but frequently pathological, and values over 1.5 mg/100 ml are regarded as definitely pathological. The possible influence of hereditary factors on the normal serum bilirubin level is mentioned.

2. Serum Bilirubin in Infancy: Icterus Neonatorum, Kernicterus, and Hepatitis Foetalis

A large number of newborns exhibit a manifest jaundice a few days after birth, and all have serum bilirubin above normal adult levels. Studies on the serum bilirubin of newborn animals are surprisingly scarce. W. Koch (1928) found increased serum bilirubin in freshly hatched chickens. Beijers (1923) examined a total of 500 newborn domestic animals (calves, sheep, pigs, and goats). Beijers *et al.* (1950) reported neonatal jaundice in foals. In addition, Hutyra and Marek (1913), Metzger (1927), Wakabayashi (1932), and Radeff (1943) investigated this phenomenon. All their studies involved only domestic animals; laboratory animals and wild animals have not been included.

About 30–80% of newborns develop manifest jaundice (Hirsch, 1913; Waugh *et al.*, 1940). However, the subjective factor plays an important role in the diagnosis, and in many cases jaundice might become visible only under the pressure of a glass spatula, and without this test might escape observation. Recently Gosset (1960) introduced a quantitative evaluation of this phenomenon, a so-called "icterometer." The yellow discoloration of ischemic skin is compared with five standard yellow colors. The standards show various intensities which are designated by 0, ½, 1, 1½ . . . until 5.0. Gosset found good agreement between values obtained with his icterometer and serum bilirubin content. The investigations of Culley *et al.* (1960) and Felbo and Kragelund (1961) showed that the icterometer can save a lot of serum bilirubin determinations in newborns. The latter studied 346 infants and found serum bilirubin values above 20 mg per 100 ml in less than 1% of infants with icterometer reading below 3 units. They recommend determination of the serum bilirubin only if the icterometer reading is 3 or above. Gorten (1964) emphasizes the importance of routine searching for jaundice at 6 hour intervals in the newborn during the first 48 hours, instead of relying on casual inspection. He recommends vitropression and standardized lighting but does not mention the icterometer.

Schellong (1962*) discussed the frequency and intensity of icterus neonatorum in a monograph written in German.

It has already been mentioned (Chapter IV,B) that the serum threshold associated with icterus in the newborn is about four times as high as in adults. Beijers (1923, p. 84) observed the same phenomenon in calves, sheep, goats, and pigs.

There is no jaundice at birth; it develops only during the first days of life. However, the serum bilirubin content of umbilical cord blood is already increased. As a rule it is 1–2 mg per 100 ml, but values as high as 4 mg per 100 ml have also been observed. Values below 1 mg per 100 ml were found only in a few per cent of newborns (Weiner and Reiner, 1939; L. T. Davidson et al., 1941). According to Davidson et al. a positive relation exists between high cord blood values and high values at the peak of jaundice. However, Dine (1954) as well as Hsia et al. (1953) questioned this statement.

Lewi et al. (1965*) found values above 3.0 mg/100 ml in cord blood —the highest value being 4.6 mg/100 ml—five times among 203 newborn weighing at least 2 kg and without hemolytic disease. Thus high cord blood bilirubin does not necessarily anticipate a severe neonatal jaundice.

The serum bilirubin content increases considerably during the first 2–4 days of life in icteric as well as in nonicteric children. Only a few exceptions to this rule are known; for example, Heiniö (1933a,b) described a child in which these values decreased. F. Bang (1915) followed the hourly variations of serum bilirubin after birth. He found that 2–4 hours after birth the bilirubin content of serum was already definitely above that determined in cord blood. Since this investigation was performed with a rather primitive technique, a repetition and extension of the experiments would be desirable. The highest elevation in serum bilirubin occurs on the second or third day of life, but it can take place on the first day and can still prevail on the seventh day. Generally, the later the maximum of physiological jaundice is reached, the higher the peak becomes.

Jaundice can develop from the first to the seventh day after birth. As a rule, it becomes visible on the second or third day (Davidson et al., 1941). A pathological condition is indicated when icterus is already manifest at birth. This has never been observed during physiological neonatal jaundice. Whereas in most cases jaundice disappears in 1 week, hyperbilirubinemia continues for a few weeks. Even in more severe forms of jaundice the serum bilirubin adjusts itself to a level of about 0.5 mg per 100 ml within 4 weeks (Davidson *et al.*, 1941; Larsen and With, 1943). Icterus is severe in about 10% of newborns, and more marked in premature infants than in full term babies (Ylppö, 1924; Napp and Plotz, 1949; Claireaux *et al.*, 1953, 1955). The peak values of serum bilirubin are correlated with the body weight at birth.

Figure 44 shows the variations of serum bilirubin level in newborns (from Larsen and With, 1943). Daily fluctuations in serum bilirubin

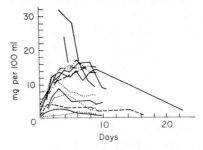
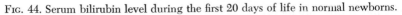

Fɪɢ. 44. Serum bilirubin level during the first 20 days of life in normal newborns.

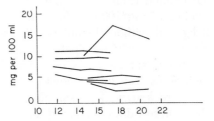

Fɪɢ. 45. Daily variations of serum bilirubin in normal newborns in hours, excepting the first 12 hours.

content are shown in Fig. 45. In the latter figure the increase occurring immediately after birth is not shown.

Practically all investigators who studied icterus neonatorum following the first publication by Biffi and Galli (1907) found the pattern of serum bilirubin in icterus neonatorum as outlined above, with the exception of Varela-Fuentes, who used the chloroform extraction method. The literature has been summarized and surveyed by Lucas *et al.* (1922), Snelling (1933), Davidson *et al.* (1941), Larsen and With (1943), and most recently by Vest (1959) and Schellong (1962*) in their monographs (in German). Davidson *et al.* (1941) examined 132 newborns using the acetone extraction method of Ernst and Förster (1924). Larsen and With carried out 300 determinations on 90 infants using the method of Jendrassik and Gróf. Schick *et al.* (1942) determined the icterus index. Napp and Plotz (1949) examined 36 newborns employing Jendrassik and Gróf's method. Vest (1959) gives a thorough treatment in a small monograph. The absolute values found by these authors vary with the method they employed. Using Jendrassik and Gróf's method, peak values of 10 mg per 100 ml were found regularly; concentrations of 20 mg per 100 ml were occasionally observed. Newns and Norton (1958) observed up to 35 mg per 100 ml in full term infants, and 43 mg per 100 ml in premature babies.

The highest value reported is 51.6 mg/100 ml in one of the cases studied by Turay *et al.* (1964*). This case was, however, atypical as most of the bilirubin was "direct" and there was bilirubinuria.

Schellong (1962*) discussed icterus neonatorum in a small monograph. He studied the curve of the serum bilirubin during the first 7 days of life and its relation to ABO blood group incompatibility between infant and mother. In 242 normal full term newborn in whom maternal antibody could be excluded, the upper limit of the serum bilirubin of the cord blood was 2.4 mg/100 ml, and the upper limit of the serum bilirubin at the age 24 hours was 7.0 mg/100 ml. The maximum serum bilirubin measured in this material was 15.2 mg/100 ml. Only 1.6% of the infants exhibited maximal values over 15 mg/100 ml. The time at which the maximum serum bilirubin level was reached was most often the 1st, 2nd, 3rd, or 4th day, in some cases the 5th, and in below 1% of the infants the 6th or 7th day. ABO incompatibility between infant and mother was without significant influence on the serum bilirubin except in cases where the ABO-Gamma test in the mother was positive in a dilution 1:10 or more. In 154 newborn with the same ABO blood group as their mothers the average serum bilirubin was 1.4 mg/100 ml in the cord blood, 4.0 mg/100 ml at the age 24 hours, 5.3 mg/100 ml at 48 hours, 6.0 mg/100 ml at 72 hours, and 5.9 mg/100 ml at 96 hours. The average time of the maximum serum bilirubin was 2.9 days after birth with a variation from 0.3 to 5.4 days.

Tuttle (1955) conducted electrophoretic studies on serum bilirubin of newborns with severe jaundice. These children obtained exchange transfusions. In cord blood, a maximum of 415 nm was found, whereas blood taken immediately before transfusion exhibited maxima of 460 and 415 nm. Paper chromatography showed that the maximum at 415 nm was due to methemalbumin. The presence of benzidine-positive substances bound to the serum proteins was demonstrated. Of the 40 normal newborns examined, 20 showed benzidine-positive fractions, which were always located in the β_1-globulin band. This was, however, only detectable in the first 12–14 hours after birth.

Gex *et al.* (1960) investigated the absorption maxima of icteric newborn sera and found four types with maxima at 460, 457, 455, and 450 nm which they named types α, β, γ, and δ. Types α and β were most often found at the peak of the jaundice in 126 sera from 47 newborns with icterus gravis or prematurity. During the ascending phase of the jaundice the maximum was most often of the γ-type, and during the descending phase it was of type α or γ. A case of bile duct occlusion in a newborn exhibited type γ.

Berezin and Antunes (1962) also performed electrophoretic studies on newborn sera using high voltage field and diazotized serum (Malloy-Evelyn technique for indirect reaction). Barbitone buffer (pH 8.6) and ion strength 0.05 were used and the time was 4 hours. In this way a yellow band migrating rapidly with the albumin and a slowly moving diazo band were separated.

Vahlquist (1941) examined *fetal serum bilirubin* levels between the fourth and the tenth month using the method of Jendrassik and Cleghorn. This author found 0.95–2.31 mg per 100 ml in 14 fetuses. *Cord blood* of 28 newborns contained an average of 1.75 mg per 100 ml. Napp and Plotz (1949) found an average of 1.98 mg per 100 ml in cord blood of normal newborns, and 2.63 mg per 100 ml in prematures (method of Jendrassik and Gróf). Claireaux *et al.* (1955, figure, p. 1155) reported comprehensive studies of the relation existing between jaundice and maturity. These authors determined the serum bilirubin on the second, third, and sixth days after birth. The following maximum serum bilirubin levels were found for various weight groups on the sixth day: 2 mg/100 ml for body weight over 3500 g (17 cases); 3.5 mg/100 ml for 2500–3500 g (29 cases); 7.5 mg/100 ml for 2000–2500 g (26 cases); and 8.5 mg/100 ml for below 2000 g (27 cases). The relation of hyperbilirubinemia to prematurity was also studied by Newns and Norton (1958) and D. Watson and Maddison (1962). They found a certain inverse correlation between birth weight and maximum serum bilirubin level. The jaundice in premature newborns is thus closely related to physiological icterus neonatorum but is often called "*jaundice of prematurity.*"

Schellong (1962*) studied the influence of various factors on the serum bilirubin of newborn in 301 mature and 133 immature infants, using a micromodification of the Jendrassik-Gróf method. In boys the maximal total bilirubin was on the average somewhat higher and was reached slightly later than in girls (7.2 mg/100 ml and 3.1 days as against 5.9 mg/100 ml and 2.6 days respectively, for mature infants). There was a definite relationship between the birth weight, the maximal serum bilirubin concentration reached, and the point of time this value was attained. With birth weight 2500–3000 g the average serum bilirubin was

8.57 mg/100 ml and was reached on an average in 3.69 days; with birth weight 3000–3500 g the corresponding figures were 6.87 mg/100 ml and 2.78 days; with birth weight 3500–4000 g, 6.26 mg/100 ml and 2.76 days; with 4000–4500 g, 5.52 and 3.00; and with birth weight above 4500 g the figures were 2.15 mg/100 ml and 1.33 days. A similar correlation was found between the length at birth and the serum bilirubin: with length 48–49 cm the figures were 8.23 mg/100 ml and 3.00 days; with 50–51 cm, 7.35 and 3.07; with 52–53 cm, 6.38 and 2.83; with 54–55 cm, 5.65 and 2.60; and with length above 55 cm the average serum bilirubin was 3.70 mg/100 ml and reached on the average in 2.36 days.

Of the 434 newborn studied by Schellong 34 were born after term (average birth weight 4075 g). The mean of the maximum serum bilirubin of this group was 4.67 mg/100 ml. The number of the birth (primi- or multigravida mother) had no significant influence on the serum bilirubin. The course of the birth (caesarean section, long duration of birth, asphyxia, etc.) likewise had no influence of the serum bilirubin of full term infants. Further, there was no correlation between the initial weight loss and the maximum serum bilirubin in full term infants. In the 133 prematures studied the highest serum bilirubin was found in the weight group 2000–2500 g (15.4 mg/100 ml and 4.28 days), the lower weight groups showing lower maximum serum bilirubin values which were reached later. In the prematures there was a certain positive correlation between the maximum serum bilirubin and the initial weight loss. Schellong found no causal relationship between hypoglycemia and hyperbilirubinemia.

Taylor *et al.* (1963a) studied the correlation between serum bilirubin and several factors including birth weight, length of gestation, race (white or colored) and delayed clamping of the umbilical cord. Their material comprised 142 full term and 173 premature infants. Inverse correlation was found between bilirubinemia and both birth weight and length of gestation, confirming the role of prematurity. Positive correlation was found between bilirubinemia and initial weight loss. Colored prematures had lower bilirubinemia than white ones. Delayed clamping was associated with increased bilirubinemia in prematures. It has been suggested that there is a correlation between the time of the first meal after birth and the bilirubinemia in prematures (cf. *Lancet,* 1963a). Haworth and Ford (1963), however, found no support for this assumption. Taylor *et al.* (1963b) studied bilirubinemia in 48 infants of diabetic mothers and found a significantly higher mean serum bilirubin on the third day than in infants of nondiabetic mothers of the same length of gestation. The figures were 9.6 versus 8.6 mg/100 ml with gestation 33–36 weeks, 8.5 versus 6.3 with 37–40 weeks. The cause of this difference is not clear, but it is believed to be due to gross increase in hemolysis.

Trolle (1965a*) studied a series from the Copenhagen University obstetric clinic (1960–1964) comprising 7900 single births. He compared the findings in underweight full term infants and prematures of the same weight range (2000–2500 g) and found that the average serum bilirubin was definitely higher in the prematures than in the matures. Further, it was found to be higher in boys than in girls. Trolle (1965b*) found that between 20 and 25% of all newborn developed jaundice (maximum serum bilirubin above 10 mg/100 ml).

Icterus gravis neonatorum or *morbus haemolyticus neonatorum* is fundamentally different from physiological jaundice of newborns and jaundice of prematurity. It is usually induced by hemolysis due to Rhesus incompatibility between fetus and mother (Mollison *et al.*, 1948; Claireaux *et al.*, 1955). Hyperbilirubinemia is already well developed at birth. The infant is either born with jaundice or it develops within 24 hours after birth. Under these conditions the bilirubin of the cord blood is practically always above 2 mg/100 ml. Mollison and Cutbush (1949a) examined 32 cases and found 1.0 to 9.3 mg/100 ml of cord blood (Haslewood and King's method, giving similar values to Jendrassik and Gróf's method). They found values below 2 mg/100 ml in only one case. Concentrations as high as 20 mg/100 ml could be reached within 12 hours in severe cases. More than 4 mg/100 ml in cord blood is highly suspicious of icterus gravis. The higher the value, the more serious the prognosis. Icterus gravis neonatorum has also been observed in horses (Beijers *et al.*, 1950), in pigs (Buxton and Brooksbank, 1953), and in chickens (Briles, 1948). Icterus gravis is dangerous because it is often accompanied by kernicterus (see Chapter IX).

Most investigators agree with the fact that the diazo reaction of the serum is always indirect in physiological jaundice of the newborn. Another similarity between icterus neonatorum and hemolytic jaundice is that neither exhibits bilirubinuria. It was assumed that bilirubin of newborn serum and adult serum are different. However, Vella (1958) could not find evidence for this. Besides indirect (free) bilirubin, there is also direct (conjugated) bilirubin in the serum of newborns. However, the latter is present only in the form of pigment I (monoglucuronide). In certain neonatal jaundice cases, this fraction can contribute up to 60% of total bilirubin content (Billing, 1955b).

Jirsová *et al.* (1958) quantitatively determined direct and indirect bilirubin in 32 cases of icterus neonatorum with a modification of Malloy and Evelyn's technique. Most of the cases showed direct bilirubin below 1 mg per 100 ml. In certain severe cases rather high values were observed: for example, 5 mg per 100 ml in 21 mg per 100 ml total bilirubin, and 19.4 mg per 100 ml in 39.8 mg per 100 ml total bilirubin. The authors assumed that, whereas in the first cases only the capacity of the liver to form glucuronides is decreased, in the latter instances the bile is also unable to excrete glucuronides.

Zuelzer *et al.* (1961) studied the serum bilirubin of 50 premature newborns with the solvent partition method of Eberlein (1960). They found considerable variation in the proportion between free and conjugated bilirubin falling in four main groups: (A) moderate hyperbilirubinemia with dominance of monoglucuronide, presumably due to failure of the liver to convert mono- to diglucuronide; (B) severe and long-standing hyperbilirubinemia with dominance of monoglucuronide, presumably of the same origin as type A but more severe; (C) high hyperbilirubinemia with dominance of free bilirubin, presumably due to marked depression of the ability to conjugate bilirubin not only in the liver but in extrahepatic tissues as well; (D) a type where the depression of the ability to conjugate bilirubin is not pronounced at birth, but develops several days after birth as shown by increase of the relative and absolute quantity of free bilirubin during the neonatal period. Types A and B have generally a favorable prognosis, while the course is more serious in types C and D.

L. E. Harris *et al.* (1962) studied 285 infants with fetal erythroblastosis, employing the analytical method of Powell (1944), and found significant quantities of conjugated bilirubin (above 1.5 mg/100 ml) present in 38 cases. The mortality rate of these 38 cases was 21% as against 10.5% in the group of 247 infants without demonstrable conjugated bilirubinemia. In the infants who died, no histopathological evidence of hepatocellular, hepatocanalicular, or obstructive jaundice was demonstrated. These observations are difficult to understand in the light of prevalent theories, but in good agreement with Schalm and Weber's (1964) observations of high concentrations of conjugated bilirubin after large bilirubin loads and gross hemolysis in normal adult humans. The findings of Harris *et al.* are, however, apparently contradictory to those of Zuelzer *et al.* (1961), cf. above.

The presence of conjugated bilirubin in the serum of newborns is most likely to be regarded as an indicator of severe hemolytic processes and, as Schalm and Weber (1964) found the highest concentrations of conjugated bilirubin after the unconjugated bilirubin had reached a maximum, it is presumably wise not to rely exclusively on the concentration of unconjugated bilirubin when evaluating the serum bilirubin in a case of jaundice in newborns.

Murano (1964*) maintained that serum bilirubin is still the most important factor determining the severity of icterus neonatorum. He found that the method of Eberlein often gives a high percentage of monoglucuronide although paper chromatography of the azo pigments yields only one band (pigment A), thus casting doubt on the reliability of Eberlein's method. He recommends diagnostic parenteral administration of 10–20 mg doses of water-soluble prednisolone daily for 10–20 days—under antibiotic cover—to differentiate between severe hemolytic icterus neonatorum and icterus due to metabolic errors.

Romano (1965*) confirmed Zuelzer's observations employing the Eberlein method.

The recent studies of Ibbot and O'Brien (1964*) have cast serious doubt on the validity of all results obtained with Eberlein's method. Generally, it is necessary to regard all fractionate determinations of bilirubin and its conjugates with reservation because of the serious inherent difficulties in these analyses (cf. Section E of this chapter).

The *pathogenesis* of neonatal jaundice stimulated numerous discussions, and an extensive amount of literature is available on this subject. For older publications and survey articles the reader should consult Ylppö (1924), Kramer (1926), Heiniö (1933a,b), E. Schiff and Faerber (1922), and Snelling (1933). The articles by Vahlquist (1941) and Künzer (1951a,b) are important, although they do not deal primarily with neonatal jaundice. The most comprehensive reviews are those of Vest (1959) and Schellong (1962*).

It is peculiar that observations on animals have been almost completely neglected in the study of the pathogenesis of neonatal jaundice. Nevertheless, some of the most valuable contributions come from veterinary medicine.

Kehrer (1871) and Epstein (1880) assumed that mechanical obstruction is the cause of neonatal jaundice; however, there is no evidence to support this (Snelling, 1933). Quincke (1885) believed that an open ductus venosus is responsible. Quisling (1894) thought that the reason is a catarrhal infection of the duodenum. The hemolysis theory of Virchow (1847) was widely accepted by early authors (Hofmeier, 1882). This theory was modified by Ziegelroth (1926). Liver insufficiency was first proposed as a cause by Violet (1880) and was more clearly formulated by Mensi (1910), Ylppö (1913), and Hirsch (1913). Metzger's (1927) observations on calves supported this hypothesis. Schick (1921) and Wagner (1921) considered the placenta as the site of formation of bilirubin in icterus neonatorum. It has also been assumed that intrauterine anoxia and consecutive polycythemia due to placental degeneration gave rise to enhanced hemoglobin degradation and bilirubin production in newborns (Gottlieb and Kearns, 1931; Goldbloom and Gottlieb, 1932).

These problems were recently investigated by means of labeled bilirubin. Schenker (1963) injected bilirubin-C^{14} into fetuses from late pregnancy guinea pigs. Of the injected radioactivity, 56.6% on the average appeared in the maternal bile during the ensuing 2 hours, and the percentage was independent of the bilirubin load injected. To decide whether bilirubin passed the placenta, bilirubin-C^{14} and guinea pig albumin-I^{131} were injected simultaneously. In this experiment no radioactive-albumin penetrated into the maternal circulation, from which it can be concluded that bilirubin passes the placenta in free condition. In contrast to unconjugated bilirubin, conjugated bilirubin-C^{14} appeared only as traces in the maternal bile. Grodsky *et al.* (1963) injected bilirubin-H^3 intravenously into 19–21 day old fetal rats. Two hours later only 1–4% of the radioactivity had appeared in the maternal bile, while 93–98% remained in the hemogenates of the fetuses, 27% in the carcasses, 21% in the serum, 10% in the livers, and 2.5% in the intestines. This differs much from Schenker's findings in guinea pigs with bilirubin-C^{14}. Repeated investigations including more species are required (cf. also Chapter II,D).

Today the prevailing theories explaining the genesis of icterus neonatorum are those of *hemolysis* and *liver insufficiency*. To this can be added the possible role of intestinal reabsorption of unconjugated bilirubin as a contributory factor (Brodersen and Hermann, 1963), but this can hardly play any important role. According to the hemolysis theory the relatively low oxygen tension characteristic of intrauterine life leads to polycythemia and high hemoglobin level in the fetus. After birth this hypoxia disappears. Consequently, the excess hemoglobin is degraded and bilirubin formation increases. This theory is supported by many observations, but has been criticized by several authors (Vahlquist, 1940; Waugh *et al.*, 1940; L. T. Davidson *et al.*, 1941; Findlay *et al.*, 1947). The hyperbilirubinemia of cord blood can hardly be explained by this hypothesis, because neonatal hemolysis does not begin before birth. Another fact contrary to the hemolysis theory is that the serum bilirubin is never as high in hemolytic icterus of adults—where it rarely exceeds 10 mg per 100 ml—as in neonatal jaundice (Biering-Sørensen and With, 1947). Mollison's (1948) experiments, which established the survival time of erythrocytes in transfusion experiments, merit special consideration. He found a definitely decreased lifetime of erythrocytes in newborns, and calculated that the rate of hemoglobin degradation per unit body weight is about three times as high in infants as in adults. As pointed out in Chapter IV, the liver of adults is unable to compensate for a threefold increase in bilirubin production rate without developing jaundice; thus, it seems that neonatal jaundice could be at least partially explained as a consequence of increased blood degradation. Hemolysis, however, can not alone explain the jaundice of newborns because a threefold increase in bilirubin production can only induce a slowly developing jaundice, whereas icterus neonatorum develops extremely rapidly.

Recently Vest and Grieder (1961) studied the erythrocyte destruction in 6 full-term newborns and 33 prematures by means of autologous transfusion of red cells labeled with Cr^{51}. The serum bilirubin was determined simultaneously. The half-life of tagged erythrocytes was 14.5–36 (average 22) days in the prematures and 10–31 (24) days in the full-term babies. The prematures with their higher and more prolonged hyperbilirubinemia thus did not show a significantly shorter half-life than the full-term newborns. This finding does not support the view that hemolysis plays a dominating role in jaundice of the newborn. The hemoglobin degradation in newborns was recently discussed by D. Watson and Porter (1963) with special regard to hemolytic disease in the newborn.

The occurrence of an increased hemoglobin catabolism during the newborn period is supported by studies on the endogenous formation of CO-hemoglobin in most newborn during the first 2–3 days of life (Fällström and Bjure, 1965*).

According to the *liver dysfunction* theory, the newborn liver, because of immaturity, has a low functional capacity which causes retention and jaundice. The fact that jaundice is more predominant in premature infants seems to substantiate this theory. The low kidney function in newborns found by McCance and Young (1941) points in the same direction. Herlitz (1926), Weech et al. (1941), Fashena (1948), and Mollison and Cutbush (1949a) reported findings indicating decreased liver function, but the evidence is not completely convincing. Neither Lin and Eastman (1937) nor Mollison and Cutbush (1949b) could predict—by means of the bilirubin and the bromsulphalein excretion tests—which newborns would develop jaundice and which would not. Furthermore, if the theory of decreased liver function were true, this condition should prevail during an extended period and would not disappear as quickly as hyperbilirubinemia disappears in neonatal jaundice.

As discussed above (Section G, this chapter) the elimination of bilirubin with the bile is largely dependent on the activity of the uridine diphosphoglucuronyl transferase enzyme system of the liver, and several studies have shown that the liver of various species of newborn mammals is deficient in this enzyme. In the chick embryo this enzymatic deficiency is much less pronounced; the liver of the chick embryo resembles that of the adult mammal (Dutton, 1963). Studies in more mammalian as well as avian species and lower vertebrates are required. Holton and Lathe (1963) found substances that inhibit bilirubin conjugation by liver slices from humans and rats to be present in newborn serum. Four different inhibitors were found to be active with rat liver slices. Two were identified as pregnanediol and pregnanolone glucuronides. Only one of the four compounds was active with human liver slices and its nature is not yet known. Hsia *et al.* (1963) studied glucuronic acid inhibitors which may play a role in jaundice of newborns receiving drugs. They found that progestational steroids act as competitors, while Synkavit and novobiocin act as noncompetitive inhibitors. Vest (1958a,b) compared the excretion of glucuronides in newborns after loading with acetanilide with that of adults; while the newborn excreted only 10% of the acetanilide as glucuronides, the corresponding figure in adults was 80%. Vest and Streiff (1959) studied the acetanilide conjugates in serum after oral loading and found that the appearance of glucuronides was greatly retarded in the newborn compared with older infants.

Recent studies have shown that the deficient glucuronide synthesis of the newborn liver and the closely related problem of the occurrence of β-glucuronidase in the newborn organism are more complicated than first believed. Dutton *et al.* (1964*) found that the neonatal rat liver is well equipped to form glucuronides both with *o*-aminophenol and *p*-nitrophenol for which its hepatic glucuronide-forming ability is at least as "mature" as in the adult. This is in contrast to most other newborn mammals investigated. For this reason experiments with rats or rat liver slices are unsuited for testing drug toxicity in newborn.

The development of the UDP-bilirubin transferase and other enzyme systems of mainly microsomal character in the liver of the rabbit during the neonatal period was studied by Flint *et al.* (1964*). They found that the development patterns vary widely from enzyme to enzyme, some enzymes even displaying greater than adult levels at birth. Consequently low glucuronyltransferase activity at birth cannot be due primarily to a gross lack of endoplasmatic reticulum or to "immaturity."

The bilirubin conjugation in the liver of chick embryos and newly hatched chicks as well as their content of β-glucuronidase were studied by Tenhunen (1965a*,b*); the β-glucuronidase activity of different organs of human fetuses was investigated by Jirsová *et al.* (1965*); and its development during the postnatal period in the jejunum and ileum of rats was studied by Heringová *et al.* (1965*).

That the deficiency of the newborn liver to eliminate bilirubin is not exclusively due to reduced power of glucuronide formation was pointed out by Schenker and Schmid (1964). They found that in the newborn guinea pig excretion of unconjugated bilirubin-C^{14} was reduced by more than half while that of conjugated bilirubin-C^{14} was reduced by one third compared with the excretion in the adult animal.

It must be concluded that neither decreased liver function due to immaturity nor increased hemolysis can alone explain the genesis of neonatal jaundice. As Künzer (1951a,b) emphasized, both processes can operate simultaneously. However, the *characteristic increase and decrease of the serum bilirubin curve during neonatal jaundice* (Fig. 44) cannot be explained by a simple combination of insufficiency of the immature liver and bilirubin overproduction due to hemolysis. Künzer's (1951a, table on p. 67) data suggest that the sum of average fecal bilirubin and urobilinoid excretion remains constant (about 10 mg) during the first 6 weeks, and starts to decrease only during the seventh. Vest (1959, Table VII, p. 45) also found the total daily bile pigment excretion per day unchanged during the first 2–3 weeks of life.

Finally, it would be absurd to assume a parallelism between the rapid increase and drop in the serum bilirubin curve and a considerably slower variation of liver function during the first few weeks of life.

The physiological event offering the most reasonable explanation of the time curve of serum bilirubin during the neonatal period is the profound changes in the liver circulation at birth. Quincke (1885) originally suggested that the closure of the ductus venosus Arantii is responsible for neonatal jaundice. Independently, Beijers (1923) and Elton (1935b) arrived at the same conclusion. Beijer's observations on the closure of this duct in domestic animals are important because they showed good agreement between disappearance of jaundice and duct closure. The ductus venosus functions as a natural Eck's fistula. It becomes obliterated a few days after birth, which coincides with the appearance and disappearance of hyperbilirubinemia.

Recently J. Lind (1963) performed radiological studies of the hepatic vascular tree in human fetuses and of the circulatory changes following birth. He also investigated the closure of the ductus venosus and writes: "Because of the pressure gradient 8 to 13 mm Hg across the ductus venosus in newborn infants there must be a flow of blood through it, if open, thus creating a by-pass channel around the liver. This might be a factor contributing to the hyperbilirubinemia in the neonatal period." The ductus venosus has been demonstrated to be passable to dyes during the first week of life, but this does not mean that it really functions *in vivo* during this period.

The profound alterations of the hepatic circulation at birth were described by Emery (1963), J. Lind (1963), and Montagnani (1963) and seem to offer a reasonable explanation of the time curve of the serum bilirubin in the newborn. Montagnani regards these circulatory changes as more disturbing than the physiological changes following birth in any other organ. The pressure in the umbilical vein is reduced to zero and subsequently the pressure gradient through the liver and the oxygenation of the portal blood fall markedly and rapidly. This is compensated by the fact that the blood of the hepatic artery becomes oxygenated at birth and that its tree is proportionately more well developed in the newborn than later in life. Another important factor is that the left lobe of the liver is relatively large in the newborn and receives its blood supply mainly from the umbilical vein while the right lobe is relatively small and receives its blood supply mainly from the portal vein. This means that the blood reaching the relatively large left lobe is suddenly changed from highly oxygenated blood to portal venous blood after birth, a circumstance requiring a profound and rapid adjustment. While this adjustment is going on, the liver function will most likely be markedly impaired. From what is known of the regenerative capacity of liver tissue (cf. Chapter IV,C,1), a period of adjustment of about 1 week seems reasonable. This offers an acceptable explanation of the time curve of the serum bilirubin in the newborn. The closure of the ductus venosus may be a contributory cause, but is most likely of secondary importance.

Another vascular factor hitherto overlooked was pointed out by Jäykkä (1964*), namely the blood flow through the hepatic arteries. This is probably negligible during fetal life, and Jäykkä found that the arterial bore is very small in the hepatic arterioles of 3-month-old human fetuses. The widening of the lumen of the hepatic arterioles during the postnatal period may be an important factor explaining the disappearance of icterus neonatorum. Studies on this problem are required.

The possible role of lymphogenism and synthetic bilirubin production in icterus neonatorum was pointed out by With (1947; 1949, p. 336; 1954, p. 224) who also suggested a method of experimental study of these phenomena: "The possibility of a synthetic bilirubin production does not seem unlikely, but this can only be tested in experiments with feeding N^{15}-labeled glycine to newborn." Such experiments have now been carried out by Vest *et al.* (1965*) who administered N^{15}-glycine i.v. to two newborns and found that at least 21–25% of the bile pigment excreted with the feces is derived from isotopically labeled precursors different from the hemoglobin of circulating mature erythrocytes. The relative role of the hepatic and the early erythropoietic bile pigment peaks in the newborn remains to be investigated. Vest (1967*) extended these studies. Claireaux *et al.*'s (1953) and Jirsová *et al.*'s (1958) finding of significant amounts of conjugated bilirubin could indicate lymphogenic–regurgitational factors. An experimental approach to this question by cannulation of the lymphatic vessels of the liver or the thoracic duct in order to determine the bilirubin content of blood and lymph would be desirable.

Also variations in catabolism of bilirubin to unidentifiable compounds may play a certain role in the manifestations of jaundice in the newborn, a possibility pointed out by Lester *et al.* (1963*).

Recently Newman and Gross (1963) described a special form of neonatal *jaundice due to breast feeding.* They reported 11 cases with prolonged hyperbilirubinemia for 2–4 weeks with dominating indirect bilirubin. When cow's milk was given instead of breast milk the serum bilirubin dropped to normal values in a few days. The authors believe that the condition is due to interference with the normal bilirubin conjugation mechanism by a substance present in breast milk.

Arias and Gartner (1964*) and Arias *et al.* (1964*) demonstrated that breast milk from mothers of affected infants inhibits glucuronyl transferase activity *in vitro* in guinea pig liver slices. In contrast milk from mothers of nonjaundiced infants and cow's milk caused no inhibition. They isolated the inhibitory substance from breast milk and identified it as pregnane-3(α)-20(β)-diol. This substance was given to newborns and it was found to induce an increased unconjugated hyperbilirubinemia.

Katz and Robinson (1965*) described a case of 70-days duration. The mother's milk was strongly inhibitory to glucuronyl transferase *in vitro.* Stiehm and Ryan (1965*) reported 8 cases. In one case the serum bilirubin reached 30 mg/100 ml. The bilirubin was predominantly indirect-reacting. Within 48 hours after cessation of breast feeding the serum bilirubin began to fall, and if breast feeding was resumed the serum bilirubin increased.

Rosta and Szöke (1965*) studied two comparable groups of infants with prolonged jaundice of unknown origin fed exclusively on human milk, one receiving milk from their own mothers, and one receiving milk from other women. The jaundice was found to subside much more rapidly in the infants receiving milk from other women (average daily decrease in serum bilirubin 2.45 mg/100 ml and initial serum bilirubin 20.8) than in those receiving the milk of their own mothers (daily decrease 0.84 mg/100 ml with initial serum bilirubin 17.5 mg/100 ml). This observation renders it likely that certain women excrete substantial amounts of glucuronyl-transferase inhibitors with their milk, whereas most women do not.

Another special form of jaundice in the newborn is *transient familial hyperbilirubinemia* or Lucey-Driscoll syndrome, recently described by Lucey *et al.* (1960*) and Arias *et al.* (1965*) who reported 24 infants belonging to 8 unrelated healthy Caucasian mothers. One of the infants developed cerebral palsy. Sera from the 8 mothers and their newborn infants were found to inhibit glucuronidation of bilirubin and o-aminophenol in rat liver slices and homogenates. This phenomenon occurred in the serum of the mothers from the second trimester of pregnancy. Attempts to identify the inhibiting factor were unsuccessful. The mechanism of this form of neonatal hyperbilirubinemia is unknown and requires further study.

Ströder's (1957) studies on the blood glutathione in neonatal jaundice are interesting. He found that the glutathione content of the blood is always normal in physiological neonatal icterus; in all other forms of icterus, including hemolytic icterus of adults, however, it shows a considerable depression. The pathogenetic significance of these findings is not clear.

In certain cases of icterus neonatorum, elevation of the direct serum bilirubin together with other biochemical findings (increased serum transaminase) suggest biliary occlusion. Still (1927) and Hawksley and Lightwood (1934) early drew attention to this, and Hsia *et al.* (see 1952a,b) called it *"inspissated bile syndrome."* The condition was studied systematically by Oppé and Valaes (1959) and P. Dunn (1963) who called it "obstructive jaundice and hemolytic disease in the newborn." In this condition gross anemia, hyperbilirubinemia including an elevated conjugated fraction, as well as hepato- and splenomegaly are as a rule present at birth. The infants often take on a greenish hue and develop a tendency to bleed. They are often very ill. Oppé and Valaes found no cases in prematures of less than 36 weeks gestation, but Dunn observed three typical cases below this age. The condition can be detected at birth by measuring the direct bilirubin of the cord blood; a figure of above 1 mg per 100 ml with the method of Lathe and Ruthven (1958) is highly suggestive. Clinically all neonates severely affected by jaundice ought to be suspected, and the correct diagnosis is important because it helps to avoid unnecessary exchange transfusions which may be dangerous in these patients. In lethal cases the hepatic architecture is disorganized by necrosis and giant cell regeneration and other evidence of gross hepatic damage. Fibrosis may be present at birth or develop during the following weeks. This is in contrast to hemolytic disease of newborn where the liver regularly exhibits abundant extramedullary erythropoiesis but retains a normal lobular architecture. The so-called inspissated bile syndrome, however, is poorly defined and difficult to distinguish from congenital atresia of the bile ducts (*Lancet,* 1963a; cf. Chapter IV,E,3).

A connection between the high nonesterified fatty acid (NEFA) concentration characteristic of newborns (van Duyne and Havel, 1959) and neonatal hyperbilirubinemia was suggested by E. Werner and Möhlmann (1962), who found that variations of the serum bilirubin and serum NEFA in newborns showed a certain parallelism. Melichar *et al.* (1962), however, found a fall in serum bilirubin after intravenous administration of fat while it increased after glucose infusion. Novák *et al.* (1962)

found in experiments *in vitro* that NEFA competes with bilirubin for the sites on serum albumin.

The frequency of severe neonatal hyperbilirubinemia has been claimed to be high in infants with congenital intestinal obstruction by Aicardi (1963), who presented 9 cases.

Boggs and Bishop (1965*) found that among 48 infants with high intestinal obstruction about 50% developed severe hyperbilirubinemia. This was more pronounced in infants with duodenal atresia than in those with jejunal atresia.

Another condition in which prolonged and severe icterus neonatorum has been reported is mongolism (Zuelzer and Brown, 1961; Panizon, 1965*).

Recently a new form of genetically determined neonatal jaundice has been described, i.e., neonatal jaundice associated with deficiency of erythrocyte enzymes (cf. Valaes, 1961), especially glucose-6-phosphate dehydrogenase (G-6-PD) (cf. Zinkham and Lenhard, 1959; G. D. Smith and Vella, 1960; Panizon and Meo, 1959; Weatherall, 1960; Doxiadis *et al.*, 1961; C. Lee *et al.*, 1961; Harley, 1961; Harley and Robin, 1961). This jaundice resembles other severe forms of jaundice in the newborn, but differs from them by the late development of kernicterus which may take place as late as the tenth day of life (Doxiadis *et al.*). This disease is almost exclusively observed in infants of Mediterranean races and has not been observed in newborns of Scandinavian stock (Engelson and Kjellman, 1963). It is especially frequent in Greek infants where Fessas *et al.* (1962) found 23 cases of G-6-PD deficiency among 786 male neonates (nearly 3%). Far from all infants with G-6-PD deficiency do, however, develop severe jaundice. Pronounced icterus is far more frequent in the families of other severe cases than among neonates in whom G-6-PD deficiency is accidentally discovered. Fessas *et al.* believe that severe G-6-PD jaundice depends on more than one hereditary factor. Schettini *et al.* (1963) determined the Cr^{61} half life of the erythrocytes in jaundice of newborns with G-6-PD deficiency and found it to be 12–22 days. Capps *et al.* (1963) studied a series of 196 G-6-PD deficient Nigerian newborns. As many as 20.6% of the male newborns and 10.7% of the female ones exhibited the deficiency, but jaundice developed in only ca. 20% of the affected babies. The pathogenetic role of prophylactic administration of vitamin K was considered, but no support could be found for this. Kirkman *et al.* (1964a,b) studied variants of the enzyme G-6-PD present in congenital nonsferocytic hemolytic disease and in Mediterranean G-6-PD deficiency.

Yue and Strickland (1965*) found 3.74% cases of G-6-PD deficiency among 1177 cord blood specimens from male Chinese babies in Hong

Kong. Of the 3.74%, 27% reached serum bilirubin levels above 15 mg/100 ml. Freier *et al.* (1965*) described 8 severe cases of G-6-PD jaundice in newborn in Israel and stated that severe jaundice is rare although G-6-PD deficiency is not uncommon in Israel.

Another enzymatic deficiency in the erythrocytes causing severe neonatal jaundice is 6-phosphogluconate-dehydrogenase deficiency, recently described by Brewer (1964*) and Lausecker *et al.* (1965*).

The prognosis and treatment of icterus neonatorum and other forms of jaundice in the newborn is discussed in this chapter, Section M and Chapter IX,D, where the problems of exchange transfusion in relation to serum bilirubin are also discussed.

The intensified interest in neonatal jaundice during the last two decades, beginning with clarification of the pathogenesis of the most common form of hemolytic disease of newborns and followed by some elucidation of the pathogenesis of kernicterus, has also given rise to renewed interest in the *rarer types of icterus in* newborns. Among these are both *hemolytic* and *nonhemolytic* varieties.

Lelong *et al.* (1961, 1964) discussed hemolytic diseases in newborns due to other factors than blood group incompatibilities and collected 17 cases of neonatal hereditary sferocytosis and 11 cases of nonsferocytic neonatal hemolytic anemia. Among the nonhemolytic varieties, congenital biliary atresia was discussed in Chapter IV,E,3, the "inspissated bile syndrome" was mentioned above, "neonatal hepatitis" is discussed below, and the hereditary nonhemolytic hyperbilirubinemias are discussed in Section K, this chapter.

Hepatitis foetalis ("neonatal hepatitis") is a rare form of jaundice in newborns, generally regarded as inevitably lethal. The clinical picture of this condition is closely similar to that of neonatal biliary atresia, but the histological picture is characteristic. Giant cells appear in the parenchyma, and there is no evidence of biliary obstruction. It was first described by Stokes *et al.* (1951) who believed it was due to viral infection, a view supported by Craig and Landing (1952). This was, however, doubted by Smetana and Johnson (1955). On the other hand, Kiaer (1956) believed that the disease is caused by a virus transmitted transplacentally from the mother. The histological picture is definitely distinct from hepatitis in older age groups, but this can be due to a particular reaction of the fetal liver. Kiaer and Olesen (1956) observed four cases in siblings born in succession within 5 years and assumed that this supported the infection theory. Hsia *et al.* (1958), on the other hand, suggested that the condition is inherited and depends on a recessive factor. Danks and Bodian (1963) reviewed the disease and stressed its similarities with neonatal obstructive jaundice. Their material, collected in a pediatric department in 16 years, comprized 58 cases of extrahepatic biliary atresia, 7 of intrahepatic biliary atresia, and 50 of neonatal hepatitis. Because of consanguineous parents in 4 cases of neonatal hepatitis, they suggested that the condition is hereditary and dependent on a mutant autosomal gene in homozygotous form. P. Dunn (1963) pointed out that hemolysis may also play a role in the pathogenesis of neonatal hepatitis. Ergas and Wallis (1963) described 3 cases of kernicterus due to neonatal hepatitis; one of their patients lived to the age of 4 years. Cassady et al. (1964) described 3 cases in siblings and studied 35 of their relatives, among whom several cases of jaundice were detected. They stress the importance of heredity, but admit that other factors may be active too. Neonatal giant cell hepatitis may be a syndrome with multiple causes. Its clinical picture is practically identical with that of neonatal biliary atresia. Among the relatives of their 3 patients there was apparently a case of the disease where the patient had recovered.

Shibuya (1964*) studied 22 infants with neonatal hepatitis and divided them into three groups after the histology of their liver biopsy. Wong et al. (1965*) described a case of neonatal hepatitis in one dizygotic twin while the other twin was normal—a finding which is difficult to bring in accordance with transplacental transmission of an infectious agent, although it is easily explained by genetic origin. On the other hand R. A. Cole et al. (1965*) claim to have cultivated hepatitis virus— employing the Detroit 6 cell system—from three babies with neonatal hepatitis and from one of three infants with biliary atresia.

Danks (1965*) reviewed the problem of prolonged neonatal obstructive jaundice and emphasized the difficulty in distinguishing sharply between extrahepatic and intrahepatic biliary atresia and neonatal hepatitis. Thaler (1964*) discussed neonatal liver cirrhosis, reviewing 24 cases and comparing them with 85 cases of neonatal hepatitis. He concluded that these two conditions are distinct entities.

The serum bilirubin of *older infants and children* shows no special characteristics and has aroused only little interest. As previously mentioned, the normal level (ca. 0.5 mg/100 ml) is reached in a few weeks even in severe cases of physiological icterus neonatorum (L. T. Davidson et al., 1941; Larsen and With, 1943). According to the scarce and somewhat contradictory information available, the bilirubin values remain quite low until the eighth to tenth year. After this, the concentration increases gradually until adult levels are reached during adolescence.

Saudé (1906, p. 50) found quite high values with a simple oxidation method in a few children. Zelasco (1940) found much lower concentrations in children than in adults. In 92 children examined by Traina (1941), only values below 0.58 mg per 100 ml were obtained with the method of Heilmeyer and Krebs (1930). Ramón Guerra *et al.* (1948) found lower levels in children than in adults; the adult level was reached during adolescence (14–15 years of age). Vahlquist (1939, 1941) obtained concentrations around 1.0 mg per 100 ml with the method of Jendrassik and Cleghorn in 10 normal school children. Systematic study of serum bilirubin of normal children in various age groups with reliable analytical techniques would be desirable.

Recently Iwanami (1964*) found the following average normal values in children: 30 infants aged 1–11 months, total bilirubin (TB) 0.86 mg/100 ml, unconjugated bilirubin (NCB) 0.34, pigment I (p I) 0.15, pigment II (p II) 0.37; 34 children aged 1–6 years, TB 0.88, NCB 0.39, p I 0.18, p II 0.31; 30 children aged 7–14 years TB 0.95, NCB 0.41, p I 0.19, p II 0.35; and 23 adults, TB 1.00, NCB 0.54, p I 0.17, p II 0.29.

Summary

Moderate hyperbilirubinemia exists in humans and in mammals at birth. This increases sharply until the third to seventh day and drops more slowly thereafter. This phenomenon has only been studied in humans and domestic animals. Laboratory animals have not yet been included in the investigations. A large percentage of newborns develop clinical jaundice. The serum bilirubin level reaches high values, in most cases 10 mg per 100 ml and more. The bilirubin is present as free (indirect) bilirubin and pigment I (bilirubin monoglucuronide). Jaundice is due to the combination of two factors: increased bilirubin production (mostly hemolysis), and suppressed liver function (immaturity). Further parahematic (hepatic) bilirubin formation and probably lymphogenism are contributory factors of varying importance. Uridine diphosphoglucuronyl transferase deficiency is a major cause of the liver dysfunction. Jaundice cannot be explained by only one of these factors alone. However, the combined effect of these factors satisfactorily accounts for the high levels of serum bilirubin, although it does not explain the characteristic time curve of serum bilirubin. This curve is explained satisfactorily by the profound changes of the hepatic circulation following birth and the following adjustments of the liver. More marked jaundice and stronger hyperbilirubinemia can be observed in premature babies than in mature newborns.

Experimental investigations of the pyrrole metabolism in the newborn with labeled glycine would be of considerable interest. In order to elucidate the genesis of neonatal jaundice, it is necessary to study the role of lymphatic factors by cannulation of the liver lymph vessels and the thoracic duct; such studies should be performed in newborn domestic or laboratory animals.

Special forms of jaundice in newborns are briefly discussed including glucose-6-phosphodehydrogenase (G-6-PD) deficiency, jaundice due to bile duct atresia, the so-called inspissated bile syndrome, and jaundice due to breast milk and the Lucey-Driscoll syndrome. Hepatitis foetalis, accompanied by giant cell formation in the liver, is also discussed.

The serum bilirubin of newborns reaches a low level ($\sim$ 0.5 mg per 100 ml) within a month after birth. It remains at this level during childhood. Investigations of the serum bilirubin content of infants and children are rare. Such studies should be performed systematically using reliable analytical methods.

J. Loading the Organism with Bile Pigments; Bilirubin Excretion Test

It was plausible to devise a liver function test based on loading with bilirubin. Because it was not known with certainty whether bilirubin was absorbed from the intestine, oral administration was out of the question. Subcutaneous and intramuscular application was of dubious value, because bilirubin is bound to protein in tissues and tissue fluids. Thus, only intravenous and intraperitoneal loading remain. Such loading can be performed either with aqueous alkaline solutions or with aqueous solutions containing serum albumin to increase solubility, or with colloidal aqueous bilirubin solutions. In addition, the possibility of using aqueous solutions of conjugated bilirubin exists; however, this is difficult and has not yet been tried. Also, the administration of conjugated bilirubin for liver function tests would be less physiological, since bilirubin normally reaches the liver as unconjugated pigment. The most important liver function regarding bilirubin excretion seems to be esterification with glucuronic acid. Thus, esterification can be used to measure liver function. Bilirubin administration in the form of a bilirubin serum albumin complex simulates physiological conditions. This manner of application also avoids the unpleasant side effects of strongly alkaline aqueous pure bilirubin solutions. Nevertheless, with one exception (Massias, 1956) all investigations were performed with protein-free solutions.

Tarchanoff (1874) injected bilirubin intravenously in dogs with bile fistula. He found that bilirubin was exclusively excreted with the bile, whereas the urine remained free of bilirubin. Vossius (1879) confirmed these results. Similarly, none of the later workers were able to detect bilirubinuria. One exception is Wespi (1935), who loaded rabbits with over 10 mg bilirubin per kg body weight. With (unpublished results, 1949) administered 500 mg bilirubin intravenously to a healthy man of 70 kg body weight during 4 successive days; no bilirubinuria was detected even with the sensitive method of Naumann (1936b). Scholderer and von Ludany (1932) as well as Scholderer (1933a) established that the serum bilirubin curve is not influenced by extirpation of both kidneys after loading. Gilbert and Chabrol (1911), Fromholdt and Nersessoff (1912a,b), Kodama (1925), Bouckaert and Appelmans (1925), Appelmans and Bouckaert (1926), Verzár and Zih (1928, 1929), Schwezoff (1930), and Saiki (1931a) reported investigations carried out in rabbits, dogs, and pigeons.

Von Bergmann (1927) and his pupil Eilbott (1927) introduced bilirubin loading tests in humans. They injected 70 mg bilirubin in sodium carbonate solution and subsequently examined the serum bilirubin after 3 minutes, as well as after 3 and 4 hours. Later it was proposed to use 50 mg bilirubin (Harrop and Barron, 1931) or 1.0 mg per kg body weight (Soffer, 1933). The results of these tests were expressed in so-called "retention percentage." The equation $100(c-a)/(b-a)$ was used for the calculation, where a represents bilirubin concentration before loading, b the concentration 3 minutes after loading, and c the concentration at the end of the test. This calculation has been generally accepted. However, the various investigators used somewhat different time intervals for blood sampling (3 and 4 minutes; 3, 4, or 5 hours). Most authors maintain that this test is worthless in patients with bilirubinuria. However, this cannot be correct, because loss of bilirubin with the urine is insignificant (compare above, and Chapter VI,B,4).

The normal values of per cent retention were the subject of many discussions. Eilbott considered a retention of 0–10% normal. Other investigators regarded 5% as the limit (Soffer, 1934; Soffer and Paulsson, 1936; Soffer *et al.*, 1937a,b; Kornberg, 1942). Oviedo Bustos (1933, 1934) and Brøchner-Mortensen (1935) give 15%, Jezler (1929), Jankelson and Gargill (1931), and Strasser (1937) consider 20%, whereas Schindel and Barth (1934) propose 50% as the upper normal limit. It is necessary that the patient is fasting during the entire test (Strasser, 1937). These contradictory results warranted re-examination of the validity of test conditions. On the basis of animal experiments van de Velde (1929) and Gérard (1931) doubted the value of bilirubin loading as a liver function test. Krane (1936) found that the maximum bilirubin concentration was reached 30–50 seconds after injection in some humans, but only after 1–2 minutes in others. Therefore he concluded that the bilirubin must adhere to the intima of the vessels in some irregular fashion. In addition, Dragstedt and Mills (1937) found in experiments with dogs that about 60% of the injected bilirubin disappeared immediately after injection, and only 40% reached the liver before excretion. Hyperbilirubinemia disappeared within a few hours. Disappearance of bilirubin from blood was significantly retarded when the RES was blocked. Ligation of the common bile duct completely inhibited decrease of serum bilirubin content. However, when two thirds of the bile duct system was ligated, only slight retardation occurred.

A. L. Berman *et al.* (1941) injected 5–12 mg bilirubin per kg in dogs and observed an increase of serum bilirubin to 9–13 mg per 100 ml. The kidney vessels were ligated and the amount of bilirubin excreted through the bile was determined. The dogs were killed after 1 hour and the bilirubin remaining in the blood was measured. A total of only 34–40% of the injected bilirubin could be recovered in blood and bile. Cabello Ruz (1943a) confirmed these results in experiments with dogs, rats, and toads. He concluded that, besides excretion, the liver must be able to store, as well as destroy, bilirubin. The serum bilirubin remained high after loading in hepatectomized toads; hepatectomy without bilirubin

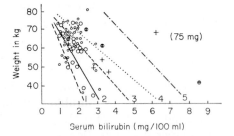

Fig. 46. The rise of serum bilirubin after loading in relation to body weight (see explanation in text). Normal subjects: large circle = 50 mg; × = 100 mg; circled × = 150 mg. Patients: small circle = 50 mg; + = 100 mg; circled + = 150 mg.

loading did not cause such increase in these animals. The serum bilirubin normalized a few hours after loading in normal toads. Experiments on partially hepatectomized rats and dogs showed that bilirubin retention and amount of available liver tissue are closely related.

With (1943f) determined the bilirubin concentration of a number of blood samples using Jendrassik and Gróf's method. The samples were taken within the first 3 hours after loading. W. Müller's (1954) investigations confirmed With's results. The expected increase was calculated from the amount injected and the volume of plasma as estimated, from the weight of patient. These results of With are shown in Fig. 46.

Line 1 represents the lowest possible increase (largest plasma volume), line 2 is the most probable increase (average plasma volume, calculated from weight), and line 3 shows the highest possible increase (lowest plasma volume). Lines 1, 2, and 3 correspond to a dose of 50 mg bilirubin. Lines 4 and 5 correspond to the average amount of plasma and 100 and 150 mg bilirubin, respectively. The experimental data reveal considerable scattering. This can be explained by insufficient mixing of bilirubin with blood during the first few minutes after injection.

In a later experiment, With (unpublished data, 1949) injected 500 mg bilirubin in a 70 kg man, and observed an increase in concentration of serum bilirubin to 17 mg per 100 ml. In similar experiments, Thompson and Wyatt (1938) found that the increase in serum bilirubin, measured 5 minutes after injections of 10 mg bilirubin per kg body weight, varied between 5.7 and 21 mg per 100 ml. Large individual variations of serum bilirubin increase occur not only after small doses (50–150 mg), but also after larger ones (500 mg; or 10 mg per kg body weight). In the newborn

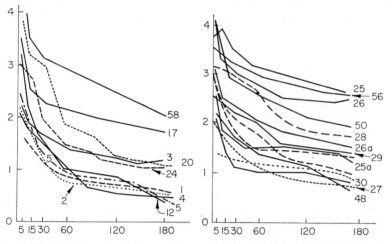

FIG. 47. Left: Bilirubin loading curves in normal subjects. From With (1943f). Right: Bilirubin loading curves in patients with hepatitis. From With (1943f).

the maximum bilirubin concentration is retarded about half an hour after injection (Lin and Eastman, 1937), whereas the peak is reached in 1–5 minutes in adults.

Figure 47 shows bilirubin loading curves for normal persons and patients with hepatitis.

Considerable individual scattering is apparent in the curves. No characteristic differences exist between normal persons and patients with liver damage. Calculation of the so-called retention percentage (see above) yielded 0–25% in 21 normal persons, 9–30% in 7 patients with slight liver damage, 0–55% in 20 cases with acute hepatitis, and 5–99% in 16 cases of chronic liver disease. Sampling was performed 3 hours and 5 minutes after injection.

On the basis of the foregoing evidence, it must be concluded that the bilirubin tolerance test is of questionable value because of both theoretical considerations and experimental evidence; its clinical value is also doubtful. Massias (1956) confirmed the uselessness of bilirubin tolerance tests for clinical purposes.

Tisdale et al. (1959) performed bilirubin loading experiments on 5 normal persons and 6 patients with liver cirrhosis. They infused 15 mg bilirubin per kg body weight intravenously within 30–60 minutes. The 1-minute-bilirubin and total bilirubin were determined before injection, in short intervals during injection, and hourly after injection; these determinations were continued for 8 more hours. Normal persons showed 0.5–1.1 mg per 100 ml total bilirubin before injection and reached a maximum of 8.5–18.3 mg per 100 ml. The corresponding 1-minute-bilirubin values were less than 0.1 mg per 100 ml and 0.7–2.3 mg per 100 ml. The maximum increase in serum bilirubin concentration was the same in normal persons and in patients with cirrhosis. However, subsequent decrease in bilirubin level was far more retarded in cirrhosis than in normal subjects.

It is noteworthy that total bilirubin and 1-minute-bilirubin increased together, although it could be shown that the injected bilirubin did not contain glucuronides. The peak of the 1-minute-bilirubin curve lagged from half an hour to 1 hour behind the peak of total bilirubin in all the experiments. This was true for normal persons as well as for patients with cirrhosis of the liver. Calculations showed that only 3% of the increase of 1-minute-bilirubin could have been due to the increase in total bilirubin. The rest must have originated from formation of water-soluble conjugates from the injected free bilirubin.

Thus, it has to be concluded that not all the conjugated bilirubin (formed from injected bilirubin) is excreted with the bile but that a certain part reaches the blood. Tisdale et al. (1959) assumed that regurgitation takes place. However, another explanation would be that during bilirubin overloading the normal excretion mechanism (from blood to bile) does not suffice to eliminate the amount present; thus a second route, namely from blood to lymph, is adopted by which conjugated bilirubin enters the general circulation. However, the lymph must pass through the thoracic duct before the bilirubin can get into the blood. Thus, this secretion is somewhat retarded as compared with total bilirubin increase. According to Shafiroff et al. (1939), this retardation is at least 15 minutes in dogs with experimental obstructive icterus; this time is probably even longer in humans because of the longer duct. In this way the retardation of the peak of the 1-minute bilirubin, which cannot be accounted for by the regurgitation hypothesis, is easily explained.

Weech et al. (1941) calculated the excretion constant for the bilirubin excretion with the bile from determinations of serum bilirubin after tolerance tests without simultaneous bilirubin determinations in the bile. This cannot be correct because a varying percentage, often below 50% (cf. above), of injected bilirubin appears in the bile. Lewis and Gershow (1961) developed a formula for calculation of the rate of bilirubin formation from the clearance of bilirubin from the plasma after intravenous injection of bilirubin. The basis of this calculation formula is open to question, although it appears to give correct values for the life-span of erythrocytes.

Most investigators have found that no bilirubin can be demonstrated in the urine after intravenous bilirubin loading in man, even with high dosage. This was studied with an especially sensitive technique by Gundermann and Kübler (1962), who found that only extremely small increases of the urinary bilirubin follow intravenous injection of unconjugated bilirubin in man. The increase was below 1% of the injected quantity of bilirubin.

Bilirubin loading in three humans with bile fistula was performed by Schalm *et al.* (1962b) who infused 100 mg bilirubin dissolved in sodium carbonate solution in the course of one half hour. The bile bilirubin was measured 1–1½ hours after the injection and found to be between 6 and 35 times the pre-injection values. After 18 hours the bile bilirubin was still 2–10 times the pre-injection value. The serum bilirubin increased 7–20 mg per 100 ml 1 hour after the loading. Chromatographic fractionation of the serum bilirubin according to P. G. Cole *et al.* (1954) showed that the increase of the serum bilirubin was mainly due to unconjugated bilirubin, but between 8 and 38% of the total serum bilirubin 1 hour after the injection was due to conjugated bilirubin, mostly the diglucuronide. Bilirubinuria was demonstrated in these three subjects. Schalm and Weber (1964) described loading experiments on rabbits and humans. To 22 rabbits, 100 or 150 mg of unconjugated bilirubin was infused intravenously during 1 hour, and blood was collected at intervals from 5 minutes to 3¾ hours after. In three of the animals, drain in the common bile duct was established. About 50% of the infused bilirubin was excreted with the bile within 2 hours. Conjugated bilirubin was determined with reverse phase partition chromatography on columns (method of Cole *et al.*) and was invariably present in all the blood samples. Loading tests with 600 or 1000 mg bilirubin were also carried out in 3 icteric human subjects with drain in the common bile duct and normal liver function. The bilirubin was infused in the course of 30 minutes. In subject A (load 600 mg) the total serum bilirubin 45 minutes after the start of the load was 10.6 mg/100 ml, the conjugated bilirubin 3.0 mg/100 ml; 15 minutes later the figures were 9.2 and 4.5, respectively. The hyperbilirubinemia had virtually disappeared 3 hours after the start of the infusion. Bilirubinuria became demonstrable 18 hours after the start of the load. Subject B (load 1000 mg) exhibited maximal serum bilirubin—19.3 mg/100 ml total, 3.4 mg/100 ml conjugated—1 hour after the start of the load. After 3 hours the figures were 11.7 and 6.3, respectively, and 18 hours after the infusion only 2.3 mg/100 ml total. Subject C (load 600 mg) exhibited maximum serum bilirubin 1 hour after the start of the load amounting to 7.9 mg/100 ml total and 3.0 mg/100 ml conjugated. After 18 hours the serum bilirubin was 1.5 mg/100 ml total. Bilirubinuria appeared after 3 hours.

Billing *et al.* (1964b*) investigated the plasma bilirubin disappearance curve after i.v. injection of 2 mg bilirubin per kg body weight dissolved in 10 ml 0.1 M Na_2CO_3, injected in 1 minute. Analyses were performed on blood taken from a limb other than the injected one, at 5-minute intervals during the first hour and subsequently every half hour for the first 4 hours after the injection. Seven normal subjects and 22 patients were studied. In the normal subjects there was a steep rise of unconjugated bilirubin to about 3 mg/100 ml and then a gradual decline; after 4 hours only 12% of the injected dose remained in the plasma. There was an increase of direct bilirubin ("15-minute bilirubin") of 0.3–0.5 mg per 100 ml, but this was regarded as an artifact having no connection with the presence of conjugated bilirubin. The form of the serum bilirubin time curve was essentially the same for all the normal subjects when plotted logarithmically against time (ordinate: logarithm of concentration; abscissa: time; nonlogarithmic scale). The curves fitted the equation: $C_t = Ae^{-k_1 t} + Be^{-k_2 t}$, where C_t is the concentration at the time t and A, B, k_1, and k_2 are constants, while e is the base of natural logarithms.

The simplest model fitting this empirical equation consists of three intercommunicating departments: (1) the plasma, (2) the pool of unconjugated bilirubin present in the liver from which some reflux to the plasma occurs, and (3) the pool of conjugated bilirubin into which it passes. If a indicates the rate of uptake of bilirubin by the liver, b estimates the rate at which the unconjugated bilirubin is being returned to the plasma, and m represents the rate of transfer of unconjugated bilirubin in the liver to the conjugated bilirubin compartment, then the following relations between a, b, m, and the constants of the above equation:

$$a = \frac{Ak_1 + Bk_2}{A + B}; \qquad b = (k_1 + k_2) - (a + m); \qquad m = \frac{k_1 + k_2}{a}$$

They calculated a, b, and m from the curves using the method of least squares and a computer, and they arrived at the following figures for normal subjects: $a = 0.035 \pm 0.01$; $b = 0.015 \pm 0.006$; $m = 0.022 \pm$ 0.018.

It is worthy of note that the mathematical analysis of the data points to a return of unconjugated bilirubin from the liver to the plasma. Direct experimental evidence for this seems required.

The studies of Billing *et al.* with this method included 8 cases of Gilbert's disease, 2 cases of hemolytic jaundice, 2 cases of posthepatitic jaundice, 4 cases with Dubin-Johnson's and one with Rotor-Stransky's syndrome, as well as 3 with portal and 2 with biliary cirrhosis. Further, three relatives of patients with Gilbert's disease, 2 relatives of a patient with Crigler-Najjar's disease, and 4 relatives of patients with Dubin-Johnson's syndrome were studied.

Bilirubin excretion proceeds significantly faster after intravenous infection in *small laboratory animals* than in humans. This could be related to different normal serum bilirubin levels in these animals and in humans. Contrary to humans these animals do not normally have bilirubin in their serum. Scholderer (1933a), who injected 4 mg bilirubin per kg body weight in *rabbits*, found that the serum bilirubin dropped to 5% of the maximum within 15 minutes after injection. This was also the case when the kidneys and spleen were removed prior to injection. The serum bilirubin level remained constant after hepatectomy. Also Schalm and Weber (1964) reported loading tests on rabbits (cf. above). Heimann (1933) could not detect bilirubin in serum of *guinea pigs*, which obtained 10 mg bilirubin per kg body weight. In rabbits, increased serum bilirubin occurred after doses as high as 20 mg per kg, but the bilirubin had already disappeared from the serum after 1 hour. When the rabbits were given acidifying food, 7.5 mg per kg sufficed to induce bilirubinemia. The *rat* exhibits a similar high excretory capacity, i.e., 3–4 mg per kg per hour (cf. Chapter IV,C,2). *Dogs*, which like small laboratory animals have normally no bilirubin in their serum, react entirely differently upon bilirubin loading. Thus, 250 mg bilirubin injected intravenously causes hyperbilirubinemia which lasts 10–12 days (Li *et al.*, 1944).

This difference in reaction of mammalian species toward bilirubin loading is very interesting, but has not yet been subject to closer investigation. Experiments performed on a larger number of animal species, which normally have a high serum bilirubin level (e.g., horses), would be valuable.

Some investigators conducted studies on bilirubin of bile after bilirubin loading. Stroebe (1932a) observed an increase of bilirubin of bile in dogs and in patients with bile fistula. The increase started 30 minutes after injection, reached its maximum after 2½ hours, and returned to normal after 5–6 hours. No exact measurements were possible, but it was estimated that about 70% of bilirubin injected appeared in the bile within 5 hours after injection. This experiment was performed in a dog, which had received an injection of 50 mg bilirubin. Cantarow et al. (1948a,b) injected 1 mg bilirubin per kg body weight in dogs and determined 50–90% of it in the bile after the first 3 hours after injection, and 60–100% after 4 hours. Similar studies in man and rabbits with bile fistula were reported by Schalm and Weber (1964) (cf. above).

Weinbren and Billing (1956) found the *maximum excretory capacity* to be 61 μg per minute per 100 g body weight in the rat, and Lathe and Walker (1958a) found 1.2 mg per hour per g liver. This corresponds, respectively, to 900 mg per 24 hours per kg body weight and 30,000 mg per 24 hours per kg liver weight. Heikel et al. (1960) loaded rabbits with free bilirubin intravenously and found that the bile bilirubin consisted of ca. 50% monoglucuronide and ca. 50% diglucuronide, i.e., a much higher proportion of monoglucuronide than normally occurring in man and the dog. Krueger and Higginson (1961) studied the effect of various hepato-toxic substances and agents blocking the RES on the bilirubin clearance of the rat liver. Only serum analyses were carried out without analyses of the bile. The bilirubin clearance thus determined showed a prompt response to hepatotoxic substances, but no parallism with the degree of histological damage of the liver parenchyma could be demonstrated. O'Donnel et al. (1961) determined the clearance of rat liver by means of bilirubin loading of prefused liver preparations. Both bile and perfusion fluid were analyzed. The maximal clearance of the normal rat liver was found to be 210 mg. Campeanu and Campeanu (1960, 1961) calculated the bilirubin clearance of the human liver from the increase in serum bilirubin following intravenous injection of 1 ml 3% nicotinic acid and its subsequent decrease. The serum bilirubin was analyzed before and 1, 2, and 3 hours after the injection. The findings were evaluated by means of a semilogarithmic diagram and compared with the clinical picture and liver biopsy. The authors found good agreement between retention per-centages and clinical findings, but only 10 cases were reported.

Stickney et al. (1965*) studied the connection between *high altitude* and the bilirubin and BSP excretion tests in rats treated in decompression chambers. It was found that the serum bilirubin 30 minutes after the loading was significantly higher in "high altitude rats" than in the con-trols. This deficiency of bilirubin excretion is most probably due to the action of chronic hypoxia on the liver.

Billing et al. (1963) investigated i.v. *loading with conjugated bilirubin*. They infused free bilirubin or diluted rat bile in doses of 0.3 mg/minute for 45 minutes i.v. in rats and found about the same hepatic clearance rate (T_m) for free and conjugated bilirubin: 54 ± 0.81 μg/

minute/100 g body weight for free bilirubin (mean serum bilirubin 43.3 mg/100 ml) and 47.8 ± 1.94 μg/minute/100 g for conjugated bilirubin (mean serum bilirubin 17.7 mg/100 ml). The animals were sacrificed and their total body bilirubin and total blood bilirubin determined. The quotient total body bilirubin/total serum bilirubin (in mg/100 ml) was on the average 4.91 after injections of free bilirubin and 9.06 after injections of conjugated bilirubin, i.e., much more bilirubin was retained in the tissues after injections of conjugated bilirubin than after free bilirubin. The liver, however, contained 25% of the total body bilirubin after loading with free bilirubin and only 10% after loading with conjugated bilirubin.

The entry of bilirubin into the liver during i.v. loading with physiological serum bilirubin concentrations was studied in the rat by means of tritiated bilirubin by Brown *et al.* (1964*). They found that after 5 minutes 50% of the label was in the liver and after 30–60 minutes most of the label had entered the bile.

The excretion characteristics of *bromsulphalein sodium* are very similar to those of bilirubin. Since this compound can be handled more easily than bilirubin, it has been used increasingly to examine liver function in excretion tests. Cantarow *et al.* (1948a,b) determined that the amount of bromsulphalein eliminated from blood over a period of time always exceeded the amount of pigment excreted with the bile during the same period. This was explained by temporary storage of bromsulphalein in the liver. Krebs and Brauer (1949) and Brauer *et al.* (1950) investigated the excretion conditions with radioactive (S^{35}) bromsulphalein. With the help of autoradiographs these authors demonstrated that the pigment was deposited in parenchymal cells and not in Kupffer's cells. A certain part of this dye stuff was degraded in the liver. It is known that bromsulphalein and bilirubin compete in the excretion mechanism of liver. This is also true for other compounds (Hanzon, 1952, pp. 37–38 et seq.). The bromsulphalein excretion of the liver was further studied by Brauer *et al.* (1955) and Andrews and Lozano (1961), who found that the excretion mechanism is complicated. As Heikel *et al.* (1960) found that bilirubin and bromsulphalein are excreted by means of different conjugation mechanisms, a further discussion is omitted here. (See also Chapter IV,C,4.)

A number of investigators have studied the *clinical value* of the bilirubin tolerance test. Bramanti (1948a,b) published a survey of results obtained with the bilirubin tolerance test in various diseases. Ljung (1948) found the highest retention percentages in jaundiced patients without severe liver insufficiency, a finding which may be explained by nonhemolytic hereditary hyperbilirubinemia in these cases. However, the bilirubin tolerance test has been generally replaced by the bromsulphalein test (compare Massias, 1956).

Experiments on rats elucidating the correlation between histologically demonstrable liver damage and the bilirubin loading test were carried by Krueger and Higginson (1961[*]) who induced liver damage by means of India ink, shellac, gum acacia, CCl_4, ethanol, chlorpromazine, $CHCl_3$, or choline-deficient diet employing a total of 100 rats. They found that the bilirubin excretion test demonstrated the liver injury at a very early stage, but that it was of no value as an indicator of the degree of histological liver damage. The results of the bilirubin loading test exhibited no correlation with the degree of hepatocellular necrosis present.

Billing *et al.* (1964b[*]) performed mathematical analyses of the loading curves obtained in humans and found characteristic deviations from the normal in patients with Gilbert's disease, Dubin-Johnson's and Rotor-Stransky's syndromes, and minor variations during posthepatitic states and liver cirrhosis.

Loading extended over longer periods, which results in artificial jaundice, is more interesting than a single loading with bilirubin. Thompson and Wyatt (1938), as well as Hench (1938), injected 10–20 mg bilirubin per kg body weight, or 1000 mg bilirubin daily, in patients with rheumatoid arthritis. The injections were continued for 13 days. They hoped that the resulting jaundice would improve arthritis. Serum bilirubin was determined 5 minutes and 24 hours after injections. Serum bilirubin increased to 5–35 mg per 100 ml after 5 minutes. The 24-hour values gave a day-by-day slowly increasing level. Values of 1–3.5 mg per 100 ml were found after the first 24 hours. After this the 24-hour values increased to about 5 mg per 100 ml after the eighth day and 8–12.5 mg per 100 ml after 11–13 days. Corresponding to these increasing values, jaundice developed slowly and became visible 2–7 days after the first injection. With (unpublished results, 1949) performed similar experiments on a normal person (38 years old, 70 kg body weight). He injected 500 mg bilirubin intravenously daily, for 4 consecutive days. The results obtained were similar to those found in the arthritic patients. After 5 minutes the maximum was 18 mg per 100 ml and after 24 hours it was 2.26 mg per 100 ml. Visible jaundice was present 3–6 days after the injections were started. Jaundice and hyperbilirubinemia slowly faded after the cessation of injections, and disappeared 3 weeks after the last injections in all these experiments.

Such experiments are very troublesome because the administration of aqueous alkaline bilirubin solutions causes fever, chills, and aseptic thrombophlebitis of the arm veins. These inconvenient side effects are avoided by injecting bilirubin in solutions containing albumin. To compensate for the irritating effect of alkali, With (1954) proposed dissolving bilirubin in dilute alkali and adding some serum of the patient, or purified human serum albumin before injection. Massias (1956) confirmed that the side effects can really be avoided in this way.

Extended loading experiments have also been performed in dogs. Li *et al.* (1944) induced hyperbilirubinemia of 10–12 days duration by five consecutive injections of 50 mg bilirubin, which were administered at 4–6 hour intervals. Snapp *et al.* (1944) continued such injections for 3 weeks. A definite icterus of the sclera developed, which continued for a few weeks after the injections. Snapp *et al.* (1947) obtained the same results by administering 200–300 mg bilirubin dissolved in dog plasma every third day or injecting 50 mg daily. The animals tolerated these injections without any detectable damage. The highest serum bilirubin value reached was 18 mg per 100 ml. About 0.5 mg per 100 ml was determined 1 week after the last injection.

Summary

Bilirubin brought into the circulation in man is only partially excreted in bile; ca. 50% of this bilirubin is destroyed in the organism. The bilirubin excretion test is without value as a measure for liver insufficiency, and has been replaced by the bromsulphalein test. Various animal species show considerable variation in bilirubin tolerance. Thus, small rodents tolerate enormous amounts of bilirubin without an increase of serum bilirubin, whereas bilirubin loading is followed by a significant rise in the serum bilirubin in humans and dogs. Investigations of this phenomenon in other animal species would be of interest. Extended loading by continued bilirubin injections has been performed on humans and dogs over a period of many days or weeks. These experiments caused hyperbilirubinemia which assumed considerable dimensions and led to jaundice.

After loading with unconjugated bilirubin not only unconjugated but also conjugated serum bilirubin apparently increases, but the few existing studies on this phenomenon are contradictory.

At amounts of 15 mg bilirubin per kg body weight and over, the liver is no longer capable of excreting all conjugated bilirubin formed from injected bilirubin. This can be explained by insufficiency of the normal excretion mechanism (blood to bile) and establishment of a secondary route, namely blood to lymph.

K. Hereditary Nonhemolytic Hyperbilirubinemia: Crigler-Najjar, Rotor-Stransky, and Dubin-Johnson Syndromes; Benign Recurrent Intrahepatic Cholestasis and Other "Functional" Hyperbilirubinemias

"Cholémie simple familiale," "physiologische Hyperbilirubinämie," "constitutional hepatic dysfunction," and *"icterus intermittens juvenilis"*

are various names introduced to designate a type of hyperbilirubinemia which occurs in apparently healthy persons. Besides this form of hyperbilirubinemia, which shows a negative direct diazo reaction conditions of a very similar nature but giving a positive diazo reaction were recently described. Hyperbilirubinemia is usually mild, but definite jaundice may develop. Cases are known where such jaundice continued through many years without becoming detrimental to health. Recently these forms of hyperbilirubinemia have been called "functional hyperbilirubinemia" (Siede, 1957; K. Beck and Kühn, 1959).

Gilbert and Lereboullet (1900, 1901a,b, 1903, 1905, 1910) were the first to describe this condition. Other French authors (Rey, 1910; Sergeant, 1910) gave a rather vague definition of the condition and considered other clinical symptoms besides hyperbilirubinemia. Sergeant found the condition in 25% of hospitalized patients in the North of France. Scheel (1911) described the disease in Norway, and Hijmans van den Bergh (1918) in Holland. The latter author coined the term "physiological hyperbilirubinemia." Later, Meulengracht (1920), Gänsslen et al. (1925), J. S. Diamond (1928), and Tecon (1936) reported similar observations. The family described by Manson (1928) also seems to belong to this form, although the symptoms were described as hemolytic jaundice at the time. Rozendaal et al. (1935), M. W. Comfort and Hoyne (1944), and M. W. Comfort (1945) investigated this condition more thoroughly and introduced the term "constitutional hepatic dysfunction." Meulengracht (1938, 1939, 1944, 1947) used the name "icterus intermittens juvenilis." Dameshek and Singer (1941), Curry et al. (1942), and Baroody and Shugart (1956) introduced the term "familial, nonhemolytic jaundice." Other investigators of the condition have been Alwall et al. (1946b), Hult (1950), W. Müller (1954), Weiss (1955), Wildhirt (1955), Eanet and Brick (1955) and Blanton and Blanton (1955).

Most of the investigators listed above confirmed the familial nature of this condition. Krarup and Roholm (1941), Curry et al. (1942), Welin (1945), Alwall (1946), Meulengracht (1947), Hult (1950), W. Müller (1954), Eanet and Brick (1955), Blanton and Blanton (1955), and Wildhirt (1955) studied the pathological anatomy of liver. They found either completely normal conditions or only slight deviations from the normal in most cases as, e.g., deposition of fat in liver cells, which was assumed to be a consequence of hepatitis. If the latter assumption is correct most of the cases are latent or protracted hepatitis (Hult, Müller). This interpretation is surely correct (cf. Margadant, 1961). However, Hult's assumption that all these cases are latent hepatitis or posthepatitic conditions is erroneous. There are cases of persistent jaundice which last from early adolescence to old age.

Parkes Weber (1946, 1948) described the most famous case in which autopsy showed a definitely normal liver. L. Schiff (1946, p. 199) and Berk (1946) reported similar findings. In addition, observations made on rats (so-called Gunn rats) with similar hereditary traits, normal liver function, no bilirubinuria, and no signs of any hemolysis, revealed that at least one part of this type of hyperbilirubinemia in humans must be due to hereditary anomalies of metabolism.

Electron microscope studies in two pronounced cases of this condition were reported by Simon and Varonier (1963). In these cases hepatitis could be excluded with certainty. The findings were ruptures of the hepatocytic membranes; disappearance or reduction in number of the microvilli of the hepatic cell and its vascular pole; obstruction of spaces of Disse's by cytoplasmic elements liberated by rupture of the cellular membrane; and partial destruction of the sinusoidal endothelium. These alterations were regarded as very probably reversible.

Hereditary, nonhemolytic hyperbilirubinemia is clinically characterized by latent hyperbilirubinemia or a form of jaundice, which usually has a mild or intermittent course. It shows a negative, direct diazo reaction, proceeds without bilirubinuria, and does not show any signs of hemolysis or increased excretion of urobilin compounds. The familial occurrence is characteristic of these cases. The disease is usually observed in young men, but it is also found in women (e.g., Simon and Varonier), and can occur even at birth and can continue to advanced age (Parkes-Weber). These patients often complain of weariness and mild dyspepsia. However, it is not entirely clear whether these symptoms are characteristic of this condition or if they are observed only in those cases of subclinical hepatitis erroneously diagnosed as cases of nonhemolytic constitutional hyperbilirubinemia.

The nature of this disease has been studied: (a) by examining subjects with high serum bilirubin detected during systematic studies of serum bilirubin of apparently normal individuals; and (b) by examining icteric patients. It is known that, during epidemics of virus hepatitis, latent cases occur with only very few symptoms. Thus, it is often difficult to decide whether one is dealing with a subclinical case of hepatitis or an hereditary condition. The determination of frequency of hereditary nonhemolytic hyperbilirubinemia is therefore difficult.

Systematic studies on high normal serum bilirubin by Weiss (1955) and O'Hagan *et al.* (1957) were discussed in Section I,1 of this chapter.

W. Müller (1954) described 8 personal cases and analyzed 94 cases reported in the literature. He agreed with Hult that this condition is often caused by virus hepatitis, and increased blood degradation could only be demonstrated on rare occasions. It is possible that the liver has a decreased excretion capacity for bilirubin. However, this has not yet been proved unequivocally. Based on the analysis of 14 cases, Wolf (1956) reached the same conclusions. Over a period of 5 years Wildhirt (1955) investigated 115 cases. Of these patients, 88 showed definite signs of earlier virus hepatitis, whereas this could not be detected in the remaining 27. Contrary to other investigators, Wildhirt found mild hemolysis in the majority of his patients. Therefore he spoke about an "acquired hemolytic icterus after hepatitis." The evidence presented for this interpretation, however, is not convincing; no quantitative excretion studies of urobilin compounds in feces were reported.

Another hypothesis is that true, nonhemolytic, familial hyperbilirubinemia (i.e., not caused by virus hepatitis) constitutes a variant of the normal, characterized by high serum bilirubin levels. But it seems more likely to assume that it is an inborn error of metabolism. Recently, Schmid *et al.* (1957a,b, 1958c) and Lathe and Walker (1957a,b, 1958a,b) shed new light on the biochemical mechanism of jaundice during this anomaly by means of rats suffering from hereditary nonhemolytic jaundice (so-called Gunn rats) (cf. Chapter IV,E,3). Livers of such rats were studied *in vitro,* and it was found that the enzyme system in the microsomes of normal rat liver, which is capable of synthesizing bilirubin glucuronides from bilirubin and uridine diphosphoglucuronic acid *in vitro,* is missing from homozygote Gunn rats. Bilirubin is retained in the serum of these animals, and no bilirubinuria is present. Otherwise these rats are normal except that their bile is colorless.

Arias (1962) studied 23 adolescent or adult patients with chronic unconjugated hyperbilirubinemia without overt signs of hemolysis. Menthol loading tests were performed to control glucuronic acid synthesis, liver biopsy with *in vitro* studies of UDP-bilirubin transferase activity were carried out, and erythrocyte survival time determinations with Cr^{31} were included. Of the 23 cases 8 were found to suffer from hereditary defects of glucuronide formation. The serum bilirubin in this group was rather high, 6.4–10.9 mg per 100 ml, and showed comparatively small variations in the single patient; it consisted almost completely of unconjugated bilirubin. The hepatic UDP-bilirubin transferase activity was significantly decreased, and after loading with 1 g of menthol the excretion of glucuronide increased 2–26% as compared with 39–72% in normals. The condition appeared to be transmitted by a single autosomal recessive gene as in Crigler-Najjar syndrome and in Gunn rats. Four of the 23 patients were shown to be suffering from latent hemolytic states with erythrocyte survival times (half-life) of 19–23 days. The serum bilirubin in this group varied from 0.3 to 4.6 mg per 100 ml. Another 4 of the 23 cases exhibited latent viral hepatitis (posthepatitis syndrome), to judge from liver function tests and liver biopsies. Their serum bilirubin ranged from 0.4 to 4.1 mg per 100 ml. In the remaining 7 patients the studies revealed no clue to the nature of the condition. Their serum bilirubin varied from 0.7 to 3.4 mg per 100 ml. Only in one of these 7 patients family studies revealed hyperbilirubinemia. This case may be of a similar nature as those of the first group. This investigation of Arias clearly shows the diagnostic difficulties encountered in chronic unconjugated hyperbilirubinemia and emphasizes the necessity of placing the patient in the correct diagnostic group and of avoiding such vague terms as "constitutional hepatic dysfunction," "physiological hyperbilirubinemia," and "Gilbert's disease."

An interesting case was published by Sagild *et al.* (1962*). The patient was a man aged 22 with serum bilirubin between 10 and 15 mg/ 100 ml of which over 95% showed indirect reaction. All liver function tests were normal including the BSP retention test. A liver biopsy showed coarse pigment granula resembling those found in the Dubin-Johnson syndrome. Also on electron microscopy the granula fitted the description of those present in the liver of patients with the Dubin-Johnson syndrome. A family study disclosed no cases of jaundice with the possible exception of a sister dying in infancy several years before.

Recently a 5-year study comprising 366 adolescent and adult patients with unconjugated hyperbilirubinemia in absence of overt hemolysis was published by Levine and Klatskin (1964*). The patients were selected from a total of 33,560 subjects studied in a liver unit. Most of the patients had an acquired disturbance of bilirubin metabolism due to disease and only relatively few of the cases were of "idiopathic" or genetic origin. They emphasized the necessity of careful search for underlying disease. Only after such search has disclosed no disease the patient can be classified as "idiopathic unconjugated hyperbilirubinemia" unless its hereditary nature can be appropriately demonstrated. Names such as Gilbert's disease, constitutional hepatic dysfunction, and familial nonhemolytic jaundice are regarded as misleading because they employ unwarranted conclusions regarding etiology.

Billing *et al.* (1964b*) reported careful bilirubin tolerance tests in 8 patients with "Gilbert's disease" and found curves significantly different from those of normal subjects, i.e., a definitely slower fall of the serum bilirubin both in the period immediately after the steep rise and later.

Perona *et al.* (1964*) published a case of Gilbert's disease in a 16-year-old boy on whom electron microscopic and enzymatic investigations on a liver biopsy were carried out. The glucuronyl transferase activity was found to be less than one-tenth of the normal.

Klaus and Feine (1965*) reported a case in a man aged 43 in great detail. He developed jaundice at 20 years of age and the icterus remained asymptomatic for 19 years. When he was 40 gallstones were found and a cholecystectomy carried out, but the jaundice persisted. The serum bilirubin was unconjugated and liver function tests were normal. Erythroid hyperplasia in the bone marrow, reticulocytosis in the peripheral blood, increased plasma-Fe turnover, and increased fecal urobilinogen suggested chronic hemolysis, but the erythrocyte longevity was normal, pointing to the presence of ineffective erythropoiesis. The patient was studied for 9 months. His serum bilirubin varied between 2 and 6 mg/100 ml and was unchanged during a 14-day course of 15 mg daily doses of prednizolone. During an 8-day course of 5 g cholestyramine resin daily it fell from 4.95 to 2.20 mg/100 ml.

Familial, nonhemolytic jaundice merits consideration because severe cases can induce *kernicterus* in young children (Crigler-Najjar Syndrome, cf. Chapter IX,D). This is understandable since most of the serum bilirubin is unconjugated in this case. Schmid *et al.* (1957b), who examined three such children with serum bilirubin between 20 and 35 mg per 100 ml, found that the bile was practically free from bilirubin. No bilirubinuria was noted and the serum of the children showed an indirect diazo reaction. The secretion mechanism for bromsulphalein and iodipamide (cholografin) was normal in these children. Similarly, liver biopsy or liver function tests did not show any pathological abnormalities. Arias and London (1957) demonstrated the same enzyme defect in the liver of human patients with familial, nonhemolytic jaundice as was found by Schmid (1957b) in the Gunn rats.

Sugar (1961) described a family with Crigler-Najjar syndrome. Szabó *et al.* (1962) reported two cases of this syndrome in two Hungarian infant siblings who both developed kernicterus. In one of them pronounced decrease of hepatic uridine glucuronyl transferase activity was demonstrated *in vitro*. As acetanilide was conjugated normally, it was concluded that at least two kinds of this transferase must be present in human liver. Both patients showed progressive hepatomegaly, and the liver of one stored an unidentified substance of polysaccharide structure. The bladder bile of this patient contained 10 mg direct reacting bilirubin per 100 ml.

Schmid and Hammaker (1962) studied a patient with the Crigler-Najjar syndrome, who exhibited a serum bilirubin of about 25 mg per 100 ml, using intravenous injection of C^{14}-bilirubin. During the first few minutes after the injection the radioactivity of the plasma decreased steeply, but later the decrease became slower, and after the 30th hour the specific activity of the plasma decreased logarithmically corresponding to a $T\frac{1}{2}$ of 156 hours. The total miscible pool of bilirubin was determined to be 568 mg and the bilirubin turnover to be 60 mg per 24 hours. Most of the isotope was recovered from the stool, only ca. 7% from the urine, and in both, the major part was present as diazo-negative catabolites different from urobilin and mesobilifuscin.

François *et al.* (1962) described a case of Crigler-Najjar disease in a 3-year-old girl. Bamatter *et al.* (1962) presented a case of congenital nonhemolytic jaundice in a 6-year-old boy born prematurely, showing kernicterus but a normal liver UDP-bilirubin transferase system. They regarded the case as caused by prematurity in a patient with a mild degree of hereditary unconjugated hyperbilirubinemia, and not as one of true Crigler-Najjar syndrome. Szabó and Ebrey (1963) supported the concept of Crigler-Najjar syndrome as a hereditary condition by performing oral menthol loading tests in 11 of 16 close relatives of their two patients. It was found that the 11 relatives excreted reduced amounts of conjugated glucuronic acid after the loading compared to normal controls. To judge from these results Crigler-Najjar disease is dependent on a recessive gene, and the heterozygote carriers can be detected by oral menthol loading tests. This is an interesting finding worthy of further study.

Billing *et al.* (1964a*) studied a 6-year-old child with Crigler-Najjar's syndrome and cerebral palsy due to kernicterus, employing C^{14}-bilirubin and found the pool of exchangeable bilirubin to be 1400 mg, the half-life of the plasma bilirubin to be 80 hours, and the daily bilirubin turnover to be 290 mg. A study with ingestion of N^{15}-glycine showed fecal peaks on the 2nd and 7th days, as well as on the 133rd day. The observations indicated abnormal initial bile pigment peaks, but the knowledge of the variation of these peaks in normals is too incomplete to allow definite conclusions. Billing *et al.* (1964*) subjected 3 relatives of patients with Gilbert's disease and 2 relatives of the patient with Crigler-Najjar's disease to i.v. bilirubin loading and found normal loading curves.

Israels *et al.* (1959) described four cases of familial icterus which were caused mainly by parahematic bile pigment formation, i.e., bilirubin production during the "first peak" (Fig. 29, Chapter II,A). Israels and Zipursky (1962) studied one of these patients after loading with 2-C^{14}-glycine. Heme was isolated from the blood and stercobilin from the feces. The curve constructed from the radioactivity data of the isolated substances showed that at least 82% of the stercobilin was excreted during the "first peak" as compared with only 6–10% in four normal control subjects. The hyperactive normoblastic bone marrow found in these patients suggests that the erythroblasts constitute the site of the bilirubin overproduction, either catabolically from heme or by a more direct metabolic pathway. Israels *et al.* (1963a,b) confirmed and extended these experiments and found that in patients with this "shunt hyperbilirubinemia," radioactive bilirubin appears in the bile before radioactive heme is demonstrated in the bone marrow (cf. Chapter II,A,1).

The so-called Crigler-Najjar syndrome and its counterpart in rats, the Gunn rat (cf. Chapter IV, Section E,2) is possibly a special hereditary disease distinct from the more benign form of familial nonhemolytic jaundice with unconjugated bilirubin, the so-called Gilbert's disease.

Several studies on Gunn rats have been reported, some of which have been discussed in Section F, this chapter. This condition in rats is due to a recessive gene, and only the homozygous rats exhibit the syndrome. Van Leusden *et al.* (1962) found that homozygous Gunn rats exhibit deficient conjugation of a number of substances while the heterozygotes show the same conjugation capacity as normal rats. Van Leusden and Stolte (1963) found that female homozygous Gunn rats show precocious puberty. Also the formation of thyroxine glucuronide was decreased in Gunn rats (Kock *et al.*, 1963). Hargreaves and Lathe (1963) pointed out that the excretion of bromsulphalein and iodipamide is not decreased in Gunn rats or patients with nonhemolytic familial hyperbilirubinemia, from which it can be concluded that these compounds must be excreted by the liver by means of mechanisms not identical with its bilirubin excretion mechanism.

Recently several studies on Gunn rats have appeared. Maggiore *et al.* (1963b*) found in loading experiments with bilirubin that the capacity of the liver to store bilirubin is the same in Gunn rats and normal rats. The difference lies in the power to conjugate bilirubin. Hargreaves and Thom (1964*) found that the serum level of transaminases, lactic dehydrogenase, aldolase, and cholinesterase is the same in Gunn rats and normal rats. Huttunen and Miettinen (1965*) found that the power of glucuronidation in rats varies considerably with the age of the animals and the strain, and they regarded the Gunn rats as an extreme variety of rat strains in this respect. Garay *et al.* (1966a*) studied the formation of bilirubin as a by-product of hepatic heme synthesis in Gunn rats and normal rats in 5-hour perfusion experiments of isolated livers employing C^{14}-δ-aminolevulinic acid. While normal rat livers incorporated 12–14% of C^{14}-ALA injected into the portal vein into the bile bilirubin, the corresponding figure for Gunn rats was only 5% into the plasma bilirubin, and the incorporation into the bile bilirubin was very low. Garay *et al.* (1966b*), who collected the bile from rats with bile fistulas as well as from isolated perfused rat livers, found that the bilirubin excretion in the Gunn rat was only about one-sixth as high as that of the normal rat. Only very little conjugated bilirubin appeared in the bile of the Gunn rat. The distribution of bilirubin in the tissues of Gunn rats with particular reference to the liver was studied by Hargreaves and Scrimegeour (1966*).

The problem of nonhemolytic, familial jaundice is not exhausted with the foregoing discussion, since only hyperbilirubinemia with indirect diazo reaction was mentioned. Forms exhibiting *direct diazo reaction* are also known. Rotor *et al.* (1948) and Stransky (1950) from the Philippines were the first who reported such cases. Although direct diazo reaction of serum was present, there was no bilirubinuria. However, the serum bilirubin level was not very high. The highest value reported was 6.5 mg per 100 ml. Liver biopsy, which was performed in one of these cases, did not reveal any pigment agglomeration which is characteristic for the Dubin-Johnson syndrome (see below). Apparently a hereditary disease was involved here. L. Schiff *et al.* (1959) described another case believed to be this "Rotor-Stransky syndrome." A 29-year-old Japanese woman was involved. The patient had pigments I and II in her serum, had normal urinary urobilinogens, normal serum phosphatases and transaminases, increased bromsulphalein retention, and did not show a gallbladder after cholecystography. They regarded the condition as hereditary.

Porush *et al.* (1962*) published a case concerning Rotor-Stransky's syndrome in an Italian woman aged 40 who had been icteric from her 7th year and had normal liver biopsy. He surveyed the literature and found 9 published cases of this syndrome with liver biopsy. He maintained that the only difference between Rotor-Stransky's and Dubin-Johnson's syndromes (cf. below) is the pigment in the liver cells.

Haník (1964*) published a study of a male suffering from Rotor-Stransky's syndrome who was born 1917, was observed at intervals from 1949 to 1962, and was subjected to two liver biopsies (1951 and 1961), both normal. His serum bilirubin was about 11 mg/100 ml with ca. 50% direct-reacting. Poland *et al.* (1965*) reported a case of Rotor-Stransky's syndrome in a 12-year-old girl who had entirely normal liver biopsy. They discussed the literature and concluded that the symptoms of this condition are completely identical with those of Dubin-Johnson's syndrome with the exception of the liver pigment and that the two syndromes may well be variants of the same condition. The maximum serum bilirubin concentration recorded in Rotor-Stransky's syndrome is 23 mg/100 ml.

Pereira Lima *et al.* (1966*) described a Brazilian family with three members suffering from Rotor-Stransky's syndrome as indicated by history, laboratory studies, and liver biopsies. Relevant information including 72 relatives in 6 generations was obtained pointing to an autosomal recessive gene. As some earlier observations suggest a dominant heredity of this syndrome, the possibility of similar conditions differing in mode of heredity cannot be excluded. Only further careful studies can decide, and the possibility of jaundice being due to other causes in some relatives must be taken seriously into account. These authors also discussed the relationship between Rotor-Stransky's and Dubin-Johnson's syndromes and regard it as likely that the two conditions may be determined by the same genetic factor and pointed out that caution should be exercised in establishing genetic models for these conditions.

Summerskill and Walshe (1959) reported two cases in England of intermittent jaundice with direct diazo reaction and bilirubinuria. Both cases showed maximal serum bilirubin concentrations of 40 mg per 100 ml, and exhibited "intrahepatic obstruction" without black pigment on numerous liver biopsies. Tygstrup (1960) reported two cases of non-hemolytic hyperbilirubinemia in two boys from the Faroe islands. Both suffered from intermittent jaundice since early infancy. The serum bilirubin gave direct diazo reaction and liver biopsy showed intrahepatic cholestasis. The conditions showed great similarity to the cases of Summerskill and Walshe. The fact that the disease occurred at a much earlier age may be due to inbreeding of the inhabitants of the Faroe islands. One of Tygstrup's cases exhibited distinct hypokalemia. Similar cases in two brothers, aged 14 and 17 years, were reported by Kühn (1962, 1963). Liver biopsy showed "intrahepatic cholestasis." Schapiro and Isselbacher (1963) described a similar case in a 41-year-old woman who had had 27 attacks of jaundice in 38 years. During the attacks her liver showed the picture of "intrahepatic cholestasis," but during remission the histologic picture was normal. The serum bilirubin reached 14.8 mg per 100 ml with a direct reaction of 11.8 mg per 100 ml. The bromsulphalein retention was increased. Summerskill and Walshe and Kühn assumed that an inherited anomaly of metabolism was involved. Schapiro and Isselbacher (1963) proposed the name "benign recurrent intrahepatic cholestasis" for this condition. The liver showed normal histology outside the attacks. The pigment characteristic of the Dubin-Johnson syndrome is not found in the syndrome.

Williams et al. (1964*) reported three new cases and Spiegel et al. (1965*) one new case of Summerskill-Walshe's syndrome. In the latter —a girl aged 14—recurrent seasonal pruritus preceded the onset by 8 years; no evidence of extrahepatic biliary occlusion could be found despite two surgical explorations, and treatment with cholestyramine resin decreased her abnormally increased serum bile acid and relieved her pruritus.

Summerskill (1965*) described a new case of this syndrome in a woman aged 59. Intra- and extracellular vesicules were found in liver biopsy during attacks of jaundice, but their significance was not clear.

The *Summerskill-Walshe syndrome*—a more handy name than *"benign recurrent intrahepatic cholestasis,"* because the term "intrahepatic cholestasis" is in itself misleading (cf. Chapter IV,E,5)—is clearly distinguishable from the Rotor-Stransky and Dubin-Johnson syndromes by biopsy and the elevation of the serum alkaline phosphatases. It is of interest because it demonstrates that the histological picture of "intrahepatic cholestasis" can apparently be developed on a purely hereditary basis.

Two highly interesting cases of *malignant hereditary intrahepatic cholestasis* in infancy in two sisters were reported by O. P. Gray and Saunders (1966*). The symptoms and biopsy findings were closely similar to those found in the Summerskill-Walshe syndrome, but the fluctuating jaundice never completely disappeared. It became much worse after infections and operations and gradually deepened until the children died before the age of 3 years. The children became dwarfed, suffered from severe itching, and had steatorrhoea, acholic stools, gross bilirubinuria, and excess of lanugo hairs. The serum bilirubin reached very high values—32 mg/100 ml—during the peaks of the jaundice. About 60% of the serum bilirubin was conjugated, and about half of the conjugated bilirubin was alkali-stable. The serum enzymes were normal initially, but rose with time. Bromsulphalein retention was much increased. The liver biopsies initially were essentially normal, but 2 years later fine fibrous trabeculas in the liver substance were visible, and the lobules were distorted. A puzzling feature was microscopic bile thrombi in some canaliculi which could hardly be due to obstruction because very little canalicular dilatation or other evidence suggesting obstruction was observed. A more likely explanation was believed to be an alteration of bile viscosity due to diminished bile acid excretion.

Peck *et al.* (1960) described a somewhat different case in a 23-year-old Turkish male who had been jaundiced from birth and had 11 relatives with persistent jaundice as well as various other anomalies in unjaundiced relatives (dwarfism, six fingers, exostoses). There was no hepato- or splenomegaly. The serum bilirubin was 6 mg per 100 ml with 3.58 "direct" and 2.42 "indirect." The bromsulphalein retention was 49% 45 minutes after injection of 5 mg per kg body weight. Closer study disclosed that only 1.4% of the retained BSP was in conjugate form, which is low. Other liver function tests were normal in Peck *et al.*'s patient. The urine showed a slightly positive bilirubin reaction. Urobilin was normal or slightly elevated. Liver biopsy was normal without black pigment. The gallbladder was normally visualized on oral cholecystography. Vest *et al.* (1960) reported a similar case in a 7-year-old Swiss girl with jaundice from the age of 4 weeks, serum bilirubin 4–7 mg per 100 ml with 50–70% "direct bilirubin," bilirubinuria, normal urobilin in the stool but slightly increased urinary urobilinoids, 50% bromsulphalein retention after

30 minutes, and normal gallbladder on oral cholecystography. Liver biopsy was normal without pigmentation.

Yet another type of hereditary nonhemolytic jaundice was described by Satler (1966*) in two siblings—brother aged 41 and a sister aged 39 —from Yugoslavia. Both suffered from intermittent jaundice from early childhood, whereas their 8 other siblings and their parents did not complain of jaundice. The patients were studied at intervals for over 10 years. The ratio conjugated/free bilirubin in their serum varied periodically (extreme values 20 and 80%) with presence of bilirubinuria in periods with high direct diazo reaction in the serum and absence of bilirubinuria in periods with weak direct reaction. The total serum bilirubin varied between 3.5 and 10 mg/100 ml. The BSP retention test was grossly pathological in both cases and the gallbladder could not be observed on cholecystography. Both were subjected to laparotomy, the liver and bile passages were found to be normal, and in both liver biopsy showed an essentially normal picture. The condition was completely benignant in both patients. The interesting feature in this "Satler syndrome"—named "Hyperbilirubinemia alternans benigna" by the author —is the alternation between periods with dominating conjugated and unconjugated hyperbilirubinemia. Apart from this the Satler syndrome is closely similar to Rotor-Stransky's syndrome.

A considerable number of patients with nonhemolytic familial jaundice with direct serum bilirubin, differing from the cases described above by the presence of black pigment in the liver, have been reported from all over the world under the designations *chronic idiopatic jaundice, Dubin-Johnson syndrome,* or *Dubin-Sprintz disease.* The characteristic symptoms are hyperbilirubinemia, which can increase to jaundice, a prompt direct diazo reaction, bilirubinuria, absence of hemolysis, accumulation of an amorphous granular brownish pigment in the centrilobular liver cells, and mild signs of liver dysfunction (i.e., retention of bromsulphalein, positive thymol and cephalin tests, and no gallbladder after cholecystography). The nature of the amorphous brownish pigment is unknown at the present time. This disease shows certain similarities to the nonhemolytic, familial hyperbilirubinemia with indirect diazo reaction. Thus, the two conditions are chronic and intermittent, mainly young people are afflicted, malaise and dyspepsia occur, and the prognosis is good. The highest serum bilirubin concentration observed was 19 mg per 100 ml during this disease. Increased urobilinogen excretion can often be observed (Dubin, 1958). Cinotti *et al.* (1957) described several cases of this disease in the same family. The description of the condition goes back to Dubin and Johnson (1954), who found 12 cases among 4000 patients with liver diseases. Shortly thereafter Sprinz and Nelson (1954) reported four more cases. Further contributions were made by Klajman and Efrati (1955); John and Knudtson (1956), who described two cases in brothers and sisters; N. L. Brown and Shnitka (1956), Tamaki and Carfaguo (1957), Hamperl (1957), and Dubin (1958), who compiled 50 cases. Campbell *et al.* (1956) reported three cases in elderly men. C. J. Watson (1956b) disclosed that the 1-minute-bilirubin constitutes about 40% of the total bilirubin in this syndrome. This is in opposition to the common familial, nonhemolytic hyperbilirubinema, in which the percentage of 1-minute-bilirubin is very low. Smiley *et al.* (1958) described a case in which the diagnosis was made by laparoscopy. A deep black discoloration of the liver was observed.

Sørland (1960) described a case in a 16-year-old Norwegian boy. The serum bilirubin was 1.5–2.5 mg per 100 ml and the bromsulphalein retention 3–10% after 45 minutes. Burka (1960) presented a case in a 51-year-old man with 2.2–4.3 mg bilirubin per 100 ml of serum, of which 60% was "direct." Chromatographic studies revealed that 78% of the direct bilirubin was mono- and 22% diglucuronide. Mandema *et al.* (1960, 1961) published 5 Dutch cases, two of whom suffered from cholelithiasis. In the remaining three the gallbladder could be well visualized after intravenous cholecystography, but only after a delay of 5 hours. The biliary excretion of conjugated bromsulphalein was impaired in these patients, presumably because of re-entry of some conjugated BSP from the liver cells into the blood stream and excretion of the excess conjugate with the urine. Four of the 5 cases were siblings.

Wegmann *et al.* (1960) studied a 39-year-old patient of Turkish descent with jaundice from the age of 6 years. The investigations included splenectomy and liver biopsy with infrared spectrophotometric study of the black pigment. The bromsulphalein retention was studied in detail, including chromatographic investigations. Abnormal bromsulphalein conjugates with amino acids were demonstrated. The black pigment from the liver and spleen could not be definitely identified, but the findings suggested a melanin closely related to adrenaline and adrenochrome. E. P. Hurst and Walters (1961) reported two cases—father and daughter—from Western Australia. Bergquist (1963) reported 4 cases, a sister and 3 brothers from Sweden. D. S. Smith (1963) reported a case in a Korean woman. Rezza *et al.* (1963) described a family where 4 to 6 siblings exhibited neonatal jaundice of 2–3 months' duration with direct bilirubin. The liver biopsy was normal, but the authors classified the case as "chronic idiopatic jaundice."

Recently a considerable number of observations on the Dubin-Johnson syndrome have appeared all over the world. Burka *et al.* (1961*) found the pigment present in the liver of apparently normal relatives of the patients. Two familial cases from Russia were described by Tarel (1964*). Cases with *melanuria* were reported by Levrat et al. (1964*) and Bernhardt (1964*); the connection between the hepatic and the urinary pigment in these cases is interesting and invites further study. Ten Japanese cases were described by Ichida and Funahashi (1964*) who subjected the liver pigment granula to electron microscopic studies. They appeared as dense bodies evidently characteristic of lysosomes, but some of them resembled altered mitochondria. Kasza et al. (1965*) published 9 cases from Rumania and discussed the relation with Rotor-Stransky's syndrome.

Billing et al. (1964b*) performed bilirubin tolerance tests with unconjugated bilirubin in four patients with Dubin-Johnson's syndrome and found the same characteristic curve as in one case of Rotor-Stransky's syndrome, i.e., an initial steep rise of unconjugated bilirubin followed by a gradual drop and a simultaneous gradual increase in the conjugated bilirubin. In some of the normal relatives of the patients, minor but definite anomalies of the bilirubin tolerance curve were established.

Cornelius et al. (1965*) described a syndrome in *Corriedale sheep* resembling the Dubin-Johnson syndrome, characterized by an acute photosensitivity syndrome, conjugated hyperbilirubinemia, retention of BSP and iodopanic acid, and a brownish-black pigment in the liver cells. The pigment was concentrated and subjected to closer study. It was insoluble in most organic solvents, but soluble in alkalies, it had an absorption peak at 268 nm at pH 8.6, which disappeared on acidification, and from electron spin resonance studies it revealed the same stable free radical content as naturally occurring and synthetic melanins. The photosensitivity was apparently due to retention of phylloerythrin. To judge from tolerance tests it was apparently not the hepatic uptake of bilirubin, BSP, and phylloerythrin that was deficient, but only their excretion with the bile. No hepatotoxic plants were found in the pasture of the animals. Cornelius et al. suggested that these Corriedale sheep should prove useful in the study of hepatic excretory function and its regulation.

Tygstrup et al. (1965*) studied the occurrence of "brown lipofuscin pigments" in 195 consecutive liver biopsy specimens from hospital patients. Marked pigmentation of this type was present in 15% of the biopsies, and it occurred in a variety of hepatic and extrahepatic diseases. The relation of these "brown lipofuscins" with the black pigment of Dubin-Johnson's syndrome was discussed. It has been claimed that the two types of pigment are distinct, but at least with usual histological techniques only minor quantitative differences were demonstrable. Furthermore, the association of the black pigment with Dubin-Johnson's syndrome is far from constant as both cases with and without pigment have been observed in families with typical Dubin-Johnson cases and pigmentation without jaundice has been encountered in relatives.

Sagild *et al.* (1962*) found the typical pigmentation in a case with unconjugated hyperbilirubinemia. A case with coincidence with idiopathic thrombopenic purpura—possibly accidental—was reported by Du *et al.* (1965*).

Accumulation of lipofuscin pigment in the liver following excessive intake of analgetics, especially phenacetin, was reported by Abrahams *et al.* (1963*). Their findings point toward the possibility that the variations of the amount of liver pigment in patients with Dubin-Johnson's syndrome may depend on exogenic factors like drugs, but the authors do not discuss this possibility themselves.

The pigment cell system of the liver of lower vertebrates was recently investigated by Hack and Helmby (1964*); it was generally most evident in amphibia and absent in birds and mammals. The pigment was unmasked by salivary amylase which permitted visualization by removing glycogen. The pigment cells are regarded as a special system of cells different from the liver cells. A connection between these pigment cells of lower vertebrates and the Dubin-Johnson pigment therefore seems unlikely although the pigment cell granules were believed to consist of melanin.

De Sandre *et al.* (1964*) reported 3 cases of hereditary nonhemolytic jaundice with direct diazo reaction; two showed pigmented granules in the liver cells, while the third, who was a cousin to one of the others, exhibited no pigment in the liver. They concluded that the distinction between Dubin-Johnson's and Rotor-Stransky's syndromes is not clear and that current classification of hereditary nonhemolytic hyperbilirubinemias is premature. A permanent classification must await further developments.

Masuda (1965*) described a case of Dubin-Johnson's syndrome in a man aged 41 who was thoroughly studied for 5 years. A liver biopsy performed in 1961 showed the typical pigment in the liver cells and no signs of hepatitis. The diagnosis was verified during a surgical operation in 1964 by observation of a typical black liver. During the operation a blood transfusion was given, and 37 days later inoculation hepatitis developed, confirmed by liver biopsy 50 days after the transfusion. Five months after the operation a new liver biopsy was performed showing disappearance of the inflammatory cell reaction and simultaneously a remarkable reduction of the brown pigment granules in the liver cells compared with the former biopsies. This observation suggests that the amount of pigment in Dubin-Johnson's syndrome is significantly influenced by environmental factors.

Blanck et al. (1966*) found Dubin-Johnson's syndrome in three sisters aged 18, 16, and 12 years of whom only two exhibited the typical brown pigmentation of the liver cells, while the third who had a very mild jaundice had very little pigment in her liver cells. These authors discussed the nature of the liver cell pigment on the basis of histochemical observations. Their own findings were compatible with a lipofuscin, but histochemical observations of other investigators are confusing; therefore, the nature of the pigment is still to be regarded as uncertain.

The mutual relationship of the different forms of nonhemolytic familial hyperbilirubinemia is complicated. The difficulty of the distinction between Rotor-Stransky syndrome and Dubin-Johnson's is clearly illustrated by the case of Petersen (1964), who reports on biopsies studied independently by Dubin and by Johnson. While Dubin classified the case as Rotor-Stransky syndrome, Johnson was of the opinion that it was Dubin-Johnson syndrome. This difference in opinion was due to different evaluation of the amount of lipofuscin pigment present in the preparations, one of the pathologists regarding it as within normal limits, the other as pathological. L. Schiff and Billing (1959) and Billing (1961a,b) differentiated between constitutional hepatic dysfunction (Gilbert's disease), chronic idiopatic jaundice (Dubin-Johnson syndrome), and chronic familial nonhemolytic jaundice with conjugated serum bilirubin (Rotor-Stransky syndrome). Sørland (1960) differentiated between Gilbert's benign familial jaundice, congenital familial nonhemolytic jaundice with kernicterus (Crigler-Najjar syndrome), chronic idiopatic jaundice (Dubin-Johnson), and familial nonhemolytic jaundice with conjugated serum bilirubin (Rotor-Stransky), to which forms he added as a new form the benign recurrent intrahepatic "obstructive" jaundice described by Summerskill and Walshe (1959). The "shunt hyperbilirubinemia" of Israels et al. (1959, 1963a) and the Turkish cases of Peck et al. (1960) accompanied by other inherited abnormalities may present other separate genetic entities and probably several others exist.

The pitfalls of regarding all cases of "benign unconjugated hyperbilirubinemia" as "Gilbert's disease" without a closer study was pointed out by Arias (1962) and Levine and Klatskin (1964*). The probable identity of Rotor-Stransky's and Dubin Johnson's syndromes was emphasized by Schiff and Billing (1959), Sørland (1960), Porush et al. (1962*), Ichida and Funahashi (1964*), and Tygstrup et al. (1965*) because of observations of cases with and without pigments in the liver cells in the same family.

A close relationship exists between the pathogenesis of nonhemolytic, familial hyperbilirubinemias and the *regulative mechanisms of normal serum bilirubin level.* These mechanisms were explained by variations in intravascular hemolysis (Aschoff, 1932), by bilirubin absorption from the intestine (Retzlaff, 1923a,b), and by varying permeability of liver cells for bilirubin (Isaac, 1925). However, experimental evidence has not been presented. With (1954, p. 237) pointed out that another explanation could be a reversion of the normal blood/bile route to a blood/lymph directed excretion mechanism. It is entirely plausible that such a change in mechanism takes place during the Dubin-Johnson or Rotor-Stransky syndrome with direct diazo reaction in serum. However, no studies were reported on the visceral lymph in these patients. With (1949) pointed out another possibility, i.e., an inherited abnormal metabolism, similar to the abnormal pyrrole mechanism in porphyrias. To test the theories, experiments should be carried out with C^{14}- or N^{15}-labeled glycine with subsequent determination of the radioactivity or the N^{15} content of isolated bilirubin. Experiments by Schmid *et al.* (1957a,b, 1958c) indicate that hemolytic familial hyperbilirubinemia is caused by an enzymatic defect invalidating the conjugation with glucuronic acid in the liver cells. However, this theory does not explain nonhemolytic familial jaundice with direct diazo reaction. As previously mentioned (Chapter II,D), the bilirubin degradation mechanism, which is prevalent in horses and cattle, can also become effective in humans. It is therefore possible that a disruption of this mechanism may be active in familial nonhemolytic hyperbilirubinemia.

According to K. Beck and Kühn (1959), the problem of the pathogenesis of "functional hyperbilirubinemia" (comprising nonhemolytic hyperbilirubinemia, the Dubin-Johnson syndrome, and posthepatitic hyperbilirubinemia) is a very complex one. Three different mechanisms interact: (a) excretion disturbances by enzyme defects (e.g., of conjugation of bilirubin in the liver); (b) increased erythrocyte destruction (hemolysis); and (c) increased parahematic bilirubin production (bilirubin formation from sources other than mature circulating erythrocytes). These three mechanisms are affected in varying degrees during different forms of functional hyperbilirubinemia. Kühn *et al.* (1958) studied the nature of disturbances of the glucuronide synthesizing enzyme system with menthol tolerance tests. These authors found that total excretion of glucuronic acid deviates only slightly from normal levels after administering menthol to patients with intermittent juvenile jaundice (Meulengracht, 1938, 1947). However, whereas healthy individuals excreted the glucuronic acid during the first 3 hours after loading, patients with hyperbilirubinemia reached the maximum value only after 3–6 hours. This finding indicated disturbances in the glucuronide-forming enzyme system of the liver. K. Beck and Kiani (1960) supplemented these investigations with similar studies including determination of serum glucuronides and glucuronide clearance after loading with menthol. The retardation of glucuronide production in functional hyperbilirubinemia was confirmed. The 20 patients studied suffered from slight hyperbilirubinemia, secondary to various diseases, not from the more severe hereditary syndromes.

The role of hemolysis in the genesis of functional hyperbilirubinemia, especially the posthepatitic type, was studied by Heimpel et al. (1962) in 64 patients with chronic jaundice, of whom 41 had a history of viral hepatitis. The erythrocyte survival was determined with Cr^{51} and only three patients exhibited decreased erythrocyte longevity; in the remainder it was normal. It was concluded that hemolysis cannot play a significant role as a cause of "functional hyperbilirubinemia." This finding differs from that of Arias (1962; cf. above) who found significantly decreased Cr^{51} $T\frac{1}{2}$ in 4 of 23 patients with chronic unconjugated hyperbilirubinemia.

At present it is too early to attempt a rigid classification of the nonhemolytic hereditary hyperbilirubinemias. It is important to exclude subclinical forms and residual cases of viral hepatitis. The genetically determined forms are to be looked upon as a series of enzymopathias which may arise as mutations in different loci. These conditions have much in common with other genetically determined anomalies of the pyrrole metabolism as porphyrias and hemoglobinopathias (cf. With, 1962). There may be close connections between certain forms of nonhemolytic hyperbilirubinemia and certain forms of porphyria as indicated by the case described by Gray et al. (1948) where recurrent jaundice developed in a case of porphyria. To understand these genetically determined diseases it will be necessary to look upon them primarily as enzymopathias and secondarily as hereditary anemias, porphyrias, or hyperbilirubinemias.

Summary

Hereditary nonhemolytic hyperbilirubinemias exist in two groups, one where unconjugated bilirubin dominates and another where conjugated bilirubin dominates in the serum. Within each of these two groups several distinct forms exist. Among the forms with dominating unconjugated bilirubin, a relatively mild form—most often called Gilbert's disease—as well as a severe one called Crigler-Najjar syndrome exist; the latter is associated with kernicterus in infants. The shunt bilirubinemia of Israels et al. (1959, 1963a) seems to constitute a third form. Of hereditary hyperbilirubinemias with dominating conjugated bilirubin, the Dubin-Johnson and the Rotor-Stransky syndromes characterized by relatively constant hyperbilirubinemia have been known for some years, but recently a third type, the Summerskill-Walshe syndrome has been clearly delineated, and also other, more or less rare, hereditary types undoubtedly exist. Our knowledge today is not sufficient to allow a schematic subdivision of these syndromes. The Dubin-Johnson syndrome is defined by a characteristic pigmentation of the liver cells, but this may be weak and even entirely absent in some cases. In the original description of Rotor *et al.* (1948) and Stransky (1950) histological observations of the liver cells were scanty, and consequently the differentiation between the Dubin-Johnson and the Rotor-Stransky syndrome is problematic. Knowledge of many of these syndromes is insufficient, and further observations are highly desirable.

During future studies nonhemolytic hyperbilirubinemias ought to be looked upon primarily as inborn errors of metabolism. Therefore the biosynthesis of pyrroles—including excretion of porphyrin precursors—must be studied in these patients. In shunt hyperbilirubinemia it has been shown that the so-called first peak of bile pigment synthesis is primarily affected. The mechanisms of bilirubin conjugation must also be studied.

Terms such as "functional hyperbilirubinemia," "constitutional hepatic dysfunction," "icterus intermittens juvenilis," and "idiopatic jaundice" are to be avoided because they are too vague and may include different forms of inborn metabolic errors as well as latent hepatitis and latent hemolytic states. So far as possible, well-defined hereditary and biochemical mechanisms should be delineated.

L. Serum Bilirubin in Various Diseases and in Menstruation, Pregnancy, and Childbed

Whereas the serum bilirubin concentration can only reach values around 60 mg per 100 ml in humans, concentrations of 100 mg per 100 ml have been observed in horses (Zenglein, 1930). The bilirubin content during mild jaundice is around 2–5 mg per 100 ml in humans, 5–20 mg per 100 ml in moderate jaundice, and it often exceeds 20 mg per 100 ml in severe icterus. The following values have been found for obstructive jaundice in a number of different animal species: 12 mg per 100 ml in rabbits, 9 mg per 100 ml in pigs, 20 mg per 100 ml in monkeys (*Cebus paraguayiensis*), 12 mg per 100 ml in dogs, 30 mg per 100 ml in cats (Lopez Garcia *et al.*, 1943). Nevertheless, as yet no systematic studies of species differences on this point have been conducted with reliable methods.

Sova (1964*) presented an exhaustive review on serum bilirubin in the horse and personal studies on the serum bilirubin of horses with various diseases with a diazo micromethod with photometric reading. He found in 125 horses with hepatitis an average of 5.67 ± 1.78 mg/100 ml, in 87 with degenerative liver diseases 3.44 ± 1.42, in 37 with diffuse liver necrosis 14.29 ± 4.76, and in 42 with chronic liver diseases 3.15 ± 0.39 mg/100 ml as against 1.33 ± 0.05 mg/100 ml in 33 normal horses.

Medway *et al.* (1966*) found serum bilirubin reaching 17.2 mg/100 ml in a dolphin suffering from hepatic fibrosis and atrophy as against an average of 0.43 mg/100 ml in 3 normal dolphins.

The serum bilirubin level shows definite differences in the various forms of jaundice. As previously mentioned, the concentration is usually low during hereditary nonhemolytic jaundice, although values around 20 mg per 100 ml can occur. A low serum level is also found in hemolytic jaundice (Meulengracht, 1918). Here the serum bilirubin content is 2–5 mg per 100 ml in most cases, but higher concentrations are also observed under certain conditions (Katznelson, 1920; Weir, 1932; C. J. Watson, 1937b; Cantarow and Trumper, 1945, p. 443; Dameshek and Schwartz, 1940b, p. 245; Enanesco *et al.*, 1947; Lichtman, 1949, p. 223). The serum bilirubin in 12 cases of acute hemolytic favism in children was reported by Rindone and Mollica (1962). The highest figure reached was 6.7 mg per 100 ml. The highest value yet reported was 14 mg per 100 ml following a hemolytic transfusion reaction (Barac, 1947). Bendixen and Carlström (1928) found 40–80 mg per 100 ml in a horse with hemolytic icterus. However, the serum bilirubin level is normally high in this animal; for example, 25–75 mg per 100 ml can be observed during infectious anemias (Zenglein, 1930). In cattle, serum bilirubin levels are significantly higher during hemolytic processes than during hepatitis or obstructive jaundice (Garner, 1953). In man values above 10 mg per 100 ml are regularly found during the peak of physiological icterus neonatorum, but 50 mg per 100 ml is occasionally observed. Compared to other forms of jaundice with indirect diazo reaction, these values are extraordinarily high.

Individual variations in the bilirubin production level play a role (Chapter III,G), and one cannot judge the severity of the disease from the serum bilirubin level. Thus, the clinical value of quantitative serum bilirubin determination is limited. It is also worthless for the differential diagnosis between hepatic and obstructive jaundice, although higher concentrations are usually found during obstruction than during the hepatocellular form (Mendioroz and Castro, 1959). Neoplasms generally show higher concentrations than obstructions by stones (Adler and Jeddeloh, 1929a,b; Weir, 1932; C. J. Watson, 1937b, 1940; Royer, 1943; Lopez Garcia, 1943, pp. 110–118; With, 1944b; Verniory, 1946; Lattanzi, 1948a; Lichtman, 1949, p. 223). No definite relation was found between serum bilirubin level and liver damage in liver biopsies (Schaffner *et al.*, 1950).

Figures 49–52 (Chapter VI) show variations of serum bilirubin level during acute hepatitis. The differences can be very distinct in the initial stages of hepatitis and can change rapidly (see Chapter, III,G). The same is true for obstructive icterus due to bile stones (see With, 1944b, cases 4 and 6), as well as for beginning icterus neonatorum. Serum bilirubin variations are more gradual in hemolytic icterus, in nonhemolytic familial hyperbilirubinemia, in later stages of hepatitis and icterus neonatorum, and in cardiac icterus. Usually constant values are found in complete (neoplastic) obstruction, but certain variations can occur even here (Chapter III,G); however, these variations take place slowly and gradually, especially when the obstruction is not complicated by hemolysis or infection.

Differentiation between complete and incomplete bile duct closures has been claimed to be facilitated by repeated serum bilirubin determinations several times a day, and serial determinations performed on different days are believed to be valuable for the differentiation between hepatocellular jaundice and complete bile duct obstruction. Unfortunately, experimental evidence which would substantiate the diagnostic value of such determinations is still lacking. Aronsen's (1962) experimental studies on obstructive jaundice in dogs disclosed a maximum of the serum bilirubin after 7 days' stasis. Then followed a slow decrease in spite of persisting obstruction. The return of the serum bilirubin to normal level after removal of the obstruction took place at a rate dependent on the degree of stasis. These observations are, however, not directly applicable to patients because man is much more resistent toward biliary obstruction than the dog.

Wiechel (1963) correlated the serum bilirubin and the patency of the bile duct system in 54 surgical cases of jaundice subjected to percutaneous transhepatic cholangiography. The range of the serum bilirubin concentration was 1.3–16.1 (mean 5.5) mg per 100 ml in 11 patients with free bile duct system, 0.8–19.6 (8.0) in 18 with gall stones in the bile ducts, 2.0–24.9 (10.9) in 9 with benign strictures of the bile ducts, and 4.0–41.1 (22.3) mg per 100 ml in 16 patients with malignant bile duct occlusion. Thus there was a significantly higher mean serum bilirubin level if bile duct obstruction was present than when no obstruction was demonstrable, but the figures overlapped too much to be of diagnostic significance. There was a tendency toward higher serum bilirubin with longer duration of jaundice. In several of the patients, operation with cholecystectomy or removal of the biliary obstructions was carried out, and in them the time elapsing before the serum bilirubin reached the normal level was determined. In 7 patients with free bile passages 4–28 (mean 16) days elapsed, in 16 with stones in the bile ducts 2–51 (21) days, in 5 with benign bile duct obstruction 6–51 (30) days, and in 19 with malignant occlusion 25–64 (49) days elapsed. In this study the time required to reach the normal level was clearly correlated to the serum bilirubin level, but not to the duration of the biliary obstruction.

The serum bilirubin is important for the diagnosis of bile stone attacks without icterus, because a pronounced increase can take place in the hours following the attack (Meulengracht, 1919; Strausz, 1923). However, when the obstruction is removed, the serum bilirubin concentration normalizes itself rapidly, and can show a drop of 10 mg per 100 ml within 12–24 hours. A prerequisite for such rapid decreases is unimpaired liver function (With, 1944b, cases 4 and 6).

Interesting observations on the influence of steroid therapy on the serum bilirubin of jaundiced patients are due to Williams and Billing (1961). They found that such therapy must cause or enhance degradation of bilirubin to unidentifiable compounds.

Pruzanski (1965*) compared 28 cases of viral hepatitis treated with prednisone with 28 similar cases treated identically but without this substance. After 15 days of therapy the average decrease in serum bilirubin was 71% in the treated group as against 83% in the control group, i.e., no significant difference. Murano (1964*) found that in jaundice of the newborn large doses of prednisolone (10–20 mg daily for 10–20 days) caused a marked decrease in total serum bilirubin and bilirubin monoglucuronide (Eberlein method), but no change in the free bilirubin. In severe jaundice due to Crigler-Najjar's disease prednisolone was without effect.

Del Piano and Lisi (1964*) found that i.v. injection of high doses of ascorbic acid gave a decrease of the serum bilirubin—measured with a diazo method—in various forms of jaundice. This depression of the serum bilirubin was culminated ca. 3 hours after the injection. These authors did not contemplate the possibility that this effect might be due to the inhibitory action of ascorbic acid on the diazo reaction rather than to a depression of the bilirubin concentration.

The questions of "direct" and "indirect" serum bilirubin, and of conjugated and unconjugated bilirubin during various diseases, have been discussed previously (see Section H, this chapter).

For detailed discussion of the serum bilirubin in various forms of jaundice the reader should consult clinical monographs, for example Lichtman (1942, 1949, 1954). For the discussion of drug-induced jaundice the reader is referred to Chapter IV,E,5.

In addition to jaundice, the serum bilirubin has been investigated in many diseases and other conditions which do not result in manifest icterus, but which may be accompanied by *latent hyperbilirubinemia*. *Menstruation, pregnancy,* and *childbed* are of interest here.

Senator (1872) described four cases of "*menstrual icterus*" in patients who went through catarrhalic jaundice (acute hepatitis) and since that time exhibited jaundice attacks during menstruation. This condition is most likely a harmless consequence of posthepatitic hyperbilirubinemia, the process being activated during menstruation. Lingjaerde (1934, pp. 91–93) found regular variations of serum bilirubin content during the menstrual cycle in 16 patients. No more studies of this nature are available, although they would be of interest, if performed with modern methods.

Numerous investigators studied serum bilirubin during *pregnancy*. The results of these studies are somewhat contradictory. With (1954, pp. 242–243) summarized early findings. Väyrynen (1934) studied the largest material, 600 women. However, this author used the method of Kerppola and Leikola (1932) which is not quite reliable. Increased serum bilirubin concentration was observed during the second month of pregnancy. After the second month the values decreased again. Average values fell below those of nonpregnant women during the sixth month of pregnancy. These low values continued until the ninth month, after which a slight increase took place, but the average of normal women was not reached. A sudden increase occurred during birth and the average concentrations determined were distinctly above those of nonpregnant women. This picture can be explained by general fasting and muscle activity during labor. A sharp decrease takes place during the first 2 days of childbed. Thereafter, a gradual increase follows until the normal level is reached. Eufinger and Bader (1926a,b), Walter and Williencourt (1928), Mikeladse (1928), Breda (1929), Shinomura (1930), Wíslański (1930), Väyrynen (1934), and R. Wolf (1935) reported serum bilirubin determinations during puerperium.

Thorling (1955) determined the serum bilirubin in 169 pregnant women (third to tenth month) and 33 women during labor. He found variations between 0.1 and 1.0 mg per 100 ml during pregnancy and between 0.1 and 1.1 mg per 100 ml during labor. The average value was determined for each month of pregnancy and varied between 0.4 and 0.3 mg per 100 ml.

Several recent investigators have studied *jaundice during late pregnancy*. Thorling (1955) studied 72 cases and pointed out that this jaundice was much more often diagnosed as hepatitis after 1940 than before 1940. On close scrutiny only 38 of his 72 cases could be grouped as hepatitis. Sheehan (1961) reviewed a 10-year material of jaundice in an obstetric service, comprising 34 recovered and 50 fatal cases. Hyperemesis was not a significant cause of jaundice. About 10% of the patients dying from eclampsia suffered from hemolytic icterus. Samuels (1961) also discussed a 10-year series without adding anything new. Siegler and Keyser (1963) found 25 cases of acute hepatitis among 80,000 obstetric records. The highest icterus frequency is reported by D'Elia and Caporale (1963) who studied ca. 5000 obstetric records from a maternity hospital at Naples and found 26 patients with jaundice, i.e., 53 per 1000 pregnancies; the figures reported by earlier investigators vary between 0.17 and 20 per 1000 pregnancies. Of their 26 cases 18 were due to hepatitis and one to acute yellow atrophy of the liver. Ikonen (1964) reported a series of 66 cases of jaundice in late pregnancy from a maternity hospital at Helsinki, Finland. The 51 cases were classified as "obstetric hepatosis" (cf. below) and only 4 as virus hepatitis. Two were regarded as due to familial nonhemolytic jaundice with exacerbations in pregnancy.

More recently Haemmerli (1966*) published a monograph on the study of jaundice in pregnancy.

A special form of icterus in pregnancy is *idiopathic* or *recurrent jaundice of pregnancy*. Cases of this form of icterus were first reported by Kehrer (1907), Schwalm (1932), Martini *et al.* (1953), With (1954), Svanborg (1954), Thorling (1955), Gros (1958), Svanborg and Ohlsson (1959), and Ikonen (1964). This jaundice is mild and benign, usually develops during the last trimester of pregnancy, fades away rapidly after delivery, and has a strong tendency to recur in subsequent pregnancies. With's patient was a 31-year-old woman who developed jaundice in the fifth month in all her five pregnancies. Svanborg (1954) reported positive direct diazo reaction in the serum of these patients. Several recent investigators have studied the liver histology of these patients on biopsies and found either normal conditions or hepatocanalicular jaundice without necrosis of parenchymal cells (Svanborg, 1954; Gros, 1958; Hausheer and Lauer, 1962; J. M. M. Brown *et al.*, 1963; Moore, 1963; King and Kerrins, 1963). Sheehan (1961) found only one case in his material and believed that the condition is most frequent in Scandinavia since Svanborg and Ohlsson (1959) were able to collect 22 cases of their own. D'Elia and Caporale's Italian material comprised two cases of recurrent jaundice in late pregnancy. Recently a number of publications from England and the United States have shown that this condition cannot be infrequent. Hausheer and Lauer (1962), King and Kerrins (1963), and Simmons (1963) each published one case, while Moore (1963) and J. M. M. Brown *et al.* (1963) were each able to collect 3 cases of their own. The latter reviewed the literature and reported electron microscope studies of the liver of their three patients. The most conspicuous alterations were in the microsomal component of the parenchymal liver cells. Brown *et al.* (1963) further called attention to the similarity between recurrent jaundice of late pregnancy and the jaundice due to certain steroids (cf. Chapter IV,C,7).

Ikonen (1964) studied 66 selected cases of jaundice late in pregnancy and introduced the term *"obstetric hepatosis"* for a certain type of liver disorder, which is connected specially with late pregnancy and characterized by an intense itching and moderate jaundice and has a tendency to recur in successive pregnancies. Of Ikonen's 66 cases of jaundice in pregnancy, 51 were classified as obstetric hepatosis. Several multigravidae were included, and several had jaundice during more than one pregnancy. The condition, however, did not regularly recur in every pregnancy; in several cases one or more pregnancies took place without jaundice. Ikonen believed that the special hormonal conditions associated with pregnancy together with the stress of the condition are important pathogenic factors, but did not associate the condition more closely with steroid jaundice.

The similarity between jaundice due to 17α-alkylated anabolic steroids and recurrent jaundice of late pregnancy was further stressed by Adlercreutz (1964), who pointed out that high concentrations of steroids in the tissues of certain women during late pregnancy probably is the main pathogenetic factor of this condition. Adlercreutz also reported observations of jaundice during use of ovulation-inhibiting gestagens for contraceptive purposes.

Recently several papers on recurrent idiopathic jaundice in pregnancy appeared from various countries. Fast and Roulston (1964[*]) reported 14 cases with recurrence in half of them and 7 liver biopsies in 5 of the patients. Pavone and Pietropaolo (1964[*]) described two cases of familial jaundice during pregnancy. Elliot and Hendry (1965[*]) reported one case of idiopathic jaundice in pregnancy with recurrence 1 year after delivery during Enovid treatment; liver biopsy was normal. In the case of Sallomi and Belew (1965[*]) jaundice persisted after delivery; subsequent to uterine curretage the jaundice subsided within 1 week. Boake *et al.* (1965[*]) and Larsson-Cohn and Stenram (1965[*]) each presented one case with jaundice recurring during successive pregnancies as well as following Enovid treatment. In both cases liver biopsy showed dilated bile canaliculi with bile thrombi such as seen in hepatocanalicular jaundice. For this reason Boake *et al.* proposed the term "intrahepatic cholestasis of pregnancy." Kaern (1966[*]) found 8 cases of obstetric hepatosis among his 30,000 patients in a Copenhagen obstetric clinic, i.e., one case in 2000–3000 pregnancies.

Eliakim *et al.* (1966[*]) presented 5 cases from Israel exhibiting a total of 13 occurrences of recurrent jaundice. They stressed the similarity of this condition and jaundice due to 17-alkylsteroids.

Haemmerli (1966[*]) published a monograph on the treatment of recurrent jaundice in pregnancy based on 5 personal cases and a review of the world literature. A total of 132 cases was reviewed, 23 with liver biopsy. The highest serum bilirubin level found was 8.4 mg/100 ml. The jaundice was essentially benign and recovery after delivery was rapid and complete. The histological picture of intrahepatic cholestasis found on liver biopsy was always mild with focal or irregular changes contrasting with the impressive clinical and biochemical signs of hepatocanalicular jaundice (marked rise in bilirubin, alkaline phosphatases, and cholesterol, and often in GP and GO transaminases too). Haemmerli found it most reasonable to believe that recurrent jaundice in pregnancy is an extreme variant of a physiological derangement of liver function during normal pregnancy.

Del Piano et al. (1962*) studied the serum glucuronides and the ability of the liver to form glucuronides (menthol loading) during the last weeks of pregnancy and concluded that the power of the liver cells for formation of glucuronic acid is lower during late pregnancy.

A different form of jaundice in pregnancy develops earlier in pregnancy in association with toxicosis because of severe liver dysfunction (Lichtman, 1954). S. Stein (1903) and Stroebe (1932b) investigated this type of jaundice.

Horowitz and Küttner (1927) studied the serum bilirubin content of patients during extrauterine pregnancy, and could not detect any differences between these and nonpregnant patients.

The postoperative condition after surgical procedures is another important physiological state in which increased serum bilirubin concentrations occur. Elton (1931c) reported a "postoperative latent jaundice," i.e., increased serum bilirubin level 2–3 days after abdominal operations. Zacho and Larsen (1946b) confirmed these findings. A sharp increase was reported within the first 24 hours and a gradual decrease followed in the next 12 days. The highest values attained were often more than twice the starting level. Geller and Tagnon (1950) reached the same conclusions. They compared the increase of serum bilirubin with the amount of transfused blood which was administered during the operation, and found a certain, but not too close, relationship between these two values. The assumption of increased blood degradation explains, at least partially, enhanced bilirubin level. Depressed liver function seems to play a role also, since bromsulphalein clearance shows a postoperative drop. Anesthesia must also be considered as a causative factor, since Boshamer (1928) observed bilirubin retention in tolerance tests during anesthesia. An obvious possibility would be a lymphogenetic mechanism. It was demonstrated that the lymph of the liver shows yellow discoloration even after simple laparotomy in dogs (W. Volwiler, personal communication, 1950). Further examination of the bilirubin content of liver lymph during laparotomies in animals would be interesting.

Recently Pilchmayr and Stich (1962) described a new form of jaundice occurring after simultaneous operation, narcosis, and blood transfusion which they called "bilirubinostatic jaundice." The serum bilirubin varied from 2 to 30 mg per 100 ml with domination of conjugated bilirubin. The cause seems to be an acquired defect in the bilirubin excretion mechanism similar to the inborn defect known from the Rotor-Stransky syndrome.

M. Schmid *et al.* (1965*) described 12 patients with benign postoperative jaundice without infection. Liver biopsy was carried out in 9 patients and showed "intrahepatic cholestasis." The jaundice usually appeared on the first or second postoperative day, culminated on the 4th to 10th day and subsided in 14–18 days. M. Schmid and Hefti (1966*) reported 16 cases of benign postoperative jaundice with a histologic picture corresponding to "intrahepatic cholestasis." The peak value of the serum bilirubin varied between 5.4 and 27.6 mg/100 ml and all patients exhibited clinical jaundice. About two-thirds of the serum bilirubin was of the direct type. The jaundice commenced as a rule 1–2 days after the operation, culminated on the 3rd to 10th day, and regressed within 14–18 days. The patients were so-called "poor risks" suffering from a variety of serious diseases and many subsequently died from their primary disease.

A special form of hyperbilirubinemia caused by surgery is that following portocaval anastomosis. Da Silva *et al.* (1963) studied 10 unselected patients subjected to this operation because of portal hypertension of varying etiology. All the patients had normal serum bilirubin before operation, and their postoperative serum bilirubin increased to figures between 1.4 and 4.4 mg per 100 ml (total bilirubin) with dominating indirect diazo reaction. All the patients were followed for more than 3 months, and 6 of them were subjected to splenectomy. In all these 6 the serum bilirubin decreased substantially after this operation, and in the 3 it fell to normal figures. It was concluded that this hyperbilirubinemia is caused mainly by hemolysis.

A number of diseases lead to hyperbilirubinemia without inducing jaundice: *latent hyperbilirubinemia.* This phenomenon is observed during slight and disappearing hepatitis as well as in mild hemolytic conditions and pernicious anemia. Sonnenfeld (1924) and Broun *et al.* (1923b) established relations between the decrease of hemoglobin concentration and increase of bilirubin level in such cases. Hyperbilirubinemia is often found during cardiac congestion (F. Bang, 1915; Meulengracht, 1920; Joliffe, 1930; Robertson *et al.*, 1932; Kugel and Lichtman, 1933; Cantarow, 1935; Chavez *et al.*, 1943; Sherlock, 1951). Although infrequently, distinct jaundice can accompany this condition. Sherlock compared serum bilirubin values with the results of liver biopsies, and found the highest serum bilirubin level when necrosis of the liver was most extensive. Definite jaundice occurred only in patients with mitral stenosis or tricuspidal insufficiency. No relation was found between serum bilirubin concentration, heart volume, or arterial oxygen saturation. Serum bilirubin showed a tendency toward increase during lung infarctions. Recently Loiseleur and Petit (1963) described hyperbilirubinemia in rats after total X-ray irradiation of the body.

Numerous infectious diseases without primary liver lesions are accompanied by hyperbilirubinemia. Zenglein (1930) observed 10–50 mg bilirubin per 100 ml serum in horses with pneumonia and other infections. Elton (1928, 1929a,b, 1931a) showed that serum bilirubin increases during pneumonia in humans. He regarded the serum bilirubin level as a valuable prognostic sign. It is not surprising that hyperbilirubinemia and jaundice are often present during acute and chronic malaria with distinct hemolysis (Kinsbury, 1926; G. R. Ross, 1927; Schachsuvarly, 1927; Arellano, 1928; Pollock, 1945; Pellegrino *et al.*, 1947). Also therapeutic malaria can lead to hyperbilirubinemia (O'Leary *et al.*, 1929). Hyperbilirubinemia is probably most marked in the malarial attack. However, no investigations on serum bilirubin content during malarial attacks have been carried out with modern analytical methods. Pollock (1945) found increased serum bilirubin concentrations in most cases of infectious mononucleosis. Molinelli and Royer (1929) found normal serum bilirubin in leprosy. Normal or low values were reported in tuberculosis of the lungs (Castaigne, 1934; Jalavisto and Leppo, 1934).

Some investigators found normal serum bilirubin in thyrotoxicosis (Lichtman, 1941), whereas others reported somewhat increased values (Youmans and Warfield, 1926; Maddock *et al.*, 1936). Increased serum bilirubin levels have been frequently reported in mental diseases (Lingjaerde, 1934, pp. 93–118). However, these studies should be repeated with reliable analytical methods. Mehaut (1951) reported that serum bilirubin determinations are important for the differential diagnosis of cerebral apoplexy, since hyperbilirubinemia is generally found in cerebral hemorrhage, in contrast to thrombosis and embolism where serum bilirubin is most often normal.

Doucett (1965*) described a case of myxoedema in an 11-month-old girl presented as jaundice (4.7 mg bilirubin per 100 ml serum with equal quantities of "direct" and "indirect") without bilirubinuria. The hyperbilirubinemia disappeared under thyroid treatment within a few weeks.

Nephropathy is claimed to be accompanied by low serum bilirubin (Castaigne, 1934; Graña, 1941); however, pyelitis in pregnancy showed normal concentrations (Siggelkow, 1935).

A tendency toward hyperbilirubinemia has been claimed in cases of peptic ulcer (J. S. Diamond, 1928; Chrometzka, 1929a; Welin, 1945). However, Alwall (1946) refuted this finding. Yamaoka *et al.* (1952a,b,c) found increased serum bilirubin in bleeding ulcers and attributed this to bilirubin formation from blood which reached the intestines. It is, however, questionable if heme derivatives could be transformed into bilirubin in the intestines.

Summary

The serum bilirubin level is, as a rule, 2–5 mg per 100 ml in mild jaundice, 5–20 mg per 100 ml in medium jaundice, and 20–60 mg per 100 ml in severe icterus. These concentrations are valid for humans; in animals, distinct variations with the species occur. The average (and maximum) serum bilirubin levels during various types of icterus in humans are as follows: 2–5 (20) mg per 100 ml in idiopathic nonhemolytic hyperbilirubinemias with indirect as well as such with direct diazo reaction (Dubin-Johnson syndrome and others), 2–5 (14) mg per 100 ml during hemolytic icterus, 2–20 (50) mg per 100 ml during physiological icterus neonatorum. Every concentration up to 60 mg per 100 ml can occur in hepatic and obstructive icterus. The peak value of the concentration depends on the severity of the particular condition and on the level of bilirubin production. Series of serum bilirubin determinations are claimed to be valuable in differential diagnosis between gallstone obstruction and neoplastic occlusion. Determinations should be performed either daily at different points of time, or over a number of consecutive days during the morning hours (in fasting blood).

Drug-induced jaundice is discussed in Chapter IV. Variations in the serum bilirubin during menstruation, pregnancy, birth, and childbed are discussed, including jaundice in pregnancy, especially the form of icterus known as idiopatic or recurrent jaundice of pregnancy (obstetric hepatosis).

Latent hyperbilirubinemia following abdominal surgery is discussed. It is pointed out that a lymphogenetic mechanism could play a role. To clarify these questions studies of bilirubin contents of liver lymph in laparotomy are suggested.

The appearance of latent hyperbilirubinemia during the course of various diseases is mentioned. Reliable studies of serum bilirubin variation during malarial attacks are wanted.

M. Therapeutic Approach to Unconjugated Hyperbilirubinemia

While hyperbilirubinemia due to conjugated bilirubin is a harmless condition *per se*, that due to unconjugated bilirubin is a menace to various tissues, especially to the nervous system and particularly in newborn and young infants (cf. Section G, this chapter and Chapter IX,E). It is therefore of therapeutic importance to reduce high unconjugated hyperbilirubinemia in infants, and the only reliable method to achieve this, known at present, is *exchange transfusion*. In this procedure portions of the patient's blood are withdrawn and substituted with corresponding volumes of donor blood. In this way bilirubin-rich plasma is substituted with plasma poor in bilirubin, and simulatenously the antibody-coated erythrocytes of *morbus haemolyticus neonatorum* are exchanged with normal and viable erythrocytes. As only a limited volume of the patient's plasma can be exchanged in this way in one session, the procedures will most often have to be repeated several times before the desirable reduction of serum bilirubin is achieved. Further, bilirubin from the tissues will penetrate into the circulation following the reduction of serum bilirubin level, and this will cause a slower reduction of the serum bilirubin than calculated from the serum bilirubin level and the amount of plasma exchanged; this is called the *rebound phenomenon*.

The behavior of serum bilirubin during exchange transfusion and the therapeutic value of this procedure in hemolytic disease of the newborn have been studied by several investigators. The procedure was originally introduced as a therapeutic measure in jaundice due to blood group incompatibility, but was subsequently found to be of value in jaundice of prematurity too (B. D. Corner, 1958). It lowers the serum bilirubin and thus reduces the risk of kernicterus. Lathe (1955) found that the decrease in serum bilirubin level during exchange transfusion lagged behind the theoretical curve calculated from the blood exchange. A. K. Brown and Zuelzer (1957) investigated this further and called it the "rebound phenomenon." Forfar et al. (1958) studied the amount of bilirubin removed from the circulation during exchange transfusion and found that the procedure was most efficient if the volume of blood exchanged was 170–200 ml per kg body weight and the rate 1.6 ml per kg per minute. Rosta (1962) investigated the rebound phenomenon in 30 exchange transfusions, and found the amount of bilirubin removed from the organism considerably in excess of the amount of bilirubin present in the circulation before the transfusion, provided the exchanged blood volume was sufficient. There was a positive correlation between the volume of exchanged blood and the amount of bilirubin removed. The rebound phenomenon is probably still active some time after the transfusion has been completed. The phenomenon is really the same thing as the rise in serum bilirubin and the drainage of bilirubin from the tissues following infusions of salt-free albumin (cf. L. Johnson et al., 1961; F. Koch and Rind, 1962; Theile et al., 1963a,b).

According to Oski and Naiman (1963), the capacity of the erythrocyte membrane is of importance in the mechanism of exchange transfusion, especially in autoimmune hemolysis. The transfused erythrocytes will bind bilirubin present in serum to a higher degree than the patient's own antibody-coated ones.

Exchange transfusions in the treatment of hyperbilirubinemia in the newborn was recently discussed in two books (Daetwyler, 1963; Valaes, 1963). Daetwyler's material consisted of the first 100 infants who had received exchange transfusion for icterus gravis due to Rhesus incompatibility in the University obstetric clinic at Berne. They were subjected to follow-up study after 11 months to 6 years. Four died during the newborn period, 78 were perfectly healthy, and the remainder suffered from various anomalies. Valaes' material consisted of 63 cases of severe hyperbilirubinemia in the newborn from the Department of Child Health at the University of Bristol. Of the total, 28 suffered from immaturity, 35 from hemolytic disease. The blood volume exchanged was on the average 2.4 times the estimated blood volume, and the average rate of exchange 33 minutes for each unit of blood volume. The blood was analyzed before and at the end of the infusion, and in 14 cases 30 minutes later as well. In 36 cases analysis was also performed on the blood removed during the exchange. Comparison of the intravascular mass of bilirubin with the bilirubin removed during the exchange demonstrated that a shift of bilirubin from tissues into the vascular compartment took place. In all the cases the amount of bilirubin removed exceeded the estimated initial intravenous mass of bilirubin. This shift of bilirubin from tissue to blood continued after the exchange, and equilibrium was attained about 30 minutes after the exchange. The drop in serum bilirubin expressed as percentage of the initial value ranged from 38% to 73% (average 55%). The amount of bilirubin removed from tissues expressed as percentage of the initial intravenous bilirubin mass varied from 40% to 180%. The drop was larger when exchange was performed as a two-stage procedure (on the average, 150%) than when it was carried out as a one-stage procedure (on average 130%). Valaes discussed the problems, including techniques, of exchange transfusion in detail. Kernicterus and the tissue pool of bilirubin are treated in Chapters IX,E and V,B,12, respectively.

Sproul and Smith (1964*) studied the bilirubin equation during exchange transfusion in hemolytic disease of the newborn in 10 infants by means of the tracer dilution technique (Cr^{51}-tagging of erythrocytes and I^{131}-albumin). Dilution of the circulating blood volume could be expressed by a simple exponential equation: Remaining blood volume = antilog [2 − 0.4343 exchange vol./blood vol.]. The extravascular equilibration rate was proportional to the initial serum bilirubin and the ratio of plasma volume to body weight: Extravascular bilirubin conc. = 0.9646

$\times$ initial plasma conc. $\times$ [plasma vol./body weight $-$ 0.9092]. Equations were derived for calculation of the final plasma bilirubin concentration and the total quantity of bilirubin removed during the exchange transfusion of any given blood volume. The findings supported the theory that the extravascular bilirubin consists of two compartments: (1) a "labile pool" in constant rapid equilibration with the plasma and (2) a "stable fraction" largely responsible for the rebound phenomenon after the exchange.

There is still much discussion concerning the indications for exchange transfusion in newborns. McKay (1964*) emphasized that the decision as to whether or not to perform exchange transfusion should be made on an individual basis after taking into consideration factors other than the serum bilirubin level. It is a complicated clinical situation which requires sound judgment and not the use of thumb rules! The only absolute indication for exchange transfusion is the appearance of clinical signs of early kernicterus whatever the serum bilirubin.

Koch (1964*) published a follow-up study of 100 consecutively born premature infants. Of these 8 died during the neonatal period, 2 had kernicterus, and 68 were examined at 7 years of age. There were no major neurological abnormalities, exclusive of mental retardation, in the 27 children who had serum bilirubin reaching above 20 mg/100 ml; 6 (22%) of them had brain damage in the genesis of which hyperbilirubinemia may have been an important factor. All these patients received relatively large vitamin K doses during the neonatal period. In the children with serum bilirubin below 10 mg/100 ml during the newborn period abnormal EEG's were found in 59%, in those with 10–20 mg/100 ml in 46%, in those with 20–30 mg/100 ml in 63%, and in those with 30–40 mg/100 ml in 83%.

Wishingrad *et al.* (1965*) performed a prospective clinical study of hyperbilirubinemia in prematurity including 187 infants, 100 with serum bilirubin reaching above 18 mg/100 ml and 87 with serum bilirubin not exceeding 15 mg/100 ml. The first group was evenly divided at random —one group receiving exchange transfusions and another receiving none. Of the 50 transfused infants bilirubin levels were adequately studied in 48. There was no mortality after the exchange transfusions. Follow-up study after 1 year failed to disclose any definite evidence of kernicterus. In the 50 infants with no transfusions 10 exhibited serum bilirubin levels above 24 mg/100 ml for 48 hours or longer. One of these developed a fatal kernicterus. Of the remaining 9 with serum bilirubin above 24 mg/100 ml 8 were subjected to follow-up examination after 1 year and showed no evidence of kernicterus. The same was the case with three of the infants with serum bilirubin between 18 and 24 mg/

100 ml. Of the 87 infants with serum bilirubin below 15 mg/100 ml 75 were subjected to follow-up study after 1 year and none of these exhibited evidence of kernicterus. It was concluded that in prematures the critical serum bilirubin level is 24 mg/100 ml. Only if other factors enhancing kernicterus are present exchange transfusions are to be given at lower serum bilirubin levels. If the serum bilirubin reaches 20 mg/100 ml between the 73rd and 96th hour or 22 mg/100 ml between the 96th and 120th hour after birth, a serum bilirubin level exceeding 24 mg/100 ml may be anticipated.

Besides exchange transfusion, several other methods have been proposed in order to reduce unconjugated serum bilirubin. Lester *et al.* (1962) proposed to remove unconjugated bilirubin from the gut with the bilirubin-binding resin *cholestyramine.* This method is based on the finding of Schmid and Hammaker (1962) that the gut contains a pool of unconjugated bilirubin exchanging across the intestinal mucosa with the serum bilirubin. Lester *et al.* studied adult Gunn rats receiving 2–5% of cholestyramine in a ground rat chow offered *ad libitum.* At varying intervals the resin was withdrawn and readministered, and the consecutive variations of serum bilirubin were followed. There was a marked decrease of serum bilirubin associated with cholestyramine feeding, and 5% in the ground rat chow invariably caused a decrease of the serum bilirubin level to 30–54% of the prefeeding values. In an experiment with C^{14}-bilirubin, cholestyramine feeding resulted in a significant acceleration of the clearance of radioactivity from the serum. This method was tried with apparent success in a 6-month-old boy with intrahepatic biliary atresia by Lottsfeldt *et al.* (1963), but Schmid (1963) could demonstrate no reduction of the hyperbilirubinemia in a study of 32 infants suffering from jaundice of prematurity, of whom 16 served as control group.

Infusion of salt-free albumin has also been used to reduce serum bilirubin. L. Johnson *et al.* (1961) removed bilirubin from the brain into the blood in Gunn rats by injection of salt-free albumin, and Koch and Rind (1962) used the same procedure in infants. They employed 1 g albumin per kg body weight and reported the serum bilirubin before and 30 minutes after this infusion. Nine infants were treated with salt-free albumin, and 8 served as controls. In the latter no significant change of serum bilirubin took place, whereas the albumin infusion caused an average rise of the serum bilirubin of 33%. This effect was ascribed to a flow of bilirubin from tissues to blood plasma. On the other hand, Theile *et al.* (1963a,b) found, in experiments with rabbits as well as in clinical studies on the newborn, that infusion of albumin could not significantly influence the course of hyperbilirubinemia. The rise in serum bilirubin following albumin infusion was only of short duration.

Further, ultraviolet irradiation, which is known to destroy unconjugated bilirubin (Cremer *et al.,* 1957, 1958; A. W. Franklin, 1958), administration of sodium glucuronate (Danoff *et al.,* 1958; Schmid *et al.,* 1958a; Jeliu *et al.,* 1959; T.-C. Lee and Hsia, 1959), as well as the β-glucuronidase inhibitor saccharolactone (Anke *et al.,* 1959), have all been tried, but did not significantly reduce unconjugated serum bilirubin. Injections of 6,8-dithiocaprylic acid intramuscularly, proposed by Jirsová *et al.* (1958), and triiodothyronine treatment, recommended by Lees and Ruthven (1959), are other measures proposed, but they have not been subjected to further trial.

Künzer *et al.* (1963*) found that charcoal completely adsorbs bilirubin from duodenal juice of newborn and proposed to try oral administration of charcoal to newborns to reduce jaundice.

Ulstrom and Eisenblom (1964*) studied infants after oral administration of charcoal. Their series I consisted of 17 controls and 15 test infants chosen by weight and group pairing and weighing from 2500 g and upwards. Their series II was similar, but comprised infants weighing from 3000 to 4000 g. In series I the charcoal treatment was started at the age of 12 hours and in series II at the age of 4 hours. There was no significant difference between treated and controls in series I, but in series II (early start of treatment) the average serum bilirubin was clearly lower in the treated than in the controls (5 and 8 mg/100 ml on the fourth day, respectively). This effect is ascribed to the bilirubin binding capacity of charcoal and the resulting interruption of the enterohepatic circulation of bilirubin.

Waters and Porter (1964*) discussed indications for exchange transfusions and emphasized that many individual factors must be taken into account and recommended the *reserve albumin binding capacity* of the serum as a useful test, i.e., the ability of the albumin of the patient's serum to bind phenolsulfonphthalein. If over 100 mg phenolsulfonphthalein is bound per milliliter of serum the binding capacity is satisfactory; if below 50 mg/ml is bound, exchange transfusion is immediately required. The test is a simple dialysis test taking 2 hours. If an infant has an adequate reserve of serum albumin binding capacity exchange transfusion is not immediately necessary and further observation is advisable. They further recommend using donor blood enriched with albumin to a concentration of 7 g albumin per 100 ml for exchange transfusion.

Brodersen (1965*) proposed to try oral administration of orotic acid and parenteral administration of uridine in order to promote the enzymatic systems responsible for bilirubin glucuronidation.

Irradiation of jaundiced infants and Gunn rats with artificial blue light was found to decrease the serum bilirubin level, but this therapy was not effective with rapidly increasing serum bilirubin (Broughton *et al.*, 1965*).

The use of prednisolone and liver extract in the treatment of severe jaundice of the newborn, which was advocated by several investigators, was studied systematically on a series of over 200 cases, including 50 controls, by Lewi *et al.* (1965*). This therapy was found to be without effect, and it was concluded that large doses of steroids are dangerous.

Koch and Rind (1965*) presented 3-years' experiences with treatment of icterus neonatorum with 20% salt-free human albumin. Their material comprises 200 patients and they employed 1 g albumin per kg body weight. No complications were encountered in spite of the fact that severe anemia and shock were not regarded as contraindications. They recommend infusing 1 g albumin per kg body weight 30 minutes before exchange transfusion is given.

Porter and Waters (1966*) proposed a micromethod for determining the reserve albumin binding capacity by means of the dye 2-(4′-hydroxo-benzeneazo)benzoic acid (HABA). This method gave the same result as their previous method using phenolsulfonphthalein and dialysis, and it is more simple and rapid.

Kaufmann and Blondheim (1966*) discussed binding of bilirubin to erythrocytes in relation to exchange transfusion and found that if the bilirubin/albumin molar ratio exceeded 1 (corresponding to 33 mg/100 ml in the serum of the infant) the uptake of bilirubin by erythrocytes suddenly increased fourfold. These findings appear to provide an experimental basis and explanation for the empirically determined bilirubin concentration above which exchange transfusion is indicated to prevent kernicterus.

N. Serum Biliverdin

Biliverdin, and not bilirubin, is the first degradation product of hemoglobin (Chapter II,B). Methods of determination of biliverdin in serum are discussed in Chapter I,D. Although bilirubin is the principal pigment in the serum, it is conceivable that at least traces of biliverdin can be present during jaundice. It is a well-known fact that the skin shows green discoloration in cases of prolonged, severe obstructive or hepatic icterus (Davies and Dodds, 1927; Brugsch, 1935; Eppinger, 1937; Horsters, 1939). In addition to this phenomenon, a greenish discoloration of the sera of these patients has been described (Herscher, 1902, pp. 97–101). This can be present in quite fresh sera.

Kunde (1850, pp. 16–17) found a green tint in alcohol extracts of sera of hepatectomized frogs. Cabello Ruz (1943c) confirmed this observation in toads. Penati and Pagliardi (1943) were not able to detect biliverdin in human serum with the spectrophotometric technique. However, Larson and Evans (1945) and Larson et al. (1947) claimed that biliverdin absorption could be determined by photoelectric measurements at 6600 Å and found biliverdin concentrations up to 2.2 mg per 100 ml in various icteric sera. The pigment was never present in normal sera or in sera of patients with hemolytic jaundice. It could only be demonstrated in sera of obstructive or hepatic icterus. However, the method is not absolutely reliable. It is affected by errors due to traces of hemoglobin. Biliverdin concentrations of 0.3 mg per 100 ml sufficed to cause a green tint of the serum. Individual patients showed considerable daily variations. Biliverdin was only found in severe cases of icterus and most frequently during obstruction caused by neoplasms.

The absence of biliverdin during hemolytic jaundice and its appearance during obstructive icterus and hepatitis indicate its formation by oxidation of conjugated bilirubin which is more readily oxidized than unconjugated bilirubin.

Zaroda (1966*) determined the serum biliverdin plus bilirubin by an oxidation procedure with a reagent containing $HgCl_2$ and HNO_3 and subtracted the serum bilirubin. Significant biliverdin concentrations were observed in 14 patients with marked jaundice of differing origin. Biliverdin determination was of no use in distinguishing between obstructive and hepatocellular jaundice.

The fate of parenterally injected biliverdin, as well as the appearance of biliverdin in icteric animals, has not yet been investigated. Such studies would possibly contribute important facts to the elucidation of metabolism of bile pigments.

O. Urobilinoids of Serum

Urobilinoid concentrations in serum are low, and their determination is therefore difficult. Urobilinoids are not precipitated together with proteins from serum (Farmer-Loeb, 1932), but migrate with proteins on electrophoresis (Bennhold, 1933).

Methods for determination of urobilinoids in serum based on fluorescence measurements cannot be satisfactory because serum contains numerous fluorescent compounds (e.g., flavins). With (1954, p. 248) summarized older methods of this type (Farmer-Loeb, 1932; Heilmeyer and Ohlig, 1936; Ohlig, 1938).

Recently Lozzio and Royer (1962) published a method for determination of urobilinoids in plasma based on oxidation with $FeCl_3$, treatment with Zn-acetate in alcoholic solution at pH 7.5–8, and reading in a sensitive fluorometer. As standard they employed a solution of tripaflavine. With this method Lozzio et al. (1963a,b) found concentrations of urobilinoids in human plasma varying between 0 and 30 μg per 100 ml (mean 15.1 ± 10.1) in 29 normal subjects. The following mean values were found in disease: 59.1 ± 7.7 in acute hepatitis, 54 ± 20.2 in liver cirrhosis, 48 ± 34.5 in hemolytic anemia, and normal values in metastatic carcinoma of the liver. It was concluded that determination of the plasma urobilinoid was without diagnostic value.

Bungenberg de Jong (personal communication, 1961) elaborated a method of urobilinogen determination in large samples of serum based on the benzaldehyde reaction. This was never published, but he placed his notes on the procedure at the disposal of the writer for publication here. Bungenberg de Jong employed 40–50 ml of serum acidified with a few milliliters of 20% acetic acid until the reaction was acid to litmus paper. Then cautious extraction with 100 ml of ether was performed in a separatory funnel. The ether was purified prior to use by shuttling with 40% NaOH and subsequent washing with distilled water. If emulsions formed, the separatory funnel was left in darkness until the emulsion had cleared. A known aliquot of the ether extract—as much as possible— was transformed to a new separatory funnel and extracted with p-dimethylaminobenzaldehyde and HCl as used for urine (cf. Chapter VI, B,1). Washing of the ether prior to this extraction is not necessary. Reduction of the serum prior to extraction of the urobilinogen with ether is not required, because oxidation of the urobilinogen proceeds far more slowly in serum than in urine. Even after 24 hours storage in darkness serum urobilinogen was unchanged. Spectrophotometric studies on the Ehrlich reaction of ether extracts of sera with positive reaction showed an absorption band at 550–570 nm.

Normal sera contained only faint traces of urobilinogen (10–100 μg per 100 ml), but in patients with marked pathological urobilinuria a pronounced Ehrlich reaction was found in the extracts. As the analyses were performed several years ago, Bungenberg de Jong was unfortunately unable to present quantitative data. It is highly desirable to repeat and extend studies with this technique.

Kahán (1961) studied the protein binding of serum urobilinoid by means of electrophoresis. Stercobilin (10μg) dissolved in 0.05 ml saline was added to 1 ml normal serum or 0.5 ml serum diluted with 0.5 ml saline. After incubation for 1 hour at 4°C, 0.05 ml of the mixture was subjected to paper strip electrophoresis with borate buffer (pH 8.6) for 2, 4, 6, or 8 hours. Part of the strip was stained for protein, another part with Schlesinger's reagent, and the fluorescence studied. This was repeated after acid hydrolysis, spraying with 3 ml concentrated HCl in 100 ml ethanol, and heating 5 minutes to 100°C. Similar investigations were performed on serum and heparin plasma from dogs. Plasma from the venous blood from an isolated intestinal loop of a dog was taken during the absorption of 6 mg of stercobilin dissolved in saline and introduced into the loop. The plasma sample with maximum urobilin content was subjected to continuous paper electrophoresis for 10 hours with 10 volts/cm in barbiturate buffer (pH 8.6, ionic strength 0.1). Owing to the presence of traces of Zn in serum the fluorescence of the Zn-urobilin complex could be studied directly.

It was found that stercobilin (urobilin-L) combines freely with albumin and β-globulin, but the complexes were split if the electrophoresis was continued for more than 4 hours. Most of the urobilin was bound to albumin, and the albumin linkage was the more stable. The serum proteins exhibited a marked stabilizing effect on urobilin in solution. In heparin plasma, part of the urobilin was bound as a distinct reddish band migrating directly ahead of the albumin. This band showed no fluorescence, but after acid hydrolysis it developed marked green fluorescence. If heparin was added to the urobilin prior to its addition to serum, all the urobilin appeared in the reddish band ahead of the albumin. This must be due to a strong affinity of urobilins to heparin (i.e., mucopolysaccharides).

Kahán et al. (1962) found that crystalline urobilin absorbed from isolated intestinal loops appears in the venous blood of the loop bound to albumin and β-globulin as well as to the heparin employed as anticoagulant in the experiment.

Lozzio et al. (1963a) studied the urobilinoid present in normal human plasma by electrophoresis. They subjected 50–60 ml of plasma to continuous agitation with equal volumes of alcohol at 60°C and added 10 ml 20% $FeCl_3$ for every 20 ml of plasma. Then followed addition of 20% ammonia and addition of distilled water. The alkaline filtrate was acidified to pH 1 with 3 N HCl, after which the urobilin was extracted with $CHCl_3$. The extract was dried and concentrated by evaporation. Then followed application to Whatman No. I paper and electrophoresis in a pyridine–acetate buffer of pH 6.1 with 14 volts/cm for 3 hours. Most of the 29 sera studied contained only urobilin-I, two contained only urobilin-L and two contained both. This finding is surprising because most of the urinary and fecal urobilinoid is of type L (cf. Chapter I,E).

Also Lozzio and Royer (1965*) determined the type of urobilinoid present in the plasma in 25 normal humans. The serum extracts were subjected to the $FeCl_3$ reaction, paper chromatography, and paper electrophoresis. Urobilinoids were demonstrated in the serum of 92% of the normal human subjects with type I dominating. Type L was only present in one case where it accounted for one-third of the total urobilinoid.

An interesting phenomenon in this connection is the *yellow diazo reaction* mentioned in Chapter I,J. Varela Fuentes and Canzani (1938, 1939) first described this phenomenon. Later it was studied by Varela Fuentes *et al.* (1939), Lopez Garcia (1941), and Castex and Lopez Garcia (1941). It was found that urobilinogen-I gives the yellow diazo reaction; the behavior or urobilinogen-L has not been studied. The reaction was carried out in $CHCl_3$ extracts of sera and was found to be positive in about 5% of icteric sera. In patients suffering from insufficiency of the liver, as well as the kidney, the reaction was particularly strong. It was claimed that this reaction indicates a serious prognosis.

M. Salvini and Gonzato (1947b) claimed that the absorption spectrum of the diazo reaction of urobilinogen is very similar to the diazo reaction of most normal sera. However, according to studies of Farmer-Loeb (1932), Heilmeyer and Ohlig (1936), and Ohlig (1938), normal sera do not contain urobilinoids and according to recent investigations the concentration is very low (cf. above); thus, these cannot be held responsible for the absorption curve of the diazo reaction of normal sera. The extent to which the yellow diazo reaction can be useful for the determination of urobilinogens in pathological sera requires investigation.

The behavior of urobilinoids introduced into the circulation has been discussed in Chapter II,D.

Additional Readings

Section B

Lathe, G. H., Lord, P., and Toothill, C. (1965). Bilirubin transport by plasma protein. *In* "Transport Function of Plasma Proteins" (P. Degrez and P. M. de Traverse, eds.), West-European Symp. on Clin. Chem., Vol. 5, pp. 129–135. Paris.

Section B,12

Abei, T., and Iber, F. L. (1967). Kinetics of bilirubin-C^{14} distribution in the dog with bile duct ligation. *In* "Bilirubin Metabolism" (I. A. D. Bouchier and B. H. Billing, eds.), pp. 217–224. Blackwell, Oxford.

Billing, B. H., Ali, M. A. H., and Cartter, M. (1967). Bilirubin-C^{14} metabolism in the bile duct ligated rat. *In* "Bilirubin Metabolism" (I. A. D. Bouchier and B. H. Billing, eds.), pp. 225–230. Blackwell, Oxford.

Section C

Roth, M. (1967). Fluorimetric assay of bilirubin in serum. (In French.) *Clin. Chim. Acta* 17, 487–492.

Section C,2

Jackson, S. H. (1966). Effect of nonionic detergent on the spectral absorption of oxyhemoglobin in the presence of bilirubin. *Clin. Chem.* 12, 509–512.

Section C,4

Baer, D. M., and Wood, D. C. (1967). Artificial lowering of the total bilirubin value in serum as determined with the method of Michaelsson-Jendrassik-Gróf. *Clin. Chim. Acta* **17**, 1–3.

Section D,2

Takita, H. (1965). Serum bilirubin in children. I. The quantitative fractionation by the method of Eberlein, and the age difference in serum bilirubin measured with this method. II. Fractionation in various kinds of jaundice by Eberlein's method. III. A comparison of Eberlein's and Malloy-Evelyn's methods. *Acta Paediat. Japon.* **69**, 685–697, 761–766 (Japanese).

Section D,3

Howe, R. B., and Pinto, S. De T. (1966). Ether-soluble bilirubin. *Medicine* **45**, 523–528.

Section D,6

Fog, J., and Bakken, F. (1967). Conjugated and unconjugated bilirubin determined in icteric sera by direct spectrophotometry. *Scand. J. Clin. Lab. Invest.* **20**, 88–92.

Section F

Brodersen, R. (1966). Bilirubin diglucuronide in normal human blood serum. *Scand. J. Clin. Lab. Invest.* **18**, 361–379.

Hargreaves, T., and Price, V. (1966). The uptake of conjugated bilirubin by rat liver. *Biochem. Pharmacol.* **15**, 657–667.

Heirwegh, K. P. M., van Roy, F., and De Groote, J. (1967). Comparative study of conjugated bile pigments in different animal species. In "Bilirubin Metabolism" (I. A. D. Bouchier and B. H. Billing, eds.), pp. 107–110. Blackwell, Oxford.

Tomlinson, G. A., and Yaffe, S. J. (1966). The formation of bilirubin and *p*-nitrophenyl glucuronides by rat liver. *Biochem. J.* **99**, 507–512.

Section G

Flitman, R., and Worth, M. H. (1966). Inhibition of hepatic alcohol dehydrogenase by bilirubin. *J. Biol. Chem.* **241**, 669–672.

Lozzio, B. B., and Machado, E. (1966). Biliary pigment changes during sedormid and allylisopropylacetamide (AIA) administration. *Experientia* **22**, 513.

Section H

Fevery, J., Claes, J., Heirwegh, K., and De Groote, J. (1967). Hyperbilirubinemia: Significance of ratio between direct reacting and total bilirubin. *Clin. Chim. Acta* **17**, 73–79.

Section I,1

Brodersen, R. (1966). See reference quoted in Section F.

Brodersen, R., and Jacobsen, J. (1967). Serum bilirubin diglucuronide in the human adult and newborn child. In "Bilirubin Metabolism" (I. A. D. Bouchier and B. H. Billing, eds.), pp. 111–115. Blackwell, Oxford.

(*Continued on p. 743.*)

CHAPTER VI

The Bile Pigments of Urine

A. Introduction

Bilirubin and urobilinoids are present in normal urine. In addition, biliverdin and often propentdyopent can be found in pathological urines. The normal urinary pigment, urochrome B, is a dipyrrole bile pigment (see Chapter I,G). The renal excretion mechanism of bilirubin is significantly different from that of urobilinoids: bilirubin has an extremely low clearance, whereas urobilinoids show a very high one. Biliverdin does not seem to enter the urine in mammals. However, this can be due to low biliverdin concentrations in blood serum. Investigations with intravenous biliverdin loadings would contribute to the clarification of this problem. Biliverdin appears regularly in the urine of pigeons, although tissue fluids contain mainly bilirubin (H. Stern, 1885; F. Rosenthal and Melchior, 1922). In the tissues as well as in the urine of turtles, intense green discoloration occurs after AsH_3 poisoning (Valentini, 1888). Similary, green discoloration of urine is observed in hepatectomized frogs and toads (Lesieurs et al., 1908; Cabello Ruz, 1943c).

Urinary bilirubin is attached to colloids; it cannot be extracted with chloroform (Fischer and Reindel, 1923), and it is not dialyzable (Hartog, 1935; Bungenberg de Jong, 1937; A. Müller, 1938a,b). Spectroscopic studies indicate that urinary bilirubin is not a simple molecular solution. Thus, icteric urines show an absorption maximum at 420 nm, whereas pure bilirubin solutions show one at 430 nm at the same pH (Bénard et al., 1949a,b). Furthermore, addition of albumin to icteric urines does not shift the absorption maximum, as in pure bilirubin solutions.

Barac (1949) reported that icteric urine contains a dialkali salt of bilirubin, in which the alkali metal is on the two carboxylic groups, and a tetraalkali salt, in which the two phenol groups contain additional akali. The solubility of the tetraalkali salt is higher than that of the dialkali salt and it increases significantly with increasing pH. Barac assumed that the pH of the urine exerts a considerable influence on the amount of bilirubin present in the urine. However, he did not support his assumption with bilirubin determinations at various pH values in icteric urines.

Mesobilirubin was identified by Pearson and Watson (1963*) in the urine from a patient with severe hepatic failure and no gallbladder; the patient had pronounced bilirubinuria. As the same writers found no mesobilirubin or mesobiliverdin in samples of human bile they believe that its occurrence in urine is due to absorption from the intestine and subsequent excretion.

B. Bilirubin in Urine

1. Methods of Analysis

While the first serum bilirubin determinations were performed about 50 years ago, attempts to determine urinary bilirubin are almost 100 years old. A number of difficulties interfere with the quantitative measurement of urinary bilirubin, arising because of the natural yellow color of urine, the easy oxidation of urinary bilirubin, and the simultaneous presence of urobilinoids and bilirubin in urine. Thus, the measurement of yellow color, oxidation tests, or the diazo reaction cannot be used directly for quantitative bilirubin determination in urine. Before quantitative measurements can be carried out, it is necessary to perform certain purification steps.

Fresh urine shows considerable bilirubin losses, due to oxidation processes, after a few hours (Sivo and Forrai, 1927; With, 1942a; Barac, 1945a). However, such losses can be avoided by addition of ascorbic acid (Lauersen and Sauerbruch, 1936; Sauerbruch, 1937; Barac, 1939). Since oxidation processes commence in the urinary passages, it is necessary to saturate the organism with ascorbic acid. Similarly, proteins considerably increase the stability of urinary bilirubin (Sivo and Forrai, 1927). When the urine contains 100 mg ascorbic acid per 100 ml urine no losses occur within 24 hours without taking special precautions (Barac, 1945a). However, it has to be borne in mind that the presence of high concentrations of ascorbic acid renders the diazo reaction useless (Michaëlsson, 1961, p. 64).

Most of the earliest workers, as well as some modern investigators, used *oxidation processes* for bilirubin determination. The oldest oxidation method is the *Gmelin test* using fuming nitric acid (Tiedemann and Gmelin, 1826). Many authors modified this test, without improving it fundamentally (With, 1954, pp. 252–254). The usual procedure was a ring test (zone reaction) between the contact layer of urine and acid. Scherer (1845) precipitated with alcoholic HCl. C. Neubauer and Vogel (1858) precipitated with lead acetate and eluted with alcohol containing sulfuric acid. Schwanda (1865) evaporated the urine to dryness, extracted the residue with water, filtered and dried the extract, and extracted it with $CHCl_3$ in which Gmelin's test was carried out. Other investigators introduced iodine as reagent. Besides fuming HNO_3 and iodine, a number of other oxidizing agents have been suggested. Hammarsten (1899) used a colorless, stable, and constant reagent of the following composition: stock solution, 19 parts 25% $HCl + 1$ part 25% HNO_3; dilution, before use with 4 parts 95% alcohol. Nakayama (1902) precipitated with $BaCl_2$ and oxidized with a reagent consisting of 0.4% $FeCl_3$ and 1% HCl in 95% alcohol. Steensma (1908b, 1909) modified Gmelin's reaction by the addition of $NaNO_3$.

Auché (1907, 1908a) discovered that bilirubin can be adsorbed on talcum powder and other neutral adsorbents from which it can be eluted with alcohol containing 5% HCl. Hooper and Whipple (1916) first added Na_2CO_3 and then precipitated with $CaCl_2$, centrifuged the precipitate, and washed it with water. Finally they dissolved the residue in a solvent composed of 100 ml 95% ethanol + 0.4 ml concentrated HNO_3 + 2 ml concentrated HCl. The green color was determined colorimetrically. This was the first truly quantitative method described.

G. A. Harrison (1930) used the Fouchet (1917) reagent: 25 g trichloroacetic acid, 100 ml water, and 10 ml 10% $FeCl_3$ solution which gives blue coloration with bilirubin. Naumann (1936b) filtered the urine through a layer of talcum. In this way he obtained a very sensitive qualitative procedure. Von Purjesz (1937) and Maini (1940) employed 20% sulfosalicylic acid in a rough, qualitative method. Maher (1941) used 20% toluenesulfonic acid solution and 0.1% $NaNO_2$ solution. Singer and Kubin (1943) used Hammarsten's reagent without prior precipitation. Thoma and Kitzberger (1948) described a spectrophotometric method based on an oxidation reaction employing a modified Fouchet reagent: 0.25 g trichloroacetic acid + 2 ml 10% $FeCl_3$ solution filled up with water to 200 ml total volume. Four ml 95% ethanol and 2 ml reagent were added to 4 ml urine, and the extinction at 670 nm was measured after 10 minutes. A mixture where the reagent was replaced with 0.125% trichloroacetic acid was used as blank. The concentration was calculated from calibration curves; it was established that Beer's law was valid for the conditions of the test. Another spectrophotometric method based on oxidation was proposed by Garay et al. (1962). They precipitated with $BaCl_2$, oxidized with H_2O_2 dissolved in HCl–alcohol, and read at 660 nm in a spectrophotometer. They claimed an accuracy of 3% and recovery of added bilirubin close to 100%.

A few investigators have employed the yellow color of bilirubin as a basis for determination. Such methods would require precipitation and elution, or extraction before measurement (Schilling, 1923; Kerppola and Leikola, 1932).

The diazo reaction was employed by a number of investigators.

Krokievicz and Batko (1898) mixed equal volumes of urine and diazo reagent. Riegler (1899) extracted with $CHCl_3$ before using the diazo reaction. Raphael (1905) used equal volumes of urine and a strongly acid diazo reagent. Adler and Meyer (1923) precipitated with $BaCl_2$, eluted with HCl alcohol, and added the diazo reagent to the eluate. The azobilirubin formed was extracted with chloroform.

Terwen (1928) precipitated with Na_2HPO_4 and $CaCl_2$, washed the precipitate, and eluted with a mixture of methanol and diazo reagent. The eluate was purified by adsorption on talcum and subsequently eluted with 5% alcoholic HCl. The concentration was determined by a colorimetric method. Bilirubin added to the final solution could be recovered quantitatively. G. Hunter (1930a) acidified the urine, precipitated with $BaCl_2$, and eluated with diazo reagent and alcohol. After addition of a phosphate buffer, he determined the bilirubin content colorimetrically. Godfried (1934) used a similar method, but extracted the azobilirubin with $CHCl_3$ before determination. However, the extraction cannot be considered complete, and the final volume subjected to measurement was not exactly known (With, 1942a). Hoitink (1935) precipitated with $BaCl_2$, filtered, and added Fouchet reagent dropwise to the filtered precipitate.

Jendrassik and Gróf (1938a) described the following technique: 1.5 ml 11% $Na_2HPO_4 \cdot 12 H_2O$ solution and subsequently 0.5 ml 20% $CaCl_2 \cdot 6 H_2O$ solution was added to 1.5 ml icteric urine in a centrifuge tube. After standing for 10 minutes, the mixture was centrifuged at high speed for another 10 minutes. The supernatant was discarded and the residue was washed 3 times with 2–5 ml 0.2% $CaCl_2$ solution. After decanting the bulk of the washings the remaining liquid was removed with filter paper strips, and the precipitate was suspended in 5 ml 95% ethanol by stirring with a spatula. After the addition of 1 ml of diazo mixture (5/1000 + 15/1000 + 0.15; see Chapter V,C,5) the contents of the tube was stirred and, after standing for 10 minutes, 2 ml concentrated HCl was added and it was mixed again. The acid dissolved the precipitate and a blue solution was obtained. The color of the solution was measured with water as blank in a Pulfrich photometer (filter S 57). Bilirubin introduced to such solutions could be recovered quantitatively. This technique can be improved by adjusting the volume in a volumetric flask (With, 1942a).

Goodson and Sheard (1940) attempted to eliminate the disturbances caused by other colors with the use of spectral filters. However, Halász (1949) found that it is impossible to eliminate all interfering absorptions in the urine. Castex and Lopez Garcia (1940a; see also Lopez Garcia, 1943, p. 304) employed a method which resembles that of Jendrassik and Gróf; however, it is more complicated from the point of view of laboratory manipulation. Bilirubin added to test solutions was also recovered quantitatively with this method. The authors maintained that the color of the diazo reaction was not characteristic for bilirubin in urine samples containing small amounts of this pigment. Nevertheless, they accepted the extinctions obtained in such dilute solutions, and assumed that the color was caused by bilirubin. This assumption can easily lead to error, as shown by With (1942a) who used Jendrassik and Gróf's method in his investigations. The nonspecific absorption at 570 nm was often high enough to be misinterpreted as 3 mg bilirubin per 100 ml. This error was most marked in urines rich in urobilinoids. In contrast to azobilirubin, these disturbing pigments were not extractable with $CHCl_3$. However, since azobilirubin cannot be extracted quantitatively with $CHCl_3$ either, this process is unsuitable for quantitative bilirubin determinations.

L. D. Scott (1941) described a method based on $CHCl_3$ extraction of azobilirubin formed by diazotation of $BaCl_2$ precipitate. Golden and Snavely (1948) found that the diazo reaction yields good results in strongly icteric urines, but disturbing reddish-brown discolorations developed in urines with low bilirubin concentrations. They tried to avoid this by reading at 575 and 450 nm and by the use of suitable corrections. Although added bilirubin could be quantitatively covered with this process, the specificity is, nonetheless, questionable.

J. Watson *et al.* (1945) and C. J. Watson and Hawkinson (1946) modified the oxidation method of G. A. Harrison (1930) to a spot test ("Harrison spot test"). This oxidation method is based on the Fouchet reagent, and the spot test shows a positive reaction with concentration levels of 0.1–0.25 mg per 100 ml. It is a simple test which can be performed rapidly, and is well suited for large series. M. Franklin (1949) and Harvig and Bang (1954) modified this test by introducing reagent tablets. Barac (1945a) precipitated with $BaCl_2$ and extracted the bilirubin from the precipitate with dilute alcoholic KOH; 97–98% of bilirubin added to the test solution could be retraced. The diazo method and the direct spectrophotometric technique were used to measure the yellow color. Before $BaCl_2$ treatment some Na_2SO_4 was added to the solution in order to obtain a voluminous precipitate binding all the bilirubin present in the urine. Brereton and Lucia (1948) used NaClO as an oxidizing agent without prior precipitation. Thoma and Kitzberger (1948) oxidized with the Fouchet reagent; after addition of alcohol they read at 670 nm with a blank containing only urine, alcohol, and trichloroacetic acid. The authors found that salicylates disturb the reaction by causing pink discoloration. However, according to the proposition of Barac this source of error can be avoided by precipitation and elution.

Halász and Engel (1948), using the method of Jendrassik and Gróf, investigated the influence of the amount of urine and the nature of adsorbents on bilirubin determinations. They found that analytical results varied as much as 50% by changing the ratio urine/precipitating agent (solutions of phosphate and calcium). The results were rather irregular, variations becoming smaller as the bilirubin concentration became higher; the errors were attributed to incomplete absorption and losses during the washing of the precipitate. Losses due to washing were demonstrated by the qualitative test of Naumann (Section B,2, this Chapter) in the washings. Later, Halász (1949) compared the method of Jendrassik and Gróf (which includes precipitation and elution) with that of Goodson and Sheard (diazo method without precipitation). He found that the latter procedure yields higher values than the former because of the presence of nonspecific adsorptions in urine. Consequently, direct measurements without prior purification yield too high values, and it appears that precipitation and elution are the most useful purification procedures today.

Ingham (1951) described a simple and sensitive qualitative test using a modified Fouchet reagent. The urine was adsorbed on a layer of colloidal iron ammonium sulfate gel on absorbent cotton.

Free and Free (1953) introduced a test based on reagent tablets consisting of p-nitrobenzene diazonium-p-toluenesulfonate (0.2 mg), sulfosalicylic acid (100 mg), sodium bicarbonate (10–20 mg), and boric acid (15–25 mg). Five drops of urine are placed on a cellulose asbestos mat whereby the bilirubin is adsorbed. A tablet is placed on the urine spot and is moistened with 2 drops of water. Positive reaction is indicated when a blue or violet color develops within 30 seconds. Klatskin and Bungards (1953), as well as Shutkin and Caine (1955), studied the clinical value of this test. This method is somewhat more sensitive and yields more specific results than the Harrison spot test advocated by C. J. Watson (see Sobotka et al., 1953; Giordano and Winstead, 1953). These tablets are commercially available under the trade name Ictotest. Tallack and Sherlock (1954) considered this method at least as sensitive as the Fouchet test (1917), with the added advantage of simpler manipulation. However, they proposed placing one drop of Fouchet reagent on the cellulose asbestos mat instead of the diazo tablet. Positive reactions were observed at concentrations as low as 0.02 mg/100 ml.

The oxidation procedures described by Zak et al. (1954) have only been studied in connection with serum (Chapter V,C,1); they possibly may also be useful in determinations in urine.

Bryant and Flynn (1955) found that Ictotest was somewhat less sensitive that the Harrison spot test and the Fouchet layer test proposed by Tallack and Sherlock. However, all these were found to be more sensitive than the classic iodine ring test.

Hoenig (1955) used talcum powder adsorption for the qualitative determination of bilirubinuria. The author added a small amount of talcum powder to 5–10 ml acidified urine, mixed it and filtered the mixture through filter paper. After letting it stand for 10 minutes, dilute HNO_3 was added. When the test is positive, a bluish-green spot forms immediately. The sensitivity of the test is claimed to be 0.025 mg/100 ml.

F. A. Gries and Gries (1956) studied quantitative bilirubin determinations in urine. In spite of the criticism of Halász and Engel (1948) and Halász (1949), these authors consider the Jendrassik and Gróf (1938a) method [slightly modified by With (1942a)] the best process existing at the present time. They recommend adding HCl to the solution after 30 minutes instead of after 10 minutes, and reading the results 30 minutes after acidification. They claimed to obtain more consistent values by this process. Bilirubin added to their solutions could be recovered quantitatively. It was shown that the reaction follows Lambert-Beer's law at urine concentrations between 3 and 23 mg/100 ml. Very reliable values were obtained when a calculation factor (4.29) was used that was somewhat higher than the one employed by Jendrassik and Gróf and by With (3.46). With 2 ml urine in 10 ml final volume, the urine concentration is

$$c \text{ (mg/100 ml)} = E \times 4.29$$

where E is the extinction in a layer of 1.0 cm, using filter S57 (Pulfrich photometer).

F. A. Gries and Gries (1957) also described a method for a separate direct and indirect bilirubin determination in urine. This method is analogous to their procedure used for total bilirubin determination; however, one difference exists: whereas the precipitate is suspended in alcohol in the former method, the washed phosphate precipitate is suspended in a buffer solution of pH 3.8, prior to the addition of the diazo reagent in this test. The pH of the solution is checked after addition of the reagent, and if it falls outside the range of 3.0–4.2, it is readjusted. One hour after the introduction of diazo reagent, 25% HCl is added, the final volume adjusted with water and measured in a Pulfrich photometer using filter S57. The calculation is performed with the formula given above. The buffer solution employed consists of 9 volumes 1.5 N acetic acid and 1 volume 1.5 N sodium acetate. Precipitation and elution did not affect the ratio between direct and indirect bilirubin. Similary, dilution of the urine had no effect on this ratio.

Bolotov (1958) proposed a modification of the Fouchet test: 5 drops glacial acetic acid and 20 drops 10% lead acetate solution are added to 50 ml urine and filtered. The residue on the filter is washed with water, dried and treated with one drop of chloramine reagent (1 g chloramine B, 3 g NaCl, 5 ml concentrated HCl, filled up to 100 ml with distilled water). When the reaction is positive, the residue develops a green color. According to Bolotov, a blue color corresponds to a bilirubin concentration of about 0.005 mg. In a simplified version of this method, the urine is added dropwise to tablets of gypsum or talcum, and finally 1 drop of chloramine reagent is added. Another version consisted of adding a bichromate reagent to the urine. The bichromate reagent consisted of 0.05 g potassium bichromate, 2.0 g $FeCl_3$, 5.0 g concentrated H_2SO_4, 20.0 g crystalline Na_2SO_4, filled up to 100 ml with distilled water. Bolotov found that whereas conjugated bilirubin reacts rapidly with this reagent, free bilirubin dissolved in $CHCl_3$ reacts positively only after 5–10 minutes.

Michaëlsson (1961) introduced a new method based on a *copper complex of azobilirubin*. This is more stable than azobilirubin itself. He studied the conditions of the formation of the complex and its spectral absorption, but did not succeed in isolating it in pure crystalline condition or determining its exact structure. The complex consists, according to the evidence collected, of equimolar quantities of copper and azobilirubin. The addition of copper to azobilirubin resulted in a displacement of the absorption maximum toward longer wavelengths—from 530 to 615 nm at pH 6.2. The absorption curve of Cu-azobilirubin varies with pH but presents an isobestic point at 570 nm for pH values above 3. At pH below 2 no Cu-azobilirubin was formed. Its extinction at maximum was about 55% of that of azobilirubin. Michaëlsson's copper method *makes it possible to read the diazo reaction directly on the mixture of urine and reagents* without previous purification procedure because the absorption maximum of the Cu complex (615 nm) is sufficiently far from that of urine to eliminate errors from normal urine color. Furthermore, the complex is stable, unlike alkaline azobilirubin which has a similar color.

Michaëlsson's method is as follows:

I. *Reagents:*

(1) 5 g 7-(2,3-dihydroxypropyl) theophylline (dyphylline) and 12.5 g sodium acetate (3 H_2O) in 100 ml distilled water; heated at 30–40° to dissolve more quickly.

(2) Diazo reagent: 1.0 ml 0.5% (w/v) $NaNO_2$ solution added to 10 ml of the following solution: 5 g sulfanilic acid, 15 ml conc. HCl, diluted

to 1000 ml with distilled water. The mixture of nitrite and sulfanilic acid solution has to be used within 30 minutes.

(3) Diazo blank: 15 ml conc. HCl diluted to 1000 ml with distilled water.

(4) 1.596 g anhydrous $CuSO_4$ dissolved in 1000 ml distilled water.

II. *Procedure:* Four tubes are prepared as follows:

(A) Copper sample consisting of 1 ml urine, 2 ml reagent (1), 0.5 ml reagent (2), and after 5 minutes 0.25 ml reagent (4).

(B) Copper blank consisting of 1 ml urine, 2 ml reagent (1), 0.5 ml reagent (3) and 0.25 ml reagent (4).

(C) Water sample consisting of 1 ml urine, 2 ml reagent (1), 0.5 ml reagent (2) and, after 5 minutes, 0.25 ml water.

(D) Water blank consisting of 1 ml urine, 2 ml reagent (1), 0.5 ml reagent (3), and 0.25 ml water. The copper sample (A) is read against the copper blank (B) giving the extinction E_1 and the water sample (C) against the water blank (D) giving E_2. Read at 615 nm. If extinction is above 0.8, dilute the urine with water and repeat the procedure.

III. *Calculation:*

c (mg bilirubin/100 ml of urine) $= 6.52 \times (E_1 - E_2 - 0.020)$ if E_1 and E_2 are read in 1-cm layer.

The method includes both a copper sample and a copper-free sample to increase the specificity.

Sato and Saitoh (1965[*]) described a fractionation method for urine and bile bilirubin in which a water-soluble as well as a $CHCl_3$-soluble fraction was obtained; the lipo-soluble fraction from bile contained phospholipids and bile acids and gave the direct diazo reaction (cf. Chapter VII, Section A).

Some other methods based on various chemical reactions should also be mentioned. Rissel (1939) precipitated urine with $BaCl_2$ and, after addition of concentrated HCl, measured the red color reaction described by Heilmeyer (1938). A number of investigators employed the methylene blue test, introduced by Chelchowsky (1897). When bilirubin is reacted with methylene blue, a green color develops. This test was forgotten and revived by Franke (1931). The nature of this reaction caused some discussion. Reinhold and Fowler (1946) mixed solutions of bilirubin and methylene blue and measured the absorption spectra. They arrived at the conclusion that bilirubin and methylene blue form a complex, in which two equivalents of methylene blue are reacting with one equivalent bilirubin. W. Müller (1952) confirmed these findings. Helfferich (1960) could not, however, confirm the formation of a bilirubin-methylene blue compound in paper chromatographic studies. In chloroform methanol they behaved as two separate substances. Vella (1962) arrived at the same conclusion.

Hoesch (1922) and A. Müller (1938a,b) investigated the green coloration of certain icteric urines after addition of Ehrlich's aldehyde reagent. Green color was regularly found when nitrites of bacterial origin were present. However, in some cases the green color was also obtained after removal of the nitrites by dialysis. The color is due to biliverdin formation after the addition of the aldehyde reagent.

Godfried (1934), Foord and Baisinger (1940), Vickers (1950a), and Bryant and Flynn (1955) compared the sensitivity of various qualitative methods. They used serial dilutions of icteric urine and pure bilirubin solutions. Tests performed directly in urine were much less sensitive than those performed after precipitation or adsorption. It was found that Rosin's (1893) old iodine test, which is still widely used, was much less sensitive than modern "spot tests."

Bleyler and Steigmann (1958*) compared four screening tests for bilirubinuria, that are in general use—Rosenbach's modification of the Gmelin test, Smith's iodine test, Franklin's tablet modification of Fouchet's test, and the Ictotest method—on 247 urine specimens from jaundiced patients. Ictotest was found to be the most sensitive, but the simple and economic Rosenbach test came close to the sensitivity of Ictotest.

Summary

Since urinary bilirubin is not stable, determinations must be carried out as quickly as possible; direct sunlight should be avoided. Oxidation is retarded by addition of ascorbic acid, but it should be kept in mind that ascorbic acid can interfere with the diazo reaction. Several investigators have proposed purification procedures, but such measures inevitably involve losses. Purification can consist of precipitation with barium or calcium chloride and phosphoric acid or by adsorption on talcum powder and subsequent elution. The most efficient quantitative method, working directly on the urine without previous purification and based on the formation of an azobilirubin-copper complex is that of Michaëlsson (1961), which is given in detail above. A method permitting the separate determination of direct bilirubin has been proposed by Gries and Gries. A number of excellent spot tests have been proposed. The most sensitive of these tests is that recommended by Naumann with adsorption on talcum powder (cf. below).

2. Bilirubin in Normal Urine

The presence of bilirubin in normal urine has been much discussed. Obermeyer and Popper (1908), as well as Rabinowitch (1932), claimed to have found bilirubin in urine of normal subjects (and of patients with normal serum bilirubin). Kühle (1926) found it in about 25% of urines of normal cattle. However, Pollock (1945), who like Rabinowitch (1932) used G. Hunter's (1930a) diazo test, could not detect bilirubin in the urine of normal humans. Nevertheless, Naumann (1936b) adsorbed urine on talcum powder and found traces of bilirubin in urine of most normal humans examined. According to Naumann, the limit of positive reaction is 0.9–6.0 ppm. However, he corrected this value to 0.009–0.06 ppm (0.0009–0.006 mg/100 ml). With (1954) repeated these experiments, using larger amounts of urine (50 ml instead of 5 ml as used by Naumann), and employing following technique:

Filter paper is moistened and placed into a Büchner funnel of corresponding size and fixed there by suction. Subsequently, 5 ml of an about 10% talcum powder suspension is placed on the filter without suction. After the suspension is spread out uniformly on the filter paper and some alcohol is added to prevent foaming, the vacuum is established again. This technique should give a smooth talcum surface. Thereafter, 50 ml urine, acidified to pH 3–4 with glacial acetic acid, is carefully added to the talcum layer and sucked through the adsorbent. The surface of the talcum assumes a yellowish-orange color, the intensity of which depends on the color and amount of urine employed. The reaction is performed with Fouchet's reagent, 10% nitric acid, or diazo reagent, the reagent being added dropwise to the talcum surface. For the diazo reaction, one drop of alcohol is placed on the surface. The alcohol partially discolors the area where it has been applied. Then 1 drop of diazo reagent is added to this spot. In the case of positive diazo reaction, a distinct red color is obtained. When one drop of concentrated HCl is added, the color changes to violet. The diazo test is not as sensitive as the Fouchet test. However, the color change occurring after acidification is considered more specific. Usually Büchner funnels 12 cm in diameter and water suction was used.

Employing this method, With examined 100 urine samples of persons who did not suffer from diseases of liver or bile ducts and who did not show increased hemolysis. Of the total, 70 showed a positive reaction with Fouchet as well as with the diazo reagent. Of the remaining 30, 19 showed a positive Fouchet reaction, i.e., bilirubinuria was demonstrated in 89% of normal human urines. The concentration limit of positive reaction was 0.015 mg/100 ml in icteric urines diluted with water. However, the concentration limit for normal urine samples was higher, since they contain more nonbilirubin-colored compounds to mask the reaction than do icteric urines. Thus, the bilirubin concentration of normal humans is in the order of magnitude of 0.03 mg/100 ml.

Castex and Lopez Garcia (1940a) and Lopez Garcia (1943, p. 127) determined bilirubin in normal urine. They precipitated with $BaCl_2$, subsequently carried out the diazo reaction, and found that the color reaction is yellow in urines poor in bilirubin. They found 0.20–0.60 mg per 24 hours, i.e., 0.01–0.03 mg/100 ml with a diuresis of 2000 ml. Because of the uncharacteristic color of the diazo reaction, these results do not prove the presence of bilirubin. Barac (1945b), who used the diazo test of Hunter, reported traces of bilirubin in various normal urines. Bolotov (1958) examined the bilirubin content of 40 normal urine samples with his oxidation method (see Chapter V,B,1). The test was regularly positive when a 50-ml urine sample was used, but it was often negative when only 10 ml was employed. This would correspond to 0.05 mg bilirubin/100 ml urine. The tablet test proposed by Bolotov was always negative for normal urines.

Michaëlsson (1961) studied freshly voided urine samples from 47 adults and 34 children (aged 2 weeks to 15 years), using his Cu-azobilirubin method, and found concentrations between 0.06 and 0.16 mg/100 ml (average 0.11 mg/100 ml) in the adults and 0.06–0.12 (average 0.09) in the children. The extinctions read, however, were very low ($e_{1\,cm} =$ 0.009, corresponding to 0.06 mg/100 ml).

The studies of Gundermann and Kübler (1962) are of particular interest because they concentrated 200 ml of normal urine and proved the presence of bilirubin in the concentrate by paper chromatography. They used freshly voided urine saturated with ammonium sulfate (just above 70% w/v) and added 1% (v/v) of n-butanol. The mixture was left for 1 hour in a separator funnel, after which the lower (aqueous) phase was extracted once more with 1/100 volume butanol. The butanol phases, including the brown intermediary layers, were pooled and centrifuged. Then 3–4 volumes of 66% ethanol were added, and the precipitate that formed was brought into homogeneous suspension, after which 1–1.55 ml of diazo reagent was added. After 10 minutes the solution was saturated with sodium acetate, which results in formation of a slightly rose-colored ethanolic phase and a darker butanol phase. The former was re-extracted with butanol after addition of more water and ammonium sulfate. The pooled butanol phases were washed several times with saturated ammonium sulfate in order to increase the concentration. Finally, the butanol phase was dried over anhydrous Na_2SO_4 overnight. Then followed decantation was washing of the Na_2SO_4 with butanol. The final volume of the butanol extract was 6–10 ml (corresponding to 200 ml of urine). Between 0.25 and 0.5 ml of this extract was subjected to paper chromatography. The spot was dried with cool air. The paper was Schleicher & Schuell No. 2043 b, the solvent was methyl ethyl ketone–propionic acid–water (75/25/30), ascending technique. The spots were eluted with 10%

alcoholic HCl and subjected to spectrophotometric reading in microcells.

Gundermann and Kübler studied 45 urines from 15 healthy adults with this method, and in every case a well-marked blue spot of free pigment A (azo pigment of unconjugated bilirubin) was present. After i.v. bilirubin tolerance tests, a definite small increase of the urinary bilirubin was found, the concentration showing an increase ammounting to five times the pretolerance test level if the bilirubin dose was 50 mg i.v. Calculation showed that the bilirubin excreted with the urine was always under 1% of that passing through the kidneys during the time of the production of the urine. In newborns, small amounts of unconjugated bilirubin were also demonstrated (Kübler, 1959).

Garay *et al.* (1962), using their oxidation method, found an average of 0.024 mg/100 ml (0.247 mg/24 hours) in a study of 70 normal urines.

Only a few studies on the urinary bilirubin content of *normal animals* have been carried out. Kühle's (1926) findings on the bilirubin content in urine of normal cattle have already been mentioned. Bierthen (1906) could not detect bilirubinuria in normal horses; the method he used, however, was insensitive. Studies using sensitive detection methods on different animal species would be of interest.

Klatskin and Bungards' (1953) peculiar opinions should finally be mentioned in this connection. These authors claim that positive bilirubin reaction in urine of individuals without proved liver damage and without bilirubinemia, must be erroneous. This line of reasoning is wrong, since the question of whether the positive reaction is real or artificial (i.e., specific or nonspecific) is a chemical one, and cannot be decided by clinical observations.

Summary

With sufficiently sensitive methods, bilirubin can be detected in about 90% of normal human urines. The bilirubin concentration is about 0.03 mg/100 ml in these cases. This is the case in adults, children, and newborns. Only unconjugated bilirubin has been found in normal urine. Investigations on animals should be carried out using a sensitive method, which was described in detail.

3. PATHOLOGICAL BILIRUBINURIA: THE PLASMA THRESHOLD FOR BILIRUBIN AND THE ROLE OF THE DIRECT DIAZO REACTION

It has been known for a long time that, in the majority of cases, gross bilirubinuria is not present in hemolytic jaundice (Leyden, 1866; Quincke, 1884; Hijmans van den Bergh, 1918). The same lack was reported for jaundice of newborns (Léreboullet, 1901; Gilbert and Herscher, 1907b, footnote p. 455; Ylppö, 1913; S. G. Ross *et al.*, 1937). Originally, this fact was attributed to the relatively low serum bilirubin level during hemolytic jaundice (Hijmans van den Bergh, 1918, pp. 59 and 107). However, it soon became clear that serum bilirubin concentrations, which during hemolytic icterus are not accompanied by bilirubinuria, during obstructive or hepatic icterus are accompanied by gross bilirubinuria (Hijmans van den Bergh, 1921). During icterus neonatorum, bilirubinuria was only found when the serum bilirubin concentration exceeded 18 mg/100 ml (With, 1943d; Larsen and With, 1943). Cases were reported in which serum bilirubin concentration was higher than 22 mg/100 ml, but no bilirubinuria could be demonstrated (Deenstra, 1950). High threshold levels were reported in various forms of jaundice in newborns; for example, in one case of bile duct atresia, over 13.5 mg/100 ml serum was demonstrated, but no bilirubinuria (Ströder, 1957). Thus, jaundices characterized by indirect diazo reaction in serum are not accompanied by bilirubinuria, whereas jaundices with direct reaction show bilirubinuria. On the basis of these findings it was natural to conclude that only direct-reacting bilirubin could pass the kidneys, whereas bilirubin, which gives the indirect reaction, cannot be excreted in the urine (McNee, 1923, 1924; Bensley, 1933; Faltitscheck and Hess, 1936).

In the light of newer studies, these facts appear to be easily understandable. Recent investigations show that direct-reacting bilirubin consists mostly of water-soluble bilirubin conjugates, whereas the indirect-reacting modification represents the insoluble, free bilirubin. However, the mechanism is more complicated than it first appears because the entire amount of bilirubin in blood (indirect as well as direct) is strongly bound to serum albumin. The plasma threshold is that serum bilirubin concentration at which pathological excretion of urinary bilirubin occurs. Because only "direct" bilirubin gives rise to significant bilirubinuria, it is most correct only to take the concentration of "direct bilirubin" into account in studies of the plasma threshold. However, most investigators limited their studies to total serum bilirubin, and the majority of direct bilirubin determinations were carried out with unreliable analytical techniques.

Hijmans van den Bergh (1918) found a threshold concentration of about 4 units; this corresponds to about 1.6 mg/100 ml. Meulengracht (1920) gave 40–50 icterus index units, equivalent to 8–10 mg/100 ml. Retzlaff (1923a,b) and Andrewes (1924a) observed significant variations from case to case. E. Schiff and Eliasberg (1922) were not able to establish any relation between bilirubinuria and direct diazo reaction of the serum. Adler and Jeddeloh (1929a,b) found threshold concentrations of 8–9 mg/100 ml in jaundice cases caused by liver metastases. But the threshold concentration was 5–20 mg/100 ml during the initial phase of acute hepatitis, and dropped to 4.5–9 mg/100 ml during regressing icterus.

Faltitscheck and Hess (1936) found high threshold levels in hepatitis patients with renal insufficiency. Bensley (1933) found no correlation between urinary bilirubin and total serum bilirubin, but did note a certain correlation between urinary bilirubin and direct serum bilirubin.

With (1943d) examined the relation between serum bilirubin and urinary bilirubin in 23 hepatitis patients and 9 cases of obstructive jaundice. The results are shown in Fig. 48.

He found significant variations in threshold values: 3 mg/100 ml to 12 mg/100 ml. Most often the threshold value lay between 4 and 6 mg/100 ml serum. Lopez Garcia (1943, p. 127 et seq.) carried out similar

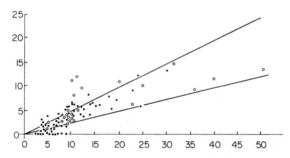

Fig. 48. Bilirubin in blood serum and in urine in acute hepatitis and in obstructive jaundice. Abscissa: serum bilirubin in milligrams per 100 milliliters. Ordinate: urinary bilirubin in milligrams per 100 milliliters. Dots represent cases of hepatitis, circles represent cases of obstructive jaundice. The lines correspond to urinary concentrations 25 and 50% of the serum concentration.

investigations and found in jaundice with direct diazo reaction a urinary excretion which corresponded to an hourly rate of 1–2% of the bilirubin present in 1000 ml serum. He found 0.15–0.3% per hour in normals and 0.03–0.13% in hemolytic jaundice. The levels were very low during jaundice complicated by renal insufficiency. As in the cases examined by With, there were no distinct differences between the percentage of bilirubin excretion during hepatic icterus and obstructive icterus.

Barac (1945b, 1947, 1951) reported threshold levels of 2–4 mg/100 ml with the exception of hemolytic jaundice where the threshold lay above 14 mg/100 ml. C. J. Watson (1946) found threshold values up to 3 mg/100 ml in hepatic and obstructive icterus; however, individual variations were large. These variations were somewhat less pronounced when the serum bilirubin content was expressed as 1-minute-bilirubin. The range of variation was 0.7 to 3 mg/100 ml with the average about 1 mg/100 ml. These variations were primarily caused by low values during the initial stage and high values occurring during the healing phase of hepatitis.

Bittorf and Riessbeck (1947) reported that the indirect diazo reaction is converted to a retarded direct reaction after intravenous injections of 0.4–4 g sodium dehydrocholate during hemolytic icterus. They observed a simultaneous decrease of the serum threshold. A. Salvini and Mantero (1947) maintained that the threshold levels are around 1 mg/100 ml with little variation. Halász (1948) examined 31 patients for total as well as direct serum bilirubin (method of Jendrassik and Cleghorn, 1936a,b) and urinary bilirubin (method of Jendrassik and Gróf, 1938a). He found that the relation between urinary bilirubin and total serum bilirubin approximately corresponded to that between urinary bilirubin and 3-minute-bilirubin (direct bilirubin). Lattanzi (1948a) found threshold levels of about 2 mg per 100 ml. He believed that only the immediately reacting direct bilirubin is available for excretion by the kidney.

Deenstra (1950) found considerable variations in the serum threshold (1–20 mg/100 ml). As a rule, a low serum threshold was found when direct bilirubin content was high, but numerous exceptions were observed. For instance, one patient with 20 mg/100 ml direct bilirubin (of which 45% was 1-minute-bilirubin) did not show bilirubinuria. The renal bilirubin excretion during obstructive jaundice showed great variations. The threshold was significantly lower during the initial stages of virus hepatitis than during the healing phase.

Vickers (1950b) observed significant fluctuations of the serum threshold in 53 cases of virus hepatitis. He often found levels below 1 mg/100 ml. Pollock (1951, pp. 78–80) pointed out that bilirubinuria is relatively independent of the serum bilirubin level. On the average, the lower the threshold during hepatitis, the lower the maximum serum bilirubin concentration. This author observed variations ranging from 35 mg/100 ml (in one case of severe jaundice) to 0.5 mg/100 ml (in a definitely mild case). He considered the relation between direct diazo reaction and bilirubinuria a puzzling and yet unsolved problem. Klatskin and Drill (1950) also contended that the urinary bilirubin level can hardly depend on the 1-minute-bilirubin concentration of serum. Weicker (1957) assumed that variations in kidney threshold during hepatitis can be attributed to differences in serum proteins.

Rotor *et al.* (1948) and Stransky (1950) described hereditary cases of jaundice with direct diazo reaction in serum but without bilirubinuria, in spite of distinct hyperbilirubinuria. This observation is hard to explain from current theories, and Stransky writes: "In any case we are dealing here with a syndrome which contradicts all our present theories about bile pigment metabolism."

Moeller and Schroeder (1954) determined simultaneously the bilirubin excretion in urine and serum bilirubin concentrations, using the

method of Jendrassik and Gróf. Direct and indirect bilirubin were determined by the technique of Jendrassik and Cleghorn. From the results the
authors calculated the excretion quotient, i.e., concentration of urine
multiplied by diuresis per hour and divided by serum bilirubin concentration. This clearance ratio turned out to be independent of the excretion
rate and varied between 2 and 88. Nineteen cases of hepatitis were examined. In only 6 instances of 50 tests on these patients was the hourly
clearance more than 11. However, in 19 tests in 10 patients with obstructive icterus all except three gave quotients higher than 11. The diagnostic
value of hourly clearance is nonetheless questionable, since overlapping
sometimes occurred. The direct percentage (direct bilirubin concentration
divided by indirect bilirubin concentration) and the renal bilirubin
excretion are independent of each other.

Redeker and Kahn (1962) found a considerably higher threshold
value during the healing phase of acute hepatitis than during the initial
phase, and these findings were not explained by measurement of direct
serum bilirubin. They studied the total and 1-minute bilirubin in 42
hepatitis cases.

Gundermann and Kübler (1962) studied the bilirubin excretion with
the urine per hour in normal subjects before and after i.v. injection of
50 mg bilirubin (cf. above). The excretion varied between 3 and 85
μg/hour without bilirubin loading and increased to 8–176 μg/hour after
the loading. They performed 10 tolerance tests in 6 subjects.

Idiopathic bilirubinuria in a 56-year-old healthy male with normal
liver function and normal serum bilirubin of the unconjugated type has
been observed by Ilca (1964) from Roumania. The urinary bilirubin was
purified from 100-ml samples of urine by precipitation with $BaCl_2$ and
eluated with diazo reagent without addition of alcohol. It gave a positive
diazo reaction under these conditions, which showed that conjugated
bilirubin was excreted with the urine. Simultaneous determination of the
serum bilirubin showed values between 0.28 and 0.31 mg/100 ml (Jendrassik and Gróf's method) in several periods where the urinary bilirubin
excretion varied from 3.5 to 7.1 mg/24 hours. During a period where
only traces of bilirubin could be demonstrated in the urine, the serum
bilirubin was significantly higher, about 0.6 mg/100 ml. This case clearly
demonstrates that a high serum concentration of conjugated bilirubin is
not a necessary condition for bilirubinuria in man. The pathogenetic
mechanism in this case was not elucidated. Unfortunately no fractionate
chromatographic studies on the conjugates were performed, and studies
of the relatives of the patient to disclose whether the condition was
hereditary were not reported.

Later, S. Ilca (personal communication, 1964) found another case of the same type of bilirubinuria in a 14-year-old girl. The bilirubinuria was accidentally discovered during a routine health examination. Her serum bilirubin was 0.30 mg/100 ml, and a positive direct reaction could be demonstrated. The urine bilirubin was 0.70 mg/100 ml and no urobilin was demonstrable. Paper chromatography of the diazotized urinary bilirubin showed R_f 0.28 as against 0.43 of azobilirubin from free bilirubin. The finding of two cases of this type of bilirubinuria suggests that it can hardly be an extreme rarity.

Recently Ilca et al. (1965*) described 5 subjects with a slight intermittent indirect hyperbilirubinemia who excreted substantial amounts of bilirubin with their urine. These subjects were found among 103 persons with intermittent hyperbilirubinemia and were submitted to a closer clinical examination. Their urine was studied as follows: To 50 ml of urine 1 ml 10% sodium sulfate and 1 ml glacial acetic acid were added, followed by filtration and addition of 5 ml 10% $BaCl_2$ to the filtrate, then mixing, and centrifugation after standing for 1 minute. The supernatant was decanted and the remaining fluid dripped off. Then 5 ml diazo reagent was added, thorough mixing was carried out, followed by standing for 10 minutes, and then recentrifugation after which the supernatant was decanted once more. Next 3 ml distilled water and 0.3 ml conc. H_2SO_4 were added, thorough mixing carried out, followed by standing for 5 minutes and recentrifugation once more. If bilirubin is present the supernatant is now violet, and quantitative colorimetric readings can be taken.

With this method Ilca et al. found a 24-hour bilirubin excretion of 0.7 to 4.1 mg, i.e., bilirubin with direct diazo reaction, in their 5 subjects. Paper chromatographic separation of the azobilirubin was carried out with Schmid's method. Using this method only one fraction with R_f 0.28–0.33 was found, and occasionally traces of another azobilirubin with R_f 0.45–0.50, i.e., findings indicating that the bulk of the bilirubin present is diglucuronide with occasional traces of free bilirubin or monoglucuronide, were present.

Ilca et al. believed that the conjugation of bilirubin took place in the kidneys in their patients, that the bilirubin conjugation capacity of the kidney varies with each individual, and that their patients are variants with unusually high capacity for bilirubin conjugation in the kidneys.

Tisdale et al. (1959) studied bilirubinuria during hemolytic forms of jaundice. They found bilirubinuria (Ictotest positive) in 8 cases out of 23. No fixed serum threshold could be determined. In bilirubin tolerance tests they found that renal bilirubin clearance does not show a closer connection to direct (1-minute) serum bilirubin than to total serum bilirubin.

Mild bilirubinuria can develop after infusion of very large amounts of bilirubin during induced hyperbilirubinemia. The author of this monograph (cf. Chapter V,J) could not demonstrate bilirubinuria in such experiments. However, Tisdale *et al.* (1959) obtained positive Ictotest in urine when the urine sample was collected 5–7 hours after infusion of 15 mg bilirubin/kg body weight. A positive test corresponds to about 0.05 mg bilirubin/100 ml urine. Gundermann and Kübler (1962) also found a small but definite increase in the urinary bilirubin in normal subjects after loading.

The threshold concentration for bilirubinuria is very high in newborns (With, 1943e; Larsen and With, 1943).

All this indicates that there is some relation between the direct diazo reaction of serum bilirubin and urinary bilirubin excretion. However, this relation seems to be complicated. In any case, the assumption that "direct" bilirubin passes through the kidneys, whereas the "indirect" form is unable to do so, cannot be correct. Therefore, more observations are needed, including those on other animal species. Only few such observations have been recorded at present.

Bilirubinuria can be absent in *horses* in spite of high hyperbilirubinemia (Bierthen, 1906; Beijers *et al.*, 1950). The latter authors reported that a newborn foal, in which the bilirubin concentration was 180 mg/100 ml, did not show bilirubinuria. On the other hand, Bendixen and Carlström (1928) found bilirubinuria in a horse with moderate hyperbilirubinemia due to hemolysis.

In *dogs*, bilirubinuria appears within 30 minutes after hemolysis has been induced by intravenous injections of distilled water (Tarchanoff, 1874). Starving can also induce bilirubinuria (Naunyn, 1869). Similarly, bilirubinuria can be observed regularly in hepatectomized dogs, although the direct diazo reaction is negative in their sera (F. C. Mann *et al.*, 1924; Bollman and Mann, 1932). It would be interesting to know whether bilirubinuria develops after induced hyperbilirubinemia in dogs. This is not mentioned in the report of Snapp *et al.* (1947).

Some investigators reported threshold values for bilirubinuria in animals. F. Rosenthal and Meier (1921) found a serum threshold of about 0.4 mg/100 ml (one Hijmans van den Bergh unit) in dogs and about 3.6 mg/100 ml (nine units) in *cats*. Wespi (1935) had to inject over 10 mg/100 kg body weight in *rabbits* to induce bilirubinuria. When dehydrocholic acid was administered simultaneously, bilirubin excretion occurred at lower concentrations.

Alican and Hardy (1962) studied the urine bilirubin in 6 dogs with common bile duct ligation and found between 5 and 20 times higher concentrations in urine samples than in simultaneously taken serum samples.

This is in striking contrast to the findings in man where the concentration in blood serum is nearly always higher than in urine (With, 1943d).

Cameron *et al.* (1963*) studied 12 dogs with experimental biliary obstruction and found a 24-hour urinary bilirubin excretion corresponding to ca. 85% of their calculated daily bilirubin production—25–76 mg per 24 hours, average 40.7. In some of the dogs, exhibiting an initial peak level of serum bilirubin, the 24-hour bilirubin excretion was only 15 mg per 24 hours during the first 2 weeks of the biliary obstruction, but increased later to 40 mg per 24 hours simultaneously with a fall of the serum bilirubin level. This observation points toward a rather complicated relation between serum bilirubin and renal bilirubin excretion.

Cameron *et al.* (1966a*) studied 3 children with biliary atresia to whom C^{14}-bilirubin was injected intravenously after which the urine was collected over a period of 14 days. Between 44.7 and 70.6% of the injected radioactivity was recovered from the urine, and it was calculated that ca. 60% of the label if the urine was present as bilirubin. The analytical method used for urinary bilirubin was, however, not specified. The authors conclude that the turnover of bilirubin is almost entirely dependent on renal clearance, but this is not warranted—because only 44.7–70.6% of the radioactivity was recovered and because the analytical method used for bilirubin (Malloy-Evelyn) is not reliable. Further, only 60% of the urinary radioactivity was present as bilirubin, which means that destruction of bilirubin before excretion can play a major role. Cameron *et al.* (1966b*) performed similar experiments on 5 rhesus monkeys with complete biliary occlusion. The urinary bilirubin varied between 1.5 and 11.0 mg/24 hours, and the total amount of bilirubin excreted during the 14 days of the experiments varied between 3.3 and 13.4 mg. Between 34.7 and 90.9% (average 69.1) of the radioactivity injected at the start of the experiments was recovered in the urine, but only 57.6–86.4% of the urinary radioactivity was accounted for as urinary bilirubin. The analytical method used for bilirubin in urine was not specified, and consequently evaluation of the results is difficult.

These few observations on animals show significant variations even within the individual animal species. They do not support the assumption that the direct diazo reaction is of decisive significance to the renal secretion of bilirubin.

Kaneda (1963*) isolated the bilirubin of jaundiced human urine by salting out with ammonium sulfate and extracting the precipitate with methanol. The ester form of bilirubin was then precipitated from methanolic solution with two volumes of $CHCl_3$ and the supernatant dried *in vacuo* and subsequently dissolved in water. On addition of $CHCl_3$ a dark-brown amorphous precipitate appeared at the borderline between the two phases, due to an unknown bilirubinoid. The diazo reaction of ester-bilirubin and the unknown bilirubinoid was studied. The former exhibited diazo maximum 530–540 nm in methanol which changed to 560 nm on addition of HCl. The maximum of the unknown bilirubinoid was 550 nm, changing to 560 nm on addition of HCl.

Summary

The threshold level of serum bilirubin at which bilirubinuria appears varies greatly. It ranges from about 2 mg in hepatocellular and obstructive jaundice to 20 mg in hemolytic jaundice, icterus neonatorum and induced hyperbilirubinemia. Furthermore, considerable variations occur during the course of hepatitis. Only a few animal studies are available, but they suggest that great differences exist among different animal species. The role of conjugated bilirubin in the mechanism of bilirubinuria is discussed. There undoubtedly is a relation between bilirubinuria and the concentration of direct serum bilirubin in humans. The old assumption that only direct but not indirect bilirubin can be excreted with urine seems to be logical, but no specific experimental evidence supports this contention and recent knowledge about the nature of direct bilirubin—a mixture of conjugates—renders matters complicated. Before this question can be solved, chromatographic investigation of free bilirubin and its conjugates must be performed. These studies should include sera as well as urines of clinical cases. Moreover, these questions should be elucidated by human and animal experiments. Idiopathic bilirubinuria with normal serum bilirubin, described by Ilca, is mentioned.

4. The Mechanism of Renal Bilirubin Excretion and the Renal Bilirubin Clearance

To understand the mechanism of bilirubin excretion by the kidneys, it should be remembered that direct as well as indirect serum bilirubin is firmly bound to serum albumin (see Chapter V,B and D,4). Earlier it was generally assumed that "direct" bilirubin was free, whereas the indirect form was bound so that only the free form passed through the filter of the kidneys (cf. Young, 1947a,b). In reality, however, only traces of bilirubin can pass the glomerulus by filtration. Thus, it would be possible to explain the appearance of this substance in urine only by active tubular excretion (Gassmann, 1930, p. 480; Bennhold, 1933; Lopez Garcia, 1943, p. 131; With, 1945e; Barac, 1945b, 1947, 1951). Traces of bilirubin are normally found in urine; this could possibly be explained by filtration, since small amounts of serum albumin are also present in normal urine. Bilirubin present in pathological urine samples is no longer bound to albumin. Therefore, it was believed that the complex must have been split by active processes operating in the tubular epithelium of the kidneys. Thus, this epithelium should exert an excretory function similar to that of the parenchymal cells of the liver, only to a much lesser degree.

After Burnstine and Schmid's (1962) studies on the solubility of bilirubin in biological fluids, however, the problem of renal bilirubin excretion needs reinvestigation. There exists an equilibrium between free and albumin-bound bilirubin in the blood plasma, and this is the case with both unconjugated bilirubin and conjugated bilirubin, although the albumin binding of the former is believed to be much more firm than that of the latter. As conjugated bilirubin is considerably more soluble in the body fluids than unconjugated bilirubin and also less firmly attached to albumin, it is easy to understand that it is excreted more freely with the urine than unconjugated bilirubin. On the other hand, Burnstine and Schmid found that unconjugated, albumin-free bilirubin can exist in solution in water—containing electrolytes within the physiological range and at physiological pH values—in concentrations of up to 5 mg/100 ml. This solubility depends on pH and falls rapidly with slight decreases of pH. One might consequently expect that significant quantities of uncon-jugated bilirubin might pass the glomerular filter if the plasma is slightly alkaline. This possibility has, however, not been subjected to experi-mental studies.

Histological examination of kidneys of icteric patients showed that the glomeruli were colorless, whereas the tubuli exhibited a strong yellow color (Möbius, 1877). Well defined bilirubin granula were detected in the convoluted tubules, especially in Henle's loops. Very similar pictures were observed in frogs with experimental jaundice produced by injections of bile into the lymph sac. Nizet and Barac (1952a,b) performed similar experiments in dogs with experimental obstructive icterus; on examination of the kidneys of these animals they found that bilirubin was located exclusively in the proximal segments of the convoluted tubules and in the wider sections of Henle's loops.

Experimental studies on the location of bilirubin excretion in the nephrone were recently presented by Laks et al. (1963), who employed the renal stop flow technique in 15 cholecystectomized dogs with ligated common bile ducts. When the jaundice had reached a maximum (6–8 days after the operation), the left ureter was catheterized with polythene tubing. Intravenous infusions of mannitol and later inulin and p-amino-hippuric acid were employed to locate the function of the different parts of the nephrone. When urine flow exceeded 8 ml/minute in the catheter-ized ureter, the tube was clamped after which the urine rapidly filled and distended the renal pelvis and the nephrone system. Six minutes later, when the flow within the system had stopped, inulin and p-amino-hippuric acid were injected. After 2 minutes for equilibration, reabsorption, and secretion, the catheter was cut and the urine rapidly collected in wells in a Lucite bar allowing fractionation of a first portion of urine from the tubing, a second from the collecting ducts, followed by fractions from the distal tubules, Henle's loop the proximal tubules, and the glomeruli. The different portions of urine were analyzed for sodium, p-aminohippuric acid, creatinine, inulin, and bilirubin.

The bilirubin concentration in the different portions varied parallel to the creatinine concentration and inversely proportional to the sodium concentration. The influence of water reabsorption was controlled by calculation of the fraction bilirubin clearance divided by inulin clearance. This ratio showed a definite increase—30 to 45%—in the fractions corresponding to the ascending Henle's loop, distal tubules, and collecting ducts. The findings give experimental support to the concept that active secretion of bilirubin takes place in the distal part of the nephrone, including the ascending Henle's loop, distal tubules, and collecting tubes.

Another interesting recent contribution to the problem of the location of renal bilirubin excretion is the study of *aglomerular fish* (Schenker and McCandles, 1964). Two freshly caught goose fish (*Lophius piscatorius*) weighing 1.9 and 2.9 kg were infused i.v. with conjugated C^{14}-bili-rubin obtained from bile of rats loaded with C^{14}-bilirubin. Infusion of unconjugated bilirubin was not performed. The bilirubin was infused in the mesenteric vein, and bile and urine were collected through polythene tubing throughout the experiment, which lasted 140–190 minutes. The animals were in excellent condition throughout the experiment, exhibiting normal ureteral flow (0.96–1.64 ml/hour). The bilirubin loads employed were 4.8–12.0 mg, dissolved in 10–20 ml and given in divided doses at a rate of 0.5 ml/minute. Blood samples were taken at intervals throughout the experiment. The concentration of conjugated bilirubin in the serum was only 0.1 mg/100 ml before loading, but increased to between 1 and 4.3 mg/100 ml. No bilirubin could be demonstrated in any of the ureteral or bladder urine specimens with either diazo reaction or radio assay. The experiments suggest that aglomerular fish are unable to excrete conjugated bilirubin, but experiments of longer duration are necessary to confirm this finding. Since the proximal segment of the nephrone is considered to be homologous in all vertebrates, it is likely that the observations have a bearing on renal bilirubin excretion in higher vertebrates. Loading experiments with unconjugated bilirubin must also be carried out before the problem can be considered adequately covered.

Normal kidney function is a prerequisite for urinary bilirubin excretion. This is known from animal experiments (Saiki, 1931c), and from clinical investigations (Faltitschek and Hess, 1936; Lopez Garcia, 1943). Nonnenbruch (1919), moreover, could show that bilirubinuria disappeared in dogs with experimental bile duct ligature 24 hours after renal poison ($HgCl_2$, etc.) was administered. A number of authors compared the bilirubin concentration of urine and serum of icteric patients (Adler and Jeddeloh, 1929a,b; Rissel, 1939; With, 1943d, 1945e). It was demonstrated that the bilirubin concentration was nearly always higher in serum than in urine in man, but in the dog the opposite is regularly the case (Alican and Hardy, 1962). As a rule, the urine concentration was about 25–50% of the serum in severe cases of jaundice (see Fig. 48, this chapter). The lines in Fig. 48 correspond to 25 and 50% of the serum values, respectively. Rissel assumed that bilirubin excretion by the kidneys is somewhat lower during parenchymal icterus than during obstructive icterus, but With could not confirm this observation. However, Moeller and Schroeder (1954) determined that the "hourly clearance" is consistently higher in obstructive icterus than in hepatitis (see B,3 this chapter). Peremy (1932) reported a case in which jaundice and chronic kidney insufficiency were present simultaneously (serum bilirubin concentrations 3–5 mg/100 ml, residual nitrogen about 110 mg/100 ml), but no bilirubin was detectable in urine.

Renal bilirubin clearance—i.e., urine concentration divided by serum concentration and multiplied by the diuresis in milliliters per minute— is very low. With (1943d, 1945e) found values of 0.09–0.80 in six cases of acute hepatitis. Significant variations were observed when determinations were carried out at different times in the same patient (for example, 0.23–0.80, 0.90–0.17, 0.24–0.40). Alzugaray (1942) and Lopez Garcia (1943, p. 131 et seq.) obtained similar results. Barac (1945b, 1947, 1951) found pronounced variations of the ratio of urine concentration to plasma concentration during clinical jaundice and during experimental bile duct closure in eight dogs (i.e., from 3.44/2.30 to 0.1/2.20). Bilirubin concentrations of serum and of urine were determined within 9–15 hours after ligature. The following values were obtained (the figures designate mg/100 ml; the first figure represents the serum concentration, the second stands for urine concentration in each of the eight dogs examined): 6.05/3.12, 4.40/3.18, 5.10/7.30, 3.12/13.6, 5.83/1.30, 5.72/3.13, 2.10/4.60, and 14.40/36.80.

Barac carried out calculations to examine the assumption that bilirubin is excreted by glomerular filtration and subsequent reabsorption. Basing his calculations on the bilirubin concentration of urine and serum, he concluded that such filtration–reabsorption would only be possible if the ultrafiltrate was concentrated more than 3000-fold. However, it is well-known that only a 100-fold concentration takes place during urine formation. Thus, his calculations indicate that bilirubin cannot be excreted by filtration–reabsorption. Barac concluded that urinary bilirubin excretion must be due to active tubular excretion processes.

Royer (1943, pp. 156–157) found about 1.5 mg bilirubin/100 ml serum and 3.0 mg bilirubin/100 ml urine in partially hepatectomized rats. Enanesco *et al.* (1946) found that the quotient, serum bilirubin/urinary bilirubin, is regularly below 2 in obstructive jaundice, but it is over 2 in hepatic icterus.

Halász (1945) determined the hourly urinary bilirubin excretion in 7 patients with hepatic jaundice with varying serum bilirubin levels. He found urinary bilirubin excretions of 1 mg/hour, 3 mg/hour, and 10 mg/hour corresponding to serum bilirubin concentrations of 10 mg/100 ml, 20 mg/100 ml, and 40 mg/100 ml, respectively. Lopez Garcia (1943, figure on p. 130) found a similarly steep, almost exponential increase of the hourly urinary bilirubin excretion with increasing serum bilirubin concentration. Halász and Pinter (1949) studied dogs with toluenediamine icterus and others with complete choledochus obstruction. They compared hourly urinary bilirubin excretion with the rate of glomerular filtration. They found that the ratio, urinary bilirubin/serum bilirubin, is significantly higher in dogs than it is in humans. Deenstra (1950) determined the 24-hour bilirubin clearance in a series of patients with various forms of jaundice. Significant variations were discovered. In one hepatitis case variations from 680 ml (0.472 ml per minute) during the initial stage of the disease to 21 ml (0.015 ml per minute) in the healing stage were found.

Some investigators have questioned the mechanism of renal bilirubin elimination by tubular excretion. Hoenig and Schück (1954) found a close relation between urinary bilirubin excretion per minute and the amount of glomerular filtrate in six cases of virus hepatitis. They assumed that only a small fraction of serum bilirubin is ultrafiltrable. They believe it is wrong to compare urinary bilirubin concentration with that of the serum, and think it is more justifiable to relate excretion per unit time to the serum concentration. Corà (1956) came to similar conclusions by the examination of 22 icteric patients, 9 of whom had hepatic jaundice, 3 had cirrhosis of the liver, and 10 had neoplastic obstruction. Corà performed 68 clearance determinations, among which he included sodium thiosulfate-, *p*-aminohippuric acid-, as well as total and direct (1-minute) bilirubin clearance. The results of these experiments are described in detail. The clearance values—calculated in milliliters per minute per 1.73 m^2 body surface—amounted to 0.08–1.38 for total bilirubin, and 0.22–2.51 for direct bilirubin. Total bilirubin was determined by the

method of Malloy and Evelyn (1937), direct bilirubin was measured as
1-minute-bilirubin according to Zieve *et al.* (1951), and the amount of
urinary bilirubin was determined by Jendrassik and Gróf's (1938a)
method. More distinct relations were found between urinary bilirubin
and direct bilirubin than between urinary bilirubin and total bilirubin.
However, quantitative evaluation of these relations indicated that additional factors must also be active in the mechanism of renal bilirubin excretion. Experiments in which the excretion capacity of tubuli was
saturated with *p*-aminohippuric acid showed that the behavior of renal
bilirubin elimination is incompatible with the theory of tubular bilirubin
excretion. Corà assumed that part of the bilirubin-protein complex is
excreted by ultrafiltration, and is concentrated by tubular reabsorption
after filtration.

Wallace and Owen (1964*) studied 42 patients with parenchymal
or obstructive jaundice by carrying out bilirubin clearance experiments.
The serum and urine bilirubin was determined with a modified Malloy-
Evelyn procedure including 30-minute direct bilirubin determination.
Bilirubin added to urine was recovered $100 \pm 3.4\%$, but the urinary bilirubin concentration with this method was somewhat higher than the
actual concentration because certain unidentified constituents of urine
also react with the diaoz reagent. In 24 patients with normal glomerular
filtration "the clearance of direct bilirubin" varied from 0.12 to 0.52 ml/
minute with a creatinine clearance varying from 94 to 206 ml/minute
and a rather constant ratio between bilirubin and creatinine clearance of
1×10^{-3} to 4×10^{-3}. In patients with reduced glomerular filtration rate
the ratio varied from 1×10^{-3} to 8×10^{-3}. Despite varying causes of
hyperbilirubinemia the urinary excretion of "direct bilirubin" was directly
and linearly related to the "filtered load," i.e., plasma direct-reacting bilirubin concentration multiplied by glomerular filtration rate. The "direct
bilirubin" excreted and measured in μg/minute was about twice the
plasma direct bilirubin concentration (mg/100 ml) multiplied by the
creatinine clearance (ml/minute). The findings in patients with and
without proteinuria were similar. Although the analytical methods used
in this study are far from satisfactory the observations support the view
that bilirubin enters the urine primarily via the glomerular apparatus.

Fulop and Brazeau (1964*) studied the renal bilirubin excretion in
40 female dogs weighing ca. 20 kg with experimental biliary obstruction
and exhibiting serum bilirubin 2.4–8.0 mg/100 ml 6–14 days after the
operation and 87–99% "direct bilirubin." Glomerular filtration studies were
performed with creatinine or inulin, and further stop-flow experiments
using i.v. infusion of 10–20% mannitol and experiments with acute partial
ureteral obstruction were employed in addition to conventional clearance

experiments. The administration of conventional inhibitors and competitors of tubular secretory processes did not cause any decrease in the bilirubin excretion, whereas agents displacing bilirubin from its albumin linkage—such as salicylates—gave rise to increased urinary bilirubin excretion. This is attributed to displacement of conjugated bilirubin from serum albumin by organic anions. Stop-flow studies showed a peak in the bilirubin curve at the glomerular level which was interpreted as arising from glomerular filtration of protein-bound bilirubin during ureteral occlusion. A small distal peak may represent a secretory locus of moderate capacity, but has not been demonstrated consistently. The studies suggest dominance of glomerular filtration over tubular secretion in the renal excretion of bilirubin.

Fulop *et al.* (1964, 1965*) found that a small fraction of conjugated plasma bilirubin in patients and dogs is dialyzable and regarded this bilirubin fraction as the source of urinary bilirubin. Unconjugated bilirubin added to plasma is not dialyzable. The experiments were carried out on plasma from 10 patients with obstructive jaundice and 14 mongrel female dogs with experimental biliary obstruction and indwelling catheter in the urinary passages. The plasma bilirubin was 3–5 mg/100 ml in the dogs and 20–40 mg/100 ml in the patients. The conjugated bilirubin constituted 82–88% of the total bilirubin (Malloy-Evelyn's method). Five-ml plasma specimens were placed in cellophane casing and dialyzed at 4°C against 5 ml buffer (0.01 M phosphate, 0.15 M NaCl, pH 7.2) in flasks covered with aluminum foil and gassed with 5% CO_2, 95% N_2. Equilibrium was attained in 24 hours with specimens from subjects with normal renal function, more slowly with specimens from subjects with renal insufficiency. The spectral curves of the dialyzates were measured, as well as their protein content to test the integrity of the casing. Dialyzates from the icteric plasmas were definitely yellowish and exhibited positive diazo reaction as well as spectral maximum at 435–445 nm; the spectral curves were more reminiscent of the absorption curves of protein-free solutions of unconjugated bilirubin than of the absorption curves of unconjugated bilirubin dissolved in serum. Dialyzates of normal plasmas from patients and dogs with added unconjugated bilirubin were colorless, even when the bilirubin concentration was as high as 36 mg/100 ml. Further, renal clearance studies were carried out on the patients and dogs. The ratios of dialyzable to total bilirubin in both dogs and patients were very similar to the ratios of bilirubin clearance to creatinine clearance in the two species.

Moeller and Schroeder's (1954) studies on the hourly clearance have already been discussed (this chapter, B,3). These authors found hourly values of 2–88, i.e., minute clearance values of 0.03–1.47. Schachter

(1959) determined separately the mono- and diglucuronide clearance by fractionate butanol extraction (see Chapter V,D,2) and found 0.05–0.16 ml/minute for the former and 0.41–0.96 ml/minute for the latter.

Talafant's (1954b) investigations are of interest in this connection. This author dialyzed bilirubin from bile and indirect (free) bilirubin dissolved in $M/15$ phosphate buffer (pH = 7.3) in cellophane tubes. The concentration was 8 mg/100 ml. To avoid oxidation and bacterial contamination, ascorbic acid and phenylmercuric borate were added to the solutions. The dialysis of conjugated bilirubin proceeded at least five times as fast as that of unconjugated bilirubin. The rate of dialysis increased immediately after salts of bile acids were introduced.

Tisdale *et al.* (1959) examined the renal bilirubin clearance after infusion of bilirubin solutions in normal subjects and patients with cirrhosis of the liver. These authors found clearance values of 0.2–1.3 ml/minute in cirrhosis cases and 0.1–8.0 ml/minute in normal subjects. The amount of excreted bilirubin increased with increasing serum bilirubin concentration. However, the relation between the amount excreted and the increase in either direct (1-minute) bilirubin or total bilirubin were about the same.

Gundermann and Kübler (1962) found a small but definite increase in the urinary bilirubin after bilirubin loading in normal subjects (cf. Sections B,2 and 3, this chapter). The urinary concentration increased fivefold after the injection of bilirubin, but the excreted bilirubin was below 1% of the injected. Schalm *et al.* (1962b) studied the urine with Fouchet's reaction after i.v. loading with 100 mg of bilirubin in three subjects with drain in the bile passages and found bilirubinuria (positive Fouchet test) in two of them 3, 6, 18, and 42 hours after the bilirubin injection, but no bilirubinuria prior to the injection and 2 hours after the injection. The absence of bilirubinuria during the first 2 hours is remarkable because the serum concentration of conjugated bilirubin reached 3–5 mg per 100 ml in the course of the first hour. This does not support the current view that the state of conjugation of the serum bilirubin is of major importance for the excretion of bilirubin with the urine. Other factors besides the state of conjugation of the serum must be significant in the development of bilirubinuria.

On the basis of present knowledge the problem of renal bilirubin excretion mechanisms still remains unsolved. Its final clarification requires more experimentation. Tolerance tests in humans and animals with bilirubin and its conjugates, simultaneous determination of urinary bilirubin and serum bilirubin during varying diuresis, and dialysis experiments and studies with radiobilirubin are required. Such experiments would probably result in a better understanding of the mechanism of bilirubinuria if better analytical methods than those of Malloy-Evelyn are used.

The nature of bilirubin appearing in urine, *direct and indirect,* has been discussed by a number of authors. Talafant's (1954b) dialysis experiments which were discussed above are particularly important in this respect. Investigations in this field have also been presented by Japanese workers (Komuda, 1959a,b; Kondo, 1959a,b; Monobe, 1959a,b). Their results are, unfortunately, published in Japanese with brief summaries in poor English, from which evaluation is difficult.

Raices and Velasco Suarez (1935) suggested determination of direct and indirect bilirubin in urine with the help of reaction velocity and $CHCl_3$ extractability. Dirr and Sereslis (1939) and Sereslis (1938) thought that only direct bilirubin can reach urine since it is less firmly bound to protein than is indirect bilirubin. Bourrillon (1952) and Polonovski and Bourrillon (1952c,d) found that urinary and bilary bilirubin are of the same nature and called them "cholebilirubin." Urines containing bilirubin showed an absorption maximum at 410–420 nm, and frequently another one at 450 nm, i.e., the same peaks were found here as in bile. The peaks were less marked in urine than in bile. When acetone was added to urines rich in bilirubin, a water-soluble precipitate was obtained. This precipitate showed a maximum at 410 nm in aqueous solution. Additions of large amounts of acetone to the filtrate produced another precipitate which showed a maximum at 420 nm. Therefore, Bourrillon assumed that urinary bilirubin consists of two different components, which can be present in various concentrations. Chromatography on Al_2O_3 columns confirmed that urinary bilirubin behaves like bilirubin of the bile. In additional experiments, dogs with total bile fistula or total bile duct ligature were injected with dilute bile or bilirubin solutions (about 40 mg bilirubin into a dog of 11 kg body weight). Bilirubin excreted in urine was the cholebilirubin type, whether or not bile (conjugated) or bilirubin solutions (free bilirubin) were injected. This fact was explained by rapid conversion of injected bilirubin into cholebilirubin in the liver. Monasterio and Giovannetti (1954, 1955), however, found that urinary bilirubin behaves as free bilirubin and its salts, since it can be extracted with $CHCl_3$ from acidified urines.

Schmid (1956a,b,c) conducted paper chromatographic studies of purified azo pigments of urinary bilirubin of icteric patients. He found that practically all bilirubin present behaved similarly to the azo pigment of direct bilirubin of serum and of bile, but that it was distinctly different from indirect bilirubin. Hydrolysis by heat changed the chromatographic behavior of the azo pigment, and it became identical to the diazo compound of indirect bilirubin.

F. A. Gries and Gries (1957) determined the direct and indirect bilirubin in urine separately. They precipitated the bilirubin with calcium phosphate, washed the precipitate, dissolved it in HCl, and, after adjusting the pH to 3.8 with an acetate buffer, added the diazo reagent. They found that the type of reaction (direct or indirect) was not influenced by precipitation and solution manipulations. When unconjugated bilirubin was subjected to this treatment its diazo reaction remained indirect. Simultaneous total and direct bilirubin determinations in 10 icteric urines showed that considerable amounts of "indirect" bilirubin were present, although most of the bilirubin was "direct." The following values were found (total/direct in mg per 100 ml): 15.4/10.6, 7.7/6.0, 12.9/7.6, 6.2/4.0, 17.3/11.4, 4.1/3.5, 4.1/3.3, 4.5/3.8, 8.3/5.5, and 7.8/6.9.

Sakamoto et al. (1957a,b) purified urinary bilirubin of 7 patients with various forms of jaundice. They precipitated with ammonium sulfate, extracted with methanol, and flocculated with $CHCl_3$. The brown pigments obtained behaved like bilirubin ester, i.e., they were insoluble in $CHCl_3$ but became soluble after saponification. The absorption maximum was at 410–420 nm after chromatographic purification on cellulose columns at pH 7. The preparations were free from amino acids and glucuronic acid. Paper chromatographic studies showed the presence of two diazo positive substances, both giving direct reaction. No indirect bilirubin was found. Komuda (1959a,b) performed salting-out and $CHCl_3$ extraction of bilirubin in icteric urine. Several bilirubin fractions could be separated. Kondo (1959a,b) carried out ion exchange chromatography on jaundiced urine employing several different resins. He isolated ester and salt forms of bilirubin in this way. Small amounts of glucuronic acid were found in the ester fraction, but the salt fractions were free from glucuronic acid. Sometimes a $CHCl_3$-extractable fraction was found. The latter was a complex of bilirubin and bile acids. Preparations with direct diazo reaction prepared from urine lost their direct reaction on storage for 2 days at room temperature, being transformed to free bilirubin. Monobe (1959a,b) studied the ester and salt types of urinary bilirubin and found that the former contained glucuronic acid while the latter was free from this substance. The percentage of the urinary ester bilirubin consisting of bilirubin glucuronide varied from 0–60%, most often comprising 16–32% of the urinary bilirubin. If the liver function was severely impaired, the percentage of bilirubin glucuronide was reduced.

Schachter (1959) reported the presence of both mono- and diglucuronides in urine (cf. Chapter V,D,2). An ether-soluble urinary bilirubin has also been found, mainly during obstructive jaundice (Wainrach, 1956; Wainrach and del Gayso, 1958).

All these observations indicate that the question of the presence of indirect and direct bilirubin in icteric urines is a contradictory problem. It should be emphasized that (in spite of the doubtlessly reliable determinations of total and direct diazo reaction) the demonstration of diazopositive substances giving indirect reaction (Gries and Gries) is no proof for the presence of free bilirubin. All bilirubin isolated from urine to the present time has been "direct" bilirubin (see Schmid, Sakamoto *et al.*, Komuda, Kondo, Monobe, loc. cit.) but only a fraction of it is composed of glucuronides (Kondo, 1959b; Monobe, 1959b).

Thus, it must be concluded that bilirubin excreted with urine behaves like direct bilirubin, but the question of how much of it is bilirubin glucuronide must remain open.

Summary

Our understanding of the mechanism of renal bilirubin excretion is incomplete. Some investigators believe that the excretion mechanism involves a tubular process, but others think it is an ultrafiltration reabsorption mechanism. The firm binding between bilirubin and serum albumin speaks for the first assumption, but certain recent observations are incompatible with the theory of a tubular secretion mechanism. Possibly both mechanisms are active. The amount of bilirubin excreted per unit time in the urine shows a steep almost exponential increase with serum bilirubin concentration. In normal urine and urines of subjects with jaundice due to unconjugated bilirubin in the blood, the urinary bilirubin is unconjugated bilirubin, but the gross bilirubinuria associated with jaundice is caused mostly by water-soluble bilirubin conjugates. Urinary bilirubin is mostly a direct reacting, water-soluble compound; it is still undecided how much of it is present in the form of glucuronides and how much as other conjugates. It is beyond any doubt that conjugated bilirubin is excreted much more readily with urine than is the unconjugated form. Experiments involving radiobilirubin, various conjugates, dialysis experiments, and partition chromatography are urgently needed to elucidate the excretion mechanism and the nature of the bilirubin complex eliminated with the urine. These studies should include different species, and should not remain limited to humans and dogs. Thus, experiments in horses, which normally have high serum bilirubin levels, or in cats, which have a high kidney threshold, would be of interest. Dogs usually have an extraordinarily low serum bilirubin level and a very low kidney threshold. Tolerance tests with large amounts of bilirubin glucuronide (pigment I and II) and other conjugates would probably yield decisive information about the excretion mechanisms involved. Last but not least, reliable analytical methods are required. The fashionable method of Malloy-Evelyn does not suffice.

5. BILIRUBINURIA IN VARIOUS DISEASES

Gross bilirubinuria is observed mainly in hepatocellular and obstructive jaundice. Besides these icteric conditions, bilirubinuria is only known to occur during certain hereditary nonhemolytic hyperbilirubinemias, the most important of which is the Dubin–Johnson syndrome. Gross bilirubinuria is absent in hemolytic jaundice, icterus neonatorum, and in the

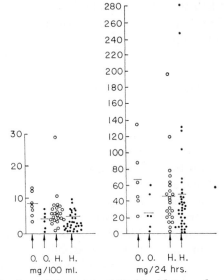

FIG. 49. Maximal values of the urinary bilirubin (dots) and urobilinogen (circles) in acute hepatitis (H) and bile duct occlusion (O).

majority of nonhemolytic familial hyperbilirubinemias. As already mentioned, if bilirubinuria during regressing hepatitis is disregarded (Section B,3, this chapter), most investigators did not find distinct differences between bilirubinuria of obstructive and hepatic icterus. During regressing hepatitis, bilirubinuria is relatively low compared with the serum bilirubin level. Therefore, urinary bilirubin determinations are of little value in the differential diagnosis of obstructive icterus and hepatitis (see Fig. 49).

Adler and Jeddeloh (1929a,b) and Lattanzi (1948a) found that during neoplastic obstruction the ratio of urinary bilirubin to serum bilirubin was significantly higher than during hepatitis. Moeller and Schroeder (1954) also found certain differences between obstructive and parenchymatous icterus. Sherlock (1951), who used a sensitive qualitative test, detected bilirubinuria in 24 of 50 patients suffering from congestive heart failure. Pollock (1951) found bilirubinuria a few days before the serum bilirubin increased in a study of 300 acute hepatitis cases. When the serum bilirubin level dropped below 1.5–2 mg/100 ml, bilirubinuria disappeared again.

The finding that bilirubinuria commences during the initial stages of hepatitis (Neefe *et al.*, 1944; Pollock, 1945, 1951; Hoenig, 1955)—before the increase of the serum bilirubin—is probably due to a different mechanism than that causing the gross bilirubinuria during the later course of hepatitis. This early bilirubinuria is perhaps rather comparable to normal bilirubinuria and the bilirubinuria found during various infectious diseases without hyperbilirubinemia, such as infectious mononucleosis, malaria, and pneumonia (Pollock; W. C. Meyer, 1947a). This mild infectious bilirubinuria is probably caused by kidney damage rather than an increased serum bilirubin level. The situation is different when gross bilirubinuria occurs, and is not accompanied by jaundice. This is due to the fact that strongly increased serum bilirubin can be present without manifest icterus. Whereas serum bilirubin increases quickly after obstruction or after sufficiently extensive parenchymal damage, jaundice requires several days to become manifest (see Chapter IV,B). Budd (1852, p. 459) was aware of bile-colored urines in individuals without jaundice; their appearance during the anicteric initial stages of hepatitis is a fact generally known (see Brugsch and Schürer, 1919); during a recent epidemic in Yugoslavia similar observations were made (D. Juričič, private communication, 1966). Whether this is due to a transient hyperbilirubinemia of too short duration to cause jaundice is not known.

The so-called *hepato-renal syndrome* should be mentioned in connection with bilirubinuria during various diseases. This term designates a secondary functional disturbance of kidney activity during liver diseases. This hepato-renal syndrome should be carefully distinguished from "hépatonéphrites" described by French investigators. The latter is a leptospirosis in which the infecting agent attacks the liver and kidney simultaneously. It has been suggested that the hepato-renal syndrome is, in reality, a kidney shock which takes place after liver damage (Lassen and Thomsen, 1957). Balcells-Gorina and Chacón (1954) described another syndrome, the so-called cirrhosis-nephropathy, which is attributed to passive congestion, ascites, hypoproteinemia, and anemia caused by cirrhosis.

Summary

Gross bilirubinuria occurs in hepatocellular and in obstructive jaundice; it is also observed in some inborn nonhemolytic hyperbilirubinemias, e.g., the Dubin–Johnson syndrome. It is absent in all other forms of jaundice. Bilirubinuria can precede manifest icterus during the initial stages of hepatitis and obstruction. Mild bilirubinuria is frequently found during the initial stage of virus hepatitis, before the serum bilirubin concentration starts to increase, as well as in certain acute infectious diseases. It can be detected by sensitive spot tests. Initial bilirubinuria is probably more closely related to normal bilirubinuria than to massive pathological bilirubinuria occurring during jaundice. The diagnostic value of bilirubinuria is limited. Quantitative serum and urinary bilirubin determinations are hardly helpful for differential diagnosis between obstructive and hepatic jaundice. Gross bilirubinuria without simultaneous icterus has diagnostic value in gallstone attacks.

C. Biliverdin in Urine

It is not known whether biliverdin is excreted primarily into the urine in man, but this is known to occur in various animals (Section A, this chapter). The interest of determination of biliverdin in urine has been limited, and only recently has a quantitative method been described by Garay and Argerich (1963), who oxidized the biliverdin to bilipurpurin and determined this compound fluorometrically. The urine biliverdin was precipitated with $BaCl_2$, eluted with HCl–methanol after addition of ascorbic acid, then extracted into ether, then extracted from the ether into dilute HCl, and, after neutralization, extracted into $CHCl_3$. The chloroform extract was treated with methanolic zinc acetate and dilute iodine, and the red fluorescence developed in this way was read in a fluorometer and compared to various standards and a urine blank to exclude errors from red porphyrin fluorescence. Of the added biliverdin, 85% was recovered, and urobilins, mesobilifuscins, and bilirubin gave no false positive reaction although they might depress the recovery percentage of the biliverdin if present in high concentrations. The method is elaborate and time-consuming.

D. Urobilinoids in Urine

1. ANALYTICAL METHODS

The fundamental questions of urobilin analysis have been discussed above, and the difficulties emphasized (Chapter I,K). These are simultaneous presence of urobilins and chromogens, and of types I, L, and D in the urine. It is important to remember that urobilinogen is the urobilinoid of fresh urine (Saillet, 1897; Fischer and Libowitzky, 1939). This is also true when urobilins are intravenously injected (Oshima, 1932a; C. J. Watson, 1936b). Thus, the urobilinogens are the primary compounds.

Urobilinoid excretion could be studied under nearly ideal conditions if their oxidation is avoided by antioxidants. Ascorbic acid would be a good choice since it is inexpensive and can be easily administered; the organism can be readily saturated with this compound and oxidation thus be avoided. It is also necessary to keep the urine samples in the dark to eliminate the effect of light on the urobilinogens. However, if precautions to prevent oxidation of urobilinogens cannot be undertaken, analysis of urobilinoids would be possible by (1) separate determination of urobilinogens and urobilins; (2) urobilinogen determination after reduction of all urobilinoids to chromogens; and (3) urobilin determination after oxidation of all urobilinoids to urobilins. High bilirubin concentration is a source of error, since bilirubin reduction to urobilinogen-I could lead to erroneous increases of positive urobilinogen reaction (K.-H. Brandt, 1957). Similarly, the formation of choletelin after oxidation can result in false positive urobilin fluorescence (Barrenscheen and Weltmann, 1923).

A detailed discussion of older methods is beyond the scope of this treatise. Older surveys on this subject have been published by Ladage (1899), Woll (1912), Wilbur and Addis (1914), Steensma (1918), and Terwen (1924). With (1954) and K.-H. Brandt (1957) published rather detailed surveys in this area; the latter author emphasized the historical evolution of analytical processes. The more important analytical methods will be discussed below.

The first clinically useful test was developed by Schlesinger (1903), and bears his name today. Actually, Schlesinger only slightly modified the methods known at this time. Following the procedure of Roman and Delluc (1900), he added equal amounts of an alcoholic zinc acetate solution to the urine and determined the fluorescence in progressive dilutions. It was assumed that the limit for visual fluorescence is at 2 mg/100 ml. Steensma (1908a,b) improved this technique by introducing alcoholic iodine solution as an oxidizing agent before performing the test. Marcussen and Hansen (1918a,b) further developed this method which, including numerous minor modifications, became widely accepted (Adler, 1922b; Herzfeld, 1922; Salén, 1924; Tützer and Adler, 1924; Opitz and Brehme, 1924a; Meulengracht and Thisted, 1925). Opitz and Brehme (1924b) vigorously criticized the modifications introduced by Adler and by Tützer and Adler; these generally yield too high values, and were considered unreliable. Elman and McMaster (1925a), Royer (1928a, 1932c), Castex and Lopez Garcia (1940b), and Lopez Garcia (1943, p. 305) introduced significant innovations and improved this zinc acetate fluorescence test.

Hausmann (1913, 1922) added copper sulfate and extracted with

CHCl$_3$. Under these conditions urobilin was extractable only from alkaline urine; therefore, the substance extracted with CHCl$_3$ is probably not urobilin itself, but a copper compound. This reaction is not identical with the biuret reaction that has been described in urine. Later, Lipp (1942) employed Hausmann's copper reaction.

Barrenscheen and Weltmann (1923) pointed out that the presence of bilirubin can lead to errors because of the formation of oxidation products giving the zinc fluorescence test (choletelins).

The fluorescence is generally observed in daylight; this is inappropriate. Fluorescence is significantly more distinct if it is observed in the dark with an analytical mercury light source ("Wood's light"). A suitable apparatus which provides this light is no longer expensive (With, 1957b).

Among recent investigators only Kahán (1961, pp. 30–34) and Lozzio and Royer (1962) recommend determination of urobilinoids after oxidation. Kahán used 50–200 ml of urine which was oxidized by standing in the air for 1 day at pH 4.5. Then followed extraction with CHCl$_3$ until colorless, after which the extract was dried over anhydrous Na$_2$SO$_4$ and evaporated to dryness *in vacuo*. The residue was dissolved in ethanol and the extinction at the maximum of urobilin read. This gives the total urobilinoids. Kahán (loc. cit., p. 33) admits that impurities such as urochrome and bilirubin may cause errors, and she proposes certain measures to avoid them. But these measures are rather elaborate and not adequate for routine use. In a separate analysis with the mesobiliviolin–ferric chloride method, closely similar to that of Legge (1949) she determined the urobilinoids of type I (cf. below). In recovery experiments Kahán (loc. cit., p. 32) found losses amounting to 20% of added urobilin-L. The concentrations given by Kahán for normal and by Kahán and Felkai (1961) for pathological urines are definitely lower than those reported by workers employing the benzaldehyde reaction after reduction with ferrous hydroxide and extraction (cf. Section D,2, this chapter). From this and from her recovery experiments, it is safe to conclude that her values are lower than those found with the latter method and that her figures are too low. Lozzio and Royer (1962) oxidized with FeCl$_3$, treated with alcoholic zinc acetate at neutral reaction, and read the fluorescence in a sensitive fluorometer under comparison with a trypaflavine standard. The pH optimum of the fluorescence was found to be 7.5–8. It was demonstrated that flavines, porphyrins, and biliviolins did not influence the results.

An interesting modification of the zinc fluorescence method was proposed by Kirkpatrick (1953*) who introduced extraction of the Zn-urobilin complex with CHCl$_3$ before studying the fluorescence, thus enhancing the specificity of the method. According to Kirkpatrick, addition of acid or alkali to the urine is unnecessary and undesirable. This method was improved by Schmidt and Scholtis (1964*) who found that the fluorescence of the Zn complex is pH dependent, being optimal at pH 7.5–8.5. Addition of a phosphate buffer to urine is, however, not practical because it abolishes the fluorescence due to precipitation of Zn-phosphate. Because phosphate is also present in normal urine it is necessary to add surplus of Zn, i.e., a 4% Zn-acetate suspended in borate buffer (0.5 M, pH 8.5, 1 ml buffer to 2 ml of urine), which does not interfere with the reaction. This fixes the pH between 7.5 and 8.5. Ammonium persulfate was preferred to iodine as an oxidant. Bilirubin interferes with the fluorimetric readings and has to be precipitated before the test if bilirubinuria is present. The procedure is as follows:

Reagents:

(1) 6.2 g of boric acid, 1.45 g NaCl, 9.55 g Na-tetraborate, 10 ml H_2O, and 2.5 g ammonium persulfate in water, diluted to 250 ml.

(2) 4% suspension of Zn-acetate in 96% alcohol.

(3) $CHCl_3$.

(4) 50 g trichloroacetic acid dissolved in 96% alcohol and diluted to 100 ml.

Procedure:

To 2 ml of urine add 1 ml of reagent (1) and mix. Add 2 ml of reagent (2) and mix; then add 3 ml $CHCl_3$, shake gently, and centrifuge. Examine the $CHCl_3$ layer in UV light (e.g., Wood's light). If a distinct greenish-yellow fluorescence is present, then aspirate off the upper layer and filter the $CHCl_3$ layer through paper, dividing the filtered solution into two equal parts. Add one drop of reagent (4) to one of the parts in order to destroy the Zn-urobilin complex (blank solution).

Reading:

The fluorescence of the filtered $CHCl_3$ solution is measured against the solution with added reagent (4) as blank using a Zeiss PMQ II spectrophotometer with ZMQ 4 fluorimetric attachment, primary filter 365 nm, secondary filter 530 nm, and a solid fluorescence standard.

The accuracy of the method was compared with the benzaldehyde method after extraction (Balikow, 1958, modified according to Henry *et al.*, 1961) and the two methods showed excellent linear correlation up to the extinction 0.40 of the benzaldehyde method. With higher extinction the fluorescence failed to increase, a deficiency easily overcome by dilution. Schmidt and Scholtis recommend their Zn-fluorescence extraction method as rapid and accurate.

Because of its extreme sensitivity, the zinc fluorescence test should be the preferred method, when only a very small amount of material is available (e.g., in small experimental animals). This situation, however, is rare in clinical chemistry. For clinical practice and for most quantitative purposes, urobilinogen determinations are preferable. However, the methods based on urobilinogen determinations were developed much later than those for urobilin analysis.

Charnas (1909, 1913a) was the first to reduce urobilins to chromogens before determination. However, he used an unreliable reduction process based on ammoniacal fermentation. After acidifying with glacial acetic acid, he extracted the urobilinogens with ether from the fermented urine; next he added a saturated solution of p-dimethylaminobenzaldehyde in ether and some HCl containing alcohol to the extract, and, finally, after suitable dilution, he spectrophotometrically determined the red coloration obtained. A considerable step forward is due to Terwen (1924, 1925), who introduced alkaline $FeSO_4$ solution as the reducing agent. After acidification, he extracted with ether and performed the benzaldehyde reaction. Terwen found that neither urobilin nor urobilinogen were adsorbed on colloidal $Fe(OH)_2$; that over 95% of urobilinogen present was extracted with the first ether extraction; and that no urobilinogen losses were encountered by washing with water. Additions of salicylic acid did not disturb the determinations. Instead of ether, petroleum ether (boiling point 40–60°) could also be used in this method. This was especially advantageous because bilirubin is very sparingly soluble in this solvent. According to Terwen, extraction with petroleum ether is a sensitive and specific qualitative test; the acidified urine is extracted with petroleum ether, the ether layer is shaken with dilute alkali, and benzaldehyde reagent is added to the alkali phase. This process is significantly more efficient than that of adding the reagent directly to urine.

Heilmeyer and Krebs (1931) and C. J. Watson (1931, 1936c) slightly modified Terwen's process. Watson found that when urobilinogen-i and -l were subjected to the benzaldehyde reaction, the maxima and extinction coefficients obtained were practically the same. Therefore it was correct to determine these two pigments together as "total urobilinogen." Watson pointed out that mesobiliviolin, which often accompanied urobilin, gives a red fluorescence on addition of zinc salts. This can lead to errors in the zinc fluorescence method. He proposed a particular, strongly acidic benzaldehyde reagent, consisting of 0.7 g p-dimethylaminobenzaldehyde, 150 ml concentrated HCl, and 100 ml distilled water, and used petroleum ether for extraction. Substances, which interfere with the reaction were formed from indole. However, they remain in the petroleum ether phase during HCl and sodium acetate extraction. He could recover 70–80% of added urobilinogen-i and urobilinogen-l.

Naumann (1936a,c) found that various substances such as indole, protein degradation products, urea, and various drugs give a color reaction with benzaldehyde reagent. These colored substances, unlike those formed from urobilinogens, cannot be extracted with ether from acidified urine. According to Naumann's findings, urobilinogens were quantitatively extracted with ether, but only partially extractable with petroleum ether. However, shaking with petroleum ether was advantageous because bilirubin, which is partially soluble in ether, is insoluble in petroleum ether. Using Terwen's method, the reduction of urobilins to urobilinogens was complete in 3 hours at 20°C, and within 5 minutes at 35°C. It was found that urobilinogen was partially destroyed during reduction. The reduction proceeded quantitatively when the concentrations involved were not very high. Bilirubin was not reduced by this process.

Eichenbronner (1938) and Voegtlin (1947) emphasized that *direct sunlight must be excluded* during the whole analysis to avoid losses. They recommended keeping the urine in a refrigerator under a layer of toluene to protect it from light and oxidation by air. Sparkman (1939a) added the benzaldehyde reagent directly to the urine, after the bilirubin was precipitated with calcium chloride. He thought that arbitrary urine volumes submitted for examination are sufficiently accurate for diagnostic purposes. However, C. J. Watson and Bilden (1941) found that this process is rather insensitive and emphasized that the analysis has to be done with the 24-hour urine. F. J. Simon (1941) treated the urine with benzaldehyde reagent, extracted it with $CHCl_3$, and finally extracted the urobilinogen–benzaldehyde compound before the reading with amyl alcohol, whereas Lipp (1942) took readings of the $CHCl_3$ solution.

With (1942b) compared Heilmeyer-Krebs' and Watson's modifications and found that of Watson preferable. He found, however, that extractions with peroxide free ether give 50–100% higher values than those with petroleum ether. This confirms Naumann's observations. Identical values were obtained when reductions were carried out for only 1 hour, or when they were extended over 24 hours in the dark at room temperature. Duplicate determinations showed ± 5% variations. With, as well as Heilmeyer and Krebs, read the reaction in a visual filter photometer (Pulfrich) and calculated the urobilin concentration (mg per 100 ml) by multiplying the extinction by 1.36 (filter S 53, 1 cm layer). The factor 1.36 was calculated from extinction values which were found for urobilinogen-I by Heilmeyer and Krebs (cf. Chapter I,K).

Schwartz *et al.* (1944) studied recovery of pure urobilinogen-I and urobilin-L. A photoelectric colorimeter was used for measurements at 565 nm. Experiments with pure solutions showed that quantitative recovery could be obtained after three extractions. About 87–100% of the added amounts were recovered, i.e., these results were better than those obtained by C. J. Watson (1931, 1936c). The authors found that it is important to use analytical sodium acetate because impurities can cause losses. They claimed that petroleum ether extraction is essential, thus ignoring Naumann's and With's findings. However, they did not give any experimental proof for the statement that the chromogens, which cannot be extracted with petroleum ether, are not urobilinogens. Since the color fades quite rapidly, it is essential to perform the measurement as fast as possible, preferably within 5 minutes after introducing the reagents.

Baumgärtel (1948b; 1950b p. 126) pointed out that phylloerythrinogen can cause significant errors in individuals who ingested food rich in chlorophyll. However, whether phylloerythrinogen can be extracted with petroleum ether from acidified urine has not yet been investigated. This substance is formed from chlorophyll by bacteria in the large intestine, absorbed and excreted primarily with the bile, although a small portion may be found in the urine. It is known that phylloerythrinogen can be extracted with chloroform from urine. After oxidation, it gives a red fluorescence in the zinc fluorescence test. Begtrup (1954) found that concentrations determined by ether extraction varied according to the amount of urine examined. With (1954, p. 284) discussed Begtrup's results and did not succeed in reproducing them. These findings are peculiar; the most likely explanation seems to be that Begtrup used too large amounts of ether for the extraction of too small urine samples. Oshima (1930a) found that the urobilinogen concentration found by extraction analysis of diluted bile was the same as that found with undiluted bile.

Balikov (1955) studied the influence of acetic acid concentration on urobilinogen extraction with petroleum ether. He found that optimum conditions were obtained with concentrations of 2%, if 5 ml of the alkaline filtrate (Terwen's method) was diluted to 50 ml and subsequently extracted. Higher as well as lower acetic acid concentrations yielded markedly lower values. Later, Balikov (1958) described a detailed spectrophotometric method in which he used solutions of Pontacyl-carmine for comparison and measured at 565 nm.

In his studies on bile, K.-H. Brandt (1957) found that a small amount of Ehrlich reagent-positive substance is formed during reduction from bilirubin present. Reduction was carried out by Terwen's method. He found lower urobilinogen concentrations when bilirubin was precipitated with calcium carbonate before reduction than when it was not removed. These findings contradict Naumann's observations. This discrepancy can possibly be due to the much higher bilirubin concentrations present in the bile. Urines rich in bilirubin, especially during complete bile duct obstruction, contain very little urobilinoids. Therefore it would surely be desirable to remove the bilirubin from urines before analysis, because even small amounts of urobilinogen, formed by reduction from bilirubin, could be important.

A few authors determined urobilinogens and urobilins together. Wilbur and Addis (1914) added alcoholic zinc acetate solution to urine, filtered, and finally added Ehrlich's aldehyde reagent to the filtrate. The filtrate was continuously diluted and the urobilin band, as well as the band of the benzaldehyde reaction, was measured spectroscopically. The dilution at which these two bands disappeared was regarded as a measure for urobilin and urobilinogen concentrations. Later, Oshima (1930a) used a similar principle and stated that urobilinogens, but not urobilins, can be extracted with petroleum ether from acidified urine. Klein (1942) described a ring test in which the benzaldehyde reagent was carefully covered with a mixture consisting of equal parts of urine and alcoholic zinc acetate in a test tube. Ehrlich's reaction appeared as a colored ring on the interface of the two liquids, whereas fluorescence became visible in the urine layer. Separate urobilin and urobilinogen determinations have not generally been accepted. Since urobilinogens are the primary excretion products, it is surely correct and simplest to determine only these compounds.

It is apparent from the above discussion that the quality of procedures based on the benzaldehyde reaction is different. Only reactions including an extraction step can be considered specific and quantitative. Since these extraction methods are rather cumbersome, other, simpler procedures have been devised for clinical purposes.

C. J. Watson *et al.* (1944) used fresh urine for the determination. The patient completely emptied his bladder at 2 PM; 2 hours later, at 4 PM, the urine was collected. An equal volume of Watson's acid Ehrlich's reagent (see above) was added, and subsequently the same volume of saturated sodium acetate. The color was measured in a photoelectric colorimeter at 565 nm. A mixture consisting of 1 volume saturated sodium acetate and 1 volume Ehrlich's reagent served as blank. The results were expressed in "Ehrlich units," one unit corresponding to 1 mg urobilinogen. This method gives somewhat higher values than extraction procedures in most urines. However, the errors were not high and the results found to permit correct clinical interpretations. Kelly *et al.* (1946) found that the benzaldehyde reaction proceeds much faster with urobilinogens than with the other benzaldehyde-positive compounds present in urine. Therefore, they recommended adding the acetate, which stops the reaction, as soon as possible after addition of benzaldehyde reagent. In this way they achieved an improved approximation to results obtained with the extraction procedure. Michel (1948) and Alliot (1949) recommended Watson's simplified procedure for clinical purposes. Young et al. (1949) developed a simple comparator, enabling laboratories without a photometer to use Watson's simplified method.

Gössner (1947, 1948) studied the red-colored compound which is formed after addition of the benzaldehyde reagent to normal urine when the mixture is subsequently heated. He found that the red compound is a condensation product of one molecule of indoxyl and one molecule of p-dimethylaminobenzaldehyde. The product was obtained in crystalline form and identified by comparison with a synthetic preparation. This indoxyl reaction does not take place at room temperature in normal urines. However, it can occur in urines which are rich in indole compounds, for example, after meals rich in tryptophan. The reaction is negative in ether extracts. Gössner's investigations show, in contrast to C. J. Watson et al. (1944), that there can be no parallelism between the benzaldehyde reaction of urobilinogens and nonurobilin chromogens in urine.

Wilson and Davidson (1949) discussed the different benzaldehyde reagents employed by various investigators. The amount of p-dimethylaminobenzaldehyde and the amount of concentrated HCl used in the reaction mixture was varied in a range of 0.06 to 0.6% and 0.35 to 11%, respectively, in the reaction mixture. The corresponding concentrations of the reagents themselves were 0.28 to 3% and 5 to 36%, respectively. Watson's strongly acidic reagent tended to give nonspecific reactions. It was found that by using analytically pure HCl these nonspecific reactions were suppressed. Addition of hydrogen peroxide leads to an erroneous increase of positive reactions. To protect the solutions from contamination by pipettes, it was recommended that the solutions be stored in dropping flasks. The nonspecific coloration was attributed to urorosein, an indole derivative which is formed in the presence of oxidizing agents in strongly acidic solutions. This nonspecific coloration can be distinguished from true urobilinogen color by extraction with $CHCl_3$. Urorosein is insoluble in $CHCl_3$. Porphobilinogen can also be excluded in this manner (Chapter I,K). The color caused by the presence of phylloerythrinogen is, as urobilinogen, extractable with $CHCl_3$.

Brereton and Lucia (1948) recommend use as a blank of a urine sample in which the urobilinogens are destroyed by sodium hypochlorite. However, this does not seem to be reliable, since nonurobilinogen-type chromogens are also degraded. Knowlton (1950) studied the influence of cold storage of urine with Watson's simplified method. Compared to concentrations determined in fresh urine, she found 60% reduction in urines stored for 18 hours in a refrigerator. However, a reduction of pathological values to normal values took place in only 13 cases of the 190 examined. Voegtlin *et al.* (1950) compared the extraction method (Schwartz *et al.*, 1944) with Watson's simplified method in 268 chronic alcoholics. Since 15% of the pathological values were not detected with the simplified method, the authors consider it unreliable for clinical purpose.

With (1942b, 1945f) and Balikov (1958) published detailed descriptions of quantitative extraction methods for urobilinogen determination. Henry *et al.* (1961) recommended adding 10 mg ascorbic acid/ml reduced filtrate to protect against oxidation. This gave about 10% higher extinction. They found for four urobilin preparations $E_{1\,cm}^{1\%} = 1180–1390$ (calculated as urobilinogen) at 562 nm. They recommend phenolsulfonphthalein (analytical) dissolved in $0.05\,N$ NaOH as standard substance because its spectral absorption curve corresponds very closely to that of the urobilinogen Ehrlich reaction. Addition of the benzaldehyde reagent to urobilinogen solutions caused some re-formation of urobilin, a fact demonstrated by the appearance of a peak at the urobilin maximum (492–494 nm) simultaneously with the development of the peak of the benzaldehyde reaction at 562 nm. If ascorbic acid (10 mg/ml) was added before the benzaldehyde reagent, the peak at 490–494 nm did not appear, and the extinction at 562 nm became higher than without ascorbic acid. They further found that only urobilinogens, not urobilins, are extracted with petrol ether. They give the values of the extinction in 1 cm layer at 562 nm for urobilinogens from various urobilinogen preparations in concentrations of 1 μg/ml reaction mixture. The figures vary from 8.8 to 13.9 $\times$ 10^{-4} with an average of 12.5 $\times$ 10^{-4} (i.e., $E_{1\,cm}^{1\%} = 1250$). No significant differences between urobilinogen-i and -l were encountered. Henry *et al.* (1964) proposed adding 200 mg ascorbic acid and 100 mg potassium borohydride to 20 ml of the alkaline-reduced supernatant from the Terwen procedure. The borohydride prevented the oxidation of chromogen by the reagent, avoiding the 490 nm absorption peak. The authors proposed to use Pontacyl dye mixture as standard for the urobilinogen-aldehyde color. Recovery experiments with UG-i added to urine were performed, and only 50–80% of the added UG-i could be recovered. If pure solutions of UG-i were extracted, the recovery was 90%. These experiments are, however, of limited interest because UG-l, which is much more stable than UG-i, is the main urinary urobilinoid.

A detailed description of the procedure proposed by Terwen and modified according to recent developments follows. It should be mentioned that small amounts of benzaldehyde-positive chromogens can be formed by the reduction of bilirubin in urines rich in bilirubin. This source of error can be eliminated by bilirubin precipitation with calcium or barium, since these precipitates do not adsorb urobilinogens. It is important that the urine is stored in a cool, dark place prior to analysis.

Recommended Procedure

Reduction: Precipitates present in the urine must be stirred up before the analysis because they might contain adsorbed urobilinoids. The volume of the urine sample is measured, after which ¼ volume of freshly prepared 16% Mohr's salt (ferrous ammonium sulfate) solution is added to 1 volume of urine; next, ¼ volume of 12% sodium hydroxide solution is added. After careful mixing, the solution is covered with a layer of liquid paraffin to exclude air oxidation. To assure complete reduction the mixture is stored for 1–24 hours in the dark at room temperature. It is practical to use 80 ml urine and a 125–150 ml measuring cylinder with glass stopper. Reduction is practically complete after 1 hour; in this case, however, $Fe(OH)_2$ has to be removed by centrifugation prior to extraction. This step can be eliminated when the mixture is stored for 24 hours before determination. During this time the $Fe(OH)_2$ settles and 50 ml of the clear, reduced urine supernatant can be pipetted for subsequent extraction.

Extraction: All the following working steps should be carried out in dim light. Bright daylight, and especially direct sunlight, can lead to the destruction of considerable amounts of urobilinoids. The volume of supernatant used for extraction depends on the urobilinogen concentration. This is determined in preliminary qualitative tests, i.e., equal amounts of urine and aldehyde reagent are mixed in a test tube. If no color develops, a 50 ml sample is used for extraction. If strong red color develops, only 1–2 ml supernatant suffice. The volume to be extracted is transferred into a 250-ml separator funnel. One ml glacial acetic acid is added per 5 ml supernatant. If the volume is less than 50 ml, it is adjusted to ca. 50 ml with distilled water, after which ca. 10 mg ascorbic acid and ca. 5 mg potassium borohydrate per ml supernatant are added. Subsequently, it is extracted three times with 35 ml petrol ether.

Ehrlich Reaction and Extraction of Reaction Products: The combined extracts are washed three times with about 100 ml distilled water. Then, 3 ml benzaldehyde reagent is added to the washed extract. The reagent consists of: 0.7 g *p*-dimethylaminobenzaldehyde, 150 ml concentrated HCl, and 100 ml distilled water. All reagents must be of analytical quality and the reagent solution must be stored in a brown bottle. The mixture is vigorously agitated in the separator funnel and 10 ml of saturated sodium acetate solution (analytical) is subsequently added. Next, agitation is repeated. A more-or-less red colored aqueous phase is formed, which is collected. Extraction is repeated with new amounts of aldehyde reagent, and sodium acetate. This process is continued until the aqueous phase becomes colorless. As a rule three extractions are sufficient. The aqueous extracts are pooled.

Reading and Calculation: The volume of the pooled aqueous phases is measured and it is subjected to spectrophotometry or colorimetry as soon as possible. The color fades rapidly: after 5 minutes significant losses of color take place. The extinction at 562 nm is determined; suitable filters or comparison with a solution of phenolsulfonphthalein (cf. above) can also be used. The layer thickness used depends on the color intensity; 5 cm is appropriate for normal urines and 0.5 cm for strongly colored extracts. Distilled water is employed as blank. The following equation is used for the calculation:

$$c \ (\text{mg}/100 \ \text{ml}) = \frac{10^3}{E_{1\,\text{cm}}^{1\%}} \cdot e \cdot t^{-1} \cdot b \cdot 10^{-2} \cdot a^{-1} \cdot 10^2 \cdot 1.5 = k \cdot \frac{e \cdot b}{t \cdot a}$$

where $k = 1500/E_{1\,\text{cm}}^{1\%}$ is a calculation factor, c is the urobilinogen concentration of urine in milligrams per 100 milliliters, e is the extinction read, t is the layer thickness in centimeters, b is the volume of unified aqueous extracts in milliliters, a is the volume of supernatant (in milliliters) used for extraction, and 1.5 is a correction factor compensating for the dilution of the urine with ½ volume of alkaline reducing reagent. With the figure for $E_{1\,\text{cm}}^{1\%}$ given by Henry *et al.* as average (1250), k is 1.20 for readings carried out at 562 nm.

No prior reduction is necessary when completely fresh urine is used, or when the patient has been saturated with ascorbic acid before the sample was taken. However, the urine must be stored in dim light until the determination.

All the above-described procedures were designed for the determination of total urobilin concentration, i.e., to measure the sum of urobilin-ɪ, -ʟ, and -ᴅ. Lemberg *et al.* (1938b) were first to propose methods for separate urobilinoid-ɪ and -ʟ analysis (see also Lemberg and Legge, 1949, p. 136). These authors used the $FeCl_3$ mesobiliviolin reaction for the separate determination of ɪ and -ʟ forms.

Baumgärtel (1950b, p. 236) extracted the urine with $CHCl_3$, concentrated the extracts, dissolved the residue in alcohol, and boiled the solution for a few minutes with concentrated HCl containing a trace of $FeCl_3$. Urobilin-ɪ and urobilinogen-ɪ yielded mesobiliviolin during this reaction. However, urobilin-ʟ and urobilinogen-ʟ gave a brown coloration, because of the formation of a complex ferric salt. After cooling, $CHCl_3$, water, and some NaOH were added and the mixture agitated; mesobiliviolin was extracted in the aqueous layer, whereas the urobilin-L–iron complex remained in the CHCl₃ layer. Phylloerythrinogen is a source of error; it gives almost the same color as mesobiliviolin, but enters the water phase with green color. Legge (1949) reported a different method which, according to K.-H. Brandt (1957, p. 95), is significantly better than those of Baumgärtel and Rudolph. Rudolph (1952, pp. 30–45) described a method for separate urobilin-I and -L determination in 30 ml urine based on the copper sulfate–glacial acetic acid reaction. The reaction is followed by CHCl₃ extraction, and treatment with boiling HCl–FeCl₃ reagent. W. Stich (1952a,b) also described a mesobiliviolin reaction for separate determination of urobilinoids-I and -L and emphasized that the pentdyopent reaction is negative with urobilin-L, but positive with urobilin-I.

Gohr (1954) reported a more reliable method: about 300 ml urine is extracted with CHCl₃ after acidifying with glacial acetic acid. After evaporation, the brown residue is dissolved in 20 ml 96% alcohol. Subsequently 2 ml of Obermeyer's reagent (25% analytical HCl containing 0.2–0.4% crystalline FeCl₃, analytical quality) is added and the mixture is heated for a short while. In the presence of urobilin(ogen)-I a reddish-violet mixture of mesobiliviolin and mesobilirhodin is formed. The alcoholic solution of the dyestuff is diluted with 5 volumes of water and extracted once more with CHCl₃ in a separator funnel. Red fluorescence can be observed in the presence of high pigment concentrations in the CHCl₃ extract. The larger part of the CHCl₃ solution is then added to a 10% alcoholic zinc acetate solution. The red color can be studied spectroscopically. The absorption bands of the zinc salts are at 510 nm for urobilin-L, and at 500–517, 563–586, and 622–644 nm for mesobiliviolin. Hartridge's reversion-spectroscope (see G. A. Harrison, 1947) is the most suitable instrument for determination of these bands. This exact and simple instrument is relatively inexpensive, but not widely known. The instrument is built by the firm of Beck in London. Gohr developed a method for the study of spectral bands by the use of the Pulfrich photometer, but the reversion-spectroscope of Hartridge is much simpler to operate and more precise.

C. J. Watson and Weimer (1959) described a method for the separate determination of UG-I, UG-L, and UG-D. After oxidation with iodine, the concentrated and purified urobilins are oxidized with HCl–FeCl₃; the extract is measured at 492, 560, and 650 nm. The ratio $E_{492}/(E_{560} + E_{650})$ equals UG-L/(UG-I + UG-D) and E_{560}/E_{650} equals UG-I/UG-D. From these equations and the total urobilinoid (= UG-I + UG-L + UG-D), the concentrations can be calculated.

For details the reader is referred to Watson and Weimer's comprehensive article.

Jirásek and Jirsa (1960) separated UG-ı, UG-ʟ, and UG-ᴅ by means of the mesobiliviolin–FeCl₃ reaction and concomitant paper chromatography. They found that the mesobiliviolin reaction is completely reliable when properly carried out. Kahán (1961) employed the modification of this reaction described by Legge (1949) with equally good results to determine urobilin-ı quantitatively in a large number of normal and pathological urines.

Summary

Reliable analysis for urobilinogen must include extraction of the fresh urine. If patients are saturated with ascorbic acid to prevent oxidation, exact determination is also possible after 24 hours. It is important that the urine sample be protected from strong light during sampling and handling until measurement is performed. In the absence of antioxidants, considerable losses can occur even during storage in the refrigerator. Urobilin is best reduced to urobilinogens with colloidal $Fe(OH)_2$ and the total urobilinoids determined as urobilinogens, when fresh urine is not available. Some negligible losses can occur during reduction. The zinc fluorescence test is a very sensitive method for urobilin determination, but the methods presently used are, in general, less specific and less accurate than benzaldehyde methods. When only small amounts of urine are available, this method should be used. Fluorescence should not be observed in daylight, but with the help of a mercury lamp ("Wood's light").

The benzaldehyde reaction is not completely specific for urobilinogens; this has to be borne in mind when the test is performed directly in urine. The chlorophyll derivative phylloerythrinogen presents the single source of error with extraction and addition of saturated sodium acetate. The various methods proposed are discussed and a recommended procedure described in detail. Simplified methods without extraction, as well as processes for separate UG-ı, -ʟ, and -ᴅ determinations are considered.

The Zn-fluorescence method of Schmidt and Scholtis (1964*) looks promising and deserves further trial.

2. NORMAL UROBILINURIA AND ITS DAILY VARIATIONS

Jaffe (1869) detected urobilinoids in normal urine. Grimm (1893) found that normal urobilinuria disappeared during 24-hour fasting, that it was low during the period of gastric digestion, and that it increased markedly 3–4 hours after meals. When the food was rich in eggs, uro-bilinuria resulted. Saillet (1897) found more urobilin during the day than during the night and also observed that urobilin excretion increased after meals. Jolles (1895) assumed that urobilins of normal urine are different from those of pathological urines.

Early investigators obtained discrepant results. However, these find-ings are only of limited interest, since their technique was only semi-quantitative. Salén (1924) and Bang (1929) reexamined the earlier results. Salén (1924) used the zinc fluorescence test of Marcussen and Hansen (1918a,b); during a period of 24 hours, this author found distinct variations which were closely related to the meals. Urobilin concentra-tion increased 2–3 hours after meals, and it decreased a few hours there-after. Therefore, he warned against conclusions drawn from analysis of random urine samples and recommended the examination of 24-hour urine. Salén found urobilin concentrations measured as dilution values up to 1/60 in random samples of normal individuals, whereas the highest limit of a 24-hour urine was 1/20. Lingjaerde (1934, p. 33), using the same technique, only rarely observed dilution levels over 1/30 in the first morning urines of healthy women.

Increase of urinary urobilinoids during periods of hunger, the so-called hunger urobilinuria, was described by Naunyn (1869), Hilde-brandt (1909a), Adler and Sachs (1923b), Fischler and Ottensooser 1925), and Heilmeyer and Oetzel (1931). It was observed that fecal urobilinoid excretion decreased simultaneously. Therefore this condition was attributed to liver damage.

C. J. Watson (1937a) demonstrated considerable 24-hour variation with the benzaldehyde reaction after extraction. However, he did not report any connection between these variations and food intake. Quod-bach (1936) examined the correlation with meals with a benzaldehyde extraction method, but did not find any relation between these two factors and assumed that variations in urobilinuria are due to an endog-enous liver rhythm.

Royer (1943, pp. 40 and 123) found a urobilinoid excretion of 0–4 mg per 24 hours in normal adults. The values fluctuate significantly in the same individual. Daily excretion values which varied from zero to a few mg, but never exceeded 4 mg were reported by Oshima (1930b), Weiss (1930), Heilmeyer and Oetzel (1931), C. J. Watson (1937a), López Pontes (1938, 1947), Lopez Garcia (1943, p. 139), Steigmann and Dyniewicz (1943a), C. J. Watson et al. (1944), With (1944b), and Balikov (1957). Of these investigators several employed modern reliable benzaldehyde extraction methods. Tsuchiya (1910), Adler (1922a), Opitz and Brehme (1923, 1924a), and Sparkman (1939b,c) reported higher excretion figures, but these are due to imperfect technique. Familial, idiopathic urobilinuria is discussed later in this chapter (Section D,4).

Kahán and Felkai (1961) studied 47 24-hour urines in 26 normal subjects with a method based on oxidation of urobilinoids to urobilins and determined the urobilinoids-i simultaneously with the mesobiliviolin–$FeCl_3$ reaction. They always found less than 1.5 mg/24 hours for total urobilinoid with an average of 0.41 mg/24 hours, i.e., significantly lower figures than the writers employing modern benzaldehyde methods after reduction and extraction. Kahán and Felkai found urobilin-i present in 49% of the normal urines tested, the maximal being 0.50 mg/24 hours, the average 0.11 mg/24 hours. Urobilin-i was absent in 51% of the subjects studied. Urobilin-l was present in 85% and absent in 15%. Its maximum figure was 1.5 mg/24 hours, its average 0.30 mg/24 hours. The ratio urobilin-i/urobilin-l was, on the average, 27/73.

The influence of muscle activity on urobilinuria has not yet been sufficiently investigated (Royer, 1943, p. 111). Isaac (1925) found that adrenalin and thyroxine cause urobilinuria. Gerhardt (1897), Tsuchiya (1910), Meyer-Betz (1913), O. Bang (1929), Royer (1943, p. 111), B. Brandt (1937), and Meebold (1938) studied the influence of the *menstrual cycle* on urobilinuria. The first five authors, using less reliable methods, could not detect any connection between urobilinuria and the menstrual cycle. However, the last two investigators, who used the benzaldehyde reaction after reduction and extraction, detected a noticeable increase of urobilin excretion at the start or one day before menstruation commenced. Enhanced urobilinuria continued for 3–7 days. Meebold's studies on 26 women over a period of 3–12 weeks showed a definitely increased urobilin excretion during the menses in 19 cases. Average urobilin excretion amounted to 1.5 mg/24 hours during menstruation and 0.5 mg/24 hours during the intervals. It is interesting to note that female dogs in season show increased urobilinuria (Woll, 1912).

Various authors discussed the question of urobilinuria during *pregnancy, birth,* and *childbed.* Huwer (1933), Mittelstrass (1936), Butz (1937), B. Brandt (1937), Meebold (1938), Hansen (1938), and Dubrowsky (1939) carried out investigations with the benzaldehyde reaction after reduction and extraction. Moderate urobilin increases were found regularly during early pregnancy. Considerably increased excretion was found in some women during the last months of pregnancy (1.7 mg/100 ml, Brandt; 9.35 mg/24 hours, Hansen). However, constantly enhanced values were found in relatively few cases. Fluctuating findings were more frequent. Most pregnant women showed excretion levels within normal limits. Increased concentrations were found during labor and during childbed in women who showed enhanced excretion during the last 2 months of pregnancy. Excretion increased noticeably a few days before labor started and lasted for about 1 week in these cases (Brandt). The values remained high for a few days during childbed; they started to decrease and reached normal level in about 1 week.

According to semiquantitative tests with the zinc fluorescence technique, urobilin excretion is lower in infants and children than in adults (see Royer, 1943, p. 121). K. T. Simon's (1939) experiments are the only relevant evidence in this area; he used the benzaldehyde method after reduction and extraction and noted excretion of 0.025–2.49 mg/24 hours in the urine of 29 normal children in the age range from a few months to 11 years. More studies including larger experimental material would be desirable. Conditions in newborns are discussed below.

Finally, Stefanini's (1949) findings should be mentioned. This author found a definite increase of urinary urobilirubinoids after intravenous injections of 30 mg *sodium nicotinate*. Concentrations, exceeding five or six times that of the starting level, were observed.

Investigations involving urinary urobilinoids of normal *animals* are rare and the findings are contradictory. In dogs, Woll (1912) reported 0.02–0.16 mg/100 ml, and Royer (1943, p. 39) 0.0024–0.1 mg/24 hours. Elman and McMaster (1925a) could not find any urobilin in the urine of normal dogs. Investigations with the benzaldehyde reaction in the dog have not been reported. Oshima (1931a) found 0.03–0.07 mg/24 hours and Lopez Garcia *et al.* (1943) found 0.03–0.20 mg/24 hours in rabbits. Royer (1943, p. 157) reported excretions below 0.004 mg/24 hours in rats. Urobilin analyses are difficult in herbivorous animals, because the presence of chlorophyll in the food can lead to the excretion of considerable amounts of phylloerythrinogens. Woll (1912) found excretions ranging from 0.09 to 0.31 mg/100 ml and Lopez Garcia *et al.* (1943) 0.115 mg/100 ml in pigs. Woll (1912), Nestlé (1913), and Beijers (1923) reported investigations in horses and cattle. Woll found concentrations of 0.005–0.22 mg/100 ml in these animals. He found 0.10–1.16 mg/100 ml in normal human urine with the same method. Except for Oshima's experiments on rabbits, no determinations have been carried out in animals with the benzaldehyde reaction after extraction. Therefore, new and extended studies should be carried out in a number of different animal species.

W. Stich (1946a) demonstrated the presence of UG-ι and UG-ʟ in normal urine with the pentdyopent reaction, and Baumgärtel (1949a, 1950b) with the mesobiliviolin reaction. Both investigators found that UG-ʟ prevails and only traces of UG-ι are present. K.-H. Brandt (1957,

p. 149) reported studies involving two normal urines with the help of the mesobiliviolin-FeCl₃ method; he found a high UG-ı concentration in one of the urines examined. Kahán and Felkai (1961) found both UG-L and UG-ı in normal urine with a preponderance of the former in most cases; the average ratio was 73/27 (cf. above). C. J. Watson (1959), who examined six normal subjects, found a UG-ı excess in two cases, UG-L excess in three cases, and one where UG-D predominated.

Lozzio and Royer (1965*) studied the urine of 25 normal male subjects employing the FeCl₃ reaction after extraction as well as chromatography and electrophoresis and found only urobilinoids of type I in amounts of 0.84 ± 0.34 mg/24 hours. They point out that their findings are in direct opposition with the findings of other workers using the oxidation method. This discrepancy is discussed without any satisfactory explanation being offered.

The urobilinuria of *newborns* is a special problem since no intestinal urobilinoid formation takes place during the first period of life. Urobilinuria appearing immediately after birth is presumably caused by urobilinogen orginating from the mother. According to Royer (1929a), the placenta is permeable for urobilin. Misleading reactions can also be obtained because of the presence of phylloerythrinogen, ingested with the mother's milk (Baumgärtel, 1949a, 1950b). The available information is contradictory and the conditions prevailing in humans and in herbivorous animals are completely different. Using the zinc fluorescence test, most of the earlier authors found considerable amounts of urobilinoids in the urine of human newborns (cf. With, 1954, p. 290). Contrary to this, Royer and Bertrand (1929a) and Royer (1943, p. 118) found only extremely low concentrations (0.001–0.004 mg/24 hours). Heilmeyer and Pfotenhauer (1933) could never detect urobilinuria at birth when using the benzaldehyde method after extraction. However, urobilinuria was often observed 8–24 hours after birth. No quantitative data are given. Using the same method, Biering-Sørensen and With (1947) could never demonstrate urobilinuria in newborns. W. Stich (1948) sometimes found UG-ı, but never UG-L. Baumgärtel (1949a, 1950b) could not detect any urobilinoids at all in the urine of newborns. Extended investigations have been carried out on newborn calves, sheep, foals, and goats (Wester, 1912a,b; Beijers, 1923; Metzger, 1927). Urobilinuria developed about 36 hours after birth, and lasted until the 8th or 15th day, i.e., it had a close time relation to icterus neonatorum of newborn animals. This urobilinuria in herbivorous animals is a peculiar and interesting phenomenon. Since urobilinoid determination in herbivorous animals easily yields erroneous results, reexamination of these results is necessary. Duplicate determinations should be carried out: first with the benzaldehyde reaction after extraction and then with the zinc fluorescence test. Moreover, determination of types I, L, and -D should be performed.

No further studies involving other mammals, birds, and other lower vertebrates are available.

According to Kahán and Kahán (1959) and Kahán (1961), urinary urobilinoids are partly free, partly bound to mucoprotein–carbohydrates, and occasionally conjugated with glucuronic acid. This has been shown by $CHCl_3$–amyl alcohol (9:1) extraction, paper chromatography and paper electrophoresis in borate buffer at pH 8.6.

Summary

Urobilinoid excretion ranges from 0 to 4 mg/24 hours in normal humans. An increase can be observed during fasting, menstruation, pregnancy, labor, and childbed. Marked daily variations can be present. Various hormones seem to influence the excretion. As far as is known, excretion is lower in children than in adults; however, insufficient evidence is available in this area. It is questionable whether urobilinoids are present in the urine of the newborn. This problem can only be decided on the basis of further studies. It seems that normal adult humans predominantly excrete urobilinoid-L; urobilinoid-I appears quite often, and occasionally urobilinoid-D has also been found. Only a few studies on urobilinuria in normal mammals exist. Research in this area with suitable methods is necessary. Especially, urobilinuria in newborn herbivorous domestic animals, as described by various authors, deserves reexamination with modern analytical methods.

3. RENAL EXCRETION OF UROBILINOIDS AND THEIR FATE FOLLOWING INTRODUCTION INTO THE CIRCULATION

Unlike bilirubin urobilinogens are eliminated through the kidneys, at extremely low concentration in the plasma. Engel and Kiener (1887b) and Carrié (1913, p. 81) described this fundamental difference between urobilinogen and bilirubin. Because of the extremely low normal plasma urobilinoid it is only possible to perform clearance studies in pathological conditions and tolerance tests. Achard and Morfaux (1899) and Morfaux (1899, p. 29) were the first to perform urobilin tolerance tests. These authors demonstrated massive urobilinuria 1 hour after subcutaneous injections of 100 mg urobilin in a normal person. Three patients suffering from kidney insufficiency did not develop urobilinuria after the same treatment. It is particularly interesting that the total amount of urinary urobilinoid excretion was eliminated in the form of urobilinogen, even when urobilin was injected.

Oshima (1932c) added urobilin-L to the perfusion fluid of surviving organs and to organ homogenates. It was found that, whereas the liver and kidneys were capable of converting urobilin into urobilinogen, all other organs examined were not able to do so. The reducing power of kidneys was 7–10 times higher than that of the liver. These findings were supported by experiments with nephrectomized rabbits, which excreted considerable amounts of unchanged urobilin through the bile (Oshima, 1931c, 1932b). In contrast, normal rabbits eliminated practically all intravenously injected urobilin-L in the form of urobilinogen through the bile. Unchanged urobilin was only found after the administration of very large amounts of urobilin-L. Urobilin could only be demonstrated in the serum for half an hour to 1 hour after injection. There was no difference when the injections were made into the auricular or the portal vein (Oshima 1932a).

C. J. Watson (1936b) performed intravenous or intramuscular injections in humans with 50 mg crystalline urobilin-L and detected a strong positive benzaldehyde reaction in the urine within 1–2 hours. He could also demonstrate small amounts of unchanged urobilin in the fresh urine half an hour to 4 hours after injection. He mentioned later (see discussion of Jankelson, 1944) that large amounts of chromogen are rapidly excreted in the duodenal fluid after intravenous injections of 50 mg urobilin-L.

Royer (1928c; 1943, pp. 69–90) conducted tolerance tests with simultaneous determinations of urobilinoids in plasma, in bile, and in urine under various experimental conditions. The author injected intravenously 0.1–0.2 mg of partially purified urobilin-L per kg body weight in dogs with bilary fistula. The solutions contained 1.2–1.8 mg urobilin-L/100 ml. Plasma concentrations of 0.06–1.12 mg/100 ml were found immediately after injection in these experiments; the concentrations decreased rapidly during the next hour. When 0.2 mg per kg body weight was injected, only traces were found half an hour later in the plasma. However, when 0.4 mg per kg was administered, measurable amounts were present even 1–2 hours after injection. The maximum concentration which was measured immediately after the injection was only 1/6–1/8 of the calculated level. Calculation was based on the amount of urobilinogen-L injected and the plasma volume of the dog. Significantly higher calculated values than those observed experimentally are also known from bilirubin tolerance tests (see Chapter V,J). In Royer's experiments only 10% of the injected urobilin was recovered in the bile, and this excretion continued for 2 more days, in spite of normal serum concentration. He explained this rapid disappearance of urobilin from the circulation and continued excretion by a fast storage of urobilin in some organs or tissues; subsequent excretion then occurs from these deposits. Royer tried to define these storage areas by tissue analysis (1928b,d; 1943, p.

75). However, because of technical difficulties, these analyses are only of limited interest. He investigated the role of the reticuloendothelial system (RES) as possible storage place by blocking with India ink in tolerance tests. Blockade noticeably changed the excretion curve; this indicated that the RES plays a significant role as storage area. In similar experiments Oshima (1931b) found distinctively accelerated excretion in the urine and in the bile of rabbits. Royer (1929c; 1943, p. 82) demonstrated the influence of the liver on the clearance by experiments in which the blocking agent was injected into the portal vein. The concentration in the plasma of the portal vein was 0.023 mg/100 ml, whereas in the hepatic vein the plasma level was 0.007 mg urobilin/100 ml. In animal preparations, in which all branches of the abdominal aorta had been ligated, urobilin concentration decreased rapidly within 10 minutes after injection, until a constant concentration level was reached. The concentration remained at this level for the next 2 hours in which the animal stayed alive.

A few authors have studied the renal clearance of urobilin in experimental *animals.* Royer and Solari (1941; see also Royer, 1943, p. 85 ff.) carried out studies on eigth dogs with bladder catheterization. The urobilin-L clearance determined was 19–71. The ratio of urobilin clearance divided by creatinine clearance amounted to 0.53/1.25 (average 1.03). The duration of clearance time, variations in serum urobilinoids, and the influence of the liver were not discussed in these studies. Experiments in dogs with obliterated common bile duct would be of interest in this connection. Royer also examined five normal men and found urobilin clearance of 138–229, and urobilin/creatinine clearance of 1.15–1.86 (average 1.48) after injection of 1.9–9.29 mg urobilin-L. Oshima (1932a) injected 0.05–0.7 mg urobilin-L intravenously in rabbits. He found that the excretion with the bile definitely increased within the first 3–4 hours. However, increased excretion with the urine was only noticeable in the first hour after injection. No difference in excretion rate took place whether the injection was given into the ear vein or into the mesenteric vein. The increased amounts of urobilinoids excreted and detected in the bile and in the urine corresponded to the amount of urobilin injected. Oshima's findings of increased and rapidly diminishing excretion contradict Royer's observations. The latter author found a rather protracted decrease of concentration. These differences can be due to the use of different animals and to different analytical methods.

A few investigators have used urobilin injections as liver function tests. C. J. Watson (1936b) performed intravenous or intramuscular injections in four normal subjects, one patient with common bile duct obstruction, and three patients with hepatocellular jaundice. He injected 50 mg recrystallized urobilin-L. The injections were tolerated without side effects. A distinct increase in urinary urobilinogen was observed during the first 30 minutes to 2 hours after the injection, but disappeared within the next 6–8 hours. The amount of urobilinogen excreted after injection was compared with the amount excreted the previous day and the increase was calculated from the difference. Excretion increment was 4–5% of the injected amount after intramuscular injections and 10% after intravenous ones in normal subjects. Corresponding values were 25% after intramuscular injections and about 45% after intravenous ones in patients with bile duct obstruction; in patients with parenchymal damage the values were 10–18% after intramuscular injections and 10–60% after intravenous ones.

Watson studied the excretion of urobilinogen in the bile after injection of 450 mg urobilin-L in 50-mg doses on 6 consecutive days. He determined the fecal urobilinoids on these 6 days, and on an additional 2 days. The excretion determined during this period was compared with the spontaneous excretion found during 4 days before and 4 days after urobilin injection. The increment was calculated from the difference of these values. A total of 400 mg was excreted during the 8 experimental days; the calculated spontaneous excretion was 268 mg. Thus, the excess is 132 mg, which amounts to 29% of the amount injected. Since only insignificant amounts were eliminated in the urine, the balance must have been retained in the organism, or destroyed in the intestines after excretion with the bile.

With (1946c) injected a urobilinogen-I preparation intravenously in 10–50 mg doses. No side effects were noticed. The urine was examined 3, 10, and 24 hours after injection. Before injections the daily amounts of spontaneous urinary excretion were determined over a period of 3 days. The daily excretion increment due to these injections was calculated from the difference between these values. An increment of 0.5–5% was found in 15 normal subjects. In 10 acute hepatitis cases the corresponding values were 15–40% during the active phase of the disease and dropped to 2–20% during the regressing stage. In 11 chronic hepatitis cases, the increments were 1–35% and values of 9–40% were found in five patients with obstructive jaundice. These increments do not indicate that the urobilin tests have any practical usefulness.

In addition to this, Biering-Sørensen and With (1947) conducted similar experiments with urobilinogen-I in newborns. These authors administered 1 mg urobilinogen-L per kg body weight and collected the urine for 6 hours thereafter. Since no spontaneous urobilin excretion had to be accounted for in these cases, the determinations were simple. Excretion was 0–7% and the values did not show any correlation with the serum bilirubin content.

Lester and Schmid (1965*) performed i.v. tolerance tests with C^{14}-urobilinogen-I dissolved in rat serum on two normal rats and one Gunn rat and found that 85–92% of the label appeared in the bile within 4 hours in both the normal and the Gunn rat.

Summary

Information on the urobilinoid excretion by the kidney is limited and the available information contradictory. Further experiments with improved analytical methods are desirable: these should include human and animal experiments involving many species. Investigations of the fate of urobilinoids during tolerance tests are also required. Possible differences between urobilinoid-I, -L, and -D excretion have not yet been systematically studied. Urobilin tolerance tests are clinically worthless in both adults and newborns.

4. URINARY UROBILINOIDS UNDER PATHOLOGICAL CONDITIONS

Since the discovery of urobilinoids, pathological urobilinuria and its clinical significance have stimulated great interest and have become the subject of numerous discussions.

Lesieurs et al. (1908) demonstrated very elegantly the central role of liver in this area. They used normal and hepatectomized frogs in their experiments. When aqueous urobilin solutions were administered to these animals by gavage, urobilinuria occurred only in the hepatectomized frogs, not in the normal animals. Royer's (1929a) observations also demonstrated the role played by the liver. When urobilin was intravenously injected into pregnant animals, accumulation of this compound in the fetal liver was found. Partially hepatectomized rats exhibited urobilinuria (Royer, 1943, p. 156). Since the physiological and biochemical mechanism of urobilinuria has already been discussed (Chapter II,D) only clinical observations will be reported here.

Hoppe-Seyler (1891), von Müller (1892), and Hildebrandt (1909b) did not observe urobilinuria at all or only to a moderate degree during complete bile duct obstruction. Hildebrandt (1909b) described the absence of urinary urobilin in complete bile fistula. The only exceptions were cases of cholangitis caused by fecal bacteria. Based on a large amount of clinical evidence, Wallace and Diamond (1925) confirmed these findings. Gerhardt (1897), Wilbur and Addis (1914), and Salén and Enocksson (1927) reported single cases in which, in spite of complete bile duct obstruction, urobilin appeared in the urine. However, this phenomenon was explained by cholemic bleedings and the subsequent presence of bilirubin in the intestines. Hoppe-Seyler (1891), von Müller (1892), Hildebrandt (1909b), and Carrié (1913) often found considerably increased urobilinuria during incomplete bile duct obstruction.

Urobilinuria during acute hepatitis (catarrhal jaundice), liver cirrhosis, and metastatic liver carcinoma was described by von Müller (1892), Grimm (1893), Ladage (1899), Hildebrandt (1909b), Wallace and Diamond (1925), Salén and Enocksson (1927), Adler and Jeddeloh (1929), Weiss (1930), and Oshima (1930b). Hildebrandt (1909b) was the first to emphasize that urobilinuria must be attributed to insufficiency of the liver. Earlier investigators also described urobilinuria in infectious diseases (With, 1954, pp. 297–298), including typhus, diphtheria, scarlet fever, pneumonia, tuberculosis, erysipelas, measles, poliomyelitis, malaria, and Weil's disease. Justi (1912), and especially Kingsbury (1926), reported studies on urobilinuria in malaria. Hildebrandt (1913) interpreted the appearance of urobilinuria during infectious diseases as a symptom of latent liver insufficiency.

Urobilinuria in heart diseases, especially those with distinct liver stasis, was described by von Müller (1892), Grimm (1893), Ladage (1899), Jonass (1912), Wilbur and Addis (1914), and Salén and Enocksson (1927). Hoppe-Seyler (1891) reported urobilinuria during chronic constipation. Salén and Enocksson (1927) found a decreased excretion of urinary urobilinoids during diarrhea. Grimm (1893) and Wilbur and Addis (1914) found decreased urobilin excretion during nephritis. Bang (1929) detected moderate urobilinuria in diabetes. Grönberg and Lindberg (1930) as well as Oshima (1930b) observed moderate urobilinuria during thyrotoxicosis when it was accompanied by cardiac damage, but urobilinuria was absent in uncomplicated cases. Von Bergmann (1881) described urobilinuria in patients with cerebral apoplexy. Aubel *et al.* (1925) found it in cyclic depressions; Lingjaerde (1934), who examined 532 patients suffering from mental disorders, detected urobilinuria in a number of cases of manic-depressive psychoses, senile dementia, general paresis, alcohol phychosis, epileptic psychosis, and especially during the active phases of schizophrenia. He maintained that starvation is an essential pathogenetic factor for urobilinuria in mental diseases.

Morfaux (1899), Clemens (1901), and Hildebrandt (1913) observed that urobilinuria present at admission to the hospital disappeared after a few days. They assumed that this was due to the elimination of the daily stress from the life of the patients. Genner (1936) and Genner and With (1938a,b) confirmed these observations. Wilbur and Addis (1914) pointed out the marked hourly fluctuations of urobilin excretion and warned against drawing fundamental conclusions from urine samples collected during less than a 24-hour period (see also Section C,2, this chapter). Kast and Mester (1891), Doyon and Gautier (1909), Brun (1910), and Royer (1929d) found urobilinuria during various forms of anesthesia. Ostrowski (1912) compiled the earlier literature on urobilinuria in the newborn and children. Lemaire (1905) surveyed the early literature of pathological urobilinuria.

Filinski (1923) found that *ingestion of 100 g glucose* causes urobilinuria in persons with latent liver disease. Malach (1913), Gerhartz (1917), Gottschalk (1922), and Isaac (1925) also made this observation. However, this phenomenon has not yet been studied with reliable analytical methods. Strauss (1919) reported preliminary experiments, according to which urobilinuria occurred in certain individuals with hyperlordosis of the vertebral column. Falta *et al.* (1921) and Falta and Högler (1922) observed urobilinuria after administration of dried bile and *alcoholic chlorophyll solutions.* This is claimed to be more distinct in individuals with liver diseases than in normal persons. However, Eppinger (1937, p. 208) could not confirm these findings. As Baumgärtel (1950b) has pointed out, this urobilinuria after chlorophyll administration is probably caused by phylloerythrinogen.

Whereas data presented in the earlier literature are primarily qualitative, or at best semiquantitative, in nature, more recent investigations yielded generally quantitative statements. These more recent data are compiled below.

C. J. Watson (1937a) found that in afebrile infections and weight loss of *psychogenic origin* the urobilin values were within normal limits; infectious diseases accompanied by fever exhibited excretions of 0.8–37.6 mg urobilin/24 hours. The degree of excretion was correlated with the severity of the infection and was independent of the degree of elevated temperature. Steigmann and Dyniewicz (1943a) reported similar findings using a benzaldehyde method after extraction, similar to Watson's method. Royer, with the zinc fluorescence test, found normal values in mild *chronic infections,* but concentrations up to 42 mg/24 hours in acute general infections (Royer, 1943, p. 155). De Vries (1946), who used Watson's benzaldehyde extraction, found levels of 3–50 mg/24 hours in acute cases of malaria. Siggelkow (1935) measured excretion values up to 12 mg/100 ml in pyelitis of pregnancy. In *hemolytic jaundice* Posthuma (1931) observed values of 2–123 mg/24 hours. C. J. Watson (1937b) found 1–20 mg/24 hours in uncomplicated cases, but various complications caused these values to go up to 380 mg/24 hours. After splenectomy, most cases returned to normal. Steigmann and Dyniewicz (1943a) found 5–90 mg/24 hours. With (1944b) found 8–15 mg/24 hours; Monasterio and Lattanzi (1947) and Lattanzi (1948c), 3.7–26 mg/24 hours. All these data refer to analyses with the benzaldehyde reaction after reduction and extraction. Royer (1943, p. 171) observed excretion of 0.9–12 mg/24 hours in uncomplicated cases, but in more complicated ones the values went up to 286 mg/24 hours. C. J. Watson (1931) found increased excretion in *pernicious anemia*. Urobilinuria disappeared on treatment simultaneously with the increase of reticulocytes. Escola (1950), who examined pernicious anemia caused by tape worms, observed values of 2.5–10 mg/24 hours which increased to 30 mg/24 hours during the reticulocyte crisis and then gradually dropped back to normal.

Varying values were found during *nonhemolytic blood diseases*, but as a rule, a slight increase was observed (Watson, 1937a; Steigmann and Dyniewicz, 1943a). Similarly, Watson found somewhat increased concentrations in constipation and ileus. Waller *et al.* (1940) reported 0.20 mg/24 hours in congestive heart failure; Chavez *et al.* (1943) found 6.2 mg/100 ml, and Sherlock (1951) 2.2–45 mg/24 hours. With progressing liver damage ascertained by biopsy, the excretion increased. Royer (1943) observed a moderately increased urobilinuria in thyroid hyperfunction and in some cases of diabetes. Values determined in ovarial insufficiency were within normal limits. Baumgärtel (1949a; 1950b, pp. 221 and 238) found increased urobilinuria in agitated psychotic patients and in those with severe headache.

C. J. Watson (1937b) found normal urobilin excretion in uncomplicated cholelithiasis, but when complications occurred (anemia, infections, cirrhosis) values of 3.9–112.3 mg/24 hours were observed. Royer (1943, pp. 167–170 and 182) found 0.9–72 mg/24 hours in obstruction caused by gallstones and 0.2–23 mg/24 hours in cholecystitis. Lopez Garcia (1943, pp. 144–146) generally found increased values in obstruction by stones, occasionally even as high as 30 mg/24 hours. Such high concentrations occurred especially in cases of cholangitis. Steigmann and Dyniewicz (1943a,b), Monasterio and Lattanzi (1947), and Lattanzi (1948c) made similar observations. In contrast, urinary urobilin content was very low during *complete (neoplastic) bile duct closure*. Thus, Watson (1937b) found values under 0.3 mg/24 hours, except for one case with excretion of 1.6 mg/24 hours. C. J. Watson (1940) later reported values below 0.3 mg/24 hours in 90% of a larger group of patients. Royer (1943) reported values up to 1.6 mg/24 hours. Lopez Garcia (1943) also emphasized the extremely low excretion in this condition. Steigmann and Dyniewicz (1943a) found 0.0–0.5 mg/24 hours. Similarly, low values were also reported by With (1944b) in most of the cases examined, but he also reported two cases confirmed by necropsy which showed noticeably increased excretion. In one of these the excretion was 23 mg/24 hours. Monasterio and Lattanzi (1947) found a similarly high value in one of their cases. López Pontes (1947) and K. A. Meyer *et al.* (1949) confirmed this low excretion in neoplastic obstructions.

In *liver cirrhosis* C. J. Watson (1937b) found normal or only moderately increased excretion levels (0.6–32.4 mg/24 hours) when it was accompanied by jaundice; when icterus was absent, however, higher concentrations prevailed (4.6–113 mg/24 hours). The same worker found 224 mg/24 hours in cases with blood destruction. Royer (1943) observed 0.3–50 mg/24 hours in anicteric cases, whereas Steigmann and Dyniewicz (1943a) found values within the normal limits, but levels of 5–300 mg/24 hours were observed in icteric patients with cirrhosis. With (1944b) found 0–130 mg/24 hours. On the basis of tolerance tests in cirrhotic patients, With (1946c) was able to show that urobilinuria in liver cirrhosis is caused primarily by liver insufficiency, and not by by-pass of the liver on account of collateral circulation.

Urobilin excretion in *acute hepatitis* depends mainly on the course of the disease. C. J. Watson (1937b) observed concentrations of 0.5–207 mg/24 hours, varying with the severity and stage of the disease. During an epidemic, Hallgren (1943, pp. 87–89) investigated the first stage of the disease which is usually difficult to detect, and observed that urobilinuria precedes massive bilirubinuria. Unfortunately, the measurements were not quantitative. Royer (1943) found values of 0.15–16 mg/24 hours. In the most severe acute cases of hepatitis Steigmann and Popper (1943) found that no urobilin can be detected in the urine during the peak of jaundice (about 10% of the cases). This phenomenon, called *intrahepatic biliary obstruction,* is caused by a temporary complete suppression of bile excretion. As a rule, such complete absence of urobilinoids continued only for a few days, but it can last for 1 week, or on rare occasions it even can extend over 30 days. Steigmann and Dyniewicz (1943a) observed values of 5–300 mg/24 hours in acute hepatitis.

With (1944b), Monasterio and Lattanzi (1947), and Lattanzi (1948c) illustrated with curves their studies of urobilin excretion during hepatitis. Four of With's curves are shown in Figs. 50–53. Mutual relationships existing between serum bilirubin as well as urinary bilirubin and urinary urobilinoid concentrations are demonstrated. Generally, urobilin levels are low when bilirubin values are high, but simultaneously increased bilirubin and urobilin levels can also exist. According to the variations discussed in Chapter III, this situation is easy to explain. With (1944b) thoroughly studied this question and pointed out that the serum bilirubin level and bilirubinuria are indications of the bilirubin production level as well as the presence of liver damage, but that urobilinuria is independent of the height of bilirubin production level. It merely indicates the severity of liver damage. The level of the bilirubin production of the

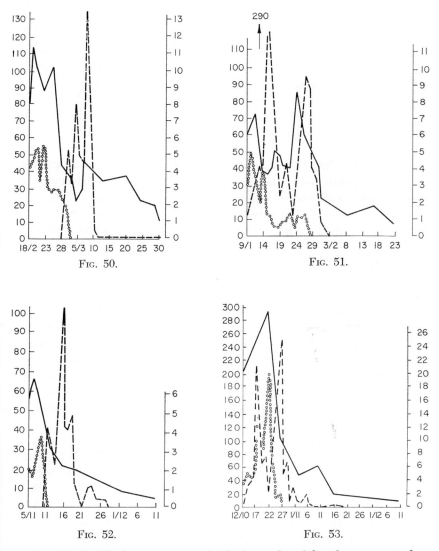

FIGS. 50–53. Bilirubin in serum and bilirubin and urobilinoids in urine in four cases of acute hepatitis. Ordinate: Concentrations in milligrams per 100 milliliters serum or milligrams per 24-hour urine. Solid line: serum bilirubin (right scale); dashed line: urinary bilirubin (left scale); dotted line: urinary urobilinoid (left scale). Abscissa: day and month. Examples from With (1944b).

subject indicates the highest possible limit of the urobilin excretion; this is the only connection of urobilinuria with the amount of bilirubin formed in cases of liver insufficiency. For this reason, urobilinuria is a much more reliable expression for the degree of liver damage than is hyperbilirubinemia or bilirubinuria. In addition, With (1944b) showed that the urobilinuria, which can be observed during bile duct obstruction, can be explained without the assumption of parenchymal liver damage.

In most of the acute hepatitis cases, urinary urobilin reached normal values before serum bilirubin (With, 1944b). This confirms Meulengracht's (1919) observations, but contradicts Eppinger's (1937, p. 280) findings.

Kahán and Felkai (1961) studied 170 24-hour urines from 22 patients with viral hepatitis, using their method based on urobilin determination after oxidation (cf. above). Simultaneously, they determined the concentration of U-I with the mesobiliviolin–$FeCl_3$ method of Legge. They give the time curves of the excretion in 6 of their cases. These curves are very similar to those found by With (1944b) and Lattanzi (1948c), with the exception that Kahán's figures are lower. The maximum 24-hour excretion of total urobilin found by the latter was 15 mg, whereas the former often found 50 mg or more. Kahán found increases of both U-I and U-L in her hepatitis patients, their ratio being close to 1/1 but varying somewhat with the stage of the disease. They warned against conclusions drawn from single analyses because the day-to-day variations were much more pronounced in hepatitis than in normal subjects. Serial studies are of clinical value. No clinical significance of separate determination of urobilin-I and -L was demonstrated. They noted that constipation in their patients was associated with higher figures for the 24-hour total urobilin than normal stool (averages 6.0 and 3.84 mg, respectively).

As is clear from the above facts, urobilin determinations are only of limited value for the differential diagnosis between obstructive and hepatic jaundice. In these two types of icterus, urobilinuria of various degrees can be present, but it can also be completely absent. Weir (1932) substantiated this opinion. However, as C. J. Watson (1940) already emphasized, values below 0.3 mg/24 hours are found in most cases of neoplastic obstruction. The finding of such low values constantly over a number of weeks suggests this diagnosis.

C. J. Watson *et al.* (1944), Pellegrino *et al.* (1947), and Lindberg and Le Roy (1947) reported observations made with the simplified benzaldehyde method without extraction. These authors found that this test has about the same clinical value as the more complicated extraction procedures.

Only few investigators have performed *separate urobilinoid-*L *and -*I *determinations* on clinical cases. W. Stich (1946a,b, 1948) found about the same increase in urobilin-I and -L contents in hemolytic anemia and in malaria, but in pernicious anemia only urobilin-L was increased. He found urobilin-I in complete bile duct closure, urobilin-I as well as -L in partial obstruction, whereas in regressing hepatitis only urobilin-L was detected. According to Baumgärtel (1947b, 1948a, 1950b, pp. 237–238), urobilin-L prevails in hemolytic conditions, urobilin-I in parenchymal damage. These two compounds were found in approximately equal proportions in malaria and in hereditary hemolytic jaundice. Only urobilin-L was present in heart diseases and only urobilin-I in complete biliary fistula. In addition, Baumgärtel (1950b, p. 225) found that urobilinuria due to physical exertion or glucose intake in convalescents after acute hepatitis can be attributed to urobilin-I. Rudolph (1951, 1952) and Maier and Schwartz (1953) more or less confirmed Baumgärtel's results; Eisfeld (1953) could not add any observations to clarify the situation.

K.-H. Brandt (1957, pp. 149–151), who examined 6 cases, found considerable amounts of urobilin-L as well as urobilin-I in one patient with paralytic ileus, in one with acute hepatitis, in one with chronic hepatitis, and in one with gallstones accompanied by cholecystitis. Relatively large amounts of urobilin-L and only small amounts of urobilin-I were found in a patient with hemolytic jaundice. A similar situation was found in a case of prostatic hypertrophy, which excreted much urobilin-L but only traces of urobilin-I. He concluded that these determinations are without practical clinical value. To the same conclusion came C. J. Watson (1959), on the basis of separate determinations of U-I, U-L, and U-D. Kahán and Felkai (1961), who performed 170 determinations of U-I and U-L on 22 patients with viral hepatitis, hold the same opinion.

Moravec (1963*) studied 30 cases of posthepatitic hyperbilirubinemia and found urobilinemia due to type I in 63%. This was ascribed to intracellular enzymatic processes in the liver. His technique is, however, not described in detail and seems, according to the information given, not quite satisfactory.

"Orthostatic urobilinuria" or better "idiopathic familial urobilinuria," as Steensma (1914; 1918, p. 59) calls it, presents a peculiar condition. This benign familial urobilinuria was observed in three generations in two families in a total of 39 individuals. It has not been mentioned since, but Steigmann and Dyniewicz (1943a) reported that some normal subjects (about 2% of their normal material) showed excretion of 3–15 mg/24 hours; these cases could perhaps be included in this type of urobilinuria. Newer studies of this condition, with simultaneous serum bilirubin determination, would be of interest. It is possibly due to abnormal liver function or to an inherited dysfunction of pyrrole metabolism.

Investigations on pathological urobilinuria of *animals* are rare. Woll (1912) described urobilinuria in cattle with tuberculosis; Nestlé (1913) observed it in horses suffering from hemolytic diseases or from infectious fevers. Beijers (1923) could only find a just noticeable urobilinuria in tuberculous cattle, but it appeared regularly in tuberculous guinea pigs. Urobilinuria also occurred in cattle suffering from pneumonia, cardiac insufficiency, or hemolytic diseases. Beijers was able to induce urobilinuria by rapid intravenous injections of 100–500 ml distilled water in calves. Urobilinuria appeared 4 hours after the injection and reached its peak after 24 hours. Lopez Garcia et al. (1943) investigated urobilinuria caused by bile duct ligation in rabbits, pigs, monkeys, dogs, and cats (zinc fluorescence method). All animals examined showed only slight urobilinuria after complete obstruction.

Cameron et al. (1963*) studied the excretion of urobilinogen in 13 dogs with complete biliary obstruction. The benzaldehyde extraction test (Balikow, 1958) was employed. They found urobilinogen excretions of 0.07–0.14 mg/24 hours in 7 normal dogs and no demonstrable urobilinogen in the dogs with biliary obstruction with the exception of one exhibiting a 20-fold increase which was ascribed to cholangitis.

Cameron et al. (1966b*) studied 5 rhesus monkeys with complete biliary occlusion in which C^{14}-bilirubin was injected after a steady state had been achieved. Values of the 24-hour urinary urobilinoid excretion were determined for the 14 days following the C^{14}-administration (method of Balikov, 1958) and values between 0.2 and 1.2 mg per 24 hours were found.

Summary

The urinary urobilinoid is increased in parenchymal liver damage, hemolytic conditions, and partial bile duct obstruction; however, it is decreased or often absent and only very rarely increased during complete bile duct obstruction (neoplastic obstruction). Urobilinoids are temporarily absent from urine in many cases of acute hepatitis. Consistent absence of urinary urobilinoids for a week or longer, or very low concentrations (below 0.3 mg/24 hours), indicate neoplastic bile duct obstruction. Besides this phenomenon, urobilin determinations are of little clinical diagnostic value. Urobilinuria fluctuates with the severity and course of acute hepatitis. Urobilinuria is often detectable during severe, general infections, but this is due to latent liver damage. Urobilinuria occurring during cardiac failure shows a certain parallelism to the severity of decompensation and to liver congestion. Unlike hyperbili-rubinemia and bilirubinemia, urobilirubinuria reflects liver function more reliably since it is independent of the magnitude of bilirubin pro-duction level. Separate determinations of the urobilin types -ɪ, -ʟ, and -ᴅ are worthless for clinical evaluation. The condition "orthostatic uro-bilinuria," also called "idiopathic familial urobilinuria" (Steensma), is mentioned. The few existing investigations on pathological urobilinuria in animals are briefly discussed.

E. Fuscinuria

The excretion of bilirubin and urobilinoids in the urine has been discussed above. Dipyrrole bile pigments can also occur in the urine, how-ever. In Chapter I it was mentioned that propentdyopents can occur, but these pigments are most likely formed secondarily from bilirubin and urobilinoids in the urine. The normal urinary pigment, urochrome B, is probably a fuscin (Chapter I,G) and it could therefore be anticipated that pathological increase of fuscin excretion will occur. This is really the case, since a hereditary form of hemolytic anemia associated with black urine due to mesobilifuscin and allied pigments has been de-scribed.

The first observation is due to Schmid *et al.* (1958b, 1959), who described two cases with congenital hemolytic anemia and black urine due to mesobilifuscin or closely similar pigments, as well as special inclusion bodies in the erythrocytes. A patient previously described by Cathie (1952) seems to belong to the same syndrome, although black urine was not noted. Further cases have been reported by Lange and Akeroyd (1958), Scott *et al.* (1960), Worms *et al.* (1961), M. Lelong *et al.* (1961), and Mozziconacci *et al.* (1961). At present 8 cases of this inborn error of metabolism are known; 2 were females, 6 males, and the age varied from newborn to 45 years. It is inherited as a dominant auto-somal trait. It manifests itself as a chronic hemolytic anemia with acute exacerbations. In most cases the erythrocytes contain specific inclusion bodies, closely similar to Heinz bodies, but these were absent in Lelong *et al.*'s case, just as the fuscinuria was not reported in Cathie's case. It is therefore possible that in some cases the syndrome can be incomplete.

Schmid *et al.* (1959) believed that the pigment is of catabolic origin, but the possibility of a by-product of an abnormal pyrrole synthesis requires serious consideration. As mentioned above (see Chapter II,A), nonporphyrin pigments, probably of a dipyrrol nature, are formed in large quantities in congenital porphyria. This question requires further study before final conclusions can be drawn.

In the patient of Lelong *et al.*, the erythrocytes contained abnormally low amounts of adenosine triphosphate (ATP) and 2,3-diphosphoglycerate (2,3-DPG).

Further cases were published by Goudemand *et al.* (1964*) and Sansone and Pick (1965*) who found an abnormal Hb in addition to the erythrocyte inclusion bodies and the bilifuscinuria. In the case of Goudemand *et al.* substantial improvement was achieved after splenectomy.

Recently André *et al.* (1963) described a case of *acquired mesobilifuscinuria* in a patient with Hodgkin's disease. The condition arose under an episode of intense hemolysis due to antigen-antibody reaction. The patient also suffered from a hypertrophic liver cirrhosis.

A thorough study of the black pigment—or pigments—excreted is required. Before this has been done the postion of this metabolic error in the system of errors of pyrrole metabolism—porphyrias, hemoglobinopathias, bile pigment anomalies (cf. Chapter V,K)—cannot be decided. Perhaps several closely related, separate forms exist.

Additional Readings

Section B,1

Heirwegh, K. P. M., Jansen, H., and van Roy, F. (1966). Determination of total bilirubin in urine. A modification of the method of Michaëlsson. *Clin. Chim. Acta* **14**, 124–130.

Section B,4

Ali, M. A. M. (1967). Urinary excretion of bilirubin in the bile duct ligated rat. *In* "Bilirubin Metabolism" (I. A. D. Bouchier and B. H. Billing, eds.), pp. 245–252. Blackwell, Oxford.

Ali, M. A. M., and Billing, B. H. (1967). Effect of acid-base changes on renal clearance of bile pigments. *Clin. Sci.* **30**, 543–552.

De Groote, J., Fevery, J., and Heirwegh, K. P. M. (1967). Urinary clearance of bilirubin in parenchymatous and obstructive jaundice. *In* "Bilirubin Metabolism" (I. A. D. Bouchier and B. H. Billing, eds.), pp. 263–272. Blackwell, Oxford.

Fevery, J., Heirwegh, K., and De Groote, J. (1967). Renal bilirubin clearance in liver patients. *Clin. Chim. Acta* **17**, 63–71.

Fulop, M., and Sandson, J. (1967). The role of bile salts in urinary bilirubin excretion. *In* "Bilirubin Metabolism" (I. A. D. Bouchier and B. H. Billing, eds.), pp. 253–262. Blackwell, Oxford.

Leyssac, P. P. (1966). The regulation of proximal tubular reabsorption in the mammalian kidney. *Acta Physiol. Scand.* **70**, *Suppl.* **291**, 1–151.

Owen, E. E. (1967). Observation on the mechanism of bilirubin excretion by the kidney. *In* "Bilirubin Metabolism" (I. A. D. Bouchier and B. H. Billing, eds.), pp. 233–244. Blackwell, Oxford.

Section D,3

Bourke, E., Milne, M. D., and Stokes, G. S. (1965). Mechanisms of renal excretion of urobilinogen. *Brit. Med. J.* II, 1510–1514.

Milne, M. D. (1967). Excretion of urobilinogen. *In* "Bilirubin Metabolism" (I. A. D. Bouchier and B. H. Billing, eds.), pp. 271–278. Blackwell, Oxford.

Section D,4

Lethonen, V., Näntö, V., and Brummer, P. (1967). Serum and urinary urobilinoids in hepatic diseases. *Acta Med. Scand.* 180, 235–239.

Section E

Bannerman, R. M., Kensch, G., Kreimer-Birnbaum, M., Vance, V. K., and Vaughan, S. (1967). Thalassemia intermedia with iron overload, cardiac failure, diabetes mellitus and porphyrinuria. *Am. J. Med.* 42, 476–486.

Kreimer-Birnbaum, M., Pinkerton, P. H., Bannerman, R. M., and Hutchison, R. M. (1966). Dipyrrolic urinary pigments in congenital Heinz-body anemia due to Hb Köln and in thalassemia. *Brit. Med. J.* II, 396.

CHAPTER VII

Bile Pigments in Bile

A. Introduction

Bile occupies a particular position among the other fluids of the body because of its high bile pigment content. The mechanism of bile secretion is discussed in Chapter IV,C,4. The secretion from the liver, the liver bile, is stored in the gallbladder where it undergoes considerable concentration thanks to active reabsorption (see J. M. Diamond, 1962). The contents of the gallbladder, the bladder bile, have a much higher concentration of bile pigments than the liver bile because the bile pigments are not absorbed from the gallbladder because they are present mainly in conjugated form. Ostrow (1963) showed in experiments on guinea pigs with conjugated and unconjugated C^{14}-bilirubin that mainly unconjugated bilirubin was absorbed from the gallbladder; conjugated bilirubin was absorbed to a considerably lesser degree. Further, much bilirubin was degraded to colorless diazo-negative compounds during the concentration of the bile in the gallbladder.

Bile can be obtained by surgery, at autopsy, or from animals and patients with biliary fistula. Pure gallbladder bile and fistula bile, also called liver bile, cannot be obtained from humans under normal conditions. Generally, only duodenal fluid is obtained. Attempts have been made to obtain pure bile by the duodenal tube after stimulation of bile excretion, and by various methods of emptying the gallbladder. Although concentrated bile fractions closely similar to bladder bile have been obtained, it is difficult to decide to what extent contamination with other secretions occurs. However, Schalm (1953b) introduced a method called *"bilitinction,"* to differentiate between gallbladder bile and liver bile obtained by the duodenal tube. This process consists of injection of 200 mg bromsulphalein 1 day prior to applying the duodenal tube. Bromsulphalein sodium which can be very easily detected, is excreted extremely rapidly with the liver bile which is free of this dyestuff within 6 hours. On the other hand, this substance is concentrated in the gallbladder where it is stored for over 24 hours. Consequently, bile fractions obtained by the duodenal tube and subsequent stimulation are free from gallbladder bile when no bromsulphalein can be detected, whereas they contain gallbladder bile when the dye is still detectable. This is the case for fractions collected between the 6th and 24th hour after the injection of the dyestuff.

Biliary bilirubin is bound to colloids. This was pointed out by Fischer and Reindel (1923), who could not extract biliary bilirubin with $CHCl_3$. Pedersen and Waldenström's (1937) studies with the aid of ultracentrifuge and boundary electrophoresis confirmed this assumption. Furthermore, Verschure and Hoefsmit (1956) demonstrated by paper chromatographic studies that the bilirubin of the gallbladder is bound to lipoproteins, whereas no binding of the bilirubin of liver bile on proteins

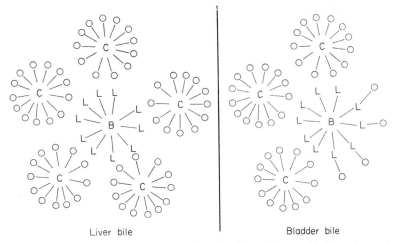

Liver bile   Bladder bile

FIG. 54. Probable composition of bilirubin–lecithin–cholesterol–bile acid complexes in normal bile according to Mendioroz (1963a,b,c). B = 1 mole bilirubin; L = 1 mole lecithin; C = 1 mole cholesterol. Circle = 1 mole bile acid.

or lipids could be demonstrated. Ichikawa (1956a,b,c) found that biliary biliverdin of rabbits is bound to high molecular weight compounds.

Mendioroz (1963a,b,c; personal communication, 1962; see also Section B,2, this chapter) suggested that the bilirubin of human liver bile is present in macromolecular complexes in which 1 mole of bilirubin is attached to 10 moles of lecithin, 5 moles of cholesterol, and 60 moles of bile salts. In humans bladder bile, 1 mole of bilirubin was found to be bound to 10 moles of lecithin, 3 moles of cholesterol, and 40 moles of bile salts (see Fig. 54). In liver insufficiency these complexes were found to contain only 2–3 moles of lecithin, 1–2 moles of cholesterol, and 18–22 moles of bile salt for every mole of bilirubin. These interesting findings deserve further study.

Polonovski and Bourrillon (1952a) and Bourrillon (1952) studied the gallbladder bile of humans, cattle, and pigs. They found a major maximum at 420 nm and a secondary one at 450 nm, whereas human liver bile showed the strongest maximum at 450 nm. However, liver bile of dogs showed equally strong maxima at 420 and 450 nm. When the bile was stored for several hours, the maximum shifted from 450 to 420 nm. Absorption spectra indicated that this was not due to biliverdin formation. This displacement was accelerated by boiling the bile in alcoholic solutions. Shifting occurred immediately when NaOH was added. The change is not due to fermentation, since enzyme inhibitors do not prevent it. It was concluded that biliary bilirubin is not present as a bilirubinate, but rather in two different modifications: a stable form with a maximum at 420 nm, and a labile form having a maximum at 450 nm. When excess ethanol or methanol was added to the bile, a precipitation occurred; the precipitate, when redissolved in water, showed a maximum at 420 nm. When bile was subjected to chromatography on aluminum oxide columns and developed with $CHCl_3$, practically the total pigment content remained on the top of the column; only a light yellow front migrated, which represented bilirubin. The zone which remained on the top of the column could be eluted with alkali or pyridine. Diazotized bile behaved similarly in this respect. Only a small portion of the pigment passed the membrane during dialysis, whereas the larger part remained in the dialyzing tube. Bourrillon assumed that billiary bilirubin is bound to bile acids and therefore called it "cholebilirubin." However, no defined compound could be identified. Verschure and Hoefsmit (1956), who used paper chromatography, were unable to demonstrate binding of biliary bilirubin to bile acids.

The predominant part of biliary bilirubin shows direct diazo reaction; however, a certain portion reacts indirectly (Gastaldo and Testoni, 1947a). According to Billing (1955b), over 80% of the pigment of human bile is present as bilirubin diglucuronide. One part of the pigment can be extracted with $CHCl_3$, but there is no parallelism between this fraction and the indirect reaction form. With decreasing pH, the $CHCl_3$-extractable fraction increases (Gastaldo and Testoni, 1947a; Salvini and Feruglio, 1949). The presence of significant amounts of indirect bilirubin was demonstrated, as was the direct form by column chromatography and paper chromatography (Yamaoka et al., 1956b; Sakamoto, 1956a,b; Sato, 1955 a,b). Vest (1959, p. 51) found small amounts of pigment A but domination of pigment B on paper chromatography of the azobilirubin of biliary bilirubin from newborn infants. Yamamoto (1951) also found "indirect" ($CHCl_3$-soluble) in addition to "direct" (water-soluble) biliverdin by paper chromatography.

Besides bilirubin, biliverdin, and small amounts of urobilinoids, Garner (1954) found a biliviolinoid pigment in the bile. This pigment was detected in the ethyl acetate extract of acidified fresh ox bile; it behaved like a violin and not like a rubin. Garner viewed this compound as another bile pigment present besides bilirubin and biliverdin. A. Beck (1895) could also detect violinoid pigments in the bile of dogs, and Fischer *et al.* (1925) demonstrated their presence in gallstones.

In mammals, practically all bile bilirubin is present as conjugates. This is not the case in all vertebrates, as Arias (1963b) found that 5–15% of the bilirubin of dogfish bile is unconjugated. The conjugation state of bile pigments in other lower vertebrates is unknown.

Yahata (1959) studied the pigments of dog bile by means of ion exchange chromatography with various Amberlite resins. On IRA-400 all types of bilirubin were bound from aqueous solutions while only indirect and salt-form bilirubins were fixed on IRC-50 and IRC-20. On IR-4B only indirect bilirubin was bound, while both salt and ester bilirubin passed. The ester form was isolated by passage through IRC-50. Solutions having passed columns of IR-4B before the run through IRC-50 contained ester bilirubin free from bile salts. Pure salt from bilirubin could be eluted from the same IRC-50 column with $2 N$ NaCI and ethanol. The fractions were subjected to paper chromatography, and no glucuronic acid was demonstrated in any of them. The azo pigments of the various bilirubin fractions from dog bile were subjected to paper chromatography and the absorption maxima of the isolated pigments determined. They were 540–550 nm for indirect bilirubin, 550 nm for salt-form bilirubin, and 540–550 for ester-type bilirubin. After addition of concentrated HCl, the maxima changed to 580, 555, and 550–555 nm, respectively.

Cornelius *et al.* (1960a,b) studied the azo pigments of biliary bilirubin in the horse, ox, pig, sheep, and cat. In the sheep and the pig, unconjugated bilirubin was present in the bladder bile, but not in the liver bile. The azo pigments of the biliary bilirubin showed the same behavior in all four species.

Schoenfield *et al.* (1962, Table I) subjected rat bile to reverse phase partition chromatography and found that 10–20% of the bilirubin present was pigment I (monoglucuronide) and the remaining 80–90% pigment II (diglucuronide).

A method of quantitative fractionation of normal human bladder bile —obtained during operations on subjects with normal bile passages— was described by Sato and Saitoh (1965*). They added 5 volumes of 98% ethanol and 1–3 volumes of saturated ammonium sulfate to 1 volume of bile and allowed the mixture to stand for a while before centrifugation.

The supernatant contained all the bile pigments except protein-bound ones which are minimal on most occasions. In normal bile a small amount of pigment was bound to the precipitate. It was soluble in water, but not in organic solvents, and gave a direct diazo reaction.

A small sample of the supernatant was mixed with methanol and used for quantitative estimation of total bile pigments (diazo reaction). The remaining portion of the supernatant was dried by freezing *in vacuo* with acetone-dry ice. The resulting desiccated material was immediately suspended in $CHCl_3$, taking precautions to prevent contact with air, transferred to a G 4 glass filter, and extracted repeatedly with anhydrous $CHCl_3$ until the filtrate became colorless. The $CHCl_3$ extracts were pooled and their bile pigment content measured. The residue after the extraction was soluble in water, but insoluble in $CHCl_3$, ethyl acetate, ether, and acetone, and gave direct diazo reaction. It consisted mainly of esterified bilirubin, and it could be separated into two fractions by means of reverse phase chromatography a.m. Cole and Lathe. On paper chromatography with the solvent systems butanol/ethanol/water, 1/1/1 (v/v/v), the esterified bilirubin yielded two fractions with R_f 0.46 and 0.60.

The $CHCl_3$ extracts were frozen *in vacuo* to evaporate the $CHCl_3$ and the residue extracted with ethyl acetate. The residue from the ethyl acetate extraction was $CHCl_3$-soluble. The recovery rate of the $CHCl_3$ extraction was controlled with suspensions of free bilirubin in water; percentage values of 90.4–95.4 were found in four experiments. The $CHCl_3$ extract fraction from bile differed from free bilirubin in several respects. Thus its direct diazo reaction was positive. Paper chromatographic fractionation suggested that the bilirubin of this fraction was conjugated with phospholipids or bile acids, while the presence of bilirubin glucuronides was not disclosed. Further, this fraction gave no liberation of glucuronic acid on treatment with β-glucuronidase. Paper chromatography was carried out with $CHCl_3$ and the solvent systems propanol/water, 1/1 (v/v) and butanol/ethanol/water, 1/1/1 (v/v/v).

The ethyl acetate extract was soluble in ethanol, ether, acetone, and $CHCl_3$, but insoluble in water. Paper chromatographic studies suggested the presence of phospholipids or bile acids. The diazo reaction was indirect. It is noteworthy that a considerable part of the "direct" bilirubin from bile was $CHCl_3$-extractable, a feature usually regarded as characteristic of unconjugated bilirubin. Association with phospholipids or bile acids is presumably the explanation.

The state of biliverdin in bile was studied by Noir *et al.* (1965*) on fresh human liver bile collected through a T-tube and on human gall-bladder bile obtained *post mortem*. The pigment was extracted with ethanol and the extract evaporated to dryness *in vacuo* at 50°C and subsequently subjected to reverse phase chromatography on silicone-treated kieselguhr employing the solvent system ethyl acetate/0.2 M phosphate buffer, pH 5/water, 4/1/5 (v/v/v). Further purification of the biliverdin fractions was achieved by means of ascending paper chromatography on Whatman No. 3 paper carried out overnight (14–16 hours) with the solvent system butanol/ethanol/water, 3/1/1.5 (v/v/v). Purified preparations of conjugated biliverdin were prepared by oxidation of crude preparations of conjugated bilirubin with iodine and subsequent purification by reverse phase chromatography and paper chromatography. The biliverdins were identified by (1) their green-blue color, (2) by development of red fluorescence on UV irradiation by spraying dried chromatograms with 5% Zn-acetate in methanol followed immediately by 0.006% iodine in methanol—the sensitivity of this method is great enough to detect less than 1 μg of biliverdin—and (3) by the spectral maxima of their solutions in methanol and water and the ratio of the extinctions at these maxima.

In this way two components were separated from green *post mortem* bile, apparently being biliverdin mono- and diglucuronide. They are presumably formed from the corresponding bilirubin conjugates present in liver bile by oxidation. The evidence for the existence of biliverdin monoglucuronide is based solely on the molar ratio. This pigment may equally well consist of a complex of free biliverdin and its diglucuronide.

The three bilirubin fractions and the three biliverdin fractions (free, mono-, and diconjugates) were separated by paper chromatography. The chromatographic behavior of the biliverdin fractions formed on oxidation of the corresponding bilirubin fractions was indistinguishable from that of the green pigments in native bile.

The occurrence of unconjugated bile pigments in bile was reported by Tenhunen (1965a*,b*) who found considerable amounts of unconjugated bilirubin and biliverdin in bladder bile of developing chick embryos and chicks, a finding explained by a considerable β-glucuronidase activity in their bile with a peak at the time of hatching and a slight decrease after hatching. In human bile the β-glucuronidase activity is much lower according to Maki *et al.* (1962*). Unconjugated bile pigments may be found in bile because they are excreted as such or because they are excreted as conjugates which are subsequently split by enzymes in the bile. Arias (1963b) found that 5–15% of the bile bilirubin of dogfish bile is unconjugated. Before observations of free bilirubin and biliverdin are interpreted as primary, it is necessary to study the β-glucuronidase activity of the bile in the species in question.

Garay *et al.* (1965*) studied the bile of humans, rabbits, chickens, turkeys, snakes, and toads using the methods of Noir *et al.* (1965*) and found that the bile of turkeys, toads, and most snakes contained biliverdin that behaved chromatographically like a bile acid complex of the sodium salt of biliverdin, whereas the bile of humans and rabbits contained biliverdin mono- and diglucuronides. Most biles contained some unconjugated biliverdin, presumably formed from its conjugates on hydrolysis.

The high concentration of bile pigments in bile, especially in bladder bile, often results in formation of *pigmented concrements* containing bilirubin in high concentration. This bilirubin is present as insoluble salts of unconjugated bilirubin with some inorganic base, although practically all bile bilirubin is present as conjugates. Bilirubin can be freed from such concrements by dilute strong acids (Sato, 1962).

Maki *et al.* (1962*, 1964*) studied the β-glucuronidase content of human bile and its role in the formation of pigmented calcium stones. They suggested that these stones are formed as follows. First, bilirubin glucuronides are hydrolyzed by β-glucuronidase of bacterial origin in the bile. Then calcium and free bilirubin combines to form the insoluble Ca-bilirubinate. However, other labile forms of bilirubin with free carboxyl groups may participate in the formation of these stones.

Pearson and Watson (1963*) were unable to detect mesobilirubin or mesobiliverdin in 6 samples of human liver bile and 3 samples of human bladder bile.

B. Bilirubin and Biliverdin in Bile

1. ANALYTICAL PROCEDURES

The determination of biliary bile pigments is difficult, because of the simultaneous presence of bilirubin and biliverdin. The bile is mostly yellow in humans as well as in carnivorous and omnivorous mammals, whereas it is described as green in herbivorous mammals. The bile of amphibia is green (see below). Earlier investigators (cf. Létienne, 1891) generally reported that the gallbladder bile of executed persons is always yellow or brown but never green. The green bile often found at autopsy is due to pathological conditions or cadaverosis (Létienne, 1891, pp. 22–23 and 111–112). Garner (1955) critically reexamined the claims made by Kämmerer and Miller (1923) as well as those by C. R. Schmidt *et al.* (1936), according to whom carnivorous animals have yellow biles and herbivorous animals have green ones. He found that whereas the bile of herbivorous animals was described as green by some authors (Colin, 1873; Ramsay, 1946), others reported green, brown (Ellenberger and Scheunert, 1925; Dukes, 1934; Marshall and Halman, 1945), or yellow biles (Lemberg and Legge, 1949). Garner found considerable amounts of bilirubin in fresh ox bile. He prepared this compound either by extraction with petroleum ether or by precipitation with barium hydroxide from acidified bile. In any case, chromatography on alumina columns followed these steps. Biliverdin was obtained from ox bile by the addition of equal amounts of ethanol or by extraction with acetic acid–ether or ethyl acetate. Besides biliverdin, other green oxidation products of bilirubin were also present.

Biliary bilirubin is extremely sensitive to oxidation, so that its analysis is difficult. Barry and Levine (1924) pointed out the oxidation sensitivity of biliary bile pigments. They attributed this partly to the alkalinity of bile and partly to fermentation processes. For the study of earlier methods of biliary pigment determinations, the reader is referred to the survey by With (1954, p. 310–312). Some of the newer methods are discussed below. Kerppola and Leikola (1932) diluted the bile with water and subjected it to Hijmans van den Bergh's serum analysis. This caused no precipitation with diluted bile. Furthermore, they found that biliary bilirubin can be quantitatively extracted with $CHCl_3$ when it is acidified with an equal amount of 10% acetic acid. However, a large part of the pigment accumulated in the thin interface between $CHCl_3$ and water. Held (1933b, p. 740) and Gebhardt (1939a, p. 217) used Heilmeyer and Krebs' serum method for the diluted bile. Peterman and Cooley (1933b) oxidized with hydrogen peroxide in alcohol and determined the concentration after 30 minutes. Varela et al. (1934) extracted the diluted bile with acetone after addition of saturated ammonium sulfate solution, carried out the diazo reaction in this acetone extract, and determined the color colorimetrically. C. R. Schmidt et al. (1936) diluted with alcohol containing acetic acid, added 2% ammonium persulfate solution, and measured the concentration colorimetrically after 16–24 hours. They reported that added bilirubin could be recovered with ±2% error. They found about 100% higher values with this method than with the diazo method of Hijmans van den Bergh.

Malloy and Evelyn (1938) diluted with hydrogen peroxide containing alcohol and HCl, filtered after 1 hour, and determined the color in a photoelectric colorimeter at 660 nm. In this way bilirubin and biliverdin are determined together as biliverdin. Added bilirubin was recovered with ±2% error. Barac (1939) prevented oxidation by adding ascorbic acid, diluted with 0.01 N NaOH and measured the yellow color in a Pulfrich photometer (Filter S 43). Josephson and Larsson (1941) determined the extinction of diluted bile in a Pulfrich photometer with filter S 57; this filter, however, is not useful for bilirubin and biliverdin determinations, since the absorption maximum of bilirubin is 420–460 nm and that of biliverdin is around 660 nm.

Amada (1941) added 2 ml of 0.23% $NaNO_2$ solution and 2 ml glacial acetic acid to 1 ml of diluted bile and measured the blue color either in a Pulfrich photometer using filter S 61, or colorimetrically using a copper sulfate solution for standard. This oxidation method yields biliverdin as well as bilirubin, and was supplemented by separate bilirubin determination with the diazo reaction. It was found that biliary bilirubin is much more sensitive to an excess of diazo reagent than bilirubin in pure solution, and that the color is rather labile. However, this situation could be improved by adding alcohol or acetone before the diazo reagent. About 93–99% of added bilirubin was recovered.

With (1945d), using Jendrassik and Gróf's serum method, was able to recover 99.5% bilirubin in diluted bile. With (1954, p. 312) attempted to carry out determinations with the diazo reaction in neutral or acid solution in addition to the alkali method of Jendrassik and Gróf (see With, 1945d). However, he found differences up to 20% between these three processes. The explanation is the sensitivity of biliary bilirubin against an excess of diazo reagent. Since With quantitatively recovered the added bilirubin by the alkali technique, this test should be preferred.

Spiegelhoff and Gnann (1950) diluted the bile with a mixture consisting of one volume 10 N sulfuric acid and six volumes 96% alcohol. The ratio of bile to diluent was 1 to 20. The final solution was heated to 50° for 10 minutes on a water bath, and the green color obtained was colorimetrically measured in a Pulfrich photometer (filter S 61), or in a photoelectric colorimeter at 620 nm. The compound obtained had a flat maximum at 690 nm and a minimum at 500 nm, i.e., it differed from biliverdin. The authors assumed that a sulfur compound was involved. The spectrophotometric methods of Zak *et al.* (1954) have not been employed for bile.

Royer and Garay (1960) determined biliverdin by direct spectrophotometric reading at 660 nm and bilirubin by the diazo method of Jendrassik and Gróf, as well as bilirubin plus biliverdin by the oxidation method of Peterman and Cooley. They constructed spectral curves in a number of different human biles using purified biliverdin as standard. As a rule, they found good agreement between separate determinations of bilirubin and biliverdin and determinations with the oxidation method of the two pigments together. Added biliverdin was recovered with a percentage of 94–108.

Garay and Argerich (1963) described a method for determination of biliverdin in bile based on the formation of Zn–bilipurpurin and fluorometric measurement of this compound. Recovery of 85% of added biliverdin is claimed, and the addition of urobilinoids, mesobiliviolin, and bilirubin gave no false positive results.

Summary

Bilirubin is the bile pigment occurring in the normal fresh bile of humans, and carnivorous and omnivorous mammals. Biliverdin may predominate in the bile or herbivorous mammals, but considerable quantities of bilirubin are always found in the fresh bile of these animals. Bile pigments can be determined with the diazo reaction in red or yellow biles. However, in green bile the total bile pigment (biliverdin + bilirubin) is determined by oxidation methods, and the bilirubin is subsequently measured by the diazo method. The difference gives the amount of pigment which is not bilirubin. Even if biliverdin represents the major part of nonbilirubin pigments, other pigments (e.g., biliviolins) and various oxidation products can be present. Malloy and Evelyn (1938) and Amada (1941) described the most useful oxidation methods. The most useful diazo method is that of Jendrassik and Gróf. Determinations of the yellow color (icterus index, spectrophotometry) yielded useful results in bile free from biliverdin. Spiegelhoff and Gnann's (1950) sulfuric acid method and Garay and Argerich's (1963) Zn-bilipurpurin method are interesting and deserve further study.

2. Bilirubin and Biliverdin of Human Bile

Numerous authors studied the occurrence of bilirubin and biliverdin in human bile. For a discussion of the early literature the reader is referred to the monograph of With (1954, p. 313). Lepehne (1921d) reported pigment contents of 50–970 mg/100 ml in 25 gallbladder biles obtained by autopsy. He considered values around 50–125 mg/100 ml as normal. Concentrations of 130–540 mg/100 ml were determined in three persons deceased from pernicious anemia, and 2–13 mg/100 ml were found in three newborns. The concentrations present in the duodenal fluid were only about one-third of these values. When the fluid was obtained from normal subjects by duodenal tube but without stimulation (so-called "A bile"), it contained 1.5–4.5 mg/100 ml. After stimulation with magnesium sulfate ("B bile"), various concentrations were obtained; these were sometimes close to that of A bile, but sometimes they approached the amounts found in autopsy gallbladder bile. During acute hepatitis at the height of the jaundice the levels were very low (0.5–1 mg/100 ml in A bile). Three normal and six increased levels (8–24 mg/100 ml in A bile) were found in nine active pernicious anemia cases examined. In a patient with hereditary hemolytic jaundice, 15 mg/100 ml was found in the A bile, and 3.2 mg/100 ml was detected in an infant with icterus neonatorum.

Hetényi (1922) reported 7–16 mg/100 ml in the duodenal fluid (A bile), and considered values below 6 mg and above 20 mg/100 ml pathological. Diminished concentrations occurred in liver carcinoma, but increased values were observed in polycythemia. By means of Hijmans van den Bergh's method, Strisower (1922) found dilution values of from 1–1500 to 1–10,000 in human fistula bile, and 1–10,000 to 1–30,000 in normal duodenal fluid (A bile). Regularly increased values were found in hemolytic conditions, whereas diminished concentrations were detected during obstructive jaundice and parenchymal liver damage. There was only one exception: as a rule, higher values were found in regressing hepatitis. Sonnenfeld (1923, 1924) examined 15 patients with pernicious anemia and found bilirubin concentrations of 1–28,000 to 1–550 in the A bile. As a rule, the values were increased when the serum bilirubin was high and the hemoglobin was low, but no closer correlation could be found. In addition to these investigations, Felsenreich and Satke (1924), Hoesch (1926), Lepehne (1932), Eppinger and Walzel (1926), and Polack (1930) reported numerous studies which were performed with rather primitive analytical techniques.

Royer (1939; 1943, pp. 169, 174–184) found 1.25–30.0 mg/100 ml in A bile from 25 normal persons, 1.0–37.5 mg/100 ml in gallbladder diseases (70 cases), and 0.8–10.0 mg/100 ml in 4 patients with hepatic jaundice. Franke and Banda (1941) found 3.4–16.6 mg/100 ml in normal duodenal fluid (A bile) and 5.0–164 mg/100 ml after stimulation (B bile). Differences of diagnostic value between normal persons and patients with bile diseases were not observed.

With (1945d) examined the fistula bile of 35 cholecystectomized patients. The bile was obtained by drainage over a period of 6–12 days after surgery. The daily rate of bilirubin excretion was significantly higher during the first days after the operation than during later periods. About 7 days after the operation a reasonably steady excretion level was reached. McMaster *et al.* (1923a,b) obtained similar results in dogs. With differentiates between the initial excretion level and the final excretion level; the former was 50–900 (usually 200–400) mg/24 hours, and the latter 50–400 (generally 50–250) mg/24 hours. These varying excretion levels can possibly be explained by an enterohepatic circulation of bilirubinoids, which is active during the initial period but is suppressed later on, due to the bile fistula; but the veracity of this explanation has not been proved. Daily variations of bilirubin excretion were irregular and often considerable; nevertheless, the values fluctuated around a certain level in each patient (e.g., 100 mg/24 hours). It was found that the bilirubin concentration could vary between 10 and 827 mg/100 ml; however, in most cases concentrations of 20–200 mg/100 ml were found during the first 7 days, and 20–100 mg/100 ml from the twelfth day. The excretion calculated for the body weight was 0.84–6.67 mg/24 hours/kg.

Schalm *et al.* (1962a) determined the bile bilirubin in 3 patients with drainage of the bile passages before and after i.v. loading with 100 mg unconjugated bilirubin. During the first half hour after the injection the bile bilirubin increased threefold and during the next half hour sevenfold. Reverse phase chromatography with the technique of P. G. Cole and Lathe (1953) was carried out. The biliary bilirubin began to increase 1½ hour after the injection—shortly after the serum bilirubin had topped and begun to decrease. Although unconjugated bilirubin was injected and the bile flow was free, considerable quantities of conjugated bilirubin appeared in the serum. Thus, about 50% of the serum bilirubin was conjugated 3 hours after the injection, containing ca. 25% of pigment I and ca. 25% of pigment II in one of the three patients.

Wiechel (1963) determined the bilirubin concentration of the bile with the Jendrassik-Gróf technique in 37 surgical patients with jaundice in whom bile was obtained by percutaneous transhepatic cholangiography. In 7 patients with free bile passages, the bile bilirubin was 24–112 (mean 58.3) mg/100 ml, in 12 with gallstones in the bile ducts it was 0–155 (46.6), in 7 with benign obstructions of the bile ducts it was 0–35 (12.5), and in 14 with neoplastic obstructions it was 0–67.5 (mean 13.6) mg/100 ml. Thus a permanent obstruction was associated with a significantly lower bile bilirubin than an intermittent one. After operative removal of the obstruction the bile bilirubin increased rapidly and reached a maximum, as a rule of 200–300 mg/100 ml during the first to third day, after which it fell again to a lower level, as a rule, 20–50 mg/100 ml, which remained rather constant during the fourth to thirtieth day after the operation. Wiechel emphasized the considerable individual variations in the bilirubin concentration of the liver bile.

McMaster *et al.* (1923b) stated that a rapid decrease of bile volume and bile pigment concentration occurred during partial bile duct ligature. The decrease changed abruptly and the volume and concentration started to increase when the obstruction was removed.

Cheadle (1903) and Quioc (1909) concluded from stool analyses that infants often have very low biliary pigment content. Gillman and Gillman (1951, p. 198) observed the same thing in severely undernourished children.

Nissen (1957) found 20–60 mg bilirubin/100 ml in duodenal juice (A bile) and 180–600 mg/100 ml after stimulation (B bile). Concentrated B bile was often encountered in cholecystectomized patients for which high bilirubin concentrations in bile cannot be reliable evidence of

this bile being bladder bile. Royer and Garay (1960) found values between 2.3 and 20 mg/100 ml in A bile and 70–200 mg/100 ml in B bile.

Thureborn (1962, Table 9, p. 40, and Figs. 17 and 18) studied the
bilirubin of fistula bile from four women with drainage of the bile
passages after operations for uncomplicated cholelithiasis. He used the
Jendrassik-Gróf method in his analyses. The bilirubin concentration of
the fistula bile varied from 20 to 70 mg/100 ml, but the total output of
bilirubin was more constant: 5–10 mg/hour or about 200 mg/24 hours.
Interruption of the enterohepatic circulation by means of the bile drain
resulted in a rise in the bilirubin concentration to about twice the former
value after 3 hours, but simultaneously the bile output was slightly
decreased.

Mendioroz (1963a,b,c; personal communication, 1962) compared the
content of human bile of bilirubin, bile salts, cholesterol, and alkaline
phosphatase. She studied 159 samples obtained by duodenal drainage
from normal and jaundiced humans. A, B, and C biles were studied (cf.
below). The concentrations of the substances were calculated in moles
per liter. Biles with bilirubin below 45 mg/100 ml contained 3 moles of
cholesterol and about 45 moles of bile salts per mole of bilirubin. In more
concentrated biles there were 2 moles of cholesterol and 30 moles of bile
salts for every mole of bilirubin. The cholesterol/bile salt molar ratio was
about 1/14, independent of the concentration of the bile. The lecithin
concentration was also determined, and showed similar characteristic
molar ratios (cf. Section A, this chapter). Studies on biles from patients
with liver diseases showed that the number of moles of the other substances per mole of bilirubin was significantly lower than in normal biles.

Mendioroz believed that these molar ratios are due to formation of
bilirubin–cholesterol–bile salt–lecithin complexes and that bilirubin
plays an important role in these macromolecular complexes by functioning
as a protecting substance against the lytic action of the bile salts.
Although these studies are based solely on quantitative analyses expressed
as molar concentrations, the suggestions put forward are interesting and
deserve further study by means of more direct attempts to investigate and
isolate the macromolecular complexes of biliary bilirubin (cf. Fig. 54).

In inborn errors of metabolism where the conjugation of the liver is
involved, the bile may be very low in bilirubin. This is most pronounced
in Crigler-Najjar's syndrome in man and in Gunn rats. In the former
condition the bilirubin content of the bladder bile may be as low as 10
mg/100 ml (Szabó *et al.*, 1962).

The question of the occurrence of mesobilirubin in human bile is
discussed by Pearson and C. J. Watson (1963). They were unable to

detect mesobilirubin with sensitive chromatographic methods, although they succeeded in identifying it in a urine containing large amounts of bilirubin.

Summary

Human fistula bile and the duodenal fluid, the so-called A bile, as a rule contain, 20–200 mg bilirubin/100 ml, while the gallbladder bile (which is obtained either by autopsy or by duodenal tube after stimulation; so-called B bile) contains considerably more bilirubin (up to 1 g/100 ml). Concentrated B bile can, however, occur despite absence of the gallbladder. Examination of cholecystectomized patients by gallbladder drainage revealed that the average bilirubin excretion is usually 50–250 mg/24 hours. Hemolytic diseases showed increased biliary bilirubin levels, and an increase of the daily amount excreted was also observed. Bile pigment excretion seems to be very irregular in children; it is probably completely suppressed during severe infectious diseases and nutritional deficiencies. Observations pertaining to the bile pigments of bile are still incomplete, and further studies including periodic fluctuation in healthy humans and under pathological conditions would be desirable.

3. BILIRUBIN AND BILIVERDIN OF ANIMAL BILE

Aside from common experimental animals (dogs, rabbits, rats), investigations in animals are rare. Quantitative investigations which avoid the disturbing side effects of a biliary fistula (e.g., loss of fluids, of minerals and alkali, risk of infection, and nutritional deficiency) have rarely been carried out with reliable analytical techniques. Rous and McMaster (1923), McMaster and Elman (1925a), and Adler and Brehme (1925) developed methods which permit the total, partial, continuous, or intermittent collection of bile under sterile conditions. Later, J. E. Thomas (1941) was able to keep dogs alive for years with duodenal fistula and complete loss of bile by maintaining normal nutritional conditions and normal liver function (see Hart and Thomas, 1945; W. J. Snape *et al.*, 1947). A peculiar form of biliary fistula is the biliary–renal fistula described by Kapsinow *et al.* (1924). This fistula forces the bile to mix with the urine (see Sribhishaj *et al.*, 1931; Hawkins and Johnson, 1939). F. A. Harrison (1962) described a device for continuous observation of the bile in sheep under physiological conditions, and a method for chronic bile duct cannulation in the dogs for up to 6 months without disturbance of normal physiological conditions was described by Marshall *et al.* (1964*).

The more significant publications concerning bile pigments of animal bile are compiled here. Tiedemann and Gmelin (1826, pp. 80–81) found a positive Gmelin reaction in all animal species studied, including mammals, birds, reptiles, amphibia, and fish. Vossius (1879) found that a 25-kg dog with bile fistula excreted 48.7–67.9 mg (average 56 mg) bile pigment in 24 hours. According to Stadelmann (1891), maximal excretion of bilirubin is 7 mg/kg body weight/24 hours in dogs. In the bile of cattle, Jolles (1894) found 24–27 mg bilirubin/100 ml, and 21–206 mg/100 ml in pig bile. Bierthen (1906) examined the bile of 32 healthy horses post mortem, but he could only collect 4–5 drops of brown or yellow bile in each of the animals. This bile showed a negative Gmelin reaction and a negative diazo reaction. The bile of cattle gave positive reactions in both tests.

Brugsch and Retzlaff (1912) found 20–30 mg bilirubin/100 ml/24 hours in dogs with bile fistula during the first days after it was established. Rosenthal and Melchior (1922) observed green and clear bile in pigeons. Beijers (1923) found bilirubin present in the bile of 20 horses, but mentioned that the amount of bile available was always very small. He could not find bile pigments in newborns and fetal calves. Cattle, sheep, and goats had green bile; when the animals were grazing the absorption spectrum of the bile changed because of the large amounts of chlorophyll derivates ingested (phylloerythrins). These compounds were not detected in horse bile.

Nishimaru (1931) found that the bile of bull frogs is greenish-blue, but he did not perform any quantitative determinations. Held (1933a,b) and Gebhardt (1939a,b) found 7.4–8.4 mg bilirubin/kg body weight/24 hours in dogs with bile fistulas. Lemberg (1935) showed that the bile of frogs contains pure biliverdin without any degradation products; Cabello Ruz (1943b) confirmed this finding in studies of toad bile. C. E. Cornelius (personal communication, 1961) found 4.2 and 30.5 mg bilirubin in the bile of 2 horses.

Hanzon (1952) examined biliary bilirubin before and after intravenous injections of this compound in rats. The normal liver bile contained about 8 mg bilirubin/100 ml. Other investigators found about 4 mg/100 ml under the same conditions. Unanesthetized rats showed concentrations of 24 mg/100 ml. He loaded the animals with 0.5–10 mg bilirubin/100 g body weight and followed the biliary bilirubin for 3 hours. Immediately after injection an increase was noticeable, which reached its maximum 10–15 minutes after injection. The maximum level was about 500 mg/100 ml after injections of 0.5 mg/100 g; after administering 2–10 mg/100 g body weight, concentrations around 1500 mg/100 ml were reached. After reaching the maximum, the biliary bilirubin started to drop. A very sharp decrease occurred during the first 20–40 minutes, which was followed by a flatter curve. The smaller the injected amounts, the faster normal values were attained. Hanzon also reported bilirubin excretion experiments in which compounds which compete with bilirubin excretion (e.g., cholates and uranin), were also administered besides intravenous injection of bilirubin.

O'Donnel et al. (1961) investigated the bilirubin clearance of isolated perfused rat liver on 37 specimens. Bilirubin was determined in the bile and perfusion fluid for 1 hour after the infusion of a known amount of bilirubin in the course of 1 minute. The livers were weighed after the experiment. The maximum clearance of the normal rat liver was found to be 0.21 g bilirubin.

Royer et al. (1962) studied the biliary elimination of bilirubin and biliverdin in 40 rats with cannulated common bile duct. In the 20 rats, 2 mg of biliverdin was injected intraperitoneally while the remaining 20 served as controls. Biliverdin and bilirubin were determined separately in the bile during the 7 hours following the injection. In the control rats the bile contained 2.0–2.7 mg bilirubin/100 ml and 7.5–8.9 mg biliverdin/100 ml during the first 3 hours, while the figures rose to 3.3–4.6 and 9.4–11.4, respectively, during the fourth to seventh hour. In the rats injected with biliverdin, the figures were 2.6–7.3 mg bilirubin 100 ml and 4.9–7.3 mg biliverdin/100 ml during the first 2 hours. From the third hour, the biliverdin increased to 19.5–26.6 mg/100 ml, while bilirubin increased to 9.5–13.4 mg/100 ml from the fourth hour. It was calculated that 50% of the injected pigment was excreted with the bile in the course of 5 hours, and that about 30% appeared as biliverdin and about 20% as bilirubin.

Cantarow et al. (1948a,b) investigated biliary bilirubin excretion after intravenous hemoglobin and bilirubin injections in dogs. They compared bilirubin excretion with the excretion of bromsulphalein, and found 12–161 mg bilirubin/100 ml bile, which corresponds to 0.019–0.289 mg/kg body weight/24 hours. Daily fluctuations were considerable, e.g., 23–153 mg/100 ml. Polonovski and Bourrillon (1952a) found 42–55 mg bilirubin/100 ml in the liver bile of dogs, whereas the gallbladder bile contained 92–170 mg/100 ml. Corresponding values in six pigs were 36–62 mg/100 ml. Yamaoka et al. (1952a) studied the ratio of biliverdin to bilirubin in rabbit bile, and found it to be 2 to 1 in normal animals.

Garner (1955) found that bilirubin is the predominant pigment in fresh ox bile and that the occurrence of biliverdin varies. Addition of HCl to green ox bile intensifies the green color because the color of biliverdin hydrochloride is deeper than that of free biliverdin. Garner assumed that biliverdin is normally present in the winter bile, whereas it is absent in the summer bile; if it should be present it is formed from bilirubin. He does not mention anything about phylloerythrins occurring in the summer bile (cf. above, Beijers).

Already during *intrauterine life* the bile is rich in bilirubin. Thus Lester *et al.* (1963*) found values as high as 50 mg/100 ml in the bile of fetal rhesus monkeys just before term. Also in the chick embryo high bilirubin concentrations are found in the bile (Tenhunen, 1965a*,b*).

Garay *et al.* (1965*) studied the nature of the green pigments of the bile in 22 chickens, 8 turkeys, 12 toads, and 10 snakes of three different species by means of reverse phase partition chromatography, paper chromatography, and comparison with synthetic biliverdin derivatives. In toad bile free biliverdin and its sodium salt were found besides biliverdin-bile acid complexes, but in the other biles the green pigments all behaved like bile acid complexes of sodium biliverdinate. In green human biles, rabbit bile, and the bile of certain species of snake the dominant green pigments were biliverdin glucuronides.

In important studies on bile fistula rats using dual labeling technique and tritiated bile pigments Lester and Klein (1966*) compared the excretion rate of intravenously injected unconjugated bilirubin, bilirubin glucuronide, and urobilinogen-I and found that unconjugated bilirubin was excreted at lower rates than the other two compounds.

Garay *et al.* (1966a*,b*) found that the bile of Gunn rats contains about one-sixth as much bilirubin as the bile of normal rats.

The bile of *wild animals* has only exceptionally been investigated. Barac (1963) studied the bladder bile in four sloths and found 20–45 mg biliverdin/100 ml, with a typical absorption maximum and no bilirubin (negative diazo reaction). Of special interest is the observation of Arias (1963b) that 5–15% of the bilirubin of dogfish bile is unconjugated, unlike the bilirubin of mammal bile of which practically all is present in the conjugated state.

Tenhunen (1965a*,b*) found substantial amounts of unconjugated bilirubin and biliverdin in bladder bile from chick embryos and newly hatched *chicks* and ascribed this to β-glucuronidase present in their bile.

Summary

Available evidence indicates that biliverdin is the predominant bile pigment present in amphibia and birds. The theory that herbivorous mammals have green bile and carnivorous and omnivorous animals have yellow or brown bile cannot be true, because it is now known that completely fresh ox bile contains bilirubin as the principal pigment. Horses have only small amounts of bile, and excrete only small amounts of bilirubin. This is interesting since normal horse serum shows a high bilirubin content.

Substantial concentrations of bile pigments are already present in the fetus. In lower vertebrates the bile contains high amounts of unconjugated bilirubin and even in higher vertebrates this can be the case, presumably due to the presence of β-glucuronidase in the bile.

4. WHITE BILE

The so-called "white bile"—"*bile blanche*" and "*bile incolore*" of the French—occurs during complete bile duct obstruction with hydrops of the entire biliary tract, but never during hydrops of the gallbladder, when only the cystic duct is obstructed. Furthermore, white bile can occur because of certain poisonings or because of other forms of liver damage. White bile can develop very rapidly. Klose and Wachsmuth (1923, p. 17) quote a case with white bile 14 days after the first gallstone attack. Melchior (1931) observed white bile in a patient where bile was obtained on duodenal drainage 30 hours prior to surgery. Létienne (1891, pp. 17–20), who examined a case of liver damage without obstruction, mentioned that bile acids can be present in white bile. Hanot (1895) reported a similar observation. Rous and McMaster (1921b) observed accumulation of white bile in dogs, cats, and monkeys when the common bile duct and the cystic duct were ligated at the same time. When only the ductus choledochus was ligated, a concentrated, dark, and viscous bile was obtained. This difference was attributed to absorption by the gallbladder (McMaster and Rous, 1921). Rous and McMaster (1921b) established that the white bile found in the bile duct system during hydrops is mainly composed of secretion products of mucous glands situated in the walls of larger bile canals. When the common bile duct of dogs was ligated at two different places, a clear, colorless liquid accumulated between the two ligatures. In an experiment which lasted 6 days, 8.5 ml of this liquid was obtained.

According to Shafiroff *et al.*'s (1939) experiments on dogs and Edlund's (1948, p. 59) observations on rats, bile excretion stops within a few hours after complete obstruction because of the increased pressure. Only when the gallbladder absorbs the liquid from the system can the pressure remain low enough to assure continuous bile excretion. In such cases a dark, concentrated bile is accumulated in the biliary tract. If the gallbladder is missing or if it is diseased, pressure builds up in the system and bile excretion stops. However, the secretion of the mucous glands of larger bile canals continues. This results in a continuous dilution of the bile present in the biliary tract. In addition to this, the available bile pigment can also be degraded enzymatically. Thus, the liquid accumulating in the biliary tract eventually becomes colorless, and white bile appears.

Haber and Rees (1963) found that white bile was formed in rats 17–21 days after obstruction of the common bile duct. It is a clear, colorless, watery fluid of low specific gravity differing so much from normal bile that the term "white bile" is misleading. Its chemical composition is that of a product of passive filtration and diffusion through intact capillary membranes, and not that of a product of active secretion. Therefore, Haber and Rees believe that white bile can hardly be a product of the secretion of the mucous glands of the larger bile ducts. The finding that ionized I^{131} injected into the distended common bile duct appears in the circulation soon after the injection demonstrates that diffusion actually takes place between the content of the bile sac and the circulating blood. On the other hand, the studies of Edlund (1948; cf. Chapter IV,E,3) strongly suggest that the secretion of the mucous glands of the larger bile ducts play an important part in the production of "white bile." More material is required before the relative role of filtration-diffusion and active secretion in the formation of white bile can be decided.

Wiechel (1963) measured the pressure in the hepatic veins and the intrahepatic bile ducts simultaneously during percutaneous transhepatic cholangiography in 7 patients with white bile due to biliary obstruction with abolished absorptive function of the gallbladder. The pressure in the bile ducts was 230–375 (mean 273) mm H_2O, while that in the intrahepatic veins was 80–195 (119) mm H_2O. The venous pressure was on the average about 100 mm lower than the bile duct pressure. This finding does not support the hypothesis of an active role of ultrafiltration in the genesis of white bile.

Bouchier and Cooperband (1965[*]) reported on two patients; one with white bile in the gallbladder with a gallstone obstructing the infundibulum, the white bile was highly mucous; the other patient had undergone cholecystectomy and the biliary tree contained a thin, watery, translucent, colorless fluid. They concluded that white bile can be found in either the gallbladder or the bile ducts, a fact often ignored, and that its composition is far from constant—a fact illustrated by meticulous chemical analysis of the white bile in the two patients studied.

In light of recent investigations, the above theory of the formation of white bile becomes even more questionable. Barber-Riley (1963b) and Harth and Waldeck (1964)—see Chapter IV,C,5—found that bile formation continues in spite of increased pressure in the bile duct system. The fluid is removed by back-flow into the lymphatic system and into the blood. Thus the question of the formation of white bile cannot be regarded as finally solved, and reinvestigation is needed.

Various observations indicate that under certain conditions white bile can be excreted by the liver and is not necessarily a secretion product of the mucous glands of large biliary ducts. The most interesting observations are the formation of white bile in sheep after poisoning with *Lippia rehmanni* (cf. Chapter IV,C,7). In the publications of Quin (1936) and Rimington *et al.* (1937), colored illustrations of the disappearance and reappearance of the stain of the bile under these conditions are found. In addition to this, Hawthorne and Sterling (1954) reported two cases of secretion of colorless bile. In the first case the patient excreted less than 50 ml of water-like bile through a T-shaped drainage tube for 3 weeks after cholecystectomy. Postoperative conditions were normal. Thereafter the excretion of colored bile started again. Bile acids and cholesterol were absent from the colorless bile. The patient developed jaundice during the acholic period (maximum serum concentration was 20 mg/100 ml and dropped to 1 mg/100 ml). The other case involved a patient who had a gallstone operation. The patient exhibited strong jaundice for 72 hours after the operation and excreted a small amount of clear, colorless liquid through a T-drain. After 72 hours, colored bile started to appear; simultaneously, jaundice began to regress.

Kjellgren (1955a,b) studied bile production of rabbits with local abdominal hyper- or hypothermia. His experiments indicated that bile pigment formation can be reduced by liver damage. Production of bile was diminished when the liver was heated locally to 41° and the rectal temperature was kept at a normal level. The bile pigment concentration was unchanged in the bile. However, when the liver was chilled locally to 18° the amount of bile excreted was reduced to 1/10 of its original volume. Simultaneously, the bile pigment concentration decreased; however, this decrease was not as steep as the reduction of bile volume.

Sato (1955b) reported a case in which a dark but bilirubin-free bile was observed during complete bile duct obstruction and severe swelling of the gallbladder. The bile was dark brown with a greenish tinge and was highly viscous. Bile pigment reactions were negative. Paper chromatographic experiments confirmed the absence of the bile pigments usually detectable in the bile. Therefore, complete obstruction does not necessarily result in white bile formation. However, bilirubin can be converted into colored compounds, which cannot be identified as bile pigments.

Summary

White bile is formed during simultaneous closure of the common bile duct and cystic duct. It is a clear, colorless, watery fluid with low protein content. The mechanism of its formation is not quite clear, but most likely both passive processes (filtration, diffusion) and active secretion from the mucous glands of the larger bile ducts play roles. The colorless bile formed by secretion of the liver during special conditions such as icterogenin poisoning is a quite distinct phenomenon.

C. Urobilinoids of Bile

1. ANALYTICAL PROCEDURES

Urobilinoids in bile are determined by the same method as in urine, but in this case bilirubin must be removed. The earlier methods have been surveyed by With (1954, pp. 319–320). With (1945d) employed the same method for bile as that used for the analysis of urine. K.-H. Brandt (1957) employed a similar method and considered it advantageous to remove bilirubin before analysis by precipitation with $CaCl_2$ and Na_2CO_3. Without removing bilirubin he found in one specimen 2.14 mg urobilinoid/100 ml, but only 0.89 mg/100 ml after bilirubin precipitation. Garner (1955) acidified ox bile with HCl and extracted it with chloroform; finally he added a saturated alcoholic zinc acetate solution to the extract.

Bungenberg de Jong (1959) mixed 5 ml bile with 25 ml water, added 25% of 1%(w/v) solution of Mohr's salt and 25 ml of 12% NaOH, and mixed well. The bilirubin of the bile was adsorbed to colloidal ferrous hydroxide in this way, and extraction of the filtrate with acetic acid ether was performed as with urinary urobilinoid. He found identical results with extraction with ether and petrol ether; reduction times between 1 and 72 hours gave identical values.

Lozzio and Royer (1962) described a quantitative fluorescence method for the determination of biliary urobilinoids. All the urobilinoid was oxidized to urobilin by $FeCl_3$, and the fluorescence of the Zn salt was read in alcoholic solution and compared to a trypaflavine standard which was calibrated by comparison with stercobilin solutions.

K.-H. Brandt (1957) described a method for the differentiation between biliary urobilinoids-I and -L. C. J. Watson (1959) reported a method for separate urobilinoid-I, -L, and -D determination.

Summary

Urobilinoids in bile are determined after bilirubin and biliverdin have been removed by precipitation with calcium carbonate, calcium phosphate, or barium salts or by adsorption on ferrous hydroxide.

2. UROBILINOIDS OF HUMAN BILE

Human bile contains only small amounts of urobilinoids. However, the concentrations of these compounds can increase under pathological conditions. Jaffe (1869a), MacMunn (1880a,b), Tissier (1889), Gerhardt

(1889), von Müller (1892), Brand (1901, p. 82), Braunstein (1903), and Kimura (1904) demonstrated the presence of urobilinoids in human bile. Carrié (1913, p. 89) surveyed the earlier literature. Hildebrandt (1908, 1909a,b) found considerable amounts of urobilinoids in the gallbladder of a premature baby whose intestinal contents were free from urobilin. Since the mother suffered from urobilinuria, he concluded that the urobilinoids had passed the placenta. Wilbur and Addis (1914) examined the urobilinoid contents of bile from gallbladder obtained by autopsy, but free from detectable cadaverous changes. Dilution values of 0 (urobilin free bile) to 4500 were observed. No connection was found between urobilin content and the nature of the disease. A few cases with biliary fistula were also examined. In these instances, biliary urobilin increased when bile started to reach the intestines. However, no closer connection between biliary and fecal urobilinoid could be detected. In one case considerable amounts of urobilin were found in the bile, although the feces were free from urobilin (Wilbur and Addis, 1914, case 14, p. 273). Unfortunately, no clinical details were given concerning this interesting case. It is possible that urobilin was formed by bacterial action in the biliary tract.

Strisower (1922) found positive benzaldehyde tests in the duodenal fluid in hemolytic diseases and during regressing hepatitis. Oshima (1930b) could demonstrate small amounts of urobilinoid in duodenal fluid (A bile); however, considerably higher concentrations were observed after stimulation with magnesium sulfate (B bile). Weiss (1930) observed 0.8–1.5 mg/100 ml in A bile and 2.5–3.5 mg/100 ml in B bile (healthy individuals). In patients with pernicious anemia, 1.2–12.5 mg/100 ml were found in B bile, and 12–100 mg/100 ml in gallbladder bile after autopsy. Lepehne (1932, p. 1007) obtained only a weak or negative benzaldehyde reaction in the duodenal fluid, whereas it was rather strong in hemolytic conditions. He always observed a positive benzaldehyde reaction in normal B bile. In acute hepatitis this test was positive only in the regressive stages. Polack (1930) reported similar observations.

Royer (1932b, 1939; 1943, pp. 169–184) found 0.04–0.6 mg urobilinoid/100 ml in normal A bile, 0.015–0.034 mg/100 ml in patients with hepatitis, and 0.06–1.2 mg/100 ml in patients with gallbladder diseases. According to Royer, the ratio of bilirubin to urobilin is diagnostically important. Royer et al. (1933) found 0.016–1.115 mg/100 ml in A bile in 23 normal subjects; no connection was detected between urinary and biliary urobilin. The urobilin concentration in the bile was usually reduced in hepatitis, and urobilin was often completely absent.

Jankelson (1944) performed the benzaldehyde test in duodenal fluid of 56 patients. Fourteen of these patients who did not suffer from disorders of the liver or the biliary tract gave a positive benzaldehyde reaction. Furthermore, he examined the fistula bile of 13 patients whose common bile duct was drained. All exhibited a positive reaction immediately after surgery, but it disappeared within a few days. In the discussion of this publication, C. J. Watson, (1944) mentioned that rapid excretion of biliary urobilinogen-L takes place after intravenous injection of 50 mg urobilin-L; the major part of this excretion occurs within the first 15–20 minutes.

With (1945d) examined 25 cholecystectomized patients whose biliary tracts were drained. He usually observed concentrations above 1 mg/100 ml (maximum 5.3) within the first days after the operation; thereafter, the concentration rapidly decreased and in some cases urobilinoids disappeared completely within 1 week after the operation. When the tube was clamped and the bile forced to flow again into the intestines, the urobilinoids reappeared in the bile. In this case the biliary urobilinogen concentration was usually below 1% of that bilirubin. The amount of biliary urobilinoid excreted was only 0.5–4 mg/ 24 hours. This amount is significantly below the difference between the daily biliary bilirubin excretion (50–400 mg) and the daily fecal urobilin excretion (25–250 mg). Therefore, the classic theory of enterohepatic urobilin circulation can hardly be maintained (see also Chapter II,D).

K.-H. Brandt (1957, pp. 116–117 and 119–132) essentially confirmed With's findings. He examined B and C biles by the duodenal tube from 20 patients, and found concentrations of 0.1–4.5 mg/100 ml and 0.06–1.3 mg/100 ml, respectively.

Bungenberg de Jong (1959) found between 10 and 92 mg urobilinogen/100 ml in 5 gallbladder biles obtained at autopsy from patients with various diseases.

Schwartz and Watson (1942) found urobilin-D in infected human fistula bile. Sborov and Watson (1949) observed a complete disappearance of biliary urobilinoid in seven of eight cases, in which the intestinal bacterial flora was suppressed by Aureomycin. Eisenreich (1948) and Baumgärtel (1949a, 1950b) found "3-urobilin" and urobilinogen-I in the bile, but no urobilinogen-L. In an excellent study performed on clinical material, K.-H. Brandt (1957) showed that the bile does not contain urobilinogen-L and urobilinogen-I providing bile does not reach the intestines. This author substantiated his results with 32 absorption curves. In contrast to Baumgärtel's findings Brandt found urobilinogen-L in normal human bile but only traces of urobilinogen-I. However, when the liver function was impaired, urobilinogen-I in the bile increased. Thus, the presence of urobilinogen-I in the bile indicates liver damage;

however, this has only moderate significance in clinical diagnosis. According to C. J. Watson (1959), urobilinogen-L usually predominate, although urobilinogen-I can occasionally prevail. Mitsuda (1959a,b) found that urobilinogen-L dominated in the bladder bile in 20 patients with cholecystopathy. He was unable to demonstrate urobilinogen-D.

Blažek *et al.* (1964*) performed the mesobiliviolin reaction on extracts of duodenal juice (B- and C-bile) from 125 patients with gastrointestinal complaints subjected to duodenal drainage. The juice was extracted with $CHCl_3$, the extract evaporated to dryness and redissolved in ethanol on a boiling water bath. Then $FeCl_3$ in concentrated HCl was added and the mixture placed on a boiling water bath for 10 minutes. The reaction is considered positive if a violet color developed. Positive mesobiliviolin reaction, i.e., presence or urobilinoids-I, was seldom seen in subjects without liver disease and only in the B-bile. In patients with chronic liver affections (positive Takata reaction) the mesobiliviolin reaction was, on the other hand, positive in about half of the cases.

Summary

Small amounts of urobilinogen-L are present in normal human liver bile. Only traces of urobilinogen-I can be detected. The concentration is significantly higher in gallbladder bile. The concentration of biliary urobilin is usually less than 1% that of bilirubin. Increase of the biliary urobilin level is observed in hemolytic disease and in the regressing stages of acute hepatitis. However, these earlier findings have not yet been reconfirmed by modern quantitative analytical methods. When the liver function is impaired, urobilin-I appears in the bile in addition to urobilinogen-L. Urobilinogen-D can also be present in infected bile.

3. UROBILINOIDS OF ANIMAL BILE

Investigations on the biliary urobilinoid of animal biles are scarce. MacMunn (1880a,b) detected urobilin in the bile of pigs, cattle, and sheep. Auché (1908c) found very low urobilin concentrations in cattle and sheep, unlike pigs and carnivorous animals, which showed considerably higher levels. Only gallbladder bile was examined; variations in urobilin concentration were large. Steensma (1918, p. 53) found urobilinogen in the bile of rabbits, pigs, and cattle, but not in that of dogs. Kämmerer and Miller (1922a,b, 1923) claimed that carnivorous but not herbivorous mammals excrete biliary urobilinogen. This statement was based on the assumption that the bile of carnivora contains bilirubin, that of herbivora biliverdin, and that biliverdin cannot be converted into urobilinogen by bacterial reduction in the intestines. This view was supported by *in vitro* experiments, which also showed that biliverdin could be converted to urobilinogen by inoculation with feces of carnivora, but not with feces of herbivora.

Royer (1932c) found 4–50 mg urobilin/100 ml in gallbladder bile of 11 of 12 dogs. Beijers (1923, Chapter 11) found urobilin in the bile of herbivorous mammals, if it was also present in the stool. Oshima (1931a) found an average of 0.70 mg urobilinogen/100 ml (corresponding to 0.068 mg/24 hour) in fistula bile from rabbits. This is more than eigthy times the amount excreted with the urine. Urobilin excretion decreased markedly after $CHCl_3$ poisoning. Royer (1932c) observed excretion of 0.2–0.7 mg urobilin in 24 hours in the bile of dogs on the first day after a biliary fistula had been established. Garner (1957) found urobilinogen-L in gallbladder bile of oxen, whereas he could not find urobilinogen-I.

Lozzio and Royer (1965*) studied the bile of 10 dogs and 10 cats and found that urobilinoids-I made up the bulk of the urobilinoids present. In 6 of the dogs and 6 of the cats urobilinoids-L were present—in the dogs making up ca. 50% of the total urobilinoid, in the cats only 20%. In the bile of white rats and guinea pigs only urobilinoids-I were present.

Lester and Schmid (1965*) carried out i.v. tolerance tests in rats using C^{14}-UG-I and found that 85–92% of the label appeared in the bile within 4 hours.

Garay *et al.* (1966a*,b*) found that Gunn rats excrete 11 μg urobilinogen every 2 hours as against 16 μg every 2 hours in normal rats. After the establishment of bile fistula the biliary urobilinogen decreased progressively in normal rats but not in Gunn rats. On oral administration of the antibiotic neomycin the biliary urobilinogen of Gunn rats decreased greatly.

Summary

Reports on the presence of biliary urobilinoids in animals are scarce and contradictory. Existing observations involve only mammals. It was claimed that urobilinoids are only present in carnivorous mammals, and not in herbivorous ones. However, it is now known that this cannot be correct because urobilinogen-L was detected in ox bile. Further investigations are necessary in this area.

Additional Readings

Section A

Bouchier, I. A. D., and Cooperband, S. R. (1967). Isolation and characterization of a macromolecular aggregate associated with bilirubin. *Clin. Chim. Acta* **15**, 291–302.

Bouchier, I. A. D., and Cooperband, S. R. (1967). Sephadex filtration of a macro-molecular aggregate associated with bilirubin. *Clin. Chim. Acta* **15**, 303–313.

De Palma, R. G., Hubay, C. A., and Levey, S. (1966). The micellar properties of bile. *J. Am. Med. Assoc.* **195**, 943–945.

Nakayama, F., and Miyake, H. (1966). Species differences in cholesterol-complexing macromolecular fractions in bile in relation to gallstone formation. *J. Lab. Clin. Med.* **67**, 78–86.

Section B,2

Saitoh, T. (1964). "On Bilirubin in Bile." Reports on the 10th anniversary symposium on glucuronic acid, p. 87. Tokyo Biochemical Research Foundation, Tokyo.

Section B,3

Acocella, G. (1967). A symbiotic system for the study of the excretion of bile pigments in rats. *In* "Bilirubin Metabolism" (I. A. D. Bouchier and B. H. Billing, eds.), pp. 207–210. Blackwell, Oxford.

Berthelot, P. (1967). Excretion of unconjugated bilirubin in rat bile. *In* "Bilirubin Metabolism" (I. A. D. Bouchier and B. H. Billing, eds.), pp. 189–197. Blackwell, Oxford.

Hargreaves, T. (1966). Bilirubin, bromsulphthalein and indocyanine green in bile. *Quart. J. Exptl. Physiol.* **51**, 184–195.

Lester, R., and Klein, P. D. (1967). Why conjugation? Molecular structure and bilirubin glucuronide formation. *In* "Bilirubin Metabolism" (I. A. D. Bouchier and B. H. Billing, eds.), pp. 89–97. Blackwell, Oxford.

Section C,3

Lester, R., and Klein, P. D. See reference quoted above for Section B,3.

CHAPTER VIII

Bile Pigments in Feces

A. Introduction

Under normal conditions, biliary bilirubin is converted into urobilinogen in the large intestine. Thus, the small intestine contains bilirubin, whereas urobilinogen predominates in the large intestine. This was shown in impressive observations of the intestinal contents with the help of $HgCl_2$, the sublimate reaction (Schmidt, 1895; Quioc, 1909, p. 30). Similar studies with modern methods by Matsui (1959a,b,c) confirmed these early observations. Exceptions to this rule are conditions found in newborns where the bacterial flora of the intestinal tract is not capable of converting bilirubin into urobilinogen and, therefore, bilirubin and biliverdin are eliminated in the stool. If intestinal bacteria are suppressed by antibiotics, a condition very similar to that found in newborns develops.

Fecal urobilinoids are always present as chromogens. Type L predominates, but types I and D can also occur. Other bile pigments, for example mesobiliviolin, can also be present besides bilirubin, biliverdin, and urobilinoids. Görges and Gohr (1954) isolated dihydromesobilirubin in crystalline form from 2 kg stool of a patient with hemolytic jaundice. Minoru (1958a,b) isolated dihydromesobilirubin from the stool of three patients receiving oral antibiotics, and mesobilirubin from the stool of two patients receiving similar treatment. Dihydromesobilirubin is an "intermediate" between mesobilirubin and urobilinogen-I, and is formed during hydrogenation of bilirubin. Imai (1959a,b) identified mesobilirhodin and mesobiliviolin by column chromatography of fecal extracts of two patients receiving long-term oral antibiotics, and bilirubin, mesobilirubin, and dihydromesobilirubin from eight patients on such treatment. If fecal filtrates from such patients were incubated with bilirubin, mesobilirubin could be demonstrated after 12–24 hours' incubation, dihydromesobilirubin after 26 hours, and urobilinogen began to appear after 48 hours. After 72 hours only urobilinogen was found.

The dipyrranes, for example mesobilifuscin, are probably the most important coloring matters of feces, as was pointed out by C. J. Watson

(1956a,b,c). Unfortunately, these substances are very difficult to determine quantitatively. In addition, the occurrence of other compounds such as "stercorubin" and "stercofulvin" was claimed (Baar and Hickmans, 1941).

Heringová et al. (1964a*) and Jirsa et al. (1967*) isolated a urobilinoid from the feces of healthy infants 3 months of age and found it to be different from U-I, U-D, and U-L. It did not seem to be a racemate of any of the known urobilinoids either. They believed it to be a new type of urobilin not previously known.

When the intestinal content passes very rapidly through the colon, the reduction of bilirubin to urobilinogen is incomplete. Bilirubin can be detected in the feces of normal persons after severe diarrhea.

The occurrence of bilirubin, biliverdin, and urobilinoids will be discussed separately. For questions involving mesobiliviolins and fuscins, the reader is referred to Chapter I,F and G.

B. Bilirubin and Biliverdin of Feces

1. METHODS OF DETERMINATION

The determination of bilirubin and biliverdin in stool of adults is difficult because of the presence of large amounts of brown pigments. The analysis of these compounds in the feces of newborns and infants presents fewer difficulties since in this case the actual bile pigments constitute the predominant part of the fecal pigments. Results obtained with the Gmelin reaction are difficult to evaluate in stool of adults where other pigments give color reactions with oxidizing agents. But in meconium, bilirubin determination is simple with the Gmelin reaction (J. F. Simon, 1840; Zweifel, 1875).

Schmidt (1895) used concentrated $HgCl_2$ solutions for bilirubin determination. In the presence of bilirubin, a green color developed 15–20 minutes after the addition of the reagent. However, when urobilin was present, red coloration occurred; in the presence of both pigments a mixed color developed. Schorlemmer (1900) found that the test was most conveniently read 24 hours after the addition of the reagent. He also recommended microscopic observations for the detection of bile pigments which were adsorbed on smaller particles. For a thorough discussion of earlier methods, the reader is referred to With's treatise (1954, p. 325). The work of Triboulet (1909a,b), Quioc (1909), and Borrien (1911) should be mentioned here; Quioc published beautiful color pictures.

Ylppö (1913) dried the feces on a water bath, powderized the dry substance, and removed the lipids by extraction with ether for 6–8 hours.

Then the residue was extracted with 0.1 N HCl for 2 minutes and 250 ml H_2O was added to the extract to precipitate bilirubin and biliverdin. After filtration, the precipitate was extracted with $CHCl_3$ and the combined extracts subjected to photometric determination at 493 and 538 nm in a König-Martens spectrophotometer. Ylppö claimed recovery of 91–107% of added bilirubin, in spite of the many possibilities of oxidative losses during this procedure. However, his values for the daily excretion were considerably lower than those of more recent authors. E. Meyer and Adler (1924) used the diazo reaction in quantitative studies of stool. Their method has not been described in detail and their values for bilirubin in meconium are surprisingly high. Zamorani (1925) ground feces with 1% NaCl solution and added 2 parts of 96% alcohol; then he added 1 part diazo reagent to 1 part stool suspension. After maximal color had developed, the mixture was centrifuged and the pigment concentration in the supernatant liquid was determined colorimetrically. Kerppola and Leikola (1932) acidified with glacial acetic acid, extracted with chloroform, and measured the yellow color of the extracts. S. G. Ross et al. (1937) prepared a suspension by grinding the stool with an oxidizing agent (2 ml concentrated HNO_3 and 10 ml concentrated HCl filled up with alcohol to 500 ml) and determined the blue color in a photoelectric colorimeter. Malloy and Evelyn (1938) used a reagent which consisted of 0.4 ml 30% H_2O_2, 2 ml concentrated HCl, and 100 ml 94% alcohol. The stool was collected over a 24-hour period and homogenized in a mechanical homogenizer with 200–500 ml water. A 10-ml aliquot of this homogenate was vigorously shaken with 15 ml 94% alcohol and 25 ml reagent and subsequently centrifuged. The volume of the supernatant was determined, and the residue extracted once more. After filtration through a paper filter, the pigment contents in the combined extracts were determined in an Evelyn colorimeter (filter 660; 94% alcohol as blank). Added bilirubin was recovered within ±5% error. Squarcetta Romano (1942) described oxidation reactions with three different reagents; these, however, were only useful for qualitative purposes.

With (1942b) dried the stool by grinding with anhydrous Na_2SO_4 in the presence of a few drops of glacial acetic acid. Subsequently, 96% alcohol and diazo mixture were added to the dried powder, stirred, let settle in a flask, and the extract was decanted. This extraction was continued until no color was noticeable; the combined extracts were acidified with concentrated HCl. Color determinations were performed in a Pulfric photometer (filter S 57). The typical color change on acidification, from red to blue, of the diazo reaction of bilirubin was often missing in acidified meconium extracts. Instead, a yellowish color could

be observed, which changed to a reddish blue. Tat *et al.* (1943) regarded
bilirubin determination in stool as unreliable. Madel (1947) studied
azobilirubin extracts with the method described by With. He demonstrated that the absorption curves of these extracts differ significantly
from those of azobilirubin. To avoid this source of error, he acidified
the stool before extraction by wetting it with 0.1 N HCl in order to
liberate bilirubin from its alkali salts. In the absence of acidification, up
to 25% lower values were determined. After the stool was dried by With's
method, Madel extracted with $CHCl_3$ and the extract was concentrated
by evaporation, the residue dissolved in alcohol, and diazo mixture
added; the mixture thus obtained was filtered. Then concentrated HCl
was added. The absorption was determined in a König-Martens-Grün-
baum spectrophotometer at 10 nm intervals in the range of 400–700 nm.

According to Künzer *et al.* (1950) and Künzer (1951a,b), it is better
to use $CHCl_3$ to extract fecal bilirubin than alcohol. Bilirubin is much
more soluble in $CHCl_3$ than in alcohol, and the amount of nonbilirubin
pigments extracted with $CHCl_3$ is much less. Furthermore, they showed
that the red and yellow pigments present in diazotized alcoholic stool
extracts can simulate up to 10 mg bilirubin/100 g in bilirubin-free feces.
Finally, they studied the absorption curves of diazotized stool extracts
and tried to eliminate the error due to nonspecific coloration by using
suitable compensating solutions. Künzer's latest procedure (1951a, p.
57) was as follows: 2 g of fresh stool were ground in a mortar with
about 2 ml glacial acetic acid to adjust the pH to about 3.0 (universal
indicator paper). It was necessary to measure the amount of glacial
acetic acid added (pipette!). Subsequently, a few grams of anhydrous
Na_2SO_4 were added and grinding was continued until a dry, homogeneous
powder was obtained. This material was transferred into a dark flask
with ground glass stopper and filled up to 40 ml final volume with $CHCl_3$.
Subsequently, the mixture was shaken in a mechanical shaker for 6 hours
and filtered without washing the precipitate. A 5-ml aliquot of the filtrate
was concentrated to about 1 ml on a water bath in the presence of a few
glass beads; 5 ml methanol was added and subsequently, after cooling,
1 ml freshly prepared diazo reagent. After 15 minutes, 1 ml HCl–methanol
was added to the mixture which was then filtered, the filter washed
with methanol, and the volume adjusted to 25 ml with methanol. A blue
color was obtained which was measured in a Pulfric photometer (filter
S 57) with water as blank. The color of the extracts was not always pure
blue. Attempts were made to compensate this deviation by measurement of the same solution at pH 2.5 (Künzer, 1951a, p. 42). However,
this correction seems to be somewhat complicated and not entirely
satisfactory. Chromatographic purification would be more expedient and

would not require more work. The calculation constants used in this investigation are reported in Künzer's paper (1951a, pp. 28 and 49).

Heringová *et al.* (1964b*) studied the fecal bilirubin of newborns with special regard to its content of free and conjugated bilirubin. They subjected the stool to freezing at −30°C until analysis was performed, extracted with methanol by grinding, filtered the extract, and diazotized it. The azobilirubin was subsequently subjected to ascending paper chromatography for 6 hours on Whatman No. 3 paper employing a solvent system consisting of 3 volumes of water-saturated butanol and 2 volumes of glacial acetic acid; 20 volumes of this mixture were diluted with 3 volumes of distilled water. With this method the R_f of conjugated bilirubin ("pigment B") was 0.53–0.64, that of free bilirubin ("pigment A") 0.69–0.80.

Garay *et al.* (1964b*) extracted meconium by grinding with an ethanol-water mixture, 3/1 (v/v) and subsequently extracting three times with ⅓ volume of butanol. The pooled extracts were placed in a separatory funnel and 3 volumes of petrol ether and a few drops of water added. After mixing a small aqueous phase rich in bile pigments separated and the organic phase was extracted 1–2 times with 1–2 ml of water. The pooled aqueous extracts were centrifuged and the bilirubin determined with the Jendrassik-Gróf method, the biliverdin with the fluorimetric method of Garay and Argerich (1963).

Summary

Methods of quantitative bilirubin determination have only been developed for the stool of the newborn. Low concentrations are the rule after this period and consequently, because of many interfering substances, quantitative analysis is hardly possible. Only qualitative demonstrations can be obtained at best. The stool of patients having an abnormal intestinal flora (after tetracycline therapy) is perhaps one exception. In these cases, as in the case of newborns, biliary bilirubin persists in stool. Künzer's (1951b) method is an improvement, although the diazo reaction is not always specific with this technique. Further improvements were suggested by Herigová *et al.* (1964b*) and Garay *et al.* (1964*).

2. FECAL BILIRUBIN AND BILIVERDIN IN HEALTHY AND SICK HUMANS AND ANIMALS

Whereas significant amounts of bilirubin and biliverdin are found in infants, the stool of normal adults and older children contains only traces of these two compounds (cf. Borrien, 1911, p. 50). Sometimes, small amounts become detectable, i.e., in hemolytic jaundice (Libowitzky, 1940a) and in severe diarrhea, when passage through the colon is very rapid (Schorlemmer, 1900). Some bilirubin was found in the stool of normal adults with the help of the $HgCl_2$ reaction and by microscopic observations, but bilirubin was never found during macroscopic studies (Schorlemmer, 1900). C. J. Watson's collaborators (personal communication, 1958) found 5–20 mg bilirubin/24 hours in the stool of normal adults. The authors were able to isolate bilirubin in crystalline form from this source. When the intestinal flora was suppressed by treatment with antibiotics (tetracycline and others), the urobilinoids disappeared from the feces, and bilirubin and biliverdin appeared (Sborov and Watson, 1949; Hollan, 1950; Sborov *et al.*, 1951; French *et al.*, 1956; K.-H. Brandt, 1957, Table 6, p. 120). Although only semiquantitative determinations were performed, it was demonstrated that the combined amount of bilirubin and biliverdin excreted was less than the amount of urobilin normally eliminated in the stool (Sborov and Watson, 1949).

Hollan (1950) examined the contents of duodenum, jejunum, ileum, and cecum obtained by intubation. His analytical method was as reliable as possible. The bilirubin levels determined were 0.83–13.92 (average 5.23) mg/100 ml in the duodenum, 3.32–8.6 (5.86) mg/100 ml in the jejunum, 1.7–36.85 (13.57) mg/100 ml in the ileum, and 2.5–10.1 (4.84) mg/100 ml in the cecum. The urobilinoid concentration was, in contrast, very low, i.e., on the average 0.3 mg/100 ml in samples taken from the first three intestinal segments and 5.05 mg/100 ml in the cecum. Fecal bilirubin was not detectable in any of the 14 cases examined, but it was found in 6 patients who were treated with antibacterial agents (sulfasuxidine, streptomycin, bacitracin, polymyxin). The maximum concentration was 70 mg/100 g.

The so-called rice-water stools of cholera patients were recently studied by Cole and Greenough (1965*) who injected bromsulphalein i.v. to 3 patients with bacteriologically proven cholera and typical rice-water stools and analyzed the stool collected during 8-hour periods for BSP. A large fraction of the injected BSP—5 mg per kg body weight was injected—was recovered from the stool in all of the patients, suggesting that the colorless stool cannot be due to absence of bile. Whether the excretion of pigments with the stool is stopped during cholera, or they are rapidly reduced to chromogens, or their color is simply covered by the white stool was not investigated.

A series of studies have been performed on newborns. J. F. Simon (1840), Zweifel (1875), and Schorlemmer (1900) found bilirubin in the stool of newborns. Hoppe-Seyler (1874) found 1% bilirubin and large amounts of biliverdin in the meconium of calves. Ylppö (1913) found a total excretion of 120–160 mg in 13 newborns during the first 14 days of life. Fecal bilirubin was detectable to an age of 2½ months. E. Meyer and Adler (1924) found 300–5000 mg/24 hours in the stool of the new-born. Zamorani (1925) found 0.9–1.6 mg/g during the first 8 days of life. Twelve breast-fed infants ranging from 15 days to 9 months had 0.1–0.7 mg/g, and seven infants from 1–10 months on mixed nourishment had 0–0.4 mg/g. Twelve artificially fed infants aged 3–12 months had 0–0.2 mg/g. In infants over 3 months of age, the concentrations were never higher than 0.2 mg/g.

Schönfeld (1927) showed that the white calcium soap stool of children often contains considerable amounts of bilirubin. Giaume and Lanza (1929) found 0.4–1.2 mg bilirubin/g (9–24 mg/24 hours) in seven newborns with the method of Zamorani, and around 0.2–0.4 mg/g (2–6 mg/24 hours) in 42 children whose ages ranged from 14 days to 14 months. The maximum concentration found was 0.7 mg/g (7.86 mg/24 hours). Bilirubin could be detected for a longer period in breast-fed children than in those who did not obtain mother's milk. After the seventh month, bilirubin was absent in the majority of cases.

Kerppola and Leikola (1932) found 3–58 (average 27) mg bilirubin/100 g in the meconium. Dordi and Rossi (1936) showed that bilirubin was regularly present in the stool of infants under 8 months of age. Snelling (1933) did not find any bilirubin in the first meconium, whereas he found increasing concentrations during the second and third day. The concentrations varied from the fourth to the sixteenth day. S. G. Ross *et al.* (1937) found the following average values with an oxidation method: 24–34 mg/24 hours in newborn humans with jaundice (14 cases examined); 11–48 mg/24 hours in infants with no jaundice (21 cases examined). The average was 52.9 for the first 2 days, 23.2 for the third to the fifth day, and 14.2 mg/24 hours for the sixth to the seventh day; i.e., a distinct drop was noticeable during the first week of life. The average values were 1.5–2 times higher in normal children than in icteric ones.

Squarcetta Romano (1942) investigated the influence of nourishment (mother's milk, mixed feedings, and pure bottle feedings) and intestinal disorders on fecal bile pigment excretion in 31 children. Qualitative bilirubin tests by Fouchet's (1918) and Triboulet's (1909a,b) oxidation tests and Grigaut's (1909) urobilin test were used in these studies. A green reaction (bilirubin) was obtained in the first month of life in children fed with mother's milk; formula-fed children showed a pink reaction (urobilinoids). Urobilinoid reaction was also obtained in children 7–8 months old fed with mother's milk. Grayish white or yellowish reactions were observed in acholic stools. During diarrhea, bilirubin excretion was higher than urobilin excretion even in older children; the appearance of fecal urobilinoids in infants indicated a putrescent process in the intestinal tract. Royer (1943, p. 172) found 1.2–90 mg bilirubin/24 hours in the stool of newborns during the first 7 days.

Larsen and With (1943) examined the stool of 25 newborn humans during the first 6–10 days of life and simultaneously determined the serum bilirubin concentration each day or every second day. The bilirubin concentration of meconium was consistently low, and in ten cases no bilirubin was detectable. The total excretion was 2.5–75 mg during the first 6 days, the values being mostly around 10–60 mg. Daily excretion showed large and irregular individual variations between 0.25 to 42 mg. These large fluctuations can only be explained by assuming bilirubin destruction in the intestinal tract. No significant connection was detected between fecal and serum bilirubin concentrations. In order to establish the age level at which bilirubin disappears from the stool, 28 children ranging from 1 week to 12 months of age were studied. Three weeks was the earliest age at which urobilinoids could be detected. However, many children showed urobilinoids only after their sixth month. Bilirubin excretion was regularly 1.4–6.6 mg/24 hours until the age of 2 months. After this age, the concentrations varied considerably and values of 0–24 mg/24 hours were determined. In one case bilirubin was present even after 8 months (excretion was 2.6 mg bilirubin/24 hours and 0.4 mg urobilinoids/24 hours).

Tat *et al.* (1943) examined 30 normal newborns during the first 5 days of life, using the oxidation method of Malloy and Evelyn. In 6 of these children the fecal bilirubin excretion was followed until it completely disappeared. Bilirubin excretion was 1–23 (average 8.6) mg/24 hours during the first 5 days. The following values were determined in the 6 children who were examined continuously: 0–17 (average 5.7) mg/24 hours during the fifth to tenth days, 0.3–12 (average 5.3) mg/24 hours during the tenth to fifteenth days. Bilirubin disappeared during the eighth and tenth day in 2 children, whereas it was detectable on the 46th, 64th, 65th, and 75th day in the other 4 children. The concentrations showed marked fluctuations. It was occasionally found that the bilirubin disappeared for a while to reappear at a later date.

Madel (1947) found 0.34–17 mg/24 hours in the stool of 10 normal newborns. Fashena (1948) found 25–102 (average 58.5) mg/100 g in the first meconium of 6 newborns with the method of Malloy and Evelyn. In these children the serum bilirubin concentration was below 5 mg/100 ml. He found 16–62 (average 33.7) mg/100 g in 6 cases which had 5–10 mg bilirubin/100 ml serum and 12–37 (average 26.0) mg/100 g in 8 children having serum bilirubin concentrations above 10 mg/100 ml, i.e., the lower the bilirubin content of the meconium, the more pronounced will be the jaundice that develops later. Napp and Plotz (1949) investigated the fecal bilirubin in 22 newborns by With's method. They found 1.5–110 mg in the first meconium, a total of 0.4–85 mg in the stool eliminated during the first to the fifth day, and 4.2–55 mg in the stool excreted during the sixth to the tenth day. Generally, high fecal bilirubin excretion was found when the serum bilirubin concentration was low. The average total excretion was 118.8 mg during the first 10 days in children having a serum bilirubin content below 7 mg/100 ml. However, 41.8 mg was observed in children with serum bilirubin concentrations higher than 10 mg/100 ml. The same authors found 61.5 mg in full-term babies and 35.9 mg in premature babies.

Künzer (1951a, Tables 38–50) obtained the following values: 9–42 mg/24 hours in the first meconium (6 cases); 5.9–14.4 (average 10.0) mg/24 hours during the first week of life (8 cases); 7.2–14.3 (average 10.3) mg/24 hours during the second week of life (7 cases); 5.3–16.2 (average 10.3) mg/24 hours during the third to fourth weeks of life (11 cases); 5.3–14.4 (average 9.4) mg/24 hours during the fifth to sixth weeks of life (9 cases); 2.8–5.9 (average 4.2) mg/24 hours during the seventh to eighth weeks of life (8 cases); and 0–3.9 (average 1.3) mg/24 hours during the ninth to tenth weeks of life (9 cases). Bilirubin could be detected in the stool (1.2 mg/24 hours) of only 1 of 12 children ranging from 10 weeks to 1 year of age. No fecal bilirubin was detected in children from 1 to 12 years of age.

Vest (1959) studied the fecal excretion of bile pigments in infants from birth to the 8th week with the oxidation method of Malloy and Evelyn. He compared the excretion with simultaneous hemoglobin determinations. The following average values were found in prematures: In 31 infants during the first week of life, 9.95 mg fecal bilirubin/24 hours and a Hb turnover of 190 mg/24 hours; in 35 infants during the second week of life, 7.41 mg bilirubin and 160 mg Hb; in 32 infants during the third week, 5.86 and 160 mg/24 hours; in 27 infants during the fourth week 5.05 and 140 mg/24 hours; in 32 during the fifth, 4.38 and 120; in 22 during the sixth, 3.73 and 100; in 21 during the seventh, 3.60 and 100; and in 14 premature infants during the eighth week of life 4.45 mg bilirubin and 130 mg Hb per 24 hours. In normal newborns the figures were somewhat higher than in the prematures: in eight during the first week of life the average bilirubin excretion was 14.5 mg/24 hours and the average Hb turnover 410 mg/24 hours; in eight during the second week, the figures were 11.35 and 320 mg; in 5 during the third week, 9.0 and 250 mg; in 4 during the fourth week, 8.0 and 230 mg. Like previous investigators, Vest found a well-marked correlation between the maximum serum bilirubin and the bilirubin in the meconium: With maximum serum bilirubin below 5 mg/100 ml, the average meconium bilirubin was 29.40

and with maximum serum bilirubin above 15 mg/100 ml, the average meconium bilirubin was 7.66 mg. The same inverse relationship was present in the feces during the first to fifth day of life in both normal and premature newborns, but after the fifth day these differences disappeared.

Heringová *et al.* (1964b*) studied the feces of 113 infants 1–6 months of age and found that the diazo reaction was positive in 55 and negative in 7 cases during the 1st to 2nd week, positive in 10 and negative in one during the 3rd and 4th week, positive in 8 and negative in 4 during the 2nd month, positive in 2 and negative in 3 during the 3rd month, negative in all of the 9 infants studied during the 4th and 6th months, and positive in one of the 8 studied during the 5th month. In 90 infants the azobilirubin prepared from the stool was subjected to paper chromatography. In 21 samples of meconium the diazo reaction was negative in the 7 and in the remaining 14 only unconjugated bilirubin was found. In 41 infants 3–14 days of age both unconjugated and conjugated bilirubin were found in most of them; in 3 cases only free bilirubin occurred and in 4 only conjugated bilirubin was found. In older infants most often both conjugated and unconjugated bilirubin occurred and there was no significant difference between breast-fed and artificially fed infants.

Garay *et al.* (1964b*) determined the bilirubin and biliverdin in 50 samples of human meconium and found an average of 10 μg/g for biliverdin and 43 μg/g for bilirubin.

Murano and Di Toro (1965*) measured the fecal bilirubin during the first week of life in newborns with and without treatment with prednisolone (0.5 mg per kg body weight daily intramuscularly for 2 weeks) and found a more than twofold increase of the fecal bilirubin excretion in the treated infants as compared to the controls.

The bilirubin content of *animal feces* has been investigated only rarely. Hoppe-Seyler (1874) detected large amounts of bilirubin in meconium of calves. Wester (1912) found bilirubin in feces of newborn calves and sheep. Garner (1955) could not detect bilirubin or biliverdin in the feces of cows. Steensma (1918, p. 50), and Rosenthal and Melchior (1922) reported the presence of bilirubin in the feces of parrots, pigeons, and other birds.

Summary

Small amounts of bilirubin are present in the stool of normal adults (5–20 mg/24 hours). Larger amounts are observed in diarrhea, hemolytic diseases, and after treatment with antibiotics. Bilirubin and biliverdin are regularly present in the stool of the newborn and in the meconium. These compounds can be detected to about 8 weeks after birth, but the concentration decreases after 6 weeks. These pigments gradually disappear from the stool in the ninth to tenth weeks of life; they can only be detected occasionally and in small amounts after the tenth week. After the first year their concentration reaches the low adult level. The occurrence of bilirubin varies considerably in the stool of the newborn. There exists an inverse relation between the fecal bilirubin and the serum bilirubin level during the first week of life.

Very little has been published about studies with animals. Available evidence indicates that the situation in newborn and full-grown cattle is the same as it is in humans. Bilirubin and biliverdin are consistently present in the feces of birds.

It would be extremely desirable to conduct extended studies on many animals, including mammals, birds, and lower vetebrates. Young and mature animals should be included in these investigations. The study of fecal pigments seems to be rather neglected in the field of comparative biology.

C. Fecal Urobilinoids

1. ANALYTICAL METHODS

Fresh stool similar to urine contains only urobilinogens (Steensma, 1907; Fischer and Libowitzky, 1939; French, 1957). Therefore, as in urine, it is best to determine fecal urobilinoids as urobilinogens. In this connection it must be pointed out that urobilinoids do not contribute significantly to the color of the stool. French (1957) found that, at the most, 1/50 of the color of fresh, normal feces is caused by these pigments. Because of the light sensitivity of urobilinogens, all manipulations during analysis should be carried out in dim light. To avoid oxidation, the materials should be handled as quickly as possible. A number of methods have been suggested for determination of fecal urobilinoids; the more important ones are discussed below. For a more comprehensive treatment, see With (1954, pp. 334–340).

A. Schmidt (1895) mixed the stool with concentrated $HgCl_2$ and studied the color developed during this operation. Urobilin gives red color. Ladage (1899) collected 24-hour stool, treated it with dilute ammonia, and homogenized it until about 3 liters of a sirupy liquid were obtained. He used 1/10 of this material for analysis. He added 10 drops of tincture of iodine to the sample, and filtered. The residue on the filter was extracted once more with ammonia. The determination was performed in the combined filtrates as described for urine. Van Leersum (1899) found that, even after complete extraction with ethyl acetate, large amounts of urobilinoids can be obtained from the residue with 5% aqueous potassium hydroxide. Triboulet (1909a,b) and Quioc (1909) used the $HgCl_2$ reaction. Steensma (1907, 1908a,b; 1918, p. 39) ground the stool sample with absolute alcohol, filtered and examined the fluorescence after introducing 10% $ZnCl_2$ solution. When no fluorescence was noticed, one drop of tincture of iodine was added. Fluorescence was never observed in completely fresh stool without iodine addition.

Borrien (1910, 1911, p. 56 et seq.) found that water, 90% alcohol, and acetone are equally effective in extracting fecal urobilinoids, and that $CHCl_3$, CCl_4, amyl alcohol, ethyl acetate, and especially ether and petroleum ether are definitely inferior solvents. He employed the $HgCl_2$ reaction, which is positive for urobilin as well as for urobilinogen. A pink coloration was obtained in neutral or weakly acidic solution, whereas an amber color with red fluorescence could be observed in acidic media. A red pigment precipitated from the solution at alkaline reaction. The author compared the $HgCl_2$ reactions of A. Schmidt and Triboulet and proposed adding the reagent to the centrifuged, aqueous extract. In a semiquantitative process, he treated 2 g stool with 10–15 ml $CHCl_3$ and added 5 drops of a saturated $HgCl_2$ solution. The mixture was shaken vigorously and stored for 24 hours before filtration. During this time the filtrate assumed a red color, which was proportional to the urobilin content (Borrien, 1911, p. 73).

Eppinger and Charnas (1913) ground a 10-g aliquot of the 24-hour stool with 1% tartaric acid in ethanol, boiled the mixture for a few minutes on a water bath, filtered, and extracted the residue in the same way. Precipitation with 20% ammonium sulfate followed, and the solution was alkalized with dilute sodium hydroxide. The solution was extracted with ether, acidified with tartaric acid, and again extracted with ether. The extract was washed and dried. The color was determined in a spectrophotometer after performing the benzaldehyde reaction. All manipulations were carried out under artificial light. Glanzmann (1916) employed a very similar process. Wilbur and Addis (1914) ground the stool with water and shook the emulsion with threefold volume alcohol containing HCl. Subsequently, the same amount of saturated alcoholic zinc acetate was added and the mixture was filtered. The filtrate was treated with 0.1 volume of Ehrlich's reagent. Urobilin and urobilinogen were separately determined as described by the same authors for urine analysis.

Brulé and Garban (1920) were able to extract considerable amounts of urobilinoids from stool with 5% KOH even after exhaustive extraction with organic solvents, i.e., $CHCl_3$, amyl alcohol, ethyl acetate, 90% alcohol, and a mixture of HCl–alcohol–ether. Moreover, they found that extraction with ligroin or petroleum ether results in considerable losses of urobilinoids. These solvents had been used in earlier methods to remove indole before urobilinoid extraction. Hueck and Brehme (1923) used a technique similar to that employed by Eppinger and Charnas (1913). Opitz and Brehme (1923, 1924a), pointed out the marked fluctuations occurring in the 24-hour stools of one individual, and recommended using the average of at least 5 consecutive 24-hour stools.

Terwen (1924, 1925) ground 5 g of homogenized 24-hour stool with 40 ml water, which he added gradually in small portions. He then subjected this emulsion to the reduction process which he described for urine analysis. Elman and McMaster (1925a) homogenized the stool with water by mechanical agitation, diluted a sample, and extracted it with alcohol containing some HCl, by shaking for 1 hour. The sample was stored for oxidation overnight. The extract was examined with the zinc fluorescence test, which they also recommended for urine. Royer (1928a) homogenized stool in a mortar, extracted 1–2 g with alcohol containing HCl in a centrifuge tube, and incubated for several hours at 38–40°. The precipitate was centrifuged and the extraction continued until the zinc fluorescence test became negative in the extracts. Concentrations were determined fluorimetrically in the combined extracts as described for urine analysis. This procedure is very cumbersome and requires several days.

Heilmeyer and Krebs (1931) and C. J. Watson (1931, 1936c) employed a modification of Terwen's method. In order to exclude errors from irregular defecation, Watson, like Opitz and Brehme, emphasized the necessity of sampling the stool over a period of at least 4 days. Josephs (1934) used the improved method devised by Elman and McMaster. The fluorescence was compared with an acriflavine standard ($1/30 \times 10^{-6}$). He found that stool can be stored in a refrigerator for at least 5 days without loss of urobilinoids. S. G. Ross et al. (1937) emulsified the stool with a mechanical stirrer and precipitated 10 ml of this emulsion by adding 1 ml of concentrated ammonium sulfate solution, 5 ml 20% strontium chloride, and 50 ml water. After shaking, the mixture was stored for 20 hours and filtered. Subsequently, the zinc fluorescence test was performed and the color compared with an acriflavine standard solution.

Sparkman (1939a), With (1942b), and Schwartz et al. (1944) used a modified Terwen method. Schwartz et al. and With collected and measured the stool for 4 days, and homogenized it in a mortar or in a mechanical homogenizer. The latter used 2–5 g and Schwartz et al. used 10 g samples from the homogenate for analysis. The samples were ground with water in a mortar and diluted to a suitable volume (80 ml, With; 300 ml, Schwartz et al.). Strongly alkaline solutions of ferrous sulfate were added to the diluted mixtures for reduction. The reduced solutions were extracted and analyzed with methods used by these authors for urine analylsis. In this way, With found less than 5% variation in the averages of duplicate determinations. Schwartz *et al.* added pure stercobilin and were able to recover 98–110% with an average error of 7.7%. It was established that when the reduction mixture was stored in the dark for 1 hour at room temperature all urobilinoid was converted into urobilinogen. C. J. Watson *et al.* (1944) suggested a simplified procedure similar to the one employed for analysis in urine.

MacLagan (1946) used a large wax-lined container for the collection of stool. The container was weighed in advance and was discarded after use. In this manner he avoided the cumbersome and dirty job of cleaning containers. McDonald and Kelley (1947) thoroughly mixed the collected stool and weighed out 10 g on a filter paper. Stool and filter paper were emulsified with 150 ml water in a Waring Blendor. Reduction was performed according to Watson *et al.* The efficiency of extraction was compared by homogenizing stool samples in an homogenizer and in a mortar. Somewhat higher values were obtained when the first method was used, but the variations between these methods were below 5%. The advantage of the homogenizer is the faster emulsification.

Brereton and Lucia (1948) used random stool samples. This was also recommended by Sparkman (1939a). The authors maintained that random sampling has the same value in clinical practice as the more cumbersome 4-day sampling.

Balikov (1955) investigated the role of the amount of glacial acetic acid used for neutralization of the reduced alkaline stool extracts before petroleum ether extraction of urobilinogen. He found that optimum extraction is obtained by adding 1% glacial acetic acid. The stool extract to be analyzed was diluted with water; 0.5 ml glacial acetic acid was added to it and the suspension was filled up with water to 50 ml. This amount of glacial acetic acid could be insufficient for neutralization when only small amounts of urobilinogen were present in the stool, and thus larger amounts of the alkaline extract were used. In this case it is better to continue neutralization by dropwise addition of concentrated hydrochloric acid until the appropiate pH is obtained under control with universal indicator paper.

Balikov (1955, 1957, 1958) and Gray (1957, 1961b) published detailed descriptions of the quantitative extraction method.

The method of Gray is given below. The additions in parentheses are modifications proposed by the writer.

Recommended Technique

Apparatus:

A 100-ml measuring cylinder, 100-ml separatory funnel, 1000-ml flask, photoelectric colorimeter.

Reagents:

Modified Ehrlich reagent: 0.7 g analytical *p*-dimethylaminobenzalde-hyde dissolved in 150 ml analytical concentrated HCl, to which 100 ml distilled water is added. Saturated (analytical) sodium acetate solution, 20% (w/v) solution of iron sulfate ($FeSO_4 \cdot 7H_2O$), 10% NaOH, petroleum ether, boiling point 60–80°.

Procedure:

The stool is collected for 4 days and thoroughly homogenized (Waring Blendor or a similar electrical apparatus. The stool is stored in a refrigerator until analysis. All manipulations must be performed in dimmed light. Direct illumination must be avoided). Ten g of the thoroughly homogenized stool are transported into a mortar and extracted 5 times by grinding with 20 ml water (extraction can also be carried out in an electric mixer; since 20 ml water is not sufficient to fill up these machines, larger amounts of stool, for example 100 g, and correspondingly more water should be used). After each extraction, the liquid, which should be a fine, homogeneous suspension, is transferred into a liter flask containing 100 ml $FeSO_4$ solution. (When larger amounts of stool are used in an electric mixer, the extracts are first collected and measured, and then 100-ml aliquots are mixed with 100 ml $FeSO_4$ solution.) Mortar and pestle are washed with 190 ml water and with 100 ml 10% NaOH. The NaOH is added slowly and in small portions under shaking to the mixture of extract and $FeSO_4$. (When a blender is used, it is washed by stirring up 100 ml water twice, and the washings are combined with the extract. The solutions are carefully mixed and 100-ml aliquots are removed for analysis.) The flask containing the $Fe(OH)_2$ mixture is stored in the dark for 90 minutes. Subsequently, the mixture is filtered through Whatman No. 1 filter paper. If the color of the filtrate is deeper than pale straw yellow, it is advisable to repeat the analysis by using a smaller amount of stool.

First a preliminary test is performed: About 2–3 ml of the filtrate is transferred into a test tube and mixed with an equal volume of Ehrlich reagent and 6–8 ml of saturated sodium acetate solution. If an intense red color develops, 1 ml of the filtrate suffices for extraction. When the color is less intense, 2 ml filtrate is used; when the color is weak red, 3–5 ml filtrate is used; when it is a very pale red, 10–25 ml is used; and when it is colorless, 50 ml of the filtrate is extracted. The suitable amount of filtrate is transferred into a separatory funnel and its volume adjusted to 50 ml with water. At this moment 2 ml of glacial acetic acid is added

(Balikov prefers to add 0.5 ml glacial acetic acid; he claims to obtain better extractions this way; see above). Subsequently, it is extracted with 50, 25, and again with 25 ml petroleum ether, and the combined extracts are washed. After adding 2 ml Ehrlich reagent, it is subjected to vigorous agitation for about 30 seconds. Then 6 ml saturated sodium acetate is added before the phases separate, and after repeated mixing the phases are separated. Extraction with Ehrlich reagent and sodium acetate is continued until the aqueous phase is no longer red. The aqueous extracts are pooled in a measuring cylinder, mixed, and the color intensity determined photometrically. A mixture of 2 ml Ehrlich reagent and 6 ml sodium acetate solution is used for the blank sample. The use of a green filter (Ilford 605) is recommended. [The addition of ascorbic acid (Henry *et al.*, 1961) and potassium borohydride (Henry *et al.*, 1964) recommended for urine analysis (cf. Chapter VI,D,1) has not been tried for feces, but would undoubtedly be of value also here.]

For accurate measurements the instrument should be calibrated with pure stercobilin hydrochloride solutions. For this purpose 10 mg of the pure compound are dissolved in 2–3 drops 1 N Na_2CO_3 and the solution is diluted to 100 ml. Ten ml aliquots ($=$ 1 mg stercobilin) of this solution are filled up to 50 ml with water. Subsequently, 25 ml ferrous sulfate and 25 ml 10% sodium hydroxide are added, and the mixture is stored in the dark for 90 minutes. Thereafter, it is filtered and 50 ml of the acidified filtrate is extracted with petroleum ether and subsequently treated with the above-described method. When the calibrating solution is prepared in this manner, urobilin losses during manipulation will be compensated.

Earlier researchers compared the extinctions of the final solution with that of pure urobilinogen solutions. Gray avoided losses due to manipulations by subjection of the standard solution to the same manipulations as the test sample. According to Schwartz *et al.* (1944), losses due to manipulation are insignificant. Calibration with pure stercobilinogen in hardly necessary for clinical determinations. Calculations, which are based on literature values for $E_{1\,cm}^{1\%}$, suffice in clinical practice (see Chapter VI,C,1). According to Gray's curve, an extinction of 1 with filter 605 of the Spekker absorptiometer corresponds to ca. 0.99 mg stercobilinogen/100 ml final solution.

Finally, the concentration of 24-hour stool is calculated from the extinction observed, the calibration curve (or a certain value for $E_{1\,cm}^{1\%}$ which must always be specified in publications), and from the extracted volume compensating for the dilution.

Gray (1961b) also reported a simplified method in which the petroleum ether extraction was omitted. He recommended this simplified method only for crude, orienting tests. However, this simplified test has little justification, because the collecting and homogenizing of the stool are the cumbersome and unesthetic working steps. Final extraction is only a minor and less repulsive part of the whole operation.

Only a few authors have attempted to differentiate between urobilin-I and urobilin-L. When urobilinogen-D is present, the petroleum ether extraction yields values which are too low (see Section C,2, this chapter). Baumgärtel (1949b; 1950b, p. 240) ground a few grams of stool with 20 ml methanol in a mortar and extracted the mixture several times with petroleum ether to remove the indole derivatives. After extraction the alcohol was evaporated in vacuum, and the residue was extracted with 3 ml water. The aqeuous solution was treated with boiling concentrated HCl containing traces of $FeCl_3$. Urobilinoids-I gave a violet color reaction, whereas U-L gave brown coloration. Rudolph (1952, p. 38) recommended a very similar process. Legge (1949) covered the finely ground stool with glacial acetic acid for about 30 minutes and extracted 3 times with equal volumes of ether. The combined ether extracts were extracted with about 15 ml saturated sodium acetate solution and then repeatedly with water until only traces of urobilinoid remained in the ether. The combined aqueous extracts were treated with 10–15 ml $CHCl_3$, the $CHCl_3$ evaporated to dryness, and the dry residue was finally dissolved in 5 ml methanol. An aliquot of 0.5 ml of this methanol solution was suitably diluted and used for spectrophotometric determinations at 492 nm. Taking the dilution into consideration, the urobilin content of the original solution was calculated. The remaining 4.5 ml of the methanol solution was mixed with 0.5 ml of a 20% (w/v) solution of $FeCl_3$ in concentrated HCl and boiled under reflux for 15 minutes in a test tube. After cooling to room temperature, the mixture was neutralized with saturated sodium acetate solution, extracted with ether, and carefully washed to remove as much urobilin-L as possible. The violins which formed during this process were finally extracted with 2.8 N HCl. Spectrophotometric determination was performed at 492 and 560 nm. The violin absorption at 492 nm can be neglected; the absorption at this wavelength is due to traces of urobilin-L. Absorption at 560 nm is due to violins. The true violin extinction is obtained when the extinction at 492 nm is multiplied by 0.07 and the product subtracted from the extinction at 560 nm. K.-H. Brandt (1957, p. 94 et seq.) compared the methods of Baumgärtel and Legge and found the latter method superior to the former.

C. J. Watson (1959) described a method for the separate determination of urobilinoids-I, -L, and -D (see Chapter VI,C,1).

Heringová et al. (1964b*) employed the Schlesinger fluorescence test and the $FeCl_3$-mesobiliviolin reaction on fecal extracts from infants as qualitative tests. Garay et al. (1964b*) used the Schlesinger fluorescence test on aqueous ethanolic extracts of meconium and verified the presence of the pigments by means of paper chromatography.

Skrijver (1929) studied the destruction of urobilinoids in the feces. He was able to show that the rate of this process was much faster under aerobic conditions than under anaerobic ones. However, a small amount of degradation occurred even in the absence of air. Degradation occurred more quickly when the samples were dried in a desiccator.

Summary

The best quantitative method for urobilin determination consists of extraction of the stool with distilled water, reduction of the extracts with ferrous hydroxide (according to Terwen), and extraction with petroleum ether after suitable acidification. Subsequently, the extracts are subjected the benzaldehyde reaction; the red reaction product is extracted, neutralized with sodium acetate, and transferred into the aqueous phase. For precise quantitative work, it is important to take the sample from carefully homogenized stool collected over 4 days. The stool should be kept in a refrigerator until it can be analyzed. All manipulations should be performed in dimmed light. During collection and storage, contact with air should be avoided. Simplified methods which omit certain extraction steps are of questionable value. Methods for urobilin-I, -L and -D differentiation have been described.

2. FECAL UROBILINOIDS OF HEALTHY AND SICK ADULTS

A number of investigators studied fecal urobilinoid excretion of adults and older children. With (1954, pp. 341–345) presented a detailed discussion of the early literature.

Gilbert and Herscher (1907b) found that stercobilinogen is regularly present in normal stool, but that it disappears completely in total bile duct obstruction, as well as in severe hepatic jaundice (1907c). Adler and Sachs (1923a) determined the "urobilin quotient," i.e., urinary urobilinoid divided by fecal urobilinoid, in sick and healthy individuals and found between 0.03 and 0.1 in both groups. Liver diseases, having quotients above 0.1, and seldom higher than 1.0, were exceptions. Opitz and Brehme (1924a,b) criticized the high fecal urobilin levels found by these workers and claimed their findings were due to impurities present in the standard urobilin preparations. Opitz and Brehme found an average normal fecal excretion of 65–220 mg/24 hours. These authors recommended extending the collection of stool over a period of 5 consecutive days. Lichtenstein and Terwen (1925) found 50–193 (average 127) mg urobilinoid/24 hours in normal subjects, 917–1080 mg/24 hours in hemolytic icterus, and 240–824 mg/24 hours in recurrences of pernicious anemia.

Kingsbury (1926) found urobilin quotients below 0.04 in hemolytic jaundice and most often above 1.0 in obstructive icterus. Adler and Jeddeloh (1929a,b) examined 37 patients with neoplastic bile duct obstruction and found that these patients often excreted urobilinoids in stool. However, the quality of the analytical method used by these workers is questionable. Singer (1930) confirmed the considerable daily variations of fecal urobilinoid excretion but found that these fluctuations could be reduced by a constant diet. Weiss (1930) found an excretion of 50–110 mg/24 hours in normal individuals and 120–750 mg/24 hours in patients with pernicious anemia. Using Terwen's method, Posthuma (1931) found 1000–3000 mg/24 hours in patients with hemolytic icterus and 300–600 mg/24 hours during pernicious anemia in relapse. C. J. Watson (1931) found 70–1143 (average 557) mg/24 hours during pernicious anemia; after proper therapy the fecal urobilin concentration decreased simultaneously with the onset of the reticulocyte reaction. Huwer (1933) compared pregnant and nonpregnant women and found increased excretion in the former group (average 152 mg/24 hours during the ninth month of pregnancy), whereas the latter group showed an average of 96 mg/24 hours (method of Heilmeyer and Krebs; 1931).

C. J. Watson (1937a) observed 40–280 mg/24 hours, but mostly 100–250 mg/24 hours in normal subjects; he found 9–95 mg/24 hours during mild infectious diseases and pulmonary tuberculosis. He further found 125–325 mg/24 hours in feverish infections, 6.5–625 mg/24 hours in blood diseases without hemolysis, and 37–498 mg/24 hours in polycythemia. Watson (1937b) found 37–217 mg/24 hours in uncomplicated gallstone obstructions and, in case of complications, 7–622 mg/24 hours. Low values were observed during neoplastic obstructions (0–18 mg/24 hours). Watson found 8–212 mg/24 hours in liver cirrhosis accompanied by jaundice, 52–137 mg/24 hours in cirrhosis without jaundice, and 55–1257 mg/24 hours in cirrhosis accompanied by hemolysis. Excretion was 35–259 mg/24 hours in severe cardiac decompensation. He quotes 0–5 mg/24 hours as the usual range for neoplastic bile duct closure, 10–300 mg/24 hours for acute hepatitis, 300–2500 mg/24 hours for hemolytic jaundice during crisis, and 300–1800 mg/24 hours during the interval. Furthermore, he mentioned that fecal urobilinoid concentration was diminished during chronic constipation and in ileus. Hansen (1938) found 48–289 (average 165.5) mg/24 hours in 12 pregnant women during the last 3 months of pregnancy. The excretion was 38–672 (average 301.8) mg/24 hours during childbed; a sharp decrease occurred after the sixth day.

Sparkman (1939b,c) found 72–600 mg (average 230.5) per 100 g in random samples of stool of 100 patients selected at random. The same author found 634–2625 mg/100 g in hemolytic anemia, 75–205 mg/100 g in acute hepatitis, 36–226 mg/100 g in liver cirrhosis, and 40–68 mg/100 g in obstruction caused by gallstones. In neoplastic obstruction no fecal urobilin could be demonstrated. Expression per gram of dry substance would presumably give less variation. Such figures, however, have not been reported.

C. J. Watson (1940) examined 67 patients with neoplastic bile duct closure, 61 with gallstones obstruction, 28 with liver cirrhosis, 23 with acute hepatitis, and 5 with subacute liver atrophy. About 92% of the cases with neoplastic obstruction had under 5 mg/24 hours and 55% below 1 mg/24 hours. In contrast, only 10% of the patients with stone obstruction and with parenchymal liver damage had values below 5 mg/24 hours, and only 2% below 1 mg/24 hours. Waller et al. (1940) found 10–282 mg/24 hours in severe cardiac decompensation. Steigmann and Popper (1943) observed a temporary decrease of fecal urobilin excretion in 10% of 127 acute cases of hepatitis. They called this the "obstruction phase" of hepatitis. As a rule this period lasted only a few days, but in certain cases it lasted as much as a month. Using more than 1000 stool samples, Steigmann and Dyniewicz (1943a) compared results obtained with stool samples collected over a period of 4 days with analyses of random samples. They examined 84 normal subjects and found 20–250 mg/24 hours (70% between 40 and 120 mg/24 hours) and 15–255 mg/100 g (85% of the samples were between 50 and 185 mg/100 g). They observed a significant decrease of excretion after splenectomy in a hemolytic icterus case. Excretions of 200–1200 mg/24 hours and 30–581 mg/100 g were found in other blood diseases. The highest values were found in pernicious anemia in relapse. The excretion was usually low during the icteric period of acute hepatitis, but occasional increases to 250 mg/24 hours were encountered. Figures were within normal limits during partial obstruction, but 0.5–13 mg/24 hours (generally below 5 mg/24 hours) and 0–10 mg/100 g were determined during complete obstruction. On the basis of these findings it can be stated that urobilinoid determinations, even of samples collected at random, undoubtedly have clinical significance. Braden and DuVal (1963) studied 72-hour fecal urobilinoid in 53 patients, among whom 29 had jaundice, with Watson's extraction method. They confirmed the findings of Watson and Steigmann (cf. above). All their 9 cases of obstruction due to carcinoma exhibited figures below 5 mg/24 hours.

C. J. Watson et al. (1944) reported that results obtained with their simplified analytical method and those determined with their extraction process were generally in good agreement. With (1944) found normal values of 25–225 mg/24 hours in 20 subjects (stool collection was extended over 4 days). He found 0.9–11 mg/24 hours during neoplastic obstruction and 7–38 mg/24 hours during the icteric period of acute hepatitis. The author pointed out that fecal urobilinoid determination is unsuitable for following rapid changes of bile pigment excretion, as it occasionally occurs in acute hepatitis. He also showed that the urobilin quotient is only rarely more useful clinically than simple urinary urobilin determination.

MacLagan (1946) found 151–1136 mg/24 hours in 10 acute malaria cases with Watson's method. No connections were found between fecal and urinary urobilin excretion and serum bilirubin level. W. C. Meyer (1947b,c) discussed the appearance of urobilinogens-i and -l, as well as his so-called "urobilin-III" in the stool; however, no quantitative data were reported. Stich (1948) examined 64 patients with various diseases and found that urobilinogen-l predominates in the stool during hemolytic conditions. However, he could also demonstrate urobilin-i in these cases. He detected varying amounts of urobilinogen-l and -i in obstructive jaundice. Only urobilin-i and never the l form was present in complete obstruction. The l form prevailed in hepatocellular jaundice, but the i form occurred as well. Urobilinogen-l predominated in normal persons; only insignificant amounts of urobilinogen-i were found here.

Monasterio and Lattanzi (1947) found 0–38 mg/24 hours at the peak of the jaundice in acute hepatitis, and from 0 to normal values during stone obstruction, whereas concentrations below 5 mg/24 hours were observed in 2 patients with neoplastic obstruction, and 9–37 mg/24 hours was found in a third case. Concentrations between 181 and 1277 (average 696) mg/24 hours were found in 5 cases of hemolytic icterus (method of Heilmeyer and Krebs, 1931). Lattanzi (1948c) published a series of investigations involving icteric patients and reported detailed findings concerning the fecal and urinary urobilinoids as well as serum and urinary bilirubin. Daily determinations were also carried out over a number of weeks in 19 acute hepatitis cases. In some cases no fecal uro-bilinoids could be detected during the peak of jaundice. The concentrations became normal again during the disappearing stage of icterus. In 4 patients with stone obstruction, values ranged from 0 to normal (average 12.3 mg/24 hours); 10 cases of neoplastic obstruction showed 0–90 mg/24 hours (0 in 6 cases); and 5 with hemolytic icterus 106–1690 mg/24 hours (only 1 below 400).

In experiments with N^{15}-labeled glycine, London et al. (1949) demonstrated a 2.5-fold increase of hemoglobin formation in patients with *idiopathic polycythemia,* a disease where only slight increases of fecal urobilinoid occur (Eppinger and Charnas, 1913; C. J. Watson, 1937b, 1938). This indicates that the major part of hemoglobin was degraded to compounds other than urobilinoids (fuscins?), or that the major part of bilirubin was degraded to unidentifiable compounds. This problem requires further investigation.

Hollan (1950), using With's method, found 30–159 (average 90.8) mg/24 hours in 8 normal subjects. Escola (1950), who examined 19 patients suffering from tapeworm anemia, found excretion of 200–540 mg/24 hours with Heilmeyer and Kerbs' method. Excretion increased during reticulocyte crisis where maximum concentrations of about 1200 mg/24 hours were noted. Rudolph (1952, pp. 46–59) examined a small number of patients with various diseases but did not report quantitative data. Basu Malik *et al.* (1957) determined the urobilinoids in cholera stools. They found low values which they attributed to rapid intestinal passage.

Sborov *et al.* (1951), C. J. Watson *et al.* (1954), and French *et al.* (1956) showed that after *antibiotic treatment* (tetracyclines) the fecal urobilinogen drops to almost nil and bilirubin appears within a few days. When antibiotic therapy is stopped, urobilinogen reappears within a few days. This reappearing urobilinogen contains large amounts of urobilinogen-D. This compound is much more difficult to extract from aqueous solutions with petroleum ether than urobilinogens-I and -L. Thus, in this case, the extraction method gives lower results than Watson's simplified method without extraction. Substantial amounts of *urobilinogen*-D can also appear when antibiotic treatment is continued for extended periods.

K.-H. Brandt (1957) investigated the occurrence of urobilinogen-I and -L in stool, and found that the predominant portion of fecal urobilinogens consists of urobilinogen-L. Noticeable amounts of urobilinogen-I were observed only during hemolytic conditions. French (1957) completely extracted fresh stool with 3% NaOH and found a sharp decrease of the absorption curve between 400 and 550 nm, and only a small peak at 508 nm. No readings were carried out below 380 nm. The peak at 508 nm increased steadily, and the extinctions at shorter wavelengths decreased simultaneously when the extract was stored in dim light at room temperature. The maximum extinction at 508 nm was reached after 6 days of storage. The extinctions at all wavelengths decreased sharply when the fresh stool extracts were reduced with $Fe(OH_2)$. This was especially true for extinctions at shorter wavelengths. During storage these reduced extracts developed a much more marked peak at 508 nm than the unreduced solutions. The absorption increase at 508 nm was caused by stercobilin, whereas the diffuse absorption was ascribed to the non-tetrapyrrole pigments of the stool. The absorption of the latter is suppressed by reduction and does not reappear after oxidation. C. J. Watson (1959) found that urobilinogen-L was predominant in most cases, but he found urobilinogen-I and occasionally urobilinogen-D in hemolytic disease.

Various investigators observed low fecal urobilinoid in chronic constipation (Wilbur and Addis, 1914; Belonogowa, 1928; Paschkis and Diamant, 1930; Singer, 1930; Heilmeyer, 1931b; C. J. Watson, 1937b; 1938, p. 2502), Heilmeyer found 142 mg/24 hours in a case of constipation which lasted 5 days. Later, during a period of daily defecation, this patient showed 246 mg/24 hours for a 3-day period. The lower excretion level was generally attributed to increased absorption during the comparatively long time the feces stayed in the colon. However, E. Jacobs and Scheffer (1925) and Skrijver (1929) pointed out that destruction takes place even in the anaerobic environment of the colon.

C. J. Watson et al. (1958) administered free and conjugated bilirubin through duodenal tube and found that the amount of urobilinogen formed from bilirubin glucuronide was about double that formed from free bilirubin. When the pigment was given to patients with acholic stools, there was no difference in urobilinogen formation, i.e., free and conjugated bilirubin gave the same amount of urobilinogen. When urobilinogen-D or -I was added to broth cultures of normal stool bacteria, it was found that urobilinogen-D was converted to urobilinogen-I. The latter compound was further reduced to urobilinogen-L. This finding indicates that urobilin-D and -I are normal intermediates of bilirubin degradation to urobilin-L.

Berendson et al. (1964*) investigated the fecal urobilinoids in a patient with idiopathic dyserythropoietic jaundice having a basic abnormality of the hemoglobin synthesis in the bone marrow. The fecal urobilinoid of this patient was mostly an atypical urobilinoid hitherto not described, but closely resembling urobilin-D with regard to spectral absorption and $FeCl_3$ reaction. Although it was optically inactive at 589 nm it exhibited activity at other wavelengths and was distinguished from racemic urobilin (H_{40}).

Lozzio and Royer (1965*) studied the feces of 25 humans with the $FeCl_3$ oxidation method and found that urobilinoids-I dominated making up all the fecal urobilinoid in 8 cases and 86–98% in the remaining 17. This result is contradictory to previous studies and renewed investigations on this problem are consequently desirable.

Summary

The stool of normal human adults generally contains 50–250 mg urobilinogen/24 hours. Daily variations are considerable, and therefore the analysis of samples collected over a period of 4 days is recommended. Nevertheless, randomly collected stool samples are just as valuable for clinical purposes. The concentration of fecal urobilinoids increases during menstruation, advanced pregnancy, and the first days of childbed. The fecal urobilinoid is very low during complete bile duct obstruction. Decreased concentrations (5 mg/24 hours or 10 mg/100 g and below) which prevail over longer periods strongly indicate neoplastic obstruction. Varying concentrations are observed during partial obstruction and in acute hepatitis; however, a completely normal excretion picture can also prevail in these conditions. Transitory very low excretion is often observed in hepatitis, but as a rule this only lasts for a few days. Increased excretion of fecal urobilinoids is encountered in diseases accompanied by hemolysis, for example, hereditary hemolytic jaundice, pernicious anemia in relapse, and acute malaria. Concentrations up to 3000 mg/24 hours can occur under certain conditions. No marked increase is found during polythemia, although it is known that in this condition hemoglobin production is doubled as compared to normal.

The fecal urobilinoid consists mainly of urobilinogen-L. Urobilinogen-I can be present in excess, especially in hemolytic disease. Occasionally urobilinogen-D also appears immediately after the discontinuance of antibiotic therapy and during extended antibiotic treatment.

Recently Lozzio and Royer (1965*) employing an oxidation method found that urobilinoids-I dominate in human feces. Renewed investigations on this question with reliable techniques and preferably isolation of crystalline urobilinoids are desirable.

3. FECAL UROBILINOIDS OF INFANTS AND CHILDREN

Some investigators demonstrated urobilinogens in the stool of the newborn. However, others could not confirm this finding. Generally, it is assumed that no noticeable amounts of fecal urobilinoids are present in infants between 5 and 7 months of age. This situation changes only when the intestinal flora starts to resemble the conditions prevailing in adults. With (1954, pp. 348–350) discussed the early literature dealing with this problem.

Dordi and Rossi (1936) never found urobilinoids in children under 8 months by means of Terwen's procedure. All breast-fed infants had more bilirubin than urobilins in stool. Urobilinoid excretion was 0–6 mg/24 hours in children under 2½ years old, and it was 10–50 mg/24 hours in those between 2½ and 7 years old. S. G. Ross et al. (1937) found 22–40 mg/24 hours in icteric newborns with a fluorescence method and 33–70 mg/24 hours in nonicteric infants. K. T. Simon (1939), who investigated 9 normal children ranging from 4 to 11 years of age with the method of Heilmeyer and Krebs, found the average 7.8 mg/24 hours, and never above 20 mg/24 hours.

Larsen and With (1943) examined the stools of 30 infants with Terwen's method as modified by With. These authors could not detect urobilinoids in infants under 3 weeks of age. Among 3-week-old children, they found 2 with traces of urobilinoids and 2 others with no urobilinoids present. Children aged between 1 and 12 months excreted 0–1.7 mg/24 hours. The authors pointed out that this amount of urobilin, when calculated on a kilogram per body weight basis is very low as compared with adults, i.e., the normal adult excretion of 50–250 mg/24 hours corresponds to 0.7–3.6 mg/kg for an individual weighing 70 kg, and would yield the anticipated value of 3.5–18 mg/24 hours for a 5-kg child.

Tat et al. (1943) found 0–0.7 mg/24 hours in 30 newborns during the first 5 days of life by means of Watson's extraction method. Urobilinoids always appeared before the end of the first week. The authors found 0–13 mg/24 hours in 31 children from 3 months to 11 years of age, who suffered from various diseases. Künzer (1951a) examined a series of newborns and children with Heilmeyer and Krebs' method. He found 0–1.7 (average 0.6) mg/24 hours in 8 newborns during the first week of life. During the second week, he found 0–3.2 (average 1.2) mg/24 hours in 7 infants, and 0–4.4 (average 2.0) mg/24 hours in 11 infants during the third to fourth weeks. Values of 0.4–3.7 (average 1.8) mg/24 hours were obtained in the fifth to sixth weeks (9 cases), and 0.1–2.4 (average 1.1) mg/24 hours during the seventh to eighth weeks (7 children). In addition, the following excretions were observed: 0.2–3.3 (average 1.6) mg/24 hours during the ninth to tenth week (9 cases); 1.1–5.7 mg/24 hours during the second to twelfth month (12 cases); 5.3–19.0 mg/24 hours during the first to fifth year (9 cases); and 25–51 mg/24 hours in children between 6 and 12 years of age (6 cases). Excretion per 24 hours based on kilograms body weight was 0.2–0.8 mg/kg during the second to the twelfth month, 0.4–1.6 mg/kg during the first to fifth year, and 0.93–1.81 mg/kg during the sixth to twelfth year. Bilirubin concentration was significantly higher than the urobilinoid level during the newborn period. The bilirubin level gradually decreased when the urobilinoid concentration started to increase in the later months of the first year.

A. Frölund (1954), using With's modifications of Terwen's method, examined 59 children between 2 and 16 years of age and found the following average concentrations (in milligrams/kilograms/24 hours): 1.55 for 2 year olds; 1.80 for 3 year olds; 1.55 for 4 year olds; 1.68 for 5 year olds; 1.90 for 6 year olds; 2.16 for 7 year olds; 2.02 for 8 year olds; 2.10 for 9 year olds; 2.68 for 10 year olds; 2.45 for 11 year olds; 2.60 for 12 year olds; 3.10 for 13 year olds; 3.10 for 14 year olds; and 2.90 for 15 to 16 year olds. She found excretions of 180–210 mg/24 hours or 2.9–3.3 mg/kg/24 hours in 10 normal adults. No difference was detected between boys and girls. The excretion increased with age and the concentrations reached adult levels at puberty. Vest (1959, Table VIII) found 0.33–1.24 mg/kg body weigth in meconium using Watson's modification of Terwen's method.

Stich (1948) and Rudolph (1952) carried out investigations of the appearance of urobilinogen-I and -L in children. These workers could never find the L-form in the meconium, but occasionally observed the I-form. Similarly, Baumgärtel (1950b) could never detect urobilinogen-L before the seventeenth month of life.

Heringová et al. (1965*) found a positive mesobiliviolin reaction in some infants during the second week of life and after the third week this reaction became positive more and more often. After the beginning of the 5th month it was positive in most cases. The Schlesinger fluorescence test was positive in 9 and negative in 64 during the first month, positive in 7 and negative in 5 during the second month, positive in 3 and negative in 2 during the 3rd month, positive in all 9 studied during the 4th month, positive in 8 and negative in 1 during the 5th month, and positive in 4 and negative in 1 during the 6th month. Garay et al. (1964b*) found an average of 3.4 μg urobilinoid per gram in 50 samples of human meconium. It is, however, not clear from their paper whether this finding was chromatographically verified.

Cameron et al. (1966a*) studied 3 children aged 25 weeks to 23 months with congenital biliary atresia and found 0, 0.1, and 0.3 mg urobilinogen per 24 hours (method of Balikov, 1958). After intravenous administration of C^{14}-bilirubin between 0 and 5.2% of the radioactivity was recovered from the feces.

Summary

When examinations are performed with reliable analytical techniques, only traces of urobilinoids are found before the end of the first week of life. Small amounts of urobilinoid gradually appear from this time on. Urobilinoid occurs more frequently and in higher concentrations in the next months, especially when the fecal bilirubin concentration starts to decrease. Nevertheless, urobilinoid excretion remains steadily low and irregular during the first year of life. A slow increase of fecal urobilinoid takes place in infancy, but excretion per kilogram body weight remains substantially below adult level which is reached only during puberty. This may be due to relatively lower hemoglobin degradation in young children than in adults (see Künzer, 1951a, Fig. 51, p. 76). Another explanation might be that the amount of hemoglobin degradation by way of dipyrryl compounds is larger in children than it is in adults.

4. FECAL UROBILINOIDS OF ANIMALS

Only a few investigators have studied fecal urobilinoids of animals. Wester (1912a,b) detected urobilin in the feces of horses, cattle, goats, and dogs. He was not able to find it in newborn calves and lambs. However, urobilin appeared 2–3 days after birth, and at the same time a putrid odor could be noticed. Fecal urobilin excretion was higher in young herbivorous domestic animals fed with milk, than in full grown animals who obtained pure vegetable food and excreted large amounts of feces. Nestlé (1913) found urobilin in the feces of all 59 horses examined; however, his analytic method was not reliable. Wilbur and Addis (1914) detected only traces of urobilin in the feces of rabbits and goats; cats and dogs also showed only very small amounts of this pigment. On the other hand, these workers observed that the feces of dogs were not completely free from urobilin even when the bile was prevented from entering the intestines by ligature or by the application of a biliary fistula. Steensma (1918, p. 50) found considerable amounts of urobilin in the stool of chimpanzees, gibbons, lions, mountain lions, bears, dogs, and cats, whereas the feces of elephants, camels, zebras, and rabbits were free from this compound. Similarly, urobilin was detected in the droppings of birds. Among the reptiles, crocodiles had fecal urobilin; snakes did not show any urobilin in the stool. These findings indicate the presence of urobilin in carnivorous animals and its absence in herbivorous ones. When rabbit bile was fed to dogs or, inversely, dog bile was given to rabbits, the excretion of fecal urobilins did not change in any way (Steensma, 1918, p. 52). The author concluded that the difference is due to the different intestinal flora. He succeeded in producing feces rich in urobilin in rabbits by feeding them bread and milk without adding any food containing cellulose. However, the rabbits died from this diet within a few days because of constipation and ileus. He believed that the dry, hard feces of rabbits are responsible for the absence of urobilin.

Rosenthal and Melchior (1922) found considerable amounts of biliverdin in the droppings of pigeons, but only traces of urobilin. Kämmerer and Miller (1922b, 1923) proved that urobilinogen production took place when substrates containing protein and bilirubin were incubated with fecal bacterial cultures of carnivorous animals. No urobilin formation occurred when the feces of herbivorous animals were used. Moreover, these authors found that fecal bacteria did not reduce biliverdin, believed to be the predominant bile pigment of herbivora. Beijers (1923, Chapter 4) proved that acholia has no influence on the color of the feces in herbivora, since large amounts of unabsorbed plant pigments are present in it. Royer (1943) found 0.5–20 mg urobilin/24 hours in the feces of normal dogs. After obstructing the common bile duct, the fecal urobilinoid content dropped to about 1% of its original value (Royer, 1943, p. 116). Legge (1949) found a considerable increase of fecal urobilinoid in rats after sulfanilamide administration. At the same time large quantities of urobilinogen-I appeared in the feces, a finding which was ascribed to the influence of sulfonamide on the intestinal flora. Garner (1955) isolated urobilin-L in crystalline form from the feces of cattle, thus proving that urobilins can also be present in herbivora. The fact that oxen excrete wet feces, unlike other herbivora examined (horses, goats, and rabbits), could perhaps explain the difference.

Cameron et al. (1963*) determined the 24-hour fecal output of urobilinogen of 7 normal healthy dogs and 14 dogs with complete biliary occlusion using the benzaldehyde extraction method (Balikov, 1958) and found 15–56 (average 32.0) mg/24 hours in the normal dogs and 2.1–6.1 (average 4.1) mg/24 hours in the obstructed. Small amounts of urobilinoid was present in the feces of the obstructed dogs even 63 days after the obstruction (4.2 mg/24 hours in one case).

Lozzio and Royer (1965*) studied the fecal urobilinoid in 10 dogs, 10 cats, white rats, and guinea pigs. In four of the dogs only urobilinoids-I were present; in the remaining six there were equal quantities of type I and type L. In four of the cats only urobilinoids-I were present; in the remaining six type I made up ca. 80% of the urobilinoid and type L the rest. In the rats and guinea pigs only type I was found. These results differ markedly from other findings, for which repeated studies including other analytical methods are required.

Cameron et al. (1966b*) studied 6 rhesus monkeys before and after experimental biliary occlusion and found no bilirubin, but he did find urobilinogen 1.4–6.5 (average 4.6) mg/24 hours with the method of Balikov (1958) before the occlusion—calculated per kg body weight 0.37–1.83 mg/24 hours. After the occlusion they found 0.2–1.2 mg urobilinogen per 24 hours (average 0.8).

Summary

Observations involving fecal urobilinoids in animals are scarce. This is especially true for investigations carried out with reliable methods. Urobilinoids is absent from the feces of newborn animals. This pigment appears a few days after birth in herbivora, but it disappears again when the food of the young animals is changed from milk to vegetables. According to experimental evidence, fecal urobilin is absent in herbivora which excrete dry feces, but it is present in the moist dung of oxen. Urobilinoid is present in the feces of carnivorous mammals, but absent in birds. Some reptiles seem to excrete fecal urobilinoid, whereas it is missing in others. For a complete understanding of the biology of bile pigments, it would be necessary to extend the investigations over a larger group of animals. Amphibia and fish should be included in these studies.

Additional Readings

Section A

With, T. K. (1967). Stercobilin and the colour of faeces. A perpetual textbook error. *In* "Bilirubin Metabolism" (I. A. D. Bouchier and B. H. Billing, eds.), pp. 135–139. Blackwell, Oxford.

Section C

Wollaeger, E. E., and Gross, J. B. (1966). Complete obstruction of the extrahepatic biliary tract due to carcinoma as determined by the fecal urobilinogen test: Incidence and effect of serum bilirubin concentrations. *Medicine* **45**, 529–536.

CHAPTER IX

Bile Pigments of Tissue Fluids, Secretions, and Organs

The study of bile pigments has been concerned mainly with blood, urine, bile, and stool; more seldom other biological materials, such as lymph, various transudates and exudates, cerebrospinal liquid, tears, perspiration, milk, and other secretion products, as well as various tissues and organs, have been included in these determinations. The scattered literature in this area will be discussed on the following pages.

A. Bile Pigments of Lymph, Transudates, and Exudates

In biological fluids which contain only small amounts of cells, the analysis of bile pigments can be performed as in the blood serum. However, if strongly purulent exudates are involved, the problems become similar to those encountered in tissue analysis. The presence of bilirubin in hemorrhagic transudates and exudates has already been discussed (Chapter II,B and C). The same is true for the liver lymph (Chapter IV,C,3). The situation prevailing in the peripheral cutaneous lymph was studied in cantharidine blisters. It should be mentioned that the liquid examined in this method is not a true lymph but a fluid which is mixed to a large extent with plasma from the blood vessels.

Scherck (1928) found that the bilirubin content of the blister fluid was lower than that of the serum in 20 patients with regressing jaundice. F. Umber and Rosenberg (1928) doubted the value of bilirubin determination in the blister fluid for the study of tissue bilirubin. Julesz and Winkler (1933) found that the bilirubin content of serum was usually about 25% higher than that of the blister fluid in the 33 icteric patients examined; the blister fluid had a higher bilirubin level than that of the serum in only eight cases with regressing icterus. The ratio of direct to indirect reaction was generally the same in the serum and in the blister fluid; however, a direct reaction could occur in the blister fluid even when the serum reaction was indirect. Ottenberg (1943, p. 945) observed that the bilirubin content of serum was higher than that of the blister fluid in beginning jaundice, whereas the situation was just the opposite during disappearing icterus; he regularly obtained an indirect diazo reaction in the blister fluid. Del Bono (1949) examined 16 patients with obstructive or hepatic icterus. This author used the methods of Jendrassik and Cleghorn and of Jendrassik and Gróf and found higher bilirubin concentrations in the serum than in the blister fluid during beginning jaundice, whereas the levels were about identical during the stage of regression. The bilirubin concentration of blister fluid was never distinctly higher than that of the serum. Based on the analysis of various components, Del Bono concluded that the blister fluid consists of a mixture of true cutaneous lymph and blood extravasate.

A few workers studied bilirubin in edema fluid, transudates, and exudates of body cavities. Andrewes (1924c) found 0.25–1 mg bilirubin/100 ml in ascites of icteric patients. Meakins (1927) could obtain only a very weak diazo reaction in fluid obtained by puncturing the edematous skin of icteric patients who suffered from cardiac failure. Altschule and Volk (1937) found most often traces and always below 1.3 mg bilirubin/100 ml in hydrothorax fluid, ascites, or in edema of eight cardiac patients having serum bilirubin contents of 0.60–2.80 mg/100 ml. The bilirubin concentration was generally higher in fluids rich in proteins. Laguna (1951) examined edema and ascitic fluid in 15 icteric patients, most of whom suffered from cirrhosis of the liver. The serum bilirubin content in these cases was 0.6–24 mg/100 ml and the jaundice lasted for several months. In about half of the patients bilirubin was detected in the liquids collected by aspiration. In ascites the bilirubin concentrations were 0–50% of those of the serum, whereas the edema fluid showed only 3.2–17%. The bilirubin content expressed as milligrams bilirubin per gram albumin was 0.3–6.3 in the serum, 0–13.0 in the edema fluid, and 0–6.0 in the ascites. The highest bilirubin concentration determined in the edema fluid was 4 mg/100 ml (in a patient with 24 mg/100 ml of serum). The corresponding value for ascites was 3.6 mg/100 ml (24 mg/100 ml serum). No close correlation was found between bilirubin content and the amounts of albumin or protein present in these fluids. W. W. Hurst *et al.* (1951) found 0.1–0.8 (average 0.3) mg/100 ml in the edema fluid of cardiac patients with serum bilirubin content of 0.1–1.8 (average 0.65) mg/100 ml.

Determinations of urobilinoids in tissue fluids are scarce. Kiener and Engel (1887), as well as C. Stich (1901), occasionally found urobilinoids in the ascites of cases of jaundice. Contrary to this, Herscher (1902, p. 73 et seq.) found no urobilinoids in three cases of liver cirrhosis with massive urobilinuria. Hildebrandt (1906) found small amounts of urobilin in the lymph of the thoracic duct obtained by autopsy from a patient who died of pernicious anemia. Troisier (1909) and Tefik and Ibrahim (1909) found urobilin in the transudates and exudates of body cavities during liver cirrhosis, tuberculosis, and hemorrhagic serositis. Castex and Lopez Garcia (1937) found 5.6 mg urobilinogen/100 ml pus in liver abscess.

Summary

Bilirubin is present in the lymph, transudates, and exudates of icteric patients. However, the bilirubin concentration is lower in these liquids than it is in the serum. The bilirubin content of these fluids is not closely correlated with their protein content. Urobilinoids can also be present in these fluids of the body, but few reliable observations are available as yet.

B. Bile Pigments of Cerebrospinal Fluid, Intraocular Humors, Amniotic, and Synovial Fluid

Xanthochromic cerebrospinal fluid (CSF) contains bilirubin and is present in patients with hemorrhages and tumors of the central nervous system. Occasionally, urobilinoids were also found in it (Lemaire, 1905, p. 93; Leschke, 1921b; Naumann, 1947). Lepehne (1942b) examined CSF in 8 xanthochromic liquors and found 0.4–3.8 mg bilirubin/100 ml. Polonovski *et al.* (1942) observed a positive indirect diazo reaction and a $CHCl_3$ extractable bilirubin in the xanthochromic CSF. Naumann (1947) found 2–5.5 mg bilirubin/100 ml in the cisternal fluid in two cases of subarachnoidal hemorrhage, but he could not find any bilirubin in four other cases. Cumings (1950) found 0.01–1.25 mg bilirubin/100 ml in the fluid of brain cysts. Barrows *et al.* (1955) examined 149 xanthochromic CSF's in 68 cases using the diazo reaction which was carried out with 1 ml of the fluid, 0.5 ml methanol, and 0.5 ml diazo reagent; spectrophotometric measurement followed after 30 minutes. Besides bilirubin, oxyhemoglobin and methemoglobin were found. Oxyhemoglobin and bilirubin were demonstrated in subarachnoidal hemorrhage, but only methemoglobin was found in subdural hematomas. Only bilirubin was present in spinal and ventricular blockage; this was also true in cases of jaundice. Twenty-seven colorless fluids were examined for comparison, but were completely free from any kind of pigments. The oxyhemoglobin content reached its maximum in the CSF 2 days after the hemorrhage, whereas bilirubin appeared within 2–3 days after it and increased gradually with a simultaneous drop of the hemoglobin. The authors erroneously assumed that the presence of living cells is necessary for bilirubin formation from hemoglobin (see Chapter II,D).

As long as the blood–CSF barrier is intact, the CSF of icteric patients is colorless. However, when the barrier function is disturbed, bilirubin enters the CSF. This can occur during inflammatory diseases of the meninges, in the newborn and especially in premature infants. In severe, long-lasting jaundice, small amounts of bilirubin can be present even with normal blood–CSF barrier, but this is the exception. As a rule the CSF is colorless in all forms of jaundice except in the newborn. Since these problems are completely different in adults and in newborns, they will be discussed separately. With the exception of the newborn period children behave as adults in this respect.

Schmorl (1910) found colorless CSF, obtained by autopsy, in seven of ten severe icterus cases. The remaining three cases showed either inflammations or hemorrhages of the meninges. Borchardt (1923) examined the CSF of 33 icteric subjects and found it colorless in 25 and xanthochromic in the other 8 in whom local hemorrhages had occurred. Von Gündell and Jacobi (1926) found colorless CSF in three of six patients with severe jaundice and demonstrated traces of bilirubin in the other three. Meakins (1927) mentioned that the CSF is free from bilirubin during jaundice. De Castro (1930) observed colorless CSF in two of 7 patients whose serum bilirubin was 4–20 mg/100 ml. In the other five cases the CSF was faintly yellow or green and gave a slight diazo reaction. Saiki (1931b) stated that no bilirubin was present in the CSF of dogs as long as the blood–CSF barrier was intact. However, when it was permeable due to pathological conditions, bilirubin could be detected. N. Klein and Szentmihàlyi (1932) reported two cases of acute yellow liver atrophy whose clear, intensely yellow CSF showed a direct diazo reaction. In one of these cases the brain was found to be yellow at autopsy. In one case 52 bilirubin units were found in the blood and 2 in the CSF (about 25 and 1 mg/100 ml). A total of 12 jaundice cases were examined; 5 of them showed a colorless liquor, 4 others had a slightly yellowish one, and the remaining 3 had markedly yellow spinal fluids with positive direct diazo reaction. It was established that for the appearance of bilirubin in the CSF the duration of jaundice is more important than its intensity. Only the two cases of acute liver atrophy were recognized as exceptions; these findings were attributed to damage of the blood–CSF barrier.

Ottenberg (1943, p. 945) mentioned that the CSF is always colorless in adults, but it can be yellow in icteric children. With (1945e) observed colorless fluids in three of five severely icteric patients. The serum bilirubin concentration was 10–24 mg/100 ml. The spinal fluid was slightly yellow in the two other cases, and concentrations below 0.1 mg bilirubin/100 ml were found (i.e., less than 1% of the serum bilirubin content). Amatuzio *et al.* (1953) examined the CSF of ten icteric patients with liver cirrhosis and eleven with hepatic coma. From the former group, two exhibited yellow spinal fluid (0.11 mg/100 ml at an average of 13 mg/100 ml of serum); the cases of coma showed the same situation (average in liquor 0.35 mg/100 ml, in serum 16.2 mg/100 ml). No bilirubin was found in the CSF of 18 normal subjects.

L. B. Berman *et al.* (1954), using the diazo reaction, found traces of bilirubin in the CSF of all of 20 icteric patients examined. In these cases the jaundice lasted from 1 day to 6 weeks, the serum bilirubin content was 1.0–26.2 mg/100 ml, and that of the spinal fluid was 0.01–0.12 mg/100 ml. Similarly, 0.007–0.11 mg bilirubin/100 ml was demonstrated in the CSF of nine of eleven normal subjects with the diazo method with spectrophotometric determination at 540 nm. However, such slight reactions can hardly be considered definite proof for the presence of bilirubin. The concentration in CSF was 1/10 to 1/100 that of serum. There was a certain positive relationship between the concentrations in the serum and those of the cerebrospinal fluid; repeated experiments also confirmed this during the course of jaundice in individual patients. No cases of hemolytic icterus were examined.

Barrows *et al.* (1955) examined 12 icteric patients; they found no bilirubin in the CSF in two patients with less than 10 mg bilirubin/100 ml serum whose jaundice did not last longer than 2 weeks. The other patients showed 0.02–0.70 mg bilirubin/100 ml spinal fluid and 6–19 mg/100 ml serum, the duration of icterus being 10–40 days. The highest level, 0.70 mg/100 ml of CSF was found in a patient with 19 mg bilirubin/100 ml serum. B. A. Mendioroz (personal communication, 1957) found 0.10–0.35 mg bilirubin/100 ml CSF at serum bilirubin levels of 2–35 mg/100 ml in seven cases of hepatitis or obstructive jaundice.

Kronholm and Lintrup (1960) studied the absorption curve in the range 390–500 nm in 1250 spinal fluids from 1123 patients and developed a valuable method for diagnosis of hemorrhagic diseases of the central nervous system (Kronholm and Lintrup, 1960, 1961; Kronholm, 1960, 1961, 1962). Their method is based on separate determinations of bilirubin, oxyhemoglobin, and methemoglobin by measurements of the absorption curve of the spinal fluid in the range 390–500 nm. Their papers are illustrated with numerous examples of typical curves. In fresh hemorrhagic processes, oxyhemoglobin dominates, giving a sharp maximum at 415 nm. In hematomas of longer duration methemoglobin, exhibiting a maximum of 406 nm, and bilirubin, with a maximum at 455 nm, dominate. Patients with nonhemolytic jaundice exhibited maxima at 420, 430 and 455 nm in their spinal fluid, whereas jaundiced newborns had a maximum at 455 nm like xanthochromic spinal fluid.

Several authors studied the bilirubin content of the CSF of the *new-*

born. Framm (1925) observed intensely yellow CSF in premature babies with severe jaundice. Roberts (1925, 1928) examined the CSF of 900 newborns during the first 24 hours of life and consistently found a yellow coloration. In the normal newborn the color was usually 1/25 of the color of the serum determined as icterus index. None of the fluids examined was completely colorless. Levison *et al.* (1926) regularly found yellow spinal fluids in newborns, but could not demonstrate bilirubin. Waitz (1928) observed yellow spinal fluid in about half the newborns he examined. He assumed that the color was due to the presence of blood, since the fluid, which appeared to contain blood at birth, later turned yellow. Garrahan (1928) examined the CSF in 177 newborns; only 20 of the fluids were colorless. Samson (1930), who examined 40 newborns, found that whereas during the first 8 days a yellow CSF was practically always present, this was not true for the following days. In premature infants the color was stronger and lasted longer, 14 days in most cases, and occasionally 4 weeks. The color varied from slight traces to pronounced yellow, and the more intensely colored liquids always showed a slightly positive diazo reaction.

Otila (1948) examined 100 "healthy" premature babies by performing 200 spinal taps. The spinal fluids were divided into four groups (I to IV), corresponding to color intensity. Group I was completely colorless, group IV was definitely yellow. The fluids were all more or less yellow in premature babies at the age of 1 week or younger. However, the color faded as time progressed. After 4 weeks none of the fluids showed coloration corresponding to group IV. The yellow coloration was more intense when the jaundice of the child was more severe. Yellow spinal fluids were not unusual after the first month. It was established that bilirubin was the prevailing pigment, but other pigments were also present. It was believed that these occur because of hemorrhagic processes in the central nervous system; however, no further significance was attributed to their presence. Indeed, cases of cerebral hemorrhages were demonstrated by autopsy in which the CSF had remained colorless. The increased permeability of the blood–CSF barrier in the newborn was considered an important pathogenic factor.

Peluffo and Prado (1949a,b) examined 261 newborns, of which 183 were normal, and found that the CSF of the jaundiced newborn was always definitely xanthochromic, and contained 0.3–0.5 mg protein/100 ml and gave a positive Pandy's reaction. The spinal bilirubin content was proportional to that of the serum, but independent of hemorrhages in the cerebrospinal cavity.

Wyers and Bakker (1954) examined the cerebrospinal fluids of 50 newborns. Only one of these fluids was not xanthochromic; 26 showed a slight coloration and 23 a more pronounced one. All these children were full-term babies; the tapping was performed 2–24 hours after birth. The bilirubin concentration was 0.05–0.25 mg/100 ml in eleven of these cases. It was assumed that bilirubin was also present in the other cases, but it could not be detected by Jendrassik and Cleghorn's method because of the low concentrations.

Claireaux *et al.* (1955) found only a little over 1 mg bilirubin/100 ml in the spinal fluid of icteric newborns with kernicterus. The serum bilirubin concentration was usually over 20 mg/100 ml in these cases. These findings indicate that the concentration in the cerebrospinal fluid is only exceptionally more than 1/20 the concentration of bilirubin in serum.

Gyllensvärd and Malmström (1962) examined the CSF of 36 healthy immature infants and found bilirubin concentrations of 0–0.5 mg/100 ml. No correlation between bilirubin levels in serum and CSF was demonstrated. A high protein level and red cell count in the CSF were frequently recorded, but other signs of hemorrhage could not be demonstrated. Possible factors responsible for the elevated bilirubin in the CSF of prematures are increased permeability of the blood–CSF barrier, hemorrhage, and aseptic meningitis. Opinions on the mutual role of these factors diverge widely.

The so-called blood–CSF barrier is of significance in this area. It can be expressed by the ratio CSF bilirubin/serum bilirubin (CSFB/SB). Nasaralla *et al.* (1958) investigated this ratio in the newborn; Ernster *et al.* (1957) made similar determinations in rabbits. The quotient CSFB/SB was significantly higher in newborns than in adults; this was especially seen in premature cases. After *p*-chloromercuribenzoate injections into the cisterna of rabbits, the CSFB/SB ratio became ten times higher than normal. Herlin (1958) could demonstrate the importance of the blood–CSF barrier for the penetration of bilirubin into the cerebrospinal fluid with experiments with artificial hyperbilirubinemia in rabbits. When *p*- chloromercuribenzoate was injected in the cisterna, the bilirubin concentration in the CSF rose 4.3 times higher than that of the control animals injected with saline. T.-C. Lee and Hsia (1959) confirmed these findings. The ratio CSFB/SB was 2.7 times higher in rabbits weighing 0.5 kg than in those with 2.0 kg body weight. Furthermore, the authors observed that there is a close parallel between the protein content of the CSF and its bilirubin content in the rabbit. The ratio CSFB/SB was below 0.6 in experiments with *p*-chloromercuribenzoate. A quotient of 3.3 was reached in only one case.

Lazard and Sobotka (1962) injected 0.02 ml of a millimolar solution of *p*-chloromercuribenzoate intracisternally to adult rats, and 5 minutes later 48 mg bilirubin/kg body weight i.v. This resulted in pronounced jaundice of the brain. If 20 times higher doses of p-chloromercuribenzoate were injected i.v. simultaneously with bilirubin to normal rats, no jaundice of the brain followed. The authors concluded that p-chloromercuriben-zoate must act on the hypophysis and that the brain jaundice must be due to hormonal influences. This was confirmed in hypophysectomized rats. Such animals developed jaundice of the brain after i.v. injection of unconjugated bilirubin, whereas normal controls did not.

The *amniotic fluid* was studied by Gairdner *et al.* (1950), Bevis (1952a,b, 1953, 1956), Walker (1957), Wild (1961), and Liley (1961*), and later by an increasing number of investigators when it became clear that aminocentesis by the 36th week of pregnancy and subsequent deter-mination of the bilirubin in the amniotic fluid was a valuable method of preventing hemolytic disease in the newborn. Several analytical tech-niques were proposed; the spectrophotometric ones yield only arbitrary figures in spite of complicated and time-consuming procedures, whereas the most recent methods based on the diazo reaction give reliable quanti-tative measurements using a reasonably simple technique and, therefore, are to be preferred.

Bevis (1952–1956) examined 205 samples of 98 patients, of which 41 suffered from morbus hemolyticus neonatorum. Bilirubin concentrations between 0 and 7.5 mg/100 ml were found in the amniotic fluid. No relationship could be found between the severity of hemolytic icterus and the bilirubin content of amniotic fluid. The bilirubin concentration was high when this fluid was contaminated with meconium. Large amounts of mesobilifuscin were detected in the amniotic fluid during morbus hemolyticus. The urobilin concentration was 1–2 mg/100 ml. Wild (1961) studied amniotic fluid obtained on abdominal paracentesis during the 32nd to 35th week of pregnancy in 72 Rh-negative mothers with incompatible pregnancy. He examined 77 amniotic fluids for bili-rubin and protein and found bilirubin between 0 and 1 mg/100 ml and a marked positive correlation between bilirubin and protein concentra-tions. If the fetus died *in utero,* the bilirubin concentration of the amniotic fluid decreased. The bilirubin of the amniotic fluid is of fetal origin.

Liley (1961*) presented spectrophotometric findings in liquor speci-mens from 101 rhesus-sensitized pregnant women and suggested that such liquor analyses may be used with precision in selecting the optimal time for delivery. The liquors were obtained by amniocentesis, centri-fuged, and examined (either fresh or after refrigeration to protect from light) in a spectrophotometer in a 1-cm cell in the range 350–670 nm with readings at every 5 nm around the peaks at 415 and 450; further a reading at 700 nm was taken. Distilled water was used as a blank. The density was plotted on a logarithmic scale against the wavelength on a normal scale. From the curve the height of the 450 nm peak due to bilirubin was measured. This peak was found to be definitely higher in the presence of hemolytic anemia than without hemolysis if the maturity of the fetus was taken into account.

Mackay and Watson (1962) performed aminiocentesis in 63 patients with rhesus immunization during the 33rd week of pregnancy. Bilirubin in the amniotic fluid was determined with a diazo method with methanol as coupling reagent, reading after 10 minutes at 535 nm, and comparison with a bilirubin standard. Concentrations varying from 0 to 2.34 mg/100 ml were found. The authors discuss the value of amniotic fluid bilirubin as a guide to the decision of whether exchange transfusion in the infant is necessary. With bilirubin levels in the amniotic fluid below 0.05 mg/100 ml, exchange transfusion was very seldom necessary, with levels between 0.06 and 0.13 mg/100 ml it was necessary in about a quarter of the infants, and with levels above 0.13 mg/100 ml it was necessary in nearly all cases.

Liley (1963*) discussed pitfalls, errors, and limits of accuracy in the antenatal prediction of the severity of hemolytic disease of newborns from analysis of amniotic fluid. It is essential to be certain that the material studied is really amniotic fluid as in rare cases fetal ascitic fluid may be obtained on aspiration instead. Also multiple amniotic sacs and amniotic cysts may introduce errors of judgment. It is important to remember that it is density differences and not absolute values which count because the 450 nm density may vary considerably with procedures such as filtration and centrifugation. Therefore it is the departure of the spectral curve from linearity at 450 nm which is to be measured.

Lewis *et al.* (1964*) employed an elaborate spectrophotometric method closely similar to that of Liley on 38 Rh-sensitized mothers on whom 78 successful amniocenteses were performed as outpatient procedures. At least 3 ml of fluid was removed, the specimens were refrigerated and shielded from light until analysis was performed within 48 hours. Before analysis the specimens were centrifuged for 10 minutes at 14,000 rpm; that this procedure most likely will result in a significant increase of the temperature is not discussed. Spectrophotometric readings were now performed at 15–20 separate wavelengths between 350 and 700 nm and the result plotted on special paper. The presence of a peak at 450 nm indicates the presence of bilirubin and quantitation in arbitrary units was performed based on measuring the distance between the top of the curve at 450 nm and a certain tangential line on the curve. This method is time consuming if a recording spectrophotometer is not available and it is only semiquantitative.

Fleming and Woolf (1965*) used 10 ml liquor collected by amniocentesis between the 32nd and 35th week of pregnancy and centrifuged for ½ hour at 4000 rpm, after which spectrophotometric readings at 700, 623, 576, and 462 nm were carried out on the undiluted liquor or on an appropriate dilution if the pigment concentration was high. Then ca. 2 mg of sodium dithionite was added to the cuvette and its contents mixed by inversion until the crystals had dissolved. The reading at 700 nm was repeated. The lower of the two readings at 700 nm was used in the calculation. Four readings were taken in order to correct for methemoglobin, oxyhemoglobin, and turbidity, and the following calculation formula was used: mg bilirubin/100 ml $= 1.25\ E_{462} - 0.91\ E_{576} - 1.15\ E_{623} + 0.11\ E_{700}$.

Reproducibility studies showed a range within 0.006 mg/100 ml and a recovery percentage of 95–110%. In a private communication the authors mention that amniotic fluid bilirubin concentrations of 0.0–0.07 mg/100 ml means absence of hemolytic disease, 0.08–0.11 means slight hemolytic disease probably without need of treatment, 0.12–0.20 indicates need of exchange transfusion, and 0.20–0.75 indicates that at least two exchange transfusions are needed. The highest value encountered was 2.86 mg/100 ml. They concluded that in pregnancies where hemolytic disease is suspected amniocentesis should always be performed by the 36th week of pregnancy in order to remove the exposed fetus before damage is done.

Crosby and Merrill (1965*) performed spectrophotometric readings on the centrifuged amniotic fluid at 10 nm intervals from 350 to 700 nm and measured the distance between the 450 nm extinction and a tangential line on the curve. In this way expressions in arbitrary units were obtained. Studies on 42 pregnancies complicated by isoimmunization showed a high degree of correlation between the figures obtained and the severity of the fecal hemolytic processes.

Pennington and Hall (1966*) suggested extracting the amniotic fluid with $CHCl_3$ in order to get reasonable optical densities with the very low bilirubin concentrations in question. Samples of 10 ml were placed in a closed bottle and refrigerated until analysis was carried out and extraction performed by shaking for 10 minutes with 40 ml $CHCl_3$. The $CHCl_3$ was then evaporated to dryness in vacuo in a round-bottom 50 ml flask at temperatures not exceeding 40°C. The residue was dissolved in 2.5 ml $CHCl_3$ and subjected to spectrophotometric reading at 450, 420, and 480 nm. The method was compared to measurements with Lathe and Ruthven's diazo method and good correlation was found. The $CHCl_3$ method gave, however, systematically ca. 14% lower values than the diazo method. Added bilirubin was recovered with a loss of 5–10%. The method of Pennington and Hall which includes concentration of the very dilute samples is theoretically well founded and technically rather simple. It might, however, be possible to increase its specificity by performing diazo reaction on concentrated extract.

Bowman and Pollock (1965a*,b*) performed bilirubin determinations (method of Liley) on amniotic fluid obtained on transabdominal amniocentesis between the 30th and 34th week of gestation in 35 mothers and in some cases as early as the 24th week. The addition of this chemical analysis to the usual clinical and immunological criteria increased the accuracy of their prediction of the status of the fetus to nearly 100%. The study of the amniotic fluid permitted more accurate timing of induction of labor in threatened intrauterine death and saved less severely affected fetuses from the hazards of prematurity.

Kruijswijk *et al.* (1966*) measured amniotic fluid bilirubin with a modification of Michaëlsson's method for bilirubin in serum using Frankonite KL to adsorb the azobilirubin and subsequent elution with a solution of sodium acetate and cadmium sulfate in 2-methoxyethanol. In this way the azobilirubin was eluted into the same volume of the original sample of amniotic fluid as its blue Cd-complex. The method was calibrated with a bilirubin standard. It was claimed that concentrations down to 25 μg bilirubin per 100 ml can be determined with an accuracy of ca. 5%.

With (1945e) studied *intraocular humors.* In a patient who died of obstructive icterus of long duration (serum bilirubin content 20–25 mg/100 ml), he found only traces of bilirubin in the aqueous humor and vitreous body. Naumann and Young (1960) investigated bilirubin present post mortem in the serum, vitreous body, spinal fluid, and *synovial fluid* in 78 autopsies of 44 jaundiced and 34 nonjaundiced subjects. The average bilirubin concentrations in the jaundiced subjects were 8.6 mg/100 ml serum, 2.02 mg/100 ml synovial fluid, 0.23 mg/100 ml spinal fluid, and 0.04 mg/100 ml vitreous body. The maximum values were 36.0, 10.5, 4.0, and 0.48 mg/100 ml, respectively. In the nonjaundiced subjects bilirubin was absent from the spinal fluid and vitreous body if there were no hemorrhagic processes in the CNS or eye. The synovial fluid, however, contained bilirubin averaging 0.28 mg/100 ml in the nonjaundiced subjects, and the ratio of synovial fluid bilirubin to serum bilirubin was, on the average, 1/4. Studies of the synovial bilirubin in live subjects have not been reported.

Engel and Kiener (1887b) was unable to detect urobilin in the intraocular humors of an icteric patient, whose ascites contained urobilin.

Summary

As long as the blood–CSF barrier is intact, only unmeasurable amounts of bilirubin are present in the cerebrospinal fluid. Even in cases of severe and lengthy icterus only traces of this pigment are found. When the barrier becomes permeable for a longer period of time, for instance during the first week of life of normal or premature infants, bilirubin appears in the spinal fluid. However, the bilirubin concentrations present in the spinal fluid are, at best, 1/20 of the serum bilirubin level. The so-called xanthochromic CSF is found after hemorrhages in the cerebro-spinal canal and in some cases of tumor. The color is due to bilirubin, methemoglobin, and oxyhemoglobin, and a close spectrophotometric analysis gives information of diagnostic value. In such cases, the bilirubin concentration can reach several milligrams per 100 ml.

Bilirubin determination in the amniotic fluid is of importance in antenatal prediction of the state of the fetus in hemolytic disease of the newborn. Several analytical methods have been proposed for determination of the very low concentrations involved. Diazo methods involving concentration before measurements are recommended.

From the material available, the aqueous and vitreous humors of the eye appear to exhibit the same behavior as the CSF. Investigations on the spinal fluid bilirubin/serum bilirubin (CSFB/SB) ratio are discussed. Post mortem studies show low bilirubin concentrations in the spinal fluid in jaundice, amounting to about 1/35 of the serum bilirubin. The vitreous body contains only 1/200 of the serum bilirubin concentration post mortem. The synovial fluid contains bilirubin post mortem even in nonjaundiced subjects. In jaundiced subjects its bilirubin content was about 1/4 of the serum bilirubin. *In vivo* studies of the bilirubin of the synovial fluid have not been reported.

C. Bile Pigment Content of Various Secretions and Excretions

Several authors found small amounts of bilirubin in the *sweat* of strongly icteric patients (Frerichs, 1858, Vol. I, p. 109; von Müller, 1887, p. 73; Leube, 1888; Klemperer, 1933). Others found it free from bilirubin (Eppinger, 1937, p. 98; Ottenberg, 1943; With, 1945e). Two sources of error are present in such determinations: contamination with icteric urine and admixture of bilirubin-containing skin cells which have been scaled off. This probably explains satisfactorily the contradictions among the various authors. The pigment lanaurin, demonstrated in the sweat of sheep by Rimington and Stewart (1932), should also be mentioned here. This compound seems to be closely related to the bile pigments, and it could possibly be a dipyrrole pigment.

Tears, saliva, gastric juice, intestinal juice, pancreatic juice, and *vaginal secretion* have been found free from bilirubin even during severe jaundice (Frerichs, 1858; Leyden, 1866; von Müller, 1887; Meakins, 1927; Eppinger, 1937; With, 1945e). Nevertheless, Calvert *et al.* (1954) described a lethal case of fulminant hepatitis with hepatic coma in which the tears were yellow and gave positive reaction with Fouchet's reagent when the patient became comatose; the serum bilirubin concentration was between 5 and 8 mg/100 ml. Umber (1926, p. 27) and With (1945e) found that the *milk* of icteric mothers was free from bilirubin; in contrast, Frerichs (1858, Vol. I, p. 111) and Klemperer (1933) maintained that it contained bilirubin. However, this problem has not yet been explored sufficiently. Observations on animals would be of interest in this area.

Only *sweat* and *milk* have been investigated for the possible presence of urobilinoids. Leube (1888) was unable to find urobilin in the sweat of an icteric patient who had no urobilinuria. Paulsmeyer (1937) tried to detect urobilinogen in cow's milk with Heilmeyer and Krebs' method, after precipitation of casein with glacial acetic acid, and showed that urobilinogen is not adsorbed on the casein precipitate. He was able to detect a certain amount of this pigment in the milk of healthy cows (maximum value 0.23 mg/100 ml). However, this finding is rather surprising, and the possibility that the benzaldehyde reaction was not due to urobilinogen has to be seriously considered. This reaction could have been positive because of the presence of phylloerythrinogen ingested with food (see Baumgärtel, 1950b, p. 129). Human milk has not been investigated for the presence of urobilinoids.

Finally, it should be mentioned that excretions could contain bilirubin when hemorrhages occurred in the respective glands involved or if, in icteric patients, inflammation renders the parenchyma or the duct systems of the glands permeable for proteins.

Summary

Sweat, tears, gastric juice, intestinal juice, pancreatic juice, and vaginal secretion are free from bilirubin during jaundice. Only one case was reported in which bilirubin appeared in the tears in hepatic coma. Very little is known about the bile pigment content of milk; more studies on animals should be carried out in this area. It has been claimed that urobilinoids are present in the milk of healthy cows; this, however, is unlikely and needs confirmation.

D. Bile Pigments in Tissues and Organs

Quantitative bilirubin and biliverdin determinations are difficult to perform in the tissues because these compounds are bound to proteins, especially to elastin (see Chapter IV,B). Moreover, under certain conditions the blood of icteric organs can contain large amounts of bile pigments. To exclude the bilirubin present in the blood of these organs, perfusion is necessary before the analysis (F. Rosenthal, 1930; Gassmann, 1930). However, in the light of Rosenthal's experiments, the error introduced by this source will not be significant in severe protracted jaundice. Besides this complication, post mortem autolysis must also be considered; therefore, analysis should be carried out in completely fresh organs or in quick-frozen organs. The best analytical process would be a complete disintegration of the organs by enzymatic digestion. Elastase and pancreas extracts would be especially suitable (cf. Baló and Banga, 1950). Evidently, bilirubin destruction must be avoided during digestion. Simultaneous additions of antioxidants would probably be advantageous.

Meakins (1927) advanced the theory of a barrier between blood plasma and tissues, based on observations made in a severely ill cardiac patient whose edema fluid was colorless in spite of strongly icteric skin. This theory is supported by F. Rosenthal and Melchior's (1922) observations of yellow serum but green tissues in icteric pigeons. Further, it is supported by findings in nerve tissue which remain colorless during icterus (see Section E, this chapter).

Numerous authors have reported observations on bile pigments present in the tissues of humans and animals. Quincke (1884) found bilirubin crystals in the subcutaneous tissues of dogs 7 days after local blood injections. The number of crystals reached its maximum after 4 weeks, and thereafter decreased again. Nevertheless, a few crystals were detectable, even after 11 months. Besides bilirubin, a brown pigment was formed. No bilirubin was present in rabbits and guinea pigs after subcutaneous blood injections. Pigeons showed a green pigment 3 days after injection. Kiener and Engel (1887) injected rabbits subcutaneously with aqueous alkaline bilirubin solutions. Intense yellow discoloration of the skin and the regional lymph nodes occurred. Microscopic examination revealed that the color was localized in the elastic fibers. After urobilin bilin injections the tissues remained colorless or showed only a very faint yellow coloration. They also exposed pieces of sheep tissues (skin, tendons, eyes, arteries) to strongly icteric urine for 24 hours and found intense yellow colorations in these tissues. When urine rich in urobilin but free from bilirubin was used, no coloration occurred.

F. Rosenthal (1930) showed that purified elastin added to alkaline bilirubin solutions or to icteric serum assumed an intense yellow color. Purified collagen or brain tissue remained colorless. Moreover, Rosenthal (1930) and Gassmann (1930) showed that the yellow color of icteric tissues became more intense as their elastin content increased.

Few authors undertook quantitative bile pigment determinations in tissues. Fischer and Reindel (1923) digested tissues with pepsin and extracted with alkaline aqueous pyridine solutions (dilute sodium hydroxide with 1/3 volume pyridine). They claimed that this process permits quantitative extraction of bile pigments. Rosenthal (1930) and Gassmann (1930) extracted with alcohol and acetone, as recommended for serum analysis by Ernst and Förster (1924). Rosenthal could, at best, observe a coloration in the first two extracts. He held this extraction to be practically quantitative; however, this is an unproved and rather unlikely opinion. He found the following concentrations after toluenediamine poisoning in a dog with jaundice which had lasted for 3 days (mg/100 g): liver 4.48, kidneys 0.106, lungs 0.265, fatty tissue 0.0014, and only traces in the muscles, spleen, and brain. The serum bilirubin content was 9 mg/100 ml in this animal. He found the following values in a dog which had had jaundice for 10 days, and whose serum bilirubin concentration was 25.5 mg/100 ml, liver 72.5, kidneys 13.6, lung 3.83, heart 0.075, muscles 0.24, and only traces in the spleen, fatty tissue, and brain. These findings indicate that the bilirubin concentration of organs can exceed the level of serum bilirubin during severe protracted jaundice. Thus, errors due to blood content of organs are not always significant. Metzger (1927) extracted the tissues with 96% alcohol containing 5% sodium carbonate and found less bile pigments per gram liver tissue in grown cows than in the liver of newborn or fetal calves.

Urobilin determination in tissues presents particular problems. In this case blood plasma is not a source of error since its urobilin content is always low. Kiener and Engel (1887) found no urobilin in the tissues of icteric patients with massive urobilinuria. Royer (1928a,b) ground 2–3 grams tissue with sand in a mortar and extracted with 95% alcohol weakly acidified with hydrochloric acid. After decanting, the extract was stored for 24 hours in the dark and subsequently centrifuged. Extraction was repeated until no more fluorescence was noticeable on treatment with zinc acetate. The fluorescence was measured in the combined alcoholic extracts. Royer (1928b, 1943, p. 35) described another process where the alcoholic solution was extracted with $CHCl_3$ and the urobilin band identified spectroscopically in the extract. When the extraction was carried out fast enough, even the benzaldehyde test gave a positive reaction. However, Royer did not reduce the extracts in order to measure the benzaldehyde reaction after reduction. The following values were determined in four normal dogs and in three others in which total biliary fistula was established 2 or 3 days before analysis (mg/100 g): liver 0.044–0.177 in normal animals and 0.0006–0.009 in animals with fistula; kidneys 0.016–0.038 and 0.0004–0.007, respectively; the other organs, such as pancreas, lungs, spleen, and intestines, exhibited extremely low concentrations (Royer, 1928b, 1943, pp. 36–38).

Further, *histochemical reactions* have been employed, including identification of bilirubin crystals. However, it should be remembered that a considerable amount of histologically undetectable bilirubin can be present in tissues (Lepehne, 1930, p. 319). Daddi (1933) used 1:5000 to 1:1000 solutions of the potassium salt of iso-*p*-nitrodiazobenzene in 5–10% formalin solution for staining. For color stabilization he added a few drops of 20% sulfuric acid. Frozen sections, as well as specimens fixed with alcohol or formalin, were treated in this manner. Bilirubin appeared as pink granula or as tinted areas, whereas biliverdin was not stained. J. Stein (1935) employed short fixation in formalin; he embedded the specimens in paraffin wax, then deparaffinized and treated them with iodine solution for 6–12 hours (2–3 volumes of Lugol's solution plus 1 volume of tincture of iodine; an excess of tincture of iodine dissolved bilirubin). After washing with water the sections were treated with sodium hydrosulfite solution for 15–20 minutes. After repeated washings the sections were stained with carmine alum for 1–2 hours and washed again; the water was removed with acetone and the sections finally treated with xylene and mounted in Canada balsam. In these preparations the bile pigments appeared as beautifully stained small, intercellular green granula in the parenchymal cells, as well as in the Kupffer cells of the liver. Other oxidation agents gave similar reactions (potassium permanganate, potassium chromate, potassium chlorate, hydrogen peroxide, iron chloride, and calcium hypochlorite), but the best staining was obtained with the method described above. For the best result it was important to use acetone for washing and not alcohol.

Glenner (1957) described a rapid method for demonstrating bilirubin in frozen tissue sections based on oxidation with a buffered solution of potassium dichromate at pH 2.2. This method allows study of the mutual physical relations among bilirubin, hemosiderin, and lipofuscin in tissues.

Kutlik (1957) also described a method for histochemical demonstration of bilirubin. Leibnitz (1964) made a thorough study of the histochemical demonstration of bilirubin and biliverdin in nerve tissue. She emphasized the importance of the fixation, deparaffinizing and dying procedures. Most such procedures in common use will destroy or dissolve the bilirubin. Her material consisted of icteric brains from 3-month-old rabbits receiving continuous i.v. bilirubin infusion for 6 hours. Diazo reaction without, alcohol was positive in these brains, but the color was diffuse, making the diazo reaction unsuitable for histochemical studies. Oxidation reactions were found to be suitable for this purpose if certain fixation procedures, oxidation reagents, and histological techniques were employed.

The best results were obtained by fixation as rapidly *post mortem* as possible with 96% ethanol or a mixture of 5 volumes ethanol and 1 volume glacial acetic acid. The specimens were embedded in paraffin wax through *n*-propanol with as short duration of the single steps as possible. The oxidation reaction was carried out with a 5% solution of $FeCl_3$-containing acetic acid (pH 3–5) for 20–30 minutes. For dyeing, tropaeolin OO was used. Leibnitz concluded from the appearance of the sections in the phase-contrast microscope that so-called bilirubin in brain tissue cannot be a single well-defined compound, at least not after oxidation.

Raia (1965*) described a method for histological demonstration of bilirubin in tissues based on the diazo reaction. He claims that it is possible to distinguish between free and conjugated bilirubin with this method. He employed the following stock solutions: (A) dissolve 200 mg dichloroaniline in 100 ml distilled water containing 2.5 ml HCl and filter; (B) 1% $NaNO_2$; (C) dissolve 6 g caffeine, 10 g sodium benzoate, and 10 g urea in 100 ml of distilled water. To 35 ml of this solution add 25 ml 40% formalin and add water to make up to a volume of 85 ml, then add 15 ml methyl ethyl ketone. Solutions A and B should be prepared fresh every 2 weeks and kept in the dark in the refrigerator. From the stock solutions the following reagents are prepared daily: (1) Add 1 volume B to 50 volumes A and leave for 20 minutes in an ice bath before using; (2) add 1 volume (1) to 2 volumes C (accelerator diazo reagent).

For staining the tissue is rapidly frozen and 6-μm cryostatic sections cut, mounted directly on slides, and allowed to dry for 1 hour in the dark at room temperature. Sections can be kept in a cool dark place for several weeks without loss of staining properties. To demonstrate conjugated bilirubin the slide is immersed for 10 minutes in reagent (1), washed for 3 minutes in running tap water, fixed for 3 minutes in 10% formol saline, and counterstained with hematoxylin. Conjugated bilirubin is stained blue-violet. To demonstrate both conjugated and unconjugated bilirubin the sections are immersed for 8 minutes in reagent (2), washed with running tap-water for 3 minutes and counterstained with hematoxylin. Bilirubin is stained red.

Although such histological methods are not quantitative, they give some information about the localization of these pigments in the tissues. They are often deposited in crystalline form in icteric organs (Lepehne, 1930). Crystalline as well as amorphous bilirubin deposits can be encountered in hemorrhagic lesions. Thus, crystals can often be found in the periphery of ischemic necroses. Globular aggregates of so-called embryo crystals are found in the central parts of these necroses from which fine, truly crystalline needles radiate in spherulites (Lignac, 1923; who published beautiful colored illustrations).

The localization of bilirubin in icteric kidneys is of particular interest. Nizet and Barac (1952a) examined the kidneys of dogs with bile duct closures lasting 1–4 weeks, using the staining procedure described by Stein. Bilirubin always appeared in the form of intracellular regular granula. The pigment was usually localized in the base of the cells of the proximal convoluted tubes, and occasionally in the descending part of Henle's loop. The other parts of the tubuli, as well as the glomeruli were free from bilirubin. No cell degeneration could be observed. Lubarsch (1925) observed a similar localization of bile pigments in the kidneys of patients who died of obstructive jaundice. It is important to remember that dissolved bilirubin can also be present in other parts of the kidneys, without being detected. In another publication Nizet and Barac (1952b) reported investigations carried out with the diazo reagent in liver and kidney sections of icteric dogs. The composition of the diazo reagents used was not mentioned; it was only stated that an excess of nitrite was avoided. The sections were treated with the reagent for "various lengths of time." The reaction was always negative. In a control experiment the tissue sections were treated with the diazo reagent and were placed in icteric serum. A positive reaction took place immediately between the serum bilirubin and the reagent which remained in the tissue. The authors assumed that the negative reaction of tissues is caused by firm binding of bilirubin to tissue proteins.

A spectacular occurrence of bile pigments in tissues is *green teeth,* observed when marked jaundice is present during the period of dentin development. Thursfield (1911) was the first to report green teeth in a child. Craig (1925) described them in a 2-year-old child. Potter (1947, pp. 197–198 and Fig. 25) found that the incisors were bluish-green and occasionally also light brown in many children who had undergone a severe and protracted jaundice immediately after birth. The central and lateral incisors were usually discolored. The second dentition was normal. McRae (1952) described a similar observation; the teeth were yellowish when they first appeared, but became green later. According to McRae, the duration of the jaundice was more significant for the appearance of colored teeth than its intensity. Marsland and Gerrard (1953) as well as Claireaux et al. (1955) performed the most thorough investigations of these conditions. The later authors published beautiful colored photographs and colored microphotograms. Earlier authors believed that the color was localized in the enamel. Contrary to this opinion, Claireaux et al. could unequivocally show that the color is localized in the dentin in the form of narrow bands. It appeared in the part of the dentin formed during the jaundice period. These bands were also detected in the unerupted teeth of a 10-day-old child who died of icterus gravis.

Besides these pathological appearances of bile pigments in various tissues, several observations of their occurrence under normal conditions have been noted: for example, their presence in the tissues of certain fishes, and in the tissues enveloping the embryos of various birds and mammals. These deposits are apparently due to old blood.

Special bile pigment chromoproteins, the so-called *ichthyoerythrin* (Cyclopteridae) and *ichthyocyanin* (Labridae) occur in fish of the families Labridae and Cyclopteridae. The pigments are already present under normal conditions, predominantly in the skin, scales, testicles, eggs, muscles, and blood serum. These compounds are closely related to phycoerythrin and phycocyanin, chromoproteins of certain algae. The amount of pigment present in these fishes varies widely with the season and sexual activity (von Zeyneck, 1901, 1902; Fontaine, 1941). Further investigation of the pigments of these fish would be of great interest; determinations should be extended to organs, body fluids, and excretions. Experiments with labeled atoms should be included.

Observations on other fish have also been published. Willstaedt (1941) studied the green pigment in the bones or horned pikes (*Belone belone*) and the eelpout (*Zoarces viviparus*). After decalcification with hydrochloric acid, these green pigments became extractable with glacial acetic acid and gave positive Gmelin reactions. The peroxidase reaction with benzidine and hydrogen peroxide was also found to be positive. The methyl ester could be separated into two different green pigments by chromatography on aluminum oxide columns. Willstaedt was unable to isolate samples from these substances large enough to perform elementary chemical analysis. Nevertheless, on the basis of their behavior he concluded that they are probably bile pigments. This worker also studied the green pigment found in the common sea scorpion (*Cottus scorpius*), which is localized in the ventral fins, maxilla, and the skin around the mouth. Willstaedt established a close relationship between this pigment and the pigment of labridae (e.g., *Crenilabrus pavo* which lives in the Mediterranean Sea). Nevertheless, certain differences were detected. Thus, the pigment of the *Cottus* showed an absorption maximum at 681 nm, whereas that of the *Crenilabrus* was at 640–660 nm. Both pigments were water soluble. Cağlar (1945, 1950) confirmed that the green pigment of the *Belone* is a bile pigment. D. L. Fox and Millot (1954) studied the green pigment found in the bones of the ocean skipjack (*Katsuwonus pelamis* [Linnaeus]) and showed that the absorption spectra of this compound, as well as its methyl ester, were identical with that of biliverdin. This pigment gave a Gmelin reaction and also a weak benzidine hydrogen peroxide reaction. The latter reaction was attributed to small amounts of porphyrin impurities accompanying the main pigment.

Tsuchiya and Nomura (1955) investigated the pigment occurring in the scales of Sauries (*Cololabris sari* Brevoort). The pigment was isolated in crystalline form and it was named ichthyoverdin. About 100 kg fresh scales was extracted and only a few milligrams of the green substance could be isolated. This pigment crystallized in blue-green needles, its esters in green plates. The absorption spectrum was very close to that of biliverdin and the Gmelin reaction was positive. In addition, these authors examined the blue pigment of certain sea fishes, such as *Cololabris saria* Brevoort, bonitos (*Katsuwonus vogans,* Lesson), mackerels (*Scomber japonicus,* Temminck and Schlegel), herrings (*Clupea pallasii,* Cuvier), and sardines (*Sardinia melanosticta,* Temminck and Schlegel). They found that after removing the scales the fresh skin gave a positive Gmelin reaction. However, unlike scales this pigment could not be extracted from the skin with methanol–hydrochloric acid. Tsuchiya and Nomura (1958) subjected ichthyoverdin to spectrophotometric study in the visible and ultraviolet regions. The absorption curve of the methyl ester dissolved in various solvents was determined. In $CHCl_3$ it exhibited four bands with maxima at 665–670 nm, 378 nm, 318 nm, and 284 nm. The curve was closely similar to that of biliverdin ester described by Tixier (1945), but there were minor differences. Studies in acid and alkaline solution showed that ichthyoverdin is an amypholyte. Chromatographic investigations on ichthyoverdin reported by Tsuchiya and Nomura (1959) showed it behaved identical to biliverdin. Later, Tsuchiya and Nomura (1961) compared ichthyoverdin and synthetic biliverdin-IX, α and found a melting point of the crystals of the former of 205° as against 207° for the latter; mixed crystals resulted in no depression of the melting point. The spectral and chromatographic behavior of the two esters as well as their chemical reactions were identical. It was concluded that *ichthyoverdin* is identical to biliverdin-IX,α. Finally, Tsuchyia and Nomura (1962) studied the pigment isolated from scales of *Belone belone* L. and *Labrus berggylta* L. The pigments of the former were found to be very similar to biliverdin, whereas those of the latter exhibited minor differences.

Wicke (1858) studied the bluish-green pigment occurring in the *egg shells* of certain birds and found that they gave a positive Gmelin reaction. Sorby (1875) called this pigment "oocyan." Liebermann (1878) proved that it is localized in the outer layer of the egg shells and that it gave a Gmelin reaction. Krukenberg (1883a) believed it was identical with biliverdin. Lemberg (1932, 1934d) and Tixier (1945) finally confirmed this assumption by isolating the crystalline compound.

Poole (1965*) found biliverdin present in the superficial part of egg shells of the wild type of the Japanese quail, the deposition beginning between the second and third hours prior to oviposition.

Lieberkühn (1889) and Heinricius (1889) were the first to observe bile pigments in the *placenta*. These appeared as small, dark green zones around the poles of dog placenta. They appeared during the fifth week of pregnancy, and increased markedly thereafter, giving a characteristic appearance to the placenta. It was found that this phenomenon is caused by the deposition of maternal blood in the lateral sinus between the wall of the uterus and the chorion. Since these sinuses do not have endothelial envelopes, the free pigment is deposited in the tissue of the peripheral portion of the maternal placenta. During the latter part of pregnancy considerable amounts of pigment can be detected at this location. Strahl (1890) confirmed these observations and showed in addition that the Mustelidae have a yellow-red metallic-looking zone instead of the green zone of the dog placenta. Hematoidin crystals caused this appearance. This zone was absent in cats since the pigment was absorbed by the chorion. Duval (1893, p. 288) found this green zone in dog placenta as early as the 18th day of pregnancy. Diwany (1919, p. 40) found bilirubin crystals in the placenta of ferrets and biliverdin crystals in the placenta of dogs. Thudichum (1886, 1896) assumed that the pigment in the placenta of dogs, "uteroverdine," is really biliverdin; this was finally proved by Lemberg and Barcroft (1932).

Summary

Relatively little attention has been given to the bile pigments of organs and tissues and no suitable analytic methods are known for their determination. Bilirubin, which is bound to tissues, does not react with the regular diazo reagent. However, it is claimed that it reacts with iso-*p*-nitrodiazobenzene in formaldehyde. Investigations concerning the occurrence of urobilinoids in tissues are scarce and unreliable. Histochemical methods, which are important for the localization of bilirubin in the cells, are discussed. However, negative histochemical reactions do not exclude the presence of bile pigments.

Deposition of bile pigments occurs in the green or yellow deciduous teeth of infants who have undergone a severe and protracted jaundice during their newborn perid. This coloration is caused by the deposition of bands of bile pigments in the dentin, and not by localization in the enamel, as was assumed earlier. The coloration disappears gradually and never affects the final dentition.

Finally, bile pigments can be distributed everywhere in the tissues of various sea fishes, especially in Labridae and Cyclopteridae, under normal conditions. In addition, bile pigments are present under normal conditions in the egg shells of certain birds and in the placenta of certain carnivorous mammals. These latter accumulations originate from degradation products of maternal blood.

E. Kernicterus

The most important deposition of bile pigment in tissues is the so-called *kernicterus*, the staining of the central nervous system with bilirubin, which is important from clinical, pathological, and biological points of view. This condition deserves particular attention, because the central nervous system regularly remains colorless during jaundice of adults—it is "bilirubinophobic" (see Chapter IV,B). Nevertheless, exceptions have also been reported (cf. N. Klein and Szentmihàlyi, 1932; Section B, this chapter). In this connection the observations of Lazard and Sobotka (1962) (cf. Section B, this chapter) on the role of the hypophysis in the development of icterus of the brain are highly significant. They should be repeated on several species of animals. It looks like the blood–tissue barrier, the blood–brain barrier in particular, depends on hormonal factors.

Kernicterus is a disease of infants, and occurs especially during the newborn period. It is believed to be caused by indirect (free) bilirubin, whereas direct, conjugated bilirubin seems to be ineffective. Because of neonatal jaundice, newborn babies are especially exposed to the influence of free bilirubin. Further, newborn infants, and especially premature ones, exhibit increased permeability of the blood–CSF barrier (cf. Section B, this chapter), and kernicterus is therefore particularly common during this period of life. The more pronounced the prematurity and the intensity of the jaundice, the greater the danger; i.e., kernicterus especially threatens premature babies and infants with icterus gravis. Darrow (1938) never found kernicterus in physiological neonatal jaundice. However, later investigators occasionally detected kernicterus under these conditions (Aidin *et al.*, 1950; Gerrard, 1950; Butler and Spector, 1952; Claireaux *et al.*, 1953; B. Corner, 1955; Crosse *et al.*, 1955; Boon, 1957).

J. Orth (1875) was the first to describe icterus of the brain, but the term "kernicterus" was coined by Schmorl (1904), who illustrated his work with colored figures. The yellow coloration of the brain is especially marked on the surface of the large ganglia around the third ventricle, but it is also noticeable in other parts of the brain. Orth (1875) assumed that the coloration was related to the necrosis of nerve cells by bilirubin. Schmorl (1904) found that the yellow pigment does not become green with $HgCl_2$ treatment and that it does not give a Gmelin reaction. These facts indicate the presence of pigments other than bilirubin. Bevis (1952a,b) believed that bilifuscin is involved. Ford (1952) assumed that the coloration of the brain is secondary to necrosis and that bilirubin is not the actual cause of kernicterus. He believed that this condition is a complication of icterus gravis (morbus hemolyticus neonatorum). The belief that free (unconjugated indirect) bilirubin is the true cause of this disease and the fact that premature babies are primarily afflicted, gradually developed after 1950. Anglo-Saxon investigators were particularly active in this field (cf. below).

There is not full agreement, however, on the role of bilirubin in the pathogenesis of kernicterus. In their penetrating clinical and pathological analysis of 87 cases, Haymaker *et al.* (1960) came to the conclusion that bilirubin itself cannot be the only factor of importance. Other factors of equal importance must be active too. They found little support for the view that kernicterus develops because of functional immaturity of the blood–brain barrier and were more inclined to believe in other factors operative in prematures, such as hypothermia. They believed that the functional immaturity of the liver can induce brain damage in other ways than by means of hyperbilirubinemia, i.e., the latter is looked upon not as the sole important factor, but as one factor among others not known in detail at present.

Brodersen and Vind (1963a) present some data of interest to the explanation of kernicterus as a result of the toxic action of free bilirubin on the brain cells. They calculated the coefficients of phase distribution of bilirubin between $CHCl_3$ and serum at different pH values and discussed the distribution of bilirubin between serum and brain cells in the light of these data. They calculated the equilibrium distribution of bilirubin on either side of a lipid membrane in which bilirubin has the same solubility as in $CHCl_3$ and where the aqueous phase on one side has a constant pH at 7.4 while the pH of the other side varies. The calculation showed that minor pH variations on either side of the membrane could result in considerable bilirubin accumulation on one side of the membrane. Penetration of free bilirubin into the brain cells is thus, according to these calculations, quite possible under the conditions found in jaundice of the newborn.

Another circumstance which is most likely of importance in this respect is the fact that bilirubin is much more firmly bound to nucleic acids than to albumin, demonstrated so well by Stenhagen and Teorell (1938) in electrophoresis experiments. The observation that the large nuclei of the brain stem are primarily affected in kernicterus points to the role of bilirubin-nucleic acid linkages.

Kernicterus is not limited entirely to icterus neonatorum and to morbus hemolyticus neonatorum. This became apparent from observations made in a few rare cases such as the inclusion disease (France, 1952), severe nonhemolytic familial jaundice of older children which proceeds with high indirect serum bilirubin concentrations (Crigler and Najjar, 1952; I. M. Rosenthal et al., 1956; Childs and Najjar, 1956; Haymaker et al., 1960; Sugar, 1961; Szabó et al., 1962), congenital spherocytosis (W. H. Patterson and Forrester, 1953; Adams, 1954), and neonatal hepatitis (Ergas and Wallis, 1963).

It was recognized that bilirubin is of etiological significance to kernicterus, which occurs especially in premature babies (Aidin et al., 1950; Zuelzer and Mudgett, 1950; Hsia et al., 1952a,b; Gowan and Scott, 1953a,b). Claireaux et al. (1953) gave final proof that bilirubin appears in the nerve tissue during kernicterus. Waters et al. (1953, 1954) isolated bilirubin in crystalline form from CHCl$_3$ extracts of the brain tissue; Day's (1954) in vitro experiments, described below, should also be mentioned in this connection. Schmorl's observation that the yellow brain tissue does not become green on treatment with HgCl$_2$ is understandable since free bilirubin is relatively stable toward oxidative influences. Contrary to this, bilirubin of other icteric tissues is more easily oxidized, because the coloration is caused by conjugated bilirubin (Claireaux et al.). Buxton and Brooksbank (1953) proved that kernicterus also occurs in animals. They found that the brains of a large number of newborn pigs, which suffered from hemolytic diseases, were colored. Waters and Britton (1955) injected aqueous alkaline bilirubin solutions of pH 8–9 in 36 rats younger than 24 hours and in 25 rats 1 month old. They found that only the younger rats developed icterus of the brain. Earlier, Frölich and Mirsky (1942) had injected young rats with solutions of "concentrated bile" and arrived at the same conclusion. In these experiments, animals younger than 10 days also developed icterus of the brain.

Day (1954) studied the effect of bilirubin on brain tissue in in vitro experiments. He added 20–25 mg bilirubin/100 ml to the incubation fluid of minced rat brains with the result that their respiration rate decreased about 25%. Oxidation of bilirubin diminished this retardation; methylene blue treatment of bilirubin yielded the same effect. Similarly, cytochrome c eliminated the inhibition. In this connection Zetterström and Ernster's (1956) experiments with rat liver mitochondria are interesting (cf. Chapter V,G). The limit of active bilirubin concentration was about 20 mg/100 ml in these experiments (notice the similarity between this concentration and the commonly accepted critical bilirubin concentration for the beginning of kernicterus).

Studies on Gunn rats with congenital jaundice due to free bilirubin have shown that kernicterus develops in newborn hyperbilirubinemic rats just as in human infants (Blanc and Johnson, 1959; L. Johnson et al., 1959, 1961). Further, investigations on 44 normal newborn kittens, 43 newborn puppies, and 28 newborn rabbits were reported by Rozdilsky and Olszewski (1961). They produced a state of prolonged hyperbili-rubinemia in the animals by repeated i.v. injections of 50 mg bilirubin dissolved in albumin solution. Several of the animals died of shock a few hours after the injections, and most of the animals developed severe diar-rhea; liver and kidney damage as well as various hemorrhagic and exuda-tive processes were frequent. Several of the animals developed convul-sions, coma, and other evidence of damage to the CNS. In the rabbits and puppies, serum bilirubin of 40–50 mg/100 ml was measured immediately after the injections and was followed by a gradual decline to about 10 mg/100 ml in the course of 10 hours. Jaundice of the skin and mucous membranes became visible immediately after the injections of these large doses of bilirubin. On autopsy multiple hemorrhages, especially of the lungs, and petechiae of the serous membranes were visible, and a faint yellowish tint of the brain was often encountered. Gross nuclear jaundice closely resembling human kernicterus was produced in 33 of the 44 kittens within 24 hours, while in the puppies and rabbits additional damage to the nervous system was necessary to obtain this result. Gross staining was visible in the kittens after only 12 hours, while 18–24 hours were required to produce cellular pigmentation.

These observations on animals substantiate the belief that, besides high free bilirubin concentration, immaturity is of significance in the pathogenesis of kernicterus. They further show that species differences exist and that hyperbilirubinemia alone can cause kernicterus, at least in newborn kittens.

Claireaux *et al.* (1953) drew attention to the role of free (indirect) bilirubin in the pathogenesis of kernicterus. These authors investigated the brains of four children who died of this disease, and the sera of nine cases of icterus gravis. Partition chromatography showed that practically only free bilirubin was present in the brain; but the serum also contained considerable amounts of conjugated (direct) bilirubin. These findings indicate that the brain tissue has a pronounced affinity for free bilirubin, which was ascribed to a bilirubin retention factor. However, this factor has not yet been indentified. Control experiments, in which free and conju-gated bilirubin were added to normal brain tissue, showed after extrac-tion that the chromatographic character of these pigments had not changed. Furthermore, it was demonstrated that conjugated bilirubin was harmless to infants. The authors also observed that no kernicterus developed in three cases of high hyperbilirubinemia caused by conju-gated bilirubin (50 mg/100 ml was determined in one case).

The "retention factor" of Claireaux *et al.* may be the nucleic acid of the ganglion cells (cf. above).

Kernicterus arising from hemolytic diseases in the newborn is lethal within 4 days in most cases; however, kernicterus which arose because of prematurity terminates in death only after 6–10 days. This substantiates the fact that hyperbilirubinemia culminates earlier in icterus gravis than in icterus of premature babies (Claireaux *et al.*, 1955). The critical serum bilirubin limit for occurrence of kernicterus was usually 20 mg/100 ml. Most of the kernicterus cases showed higher serum bilirubin concentration than this (Bound and Telfer, 1956; Boon, 1957; Crosse *et al.*, 1958). There is, however, no absolutely set critical level (A. K. Brown and Zuelzer, 1957). Cases have been reported with maximal concentration as low as 12.6/100 ml (Hsia *et al.*, 1952a,b; Bound and Telfer, 1956; A. K. Brown and Zuelzer, 1957). According to Dine (1954), values over 16 mg/100 ml are dangerous. About 66% of newborn infants develop kernicterus when the serum bilirubin concentration exceeds 18 mg/100 ml (Crosse *et al.*, 1955). According to Hsia *et al.* (1952a,b), kernicterus occurs only very rarely under 10 mg/100 ml, but it is observed regularly over 30 mg/100 ml. Newns and Norton (1958) considered 30 mg/100 ml as an indication for exchange transfusion in premature babies. They believed that routine transfusions at 20 mg/100 ml were unnecessary. When the bilirubin level is equally high the risk for kernicterus seems to be the same for full-term babies, premature babies, and babies with hemolytic diseases (Dine, 1954; Dundon, 1958).

Zuelzer (1959) regarded serum bilirubin as "a very imperfect indicator of the summation of many factors involved in the genesis of kernicterus," and Haymaker *et al.* (1960, p. 193) support this view.

The lack of agreement among the various authors can be partially explained by rapid changes in the serum bilirubin level (MacLean *et al.*, 1955; Harris *et al.*, 1958) and partially by differences in analytical methods used. The best methods for bilirubin determinations in the newborn are those of Lathe and Ruthven (1958) and of Michaëlsson (1961, cf. Chapter V,D,1).

In the opinion of most investigators, exchange transfusion is necessary to prevent a possible kernicterus when the serum bilirubin increases over 20 mg/100 ml (see Forfar *et al.*, 1958, 1959). The problems concerning serum bilirubin during exchange transfusion are discussed in Chapter V,M.

The wisdom of using serum bilirubin as indication of exchange transfusion was seriously questioned by Linneweh and Bickel (1959), who compared 15 prematures with severe hyperbilirubinemia treated with exchange transfusion with 16 others not subjected to this procedure. The children were reexamined at the age of 1½–2¼ years and both groups were found to have developed normally. The maximum serum bilirubin of the transfused group was 23–44 mg/100 ml, that of the non-transfused group 20–28 mg/100 ml, except one infant with the figure of 10 mg/100 ml. The decision, transfusion or no transfusion, in these cases was based exclusively on clinical symptoms and not on the serum bilirubin. The serum bilirubin was generally higher in the transfused group than in the other, but the great majority of children in both groups exhibited serum bilirubin above 20 mg/100 ml.

Killander et al. (1963) reported a follow-up study of 93 full-term infants with hyperbilirubinemia, 46 of which were treated by exchange transfusion. Examination 2–2½ years later showed no difference between the two groups, i.e., a confirmation of the conclusions of Linneweh and Bickel.

Zuelzer and Brown (1961) and A. K. Brown (1962) state that in hemolytic disease of the newborn exchange transfusion is usually performed if the serum bilirubin approaches 10 mg/100 ml at 24 hours, 14 mg/100 ml at 48 hours, 17 mg/100 ml at 72 hours, and 20 mg/100 ml at any time. On the other hand, Jablonski (1962) regards figures below 25 mg/100 ml as safe. The observations of Linneweh and Bickel indicate, however, that it would probably be better to lay more stress on a close clinical observation than to rely on the serum bilirubin determination. This view is supported by the observations of Reiner and Thomas (1962) on the difficulties of reproducible serum bilirubin analysis, a problem fully discussed in Chapter V,C,4.

Mackay and Watson (1962) also came to the conclusion that other factors than bilirubin concentration are important to decide the need for exchange transfusion. They wrote: "There are a number of other variables to be taken into consideration, such as the previous history, the level of antibodies in maternal blood, and the clinical assessment of fetal well-being. . . ." To this list should be added the bilirubin of the amniotic fluid (see this chapter, Section B).

That hyperbilirubinemia is not the only factor important in the genesis of kernicterus was substantiated by recent clinical and experimental investigations on the role of post partum asphyxia. Thus, Lucey et al. (1963*, 1964*) found that experimental hyperbilirubinemia in newborn monkeys is not followed by kernicterus, but if it follows after a period of asphyxia typical icterus of the brain resulted. Further, Hibbard (1964*) performed polarographic determinations of the molar oxygen concentration using electrodes placed in the peritoneal cavity of 7 newborn monkeys (Maccaca mulatta) with artificial hyperbilirubinemia—sustained concentration of serum bilirubin of over 30 mg/100 ml for 3–10 hours. The bilirubin infusion was followed by a significant decrease of oxygen concentration which in the course of the first hour became established at a lower level. Post mortem studies of the brains showed, however, only diffuse yellow color but no staining of the nuclei. The hypothesis was put forward that the high serum bilirubin is followed by decreased oxygen tension in the tissues which makes the cells more susceptible to inward diffusion of bilirubin. On the other hand, asphyxia seems to be necessary to start the process of kernicterus, hyperbilirubinemia alone not being enough.

Tygstrup (1965*) performed histological studies of the brain of 25 patients with severe neonatal jaundice who died between the ages 1 and 4 years. Nineteen showed typical kernicterus, but in the remaining 6 the ganglia were not jaundiced. The material was subdivided into 5 groups: (1) asphyxia grade 0, icterus grade I; 2 cases; (2) asphyxia grade 0, icterus grade II–III, 13 cases; (3) asphyxia grade I, icterus grade I, 2 cases; (4) asphyxia grade I, icterus grade II–III, 7 cases; (5) asphyxia grade III, icterus grade I, 1 case. The severity of the histological alterations in the nervous system were also graded and found to depend on the grade of asphyxia to the same extent as the degree of hyperbilirubinemia. Thus the case in group (5) with severe asphyxia exhibited pronounced jaundice of the basal ganglia although its serum bilirubin never exceeded 10 mg/100 ml.

Chen *et al.* (1965*) produced experimental kernicterus in newborn rabbits weighing 40–60 g by subjecting them to asphyxia followed by prolonged hyperbilirubinemia. The asphyxia was produced by breathing nitrogen until the final stage of asphyxia was reached and then applying artificial respiration. Of 230 rabbits subjected to this treatment 125 died. The surviving were subjected to i.v. injection of 6 mg bilirubin over 8 hours resulting in an initial serum bilirubin of 60 mg/100 ml with a subsequent slow decrease to a permanent level of 20 mg/100 ml. Ninety-one animals survived both asphyxia and hyperbilirubinemia and 52 showed brain conditions closely resembling human kernicterus both macro- and microscopically. Also pulmonary edema, myocardial necroses, and degeneration of the renal tubuli were observed. In 43 controls with hyperbilirubinemia without asphyxia no kernicterus was found.

According to Hsia (1965*) kernicterus appears to be an all-or-none phenomenon, i.e., if an infant escapes gross neurological damage in the neonatal period it is likely to develop normally.

The value of the bilirubin concentration of cord blood as a guide to the subsequent maximum serum bilirubin level was discussed by Tovey *et al.* (1959) and Barton *et al.* (1962), who concluded that the correlation is not close enough to use the cord blood bilirubin for practical clinical purposes. If the cord blood bilirubin exceeds 12.5 mg/100 ml, it can, however, be safely concluded that severe jaundice will develop.

On the other hand, Lewi *et al.* (1965*), on the basis of a study of 203 newborns without hemolytic disease, concluded that a high cord blood bilirubin does not necessarily anticipate a severe neonatal jaundice.

Various therapeutic *procedures* have been found to *enhance the risk of kernicterus*. Thus, Bakker (1954) showed that *oxygen* treatment promotes the danger of kernicterus in premature babies; this is probably due to the fact that oxygen accelerates hemoglobin degradation. Bound and Telfer (1956) found that intramuscular injections of *vitamin K* preparations (30 mg doses of Synkavite) led to increased serum bilirubin levels in premature infants. Therefore, they advocated caution and recommended the use of smaller doses of vitamin K to avert the danger of kernicterus. A. K. Brown and Zuelzer (1957) confirmed this opinion. It was also established that prophylactic administration of sulfonamides increases the frequency of kernicterus in premature infants (Silverman *et al.*, 1956a,b). Vest (1958a,b) advocated the avoidance of large doses of Synkavite in prematures. Waters *et al.* (1958) found that vitamin K (Synkavite) inhibited bilirubin conjugation in liver homogenates. B. Corner *et al.* (1960) found that the synthetic vitamin K preparation menaphthone dipotassium bisulfate ("Viskastab") did not influence the serum bilirubin in prematures if given in doses below 60 mg. T.-C. Lee and Hsia (1959) studied experimentally the effect of sodium glucuronate, vitamin K (Hykinone), chelation (EDTA–sodium), sulfonamide (Gantrisin), and anoxemia on the blood–brain barrier in rabbits. These compounds, as well as anoxemia, did not seem to affect this barrier. Experiments with C^{14}-labeled glucuronic acid injected in dogs did not yield radioactive biliary bilirubin in these animals.

The relationships between drug therapy and kernicterus in the newborn have recently been subjected to studies by several investigators. Besides vitamin K and sulfonamides, phenothiazines and certain antibiotics (penicillin, sterptomycin, novobiocin) have been reported to increase serum bilirubin in the newborn. The literature was reviewed by Sutherland (1963). Belmont *et al.* (1963) could not detect any influence of administration of phenothiazines (e.g., promazine) to mothers in labor on the course of hyperbilirubinemia of prematurity. Arias *et al.* (1963b) studied the action of several drugs administered to mother rats on hepatic glucuronide formation in liver homogenates of their newborn. It was found that 3,4-benzpyrene, chlorcyclizine, and chloroquine increased the glucuronide formation. In clinical observations they found no influence of the administration of chloroquine, in doses adequate to suppress malaria, to mothers late in pregnancy on the hyperbilirubinemia of their infants. Hsia *et al.* (1963) studied the inhibitory effect of certain drugs on glucuronyl transferase activity in liver homogenates of newborn rats and guinea pigs. Progestational steroids, vitamin K analogs, and novobiocin were investigated and found to be inhibitors. Progestational agents acted as competitive inhibitors, Synkavite and novobiocin as non-competitive ones. Injection of Synkavite to newborn animals did not result in hyperbilirubinemia, whereas transitional jaundice followed novobiocin injections.

The most striking demonstration of the influence of drugs on the conditions producing kernicterus is the experiments of Schmid *et al.* (1965*) on Gunn rats. They used rats with a level of hyperbilirubinemia as stable as possible and injected them with a tracer dose of C^{14}-bilirubin making it possible to assess the pool of miscible bilirubin which remained reasonably constant throughout the experiment. To such rats sodium salicylate was infused i.v. for 4 hours at a rate of 16 mg/hour. This infusion was immediately followed by a sharp drop of the serum bilirubin level from ca. 12 to 4 mg/100 ml where it remained for 24 hours. Then an i.v. infusion of 500 mg salt-poor albumin was given; this gave rise to an equally rapid rise of the serum bilirubin to 11 mg/100 ml. These results can hardly be interpreted as other than an experimental support of the view that salicylates displace unconjugated bilirubin from the serum albumin to the tissues and infusion of albumin brings it back into the blood again.

Zetterqvist (1957) stressed the frequency of kernicterus in premature infants and the significance of a suitable prophylaxis. This is of great importance because kernicterus is often lethal, and because the survivors are often afflicted by residual damages such as cerebral palsy.

An important paper discusses the role of *conjugated bilirubin* in kernicterus (L. E. Harris *et al.*, 1962). These authors analyzed 285 cases of erythroblastosis foetalis from the Mayo Clinic and found conjugated bilirubin present in the serum in concentrations above 1.5 mg/100 ml in 38 cases. The method of Powell (1944) was used, and the level 1.5 mg/100 ml was chosen as dividing level because lower values can be simulated by a high concentration of unconjugated bilirubin. The mortality among the 38 infants with high conjugated bilirubin was 21% as against 10.5% among the 247 cases without conjugated bilirubin in the serum, and the mortality rate of infants showing conjugated bilirubin in the cord blood or during the first 24 hours was as high as 38%; it was zero in the cases exhibiting elevated conjugated bilirubin only after the 24th hour of life. In the infants succumbing to hemolytic disease no histopathological evidence of obstruction of bile canaliculi by hematopoietic tissue or swollen liver cells, and no regurgitation or inspissated bile could be demonstrated. This material of Harris *et al.* supports the view of Haymaker *et al.* (1960) that factors other than unconjugated bilirubin must be of importance in the pathogenesis of kernicterus.

In light of the observations of Schalm *et al.* (1962b)—who found that intravenous loading with large bilirubin doses caused an increase of conjugated serum bilirubin (cf. Chapter V,J)—the observations of Harris *et al.* are not difficult to understand.

On the other hand, Riding and Ellis (1963) regarded "direct bilirubin" in hemolytic disease of the newborn as harmless. It most often did not appear until after the first exchange transfusion. In the four cases where it was present at the first day of life (level 2–6.2 mg/100 ml), the babies were not severely affected. Riding and Ellis believed that the rise in direct level was due to complicating "inspissated bile syndrome."

The cause and clinical significance of conjugated bilirubin in jaundice of the newborn deserves further study.

The etiology and pathogenesis of kernicterus is far from clear. The role of bilirubin was discussed above, but the way in which bilirubin acts on the immature brain is not sufficiently known. The so-called *blood–brain barrier* is important in this respect. The existence of a blood–tissue barrier for bilirubin was mentioned above (Section D, this Chapter) and the blood–brain barrier has been much discussed (cf. Tschirgi, 1962). In the opinion of Crone (1961, pp. 128 and 144), the blood–brain barrier is tighter than the blood–tissue barriers of other organs because electron microscope studies show that the endothelial cells in the capillaries of the brain lie very close together without spaces of intercellular substance between them, and consequently the permability of the brain capillaries is identical to that of the endothelial cells themselves. Crone believes that the brain has an intercellular fluid as other organs.

It has been difficult to understand the penetration of bilirubin in the brain cells because of its very low solubility in aqueous solutions at physiological pH. Odell (1959a,b) tried to overcome these difficulties by pointing out that various drugs actually increased the solubility of free bilirubin considerably, and among the drugs studied were some which are known to give increased frequency of kernicterus in infants. The recent observations of Burnstine and Schmid (1962) on the solubility of bilirubin in electrolyte-containing aqueous solutions at various pH levels show, however, that the solubility of bilirubin under physiological conditions is far higher than formerly believed, based on the studies of Overbeek *et al.* (1955b), and consequently the passage of free bilirubin into the tissues during jaundice is less difficult to understand (cf. Chapter V, Section B,12).

Kahán (1964a,b) studied the binding of bilirubin to brain lipids of newborn and adult rats. Most bilirubin was bound to a lipid fraction containing neuraminic acid, but no hexosamine, corresponding to ganglioside II of Klenk. In chromatograms from newborn rats this was the most prominent lipid spot, but was a minor component in adults. By addition of Ca–EDTA, the amount of bilirubin bound to brain tissue was reduced by half.

Summary

The most important form of bile pigment accumulation in human tissues is kernicterus, which is due to deposition of free bilirubin in the brain of newborn infants and is more rarely found in small children with Crigler-Najjar syndrome. Such accumulations are most often found in morbus hemolyticus neonatorum and in premature babies with severe icterus. Kernicterus is known in animals both spontaneously and experimentally. Only very young mammals are susceptible to this disease. When the serum bilirubin content in the newborn exceeds a certain level, most often given as 20 mg/100 ml, there is danger of kernicterus. This is of importance in clinical practice. The risk of this disease is increased in premature infants by various factors such as oxygen treatment and large doses of vitamin K and sulfonamides. The various suggested treatments of kernicterus are discussed and include exchange transfusion and the rebound phenomenon. The etiology and pathogenesis of kernicterus are not quite clear. Current research is centered on the brain toxicity of unconjugated bilirubin and the enzyme systems of the liver responsible for forming bilirubin glucuronides. It is emphasized that other factors must be involved too and that hormones are important. It is to be remembered that bilirubin glucuronides are formed outside the liver, that bilirubin conjugates other than glucuronides exist, and that bilirubin can be broken down to diazo-negative substances in tissues.

A factor which may be of importance is the very firm binding of bilirubin to nucleic acids already demonstrated by Stenhagen and Teorell (1938).

Additional Readings

Section B

Bower, D., and Swale, J. (1966). Chemical test for bilirubin in liquor amnii. *Lancet* I, 1009–1011.

Gambino, S. R., and Freda, V. J. (1966). The measurement of amniotic fluid bilirubin by the method of Jendrassik and Gróf. Its correlation with spectrophotometric analysis. *Am. J. Clin. Pathol.* 46, 198–203.

Robertson, J. G. (1966). Evaluation of reported methods of interpreting spectrophotometric tracings of amniotic fluid in Rh isoimmunization. *Am. J. Obst. Gynec.* 95, 120–126.

Savage, R. D., Walker, W., Fairweather, D. V. I., and Knox, E. G. (1966). Quantitative estimation of bilirubin in liquor amnii. *Lancet* II, 816–819.

Section D

Aboliņš, L., and Rüdiger, W. (1966). On the chromophorous group of crenilabrus-blue (in German) *Experientia* 22, 298–299.

Desmet, V. J., Bullens, A. M., and Heirwegh, K. P. M. (1967). Histochemistry of bilirubin and conjugates. Staining conjugated bilirubin with the diazonium salt of ethylanthranilate. *In* "Bilirubin Metabolism" (I. A. D. Bouchier and B. H. Billing, eds.), pp. 281–284. Blackwell, Oxford.

Hargreaves, T., and Scrimegour, G. (1966). The distribution of bilirubin in rat liver fractions. *Experientia* 22, 382.

Nomura, T., and Tsuchiya, Y. (1966). Identification of the blue-green pigment of the scales of sea fishes, *Cololabris Saria*, Brevoort (in French). *Tohoku J. Agri. Res.* 16, 213–224.

Raia, S. (1967). Histochemical demonstration of conjugated and unconjugated bilirubin in cholestatic liver tissue. *In* "Bilirubin Metabolism" (I. A. D. Bouchier and B. H. Billing, eds.), pp. 285–289. Blackwell, Oxford.

Section E

Bakay, L. (1955). "The Blood-Brain Barrier," 154 pp. Thomas, Springfield, Illinois.

Chen, Hai-Chin, Lin, Ching-Shen, and Lein, I-Nan (1966). Ultrastructural studies in experimental kernicterus. *Am. J. Pathol.* 48, 683–699.

Diamond, I., and Schmid, R. (1966). Experimental bilirubin encephalopathy. The mode of entry of bilirubin-C^{14} into the central nervous system. *J. Clin. Invest.* 45, 678–689.

Herlin, L. (1958). The existence of a barrier between the cerebrospinal fluid and the boundary of the brain; including experimental investigations on rabbits, using bilirubinemia. *In* "The Cerebrospinal Fluid" (G. E. W. Wolstenholme and C. M. O'Connor, eds.), pp. 209–229. Churchill, London.

Menken, M., Barret, P. V. D., Swarm, R. L., and Berlin, N. I. (1966). Kernicterus. Development of an experimental model using bilirubin-C^{14}. *Arch. Neurol.* 15, 68–73.

Rozdilsky, B. (1966). Kittens as experimental model for study of kernicterus. *Am. J. Diseases Children* 111, 161–165.

Schenker, S., McCandless, D. W., and Wittgenstein, E. (1966). Studies *in vivo* of the effect of unconjugated bilirubin on the hepatic phosphorylation and respiration. *Gut* 7, 409–414.

Schenker, S., McCandless, D. W., and Zollman, P. E. (1966). Studies of cellular toxicity of unconjugated bilirubin in kernicteric brain. *J. Clin. Invest.* 45, 1213–1220.

CHAPTER X

Comparative Biology and Biological Significance of Bile Pigments

A. Bile Pigments in Vertebrates

Our knowledge about the occurrence of bile pigments in most vertebrates is scanty. The only exceptions are humans, common laboratory animals, and to a certain extent domestic animals. Wild animals and lower vertebrates are hardly ever investigated.

An exception is Barac's (1963) study of the bladder bile of four sloths which exhibited 20–45 mg biliverdin/100 ml with a typical absorption maximum and no bilirubin.

The disproportion which can be observed in the horse between a high serum bilirubin content and a negligible biliary bile pigment excretion, has already been mentioned; this observation, although extremely interesting, has not received proper attention. The assumption generally accepted until recently that the bile of herbivorous mammals contains biliverdin, whereas that of carnivorous and omnivorous mammals contains bilirubin, cannot be acknowledged without further studies. Garner (1955) could regularly find bilirubin in ox bile and stercobilin in the stool of cattle. Several peculiar facts reported in the earlier literature require further examination: e.g., that hepatectomized frogs excrete biliverdin in the urine (Lesieurs et al., 1908), and that bilirubin accumulates in the blood of icteric pigeons, whereas biliverdin is present in their tissues and urine (F. Rosenthal and Melchior, 1922).

Recently Arias (1963b) discovered a difference in the excretion of bilirubin with the bile in higher and lower vertebrates. Whereas mammals excrete virtually all their bile bilirubin in the conjugated form, a substantial fraction (5–15%) of the bilirubin of dogfish bile is present in the unconjugated form. This interesting observation points to the importance of studying the occurrence of conjugated and unconjugated bilirubin in a series of lower vertebrates of different levels of organization.

The presence of bile pigments in fish has been mentioned (Chapter IX,D). The fact that bile pigments occur in the skin, scales, bones, and other organs is especially remarkable because these depositions are present in normal animals and do not indicate pathological conditions. Nevertheless, the physiological role of bile pigments in these fishes, as well as their precise chemical composition, have not been sufficiently explored. Further studies are needed. Similarly, the biological significance of bile pigment depositions in the egg shells of certain birds under normal conditions is also unknown. On the other hand, bile pigments, which can be found occasionally in the placenta of certain mammals, seem to be merely by-products of maternal blood deposited at this site (cf. Chapter IX,D).

On the basis of experiments with rabbits, rats, mice, and dogs, Verzár and Zih (1928, 1929), Verzár (1929), and Verzár *et al.* (1933) assumed that bile pigments exert a certain hematopoietic function (see also Zih, 1928, 1933, 1936; Bencsik *et al.*, 1930; E. Fischer and Verzár, 1932). Other authors found indications for certain erythropoietic effects of bilirubin (Bonome, 1924; Fellinger, 1932; Uno, 1934; Patek and Minot, 1934; Schernhardt, 1937; Krumholz, 1945; Bomford, 1949). Nevertheless, it is difficult to understand this alleged hemopoietic function of bile pigments, especially since it is known that protoporphyrin can easily be formed from glycine. One is inclined to agree with Lemberg and Legge (1949, p. 626), who consider this effect doubtful.

The *noxious effect of bilirubin* on the central nervous system is discussed above (Chapter IX,E), but unconjugated bilirubin is also known to have a general cytotoxic effect (cf. also Chapter V,G). Zetterström and Ernster (1956) found that unconjugated bilirubin suppresses the respiratory activity of rat liver mitochondria, and Labbe *et al.* (1959) found that it suppresses the metabolic activity of certain bacteria. Ebnöter (1959) showed that unconjugated bilirubin in concentrations of about 20 mg/100 ml added to tissue cultures of liver and brain of mice results in a decrease of oxidation of α-ketoglutarate, succinate, and pyruvate by 24% in adult tissues and by 67% in tissues from 5-day-old mice. K. Kikuchi (1961) studied the effect of unconjugated bilirubin in concentrations of 0.1–3 mg/100 ml on tissue cultures of various kinds of cells and could not demonstrate significant effects of these rather low concentrations.

The toxic effect of unconjugated bilirubin on a long series of tissues of young kittens, puppies and rabbits was demonstrated by Rozdilsky (1961a,b) and Rozdilsky and Olszewski (1961). Necrotic lesions and various hemorrhagic and exudative phenomena were encountered in the gastrointestinal canal, liver, kidneys, and many other organs, including the brain. Bernstein and Landing (1962) found similar lesions in icteric newborn humans which they ascribed to the cytotoxic action of unconjugated bilirubin.

Künzer and Goebels (1964*) studied the effects of unconjugated bilirubin on the *in vitro* maturation of erythrocytes in plasma and found no inhibition at concentrations up to 96 mg/100 ml.

Conjugated bilirubin is generally believed to be nontoxic, but Kopéc *et al.* (1961) showed that the bilirubin glucuronides exhibit antithrombin activity in studies with jaundiced serum from patients and from cats with experimental bile duct occlusion.

Flitman and Worth (1966*) found that human bile inhibits human and equine liver alcohol dehydrogenase *in vitro* and that this effect is mainly due to conjugated bilirubin. The mechanism of this inhibition was related to the capacity of bilirubin to form complexes with the Zn ion. They pointed out that many enzymes are known to contain Zn for which hyperbilirubinemic states may inhibit enzymatic activities.

B. Bile Pigments in Lower Animals

However, bile pigments are present not only in vertebrates, but also in *lower animals* and in plants. Here their occurrence—as in fishes—is not limited to the bile and they occur normally and not only under pathological conditions, as is the case in higher vertebrates. The distribution of bile pigments is completely irregular in lower animals. They can be found everywhere in the animal kingdom; they can be present in one species and can be missing in closely related ones. Moreover, bile pigments can occur in many different organs of the lower animals. Furthermore, these pigments can show a different chemical composition here, whereas in higher vertebrates mostly bilirubin and biliverdin are present. The presence of bile pigments in the organs of certain fishes is similar to those of lower animals. As far as bile pigments are concerned, fishes seem to be the connecting link between lower animals and higher vertebrates. It is unknown whether these bile pigments have a physiological function in the particular animal species in which they occur. Possibly, they only act as pigments, without having any function in the metabolism. Nevertheless, the distribution pattern of these pigments in lower animals and fishes indicate that they are not merely metabolic by-products, as in higher vertebrates.

Various authors have investigated the bile pigments of invertebrates. Lederer (1940) compiled a survey of these studies. Even early researchers knew that the "invertebrate liver" (digestive gland) does not produce bile in the same sense as the vertebrate liver (von Fürth, 1903). Various investigators were unable to detect bile pigments in this gland (Voit, 1860, in pearl oysters; Cadiat, 1878, in snails; Krukenberg, 1882a,b, in snails and Cephalopoda; Levy, 1890, in snails; Frédericq, 1878a,b, in Cephalopoda; Frenzel, 1888, in sea snails; Roaf, 1906, in crabs and sea shells and marine Gastropoda. On the other hand, Karsten (1845) found green pigment in the "liver" of some fresh water shells (*Anodontata*) that gave the Gmelin reaction. The green color which can sometimes be observed in oysters is caused by a blue diatom (*Navicula ostrearia*), and has probably nothing to do with bile pigments (Sauvangeau, 1907).

Corresponding to their occurrence, the bile pigments of invertebrates can be divided into five groups:

(1) Bile pigments ingested with food

(2) Bile pigments which originate from the chlorophyll ingested with food

(3) Bile pigment formed from hemoglobin ingested with food

(4) Bile pigments formed from phycobilins—bile pigments of algae—ingested with food

(5) Bile pigments formed in the metabolism independent of food

Only one example is known for group (1), i.e., a protozoon (*Opalina ranarum*) in the intestines of frogs. Kedrowsky (1930), Fantham (1931), Lavier (1937), and Mohr (1948) found that biliverdin from the bile of frogs dyes these parasites green. This is true for their vegetative as well as their resting forms (cysts). In their protoplasm, bilirubin-like crystals are often present which give a Gmelin reaction. Brookes and Mohr (1963) studied bile pigments in opalinids and found that bile pigments were concentrated in the large intestine of the anuran hosts at elevated pH levels under special physiological conditions, and this gave rise to diffusion of bile pigments into the cytoplasm of the opalinids. They found that the yellow crystals occurring in the protoplasm of the opalinids were dissolved during treatment with alcohol, from which they concluded that the crystals are stercobilin and not bilirubin.

Also, only a single example is known for group (2). Metcalf (1945) detected a green Gmelin-positive pigment in the fat body (corpus adiposum) and in the pericardiac cells of the hemiptera *Anasa tristis* and *Acanthocephala terminalis*. This pigment originates from the chlorophyll of food; the chlorophyll was apparently degraded in the intestinal walls to a rusty-red substance which accumulated in the pancreas, testes, and in the hypodermis. This red pigment was converted to a green one, which gave a Gmelin reaction. Isolation and closer examination of this substance would be extremely interesting, since this is the only bile pigment known which is formed from chlorophyll.

Pigments belonging to group (3) can be found in numerous blood-sucking invertebrates. Thus, Spiess (1905) found bile pigments in the peritoneal epithelia of leeches (*Hirudo medicinalis*), which gave a Gmelin reaction after alcoholic extraction. Contrary to this, Diwany

(1919, pp. 121–122) could not find any bile pigments in *Hirudo*. The yellow pigment which was formed from digested hemoglobin in ticks (*Ixodes*) did not give a Gmelin reaction. Abeloos (1925, p. 471) detected a Gmelin-positive green pigment (*"pontobdellin"*) in the granula of certain specific connective tissue cells of the Rhynchobdella leech *Pontobdella*. Furthermore, Diwany found brown and red pigments in the epidermis of the leeches *Glossiphonia, Hemiclepsis,* and *Piscicola*. Gheorghiu (1933) found bile pigment in the leech *Protoclebsis tesselata*. Mouchet (1928) succeeded in finding it in fish leeches, Gnathidae. Voinov (1928) detected a Gmelin-positive green pigment in the specific chromophoric cells of the leech *Glossiphonia paludosa*. These cells, loaded with the pigment, migrated from the intestines into the skin, where the green pigment was converted into a yellow one. Raphael (1936, 1939) found bile pigments in some marine annelidae of the class Polychaeta (*Aphrodite*). He assumed that these compounds originated from hemoglobin degradation. However, in some cases it seemed more likely to assume that a precursor of hemoglobin was involved. Later the same author also examined the location, of bile pigments in the parasitic cirripedic crustacea *Septosaccus cuenoti* (Raphael, 1948a,b). The larva of this invertebrate leads a free, nonparasitic life. It was assumed that the small quantities of bile pigment which can be found in the eggs and in the larva originated from hemoglobin ingested by the mother. This biliverdin-like pigment was mainly located in the sucking organs of grown animals. The amount of pigment varied with the sexual cycle. Wigglesworth (1943) proved that bile pigment formation takes place both in the epithelial cells of intestines and in the mesenchymal cells of the pericardium in bloodsucking arthropodae (*Rhodnius prolixus* and others). H. M. Fox (1953) found biliverdin in the parasitic cirripedic crustaceae *Rhizocephala peltogaster* and *partenopea*. The roots of the cirripedic crustaceae, which were anchored in their host, contained a Gmelin-positive green pigment.

In group (4) only one representative is known. Green (1959) found that some crustaceae (Ostracoda)—species *Heterocypris incongruens* and *Eucypris vireus*—contain bile pigments, most likely biladienes of type a,b derived from blue-green algae in their food. These pigments are found as small granules in the cell wall of the gut. *Eucypris vireus* also transfers some pigment to the valves of its carapace. Green (1962) described the extraction, spectral absorption, and fluorescence data of the pigments.

Later Green (1962*) found a blue-green biladiene of the violinoid type in the green patches on the valves of the carapace *Eucypris virens* (Crustacea, Ostracoda) as well as in the walls of its gut, whereas *Hetero-*

cypris necongruens had no bile pigment outside the gut. Probably the color of the carapace valves of the ostracodes like *Cypridopsis aculeata* is also due to bile pigments.

Mangum (1962*) found a green pigment identified as mesobiliviolin in some populations of *Clymnella torquata* and *Clymnella mucosa* (polychate family Maldamidae), but not in other populations. Experiments showed that the deposition of the pigment was probably derived ultimately from blue-green or red algae.

The bile pigments of the sea slug *Aplysia* which feeds on red algae may also be derived from algal bile pigments (D. L. Fox, 1953; C. J. Watson, 1957; cf. also below).

The most interesting class is group (5). MacMunn (1885a,b) observed a Gmelin-positive pigment in various species of actinidae below the ectoderm of their plantar surface. Abeloos and Teissier (1926) found a violet pigment in the sea anemone *Sagartia parasitica* (*Calliactis effoeta*). This pigment was isolated in crystalline form by Lederer *et al.* (1940), who called it *calliactin* and pointed out its close chemical relation to bile pigments. D. L. Fox and Pantin (1944) reexamined the appearance of bile pigments in coelenterates and Tixier and Tixier-Durivault (1942, 1943) studied the pigment present in blue corals (*Heliopora coerulea*). This blue pigment remained intact even after decalcification with HCl and gave a positive Gmelin reaction. Its zinc salt showed red fluorescence and the methyl ester was similar to that of bile pigment esters. Tixier and Tixier-Durivault (1943) isolated the pigment in crystalline form and showed that it is a bilitriene with two vinyl groups; the pigment differs from biliverdin in its violet color. Tixier (1945), who called this pigment *helioporobilin*, studied its methyl esters.

Von Linden (1903, p. 55) investigated insects and found that the scales, intestines, and excretions of the butterfly *Vanessa* contain a yellow pigment which gave a positive Gmelin reaction. Comas (1927) detected a biliverdin-like pigment in the fat bodies of the larva of the ephemera *Chironomius* which was also slightly Gmelin positive. This pigment occurred together with a compound similar to hemoglobin and was independent of the chlorophyll ingested with food. Wieland and Kotzschmar (1937) and Wieland and Tartter (1940) found green and blue chromoproteins in the wings of the cabbage butterfly. These authors isolated the prosthetic group of these compounds in the form of a crystalline methyl ester and called it *pterobilin*. They established that the pigment has a bilitreine structure. Junge (1941) detected blue-green pigments in the hemolymph of *Sphinx ligustri*, grasshoppers, and locustidae. These pigments resembled bile pigments, but were different from glaucobilin and pterobilin. Okay (1945) found chromoproteins in the orthopera *Mantis religiosa* and *Oedipoda miniata* which were similar to phycocyanin of algae. Goodwin and Srisukh (1950, 1951) found blue chromoproteins in the hemolymph and tegument of migratory locusts. Hackman (1952) also detected blue chromoproteins in the hemolymph of the lepidoptera *Pieris rapae, Cacoecia australana,* and *Amphipyra sanguinipuncta.* These compounds contained mesobiliverdin as prosthetic groups. Passama-Vuillaume (1964) studied the bile pigments of the teguments of *Mantis religiosa.* She found that the pigment is water extractable and consists of a green and a yellow component. The former was isolated as crystalline ester and shown to be identical with biliverdin, the latter was most likely formed by oxidation of biliverdin and probably is not present in the animal *in vivo.*

Also in crustacea bile pigments occur in some species while they are absent in most species, even in those closely related to bile pigment-containing species. Bradley (1908) found a green Gmelin-positive pigment in the digestive gland and muscles of fresh water crabs although the blood and muscles of the animals were hemoglobin-free. Green (1961) found a green pigment in the eyes of the Cladocera *Polyphemus pediculus* (L) as well as in its embryos. The pigment was extracted with HCl–methanol and its close similarity to biliverdin established. The bile pigments described in two species of ostracoda by Green (1959, 1962) (see above) were derived from blue-green algae in their food. Gilchrist and Green (1962) found a bilatriene in the fresh water fairy shrimp *Chirocephalus diaphanus* Prévost. This shrimp is frequently blue-green in color, and this is partially due to a granular blue pigment in the tissues, identified as a bilatriene. This pigment is more abundant in females than in males, and the females contain more pigment if cultured in water deficient in dissolved oxygen. This finding points toward a connection between the bile pigment formation and the intensity of the heme synthesis in these animals.

Gilchrist and Green (1962) reviewed the literature finding that the occurrence of bilins among entomostracan crustaceae is rare, having been recorded only in parasitic cirripedes, some freshwater ostracodes and the eyes of the cladoceran *Polyphemus pediculus* (L). According to the literature, however, the occurrence of blue and green colors is not infrequent within this family, but the pigments have not yet been identified.

It has been known that bile pigments can occur in the shells of molluscs since Krukenberg (1882a,b, 1883b) found bluish and violet Gmelin-positive pigments in the snail shells of *Haliotis* and *Turbo.* Schultz (1904) confirmed these observations. He found that the red pigment of the snail *Haliotis rufescens* gives a strong Gmelin reaction and a positive diazo reaction. On treatment with sodium amalgam, a urobilin-type compound was formed, which was named *"rufescin."* Dhéré and Baumeler (1928, 1929), and Dhéré *et al.* (1928, 1930) found that this pigment was closely related to bilirubin. Schultz found similar pigments in *Haliotis californensis* and *Turbo olivaceus,* and Kodzuka (1921) found them in *Haliotis gigantea.* N. Schultz and Becker (1931), who later continued the investigation of snail pigments, tended to regard them as indigo derivatives ("Haliotsindigo"). However, Lemberg (1931), Tixier (1947, 1948), and Tixier and Lederer (1947, 1948, 1949) unequivocally defined these pigments as bile pigments. Tixier and Lederer found that these substances are closely related to mesobiliviolin and proposed the name *"haliotviolin."* A. Comfort (1949a) found bile pigments in turbinidae although these animals did not contain porphyrin. He also assumed that the haliotis pigment was an indigo derivative (1940b), but admitted later (1950a) that it is probably a bile pigment. Furthermore, he described an additional accompanying yellow pigment in the shells of *Haliotis cracherodii* Leach which seemed to be a bile pigment also. The same year he (A. Comfort, 1950b) found a violet pigment in the shells of the pearl oyster (*Pinctada vulgaris*). This pigment accompanied uroporphyrin I and was a mixture of two biliviolinoid compounds which were different from known bile pigments. Dor (1902) found a pigment in gastropoda which resembled urobilin. Later it was established that this compound was a true bile pigment (Schultz, 1904; Dhéré and Baumeler, 1928; Dhéré *et al.,* 1928).

Derrien and Turchini (1925) were the first to study the violet pigment of the sea slug *Aplysia,* which they called "aplysiopurpurin." They found that the pigment itself showed a red fluorescence, whereas its zinc salt gave a green fluorescence. Schreiber (1932) found this pigment in the digestive gland of the snail, as well as in its purple secretions. He confirmed its urobilinoid character and obtained a positive benzaldehyde reaction. Fontaine and Raffy (1936) found that the pigment was similar to mesobiliviolin. Lederer and Huttrer (1942) showed that aplysiopurpurin is a chromoprotein and isolated its prosthetic group in pure form. It was found to be a mixture of two bilidienes, *"aplysioviolin"* and *"aplysiopurpurin."* Christomanos (1954) studied the pigment of *Aplysia depilans* and confirmed Lederer and Huttrer's findings, but believed that the pigments had porphyrin character. He substantiated this assumption by the observations that the pigment gave an untypical Gmelin reaction and that methanol solutions of the pigment showed red fluorescence even without the addition of zinc salts. His investigations, however, did not include spectrophotometric studies in the near-ultraviolet, the region of the Soret band characteristic of porphyrins, but absent in bile pigments.

Kennedy and Nicol (1959) studied the polychate worm *Chaetopterus variopedatus* and found four bile pigments besides chlorophyll derivatives and porphyrins; three of them gave the Gmelin reaction: one was mesobiliviolin, one turboglaucobilin, and one helioporobilin or a closely related derivative.

Webb (1939) found pyrrole pigments closely related to bile pigments in *Tunicata* (Ascidia). These pigments consist of a straight chain of pyrrole rings and contain a vanadium atom. A green chromogen and a brown pigment were differentiated.

Currie (1962) studied the pigments of zooplancton feces and could demonstrate various chlorophyll derivatives but no bile pigments.

The blue pigment of a surface-living oceanic copepod (*Potella fera*, Dane) was studied by Herring (1965*) who believed it to be a chromoprotein carotenoid complex. A closer analysis was, however, not carried out. He points out that one of the most striking features of the surface plankton of the top 4 inches of tropical waters is the predominance of blue pigmented organisms of a wide variety of groups. It therefore seems likely that at least some of these plankton organisms should contain bile pigments.

The chemical nature of the reddish pigment of the dinoflagellates abundant in the waters of Tampa Bay, Florida, described by Dragovich *et al.* (1965*) was not investigated, but the possibility that bile pigments are involved exists.

C. Bile Pigments in Plants

Until recently it was believed that the occurrence of *bile pigments in plants* was limited to red algae (Rhodophyta), blue-green algae (Cyanophyta), and the root nodules of Leguminosa. It is, however, now clear that the physiologically important compound *phytochrome,* the photoreceptor controlling many aspects of growth and development of higher plants, is a chromoprotein with a bile pigment as prosthetic group. Siegelman and Firer (1964*) suggested this on the basis of comparison of the spectral absorption curves of phytochrome and those of allophycocyanin and phycobilins (Ó'hEocha, 1962*, 1963*). Later Siegelman *et al.* (1966*) cleaved the chromophore from phytochrome and found that it contains bile pigments closely similar to but distinct from the phycobilins. In Chapter I,N we suggested that this bile pigment be called *phytobilin.*

The chromoproteins phycoerythrin and phycocyanin are present in red and blue algae. Here they play an important physiological role as photosynthetic pigments. Because their absorption range complements the chlorophyll absorption, the algae become able to absorb light at wavelengths where the chlorophyll absorption is already weak. Thus algae can absorb additional radiation energy and are able to grow in less intense light.

Kützing (1843) discovered these compounds. Lemberg investigated the prosthetic groups of these substances, the *phycobilins* (Lemberg and Legge, 1949, pp. 145–158 and 571–572). Fujiwara (1955) described a novel process for the isolation of crystalline chromoproteins from algae. He also reviewed the literature in this field, including important papers of Japanese researchers. At the same time he electrophoretically examined the chromoproteins and published a tabulated survey of the absorption maxima of different algae. Furthermore, he studied the amino acid composition of the pigments (Fujiwara, 1956). Later, Fujiwara (1960) studied the chromoproteins derived from the Japanese Nori *Porphyra tenera* by means of enzymatic digestion employing chromatography and infrared spectrophotometry. In a later paper he investigated their sugar compounds (Fujiwara, 1961).

It is thus evident that *bile pigments play an important biological role* both in some of the most primitive plants existing—the red and blue-green algae—and in higher plants; these pigments are of considerably greater biological interest than formerly believed. As the Rhodophyta and Cyanophyta are among the most primitive and old organisms known the biological history of bile pigments must be correspondingly ancient, i.e., dating back to pre-Cambrian times, as is the case with the porphyrins.

C. J. Watson (1965) discussed the possibility of a more direct biosynthetic pathway for bile pigments in red and blue-green algae than that via the porphyrins known in higher organisms. He came, however, to the conclusion that such a pathway is not very likely because the algal bile pigments like those of higher organisms are of the type IX,α.

Interest in the phycobilins has been increasing considerably during the last few years because they can probably be of practical importance during future space travel (Ó'hEocha, personal communication, 1966).

Ó'hEocha (1958) thoroughly discussed the comparative biochemistry of phycoblins, including their absorption spectra. Further studies on algae chromoproteins are due to Ó'hEocha and Haxo (1960), Ó'hEocha *et al.* (1961), Ó'hEocha and Ó'Carra (1961), Ó'Carra and Ó'hEocha (1962 a,b; 1963). According to these investigators phycoerythrins and phycocyanins occur in algae of the divisions. Rhotophyta, Cyanophyta, and Cryptophyta. The prosthetic groups, called phycobilins, are firmly attached to the proteins and can only be released by concentrated acids. Because of the lability of phycobilins they are difficult to isolate, and artifacts are easily formed. Minor differences in preparation procedures can result in different pigments. Therefore the elucidation of the structure of phycobilins is exceedingly difficult.

Hattori and Fujita performed a series of important studies on the formation of phycobilin chromoproteins by the blue-green alga *Tolypotrix tenuis*. Hattori and Fujita (1959a) studied the formation of these pigments as induced by light of various colors, so-called "chromatic adaptation." Algal cultures in flat-bottomed flasks were placed in a thermostatically regulated water bath at 30° and irradiated from beneath with light which had passed different filters—red, orange, orange-yellow, yellow, blue, green, or purple. The spectral transmittance curves of the filters are given. Prior to the irradiation the algal cultures had been incubated for 24–48 hours in strong light at 20° in order to reduce their initial pigment content. The algal cultures were continually aerated with air containing 5% CO_2. Aliquots of algal suspension were withdrawn at intervals for pigment analysis and determination of packed cell volume. The phycoerythrin content increased markedly on irradiation with blue and green light but red and pink light did not induce a rise in the content of this pigment. Phycocyanin and allophycocyanin, on the other hand, increased on irradiation with red and yellow light, but did not increase with blue light, lacking the spectral range of 550–700 nm. It was clear that photochemical mechanisms were involved in the formation of phycobilin pigments and that chlorophylls or carotenoids could hardly be involved.

Hattori and Fujita (1959b) prepared the phycobilin chromoproteins from *Tolypothrix tenuis* in crystalline condition by means of an elaborate technique described in detail. This method involves disintegration of the cells with sonic oscillators and fractionations by means of centrifugation at 20,000–100,000 g, salting out with ammonium sulfate, and adsorption on tricalcium phosphate gels. *Phycocyanin* and *allophycocyanin* crystallized in microscopic thin platelets while *phycoerythrin* regularly formed thin needles and only exceptionally platelets. The pigments exhibited the following principal maxima (main visible maximum placed first): phycocyanin 620, 360, 280 nm; allophycocyanin 650, 360, 280 nm; phycoerythrin 565, 380, 308, 280 nm. The phycobilin pigments of *Tolypothrix tenuis* were compared to similar pigments from six other species of algae and studied by means of electrophoresis, ultracentrifugation, and determination of the isoelectric point. The molecular weight of phycocyanin and allophycocyanin was 134,000–138,000, that of phycoerythrin 226,000. The concentration of phycobilin chromoproteins within the cells was remarkably high, amounting to about 30% of the total cell protein. All three types of chromoproteins were found to occur regularly in substantial concentrations in both red and blue-green algae.

Detailed spectrophotometric studies of the phycobilin pigments of 8 different species of algae—4 *Rhodophyceae* and 4 *Cyanophyceae*—were reported by Hattori and Fujita (1959c). Phycocyanin and allophycocyanin obtained from different species exhibited practically identical spectral properties. These two pigments were found to share the absorption bands or shoulders at 280, 285, and 360 nm. On the other hand, the spectral properties of phycoerythrin from various species differed considerably. Their absorption maxima were, however, the same—i.e., 565, 545, 500, 370, 310, and 280 nm—but the relative intensity of these bands varied widely. Phycoerythrin forms the major phycobilin pigment of Rhodophyceae, but contrary to what is generally believed, it was also predominant in most of the blue-green algae examined.

The effect of pre-illumination of algal cultures on their content of phycobilin pigments was investigated in *Tolypothrix tenuis* by Hattori and Fujita (1959d). Illumination was carried out with a fluorescent light (20,000 lux) for 24 hours at a constant temperature of 22–24°. During this time a distinct decrease of the content of phycobilin pigments took place while the level of chlorophylls and carotenoids remained unchanged. On incubation in darkness following the illumination phycoerythrin formation took place after an induction time of 4 hours, if nitrate was added within the first 6 hours after the beginning of the dark period. If nitrate was added more than 10 hours after the beginning of the dark incubation, no pigment formation took place. The final level of phycoerythrin was reached after 14 hours dark incubation and varied with the time of nitrate application. Under the conditions described, no increase of phycocyanin took place. If, however, the algae were pre-illuminated with red light, phycocyanin was formed while no formation of phycoerythrin took place. No change of the level of chlorophylls or carotenoids took place.

Fujita and Hattori (1962a) studied the changes of composition of the cellular material of algae during the formation of phycobilin chromoproteins in *Tolypothrix tenuis*. Fujita and Hattori (1962b) investigated photochemical interconversions between precursors of phycobilin chromoproteins in the same organism. Green light induced a conversion of a phycocyanin precursor into a phycoerythrin precursor, whereas red light converted a phycoerythrin precursor into a phycocyanin precursor. The rates of these photochemical reactions was unaltered by variations in the incubation temperature from 0° to 35°, by the composition of the atmosphere (pressure of O_2 and CO_2), or by the inhibitor of photosynthesis *p*-chlorophenyldimethylurea. The most active wavelength for inducing conversion of phycocyanin into phycoerythrin precursors was 541 nm, which is near the maximum of phycoerythrin (565 nm), while the most effective wavelength for induction of the reverse process was 641 nm, which is close to the absorption maximum of phycocyanin (620 nm). A possible mechanism of these photochemical interconversions was proposed.

Fujita and Hattori (1963) extended their studies on illumination and formation of phycobilin chromoproteins in *Tolypothrix tenuis*. They found that the total amount of chromoproteins (phycoerythrin plus phycocyanin) synthesized by cells which had been pre-illuminated by exposure to green (red) light was markedly suppressed by exposing them for a short period to red (green) light (second chromatic illumination). These inhibitory effects were absent if dark incubation was carried out in the absence of nitrogen source, indicating that the nitrogen metabolism of the cells is involved. When the synthesis of chromoproteins was completely suppressed by chloramphenicol, the inhibitory effect of the second chromatic illumination became more conspicuous. A reaction scheme was proposed according to which intermediary formation of direct precursors of phycocyanin and phycoerythrin is assumed to occur on addition of a nitrogen source to the pre-illuminated cells.

The important studies of Fujita and Hattori clearly underline the basic biological importance of the bile pigment chromoproteins in the metabolism of red and blue-green algae.

The most penetrating recent studies on algal bile pigments are due to Ó'hEocha and collaborators (Ó'hEocha, 1963*, 1965a*). Ó'hEocha (1963*) obtained three different pigments from C-phycocyanin using closely related methods of isolation. The spectra of these pigments were subjected to thorough studies. One of them, phycobilin 630, obtained by $CHCl_3$ extraction after hydrolysis of C-phycocyanin with $12 N$ HCl, was believed to be the native prosthetic group of C-phycocyanobilin. Phycobilin 630 is converted to phycobilin 608 and phycobilin 655 on standing with 12 and $9 N$ HCl, respectively, and $12 N$ HCl converts phycobilin 655 to phycobilin 608. Phycobilin 608 has many of the properties of mesobilene, but differs from it in being converted to phycobilin 655 on methylation. Phycobilin 655, a dibasic tetrapyrrole, was also formed by neutralization of an aqueous solution of phycobilin 630 with sodium acetate. The findings indicate that procedures for isolation of phycobilins must be selected with caution to avoid artifacts. Earlier results, indicating interspecific differences in the prosthetic group of C-phycocyanin, were most likely due to variations in the chemical technique for isolating phycocyanobilin.

Similar studies on phycoerythrobilin were carried out by Ó'Carra *et al.* (1964*) who found that the pigment isolated from the phycoerythrins is the chemically unaltered prosthetic group of these biliproteins.

A bilidiene,IX,α structure isomeric with mesobiliviolin,IX,α is proposed for phycoerythrobilin (cf. Chapter I). The amino acid composition, C-terminal residue analysis, as well as purification and N-terminal analysis of algal biliproteins was investigated by Ó'Carra (1965[*]) and Rafferty and Ó'hEocha (1965[*]). Fujimori (1964[*]) studied the chromophores of phycoerythrin by investigation of the intermolecular energy transfer using spectral absorption and fluorescence studies and treatment with the SH-blocking agent p-chloromercuribenzoate. It was found that phycoerythrin contains at least two main units, one containing a 500 nm chromophore and the other two chromophores—545 and 465 nm. Possibly these units are composed of smaller units.

Ó'hEocha (1965b[*]) presented a general survey of algal biliproteins and bilins. Ó'Carra and Ó'hEocha (1966[*]) introduced an improved procedure for large scale preparation of phycobilins by means of extraction with hot methanol. During this extraction the chromoproteins are denatured and the phycobilins set free in modified conditions, but they can be reconverted into the original phycobilins in a solution of concentrated HCl. The separation of the phycobilins from the apoproteins was found to take place without methylation of their propionic acid side chains.

Virtanen and Laine (1946) and Virtanen and Miettinen (1949) studied the *bile pigments of leguminous plants*. They isolated a green bile pigment chromoprotein, resembling choleglobin, and called it "legcholeglobin." This compound contains biliverdin and is formed from a hemoglobin derivative, leghemoglobin, which participates in the nitrogen fixation from air. Falk *et al.* (1959) reviewed the occurrence and function of heme compounds and porphyrins in legume root nodules but did not mention observations on their bile pigments.

Summary

The comparative biology of bile pigments is a wide and interesting field of research, but our knowledge in this area is limited. Bile pigments are regularly present in higher vertebrates, where they are apparently only by-products. They occur in various tissues of some fishes and invertebrates, where they surely have significant physiological functions. They occur irregularly in many invertebrates and may be present in one species and missing in another closely related one. In invertebrates the bile pigments can be derived from the following sources: (1) absorbed from the food; (2) formed from chlorophyll of the food; (3) formed from hemoglobin of the food; (4) formed from phycobilins of algae ingested with food; and (5) formed autonomously in the metabolism. They can be present as accompanying compounds of hemoglobin or porphyrins, or as the only pyrrole pigments present. The chemical investigation of the bile pigments of fishes and invertebrates is as yet very incomplete. Some of the bile pigments from these animals have been obtained in crystalline form and some of them were shown to be different from the bile pigments of higher vertebrates. More thorough studies in this field are desirable.

In plants bile pigments occur in the chromoproteins of red and blue-green algae and in the chromoprotein phytochrome of higher plants, as well as in the root nodules of leguminous plants. The bile pigments of plants play an important biological role approaching that of the porphyrins.

Bile pigments occur as chromoproteins in the excretions and tissues of lower animals and plants. They behave like bilirubin of mammals, where the pigment is bound to serum albumin, elastin, or various macromolecular compounds of the bile.

A systematic and extended study of bile pigments in fishes, lower animals, and plants would be of extraordinary value in broadening our understanding of the biology of these pigments.

The biological action of bilirubin is briefly discussed, especially the cytotoxic action of unconjugated bilirubin.

Additional Readings

Section A

Cheung, W. H., Sawitsky, A., and Isenberg, H. D. (1966). Effect of bilirubin on the mammalian erythrocyte. *Transfusion* 6, 475–486.

Section B

Needham, A. E. (1966). The tissue-pigments of some fresh-water leeches. *Comp. Biochem. Physiol.* 18, 427–461.

CHAPTER XI

The Clinical Value of Bile Pigment Determinations: A Summary

The occurrence of bile pigments in blood, urine, stool, various fluids of the body, and tissues has been discussed in Chapters V to IX. A brief survey of the clinical significance of bile pigment determinations will be given here.

The terms "bile in blood" and "bile in urine" are widely used, but constitute a bad terminology. Whole bile cannot find its way to blood or urine except in patients with fistulas between the bile passages and the lymph vessels or the urinary passages. Nevertheless, these misleading terms have hitherto met little opposition. With (1963) wrote: "The tendency to speak of 'bile in blood' and 'bile in urine' is misleading and ought to be abandoned." Eiband and Fred (1963) expressed quite similar views in an Editorial in a leading medical journal and concluded their article with the hope: "That the foregoing will encourage some medical students, house officers, clinicians, academicians, and members of editorial boards of scientific journals to be more precise when recounting the urinary findings of jaundiced patients."

It should be remembered that the diagnostic value of bile pigment analysis, including that of urobilinoids, is limited. The results of these analyses alone can never be sufficient to make a diagnosis. These determinations gain their true value only as a part of the entire clinical picture.

It should be emphasized that differential diagnosis between obstructive (extrahepatic) and hepatocellular jaundice can hardly be made from bile pigment determinations alone. This will readily be appreciated, because every case of biliary obstruction rapidly becomes complicated by secondary inflammation phenomena, and most cases of hepatitis are complicated by secondary intrahepatic biliary occlusion. Furthermore, hepatitis can occur in forms dominated by intrahepatic obstruction (cholangiolitis) as well as in forms dominated by parenchymal cell necrosis. This was clearly recognized by Young (1947b, p. 266), who wrote that: "Repeated determinations of bilirubin in the blood and urine and of urobilinogen in the urine and stool are of distinct but nevertheless secondary value." Similarly, D. Watson (1963) doubts the value of analysis of bilirubin metabolites in this respect.

Repeated determinations are more valuable than single analyses. For example, neoplastic obstruction is strongly suspected when the serum bilirubin concentration is constantly high with small variations, and the fecal urobilinogen level low, over a number of weeks.

The most important bile pigment analysis is that of bilirubin in serum. Simple methods, e.g., the icterus index, suffice for most clinical purposes. More specific bilirubin tests are required when certain conditions, such as aurantiasis cutis or pathomimetic jaundice caused by drugs, have to be eliminated. More exact quantitative methods are necessary only for the examination of newborns (danger of kernicterus!) or for scientific investigations. The use of bilirubin standards is superfluous if thoroughly standardized spectrophotometers are employed.

Hijmans van den Bergh's direct diazo reaction is suitable for differentiation of hemolytic jaundice types, nonhemolytic jaundice with unconjugated bilirubin, and neonatal jaundice from other forms of jaundice. Thus, it permits differential diagnosis between nonhemolytic jaundice with conjugated bilirubin and nonhemolytic jaundice with unconjugated bilirubin. Galambos (1963) wrote: "In the large majority of patients, the proportion of the elevated direct and indirect reacting serum bilirubin is of no help whatever in the etiology of their jaundice." This is in accordance with the personal experience of the writer and with the fact that Danish hepatologists and hematologists—including E. Meulengracht (1918, 1921) who introduced the icterus index and P. Iversen who introduced the liver biopsy (Iversen and Roholm, 1939)— have never used the direct diazo test and never missed it.

Also quantitative determination of the direct diazo reaction is of limited value. The advocates of such analyses—C. J. Watson in the U.S.A. and Schalm in Holland—use quite different techniques, the former the 1-minute-bilirubin and the latter the 10-minute-bilirubin (cf. Chapter V). The process used by Watson for the determination of 1-minute-bilirubin is far from accurate. If a quantitative determination of the direct diazo reaction is required, Schalm's 10-minute-bilirubin is preferable. But it is also to be emphasized that even chromatographic determinations and phase separation analysis of bilirubin and its conjugates have given disappointing clinical results (cf. D. Watson, 1963; Galambos, 1963). The cause of this is that bilirubin conjugates constitute several different only partly known compounds which are labile and have not been isolated in pure condition. And it is highly questionable if exact differential analysis of bilirubin and its conjugates will ever be possible.

Quantitative determinations of the "total" serum bilirubin are of vital importance only in cases of severe jaundice of the newborn. The danger of kernicterus is generally believed to exist when the serum bilirubin concentration exeeds a certain limit which is at present set at about 20 mg/100 ml. Even though only the free (unconjugated) bilirubin is toxic, total bilirubin determinations will suffice for clinical purposes in the vast majority of cases, the only exceptions being the rare cases of congenital biliary atresia and neonatal hepatitis.

Because of these considerations, knowledge of exact serum bilirubin concentration is of little diagnostic or prognostic value except during icterus of newborn. Indeed, a normal serum bilirubin level can exist even during complete bile duct obstruction and total necrosis of the parenchyma of the liver. The height of the serum bilirubin is dependent not only on the liver function but also on the amount of bilirubin produced. Moreover, the peak of the serum bilirubin level and the maximum of parenchymal damage do not correspond in viral hepatitis (Pollock, 1951; p. 74).

Nevertheless, severe jaundice which lasts for extended periods has to be taken more seriously than a milder icterus lasting for a shorter period of time. However, jaundice *per se* is not dangerous since intense jaundice can last for a long time without bringing about severe consequences. This is especially apparent in cases of nonhemolytic familial jaundice.

Determination of bilirubin and its conjugates in urine has only slight value. They can be detected in normal urine with sensitive analytical methods. Various authors regarded the presence of traces of bilirubin in urine as an indication of early stages of virus hepatitis (cf. Chapter VI). This is not easy to understand and should be reexamined. In manifest jaundice, massive bilirubinuria—due to conjugates—is apparent even at gross examination. Therefore, it is superfluous to ascertain this fact by analysis, especially if serum bilirubin analysis is carried out. Quantitative urinary bilirubin determinations have scientific significance exclusively.

Urinary urobilinoid determinations have a certain but rather limited clinical usefulness as liver function tests. Royer (1943, p. 243 et seq.) maintained that the appearance of pathological urobilinuria is the most sensitive liver function test known. However, this extreme sensitivity presents a rather serious limitation in clinical value; indeed, this test becomes positive even in mild affections of the liver. Undoubtedly, the simplified quantitative benzaldehyde test of Watson has a certain significance, but also its shortcomings. Extraction methods are too complicated for daily clinical work, considering their limited clinical value. Determination of urobilinogen excretion over a 24-hour period is a better measure of the degree of liver damage than serum bilirubin concentration, because only the former is independent of the bilirubin production level of the patient.

Fecal urobilinoid determinations are valuable in the diagnosis of neoplastic bile duct obstruction and hemolytic jaundice. However, the necessary quantitative procedure is time consuming and distasteful to the laboratory personnel. Therefore, it is conceivable that this method will hardly be accepted, in spite of its value. For scientific purposes sampling of the stool for a period of several days is necessary, but a single random sample is acceptable for clinical purposes.

The fecal urobilinoid content is practically always increased during hemolytic diseases, and quantitative determination can be of clinical value. However, the fecal urobilinoid level should not be regarded as a measure of hemoglobin degradation. The fecal urobilinoid is always somewhat lower than calculated from the hemoglobin degradation. No constant relation seems to exist between these two factors. The ratio between urinary urobilinoid and fecal urobilinoid, the "urobilin quotient," has been regarded as a liver function test, but it does not give more information than analysis of urine alone.

The fecal urobilinoid is very low during neoplastic bile duct obstruction. C. J. Watson (1937b, 1940), as well as Steigmann and Dyniewicz (1943a,b), emphasized the diagnostic value of quantitative determinations, which are based on stool samples extended over 4 days. When the concentrations are below 5 mg/24 hours in adults with long-lasting icterus, neoplastic obstruction is indicated with great probability. Analyses of random samples are, however, sufficient for clinical purposes.

The limited clinical value of urobilinoid analyses is clearly expressed by Kahán and Felkai (1961) in the conclusion of their detailed investigations with reliable chemical methods. They correctly state that the urobilinoid metabolism is a complex process influenced not only by liver parenchyma, but also by entrance of bilirubin into the gut, rate of enteric bacterial reduction, and balance between intestinal motility and the factors of absorption.

Biliary bile pigment determinations have a very limited clinical value. In examination of duodenal fluid, Schalm's "bilitinction" based on bromosulphalein determinations is superior to bile pigment analysis.

Bile pigment determinations in other fluids of the body, excretions, and in organs are only interesting from a scientific point of view. This is also true for the differentiation between the various forms (l, i, and d) of urobilinoids. Similarly, tolerance tests with bilirubin or urobilinoids have no practical clinical value.

Bilirubin determination in amniotic fluid with very sensitive methods seems to be important in *antepartum* diagnosis of hemolytic disease of newborns.

Recently several writers expressed profound skepticism toward the value of fractionate determination of bilirubin and its conjugates. Thus McGill *et al.* (1962*) wrote: "Despite improved understanding of the chemistry of bilirubin . . . , the separation of conjugated and unconjugated bilirubin by any modification of the van den Bergh reaction is impossible. There is no precise method by which the relative amount of pigment derived from unconjugated bilirubin and pigment I can be determined"; and Schoenfield *et al.* (1964*) concluded that: "The advisability of additional chemical studies based upon existing methods and concepts is questioned." Further, D. Watson (1963) directed the attention toward the time-honored but often neglected fact that "Because most liver diseases are neither purely 'hepatocellular' nor 'obstructive' in nature it is doubtful whether analysis of bilirubin metabolites will ever assist their differential diagnosis." Finally, Jacobs *et al.* (1964) admitted that the unavailability of reference standards of bilirubin conjugates present a serious obstacle to the solution of the analytical problems involved.

It is therefore with a certain amount of justification that the writer concludes this monograph by quoting his 10-year-old discussion remark to Sherlock (With, 1957c): "In few places is so much biochemistry used with so small results as in liver diagnostics."

Bibliography

Abeloos, M. (1925). *Bull. Biol. France Belg.* **59**, 436–497.
Abeloos, M., and Teissier, G. (1926). *Bull. Soc. Zool. France* **51**, 145–151.
Abelson, N., and Boggs, T. R. (1956). *Pediatrics* **17**, 452.
Achard, C., and Morfaux, P. (1899). *Compt. Rend. Soc. Biol.* **51**, 50–51.
Adams, W. C. (1954). *J. Pediat.* **44**, 213–218.
Adler, A. (1922a). *Deut. Arch. Klin. Med.* **140**, 302–322.
Adler, A. (1922b). *Deut. Arch. Klin. Med.* **138**, 309–320.
Adler, A., and Brehme, W. (1925). *Z. Ges. Exptl. Med.* **48**, 148–153.
Adler, A., and Jeddeloh, B. (1929a). *Deut. Arch. Klin. Med.* **164**, 129–146.
Adler, A., and Jeddeloh, B. (1929b). *Deut. Arch. Klin. Med.* **164**, 282–297.
Adler, A., and Meyer, E. (1922). *Klin. Wochschr.* **1**, 2468–2470.
Adler, A., and Meyer, E. (1923). *Klin. Wochschr.* **2**, 258–259.
Adler, A., and Sachs, M. (1923a). *Z. Ges. Exptl. Med.* **31**, 370–397.
Adler, A., and Sachs, M. (1923b). *Z. Ges. Exptl. Med.* **31**, 398–409.
Adler, A., and Strausz, L. (1922). *Klin. Wochschr.* **1**, 2285–2286.
Adler, A., and Strausz, L. (1923). *Klin. Wochschr.* **2**, 932.
Adler, A., and Strausz, L. (1925a). *Z. Ges. Exptl. Med.* **44**, 1–8.
Adler, A., and Strausz, L. (1925b). *Z. Ges. Exptl. Med.* **44**, 9–25.
Adler, A., and Strausz, L. (1925c). *Z. Ges. Exptl. Med.* **44**, 26–42.
Adler, A., and Strausz, L. (1925d). *Z. Ges. Exptl. Med.* **44**, 43–68.
Adlercreutz, H. (1964). *Nord. Med.* **72**, 1004–1005.
Adlersberg, D., and Perutz, A. (1932). *Klin. Wochschr.* **11**, 942–945.
Afanassiew, M. (1883). *Z. Klin. Med.* **6**, 281–331.
Ahrens, E. H., Harris, R. C., and MacMahon, H. E. (1951). *Pediatrics* **8**, 628–647.
Aicardi, J. (1963). *Arch. Franc. Pediat.* **20**, 839–850.
Aidin, R., Corner, B., and Tovey, G. (1950) *Lancet* **I**, 1153–1154.
Akagi, K. (1960a). *Okayama Igakkai Zasshi* **72**, 645.
Akagi, K. (1960b). *Okayama Igakkai Zasshi* **72**, 655.
Akazaki, K. (1962). *Tohoku J. Exptl. Med.* **76**, 107–118.
Åkerren, Y. (1934). Experimental Changes in Liver Function. Dissertation (Med.), U. of Uppsala (284pp.).
Aldrich, R. A., Hawkinson, V., Grinstein, M., and Watson, C. J. (1951). *Blood* **6**, 685–698.
Alican, F., and Hardy, J. D. (1962). *Surgery* **52**, 366–372.
Allessandro, G., and Indovina, R. (1935). *Biochim. Terap. Sper.* **22**, 298–306.
Alliot, M. (1949). *Ann. Biol. Clin. (Paris)* **7**, 249–253.
Altman, K. I., Casarett, G. W., Masters, R. E., Noonan, T. R., and Salomon, K. (1948). *Federation Proc.* **7**, 2.
Altschule, M. D., and Volk, M. C. (1937). *Proc. Soc. Exptl. Biol. Med.* **37**, 184–185.
Alwall, N. (1946). *Acta Med. Scand.* **123**, 560–595.
Alwall, N., Laurell, C. B., and Nilsby, I. (1946a). *Acta Med. Scand.* **124**, 92–101.
Alwall, N., Laurell, C. B., and Nilsby, I. (1946b). *Acta Med. Scand.* **124**, 114–125.

Alzugaray, A. E. (1942). La bilirrubinuria en la ictericia. Thesis (Med.), U. of Buenos Aires (quoted from Lopez Garcia, 1943).

Amada, Y. (1941). *J. Biochem.* (*Tokyo*) **32**, 187–210.

Amako, T. (1957a) *Igaku Kenkyu* **27**, 1584.

Amako, T. (1957b). *Igaku Kenkyu* **27**, 1592.

Amatuzio, D. S. (1960). *Arch. Biochem. Biophys.* **86**, 77–79.

Amatuzio, D. S., Weber, L. J., and Nesbitt, S. (1953). *J. Lab. Clin. Med.* **41**, 615–618

Anderson, L. A. P., de Kock, W. T., and Enslin, P. R. (1961). *J. S. African Chem. Inst.* **14**, 58.

Anderson, W. A. D., and Morrison, D. B. (1942). *AMA Arch. Pathol.* **33**, 677–688.

Anderson, W. A. D., Morrison, D. B., and Williams, E. E., Jr. (1942). *AMA Arch. Pathol.* **33**, 589–602.

André, R., Dreyfus, B., and Sultan, C. (1963). *Nouvelle Rev. Franc. Hematol.* **3**, 189–193.

Andrewes, C. H. (1924a). *Brit. J. Exptl. Pathol.* **5**, 213–219.

Andrewes, C. H. (1924b). *Lancet* I, 590–591.

Andrewes, C. H. (1924c). *Quart. J. Med.* **18**, 19–35.

Andrews, W. H. H. (1955). *Lancet* II, 166–169.

Andrews, W. H. H., and Lozano, I. del R. (1961). *Quart. J. Exptl. Physiol.* **46**, 238–256.

Andrews, W. H. H., and Lozano, I. del R. (1963). *Quart. J. Exptl. Physiol.* **48**, 127–137.

Andrews, W. H. H., Maegraith, B. G., and Wenyon, C. E. M. (1949). *Ann. Trop. Med. Parasitol.* **43**, 229–237.

Andrews, W. H. H., Maegraith, B. G., and Richards, T. G. (1956). *J. Physiol.* (*London*) **131**, 669–677.

Anke, W. K., Fenichel, R., and Barmess, L. A. (1959). *AMA J. Diseases Children* **98**, 559.

Appelmans, R., and Bouckaert, J. P. (1926). *Rev. Med.-Chir. Maladies Foie* **1**, 294–298.

Araki, K. (1956a). *Igaku Kenkyu* **26**, 1843.

Araki, K. (1956b). *Igaku Kenkyu* **26**, 1853.

Arellano, J. M. (1928). *Rev. Med. Rosario* **3**, 336–340.

Arias, I. M. (1962). *J. Clin. Invest.* **41**, 2233–2245.

Arias, I. M. (1963a) *Ann. N.Y. Acad. Sci.* **104** (Art. 3), 1014–1025.

Arias, I. M. (1963b). *Federation Proc.* **22**, 398.

Arias, I. M., and Johnson, L. (1959). *Clin. Res.* **7**, 251.

Arias, I. M., and London, I. M. (1957). *Science* **126**, 563.

Arias, I. M., Johnson, L., and Wolfson, S. (1961). *Am. J. Physiol.* **200**, 1091.

Arias, I. M., Furman, M., Tapley, D. F., and Ross, J. E. (1963a). *Nature* **197**, 1109–1110.

Arias, I. M., Gartner, L., Furman, M., and Wolfson, S. (1963b). *Proc. Soc. Exptl. Med.* **112**, 1037–1040.

Aronsen, K. F. (1962). Liver Function Studies During and After Complete Extrahepatic Biliary Occlusion in the Dog. *Acta Chir. Scand.* Suppl. 275, 114pp.

Aschoff, L. (1922). *Muench. Med. Wochschr.* **69**, 1352–1356.

Aschoff, L. (1924). *Ergeb. Inn. Med. Kinderheilk.* **26**, 1–118.

Aschoff, L. (1928). *Acta Pathol. Microbiol. Scand.* **5**, 338–380.

Aschoff, L. (1932). *Klin. Wochschr.* **11**, 1620–1624.

Ashworth, C. T., and Sanders, E. (1960). *Am. J. Pathol.* **37**, 343–355.
Asvadourova, N. (1913). *Arch. Anat. Microscop.* (*Paris*) **15**, 153–314.
Aubel, E., Targocola, R., and Badonnel (no inits.) (1925). *Presse Med.* **33**, 403–405.
Auché, A. (1907). *Compt. Rend. Soc. Biol.* **63**, 713–715.
Auché, A. (1908a). *Compt. Rend. Soc. Biol.* **64**, 297–299.
Auché, A. (1908b). *Compt. Rend. Soc. Biol.* **64**, 299–301.
Auché, A. (1908c). *Compt. Rend. Soc. Biol.* **65**, 757–758.
Auché, A. (1909). *Compt. Rend. Soc. Biol.* **67**, 225–227.
Auld, A. G. (1896). *Brit. Med. J.* **I**, 137–141.
Axenfeld, H., and Brass, K. (1942). *Frankfurter Z. Pathol.* **57**, 147–236.
Baar, H. S., and Hickmans, E. M. (1941). *J. Physiol.* (*London*) **100**, 4P.
Bader, M. (1947). *Z. Ges. Inn. Med. Grenzgebiete* **2**, 659–665.
Bagenstoss, A. H. (1957). *J. Am. Med. Assoc.* **165**, 1099–1107.
Baikie, A. G. (1957). *Scott. Med. J.* **2**, 359.
Bakker, J. C. W. (1954). *Acta Paediat.* **43**, 529–542.
Balcells-Gorina, A., and Chacón, F. A. (1954). *Med. Clin.* (*Barcelona*) **23**, 238–244.
Baldini, M., and Pietrantonj, F. D. (1957). *Minerva Med.* **48**, 304–315.
Balikov, B. (1955). *Clin. Chem.* **1**, 264–268.
Balikov, B. (1957). *Clin. Chem.* **3**, 145–153.
Balikov, B. (1958). *In* "Standard Methods of Clinical Chemistry" (Am. Assoc. Clin. Chemists, eds.), Vol. II, pp. 192–203. Academic Press, New York.
Baló, J., and Banga, I. (1950). *Biochem. J.* **46**, 384–387.
Balzer, E. (1953). *Acta Med. Scand.* Suppl. 278, 67–70.
Balzer, E., and Schulte, P. (1949). *Deut. Arch. Klin. Med.* **194**, 550–560.
Bamatter, F., Varonier, H. S., Roullier, C., and Simon, G. (1962). *J. Suisse Med.* **92**, 111.
Bang, F. (1915). *Hospitalstidende* **8**, 637–651.
Bang, O. (1929). Klinische Urobilinstudien in Sonderheit an normalen und "leber-gesunden" Personen. *Acta Med. Scand.* Suppl. 29 (203pp.).
Barac, G. (1939). *Bull. Soc. Chim. Biol.* **21**, 1163–1170.
Barac, G. (1945a). *Compt. Rend. Soc. Biol.* **139**, 412–414.
Barac, G. (1945b). *Compt. Rend. Soc. Biol.* **139**, 414–415.
Barac, G. (1946a). *Compt. Rend. Soc. Biol.* **140**, 563–565.
Barac, G. (1946b). *Compt. Rend. Soc. Biol.* **140**, 565–566.
Barac, G. (1946c). *Compt. Rend. Soc. Biol.* **140**, 578–580.
Barac, G. (1946d). *Compt. Rend. Soc. Biol.* **140**, 901–902.
Barac, G. (1946e). *Compt. Rend. Soc. Biol.* **140**, 1222–1223.
Barac, G. (1946f). *Bull. Soc. Chim. Biol.* **28**, 632–633.
Barac, G. (1946g). *Bull. Soc. Chim. Biol.* **28**, 633–636.
Barac, G. (1946h). *Nature* **158**, 97.
Barac, G. (1947). *Bull. Soc. Chim. Biol.* **29**, 96–99.
Barac, G. (1949). *Bull. Soc. Chim. Biol.* **31**, 876–879.
Barac, G. (1951). *Rev. Med. Liege* **6**, 186–193.
Barac, G. (1953). *Arch. Intern. Physiol.* (*Liege*) **61**, 129–140.
Barac, G. (1957). *Acta Clin. Belg.* **12**, 307–317.
Barac, G. (1963). *Arch. Intern. Physiol. Biochim.* **71**, 117–118.
Barac, G., and Gernay, J. M. (1949). *Bull. Soc. Chim. Biol.* **31**, 128–133.
Barac, G., and Roseman, R. (1946a). *Compt. Rend. Soc. Biol.* **140**, 581–583.
Barac, G., and Roseman, R. (1946b). *Compt. Rend. Soc. Biol.* **140**, 899–902.
Barac, G., and Roseman, R. (1946c). *J. Wash. Acad. Sci.* **36**, 296–301.

Barac, G., Beaumariage, M. L., Cuvelier, C., and Notay, W. (1961a). *Arch. Intern. Physiol. Biochim.* **69**, 95–96.

Barac, G., Beaumariage, M. L., Cuvelier, C., and Notay, W. (1961b). *Arch. Intern. Pharmacodyn.* **131**, 239–241.

Barber-Riley, G. (1963a). *Am. J. Physiol.* **205**, 1122–1126.

Barber-Riley, G. (1963b). *Am. J. Physiol.* **205**, 1127–1131.

Barchi, L. (1926). *Giorn. Clin. Med.* **7**, 81–99.

Bárdős, G. (1936). *Sang* **10**, 920–925.

Barkan, G., and Schales, O. (1937). *Z. Physiol. Chem.* **248**, 96–116.

Barkan, G., and Schales, O. (1938). *Z. Physiol. Chem.* **253**, 83–104.

Baroody, W. G., and Shugart, M. R. T. (1956). *Am. J. Med.* **20**, 314–316.

Barrenscheen, H. K., and Weltmann, O. (1923). *Z. Physiol. Chem.* **140**, 273–278.

Barron, E. S. G. (1931). *Medicine* **10**, 77–133.

Barron, E. S. G., and Bumstead, J. H. (1928). *J. Exptl. Med.* **47**, 999–1012.

Barrows, L. J., Hunter, F. T., and Banker, B. Q. (1955). *Brain* **78**, 59–80.

Barry, W. M., and Levine, V. E. (1924). *J. Biol. Chem.* **59**, lii–liii (Proc.).

Bartholomew, R. J., Dagliesh, C. E., and Wotton, I. D. P. (1957). *Biochem. J.* **65**, 27P.

Barton, D. H. R., and de Mayo, P. (1954). *J. Chem. Soc. (London)* pp. 887–903.

Barton, D. H. R., de Mayo, P., Warnhoff, E. W., Jeger, O., and Perold, G. W. (1954). *J. Chem. Soc. (London)* pp. 3689–3692.

Barton, M. E., Wilson, J., and Walker, W. (1962). *Lancet* **II**, 847–851.

Basu Malik, K. C., Mondol, A., and Ganguly, N. C. (1957). *Brit. Med. J.* **II**, 803–806.

Bauer, R. (1905). *Zentr. Inn. Med.* **26**, 831–841.

Baumgärtel, T. (1943a). *Klin. Wochschr.* **22**, 92–98.

Baumgärtel, T. (1943b). *Klin. Wochschr.* **22**, 297–300.

Baumgärtel, T. (1943c). *Klin. Wochschr.* **22**, 416–417.

Baumgärtel, T. (1944). *Muench. Med. Wochschr.* **91**, 407–410.

Baumgärtel, T. (1945). *Z. Ges. Exptl. Med.* **112**, 459–466.

Baumgärtel, T. (1947a). *Med. Klin.* **42**, 231–233.

Baumgärtel, T. (1947b). *Med. Klin.* **42**, 489–491.

Baumgärtel, T. (1947c). *Klin. Wochschr.* **25**, 315.

Baumgärtel, T. (1947d). *Klin. Wochschr.* **25**, 378–379.

Baumgärtel, T. (1948a). *Med. Klin.* **43**, 320–325.

Baumgärtel, T. (1948b). *Klin. Wochschr.* **26**, 22–23.

Baumgärtel, T. (1949a). *Arch. Inn. Med.* **1**, 40–63.

Baumgärtel, T. (1949b). *Klin. Wochschr.* **27**, 27–28.

Baumgärtel, T. (1949c). *Klin. Wochschr.* **27**, 577.

Baumgärtel, T. (1949d). *Z. Klin. Med.* **145**, 365–388.

Baumgärtel, T. (1950a). *Deut. Arch. Klin. Med.* **197**, 138–147.

Baumgärtel, T. (1950b). "Physiologie und Pathologie des Bilirubinstoffwechsels als Grundlagen der Ikterusforschung." Thieme, Stuttgart (271pp.).

Baumgärtel, T. (1958a). *Med. Klin.* **53**, 1331.

Baumgärtel, T. (1958b). *Aerztl. Forsch.* **12**, 600–610.

Baumgärtel, T., and Zahn, D. (1951). *Deut. Z. Verdauungs- u. Stoffwechselkrankh.* **11**, 257–266.

Bax, H. R. (1956). *Arch. Chir. Neerl.* **8**, 331–344.

Beaumariage, M.-L., Barac, G., Cuvelier, C., and Notay, W. (1961). *Arch. Internat. Physiol. Biochim.* **69**, 587–588.

Beck, A. (1895). *Wien. Klin. Wochschr.* **8**, 617.

Beck, K., and Beck, E. (1960). *Acta Hepato-Splenol.* **7**, 155–159.
Beck, K., and Kiani, B. (1960). *Klin. Wochschr.* **38**, 428–433.
Beck, K., and Kühn, H. A. (1956). *Klin. Wochschr.* **34**, 630–633.
Beck, K., and Kühn, H. A. (1959). *Z. Klin. Med.* **155**, 547–567.
Beck, K., Schubothe, H., and Baumann, G. (1962). *Klin. Wochschr.* **40**, 1041–1045.
Beckmann, K. (1933). *Zentr. Inn. Med.* **54**, 737–754.
Beckmann, W. (1954). *Aerztl. Forsch.* **8**, 473–477.
Begtrup, H. (1954). Personal communication.
Behrman, R. E., and Hibbard, E. (1964). *Science* **144**, 545–546.
Beijers, J. A. (1923). Urobiliniurie en icterus bij onze plantenetende huisdieren. Akademisch Proefschrift (Vet.), U. of Utrecht (158pp.).
Beijers, J. A., van Loghem, J. J., and van der Hart, M. (1950). *Tijdschr. Diergeneesk.* **75**, 955–970.
Belmont, A. P., Cherry, J. D., and Lucey, J. F. (1963). *Am. J. Obstet. Gynecol.* **87**, 538–539.
Belonogowa, N. S. (1928). *Deut. Arch. Klin. Med.* **162**, 297–329.
Belonogowa, N. S. (1931). *Deut. Arch. Klin. Med.* **170**, 436–444.
Beltrametti, L. (1932). *Arch. Ital. Malattie App. Diger.* **1**, 577–591.
Bénard, H., Gajdos, A., Polonovski, M., and Tissier, M. (1946). *Presse Med.* **54**, 697–698.
Bénard, H., Gajdos, A., Polonovski, M., and Tissier, M. (1948). *Presse Med.* **56**, 37–38.
Bénard, H., Gajdos, A., and Tissier, M. (1949a). "Hémoglobine et pigments apparantés, Masson, Paris (350pp.).
Bénard, H., Tissier, M., Polonovski, M., and Gajdos, A. (1949b). *Compt. Rend. Soc. Biol.* **143**, 1520–1522.
Bénard, H., Tissier, M., Polonovski, M., and Gajdos, A. (1949c). *Compt. Rend. Soc. Biol.* **143**, 1579–1582.
Bencsik, F., Gáspár, A., Vérzár, F., and Zih, A. (1930). *Biochem. Z.* **225**, 278–285.
Bendien, W. M., and Snapper, I. (1931). *Acta Brevia Neerl. Physiol.* **1**, 69–71.
Bendien, W. M., and Snapper, I. (1933). *Biochem. Z.* **260**, 105–114.
Bendixen, H. C., and Carlström, B. (1928). *Maanedsskr. Dyrl.* **40**, 129–148.
Bennhold, H. (1932). *Ergeb. Inn. Med. Kinderheilk.* **42**, 273–373.
Bennhold, H. (1933). *Verhandl. Deut. Ges. Inn. Med.* **45**, 357–359.
Bennhold, H. (1938). *In* "Die Eiweisskörper des Blutplasmas" (H. Bennhold, E. Kylin, and S. Rusznyak, eds.), p. 246ff. Steinkopff, Dresden & Leipzig.
Bennhold, H., and Schubert, R. (1944). *Z. Ges. Exptl. Med.* **113**, 722–736.
Bensley, E. H. (1933). *J. Biol. Chem.* **103**, 71–79.
Bensley, E. H. (1934). *J. Lab. Clin. Med.* **19**, 1122–1126.
Berezin, A., and Antunes, M. L. (1962). *Arch. Med.-Socialis* **21**, 119–134.
Bergquist, N. (1963). *Nord. Med.* **69**, 363–365.
Bergstrand, H. (1930). "Uber die akute und chronische gelbe Leberatrophie." Thieme, Leipzig (144pp.).
Berk, J. E. (1946). *In* "Gastroenterology" (H. E. Bochus, ed.), Vol. 3, p. 681. Saunders, Philadelphia, Pennsylvania.
Berlin, N. I., Lawrence, J. H., and Lee, H. C. (1954). *J. Lab. Clin. Med.* **44**, 860–874.
Berlin, R. (1950). *Scand. J. Clin. Lab. Invest.* **2**, 37–43.
Berman, A. L., Snapp, E., and Ivy, A. C. (1941). *Am. J. Physiol.* **132**, 176–184.

Berman, L. B., Lapham, L. W., and Pastore, E. (1954). *J. Lab. Clin. Med.* **44,** 273–279.

Bernhard, F. (1930). *Zentr. Chir.* **57,** 194–196.

Bernheim, B. M., Homans, J., and Voegtlin, C. (1910). *J. Pharmacol. Exptl. Therap.* **1,** 463–468.

Bernstein, J., and Landing, B. H. (1962). *Am. J. Pathol.* **40,** 371–392.

Berzelius, J. (1841a). *Kgl. Svenska Vetenskapsakad. Handl.* pp. 1–64.

Berzelius, J. (1841b). *Ann. Chem. Pharm.* (*Liebigs*) **43,** 1–67.

Bessis, M., Breton-Gorius, J., and Thiry, J.-P. (1961). *Compt. Rend. Acad. Sci.* **252,** 2300–2302.

Beutel, A., and Heinemann, J. (1928). *Z. Klin. Med.* **107,** 693–699.

Bevis, D. C. A. (1952a). *Lancet* **I,** 395–398.

Bevis, D. C. A. (1952b). *J. Obstet. Gynaecol. Brit. Empire* **59,** 857–858.

Bevis, D. C. A. (1953). *J. Obstet. Gynaecol. Brit. Empire* **60,** 244–251.

Bevis, D. C. A. (1956). *J. Obstet. Gynaecol. Brit. Empire* **63,** 68.

Bieling, R., and Isaac, S. (1922). *Klin. Wochschr.* **1,** 373.

Biering-Sørensen, K., and With, T. K. (1947). *Acta Paediat.* **34,** 63–71.

Bierthen, E. (1906). Untersuchungen über das Vorkommen des Bilirubins in der Galle, in dem Harn und in dem Blutserum des Pferdes. Inaugural Dissertation (Vet.), U. of Bern (38pp.).

Biesold, D., Liebold, F., and Theile, H. (1962). *Acta Biol. Med. Ger.* **9,** 652–663.

Biffi, U., and Galli, P. (1907). *J. Physiol. Pathol. Gen.* **9,** 721–736.

Bilissis, P. K., and Speer, R. J. (1963). *Clin. Chem.* **9,** 552–553.

Billi, A., Heilmeyer, L., and Pfotenhauer, F. (1933). *Z. Ges. Exptl. Med.* **91,** 720–728.

Billing, B. H. (1955a). *J. Clin. Pathol.* **8,** 126–129.

Billing, B. H. (1955b). *J. Clin. Pathol.* **8,** 130–131.

Billing, B. H. (1961a). *Acta. Med. Okayama* **15,** 185–197.

Billing, B. H. (1961b). *In* "Formation and Breakdown of Haemoglobin" (C. P. Stewart, ed.), pp. 51–69. Elsevier, Amsterdam.

Billing, B. H., and Lathe, G. H. (1956). *Biochem. J.* **63,** 6P.

Billing, B. H., and Lathe, G. H. (1958). *Am. J. Med.* **24,** 111–121.

Billing, B. H., Cole, P. G., and Lathe, G. H. (1957). *Biochem. J.* **63,** 774–784.

Billing, B. H., Maggiore, Q., and Cartter, M. A. (1963). *Ann. N.Y. Acad. Sci.* **111,** (Art. 1), 319–324.

Bingold, K. (1923). *Z. Klin. Med.* **97,** 257–286.

Bingold, K. (1930). *Folia Haematol.* (*Leipzig*) **42,** 192–222.

Bingold, K. (1932). *In* "Handbuch der allgemeinen Haematologie" (H. Hirschfeld and A. Hittmair, eds.), Vol. I, Part 1, pp. 601–641. Urban & Schwarzenberg, Berlin.

Bingold, K. (1934). *Klin. Wochschr.* **13,** 1451–1452.

Bingold, K. (1941). *Ergeb. Inn. Med. Kinderheilk.* **60,** 1–71.

Bingold, K., and Stich, W. (1948). *Deut. Med. Wochschr.* **73,** 501–506.

Bingold, K., and Stich, W. (1949). *Med. Monatsschr.* **3,** 245–255.

Birch, A. J. (1955). *Chem. Ind.* (*London*) p. 652.

Bittorf, A., and Riessbeck, K. H. (1947). *Deut. Gesundheitsw.* **2,** 412–414.

Blanc, W. C., and Johnson, L. (1959). *J. Neuropathol. Exptl. Neurol.* **18,** 165–187.

Blanton, W. B., and Blanton, M. F. (1955). *Ann. Internal Med.* **43,** 589–600.

Bloch, K., and Rittenberg, D. (1945a). *J. Biol. Chem.* **157,** 749–750.

Bloch, K., and Rittenberg, D. (1945b). *J. Biol. Chem.* **159,** 45–58.

Blondheim, S. H., Lathrop, D., and Zabriskie, J. (1962). *J. Lab. Clin. Med.* **60**, 31–39.
Boardman, J. (1954). *Brit. Med. J.* **II**, 579.
Bock, E. (1924a). *Klin. Wochschr.* **3**, 587–592.
Bock, E. (1924b). *Klin. Wochschr.* **3**, 638–641.
Bollman, J. L. (1935). *Proc. Staff. Meetings Mayo Clinic* **10**, 567.
Bollman, J. L. (1958). *Lancet* **I**, 1312.
Bollman, J. L. (1961). *Physiol. Rev.* **41**, 607–621.
Bollman, J. L., and Mann, F. C. (1932). *AMA Arch. Surg.* **24**, 675–680.
Bollman, J. L., and Mann, F. C. (1936). *Ergeb. Inn. Med. Kinderheilk.* **38**, 445–492.
Bollman, J. L., and Mendez, F. L. (1955). *Federation Proc.* **14**, 399–400.
Bollman, J. L., Sheard, C., and Mann, F. C. (1926). *Minn. Med.* **9**, 227–229.
Bolotov, M. P. (1958). *Lab. Delo* **4**, 21–26 (in Russ.).
Bomford, R. R. (1949). *Brit. Med. J.* **II**, 549–551.
Bonetti, E., and Verme, G. (1960). *Sperimentale* **110**, 420–435.
Bonome, A. (1924). *Haematologica* **5**, 1–33.
Boon, W. H. (1957). *Arch. Disease Childhood* **32**, 85.
Borchardt, H. (1923). *Klin. Wochschr.* **2**, 541–542.
Borrien, V. (1910). *Compt. Rend. Soc. Biol.* **68**, 658–660.
Borrien, V. (1911). Contribution a l'étude clinique des pigments biliaires en coprologie. Thesis (Pharm.), U. of Paris (83pp.).
Boshamer, K. (1928). *Klin. Wochschr.* **7**, 445–447.
Bouckaert, J. P., and Appelmans, R. (1925). *Compt. Rend. Soc. Biol.* **93**, 843–845.
Bouma, D. J. (1902). *Deut. Med. Wochschr.* **28**, 866–867.
Bound, J. P., and Telfer, T. P. (1956). *Lancet* **I**, 720–722.
Bourrillon, R. (1952). Etude du métabolisme de la bilirubine. Thesis (Sci.), U. of Paris (88pp., mimeographed).
Bourrillon, R. (1956). *Bull. Soc. Chim. Biol.* **38**, 675–683.
Bourrillon, R. (1957). *Bull. Soc. Chim. Biol.* **39**, 385–397.
Bourrillon, R. (1958a). *Ann. Biol. Clin.* (*Paris*) **16**, 3–12.
Bourrillon, R. (1958b). *Bull. Soc. Chim. Biol.* **40**, 111–124.
Bourrillon, R. (1958c) *Semaine Hop.* **34**, 1503–1512.
Boutaric, A. (1948). *Compt. Rend. Soc. Biol.* **138**, 9.
Boutaric, A., and Roy, M. (1939). *Compt. Rend. Acad. Sci.* **209**, 1021–1023.
Boutwell, J. H. (1964). *Clin. Chem.* **10**, 197–213.
Braden, B. F., and DuVal, M. K. (1963). *AMA Arch. Surg.* **86**, 419–422.
Bradley, H. C. (1908). *J. Biol. Chem.* **4**, 26–27 (Proc.).
Bradley, S. E. (1949). *New Engl. J. Med.* **240**, 456–461.
Bramanti, P. (1948a). *Policlinico* (*Rome*), *Sez. Med.* **55**, 24–44.
Bramanti, P. (1948b). *Policlinico* (*Rome*), *Sez. Med.* **55**, 85–98.
Brand, J. (1901). Onderzoekingen over afscheiding en samenstelling van de gal bij den levenden mensch. Akad. Proefschrift (Geneesk.), U. of Amsterdam (93pp.).
Brandt, B. (1937). Quantitative Urobilinbestimmungen in der Schwangerschaft unter der Geburt, im Wochenbett und bei Fehlgeburt. Inaugural Dissertation (Med.), U. of Hamburg (29pp.).
Brandt, K.-H. (1957). Over de plaats van vorming der urobilinogenen in het menselijk organisme (The site of formation of the urobilinogenes in the human body, Engl. summary). Proefschrift (Med.) U. of Utrecht (226pp.).
Brante, G. (1956a). *Nord. Med.* **55**, 119–126.
Brante, G. (1956b). *Nord. Med.* **55**, 126–132.

Brauer, R. W. (1963a) *Physiol. Rev.* **43**, 115–213.
Brauer, R. W. (1963b) *Am. J. Digest. Diseases* **8**, 564–576.
Brauer, R. W., Krebs, J. S., and Pesotti, R. L. (1950). *Federation Proc.* **9**, 259.
Brauer, R. W., Leong, G. F., and Holloway, R. J. (1954). *Am. J. Physiol.* **177**, 103–112.
Brauer, R. W., Pessotti, R., and Krebs, J. J. (1955). *J. Clin. Invest.* **34**, 35.
Braunstein, A. (1903). *Z. Klin. Med.* **50**, 159–166.
Breda, L. (1929). *Z. Geburtshilfe Gynaekol.* **95**, 394–399.
Brereton, H. G., and Lucia, S. P. (1948). *Am. J. Clin. Pathol.* **18**, 887–890.
Briles, W. E. (1948). *Genetics* **33**, 96.
Brinkhouse, K. M., and Walker, S. A. (1941). *Am. J. Physiol.* **132**, 666–669.
Brøchner-Mortensen, K. (1935). *Acta Med. Scand.* **85**, 1–32.
Brodersen, R. (1960). *Scand. J. Clin. Lab. Invest.* **12**, 25–32.
Brodersen, R. (1962). *Scand. J. Clin. Lab. Invest.* **14**, 517–527.
Brodersen, R., and Hermann, L. S. (1963). *Lancet* **I**, 1242.
Brodersen, R., and Vind, I. (1963a). *Scand. J. Clin. Lab. Invest.* **15**, 107–114.
Brodersen, R., and Vind, I. (1963b). *Scand. J. Clin. Lab. Invest.* **15**, 225–232.
Brodersen, R., Hermann, L. S., and Vind, I. (1963). *Scand. J. Clin. Lab. Invest.* **15**, 523–528.
Brodie, B. C. (1823). *Quart. J. Sci. Lit. Arts* **14**, 341–344.
Brody, T. M. (1963). *Ann. N.Y. Acad. Sci.* **104**, (Art. 3), 1065–1073.
Brookes, J. A., and Mohr, J. L. (1963). *J. Protozool.* **10**, 138–140.
Broun, G. O., McMaster, P. D., and Rous, P. (1923a). *J. Exptl. Med.* **37**, 699–710.
Broun, G. O., McMaster, P. D., and Rous, P. (1923b). *J. Exptl. Med.* **37**, 733–757.
Brown, A. K. (1962). *Pediat. Clin. N. Am.* **9**, 575–603.
Brown, A. K., and Zuelzer, W. W. (1957). *AMA J. Diseases Children* **93**, 263.
Brown, D. F., Porta, E. A., and Reder, J. (1963). *AMA Arch. Internal Med.* **111**, 592–606.
Brown, J. M. M. (1963). *Ann. N.Y. Acad. Sci.* **104**, (Art. 2), 504–538.
Brown, J. M. M., Anderson, L. A. P., and de Kock, W. T. (1963a). *S. African J. Lab. Clin. Med.* **9**, 262–272.
Brown, J. M. M., Rimington, C., and Sawyer, B. C. (1963b). *Proc. Roy. Soc.* **B157**, 473–491.
Brown, N. L., and Shnitka, T. K. (1956). *Am. J. Med.* **21**, 292–299.
Brückner, J. (1959). *Am. J. Clin. Pathol.* **32**, 513–520.
Brückner, J. (1961). *Clin. Chim. Acta* **6**, 370–376.
Brüschke, G., and Volkheimer, G. (1956). *Z. Ges. Inn. Med. Grenzgebiete* **11**, 804. 806.
Brugsch, J. (1935). *Med. Klin.* **31**, 366–371.
Brugsch, J. (1950). *Deut. Arch. Klin. Med.* **195**, 425–436.
Brugsch, J., and Allies, F. (1948). *Z. Ges. Inn. Med. Grenzgebiete* **3**, 249–252.
Brugsch, T., and Kawashima, K. (1911). *Z. Exptl. Pathol. Therapie* **8**, 645–648.
Brugsch, T., and Retzlaff, K. (1912). *Z. Exptl. Pathol. Therapie* **11**, 508–525.
Brugsch, T., and Schürer, J. (1919). *Berlin. Klin. Wochschr.* **56**, 601–603.
Brugsch, T., and Yoshimoto, M. (1911). *Z. Exptl. Pathol. Therapie* **8**, 639–644.
Brulé, M., and Garban, H. (1920). *Compt. Rend. Soc. Biol.* **83**, 342–344.
Brulé, M., Garban, H., and Weismann, C. (1922). *Presse Med.* **30**, 986.
Brun, V. (1910). *Pediatria (Naples)* [2] **8**, 401–416.
Bryant, D., and Flynn, F. V. (1955). *J. Clin. Pathol.* **8**, 163–165.
Budd, G. (1852). "On Diseases of the Liver" 2nd ed. Churchill, London (486pp.).

Bibliography 679

Bungenberg de Jong, W. H. J. (1937). Onderzoekingen over de diazoreaktie op serumbilirubine. Akad. Proefschrift (Geneesk.), U. of Amsterdam (155pp.).
Bungenberg de Jong, W. H. J. (1942). Ned. Tijdschr. Geneesk. 86, 2405–2414.
Bungenberg de Jong, W. H. J. (1943). Deut. Arch. Klin. Med. 190, 229–251.
Bungenberg de Jong, W. H. J. (1951). Deut. Arch. Klin. Med. 198, 655–672.
Bungenberg de Jong, W. H. J. (1959). Geneesk. Gids No. 25 (quoted from reprint).
Bungenberg de Jong, W. H. J. (1962). Personal communication.
Burka, E. R. (1960). Ann. Internal Med. 52, 453–459.
Burlina, A. (1956). Progr. Med. (Naples) 12, 372–378.
Burnstine, R. C., and Schmid, R. (1962). Proc. Soc. Exptl. Biol. Med. 109, 356–358.
Bush, J. A., Berlin, N. I., Jensen, W. N., Brill, A. B., Cartwright, G. E., and Wintrobe, M. M. (1955). J. Exptl. Med. 101, 451–459.
Butler, N. R., and Spector, W. G. (1952). Brit. Med. J. I, 1168.
Butz, W. (1937). Quantitative Urobilinogenbestimmungen im Stuhl und Harn bei Schwangeren und Wöchnerinnen. Inaugural Dissertation (Med.), U. of Jena (19pp.).
Buxton, J. C., and Brooksbank, C. (1953). Nature 172, 355.
Caballo, J., and Lazo, M. (1950). Rev. Med. Chile 78, 595–599.
Cabello Ruz, J. (1943a). Rev. Soc. Arg. Biol. 19, 16–20.
Cabello Ruz, J. (1943b). Rev. Soc. Arg. Biol. 19, 71–80.
Cabello Ruz, J. (1943c). Rev. Soc. Arg. Biol. 19, 81–93.
Cabello Ruz, J. (1943d). Rev. Soc. Arg. Biol. 19, 247–260.
Cadiat (no inits.) (1878). Compt. Rend. Soc. Biol. [6] 5, 162.
Caglar, M. (1945). Nature 155, 670.
Caglar, M. (1950). Commun. Fac. Sci. Univ. Ankara 3, 265–280.
Cain, J. C., Grindlay, J. H., Bollman, J. L., Flock, E. V., and Mann, F. C. (1947). Surg. Gynecol. Obstet 85, 558–562.
Callaghan, J. P. (1949). Australian J. Exptl. Biol. Med. Sci. 27, 281–288.
Callender, S. T., Powell, E. O., and Witts, L. L. (1945). J. Pathol. Bacteriol. 57, 129–139.
Callender, S. T., Loutit, J. F., and Jope, E. M. (1946). Proc. Roy. Soc. Med. 39, 755–762.
Calvert, R. J., Smith, E., and Werren, J. P. (1954). Gastroenterology 26, 650–657.
Cameron, G. R., and Oakley, G. J. (1932). J. Pathol. Bacteriol. 35, 769–798.
Cameron, J. D. S. (1943). Quart. J. Med. 12, 139–155.
Campbell, M., Kolars, C. P., Coe, J. I., and Hoffbauer, F. M. (1956). Am. J. Med. 21, 131–134.
Campeanu, S., and Campeanu, L. (1960). Muench. Med. Wochschr. 102, 169–173.
Campeanu, S., and Campeanu, L. (1961). Z. Ges. Inn. Med. Grenzgebiete 16, 182–187.
Cantarow, A. (1935). AMA Arch. Internal Med. 56, 521–529.
Cantarow, A. (1944). Am. J. Digest. Diseases 11, 144–147.
Cantarow, A., and Trumper, M. (1945). "Clinical Biochemistry," 3rd ed. Saunders, Philadelphia, Pennsylvania.
Cantarow, A., Wirts, C. Jr., and Hollander, G. (1940). Proc. Soc. Exptl. Biol. Med. 45, 253–256.
Cantarow, A., Wirts, C., Jr., and Hollander, G. (1942). AMA Arch. Internal Med. 69, 986–996.
Cantarow, A., Wirts, C., Jr., Snape, W. S., and Miller, L. J. (1948a). Am. J. Physiol. 154, 211–219.

Cantarow, A., Wirts, C., Jr., Snape, W. S., and Miller, L. J. (1948b). *Am. J. Physiol.* **154,** 507–512.

Capps, F. P. A., Gilles, H. M., Jolly, H., and Worlledge, S. M. (1963). *Lancet* **II,** 379–383.

Caraway, W. T., and Fanger, H. (1955). *Am. J. Clin. Pathol.* **25,** 317–331.

Carithers, H. A. (1941). *J. Pediat.* **19,** 817–822.

Carrié, P. (1913). L'urobiline. Recherches cliniques et expérimentales. Thesis (Med.), U. of Paris (140pp.).

Carruthers, J. S., and Steiner, J. W. (1961). *Can. Med. Assoc. J.* **85,** 1223–1236.

Carsten, P.-M. (1961). *Z. Zellforsch. Mikroskop. Anat.* **54,** 252.

Cassady, G., Morrison, A. B., and Cohen, M. M. (1964). *Am. J. Diseases Children* **107,** 456–469.

Cassia, B., and Pittera, A. (1962). *Boll. Soc. Ital. Biol. Sper.* **38,** 1231–1232.

Castaigne, J. (1934). *J. Med. Franc.* **23,** 422–430.

Castberg, T. (1949). Leverforandringer ved kronisk stase. Disputats (Med.), U. of Copenhagen (111pp.).

Castex, M. R., and Lopez Garcia, A. (1937). *Rapp. Congr. Intern. Insuff. Hepatique, Vichy.* pp. 65–91. A. Wallon, Paris.

Castex, M. R., and Lopez Garcia, A. (1940a). *Rev. Soc. Arg. Biol.* **16,** 275–277.

Castex, M. R., and Lopez Garcia, A. (1940b). *Anales Inst. Invest. Fis. Apl. Patol. Humana* **1,** 17–36.

Castex, M. R., and Lopez Garcia, A. (1941). *Arch. Uruguay. Med. Cirug.* **18,** 525–531.

Castex, M. R., Lopez Garcia, A., and Zelasco, J. F. (1940). *Rev. Soc. Arg. Biol.* **16,** 247–250.

Castex, M. R., Lopez Garcia, A., and Zelasco, J. F. (1941). *Bol. Acad. Nacl. Med.* (Buenos Aires) pp. 282–295.

Castro, S., Vontz, F. K., and Foraker, A. G. (1963). *AMA Arch. Pathol.* **75,** 350–359.

Cathie, I. A. B. (1952). *Gt. Ormond St. J.* **3,** 42.

Chabrol, E. (1932). "Les Ictères," Masson, Paris (523pp.).

Chabrol, E., and Busson, A. (1934a). *J. Med. Franc.* **23,** 408–412.

Chabrol, E., and Busson, A. (1934b). *J. Med. Franc.* **23,** 418–421.

Chabrol, E., Böszörményi, M., and Fallot, P. (1949). *Semaine Hop.* **25,** 3437–3445.

Chadwick, D. A., and Jennings, R. C. (1964). *Lancet* **I,** 793–795.

Charbonnier, A. (1958). *Ann. Biol. Clin.* (*Paris*) **16,** May–June (quoted from reprint).

Charbonnier, A., and Poungouras, P. (1959). *Rev. Intern. Hepatol.* **9,** 589–632.

Charbonnier, A., Mendioroz, B. A., and Rodriques, J. V. (1954). *Arch. Soc. Biol. Montevideo* **21,** 64–69.

Charbonnier, A., Mendioroz, B. A., and Caroli, J. (1956). *Gastroenterologia* **86,** 439–443.

Charcot (no inits.) and Gombault (no inits.) (1876). *Arch. Physiol. Norm. Pathol.* [2] **3,** 272.

Charnas, D. (1909). *Biochem. Z.* **20,** 401–430.

Charnas, D. (1913a). *Wien. Med. Wochschr.* **63,** 1021–1023.

Charnas, D. (1913b). *Wien. Med. Wochschr.* **63,** 1731–1733.

Chavez, I., Sepulveda, B., and Ortega, I. A. (1943). *J. Am. Med. Assoc.* **121,** 1276–1282.

Cheadle, W. B. (1903). *Lancet* **I,** 1497.

Chelchowski, K. (1897). *Gazeta Lek. (Warsaw)* **17**, 397.

Chiamori, N., Henry, R. J., and Golub, O. J. (1961). *Clin. Chim. Acta* **6**, 1–6.

Childers, D. M., and Barger, J. D. (1958). *Am. J. Clin. Pathol.* **29**, 546.

Childs, B. (1955). *Bull. Johns Hopkins Hosp.* **97**, 333–342.

Childs, B., and Najjar, V. A. (1956). *Pediatrics* **18**, 369–377.

Chiray, M., and Thiebaut, F. (1929). *Bull. Mem. Soc. Med. Hop. Paris* **45**, 598–601.

Chodos, R. B., Wells, R., and Chaffee, W. R. (1964). *Am. J. Med.* **36**, 553–560.

Christomanos, A. A. (1954). *Sitzber. Athener Akad. Wiss.* **29**, 559–568.

Chrometzka, F. (1929a). *Z. Ges. Exptl. Med.* **67**, 475–481.

Chrometzka, F. (1929b). *Z. Ges. Exptl. Med.* **67**, 482–495.

Cinotti, G. A., Fabiani, F., and Pericoli, F. (1957). *Policlinico (Rome), Sez. Prat.* **43** (quoted from reprint).

Claireaux, A. E., Cole, P. G., and Lathe, G. H. (1953). *Lancet* **II**, 1226–1230.

Claireaux, A. E., Gerrard, J. W., and Marsland, E. A. (1955). *Rev. Internat. Hepatol.* **5**, 1153–1204.

Clare, N. T. (1955). *Advan. Vet. Sci.* **11**, 1182–1211.

Clarens, J. (1903). Étude critique des differentes théories sur l'origine de l'urobiline. Thesis (Med.), U. of Toulouse (78pp.).

Clemens (no inits.) (1901). *Deut. Arch. Klin. Med.* **71**, 168–174.

Cohn, E. J. (1948). *Blood* **3**, 471.

Cohn, E. J., Gurd, F. R. N., Surgenor, D. M., Barnes, B. A., Brown, R. K., Derouaux, G., Gillespie, J. M., Kahnt, F. W., Lever, W. F., Lin, C. H., Mittleman, D., Mouton, R. F., Schmid, K., and Uroma, E. (1950). *J. Am. Chem. Soc.* **72**, 465–474.

Colangiuli, A., and Barengo, A. (1940). *Haematologica* **21**, 149–216.

Cole, P. G., and Lathe, G. H. (1953). *J. Clin. Pathol.* **6**, 99–104.

Cole, P. G., Lathe, G. H., and Billing, B. H. (1954). *Biochem. J.* **57**, 514–518.

Cole, S. W. (1919). "Practical Physiological Chemistry," 5th ed., pp. 267, 307. Heffer, Cambridge.

Colin, G. (1873). "Traité de physiologie comparée des animaux," Vol. II, p. 317, Bailliere, Paris.

Collinson, G. A., and Fowweather, F. S. (1926). *Brit. Med. J.* **I**, 1081–1083.

Comas, M. (1927). *Compt. Rend. Soc. Biol.* **96**, 866–868.

Comfort, A. (1949a). *Biochem. J.* **45**, 199–204.

Comfort, A. (1949b). *Biochem. J.* **45**, 204–208.

Comfort, A. (1950a). *Biochem. J.* **47**, 254–255.

Comfort, A. (1950b). *Nature* **166**, 194–195.

Comfort, A. (1950c). *Proc. Malacol. Soc. London* **28**, 79–85.

Comfort, A. (1950d). *Proc. Malacol. Soc. London* **29**, 35–43.

Comfort, M. W. (1945). *Med. Clin. N. Am.* **29**, 982–989.

Comfort, M. W., and Hoyne, R. M. (1944). *Gastroenterology* **3**, 155–162.

Coolidge, T. B. (1940). *J. Biol. Chem.* **132**, 119–127.

Coolidge, T. B. (1942). *Federation Proc.* **1**, 106.

Corà, D. (1952). *Acta Med. Scand.* **142**, 297–313.

Corà, D. (1954). *Acta Med. Scand.* **149**, 475–483.

Corà, D. (1956). *Minerva Nefrol.* **3**, 34–40.

Cornelius, C. E., and Kaneko, J. J. (1962). *Science* **137**, 673–674.

Cornelius, C. E., Kaneko, J. J., and Benson, D. C. (1959). *Am. J. Vet. Res.* **20**, 917–920.

Cornelius, C. E., Kaneko, J. J., Benson, D. C., and Wheat, J. D. (1960a). *Am. J. Vet. Res.* **21**, 1123–1124.

Cornelius, C. E., Kilgore, W. W., and Wheat, J. D. (1960b). *Cornell Vet.* **50**, 47–53.

Corner, B. (1955). *Am. J. Diseases Children* **90**, 520.

Corner, B. (1958). *Proc. Roy. Soc. Med.* **51**, 1019–1022.

Corner, B., Berry, E., and Neale, A. V. (1960). *Lancet* **I**, 715–717.

Cossel, L. (1959). *Beitr. Pathol. Anat.* **120**, 133–158.

Cotton, D. A. (1960). *Lancet* **II**, 294–296.

Courtice, F. C. (1946). *J. Physiol. (London)* **104**, 321–345.

Courtice, F. C., Woolley, G., and Garlick, D. G. (1962). *Australian J. Exptl. Biol. Med. Sci.* **40**, 111–120.

Craig, J. (1925). *Brit. Med. J.* **I**, 453–454.

Craig, J. M., and Landing, B. H. (1952). *AMA Arch. Pathol.* **54**, 321.

Cremer, R. J., Perryman, P. W., Richards, D. H., and Holbrook, B. (1957). *Biochem. J.* **66**, 60P.

Cremer, R. J., Perryman, P. W., and Richards, D. H. (1958). *Lancet* **I**, 1094–1097.

Crigler, J. F., and Najjar, V. A. (1952). *Pediatrics* **10**, 169–179.

Cristesco, C. (1937). *Sang* **11**, 331–332.

Crone, C. (1961). Om diffussionen af nogle organiske non-elektrolyter fra blod til hjernevaev. Dissertation (Med.), U. of Copenhagen (180pp.).

Crosby, W. H. (1955). *Am. J. Med.* **18**, 112–122.

Crosby, W. H. (1958). *J. Clin. Invest.* **37**, 887.

Crosby, W. H., and Akeroyd, J. H. (1952). *Am. J. Med.* **13**, 273–283.

Crosse, V. M., Meyer, T. C., and Gerrard, J. W. (1955). *Arch. Disease Childhood* **30**, 501.

Crosse, V. M., Wallis, P. G., and Walsh, A. M. (1958). *Arch. Disease Childhood* **31**, 403.

Crus Auñon, J. (1949a). *Acta Clin. (Seville)* **3**, 329–339.

Crus Auñon, J. (1949b). *Acta Clin. (Seville)* **3**, 399–417.

Cruz, W. O., Hawkins, W. B., and Whipple, G. H. (1942). *Am. J. Med. Sci.* **203**, 848–854.

Culley, P. E., Waterhouse, J. A. H., and Wood, B. S. B. (1960). *Lancet* **I**, 88–89.

Cumings, J. N. (1950). *Brain* **73**, 244–250.

Currie, R. I. (1962). *Nature* **193**, 956–957.

Curry, J. J., Greenwalt, T. J., and Tat, R. J. (1942). *New Engl. J. Med.* **226**, 909–912.

Czike, A. (1929). *Deut. Arch. Klin. Med.* **164**, 236–242.

Daddi, G. (1933). *Riv. Clin. Med.* **34**, 78–95.

Dähne, A. (1937). Die serumfarbe in Beziehung zur Bilirubin- und Hämoglobininhalt des Blutserums, zugleich ein Beitrag zur spektralphotometrischen Bilirubinbestimmung im Blutserum. Inaugural Dissertation (Med.), U. of Jena (21pp.).

Daetwyler, A. (1963). Ergebnisse der Nachuntersuchung der ersten Hundert in Bern wegen Icterus gravis mit Austauschtransfusion behandelten Kinder. Inaugural Dissertation (Med.), U. of Bern (44pp.).

Dal Co, C. (1950). *Arch. Pathol. Clin. Med. (Bologna)* **28**, 216–232.

Dalziel, K., and O'Brien, J. R. P. (1954a). *Biochem. J.* **56**, 648–659.

Dalziel, K., and O'Brien, J. R. P. (1954b). *Biochem. J.* **56**, 660–669.

Dameshek, W., and Schwartz, S. O. (1940a). *Medicine* **19**, 109–123.

Dameshek, W., and Schwartz, S. O. (1940b). *Medicine* **19**, 231–327.

Dameshek, W., and Singer, K. (1941). *AMA Arch. Internal Med.* **67**, 259–285.

Dangerfield, W. G., and Finlayson, R. (1953). *J. Clin. Pathol.* **6**, 173–177.

Danks, D., and Bodian, M. (1963). *Arch. Disease Childhood* **38**, 378–390.

Danoff, S., Grantz, C., Boyer, A., and Holt, L. E. (1958). *Lancet* I, 316.

Danzig, L. E. (1953). *Am. J. Med. Sci.* **225**, 76–80.

Darocha, T., Murawsky, K., and Szymanovska, Z. (1962). *Clin. Chim. Acta* **7**, 729–731.

da Rocha-Lima, H. (1912). *Verhandl. Deut. Pathol. Ges.* **15**, 163–182.

Darrow, R. R. (1938). *Am. J. Pathol.* **25**, 378–417.

da Silva, L. C., Jamra, M. A., Maspes, V., Pontes, J. F., Pieroni, R. R., and Cintra, A. B. de U. (1963). *Gastroenterology* **44**, 117–124.

Davidson, C. S. (1963). *Ann. N.Y. Acad. Sci.* **104** (Art. 3), 1026–1033.

Davidson, L. T., Merrit, K. K., and Weech, A. A. (1941). *Am. J. Diseases Children* **61**, 958–980.

Davidsohn, I. (1955). *Year Book Pathol.* pp. 313–320.

Davies, D. T., and Dodds, E. C. (1927). *Brit. J. Exptl. Pathol.* **8**, 316–325.

Davis, G. E., and Sheard, C. (1934). *J. Lab. Clin. Med.* **19**, 593–608.

Davis, G. E., and Sheard, C. (1937). *J. Lab. Clin. Med.* **23**, 22–29.

Day, R. L. (1947). *Am. J. Diseases Children* **73**, 241–242.

Day, R. L. (1954). *Proc. Soc. Exptl. Biol. Med.* **85**, 261–264.

de Castro, U. (1929a). *Z. Ges. Exptl. Med.* **67**, 673–682.

de Castro, U. (1929b). *Presse Med.* **37**, 151–152.

de Castro, U. (1930). *Deut. Arch. Klin. Med.* **170**, 176–187.

Deenstra, H. (1947). Over de galkleurstof en de diazoreactie. Akad. Proefschrift (Geneesk.), U. of Utrecht (140pp.).

Deenstra, H. (1948a). *Acta Med. Scand.* **132**, 109–123.

Deenstra, H. (1948b). *Acta Med. Scand.* **132**, 223–237.

Deenstra, H. (1948c). *Ned. Tijdschr. Geneesk.* **92**, 2076–2083.

Deenstra, H. (1950). *Ann. Med.* (*Paris*) **51**, 685–700.

del Bono, N. (1949). *Riv. Gastroenterol.* **1**, 278–293.

D'Elia, O., and Caporale, F. (1963). *Rass. Intern. Clin. Terap.* **43**, 1046–1067.

Demichelis, U., and Giacchero, R. (1936). *Arch. Sci. Med.* (*Turin*) **62**, 566–574.

Derbes, V. J., and Engelhardt, H. T. (1943). *Arch. Dermatol. Syphilis* **48**, 310–311.

De Robertis, E. D. P. (1939). Estudios de histofisiologia hepatica. Thesis (Med.), U. of Buenos Aires (quoted from Lopez Garcia, 1943).

Derrien, E., and Turchini, J. (1925). *Compt. Rend. Soc. Biol.* **92**, 1030–1031.

Descomps, P. (1910). Sur un nouveau procédé de dosage de l'urobiline et de la stercobiline. Thesis (Med.), U. of Paris (95pp.).

Deubner, G. (1884). Vergleichende Untersuchungen über die neueren Methoden zum Nachweis des Gallenfarbstoffes im Harn Icterischer. Inaugural Dissertation (Med.), U. of Dorpat (57pp.).

Deutsch, F., and Hermann, B. (1931). *Med. Klin.* **27**, 1271–1273.

de Voret, J. K., Daugherty, C., and Schneider, E. M. (1956). *Gastroenterology* **31**, 395–398.

de Vries, A. (1946). *Blood* **1**, 348–356.

Deysson, G., and Charbonnier, A. (1953). *Compt. Rend. Acad. Sci.* **236**, 1912–1914.

Dhéré, C. (1934). *Handb. Biol. Arbeitsmeth.* (*Abderhalden*) Sect. II, Pt. 3, **1**, pp. 3097–3306.

Dhéré, C., and Baumeler, C. (1928). *Compt. Rend. Soc. Biol.* **99**, 492–496.

Dhéré, C., and Baumeler, C. (1929). *Compt. Rend. Soc. Biol.* **102**, 756–759.

Dhéré, C., and Roche, J. (1931a). *Compt. Rend. Acad. Sci.* **193**, 673–676.

Dhéré, C., and Roche, J. (1931b). *Bull. Soc. Chim. Biol.* 13, 987–1014.
Dhéré, C., Baumeler, C., and Schneider, A. (1928). *Compt. Rend. Soc. Biol.* 99, 722–724.
Dhéré, C., Baumeler, C., and Schneider, A. (1930). *Arch. Intern. Physiol.* 32, 55–79.
Diamond, J. M. (1962). *J. Physiol.* (*London*) 161, 442–473.
Diamond, J. S. (1928). *Am. J. Med. Sci.* 176, 321–331.
Dible, J. H., McMichael, J., and Sherlock, S. P. V. (1943). *Lancet* II, 402–408.
Dick, R. (1884). *Arch. Gynaekol.* 23, 126–138.
Dine, M. S. (1954). *Am. J. Diseases Children* 88, 820.
Dirr, K., and Sereslis, N. (1939). *Z. Ges. Exptl. Med.* 104, 337–351.
Disqué, L. (1878). *Z. Physiol. Chem.* 2, 259–272.
Diwany, H. F. (1919). Étude histologique de l'embryotrophe hématique des mammifères et du tube digestif de quelques invertebrés hématophages Thesis (Sci.), U. of Paris (174pp.).
Doljanski, L., and Koch, O. (1933a). *Arch. Pathol. Anat. Physiol.* 291, 379–389.
Doljanski, L., and Koch, O. (1933b). *Arch. Pathol. Anat. Physiol.* 291, 390–396.
Doljanski, L., and Koch, O. (1933c). *Arch. Pathol. Anat. Physiol.* 291, 397–400.
Dominguez, J. P., Orellano-Alcaide, J. M., and Etchart, M. (1962). *Gastroenterology* 42, 69–71.
Dominici, G., and Marengo, G. (1933a). *Arch. Sci. Med.* (*Turin*) 57, 504–522.
Dominici, G., and Marengo, G. (1933b). *Arch. Sci. Med.* (*Turin*) 57, 523–566.
Donohue, D. M., Motulski, A. G., Giblett, E. R., Pirzio-Biroli, G., Viranuvatti, V., and Finch, C. A. (1955). *Brit. J. Haematol.* 1, 249–263.
Dor, L. (1902). *Compt. Rend. Soc. Biol.* 54, 54–56.
Dordi, A. M., and Rossi, G. (1936). *Riv. Clin. Pediat.* 34, 594–600.
Doxiadis, S. A., Fessas, P., Valaes, T., and Mastrokalos, N. (1961). *Lancet* I, 297.
Doyon, M., and Gautier, C. (1909). *Compt. Rend. Soc. Biol.* 66, 616.
Doyon, M., Gautier, C., and Policard, A. (1908). *Compt. Rend. Soc. Biol.* 65, 574.
Drabkin, D. L. (1942). *Ann. Rev. Biochem.* 11, 531.
Dragstedt, C. A., and Mills, M. A. (1937). *Am. J. Physiol.* 119, 713–719.
Dreyfus-Brisac, L. (1878). De l'ictère hémapheique, principalement au point de vue clinique. Thesis (Med.), U. of Paris (101pp.).
Dreyfuss, F., Klein, H., and Winnik, H. Z. (1956). *Lancet* II, 1211.
Drinker, C. K. (1945). *Ann. Rev. Physiol.* 7, 389–404.
Driscoll, S. G., Hsia, D. Y. Y., Dennen, D. A., and Dowden, R. M. (1959). *Am. J. Physiol.* 197, 1322–1326.
Dubin, I. N. (1958). *Am. J. Med.* 24, 268–292.
Dubin, I. N., and Johnson, F. B. (1954). *Medicine* 33, 155–197.
Dubin, I. N., Sullivan, B. H., LeGolvan, P. C., and Murphy, L. C. (1960). *Am. J. Med.* 29, 55–72.
Dubrowsky, R. (1939). *Bol. Inst. Matern.* (*Buenos Aires*) 8, 361 (quoted in Royer, 1943, p. 125).
Ducci, H., and Roeschmann, W. (1949). *Rev. Med. Chile* 77, 192–197.
Ducci, H., and Watson, C. J. (1945). *J. Lab. Clin. Med.* 30, 293–300.
Duesberg, R. (1934). *Arch. Exptl. Pathol. Pharmakol.* 174, 305–327.
Duesberg, R. (1938). *Klin. Wochschr.* 17, 1353–1359.
Duggan, D. E., Bowman, R. L., Brodie, B. B., and Udenfried, S. (1957). *Arch. Biochem. Biophys.* 68, 1–14.
Dukes, H. H. (1934). "The Physiology of Domestic Animals," 5th. ed. Cornell Univ. Press (Comstock), Ithaca. New York.

Dulière, W. L., and Minne, R. (1937). *Compt. Rend. Soc. Biol.* **126**, 440-441.

Dumont, A. E., and Mulholland, J. H. (1962). *Ann. Surg.* **156**, 668-677.

Dumont, A. E., Doubilet, H., Witte, C. L., and Mulholland, J. H. (1961). *Ann. Surg.* **153**, 774.

Dumont, A. E., Stertzer, S. H., and Mulholland, J. H. (1962). *Am. J. Physiol.* **202**, 704-706.

Dundon, S. (1958). *J. Irish Med. Assoc.* **43**, 281.

Dunn, M., Martins, J., and Reissmann, K. R. (1958). *J. Lab. Clin. Med.* **51**, 259-265.

Dunn, P. (1963a). *Lancet* **II**, 1115.

Dunn, P. M. (1963b). *Arch. Disease Childhood* **38**, 54-61.

Dunning, M. F. (1958). *J. Am. Med. Assoc.* **167**, 1242-1243.

Dutton, G. J. (1958a). *Biochem. J.* **70**, 39P.

Dutton, G. J. (1958b). *Lancet* **II**, 49.

Dutton, G. J. (1963). *Ann. N.Y. Acad. Sci.* **111**, (Art. 1), 259-272.

Dutton, G. J., and Greig, C. G. (1957). *Biochem. J.* **66**, 52P.

Duval, M. (1893). *J. Anat. Physiol.* (*Paris*) **29**, 249-340.

Duysens, L. N. M. (1956). *Biochem. Biophys. Acta* **19**, 1-12.

Eanet, M. P., and Brick, I. B. (1955). *New Engl. J. Med.* **253**, 1062-1065.

Eberlein, W. R. (1960). *Pediatrics* **25**, 878-885.

Ebnöter, R. (1959). *Ann. Paediat.* (*Basle*) **193**, 279.

Edlbacher, S., and von Segesser, A. (1937a). *Naturwissenschaften* **25**, 461-462.

Edlbacher, S., and von Segesser, A. (1937b). *Naturwissenschaften* **25**, 557.

Edlund, Y. (1948). Studies on the Carbohydrate Metabolism and Liver Protection Therapy in Experimental Biliary Obstruction. *Acta Chir. Scand.* Suppl. 136 (187pp.).

Edlund, Y., and Hanzon, V. (1953). *Acta Anat.* **17**, 107-111.

Edmondson, P. W., and Wyburn, J. R. (1963). *Brit. J. Exptl. Pathol.* **44**, 72-80.

Ehrlich, P. (1882). *Z. Klin. Med.* **5**, 285-286.

Ehrlich, P. (1883). *Centr. Klin. Med.* **4**, 721-723.

Ehrlich, P. (1884). *Deut. Med. Wochschr.* **10**, 419-422.

Ehrlich, P. (1901). *Med. Woche* **1**, 151-153.

Eiband, J. M., and Fred, H. J. (1963). *AMA Arch. Internal Med.* **111**, 405-406.

Eichenbronner, H. (1938). Beiträge zur klinischen Verwertbarkeit der stufenptometrischen Urobilinogen- und Urobilinbestimmung im Harn. Inaugural Dissertation (Med.), U. of Zürich (25pp.).

Eichmann, M. P., Kavitz, E., and Porter, M. M. (1959). *Am. J. Med. Technol.* **25**, 250-252.

Eilbott, W. (1927). *Z. Klin. Med.* **106**, 529-560.

Eisenreich, F. (1948). *Deut. Med. Wochschr.* **73**, 506-508.

Eisfeld, G. (1953). *Z. Ges. Inn. Med. Grenzgebiete* **8**, 205-208.

Eitel, H. (1928). *Beitr. Pathol. Anat. Allgem. Pathol.* **79**, 700-712.

Ekuni, M. (1952a). *Igaku Kenkyu* **22**, 109-121 (in Jap., Engl. summary).

Ekuni, M. (1952b). *Igaku Kenkyu* **22**, 122-136 (in Jap., Engl. summary).

Elias, H. (1948). *Anat. Anz.* **96**, 454-460.

Elias, H. (1949a). *Anat. Nachr.* **1**, 8-20.

Elias, H. (1949b). *Am. J. Anat.* **84**, 311-333.

Elias, H. (1949c). *Am. J. Anat.* **85**, 379-456.

Elias, H. (1953). *Res. Service Med.* **27**, 26-51. Searle Co., Chicago, Illinois.

Elias, H. (1955). *Biol. Rev. Cambridge Phil. Soc.* **30**, 263-310.

Elias, H., and Petty, D. (1953). *Anat. Record* **116**, 9-17.

Eliassen, E. (1961). *Nature* **192**, 1047–1049.

Ellenberg, M., and Osserman, K. E. (1951). *Am. J. Med.* **11**, 170–178.

Ellenberger, W., and Scheunert, A. (1925). "Lehrbuch der vergleichenden Physiologie der Haussäugetiere," 3rd ed. Parey, Berlin (643pp.).

Elman, R., and McMaster, P. D. (1925a). *J. Exptl. Med.* **41**, 503–512.

Elman, R., and McMaster, P. D. (1925b). *J. Exptl. Med.* **42**, 99–122.

Elman, R., and McMaster, P. D. (1925c). *J. Exptl. Med.* **42**, 619–640.

Elton, N. W. (1928). *J. Michigan State Med. Soc.* **27**, 818–819.

Elton, N. W. (1929a). *J. Michigan State Med. Soc.* **28**, 451–452.

Elton, N. W. (1929b). *New Engl. J. Med..* **201**, 611–617.

Elton, N. W. (1931a). *J. Lab. Clin. Med.* **17**, 1–13.

Elton, N. W. (1931b). *J. Lab. Clin. Med.* **17**, 216–235.

Elton, N. W. (1931c). *Surg., Gynecol. Obstet.* **53**, 656–661.

Elton, N. W. (1935a). *Rev. Gastroenterol.* **2**, 331–334.

Elton, N. W. (1935b). *J. Lab. Clin. Med.* **20**, 817–826.

Elton, N. W. (1935c). *Am. J. Clin. Pathol.* **5**, 40–54.

Elton, N. W. (1936). *Rev. Gastroenterol.* **3**, 132–142.

Emery, J. L. (1963). *Ann. N.Y. Acad. Sci.* **111**, (Art. 1), 37–42.

Enanesco, M., Comanesco, V., and Zamfiresco, M. (1946). *Acta Med. Scand.* **126**, 205–222.

Enanesco, M., Comanesco, V., and Zamfiresco, M. (1947) *Presse Med.* **55**, 17–18.

Ender, F. (1955). *Nord Veterinaermed.* **7**, 329–377.

Enderlen, E., Thannhauser, S. J., and Jenke, M. (1927). *Arch. Exptl. Pathol. Pharmakol.* **120**, 16–24.

Engel (no inits.) and Kiener (no inits.) (1887a). *Compt. Rend. Soc. Biol.* **39**, 186–196.

Engel (no inits.) and Kiener (no inits.) (1887b). *Compt. Rend. Soc. Biol.* **39**, 221–228.

Engel, M. (1937). Die plasmatische Bilirubinbildung. Inaugural Dissertation (Med.), U. of Zürich.

Engel, M. (1939). *Z. Physiol. Chem.* **259**, 75–82.

Engel, M. (1940). *Z. Physiol. Chem.* **266**, 135–148.

Engelson, G., and Kjellman, B. (1963). *Acta Paediat.* **52**, 82–86.

Engstedt, L. (1957). Endogenous Formation of Carbon Monoxide in Hemolytic Disease. *Acta Med. Scand.* Suppl. 332 (61pp.).

Engstedt, L., Johansson, S., and Nyberg, A. (1964). *Biochem. J.* **92**, 39P.

Enriques, E., and Sivó, R. (1926). *Biochem.* **169**, 152–160.

Eppinger, H. (1903). *Beitr. Pathol. Anat. Allgem. Pathol.* **33**, 123–157.

Eppinger, H. (1920). "Die hepato-lienalen Erkrankungen." Springer, Berlin.

Eppinger, H. (1937). "Die Leberkrankheiten," Springer, Vienna (801pp.).

Eppinger, H., and Charnas, D. (1913). *Z. Klin. Med.* **78**, 387–398.

Eppinger, H., and Walzel, P. (1926). "Die Krankheiten der Leber mit Einschluss der hepatolienalen Erkrankungen." Thieme, Leipzig (134pp.).

Epstein, A. (1880). *Volkmanns Sammlung Klin. Vortr.* No. 180 (Gynaekologie No. 53), 1411–1434.

Ergas, M., and Wallis, K. (1963). *Ann. Paediat.* (*Basel*) **200**, 161–172.

Eriksen, L. (1955). En in vitro studie over biosyntesen av porfyriner og hemoglobin. Dissertation (Med.), U. of Oslo (53pp.).

Ernst. Z. (1925). *Biochem. Z.* **157**, 30–38.

Ernst, Z., and Förster, J. (1924). *Klin. Wochschr.* **3**, 2386–2388.

Ernst, Z., and Förster, J. (1925a). *Biochem. Z.* **157**, 39–45.

Ernst, Z., and Förster, J. (1925b). *Biochem. Z.* **157**, 492–550.

Ernst, Z., and Hallay, I. (1930). *Biochem. Z.* **228**, 354–365.

Ernst, Z., and Szappanyos, B. (1922). *Klin. Wochschr.* **1**, 614.

Enrst, Z., and Szappanyos, B. (1925). *Biochem. Z.* **157**, 16–29.

Ernster, L., Herlin, L., and Zetterström, R. (1957). *Pediatrics* **20**, 647.

Escola, O. (1950). *Acta Med. Scand.,* Suppl. 239, 96–101.

Esser, J. (1896). Untersuchungen über die Entstehungsweise des Hydrobilirubins im menschlichen Körper. Inaugural Dissertation (Med.) U. of Bonn (27pp.).

Eufinger, H., and Bader, C. W. (1926a). *Zentr. Gynaekol.* **50**, 514–517.

Eufinger, H., and Bader, C. W. (1926b). *Arch. Gynaekol.* **128**, 293–308.

Eufinger, H., and Bader, C. W. (1928). *Arch Gynaekol.* **133**, 720–732.

Evans, J. M., Zimmermann, H. J., Wilmer, J. G., Thomas, L. J., and Ethridge, C. B. (1952). *Am. J. Med.* **13**, 704–711.

Fahrak, N. (1948). *J. Egypt. Med. Assoc.* **31**, 522–540.

Fairley, N. H. (1939). *Proc. Roy. Soc. Med.* **32**, 1278–1280.

Fairley, N. H. (1941). *Quart. J. Med.* **10**, 95–114.

Falk, J. E., Appleby, C. A., and Porra, R. J. (1959). *Symp. Soc. Exptl. Biol.* **13**, 73–86.

Falta, W., and Högler, F. (1922). *Klin. Wochschr.* **1**, 1357.

Falta, W., Högler, F., and Knobloch, A. (1921). *Muench. Med. Wochschr.* **68**, 1250–1251.

Faltitschek, J., and Hess, L. (1936). *Wien. Klin. Wochschr.* **49**, 325–326.

Famulari, S. (1934a). *Biochim. Terap. Sper.* **21**, 217–221.

Famulari, S. (1934b). *Biochim. Terap. Sper.* **21**, 222–226.

Fantham, H. B. (1931). *S. African J. Sci.* **28**, 323–333.

Farmer-Loeb, L. (1932). *Biochem. Z.* **244**, 426–430.

Fashena, G. J. (1948). *Am. J. Diseases Children* **76**, 196–202.

Fasoli, A. (1949). *Experientia* **5**, 406.

Fasoli, A. (1950). *Arch. Sci. Biol. (Bologna)* **34**, 161–170.

Fasoli, A., and Franzini, P. (1950). *Minerva Med.* **41**, 1039–1040.

Feigl, J., and Querner, E. (1919). *Z. Ges. Exptl. Med.* **9**, 153–250.

Felbo, M., and Kragelund, D. (1961). *Ugeskrift Laeger* **123**, 1357–1359.

Felix, K., and Moebus, H. (1935). *Z. Physiol. Chem.* **236**, 230–236.

Fellinger, K. (1932). *Z. Ges. Exptl. Med.* **85**, 369–381.

Fellinger, K., and Pfleger, R. (1935). *Wien. Arch. Inn. Med.* **26**, 321–339.

Fellinger, K., Braunsteiner, H., and Pakesch, F. (1953). *Wien. Klin. Wochschr.* **65**, 738–740.

Felsenreich, G., and Satke, O. (1924a). *Arch. Verdauungskrankh.* **32**, 21–50.

Felsenreich, G., and Satke, O. (1924b). *Arch. Verdauungskrankh.* **32**, 149–178.

Ferrari, G. (1934). *Clin. Med. Ital.* **65**, 366–382.

Ferro, P. V., and Ham, A. B. (1963). *Am. J. Clin. Pathol.* **40**, 209–215.

Ferro, P. V., and Ham, A. B. (1965). *Am. J. Clin. Pathol.* **44**, 111–113.

Feruglio, F. S., and Salvini, M. (1947a). *Boll. Soc. Ital. Biol. Sper.* **23**, 1183–1184.

Feruglio, F. S., and Salvini, M. (1947b). *Boll. Soc. Ital. Biol. Sper.* **23**, 1184–1186.

Fessas, P., Doxiadis, S. A., and Valaes, T. (1962). *Brit. Med. J.* **II**, 1359–1362.

Feuereisen, W., and Klein, O. (1932). *Klin. Wochschr.* **11**, 1952.

Fiessinger, N. (1934). *J. Med. Franc.* **23**, 413–417.

Fiessinger, N., and Bárdŏs, G. (1936). *Sang* **10**, 912–919.

Fiessinger, N., and Gajdos, A. (1932). *Compt. Rend. Soc. Biol.* **110**, 455–457.

Fiessinger, N., and Walter, H. (1931). *Nutrition* 1, 1.

Fiessinger, N., and Walter, H. (1934). "Nouveaux procédés d'exploration functionelle du foie." Masson, Paris (171pp.).

Fiessinger, N., Jourdain, F., and Toissoul, D. (1929). *Presse Med.* 2, 1245–1249.

Fiessinger, N., Palmer, R., and Lançon, R. (1932). *Compt. Rend. Soc. Biol.* 110, 454–455.

Fiessinger, N., Gajdos, A., and Polonovski, M. (1941). *Compt. Rend. Soc. Biol.* 135, 1572–1575.

Fiessinger, N., Gajdos, A., and Polonovski, M. (1942). *Compt. Rend. Soc. Biol.* 136, 714–715.

Filinski, W. (1923). *Presse Med.* 31, 803–804.

Finch, C. A. (1959). *Ann. N.Y. Acad. Sci.* 77, 410–429.

Finckh, E. S., and Simpson, G. E. C. (1963). *J. Pathol. Bacteriol.* 86, 371–375.

Findlay, L., Higgins, G., and Stainer, M. W. (1947). *Arch. Disease Childhood* 22, 65–74.

Fischer, E., and Verzár, F. (1932). *Z. Ges. Exptl. Med.* 80, 385–394.

Fischer, H. (1911). *Z. Physiol. Chem.* 73, 204–239.

Fischer, H. (1912). *Muench. Med. Wochschr.* 59, 2555–2556.

Fischer, H. (1915). *Z. Biol.* 65, 163–182.

Fischer, H., and Barrenscheen, H. (1921). *Z. Physiol. Chem.* 115, 94–104.

Fischer, H., and Haberland, H. W. (1935). *Z. Physiol. Chem.* 232, 236–258.

Fischer, H., and Halbach, H. (1936). *Z. Physiol. Chem.* 238, 59–83.

Fischer, H., and Libowitzky, H. (1936). *Z. Physiol. Chem.* 241, 220–222.

Fischer, H., and Libowitzky, H. (1938). *Z. Physiol. Chem.* 251, 198–203.

Fischer, H., and Libowitzky, H. (1939). *Z. Physiol. Chem.* 258, 255–277.

Fischer, H., and Lindner, F. (1926). *Z. Physiol. Chem.* 153, 54–66.

Fischer, H., and Meyer-Betz, F. (1911). *Z. Physiol. Chem.* 75, 232–261.

Fischer, H., and Müller, A. (1937). *Z. Physiol. Chem.* 246, 43–58.

Fischer, H., and Niemann, G. (1923). *Z. Physiol. Chem.* 127, 317–328.

Fischer, H., and Niemann, G. (1924). *Z. Physiol. Chem.* 137, 293–316.

Fischer, H., and Orth, H. (1934). "Die Chemie des Pyrrols," Vol. I Akad. Verlagsges., Leipzig.

Fischer, H., and Orth, H. (1937). "Die Chemie des Pyrrols." Vol. II, Part 1. Akad. Verlagsges., Leipzig.

Fischer, H., and Plieninger, H. (1942). *Z. Physiol. Chem.* 274, 231–260.

Fischer, H., and Reindel, F. (1923). *Z. Physiol. Chem.* 127, 299–316.

Fischer, H., and Siedel, W. (1947). *FIAT Rev. Ger. Sci. Biochem., Part I*, pp. 109–127.

Fischer, H., and Stangler, G. (1927). *Ann. Chem. (Liebigs)* 459, 53–98.

Fischer, H., and Stern, A. (1940). "Die Chemie des Pyrrols," Vol. II, Part 2. Akad. Verlagsges., Leipzig.

Fischer, H., and von Dobeneck, H. (1940). *Z. Physiol. Chem.* 263, 125–146.

Fischer, H., and von Dobeneck, H. (1947). *FIAT Rev. Ger. Sci., Biochem., Part I*, pp. 129–139.

Fischer, H., and Wenderoth, H. (1939). *Ann. Chem. (Liebigs)* 537, 170–177.

Fischer, H., and Zerweck, W. (1924). *Z. Physiol. Chem.* 137, 176–241.

Fischer, H., Hilmer, H., Lindner, F., and Pützer, B. (1925). *Z. Physiol. Chem.* 150, 44.

Fischer, H., Halbach, H., and Stern, A. (1935). *Ann. Chem. (Liebigs)* 519, 254–260.

Fischer, H., Plieninger, H., and Weissbarth, D. (1941). *Z. Physiol. Chem.* **268,** 197–226.

Fischler, F. (1906). Das Urobilin und seine klinische Bedeutung. Habilitationsschrift (Med.), U. of Heidelberg (90pp.).

Fischler, F. (1916). "Physiologie und Pathologie der Leber," 1st ed. Springer, Berlin.

Fischler, F. (1925). "Physiologie und Pathologie der Leber," 2nd ed. Springer, Berlin.

Fischler, F., and Ottensooser, F. (1925). *Deut. Arch. Klin. Med.* **146,** 305–322.

Fleischl, E. (1874). *Ber. K. Saechs. Ges. Wiss. Leipzig, Mat. Phys. Cl.* **26,** 42–55.

Florentin, P. (1924). Recherches experimentales sur la biligénie pigmentaire normale et pathologique. Thesis (Med.), U. of Nancy. (184pp.).

Förster, J., and Förster, B. (1926). *Z. Klin. Med.* **103,** 703–714.

Fog, J. (1949). *Scand. J. Clin. Lab. Invest.* **1,** 255–257.

Fog, J. (1952). *Analyst* **77,** 457–460.

Fog, J. (1957). *Freiburger Symp.* pp. 224–226; Springer, Berlin.

Fog, J. (1958a). *Scand. J. Clin. Lab. Invest.* **10,** 241–245.

Fog, J. (1958b). *Scand. J. Clin. Lab. Invest.* **10,** 251–256.

Fog, J. (1958c). *Scand. J. Clin. Lab. Invest.* **10,** 446–447.

Fog, J. (1960). Serumfarge og bilirubin i ikteriske sera. Dissertation (Med.), U. of Oslo (106pp.)

Fog, J. (1962). "Standardization of Spectrophotometric Data in the Near Ultraviolet, Visual and Near Infrared." Johan Grundt Tanum, Oslo, Norway (64pp.).

Fog, J. (1964). *Scand. J. Lab. Clin. Invest.* **16,** 49–54.

Fog, J., and Jellum, E. (1962). *Nature* **195,** 490.

Fog, J., and Jellum, E. (1963). *Nature* **198,** 88–89.

Fog, J., Bugge-Asperheim, B., and Jellum, E. (1962). *Scand. J. Clin. Lab. Invest.* **14,** 567.

Fontaine, M. (1941). *Bull. Inst. Oceanogr. Monaco* No. 792, 1–5.

Fontaine, M., and Raffy, A. (1936). *Compt. Rend. Soc. Biol.* **121,** 735–736.

Foord, A. G., and Baisinger, C. F. (1940). *Am. J. Clin. Pathol.* **10,** 238–244.

Ford, F. R. (1952). "Diseases of the Nervous System in Infancy, Childhood and Adolescence," 3rd ed., pp. 714–719. Thomas, Springfield, Illinois.

Forfar, J. O., Keay, A. J., Elliot, W. D., and Cumming, R. A. (1958). *Lancet* **II,** 1131–1137.

Forfar, J. O., Keay, A. J., Elliot, W. D., and Cumming, R. A. (1959). *Lancet* **I,** 311–312.

Forgacs, J. (1962). *Advan. Vet. Sci.* **7,** 273–382.

Forti, C. (1958). *Arch. Fisiol.* **58,** 10–75.

Fouchet, A. (1917). *Compt. Rend. Soc. Biol.* **80,** 826–828.

Fouchet, A. (1918). *J. Pharm. Chim.* (*Paris*) [7] **17,** 44–47 (1918).

Foulkes, E. G., and Lemberg, R. (1949). *Proc. Roy. Soc.* **B136,** 435–448.

Fowweather, F. (1932). *Biochem. J.* **26,** 165–182.

Fox, D. L. (1953). "Animal Biochromes." Cambridge Univ. Press, London and New York (379 pp.).

Fox, D. L., and Millot, N. (1954). *Experientia* **10,** 185–186.

Fox, D. L., and Pantin, C. F. A. (1944). *Biol. Rev. Cambridge Phil. Soc.* **19,** 121–134.

Fox, H. M. (1953). *Nature* **171,** 162–163.

Framm, W. (1925). *Z. Geburtshilfe Gynaekol.* **88,** 319–334.

France, N. E. (1952). *Arch. Disease Childhood* **26,** 588–600.

Franchi Pade, H., and Graña, A. (1941). *Arch. Uruguay. Med. Cirug.* **19,** 293–296.

François, R., Bertholon, M. A., Bertrand, J., and Quincy, C. (1962). *Rev. Intern. Hepatol.* **12,** 753–776.

Franke, E. (1931). *Med. Klin.* **27,** 94–96.

Franke, H., and Banda, H. (1941). *Klin. Wochschr.* **20**, 1003-1004.
Franklin, A. W. (1958). *Lancet* I, 1227.
Franklin, M. (1949). *J. Lab. Clin. Med.* **34**, 1145-1150.
Franzini, P., and Arnoletti, E. (1950). *Arch. Patol. Clin. Med.* **28**, 165-192.
Frédéricq, L. (1878a). *Bull. Acad. Roy. Belg.* [2] **46**, 761-762.
Frédéricq, L. (1878b). *Arch. Zool. Exptl. Gen.* **7**, 578-581.
Free, A. H., and Free, H. M. (1953). *Gastroenterology* **24**, 414-421.
French, J. M. (1957). Personal communication.
French, J. M., Gaddie, R., and Smith, N. M. (1956). *Quart. J. Med.* **25**, 333-351.
Frenzel, J. (1888). *Verhandl. Kaiserl. Leopold.-Carol. Deut. Akad. Naturforsch.* **48**, 81-296.
Frerichs, F. T. (1858). "Klinik der Leberkrankheiten." Vieweg Braunschweig (2 vols.).
Fridrichsons, J., and Mathieson, A. M. L. (1962). *Tetrahedron Letters* **26**, 1265-1268.
Friedman, M., Byers, S. O., and Omoto, C. (1956). *Am. J. Physiol.* **184**, 11-17.
Fröhlich, A., and Mirsky, O. S. (1942). *Proc. Soc. Exptl. Biol. Med.* **50**, 25-28.
Frölund, A. (1954). Personal communication.
Froin, G. (1914). *Compt. Rend. Soc. Biol.* **76**, 762-763.
Fromholdt, G. (1907). *Z. Physiol. Chem.* **53**, 340-348.
Fromholdt, G. (1911). *Z. Exptl. Pathol. Therapie* **9**, 268-276.
Fromholdt, G., and Nersessoff, N. (1912a). *Z. Exptl. Pathol. Therapie* **11**, 400-403.
Fromholdt, G., and Nersessoff, N. (1912b). *Z. Exptl. Pathol. Therapie* **11**, 404-407.
Fujimori, E. (1964). *Nature* **204**, 1091-1092.
Fujita, Y., and Hattori, A. (1962a). *J. Biochem. (Tokyo)* **52**, 38-42.
Fujita, Y., and Hattori, A. (1962b). *Plant Cell Physiol. (Tokyo)* **3**, 209-220.
Fujita, Y., and Hattori, A. (1963). "Studies on Microalgae and Photosynthetic Bacteria," (Jap. Soc. Plant Physiologists, eds.), pp. 431-440.
Fujiwara, T. (1955). *J. Biochem. (Tokyo)* **42**, 411-417.
Fujiwara, T. (1956). *J. Biochem. (Tokyo)* **43**, 195-203.
Fujiwara, T. (1960). *J. Biochem. (Tokyo)* **48**, 317-330.
Fujiwara, T. (1961). *J. Biochem. (Tokyo)* **49**, 361-367.
Fulop, M., Sandson, J., and Brazeau, P. (1964). *Lancet* I, 1017-1019.
Gade, A. M. (1943). *Nord. Med.* **17**, 373-377.
Gänsslen, M., Zipperlen, E., and Schüz, E. (1925). *Deut. Arch. Klin. Med.* **146**, 1-46.
Gaidano, G. (1959). *Minerva Gastroenterol.* **5**, 201-205.
Gaidano, G., and Cravario, A. (1959). *Minerva Gastroenterol.* **5**, 205-209.
Gaidano, C., and Pagliardi, E. (1959). *Minerva Gastroenterol.* **5**, 161-166.
Gairdner, D., Lowrie, N. R., and Hutcheon, M. (1950). *Lancet* II, 541.
Galambos, J. T. (1963). *Southern Med. J.* **56**, 137.
Galvin, H. J. (1964). *Lancet* I, 1164.
Garay, E. R., and Argerich, T. C. (1963). *J. Lab. Clin. Med.* **62**, 141-147.
Garay, E. R., Cantor, D., and Royer, M. (1962). *Acta Physiol. Latinoam.* **12**, 400-407.
Gardicas, C., Kench, J. E., and Wilkinson, J. F. (1947). *Nature* **159**, 842.
Gardicas, C., Kench, J. E., and Wilkinson, J. F. (1948). *Nature* **161**, 607.
Gardicas, C., Kench, J. E., and Wilkinson, J. F. (1950). *Biochem. J.* **46**, 85-88.
Garner, R. J. (1953). *J. Comp. Pathol. Therap.* **63**, 247-253.
Garner, R. J. (1954). *Nature* **173**, 451.
Garner, R. J. (1955). *J. Comp. Pathol. Therap.* **65**, 271-277.

Garrahan, J. P. (1928). *Rev. Franc. Pediat.* **4**, 483–505.

Garrod, A. E., and Hopkins, F. G. (1896). *J. Physiol. (London)* **20**, 112–144.

Gartner, L. M., and Arias, I. M. (1963). *Am. J. Physiol.* **205**, 663–666.

Gassmann, F. K. (1930). *Z. Klin. Med.* **114**, 477–480.

Gastaldo, F., and Testoni, F. (1947a). *Boll. Soc. Ital. Biol. Sper.* **23**, 689–691.

Gastaldo, F., and Testoni, F. (1947b). *Boll. Soc. Ital. Biol. Sper.* **23**, 695–696.

Gastaldo, F., Debrio, G., and Testoni, F. (1947). *Boll. Soc. Ital. Biol. Sper.* **23**, 691–694.

Gates, G. A., Henly, K. S., Pollard, H. M., Schmidt, E., and Schmidt, F. W. (1961). *J. Lab. Clin. Med.* **57**, 182–184.

Gebauer, B. (1936). Der Bilirubinspiegel im Blutserum bei fieberhaften Erkrankungen der Pferde. Inaugural Dissertation (Vet.), U. of Berlin (43pp.).

Gebhardt, F. (1939a). *Z. Ges. Exptl. Med.* **106**, 213–234.

Gebhardt, F. (1939b). *Z. Ges. Exptl. Med.* **106**, 468–492.

Gedigk, P., and Gries, G. (1952). *Z. Physiol. Chem.* **289**, 261–271.

Geiger, H. (1936). Absorptionsspektren von Farbstoffen der Bilirubinreihe. Inaugural Dissertation, U. of Jena (26pp.).

Geller, W., and Tagnon, H. J. (1950). *AMA Arch. Internal Med.* **86**, 908–916.

Gellis, S. S., and Stokes, J., Jr. (1945). *J. Am. Med. Assoc.* **128**, 782–783.

Genner, V. (1936). "By-Effects of Salvarsan Therapy and Their Prevention." Munksgaard, Copenhagen (360pp.).

Genner, V., and With, T. K. (1938a). *Acta Dermato-Venerol.* **19**, 424–440.

Genner, V., and With, T. K. (1938b). *Acta Dermato-Venerol.* **19**, 453–491.

George, P., and Irvine, D. H. (1952). *Biochem. J.* **52**, 511–517.

Gérard, M. J. (1931). *Rev. Belge Sci. Med.* **3**, 217–226.

Gerhardt, C. (1877). *Wien. Med. Wochschr.* **27**, 577–578.

Gerhardt, C. (1878). *Correspondenzbl. Allgem. Aertztl. Ver., Thueringen* No. 11, 21/11 (quoted in Kunkel, 1880).

Gerhardt, D. (1887). *Verhandl. Kongr. Inn. Med.* **15**, 460–467.

Gerhardt, D. (1889). Über Hydrobilirubin und seine Beziehungen zum Ikterus Inaugural Dissertation (Med.), U. of Berlin (41pp.).

Gerhardt, D. (1897). *Z. Klin. Med.* **32**, 303–309.

Gerhartz, H. (1917). *Deut. Med. Wochschr.* **43**, 1297.

Gerrard, J. (1950). *Lancet* **II**, 35.

Gex, M., Schneegans, E., Heumann, G., Befort, P. A., and Rodier, L. (1960). *Pediatrics* **15**, 45–55.

Gheorghiu, M. G. (1933). *Bull. Soc. Chim. Biol.* **15**, 552–554.

Giaume, C., and Lanza, P. (1929). *Pediatria* **37**, 519–537.

Giannini, G. (1929). *Z. Ges. Exptl. Med.* **64**, 431–451.

Giblett, E. R., Coleman, D. H., Pirzio-Biroli, A., Donohue, D. M., Motulski, A. G., and Finch, C. A. (1956). *Blood* **11**, 291.

Gigon, A., and Noverraz, M. (1939). *Schweitz. Med. Wochschr.* **69**, 811–814.

Gigon, A., and Noverraz, M. (1942). *Schweitz. Med. Wochschr.* **72**, 1227–1229.

Gilbert, A., and Chabrol, E. (1911). *Compt. Rend. Soc. Biol.* **71**, 162–165.

Gilbert, A., and Herscher, M. (1902). *Compt. Rend. Soc. Biol.* **54**, 795–798.

Gilbert, A., and Herscher, M. (1905). *Compt. Rend. Soc. Biol.* **58**, 899–901.

Gilbert, A., and Herscher, M. (1906). *Presse Med.* **14**, 209–211.

Gilbert, A., and Herscher, M. (1907a). *Compt. Rend. Soc. Biol.* **63**, 452–455.

Gilbert, A., and Herscher, M. (1907b). *Compt. Rend. Soc. Biol.* **63**, 597–600.

Gilbert, A., and Herscher, M. (1907c). *Compt. Rend. Soc. Biol.* **63**, 802–805.

Gilbert, A., and Léreboullet, P. (1900). *Bull. Soc. Med. Hop. Paris* [3] **17**, 948–959.

Gilbert, A., and Léreboullet, P. (1901a). *Semaine Med.* **21**, 241.

Gilbert, A., and Léreboullet, P. (1901b). *Bull. Soc. Med. Hop. Paris* [3] **18**, 475–502.

Gilbert, A., and Léreboullet, P. (1903). *Compt. Rend. Soc. Biol.* **55**, 1378–1380.

Gilbert, A., and Léreboullet, P. (1905). *Compt. Rend. Soc. Biol.* **58**, 937–940.

Gilbert, A., and Léreboullet, P. (1910). *J. Med. Franc.* **4**, 110–119.

Gilbert, A., Herscher, M., and Posternak, S. (1903a). *Compt. Rend. Soc. Biol.* **55**, 530–533.

Gilbert, A., Herscher, M., and Posternak, S. (1903b). *Compt. Rend. Soc. Biol.* **55**, 584–587.

Gilbert, A., Herscher, M., and Posternak, S. (1903c). *Compt. Rend. Soc. Biol.* **55**, 1587–1590.

Gilbert, A., Léreboullet, P., and Stein, M. (1903d). *Compt. Rend. Soc. Biol.* **55**, 847–850.

Gilbertsen, S., and Watson, C. J. (1962). *J. Clin. Invest.* **41**, 1041–1049.

Gilbertsen, S., Campbell, M., and Watson, C. J. (1957). *J. Lab. Clin. Med.* **50**, 818.

Gilbertsen, S., Bossenmaier, I., and Cardinal, R. (1962). *Nature* **196**, 141–142.

Gilchrist, B., and Green, J. (1962). *Comp. Biochem. Physiol.* **7**, 117–127.

Gilligan, D. R., Altschule, M. D., and Katersky, E. M. (1941). *J. Clin. Invest.* **20**, 177–187.

Gillman, J., and Gillman, T. (1951). "Perspectives in Human Malnutrition." Grune & Stratton, New York.

Giordano, A. S., and Winstead, M. (1953). *Am. J. Clin. Pathol.* **23**, 610–612.

Giorgio, D., and Luigi, B. (1938). *Boll. Soc. Ital. Biol. Sper.* **13**, 943–944.

Gitter, A., and Heilmeyer, L. (1931). *Z. Ges. Exptl. Med.* **77**, 594–630.

Glanzmann, E. (1916). *Jahrb. Kinderheilk.* **84**, 95–135.

Glenner, G. (1957). *Am. J. Clin. Pathol.* **27**, 1–5.

Godfried, E. G. (1934). *Biochem. J.* **28**, 2056–2060.

Görges, T., and Gohr, H. (1954). *Deut. Z. Verdauungs-Stoffwechselkrankh.* **14**, 187–190.

Gössner, W. (1947). *Z. Physiol. Chem.* **282**, 262–267.

Gössner, W. (1948). *Klin. Wochschr.* **26**, 567–568.

Gohr, H. (1954). *Laboratoriumsblaetter* (*Bayer*) pp. 30–35.

Gohr, H. (1957). *IV. Freiburger Symp.*, Springer, Berlin. pp. 195–208.

Gohr, H., Heinen, W., Görges, T., and Kersten, G. (1956). *Z. Ges. Inn. Med. Grenzgebiete* **11**, 310–321.

Goiffon, R. (1920a). *Compt. Rend. Soc. Biol.* **83**, 60–62.

Goiffon, R. (1920b). *Compt. Rend. Soc. Biol.* **83**, 344–346.

Goldbarg, J. A., Pineda, E. P., Banks, B. M., and Rutenburg, A. M. (1959). *Gastroenterology* **36**, 193–201.

Goldbloom, A., and Gottlieb, R. (1932). *Rev. Franc. Pediat.* **8**, 177–187.

Golden, W. R. D., and Snavely, J. G. (1948). *J. Lab. Clin. Med.* **33**, 890–903.

Goldfarb, S., Singer, E. J., and Popper, H. (1963). *J. Lab. Clin. Med.* **62**, 608–615.

Golub, M. (1964). *Clin. Chem.* **10**, 399–405.

Gonzales-Oddone, M. V. (1946). *Proc. Soc. Exptl. Biol. Med.* **63**, 144–147.

Goodson, W. H., and Sheard, C. (1940). *J. Lab. Clin. Med.* **26**, 423–433.

Goodwin, T. W., and Srisukh, S. (1950). *Biochem. J.* **47**, 549–554.

Goodwin, T. W., and Srisukh, S. (1951). *Biochem. J.* **48**, 199–203.

Gorten, M. K. (1964). *Gen. Practitioner* **29**, 101–104.

Gosset, I. H. (1960). *Lancet* **I**, 87–88.

Gottlieb, R. (1934a). *Can. Med. Assoc. J.* **30**, 256–258.
Gottlieb, R. (1934b). *Can. Med. Assoc. J.* **30**, 365–367.
Gottlieb, R. (1934c). *Can. Med. Assoc. J.* **30**, 512–515.
Gottlieb, R., and Kearns, P. J. (1931). *J. Clin. Invest.* **10**, 319–322.
Gottschalk, A. (1922). *Z. Ges. Exptl. Med.* **26**, 34–58.
Gowan, A. T. D., and Scott, J. M. (1953a). *Lancet* **I**, 611.
Gowan, A. T. D., and Scott, J. M. (1953b). *Arch. Disease Childhood* **28**, 217–221.
Grafflin, A. G., and Bagley, E. H. (1952). *Bull. Johns Hopkins Hosp.* **90**, 395–439.
Grafflin, A. L., and Chaney, V. E. (1953). *Bull. Johns Hopkins Hosp.* **93**, 107–139.
Grafflin, A. L., and Corddry, E. G. (1953). *Bull. Johns Hopkins Hosp.* **93**, 205–224.
Graham, J. H. (1955). *Am. J. Med. Sci.* **230**, 633–635.
Graña, A. (1941). *Arch. Pediat. Uruguay* **12**, 333–337.
Grassnickel, W. (1926). *Arch. Wiss. Prakt. Tierheilk.* **54**, 479–507.
Gray, C. H. (1953). "The Bile Pigments." Methuen, London (142pp.).
Gray, C. H. (1957). *Assoc. Clin. Pathol. (Brit.) Broadsh.* [N.S.] No. 15.
Gray, C. H. (1961a). "Bile Pigments in Health and Disease." Thomas, Springfield, Illinois (101pp.).
Gray, C. H. (1961b). *Assoc. Clin. Pathol. (Brit.) Broadsh.* [N.S.] No. 35.
Gray, C. H., and Kekwick, R. A. (1948). *Nature* **161**, 274.
Gray, C. H., and Neuberger, A. (1949). *Biochem. J.* **44**, xlvi (Proc.).
Gray, C. H., and Neuberger, A. (1950). *Biochem. J.* **47**, 81–87.
Gray, C. H., and Nicholson, D. C. (1957a). *Nature* **179**, 264–265.
Gray, C. H., and Nicholson, D. C. (1957b). *Nature* **180**, 336–337.
Gray, C. H., and Nicholson, D. C. (1958a). *Nature* **181**, 183–185.
Gray, C. H., and Nicholson, D. C. (1958b). *Nature* **181**, 483–484.
Gray, C. H., and Nicholson, D. C. (1958c). *J. Chem. Soc. (London)* pp. 3085–3099.
Gray, C. H., and Nicholson, D. C. (1960). *Nature* **185**, 380–381.
Gray, C. H., and Nicholson, D. C. (1963). *Ann. N.Y. Acad. Sci.* **111**, (Art. 1), 281–288.
Gray, C. H., and Scott, J. J. (1958). *Biochem. J.* **69**, 25P.
Gray, C. H., and Scott, J. J. (1959). *Biochem. J.* **71**, 38–42.
Gray, C. H., and Whidborne, J. (1946). *Biochem. J.* **40**, 81–88.
Gray, C. H., and Whidborne, J. (1947). *Biochem. J.* **41**, 155–161.
Gray, C. H., Rimington, C., and Thomson, S. (1948). *Quart. J. Med.* **17**, 123–127.
Gray, C. H., Neuberger, A., and Sneath, P. H. A. (1949). *Biochem. J.* **45**, xvi–xvii (Proc.).
Gray, C. H., Neuberger, A., and Sneath, P. H. A. (1950a). *Biochem. J.* **47**, 87–92.
Gray, C. H., Muir, I. H. M., and Neuberger, A. (1950b). *Biochem. J.* **47**, 542–548.
Gray, C. H., Nicholson, D. C., and Nicolaus, R. H. (1958). *Nature* **181**, 183–185.
Green, J. (1959). *J. Exptl. Biol.* **36**, 575–582.
Green, J. (1961). *Nature* **189**, 227–228.
Green, J. (1962). *Nature* **196**, 1318–1319.
Gregory, C. H. (1963). *J. Lab. Clin. Med.* **61**, 917–925.
Gregory, C. H., and Watson, C. J. (1962a). *J. Lab. Clin. Med.* **60**, 1–16.
Gregory, C. H., and Watson, C. J. (1962b). *J. Lab. Clin. Med.* **60**, 17–30.
Gregory, R. L., and Andersch, M. (1937). *J. Lab. Clin. Med.* **22**, 1111–1114.
Greppi, E. (1937). *Haematologica* **18**, 1132–1137.
Gries, F. A., and Gries, G. (1956). *Klin. Wochschr.* **34**, 1084–1088.
Gries, F. A., and Gries, G. (1957). *Klin. Wochschr.* **35**, 81–85.

Gries, G., Gedigk, P., and Georgi, J. (1954). Z. *Physiol. Chem. Hoppe-Seyler's* **298**, 132–138.

Griffiths, W. J., and Kaye, G. (1930a). *Brit. J. Exptl. Pathol.* **11**, 441–446.

Griffiths, W. J., and Kaye, G. (1930b). *Biochem. J.* **24**, 1400–1407.

Grigaut, A. (1909). *Compt. Rend. Soc. Biol.* **66**, 725–727.

Grimbert, L. (1911a). *J. Pharm. Chim. (Paris)* [7] **3**, 425–430.

Grimbert, L. (1911b). *J. Pharm. Chim. (Paris)* [7] **3**, 473–478.

Grimm, F. (1893). *Arch. Pathol. Anat. Physiol.* **132**, 246–289.

Grindlay, J. H., Herrick, J. F., and Mann, F. C. (1941). *Am. J. Physiol.* **132**, 489–496.

Grinstein, M., Aldrich, R. A., Hawkinson, V., and Watson, C. J. (1949a). *J. Biol. Chem.* **179**, 983–984.

Grinstein, M., Kamen, M. D., and Moore, C. V. (1949b). *J. Biol. Chem.* **179**, 359–364.

Grinstein, M., Kamen, M. D., Wikoff, H. M., and Moore, C. W. (1950). *J. Biol. Chem.* **182**, 715–721.

Grinstein, M., Aldrich, A., Hawkinson, V., Lowry, P., and Watson, C. J. (1951). *Blood* **6**, 699–705.

Grodsky, G. M., and Carbone, J. V. (1957). *J. Biol. Chem.* **226**, 449–458.

Grodsky, G. M., Carbone, J. V., Fanska, R., and Peng, C. T. (1962). *Am. J. Physiol.* **203**, 532–536.

Grodsky, G. M., Contopoulos, A. N., Fanska, R., and Carbone, J. V. (1963). *Am. J. Physiol.* **204**, 837–841.

Grönberg, A., and Lundberg, A. (1930). *Acta Med. Scand.* **74**, 129–147.

Gros, H. (1958). *Deut. Med. Wochschr.* **63**, 383–386.

Grossmann, J. (1912). *Wien. Med. Wochschr.* **62**, 3384–3390.

Grunenberg, K. (1922). *Verhandl. Deut. Ges. Inn. Med.* **34**, 112–114.

Grunenberg, K. (1923a). *Z. Ges. Exptl. Med.* **31**, 119–146.

Grunenberg, K. (1923b). *Z. Ges. Exptl. Med.* **35**, 128–138.

Guillaumin, C. O. (1939). *Bull. Soc. Chim. Biol.* **21**, 127–133.

Gundermann, K.-O., and Kübler, W. (1962). *Deut. Med. Wochschr.* **87**, 306–308.

Gunn, C. K. (1944). *Can. Med. Assoc. J.* **89**, 230–237.

Gustafsson, B. E., and Lanke, L. S. (1960). *J. Exptl. Med.* **112**, 975–981.

Gutman, A. B. (1957). *Am. J. Med.* **23**, 841–845.

Gydell, K. (1958). *Acta Med. Scand.* **162**, 9–27.

Gydell, K. (1959). *Acta Med. Scand.* **164**, 305–320.

Gyllensvärd, A., and Malmström, A. (1962). *Acta Paediat.* Suppl. **135**, 54–62.

Haas, L., and Dobbs, R. H. (1958). *Arch. Disease Childhood* **33**, 396–402.

Haber, M. H., and Rees, K. R. (1963). *J. Pathol. Bacteriol.* **85**, 127–137.

Hackman, R. H. (1952). *Arch. Biochem. Biophys.* **41**, 166–174.

Hahn, M., Massen, O., Nencki, M., and Pawlow, J. (1893). *Arch. Exptl. Pathol. Pharmakol.* **32**, 161–210.

Halász, M. (1945). *Schweitz. Med. Wochschr.* **75**, 220–222.

Halász, M. (1948). *Gastroenterologia* **74**, 76–83.

Halász, M. (1949). *Z. Physiol. Chem.* **284**, 258–262.

Halász, M., and Engel, T. (1948). *Z. Physiol. Chem.* **283**, 258–262.

Halász, M., and Pinter, I. (1949). *Wien. Z. Inn. Med. Grenzgebiete* **30**, 252–254.

Halbach, H. (1938). *Ergeb. Inn. Med. Kinderheilk.* **55**, 1–28.

Hallberg, L. (1955). Blood Volume, Hemolysis and Regeneration of Blood in Pernicious Anemia. Studies Based on Endogenous Formation of Carbon Monoxide and Determination of Total Amount of Hemoglobin. *Scand. J. Clin. Lab. Invest.* Suppl. 16 (111pp.).

Hallgren, R. (1943). Epidemic Hepatitis in the County of Västerbotten in Northern Sweden. *Acta Med. Scand.* Suppl. 140 (103pp.).

Hammarsten, O. (1878). *Uppsala Laekarefoeren. Foerh.* **14,** 50–54.

Hammarsten, O. (1898). *Uppsala Laekarefoeren. Foerh.* [N.S.] **4,** 73–84 (Abstr. in *Maly's Jahresber. Tierchem.* p. 310, 1898).

Hammarsten, O. (1907). Lehrbuch der physiologischen Chemie, 6th ed. Bergmann, Wiesbaden (836 pp.).

Hammerberg, P. E. (1958). *Nord. Med.* **60,** 1024–1025.

Hamperl, H. (1957). *Klin. Wochschr.* **35,** 177–179.

Hampton, J. C. (1961). *Lab. Invest.* **10,** 502–513.

Hancock, J. (1950). *New Zealand J. Sci. Technol.* **A32,** 16–24.

Hanger, F. M. (1950). *Am. J. Med.* **9,** 102–113.

Hanger, F. M., and Gutman, A. B. (1940). *J. Am. Med. Assoc.* **115,** 263.

Hanot, V. (1895). *Semaine Med.* **15,** 197–199.

Hansen, R. (1938). *Klin. Wochschr.* **17,** 521–524.

Hanssen, O. (1909). *Norsk. Mag. Laegevidenskab.* [5] **7,** 1173–1180.

Hanzon, V. (1952). Liver Cell Secretion Under Normal and Pathological Conditions Studied by Fluorescence Microscopy on Living Rats. *Acta Physiol. Scand.* Suppl. 101 (268pp.).

Harboe, N. M. G. (1965). *In* "Protides of the Biological Fluids," Proc. 12th Colloq., Bruges, 1964 (H. Peeters, ed.), pp. 446–449. Elsevier, Amsterdam.

Hargreaves, T., and Lathe, G. H. (1963). *Nature* **200,** 1172–1176.

Harley, J. D. (1961). *Australasian Ann. Med.* **10,** 192.

Harley, J. D., and Robin, H. (1962). *Australasian Ann. Med.* **11,** 148–155.

Harley, V. (1892). *Brit. Med. J.* **II,** 397–400.

Harley, V. (1893). *Arch. Anat. Physiol.* (*Leipzig*), *Physiol. Abt.* pp. 291–302.

Harris, L. E., Farrel, F. J., Shorter, R. G., Banner, E. A., and Mathieson, D. R. (1962). *Proc. Staff. Meetings Mayo Clin.* **37,** 573–581.

Harris, R. C., Lucey, J. F., and MacLean, J. R. (1958). *Pediatrics* **21,** 875.

Harrison, B. A., Burwell, E. L., and Finch, C. A. (1951). *Federation Proc.* **10,** 357–358.

Harrison, F. A. (1962). *J. Physiol.* (*London*) **161,** 212–224.

Harrison, G. A. (1930). "Chemical Methods in Clinical Medicine," 1st ed. Churchill, London (534pp.).

Harrison, G. A. (1937). "Chemical Methods in Clinical Medicine," 2nd ed. Churchill, London (585pp.).

Harrison, G. A. (1947). "Chemical Methods in Clinical Medicine," 3rd ed. Churchill, London (630pp.).

Harrison, G. A., and Bromfield, R. J. (1928). *Biochem. J.* **22,** 43–45.

Harrop, G. A., and Barron, E. S. G. (1929). *Trans. Assoc. Am. Physicians* **44,** 143–147.

Harrop, G. A., and Barron, E. S. G. (1931). *J. Clin. Invest.* **9,** 577–587.

Hart, W. M., and Thomas, J. E. (1945). *Gastroenterology* **4,** 409–420.

Harth, O., and Waldeck, F. (1964). *Klin. Wochschr.* **42,** 118–123.

Hartog, H. A. P. (1935). Onderzoekingen over het serumbilirubine. Akad. Proefschrift (Geneesk.), U. of Utrecht (118pp.).

Harvig, S., and Bang, H. O. (1954). *Ugeskrift Laeger* **116,** 1108–1109.

Haselhorst, G. (1921). *Muench. Med. Wochschr.* **68,** 174–176.

Haselhorst, G. (1928). *Muench. Med. Wochschr.* **75**, 1076–1077.

Haslewood, G. E. D., and King, E. J. (1937). *Biochem. J.* **31**, 920–923.

Hattori, A., and Fujita, Y. (1959a). *J. Biochem. (Tokyo)* **46**, 521–522.

Hattori, A., and Fujita, Y. (1959b). *J. Biochem. (Tokyo)* **46**, 633–644.

Hattori, A., and Fujita, Y. (1959c). *J. Biochem. (Tokyo)* **46**, 903–909.

Hattori, A., and Fujita, Y. (1959d). *J. Biochem. (Tokyo)* **46**, 1259–1261.

Haurani, F. I., and Tocantins, L. M. (1961). *Am. J. Med.* **31**, 519–531.

Hausheer, H. J., and Lauer, D. J. (1962). *New Engl. J. Med.* **267**, 1300–1301.

Hausmann, T. (1913). *Z. Exptl. Pathol. Therapie* **13**, 373–399.

Hausmann, T. (1922). *Z. Klin. Med.* **94**, 12–21.

Havens, W. P., Jr. (1962). *J. Am. Med. Assoc.* **180**, 30–32.

Havens, W. P., Jr., Miller, W. N., Swift, W. E., Gardner, H. T., and Knowlton, M. (1950). *Am. J. Med.* **8**, 591–599.

Hawk, P. B., Oser, B. L., and Summerson, W. H. (1947). "Practical Physiological Chemistry." McGraw-Hill (Blakiston), New York.

Hawkins, W. B., and Johnson, A. C. (1939). *Am. J. Physiol.* **126**, 326–336.

Hawkins, W. B., and Whipple, G. H. (1938). *Am. J. Physiol.* **122**, 418–427.

Hawksley, J. C., and Lightwood, R. (1934). *Quart. J. Med.* **27**, 155.

Haworth, J. C., and Ford, J. D. (1963). *Arch. Disease Childhood* **38**, 328.

Hawthorne, H. R., and Sterling, J. A. (1954). *Am. J. Gastroenterol.* **21**, 355–365.

Hayem, G. (1889a). *Gaz. Hop.* **62**, 1314 (quoted in Royer, 1943, p. 93).

Hayem, G. (1889b). *Soc. Med. Hop.* **6**, 516 (quoted in Royer, 1943, p. 93).

Haymaker, W., Margoles, C., Pentschew, A., Jacob, H., Lindenberg, R., Arrayo, L. S., Stochdorph, O., and Stowens, D. (1960). *In* "Kernicterus and Its Importance in Cerebral Palsy" (Am. Acad. Cerebral Palsy, eds.), pp. 21–228. Thomas, Springfield, Illinois.

Hedenius, I. (1894). *Uppsala Laekarefoeren. Foerh.* **29**, 541–548.

Heidenhain, R. (1868). *Stud. Physiol. Inst. Breslau* No. 4, 226–247.

Heikel, T. (1958). *Scand. J. Clin. Lab. Invest.* **10**, 191–192.

Heikel, T., Sipilä, A. M., and Tenhunen, R. (1957). *Scand. J. Clin. Lab. Invest.* **9**, 342–344.

Heikel, T., Knight, B. C., Rimington, C., Ritchie, H. D., and Williams, E. J. (1960). *Proc. Roy. Soc. (London)* **B153**, 47–79.

Heilbrun, N., and Hubbard, R. S. (1938). *Am. J. Clin. Pathol.* **8**, 273–280.

Heilbrun, N., and Hubbard, R. S. (1940). *J. Lab. Clin. Med.* **26**, 576–581.

Heilmeyer, L. (1931a). *Biochem. Z.* **232**, 229–239.

Heilmeyer, L. (1931b). *Z. Ges. Exptl. Med.* **76**, 220–235.

Heilmeyer, L. (1931c). *Deut. Arch. Klin. Med.* **171**, 123–152.

Heilmeyer, L. (1938). *Biochem. Z.* **296**, 383–388.

Heilmeyer, L. (1943). "Spectrophotometry in Medicine." Hilger, London (280pp.).

Heilmeyer, L., and Krebs, W. (1930). *Biochem. Z.* **223**, 352–364.

Heilmeyer, L., and Krebs, W. (1931). *Biochem. Z.* **231**, 393–398.

Heilmeyer, L., and Krebs, W. (1934a). *Z. Physiol. Chem.* **228**, 33–46.

Heilmeyer, L., and Krebs, W. (1934b). *Z. Physiol. Chem.* **228**, 47–49.

Heilmeyer, L., and Oetzel, W. (1931). *Deut. Arch. Klin. Med.* **171**, 365–377.

Heilmeyer, L., and Ohlig, W. (1936). *Klin. Wochschr.* **15**, 1124–1126.

Heilmeyer, L., and Pfotenhauer, F. (1933). *Z. Ges. Exptl. Med.* **91**, 714–719.

Heilmeyer, L., and Toop, H. (1932). *Z. Ges. Exptl. Med.* **80**, 603–632.

Heilmeyer, L., and Wappler, B. (1928). *Z. Ges. Exptl. Med.* **63**, 630–642.

Heimann, F. (1933). *Biochem. Z.* **263**, 316–321.

Heimann, R., Pechet, G. S., Tank, R., and MacDonald, R. A. (1963). *Exptl. Mol. Pathol.* **2**, 442–449.

Heimpel, H., Frantz, H., and Schuboth, H. (1962). *Klin. Wochschr.* **40**, 929–1041.

Heiniö, P. (1933a). Über den Einfluss von Blutinjektionen auf den icterus neonatorum und den Bilirubingehalt des Blutes. *Acta Soc. Med. Fennicae "Duodecim"* **B14**, fasc. 2 (77pp.).

Heiniö, P. (1933b). *Acta Paediat.* **14**, 453–473.

Heinrichsdorff (no inits.) (1924). *Arch. Pathol. Anat. Physiol.* **248**, 48–90.

Heinricius, G. (1889). *Arch. Mikroskop. Anat. Entwicklungsmech.* **33**, 419–439.

Heinsius, A., and Campbell, J. F. F. (1871). *Arch. Ges. Physiol. (Pfluegers)* **4**, 497–546.

Held, A. (1933a). *Klin. Wochschr.* **12**, 365.

Held, A. (1933b). *Z. Ges. Exptl. Med.* **88**, 753–775.

Helfferich, K. H. (1960). *Med. Welt* pp. 625–630.

Heller, R. (1933). *Z. Ges. Exptl. Med.* **87**, 17–21.

Hench, P. S. (1938). *AMA Arch. Internal Med.* **61**, 451–480.

Henry, R. J., Golub, O. J., Berkman, S., and Segalove, M. (1953). *Am. J. Clin. Pathol.* **23**, 841–853.

Henry, R. J., Jacobs, S. L., and Chiamori, N. (1960). *Clin. Chem.* **6**, 529–536.

Henry, R. J., Jacobs, S. L., and Berkman, S. (1961). *Clin. Chem.* **7**, 231–240.

Henry, R. J., Fernandez, A. A., and Berkman, S. (1964). *Clin. Chem.* **10**, 440–446.

Henry-Cornet, J., and Henry, L. (1936). *Bull. Acad. Roy. Belg. Cl. Sci.* **22**, 553–559.

Henry-Cornet, J., and Henry, L. (1937). *Bull. Acad. Roy. Belg., Cl. Sci.* **23**, 697–702.

Herlin, L. (1958). *Ciba Found. Symp. Cerebrospinal Fluid*, p. 222.

Herlitz, C. W. (1926). *Acta Paediat.* **6**, 214–224.

Herrmann (no inits.) (1957). *Ber. 26. Tagung Deut. Ges. Hyg. Mikrobiol.* (quoted in Baumgärtel, 1958b).

Hersheer, M. (1902). Origine rénale de l'urobiline. Thesis (Med.). U. of Paris (110 pp.).

Herter, C. A. (1906). *J. Biol. Chem.* **1**, 251–256.

Herzfeld, E. (1922). *Schweitz. Med. Wochschr.* **3**, 585–586.

Hetényi, G. (1922). *Z. Klin. Med.* **95**, 469–490.

Hijmans van den Bergh, A. A. (1918). "Der Gallenfarbstoff im Blute," 1st ed. Barth, Leipzig (111pp.).

Hijmans van den Bergh, A. A. (1921). *Presse Med.* **29**, 441–443.

Hijmans van den Bergh, A. A. (1924). *Brit. Med. J.* **II**, 498–500.

Hijmans van den Bergh, A. A. (1928). "Der Gallenfarbstoff im Blute," 2nd ed. Barth, Leipzig (112pp.).

Hijmans van den Bergh, A. A., and Grotepass, W. (1934). *Brit. Med. J.* **I**, 1157–1159.

Hijmans van den Bergh, A. A., and Kamerling, A. W. C. G. (1934). *Ned. Tijdschr. Geneesk.* **78**, 4432–4438.

Hijmans van den Bergh, A. A., and Müller, P. (1916). *Biochem. Z.* **77**, 90–103.

Hijmans van den Bergh, A. A., and Snapper, I. (1913). *Deut. Arch. Klin. Med.* **110**, 540–561.

Hildebrandt, W. (1906). *Z. Klin. Med.* **59**, 350–443.

Hildebrandt, W. (1908). *Deut. Med. Wochschr.* **34**, 489–491.

Hildebrandt, W. (1909a). *Muench. Med. Wochschr.* **56**, 710–713.

Hildebrandt, W. (1909b). *Muench. Med. Wochschr.* **56**, 763–768.

Hildebrandt, W. (1910). *Muench. Med. Wochschr.* **57**, 2574–2576.

Hildebrandt, W. (1913). *Mitt. Grenzegebieten Med. Chir.* **25**, 247–263.

Hill, K. R. (1960). *Proc. Roy. Soc. Med.* **53**, 281–283.

Hirsch, A. (1913). *Z. Kinderheilk.* **9**, 196–207.

Hiyeda, K. (1925). *Beitr. Pathol. Anat. Allgem. Pathol.* **73**, 541–565.

Hiyeda, K. (1927). *Beitr. Pathol. Anat. Allgem. Pathol.* **78**, 389–407.

Hodges, R., Ronaldson, J. W., Taylor, A., and White, E. P. (1963). *Chem. Ind.* (*London*) pp. 42–43.

Hölting, H. (1938). Untersuchungen über das Verhalten des Bilirubinspiegels bei der Kolik der Pferde. Inaugural Dissertation (Vet.), U. of Hannover (38pp.).

Hoenig, V. (1955). *Casopis Lekaru Ceskych* **94**, 657–659 (in Czech, Fr. summary).

Hoenig, V., and Hoenigová, J. (1959). *Casopis Lekaru Ceskych* **98**, 1550–1552 (in Czech, Fr. summary).

Hoenig, V., and Schück, O. (1954). *Casopis Lekaru Ceskych* **93**, 1377–1379 (in Czech, Fr. summary).

Hoesch, K. (1922). *Klin. Wochschr.* **1**, 2034–2035.

Hoesch, K. (1926). *Muench. Med. Wochschr.* **73**, 369–372.

Hoffbauer, F. W. (1949). *J. Clin. Invest.* **28**, 789.

Hoffbauer, F. W. (1959). *J. Am. Med. Assoc.* **169**, 1453–1461.

Hoffman, H. N., Whitcomb, F. F., Butt, H. R., and Bollman, J. L. (1960). *J. Clin. Invest.* **39**, 132–142.

Hofmeier, M. (1882). *Z. Geburtshilfe Gynaekol.* **8**, 287–353.

Hogg, C. K., and Meites, S. (1959). *Am. J. Med. Technol.* pp. 281–286.

Hoitink, A. W. J. H. (1935). *Nedl. Tijdschr. Geneesk.* **79**, 2928–2930.

Holden, H. F. (1943). *Australian J. Exptl. Biol. Med. Sci.* **21**, 159–167.

Holden, H. F. (1945). *Australian J. Exptl. Biol. Med. Sci.* **23**, 255–259.

Holden, H. F. (1946). *Australian J. Exptl. Biol. Med. Sci.* **24**, 107–110.

Holden, H. F. (1947a). *Australian J. Exptl. Biol. Med. Sci.* **25**, 47–56.

Holden, H. F. (1947b). *Australian J. Exptl. Biol. Med. Sci.* **25**, 355–358.

Holden, H. F., and Lynikas, K. (1961). *Australian J. Exptl. Biol. Med. Sci.* **39**, 595–600.

Hollan, O. R. (1950). *Gastroenterology* **16**, 418–424.

Holle, G. (1962). *Ger. Med. Monthly* **7**, 91–93.

Hollister, L. E. (1957). *Am. J. Med.* **23**, 870–879.

Hollos, L. (1929). *Klin. Wochschr.* **8**, 1455–1456.

Holt, C. L. (1947). *New Engl., J. Med.* **237**, 580–583.

Holton, J. B., and Lathe, G. H. (1963). *Clin. Sci.* **25**, 499–509.

Holzer, P., and Mehner, H. (1922). *Klin. Wochschr.* **1**, 66–67.

Hooper, C. W., and Whipple, G. H. (1916). *Am. J. Physiol.* **40**, 332–348.

Hoover, C. F., and Blankenhorn, M. A. (1916). *Trans. Am. Assoc. Physicians* **31**, 243–260.

Hoover, C. F., and Blankenhorn, M. A. (1921). *AMA Arch. Internal Med.* **18**, 289–303.

Hoppe-Seyler, F. (1874). *Ber. Deut. Chem. Ges.* **7**, 1065–1066.

Hoppe-Seyler, G. (1891). *Arch. Pathol. Anat. Physiol.* **124**, 30–47.

Horowitz, E. A., and Küttner, T. T. (1927). *Am. J. Obstet. Gynecol.* **14**, 721–742.

Horsters, H. (1939). *Ergeb. Inn. Med. Kinderheilk.* **56**, 575–613.

Hosokawa, M. (1956a). *Igaku Kenkyu* **26**, 1165–1174 (in Jap., Engl. summary).

Hosokawa, M. (1956b). *Igaku Kenkyu* **26**, 1175–1181 (in Jap., Engl. summary).

Hosokawa, M. (1956c). *Igaku Kenkyu* **26**, 1182–1191 (in Jap., Engl. summary).

Hou, C. T., Rees, K. R., and Shotlander, V. L. (1962). *J. Pathol. Bacteriol.* **83**, 469–473.

Houssaye, M. (1949). Contribution à l'etude de la bilirubine sanguine. L'oxydo-reaction limite. Thesis (Med.), U. of Paris (75pp.).

Howard, G. A., and Martin, A. J. P. (1950). *Biochem. J.* **46**, 532–538.

Hsia, D. Y. Y., Allen, F. H., Gellis, S. S., and Diamond, L. K. (1952a). *New Engl. J. Med.* **247**, 668–671.

Hsia, D. Y. Y., Patterson, P., Allen, F. H., Diamond, L. K., and Gellis, S. S. (1952b). *Pediatrics* **10**, 243.

Hsia, D. Y. Y., Allen, F. H., Gellis, S. S., and Diamond, L. K. (1953). *J. Pediat.* **42**, 277.

Hsia, D. Y. Y., Hsia, H., Gofstein, R. M., Winter, A., and Gellis, S. S. (1956). *Pediatrics* **18**, 433–437.

Hsia, D. Y. Y., Boggs, J. D. B., Driscoll, S. G., and Gellis, S. S. (1958). *AMA J. Diseases, Children* **95**, 485.

Hsia, D. Y. Y., Dowben, R. M., and Riabov, S. (1963). *Ann. N.Y. Acad. Sci.* **111**, (Art. 1), 326–333.

Hueck, W., and Brehme, T. (1923). *Deut. Arch. Klin. Med.* **141**, 233–242.

Huhtala, A. (1937). *Duodecim (Helsinki)* **53**, 1034–1074 (in Finn., Ger. summary).

Hult, H. (1950). Cholémie simple familiale (Gilbert) and Posthepatitic States Without Fibrosis of the Liver. *Acta Med. Scand.* Suppl. 244 (96pp.).

Hunter, F. T. (1951). "The Quantitation of Mixtures of Hemoglobin Derivatives by Photoelectric Spectrophotometry." Thomas, Springfield, Illinois (226pp.).

Hunter, G. (1930a). *Can. Med. Assoc. J.* **23**, 823–824.

Hunter, G. (1930b). *Brit. J. Exptl. Pathol.* **11**, 407–414.

Hunter, G. (1930c). *Brit. J. Exptl. Pathol.* **11**, 415–419.

Hurst, E. P., and Walters, M. N. I. (1961). *Med. J. Australia* **48**, 698–702.

Hurst, W. W., Schemm, F. R., and Layne, J. A. (1951). *Am. J. Med.* **10**, 774–775.

Hutyra, F., and Marek, J. (1913). "Spezielle Pathologie der Haustiere," 4th ed., Vol. 2. Fischer, Jena.

Huwer, G. (1933). *Z. Geburtshilfe Gynaekol.* **106**, 324–383.

Hyvarinen, V., Aulis, K., and Reinold, J. G. (1958). *Federation Proc.* **17**, 247.

Ichikawa, T. (1956a) *Igaku Kenkyu* **26**, 1441–1451 (in Jap., Engl. summary).

Ichikawa, T. (1956b). *Igaku Kenkyu* **26**, 1452–1460. (in Jap., Engl. summary).

Ichikawa, T. (1956c). *Igaku Kenkyu* **26**, 1461–1473 (in Jap., Engl. summary).

Ikonen, E. (1964). Jaundice Late in Pregnancy. *Acta Obstet. Gynaecol. Scand.* **43**, Suppl. 5 (130pp.).

Ilca, S. (1964). *Z. Ges. Inn. Med. Grenzgebiete* **19**, 476–477.

Imai, H. (1959a). *Okayama Igakkai Zasshi* **71**, 8313.

Imai, H. (1959b). *Okayama Igakkai Zasshi* **71**, 8319.

Ingham, J. (1951). *Lancet* **I**, 151.

Isaac, S. (1925). *Ergeb. Inn. Med. Kinderheilk.* **27**, 423–506.

Ishimitsu, T. (1959a). *Okayama Igakkai Zasshi* **71**, 7783.

Ishimitsu, T. (1959b). *Okayama Igakkai Zasshi* **71**, 7903.

Israels, L. G. (1963). *Ann. N.Y. Acad. Sci.* **111**, (Art. 1), 288–289.

Israels, L. G., and Zipursky, A. (1962). *Nature* **193**, 73–74.

Israels, L. G., Suderman, H. J., and Ritzmann, S. E. (1959). *Am. J. Med.* **27**, 693–702.

Israels, L. G., Skanderberg, J., Gyuda, H., Zingg, W., and Zipursky, A. (1963a). *Brit. J. Haematol.* **9**, 50–62.

Israels, L. G., Yamamoto, T., Skanderberg, J., and Zipursky, A. (1963b). *Science* **139**, 1054–1055.

Isselbacher, K. J. (1961). *Biochem. Biophys. Res. Commun.* **5**, 243.

Isselbacher, K. J., and McCarthy, E. A. (1958). *Biochem. Biophys. Acta* **29**, 658–659.

Isselbacher, K. J., and McCarthy, E. A. (1959). *J. Clin. Invest.* **38**, 645–651.

Itoh, T. (1931). *Beitr. Pathol. Anat. Allgem. Pathol.* **86**, 488–516.

Itoh, T. (1932). *Beitr. Pathol. Anat. Allgem. Pathol.* **89**, 513–528.

Iversen, P., and Roholm, K. (1939). *Acta Med. Scand.* **102**, 1–16.

Iwado, M. (1957a). *Igaku Kenkyu* **27**, 18–25 (in Jap., Engl. summary).

Iwado, M. (1957b). *Igaku Kenkyu* **27**, 26–34 (in Jap., Engl. summary).

Jablonski, W. J. (1962). *New Engl. J. Med.* **266**, 155.

Jacobi, M., Finkelstein, R., and Kurlen, R. (1931). *AMA Arch. Internal Med.* **47**, 759–763.

Jacobs, E., and Scheffer, W. (1925). *Z. Ges. Exptl. Med.* **44**, 116–142.

Jacobs, S. L., Henry, R. J., and Segalove, M. (1964). *Clin. Chem.* **10**, 433–439.

Jacoby, H. (1928). *Deut. Med. Wochschr.* **54**, 1513–1515.

Jacoby, H. (1929). *Klin. Wochschr.* **8**, 1611–1613.

Jacoby, H. (1930). *Klin. Wochschr.* **9**, 307–308.

Jadassohn, J. (1923). *Deut. Med. Wochschr.* **49**, 1544–1545.

Jaffe, M. (1868a). *Arch. Ges. Physiol. (Pfluegers)* **1**, 262–273.

Jaffe, M. (1868b). *Zentr. Med. Wiss.* **6**, 241–245.

Jaffe, M. (1869a). *Arch. Pathol. Anat. Physiol.* **47**, 405–427.

Jaffe, M. (1869b). *Zentr. Med. Wiss.* **7**, 177–188.

Jaffe, M. (1871). *Zentr. Med. Wiss.* **9**, 465–466.

Jalavisto, E., and Leppo, E. (1934). *Duodecim (Helsinki)* **50**, 232–248. (in Finn., Ger. summary).

Jamieson, N. D., and Swan, J. B. (1952). *New Zealand J. Sci. Technol.* **A24**, 354–359.

Jankelson, I. R. (1944). *Gastroenterology* **3**, 292–296.

Jankelson, I. R., and Gargill, S. L. (1931). *New Engl. J. Med.* **204**, 547–549.

Jardin, P., Davis, W. D., and Beeler, M. (1963). *Southern Med. J.* **56**, 133–137.

Jeliu, G., Schmid, R., and Gellis, S. (1959). *Pediatrics* **23**, 92–97.

Jendrassik, L., and Cleghorn, R. A. (1936a). *Biochem. Z.* **289**, 1–14.

Jendrassik, L., and Cleghorn, R. A. (1936b). *Klin. Wochschr.* **15**, 1922.

Jendrassik, L., and Czike, A. (1928a). *Deut. Med. Wochschr.* **54**, 430.

Jendrassik, L., and Czike, A. (1928b). *Z. Ges. Exptl. Med.* **60**, 554–562.

Jendrassik, L., and Gróf, P. (1938a) *Biochem. Z.* **296**, 71–79.

Jendrassik, L., and Gróf, P. (1938b). *Biochem. Z.* **297**, 81–89.

Jendrassik, L., and Rébay-Szabó, M. (1937). *Biochem. Z.* **294**, 293–299.

Jenke, M. (1931). *Verhandl. Deut. Ges. Inn. Med.* **43**, 387–389.

Jespersen, H. G. (1959). *Ugeskrift. Laeger* **121**, 1489–1490.

Jezler, A. (1929). *Z. Klin. Med.* **111**, 48–70.

Jimenez-Diaz, C., Castro-Mendoza, H., Linazasoro, J. M., Dominguez, D., and Adame, E. (1948). *Bull. Inst. Med. Res. Univ. Madrid* **1**, 111–120.

Jimenez-Diaz, C., Castro-Mendoza, H., Dominguez, D., and Adame, E. (1949). *Rev. Clin. Espan.* **32**, 385–388.

Jirásek, V., and Jirsa, M. (1960). *Casopis Lekaru Ceskych* **99**, 214–218

Jirsa, M., and Jirsová, V. (1959). *Clin Chem.* **5**, 532–541.

Jirsa, M., and Sedláček, B. (1956). *Collection Czech. Chem. Commun.* **21**, 1409–1412.

Jirsa, M., and Šponar, J. (1955). *Z. Ges. Inn. Med. Grenzgebiete* **10**, 967–973.

Jirsa, M., and Šponar, J. (1956). *Z. Ges. Inn. Med. Grenzgebiete* 11, 519–522.
Jirsa, M., and Večerek, B. (1956). *Sess. 2 Fac. Med. Sci. Univ. Carolina Med.* (*Prague*) Suppl. 2, 40–48.
Jirsa, M., and Večerek, B. (1958). *Z. Physiol. Chem.* 311, 87–92.
Jirsa, M., Večerek, B., and Ledvina, M. (1956). *Nature* 177, 895.
Jirsa, M., Ledvina, M., and Večerek, B. (1958). *Z. Physiol. Chem.* 311, 93–95.
Jirsová, V., Jirsa, M., and Janovský, M. (1958). *Acta Paediat.* 47, 179–186.
Joannovics, G. (1904). *Z. Heilkunde* 25, 25–67.
Joannovics, G., and Pick, E. P. (1910). *Z. Exptl. Pathol. Therapie* 7, 185–214.
John, G. D., and Knudtson, K. P. (1956). *Am. J. Med.* 21, 138–142.
Johnson, H. C., and Doenges, J. P. (1956). *Ann. Internal Med.* 44, 589–616.
Johnson, L., Sarmento, F., Blanc, W. A., and Day, R. (1959). *AMA Diseases Children* 97, 591–608.
Johnson, L., Garcia, M. L., Figuerra, E., and Sarmento, F. (1961). *Am. J. Diseases Children* 101, 322–349.
Johnson, L. J. (1957). *J. Med. Lab. Technol.* 14, 164–168.
Joliffe, N. (1930). *J. Clin. Invest.* 8, 419–433.
Jolles, A. (1894). *Arch. Ges. Physiol.* (*Pfluegers*) 57, 1–57.
Jolles, A. (1895). *Arch. Ges. Physiol.* (*Pfluegers*) 61, 623–637.
Jonass, A. (1912). *Wien. Klin. Wochschr.* 25, 375–379.
Jones, C. M., and Jones, B. B. (1922). *AMA Arch. Internal Med.* 25, 669–683.
Jope, E. M. (1946a). *Proc. Roy. Soc. Med.* 39, 755–760.
Jope, E. M. (1946b). *Brit. J. Ind. Med.* 3, 136–142.
Jope, E. M., Jope, H. M., and O'Brien, J. R. P. (1949). *Nature* 164, 622.
Jordan, A. (1956). *Lancet* II, 1049.
Jordans, G. W. A. (1959). *Ned. Tijdschr. Geneesk.* 103, 1296–1299.
Jórg, M. E. (1941). La hepatosis aguda letal. Atrofia amarilla y roja aguda genuina de Rokitansky. Thesis (Med.), U. of Buenos Aires (quoted from Lopez Garcia, 1943).
Jorke, D., and Steiner, C. (1957). *IV. Freiburger Symp.* pp. 219–233. Springer, Berlin.
Josephs, H. W. (1934). *Bull. Johns Hopkins Hosp.* 55, 154–167.
Josephson, B., and Dahlberg, G. (1952). *Scand. J. Clin. Lab. Invest.* 4, 216–236.
Josephson, B., and Larsson, H. (1941). *Acta Med. Scand.* 107, 584–599.
Jourdain, V. (1932). *Ann. Bull. Soc. Roy. Sci. Med. Nat. Bruxelles* pp. 176–215.
Judd, E. S., and Lyons, J. H. (1923a). *Ann. Surg.* 77, 281–292.
Judd, E. S., and Lyons, J. H. (1923b). *Trans. Southern Surg. Assoc.* 35, 279–300 (Discussion pp. 316–324).
Julesz, N., and Winkler, E. (1933). *Z. Ges. Exptl. Med.* 87, 668–678.
Julian, L. M., and De Ome, K. B. (1948). *Ann. J. Vet. Res.* 9, 331–335.
Junge, H. (1941). *Z. Physiol. Chem.* 268, 179–186.
Justi, K. (1912). *Arch. Schiffs- Tropenhyg.* 16, 443–450.
Kämmerer, H., and Miller, R. (1922a). *Wien. Klin. Wochschr.* 35, 639.
Kämmerer, H., and Miller, R. (1922b). *Verhandl. Deut. Ges. Inn. Med.* 34, 85–91.
Kämmerer, H., and Miller, R. (1923). *Deut. Arch. Klin. Med.* 141, 318–347.
Kahán, I. L. (1958). *Nature* 181, 773.
Kahán, I. L. (1961). *Stud. Med. Szeged.* 1, 1–75.
Kahán, I. L. (1964a). *Nature* 202, 1216–1217.
Kahán, I. L. (1964b). *Abstr. 6th. Intern. Congr. Biochem., New York* p. 416. Pergamon Press, Oxford.

Kahán, I. L., and Felkai, B. (1961). *Acta Med. Acad. Sci. Hung.* **17**, 277–291.

Kahán, I. L., and Kahán, A. (1959). *Nature* **183**, 463–464.

Kahán, I. L., Csernay, L., and Varró, V. (1962). *Clin. Chim. Acta* **7**, 392–393.

Kaji, M. (1958a). *Okayama Igakkai Zasshi* **71**, 8567 (in Jap., Engl. summary).

Kaji, M. (1959b). *Okayama Igakkai Zasshi* **71**, 8573 (in Jap., Engl. summary).

Kalk, H. (1957). *IV. Freiburger Symp.*, pp. 130–146. Springer, Berlin

Kalk, H. (1958). *Ciba Symp.* (*Basel*) **6**, 47–54.

Kalk, H., and Ulbricht, J. (1963). *Deut. Med. Wochschr.* **88**, 213–218.

Kalk, H., and Wildhirt, E. (1956). *Gastroenterologia* **85**, 250.

Kaneko, J. J., and Cornelius, C. E. (1962). *Am. J. Vet. Res.* **23**, 913–915.

Kaneko, J. J., Cornelius, C. E., and Baker, N. F. (1961a). *Proc. Soc. Exptl. Biol. Med.* **107**, 924–926.

Kaneko, J. J., Cornelius, C. E., and Heuschele, W. P. (1961b). *Am. J. Vet. Res.* **22**, 683–685.

Kaplan, A. A. (1956). *Gastroenterology* **31**, 384–390.

Kapsinow, R., Engle, L. P., and Harvey, S. C. (1924). *Surg., Gynecol. Obstet.* **39**, 62–65.

Karrer, P., von Euler, H., and Hellström, H. (1933). Zur Kenntnis des C-Vitamins. *Arkiv Kemi, Mineral. Geol.* **B11**, No. 6 (6pp.).

Karsten (no inits.) (1845). *Nova Acta Acad. Leopold.-Carol., Ser. 21, Pt. I* pp. 318–320.

Kast, A., and Mester, B. (1891). *Z. Klin. Med.* **18**, 469–479.

Katami, S. (1959a). *Okayama Igakkai Zasshi* **71**, 8325 (in Jap., Engl. summary).

Katami, S. (1959b). *Okayama Igakkai Zasshi* **71**, 8337 (in Jap., Engl. summary).

Katznelson, P. (1920). *Wien. Arch. Inn. Med.* **1**, 563–574.

Kawaguchi, M. (1957a). *Igaku Kenkyu* **27**, 1002 (in Jap., Engl. summary).

Kawaguchi, M. (1957b). *Igaku Kenkyu* **27**, 1015 (in Jap., Engl. summary).

Kawaguchi, M. (1957c). *Igaku Kenkyu* **27**, 1027 (in Jap., Engl. summary).

Kawai, K. (1953). *Igaku Kenkyu* **23**, 572–581 (in Jap., Engl. summary).

Kay, I. T., Weimer, M., and Watson, C. J. (1963). *J. Biol. Chem.* **238**, 1122–1123.

Kayasuga, N. (1957a). *Igaku Kenkyu* **27**, 1960 (in Jap., Engl. summary).

Kayasuga, N. (1957b). *Igaku Kenkyu* **27**, 1970 (in Jap., Engl. summary).

Kaziro, K., and Kikuchi, G. (1951). *J. Biochem. Tokyo* **38**, 213–224.

Kaziro, K., and Kikuchi, G. (1952a). *J. Biochem.* (*Tokyo*) **39**, 63–76.

Kaziro, K., and Kikuchi, G. (1952b). *J. Biochem.* (*Tokyo*) **39**, 193–201.

Kaziro, K., and Kikuchi, G. (1952c). *J. Biochem.* (*Tokyo*) **39**, 357–366.

Kaziro, K., Kikuchi, G., and Ogawa, T. (1953). *J. Biochem.* (*Tokyo*) **40**, 205–225.

Kaziro, K., Kikuchi, G., and Hanaoka, C. (1955). *J. Biochem.* (*Tokyo*) **42**, 423–437.

Kedrowsky, B. (1930). *Protoplasma* **12**, 357–379.

Kehl, R., and Stich, W. (1952). *Z. Physiol. Chem.* **290**, 151–154.

Kehrer, E. (1907). *Arch. Gynaekol.* **81**, 129–159.

Kehrer, F. A. (1871). *Oesterr. Jahrb. Paediat.* **2**, 71–90.

Keilin, J. (1944). *Nature* **154**, 120.

Keilin, J. (1952). *Biochem. J.* **51**, 443–450.

Keilin, J. (1960). *Nature* **187**, 365–371.

Kelly, W. D., Lewis, J. H., and Davidson, C. S. (1946). *J. Lab. Clin. Med.* **31**, 1045–1049.

Kench, J. E. (1954). *Biochem. J.* **56**, 669–677.

Kench, J. E., and Varma, S. N. (1962). *S. African Med. J.* **36**, 794.

Kench, J. E., Gardikas, C., and Wilkinson, J. F. (1950). *Biochem. J.* **47**, 129–134.

Kench, J. E., Du Toit, F. E., and Green, M. (1963). *S. African J. Lab. Clin. Med.* **9**, 272–276.

Kennedy, G. Y., and Nicol, J. A. C. (1959). *Proc. Roy. Soc.* **B150**, 509–538.

Kerppola, W. (1936). *Acta Med. Scand.* **89**, 387–407.

Kerppola, W. (1942). *Acta Med. Scand.* **112**, 291–301.

Kerppola, W., and Leikola, E. (1931). *Acta Med. Scand.* **76**, 479–490.

Kerppola, W., and Leikola, E. (1932). *Acta Med. Scand.* **78**, 24–42.

Keyser, J. W., and Sanders, P. G. (1953). *Lancet* **I**, 422.

Kiaer, W. (1956). *Ugeskrift Laeger* **118**, 865–868.

Kiaer, W., and Olesen, M. (1956). *Ugeskrift Laeger* **118**, 868–872.

Kiener (no inits.) and Engel (no inits.) (1887). *Arch. Physiol. Norm. Pathol. (Paris)* [3] **10**, 198–224.

Kiener (no inits.) and Engel (no inits.) (1888). *Compt. Rend. Soc. Biol.* **40**, 678–681.

Kiese, M. (1942). *Klin. Wochschr.* **21**, 565–569.

Kiese, M. (1947a). *Arch. Exptl. Pathol. Pharmakol.* **204**, 190–202.

Kiese, M. (1947b). *Arch. Exptl. Pathol. Pharmakol.* **204**, 385–413.

Kiese, M. (1947c). *Arch. Exptl. Pathol. Pharmakol.* **204**, 439–445.

Kiese, M. (1948). *Arch. Exptl. Pathol. Pharmakol.* **205**, 747–758.

Kiese, M., and Kaeske, H. (1942). *Biochem. Z.* **312**, 121–149.

Kiese, M., and Seipelt, L. (1943). *Arch. Exptl. Pathol. Pharmakol.* **200**, 648–683.

Kikkawa, K. (1959a). *Okayama Igakkai Zasshi* **71**, 6321 (in Jap., Engl. summary).

Kikkawa, K. (1959b). *Okayama Igakkai Zasshi* **71**, 6323 (in Jap., Engl. summary).

Kikuchi, G., Michiko, M., and Saito, T. (1954). *J. Biochem. (Tokyo)* **41**, 227–237.

Kikuchi, K. (1961). *Japan. J. Exptl. Med.* **31**, 71–81.

Kilchling, H., and Kühn, H. A. (1950). *Med. Klin. (Munich)* **45**, 601–603.

Kilchling, H., and Kühn, H. A. (1951). *Z. Ges. Exptl. Med.* **117**, 481–496.

Killander, A., Michaëlsson, M., Müller-Eberhard, U., and Sjölin, S. (1963). *Acta Paediat.* **52**, 481–484.

Kimura, T. (1904). *Deut. Arch. Klin. Med.* **79**, 274–289.

Kimura, T. (1953). *Igaku Kenkyu* **23**, 581–591 (in Jap., Engl. summary).

King, E. J., and Coxon, R. V. (1950). *J. Clin. Pathol.* **3**, 248–259.

King, M. J., and Kerrins, J. F. (1963). *New Engl. J. Med.* **268**, 1180–1182.

Kingsbury, A. N. (1926). *Trans. Roy. Soc. Trop. Med. Hyg.* **19**, 459–481.

Kingsley, R., Getchell, G., and Schaffert, R. R. (1953). *In* "Standard Methods of Clinical Chemistry" (Am. Assoc. Clin. Chemists, eds.), Vol. I, pp. 11–15. Academic Press, New York.

Kirkman, H. N., Rosenthal, I. M., Simon, E. R., Carson, P. E., and Brinson, A. G. (1964a). *J. Lab. Clin. Med.* **63**, 715–725.

Kirkman, H. N., Schettini, F., and Pickard, B. M. (1964b). *J. Lab. Clin. Med.* **63**, 726–735.

Kirković, S., and Russew, R. (1927). *Med. Klin.* **23**, 172–173.

Kjellgren, K. (1955a). *Acta Soc. Med. Upsaliensis* **60**, 172–185.

Kjellgren, K. (1955b). *Acta Soc. Med. Upsaliensis* **60**, 199–223.

Klajman, A., and Efrati, P. (1955). *Lancet* **I**, 538–539.

Klatskin, G. (1961). *Ann. Rev. Med.* **12**, 211–250.

Klatskin, G., and Bungards, L. (1953). *New Engl. J. Med.* **248**, 712–717.

Klatskin, G., and Bungards, L. (1956). *J. Clin. Invest.* **35**, 537–551.

Klatskin, G., and Drill, V. A. (1950). *J. Clin. Invest.* **29**, 660–676.

Klein, F. (1942). *Schweiz. Med. Wochschr.* **23**, 73.

Klein, N., and Szentmihàlyi, S. (1932). *Deut. Arch. Klin. Med.* 173, 234–240.
Klein, O. (1931). *Klin. Wochschr.* 10, 2032–2035.
Klemperer, P. (1933). *N.Y. State Med. J.* 33, 1309–1317.
Klose (no inits.) and Wachsmuth, W. (1923). *Arch. Klin. Chir.* 123, 6–30.
Klotz, I. M. (1946). *J. Am. Chem. Soc.* 68, 2299–2304.
Klotz, I. M., Longfellow, I. M., and Johnson, O. H. (1946). *Science* 104, 264.
Knisely, M. H. (1949). Liver Injury. *Trans. 8th Conf.* pp. 9–17. Josiah Macy, Jr. Found., New York.
Knisely, M. H., Bloch, E. H., Warner, L. (1948). Selective Phagocytosis I. *Kgl. Danske Videnskab. Selskab, Biol. Skrifter* 4, No. 7 (93pp., Engl. text).
Knowlton, M. (1950). *J. Lab. Clin. Med.* 35, 328–329.
Knutti, R. E., Hawkins, W. R., and Whipple, G. H. (1935). *J. Exptl. Med.* 61, 127–138.
Koch, F., and Rind, H. (1962). *Klin. Wochschr.* 40, 1077.
Koch, J. (1927). Uber das Vorkommen des Bilirubins im Blutserum und des Urobilins in den Faeces von Rindern, Kälbern, Schafen und Schweinen. (Inaugural Dissertation (Vet.), U. of Zürich (34pp.).
Koch, W. (1928). *Muench. Tieraerztl. Wochschr.* 79, 557.
Kock, H. C. L. V., van Kessel, H. I. A. M., and Stolte, L. A. M. (1963). *Acta Physiol. Pharmacol. Neerl.* 12, 168–169.
Kodama, M. (1925). *Beitr. Pathol. Anat. Allgem. Pathol.* 73, 187–250.
Kodzuka, T. (1921). *Tohoku J. Exptl. Med.* 2, 287–289.
Kolpakov, Y. V. (1961). *Fisiol. Zh. Akad. Nauk Ukr. SSR* 7, 393–408 (quoted from *Biol. Abstr.* 38, No. 5442 (1962).
Komori, Y., and Iwao, C. (1928). *J. Biochem.* (*Tokyo*) 8, 195–204.
Komuda, J. (1959a). *Igaku Kenkyu* 29, 2764 (in Jap., Engl. summary).
Komuda, J. (1959b). *Igaku Kenkyu* 29, 2778 (in Jap., Engl. summary).
Kondo, T. (1959a). *Igaku Kenkyu* 29, 1120–1130 (in Jap., Engl. summary).
Kondo, T. (1959b). *Igaku Kenkyu* 29, 2678 (in Jap., Engl. summary).
Kopéc, M., Darocha, T., Niewiarowski, S., and Stachurska, J. (1961). *J. Clin. Pathol.* 14, 478–480.
Kornberg, A. (1942). *J. Clin. Invest.* 21, 299–308.
Kosaka, Y. (1959a). *Igaku Kenkyu* 29, 2652 (in Jap., Engl. summary).
Kosaka, Y. (1959b). *Igaku Kenkyu* 29, 2671 (in Jap., Engl. summary).
Koumans, J., and De Groote, J. (1961). *Tijdschr. Gastroenterol.* 4, 151.
Kramer, P. H. (1926). *Ned. Tijdschr. Geneesk.* 70, 249–253.
Krane, K. (1936). Bilirubinbelastungen bei Graviden. Inaugural Dissertation (Med.), U. of Jena (18pp.).
Krarup, N. B., and Roholm, K. (1941). *Klin. Wochschr.* 20, 193–196.
Kraus, G. E., and Beltram, A. (1959). *AMA Arch. Surg.* 79, 769.
Krebs, J., and Brauer, R. W. (1949). *Federation Proc.* 8, 310.
Kristoffersen, M. (1964). *Nord. Med.* 72, 1042–1046.
Krokiewicz, A., and Batko, R. W. (1898). *Wien. Klin. Wochschr.* 48, 173–174.
Kronholm, V. (1960). *World Neurol.* 2, 425–441.
Kronholm, V. (1961). *Acta Psychiat. Neurol. Scand.* Suppl. 150, 323–326.
Kronholm, V. (1962). *Ugeskrift Laeger* 124, 74–78.
Kronholm, V., and Lintrup, J. (1960). *Acta Psych. Neurol. Scand.* 35, 314–329.
Kronholm, V., and Lintrup, J. (1961). *Danish Med. Bull.* 8, 47–50.
Krueger, H., and Higginson, J. (1961). *Proc. Soc. Exptl. Biol. Med.* 107, 43–47.
Krukenberg, C. F. W. (1882a). *Untersuch. Physiol. Inst. Univ. Heidelberg* 2, 1–45.

Krukenberg, C. F. W. (1882b). "Vergleichend-Physiologische Studien," Vol. 2, Sect. 3, pp. 72–87. Carl Winther, Heidelberg.

Krukenberg, C. F. W. (1883a). *Verhandl. Phys. Med. Ges. Wuerzburg* 17, 109–127.

Krukenberg, C. F. W. (1883b). *Zentr. Med. Wiss.* 21, 785–787.

Krumholz, W. (1945). Die erythropoetische Funktion des Bilirubins insbesonderen beim Ikterus. Inaugural Dissertation (Med.), U. of Basel (32pp.).

Kübler, W. (1959). *Klin. Wochschr.* 37, 43–44.

Kühl, G. (1924a). *Arch. Exptl. Pathol. Pharmakol.* 103, 247–259.

Kühl, G. (1924b). *Deut. Arch. Klin. Med.* 144, 331–338.

Kühle, E. (1926). Versuche über den Nachweis von Gallenfarbstoffe im Harn bei lebergesunden und leberkranken Schlachtrindern. Inaugural Dissertation (Vet.), Friedrich Wilhelm U. (25pp.).

Kühn, H. A. (1947a). *Beitr. Path. Anat. Allgem. Pathol.* 103, 589–649.

Kühn, H. A. (1947b). *FIAT Rev. Ger. Sci., Spec. Pathol. Issue* I, 71–81.

Kühn, H. A. (1948). *Aertzl. Forsch.* 2, 389–395.

Kühn, H. A. (1950). *Z. Ges. Exptl. Med.* 115, 371–385.

Kühn, H. A. (1959). *Handb. Allgem. Pathol.* 5, Pt. 2, 390–485.

Kühn, H. A. (1962). *Acta Hepato-Splenol.* 9, 229–245.

Kühn, H. A. (1963). *Ger. Med. Monthly* 8, 185–188.

Kühn, H. A., and Beck, K. (1951). *Klin. Wochschr.* 29, 27.

Kühn, H. A., and Beck, K. (1955). *Deut. Med. Wochschr.* 80, 1105–1106.

Kühn, H. A., and Hildebrand, G. (1951). *Klin. Wochschr.* 29, 785–786.

Kühn, H. A., Schneider, R., and Spitzmüller, I. (1954). *Z. Exptl. Med.* 124, 52–64.

Kühn, H. A., Beck, K., and Deppe, E. (1958). *Gastroenterologia* Suppl. to Vol. 90, pp. 101–106.

Künzer, W. (1951a). "Über den Blutfarbstoffwechsel gesunder Säuglinge und Kinder." Karger, Basel (86pp.).

Künzer, W. (1951b). *Z. Kinderheilk.* 70, 133–135.

Künzer, W., Zanner, J., and Zeisel, H. (1950). *Klin. Wochschr.* 28, 681–683.

Kuenzle, C., Sommerhalder, M., Maier, C., and Rüttner, J. R. (1963a). *Rev. Intern. Hepatol.* 13, 225–232.

Kuenzle, C., Sommerhalder, M., Maier, C., and Rüttner, J. R. (1963b). *Schweitz. Med. Wochschr.* 93, 695.

Kuenzle, C., Maier, C., and Rüttner, J. R. (1964a). *Pathol. Microbiol.* 27, 410–418.

Kuenzle, C., Sommerhalder, M., Maier, C., and Rüttner, J. R. (1964b). *Deut. Med. Wochschr.* 89, 1475–1477.

Küster, W. (1899). *Ber. Deut. Chem. Ges.* 32, 677–682.

Küster, W. (1906). *Z. Physiol. Chem.* 47, 294–326.

Küster, W. (1909). *Z. Physiol. Chem.* 59, 63–95.

Küster, W. (1912). *Z. Physiol. Chem.* 82, 463–483.

Küster, W. (1915). *Z. Physiol. Chem.* 94, 136–162.

Küster, W. (1917). *Z. Physiol. Chem.* 99, 86–130.

Küster, W. (1922a). *Z. Physiol. Chem.* 121, 80–93.

Küster, W. (1922b). *Z. Physiol. Chem.* 121, 94–109.

Küster, W. (1922c). *Handb. Biol. Arbeitsmeth.* (*Abderhaldens*) Sect. I, Pt. 8, 321–330.

Küster, W., Reihling, K., and Schmeidel, R. (1914). *Z. Physiol. Chem.* 91, 58–77.

Kützing, F. T. (1843). *Phycologia Generalis.* F. A. Brockhaus, Leipzig (458pp.), (quoted in Fujiwara, 1955, pp. 411, 417).

Kugel, M. A., and Lichtman, S. S. (1933). *AMA Arch. Internal Med.* 52, 16–29.

Kunde, F. (1850). De hepatis ranum extirpatione. Inaugural Dissertation (Med.), U. of Berlin (21pp.).

Kunkel, A. (1875). *Ber Verhandl. Koenigl. Saechs. Ges. Wiss. Leipzig, Mat.-Phys. Cl.* 27, 232–251.

Kunkel, A. (1880). *Arch. Pathol. Anat. Physiol.* 79, 455–465.

Kupershtein, A. P., and Roomere, P. A. (1962). *Lab. Delo* 8, 29–34.

Kutlik, I. E. (1957). *Acta Histochem.* 4, 141–157.

Labbe, R. F., Zaske, M. R., and Aldrich, R. A. (1959). *Science* 12, 1741–1742.

Ladage, A. A. (1899). Bijdrage tot de kennis de urobilinurie. Akad. Proefschrift (Geneesk.), U. of Leiden (84pp.).

Laemmer, M., and Beck, J. (1934). *Presse Med.* 42, 858–860.

Laguna, J. (1951). *Acta Med. Scand.* 140, 57–62.

Laks, M. M., Pincus, I. J., and Goldberg, D. (1963). *Gastroenterology* 44, 469–474.

Lambrechts, A., and Barac, G. (1939). *Bull. Soc. Chim. Biol.* 21, 1171–1180.

Lancet (1963a). Lead article, II, 179–180.

Lancet (1963b). Annonation, II, 394.

Lancet (1963c). Lead article, II, 818–819.

Lancet (1964). Annonation, I, 1090.

Lang, K. (1952). "Der intermediäre Stoffwechsel." Springer, Berlin (423pp.).

Lange, R. D., and Akeroyd, F. H. (1958). *Blood* 13, 950.

Langhans, T. (1870). *Arch Pathol. Anat. Physiol.,* 49, 66–116.

Laniez, G. (1950). *Biol. Med.* 39, 117–195.

Lanzkron, G. (1888). Über Urobilinurie und Urobilinikterus. Inaugural Dissertation (Med.). U. of Würzburg (36pp.).

Larsen, E. H., and With, T. K. (1943). *Acta Paediat.* 31, 153–179.

Larson, E. A., and Watson, C. J. (1949). *J. Clin. Invest.* 28, 452–464.

Larson, E. A., Evans, G. T., and Watson, C. J. (1947). *J. Lab. Clin. Med.* 32, 481–488.

Laschi, R. (1963). *Sperimentale* 113, 115–118.

Lassen, N. A., and Thomsen, Å. C. (1957). *Ugeskrift Laeger* 119, 1032–1035.

Lathe, G. H. (1955). *Brit. Med. J.* I, 192.

Lathe, G. H. (1956). *Lancet* II, 683–684.

Lathe, G. H., and Ruthven, C. R.-J (1958). *J. Clin. Pathol.* 11, 155–162.

Lathe, G. H., and Walker, M. (1957a). *Biochem. J.* 67, 9P.

Lathe, G. H., and Walker, M. (1957b). *Biochem. J.* 68, 6P.

Lathe, G. H., and Walker, M. (1958a). *Biochem. J.* 70, 705–711.

Lathe, G. H., and Walker, M. (1958b). *Quart. J. Exptl. Pathol.* 43, 257–265.

Lattanzi, A. (1948a). *Rass. Fisiopatol. Clin. Terap.* 20, 245–266.

Lattanzi, A. (1948b). *Rass. Fisiopatol. Clin. Terap.* 20, 267–280.

Lattanzi, A. (1948c). *Rass. Fisiopatol. Clin. Terap.* 20, Suppl. 1, 1–47.

Lattanzi, A. (1948d). *Rass. Fisiopatol. Clin. Terap.* 20, Suppl. 1, 48–62.

Lattanzi, A. (1948e). *Rass. Fisiopatol. Clin. Terap.* 20, Suppl. 1, 63–84.

Lattanzi, A. (1948f). *Rass. Fisiopatol. Clin. Terap.* 20, Suppl. 1, 85–99.

Lauda, E. (1925). *Arch. Pathol. Anat. Physiol.* 258, 529–599.

Lauda, E. (1928). *Ergeb. Inn. Med. Kinderheilk.* 34, 1–110.

Laudicella, V. (1948). *Arch. Ital. Chir.* 70, 91–109.

Lauersen, F., and Sauerbruch, F. (1936). *Klin. Wochschr.* 15, 1137–1138.

Laurell, C. B. (1953). *Scand. J. Clin. Lab. Invest.* 5, 118–121.

Laurence, K. M., and Abbot, A. L. (1956). *J. Clin. Pathol.* 9, 270.

Lavier, G. (1937). *Compt. Rend. Soc. Biol.* 124, 1206–1208.

Lazard, F., and Sobotka, H. (1962). *Life Sciences* 1, 771–774.

Lederer, E. (1940). *Biol. Rev. Cambridge Phil. Soc.* 15, 273–306.

Lederer, E., and Huttrer, C. (1942). *Bull. Soc. Chim. Biol.* 24, 1055–1061.

Lederer, E., Teissier, G., and Huttrer, C. (1940). *Bull. Soc. Chim. France* [5] 7, 608–615.

Lee, C., Tink, A., Robin, H., and Harley, J. (1961). *Med. J. Australia* 2, 313.

Lee, T.-C., and Hsia, D. Y. Y. (1959). *J. Lab. Clin. Med.* 54, 512–524.

Lees, H., and Ruthven, C. R.-J. (1959). *Lancet* II, 371–373.

Leevy, C. M. (1961). "Progress in Liver Diseases" (H. Popper and F. Schaffner, eds.), pp. 174–186. Grune & Stratton, New York.

Leevy, C. M., Bender, J., Silverberg, M., and Naylor, J. (1963). *Ann. N.Y. Acad. Sci.* 111, 161–174.

Legge, J. W. (1949). *Biochem. J.* 44, 105–111.

Legge, J. W., and Lemberg, R. (1941). *Biochem. J.* 35, 353–362.

Legge, J. W., and Roughton, F. J. W. (1950). *Biochem. J.* 47, 43–52.

Leibnitz, L. (1964). *Wiss. Z. Karl-Marx-Univ. Leipzig, Math.-Naturw. Reihe Math.* 13, 151–152.

Lelong, M. D., Fleury, J., Alagille, D., Malassenet, R., Lortholary, P., and Para, M. (1961). *Nouvelle Rev. Franc. Hematol.* 1, 819–831.

Lelong, M. D., Alagille, D., and Odièvre, M. (1964). *Nouvelle Rev. Franc. Hematol.* 4, 110–125.

Lemaire, L. (1905). L'urobiline, sa valeur séméiologique. Thesis (Med.), U. of Paris (201pp).

Lemberg, R. (1928). *Ann. Chem. (Liebigs)* 461, 46–89.

Lemberg, R. (1929a). *Naturwissenschaften* 17, 541.

Lemberg, R. (1929b). *Naturwissenschaften* 17, 878.

Lemberg, R. (1930a). *Biochem. Z.* 219, 255–257.

Lemberg, R. (1930b). *Ann. Chem. (Liebigs)* 477, 195–245.

Lemberg, R. (1931a). *Ann. Chem. (Liebigs)* 488, 74–90.

Lemberg, R. (1931b). *Z. Physiol. Chem.* 200, 173–178.

Lemberg, R. (1932). *Ann. Chem. (Liebigs)* 499, 25–40.

Lemberg, R. (1934a). *Nature* 134, 422.

Lemberg, R. (1934b). *J. Soc. Chem. Ind.* 53, 179.

Lemberg, R. (1934c). *J. Soc. Chem. Ind.* 53, 1024.

Lemberg, R. (1934d). *Biochem. J.* 28, 978–987.

Lemberg, R. (1935). *Biochem. J.* 29, 1332–1335.

Lemberg, R. (1938). *Ann. Rev. Biochem.* 7, 421–448.

Lemberg, R. (1942). *Australian J. Exptl. Biol. Med. Sci.* 20, 111–115.

Lemberg, R. (1943). *Australian J. Exptl. Biol. Med. Sci.* 21, 239–247.

Lemberg, R. (1949). *Nature* 163, 97.

Lemberg, R. (1956). *Rev. Pure Appl. Chem.* 6, 1–23.

Lemberg, R., and Bader, G. (1933a). *Naturwissenschaften* 21, 206.

Lemberg, R., and Bader, G. (1933b). *Ann. Chem. (Liebigs)* 505, 151–177.

Lemberg, R., and Barcroft, J. (1932). *Proc. Roy. Soc.* B110, 362–372.

Lemberg, R., and Legge, J. W. (1942). *Australian J. Exptl. Biol. Med. Sci.* 20, 65–68.

Lemberg, R., and Legge, J. W. (1949). "Haematin Compounds and Bile Pigments." Wiley (Interscience), New York (749pp.).

Lemberg, R., and Purdon, P. (1949). *Abstr. 1st Intern. Congr. Biochem., Cambridge* p. 348. Cambridge Univ. Press, London and New York.

Lemberg, R., Cortis-Jones, B., and Norrie, M. (1937a). *Nature* 139, 1016–1017.

Lemberg, R., Cortis-Jones, B., and Norrie, M. (1937b). *Nature* **140**, 65–66.
Lemberg, R., Cortis-Jones, B., and Norrie, M. (1938a). *Biochem. J.* **32**, 149–170.
Lemberg, R., Cortis-Jones, B., and Norrie, M. (1938b). *Biochem. J.* **32**, 171–186.
Lemberg, R., Lockwood, W. H., and Wyndham, R. A. (1938c). *Australian J. Exptl. Biol. Med. Sci.* **16**, 169–180.
Lemberg, R., Legge, J. W., and Lockwood, W. H. (1939). *Biochem. J.* **33**, 754–758.
Lemberg, R., Legge, J. W., and Lockwood, W. H. (1941a). *Biochem. J.* **35**, 328–338.
Lemberg, R., Legge, J. W., and Lockwood, W. H. (1941b). *Biochem. J.* **35**, 339–352.
Lemberg, R., Lockwood, W. H., and Legge, J. W. (1941c). *Biochem. J.* **35**, 363–379.
Lemberg, R., Holden, H. F., Legge, J. W., and Lockwood, W. H. (1942). *Australian J. Exptl. Biol.* **20**, 161–167.
Lepehne, G. (1917). *Beitr. Pathol. Anat. Allgem. Pathol.* **64**, 55–126.
Lepehne, G. (1920). *Deut. Arch. Klin. Med.* **132**, 96–120.
Lepehne, G. (1921a). *Deut. Arch. Klin. Med.* **135**, 79–121.
Lepehne, G. (1921b). *Deut. Arch. Klin. Med.* **136**, 88–111.
Lepehne, G. (1921c). *Ergeb. Inn. Med. Kinderheilk.* **20**, 221–280.
Lepehne, G. (1921d). *Deut. Arch. Klin. Med.* **137**, 78–89.
Lepehne, G. (1923). *Deut. Med. Wochschr.* **49**, 641–643.
Lepehne, G. (1930). *Folia Haematol.* (*Leipzig*) **39**, 277–366.
Lepehne, G. (1932). *Handb. Biol. Arbeitsmeth.* (*Abderhaldens*) Sect. IV, Pt. 6, 989–1048.
Lepehne, G. (1942a). *J. Lab. Clin. Med.* **27**, 1447–1457.
Lepehne, G. (1942b). *J. Lab. Clin. Med.* **28**, 229–232.
Léreboullet, M. P. (1901). *Compt. Rend. Soc. Biol.* **53**, 988–990.
Leschke, E. (1921a). *Berlin Klin. Wochschr.* **58**, 848.
Leschke, E. (1921b). *Deut. Med. Wochschr.* **47**, 376–377.
Lesieurs (no inits.), Monod (no inits.), and Morel, A. (1908). *Compt. Rend. Soc. Biol.* **64**, 343–344.
Lester, R. (1963). *Ann. N.Y. Acad. Sci.* **111**, (Art. 1), 290–293.
Lester, R., and Schmid, R. (1961). *J. Lab. Clin. Med.* **58**, 938 (Proc.).
Lester, R., and Schmid, R. (1962). *J. Clin. Invest.* **41**, 1379.
Lester, R., and Schmid, R. (1963a). *J. Clin. Invest.* **42**, 736.
Lester, R. and Schmid, R. (1963b). *New Engl. J. Med.* **269**, 178–182.
Lester, R., and Schmid, R. (1964). *Nature* **201**, 711–712.
Lester, R, Ostrow, J. D., and Schmid, R. (1961). *Nature* **192**, 372.
Lester, R., Hammaker, L., and Schmid, R. (1962). *Lancet* **II**, 1257.
Létienne, A. (1891). De la bile a l'état pathologique. Thesis (Med.), U. of Paris (132pp.).
Leube (no inits.) (1888). *Sitzungsber. Phys.-Med. Ges. Wuertzburg*, pp. 120–122.
Leupold, E. (1914). *Beitr. Path. Anat. Allgem. Pathol.* **59**, 501–519.
Levison, A., Greengard, J., and Lifvendahl, R. (1926). *Am. J. Diseases Children* **32**, 208–218.
Levy, M. (1890). *Z. Biol.* **27**, 398–414.
Lewin, C. (1928). *In* "Spezielle Pathologie und Therapie innerer Krankheiten" (T. Brugsch, ed.), Suppl. 2, pp. 545–593. Urban & Schwarzenberg, Berlin.
Lewis, A. E., and Gershow, J. (1961). *J. Appl. Physiol.* **16**, 1140–1141.

Leyden, E. (1866). "Beiträge zur Pathologie des Ikterus." Hirschwald, Berlin.
Li, T. W., Snapp, F. E., Hough, V. H., and Ivy, A. C. (1944). *Federation Proc.* **3**, 29–30.
Libowitzky, H. (1940a). *Z. Physiol. Chem.* **263**, 267–271.
Libowitzky, H. (1940b). *Z. Physiol. Chem.* **265**, 191–209.
Lichtenstein, A., Terwen, A. J. L. (1925). *Deut. Arch. Klin. Med.* **149**, 102–112.
Lichtman, S. S. (1941). *Ann. Internal Med.* **14**, 1199–1215.
Lichtman, S. S. (1942). "Diseases of the Liver, Gallbladder and Bile Ducts," 1st ed. Lea & Febiger, Philadelphia, Pennsylvania (906pp.).
Lichtman, S. S. (1949). "Diseases of the Liver, Gallbladder and Bile Ducts," 2nd ed. Lea & Febiger, Philadelphia, Pennsylvania (1135pp.).
Lichtman, S. S. (1954). "Diseases of the Liver, Gallbladder and Bile Ducts," 3rd ed. Lea & Febiger, Philadelphia, Pennsylvania (2 vols.) (1315pp.).
Liébecq, C. (1946). *Actualites Biochim.* **7**, 5–64.
Liébecq, C. (1947). *Bull. Soc. Chim. Biol.* **29**, 52–54.
Liébecq, C. (1948). *Experientia* **4**, 56–59.
Liébecq, C., Delbrouck, J., and Prijot, E. (1946). *Compt. Rend. Soc. Biol.* **140**, 1169–1171.
Liébecq, C., Delbrouck, J., and Prijot, E. (1947). *Bull. Soc. Chim. Biol.* **29**, 71–81.
Lieberkühn, N. (1889). *Arch. Anat. Physiol. Entwicklungsges.* pp. 196–212.
Liebermann, C. (1878). *Ber. Deut. Chem. Ges.* **11**, 606–610.
Lignac, G. O. C. (1923). *Arch. Pathol. Anat. Physiol.* **243**, 273–297.
Lin, H., and Eastman, N. J. (1937). *Am. J. Obstet. Gynecol.* **33**, 317–324.
Lind, J. (1963). *Ann. N.Y. Acad. Sci.* **111** (Art. 1), 110–120.
Lindberg, H. A., and Le Roy, G. V. (1947). *AMA Arch. Internal Med.* **80**, 175–184.
Linde, S. (1958). *Scand. J. Clin. Lab. Invest.* **10**, 308–309.
Lingjaerde, O. (1934). Leberuntersuchungen bei Geisteskranken unter besonderer Berücksichtigung des Verhältnisses von Krankheitsverlauf, Leberfunktion und Nahrungszufuhr bei Schizophrenen. *Acta. Psychiat. Neurol. Suppl.* **5** (319pp.).
Linneweh, F., and Bickel, H. (1959). *Klin. Wochschr.* **37**, 963–966.
Lins, M. de Barros (1949). Contribução para o emprêgo de sulfanilamida e sulfa derivados na reação de van den Bergh e na dasagem da bilirrubina. Dissertation (Med.), U. of Recife, Brazil (50pp.).
Lins, M. de Barros (1950). *J. Med. Pernambuco* (quoted from reprint).
Lins, M. de Barros (1951). *Arquiv. Biol.* (*Sao Paulo*) **34**, 78–81.
Lins, M. de Barros (1952). *Arquiv. Biol.* (*Sao Paulo*) **35**, (quoted from reprint).
Lins, M. de Barros (1953). *Arquiv. Biol.* (*Sao Paulo*) **37**, 94.
Lins, M. de Barros (1954). "Contribução para o estudo dos complexos bilirubino-protidicos do sangüe pela eletroforese e cromatografia em papel." Recife, Brasil (104pp.).
Lins, M. de Barros (1957). *Anales Fac. Med. Recife* **17**, 261–263 (Engl. summary).
Lipp, H. (1942). *Muench. Med. Wochschr.* **89**, 627–628.
Ljung, O. (1948). *Nord. Med.* **39**, 1456–1459.
Löwitt, M. (1889). *Beitr. Pathol. Anat. Allgem. Pathol.* **4**, 225–264.
Loiseleur, J., and Petit, M. (1963). *Compt. Rend. Soc. Biol.* **157**, 1164–1165.
London, I. M. (1950). *J. Biol. Chem.* **184**, 373–376.
London, I. M., and West, R. (1950). *J. Biol. Chem.* **184**, 359–364.
London, I. M., West, R., and Rittenberg, D. (1948). *Federation Proc.* **7**, 169.
London, I. M., West, R., and Rittenberg, D. (1949). *J. Biol. Chem.* **179**, 463–484.
London, I. M., West, R., and Rittenberg, D. (1950a). *J. Biol. Chem.* **184**, 351–358.

Bibliography

London, I. M., West, R., and Rittenberg, D. (1950b). *J. Biol. Chem.* **184**, 365–371.
London, I. M., Yamasaki, M., and Sabella, A. G. (1951). *Federation Proc.* **10**, 217.
Loosmore, R. M., and Harding, J. D. J. (1961). *Vet. Record* **73**, 1362–1363.
Loosmore, R. M., and Markson, L. M. (1961). *Vet. Record* **73**, 813–814.
Lopez Garcia, A. (1941). *Medicina (Buenos Aires)* **1**, 219–248.
Lopez Garcia, A. (1943). "El sindrome coledociano." Libreria Hachette, Buenos Aires (327pp.).
Lopez Garcia, A., and Zelasco, J. F. (1942). *Medicina (Buenos Aires)* **3**, 7–29.
Lopez Garcia, A., Zelasco, J. F., and Pedace, E. A. (1943). *Anales Inst. Invest. Fis. (Buenos Aires)* **5**, 13–58.
López Pontes, J. P. (1938). Valor semiológico da urobilinuria. Thesis (Med.), U. of Rio de Janeiro (quoted from Lopez Garcia, 1943).
López Pontes, J. P. (1947). *Rev. Brasil. Med.* **4**, 883–888.
Lottsfeldt, F. I., Krivit, W., Aust, J. B., and Carey, J. B. (1963). *New Engl. J. Med.* **269**, 186–189.
Lowry, P. T., and Hawkinson, V. (1950). *J. Clin. Invest.* **29**, 831.
Lowry, P. T., Hawkinson, V., and Watson, C. J. (1952). *Metab. Clin. Exptl.* **1**, 149–154.
Lowry, P. T., Bossenmaier, I., and Watson, C. J. (1953). *J. Biol. Chem.* **202**, 305–309.
Lowry, P. T., Ziegler, N. R., Cardinal, R., and Watson, C. J. (1954). *J. Biol. Chem.* **208**, 543–548.
Lowry, P. T., Cardinal, P., Collins, S., and Watson, C. J. (1956). *J. Biol. Chem.* **218**, 641–646.
Lozzio, B. B., and Royer, M. (1962). *Rev. Soc. Arg. Biol.* **38**, 8–23.
Lozzio, B. B., Accame, E., Colombato, L., and Royer, M. (1963a). *Medicina (Buenos Aires)* **23**, 236–238.
Lozzio, B. B., Colombato, L., Accame, E., Perez, V., and Royer, M. (1963b). *Medicina (Buenos Aires)* **23**, 239–244.
Lozzio, B. B., Garay, E. R., and Royer, M. (1964a). *Gastroenterologia* **101**, 150–162.
Lozzio, B. B., Gorodisch, S., and Royer, M. (1964b). *Clin. Chim. Acta* **9**, 78–81.
Lubarsch, O. (1921). *Berlin. Klin. Wochschr.* **38**, 757–762.
Lubarsch, O. (1925). *Handb. Spez. Pathol. Anat. Histol.* **6**, Pt. I, 555.
Lucas, W. P., Dearing, B. F., Hoobler, H. R., Cox, A., Jones, M. R., and Smyth, F. S. (1922). *Am. J. Diseases Children* **22**, 525–559.
Lucké, B. (1944a). *Am. J. Pathol.* **20**, 471–494.
Lucké, B. (1944b). *Am. J. Pathol.* **20**, 595–620.
Lucké, B., and Mallory, T. (1946). *Am. J. Pathol.* **22**, 867–945.
Ludwig, G. D., Blakemore, W. S., and Drabkin, D. L. (1957). *Biochem. J.* **66**, 38P.
Lups, S., and Francke, C. (1947). *Acta Med. Scand.* **129**, 234–256.
Lups, S., and Meyer, F. D. G. (1946). *Acta Med. Scand.* **126**, 85–96.
Macaulay, D. (1951). *Arch. Disease Childhood* **26**, 241–244.
McCance, R. A. (1950). *Am. J. Med.* **9**, 229–241.
McCance, R. A., and Young, W. F. (1941). *J. Physiol. (London)* **99**, 265–282.
McCarrel, J. D., Thayer, S., and Drinker, K. (1941). *Am. J. Physiol.* **133**, 79–81.
McDonald, R. K., and Kelley, V. C. (1947). *Am. J. Clin. Pathol.* **18**, 87–88.
Macfadyen, A., Nencki, M., and Sieber, N. (1891). *Arch. Exptl. Pathol. Pharmakol.* **28**, 311–350.
McFarlane, D., Evans, J. V., and Reid, C. S. W. (1959). *New Zealand J. Agr. Res.* **2**, 194–200.

McGann, C. J., and Carter, R. E. (1960). *J. Pediat.* **57**, 199.

McGill, D. B., Hoffman, H. N., and Bollman, J. L. (1962). *Gastroenterology* **43**, 261–265.

McGowan, J. M. (1935). *Proc. Staff. Meetings Mayo Clin.* **10**, 535–567.

McGowan, J. M. (1936). Effect of Toluylendiamine on the Excretion of Bile Salts. Dissertation (Med.), U. of Minnesota (quoted in C. J. Watson, 1938, p. 2466).

Mackay, E. V., and Watson, D. (1962). *Med. J. Australia* **49**, 942–944.

MacLagan, N. F. (1946). *Brit. J. Exptl. Pathol.* **27**, 190–200.

Maclay, E., and Osterberg, A. E. (1944). *Proc. Staff. Meetings Mayo Clin.* **19**, 4–5.

MacLean, J. R., Lucey, J. F., and Harris, R. C. (1955). *Am. J. Diseases Children* **90**, 573.

McMaster, P. D., and Elman, R. (1925a). *J. Exptl. Med.* **41**, 513–534.

McMaster, P. D., and Elman, R. (1925b). *J. Exptl. Med.* **41**, 719–738.

McMaster, P. D., and Elman, R. (1926). *J. Exptl. Med.* **43**, 753–773.

McMaster, P. D., and Elman, R. (1927). *Ann. Internal Med.* **1**, 68–73.

McMaster, P. D., and Rous, P. (1921). *J. Exptl. Med.* **33**, 731–750.

McMaster, P. D., Broun, G. O., and Rous, P. (1923a). *J. Exptl. Med.* **37**, 395–420.

McMaster, P. D., Broun, G. O., and Rous, P. (1923b). *J. Exptl. Med.* **37**, 685–698.

MacMunn, C. A. (1880a). *Proc. Roy. Soc.* **31**, 26–37.

MacMunn, C. A. (1880b). *Proc. Roy. Soc.* **31**, 206–237.

MacMunn, C. A. (1883a). *Proc. Roy. Soc.* **35**, 132–134.

MacMunn, C. A. (1883b). *Proc. Roy. Soc.* **35**, 370–403.

MacMunn, C. A. (1885a). *Nature* **32**, 68–69.

MacMunn, C. A. (1885b). *Phil. Trans. Roy. Soc.* **176**, 641–663.

MacMunn, C. A. (1885c). *J. Physiol. (London)* **6**, 22–39.

MacMunn, C. A. (1889). *J. Physiol. (London)* **10**, 71–121.

MacMunn, C. A. (1899). *J. Physiol. (London)* **24**, 1–10.

McNee, J. W. (1913). *Med. Klin.* **9**, 1125–1129.

McNee, J. W. (1914). *J. Pathol. Bacteriol.* **18**, 325–342.

McNee, J. W. (1922). *Brit. Med. J.* **I**, 716.

McNee, J. W. (1923). *Quart. J. Med.* **16**, 390–420.

McNee, J. W. (1924). *Brit. Med. J.* **II**, 495–498.

McNee, J. W., and Keefer, C. S. (1925). *Brit. Med. J.* **II**, 52–54.

MacRae, D. J. (1952). *Proc. Roy. Soc. Med.* **45**, 439 (Clin. Sect. p. 17).

Maddock, S., and Svedberg, A. (1938). *Am. J. Physiol.* **121**, 203–308.

Maddock, W. G., Coller, F. A., and Pedersen, S. (1936). *Western J. Surg.* **44**, 513–521.

Madel, M. (1947). *Z. Ges. Inn. Med. Grenzgebiete* **2**, 659–665.

Maeda, T., and Morishima, T. (1929). *Japan. J. Gastroenterol.* **1**, 155–157.

Maga, Y. (1956a). *Igaku Kenkyu* **26**, 2056 (in Jap., Engl. summary).

Maga, Y. (1956b). *Igaku Kenkyu* **26**, 2062 (in Jap., Engl. summary).

Maga, Y. (1956c). *Igaku Kenkyu* **26**, 2070 (in Jap., Engl. summary).

Maggiore, Q., Niccolai, L., and Giovannetti, S. (1961a). *Ital. J. Biochem.* **10**, 329–332.

Maggiore, Q., Vivaldi, G., Niccolai, L., and Giovannetti, S. (1961b). *Ital. J. Biochem.* **10**, 319–328.

Maher, F. T. (1941). *Science* **94**, 398.

Maier, C., and Rüttner, J. R. (1955). *Schweiz. Med. Wochschr.* **85**, 445–448.

Maier, C., and Schwartz, K. J. (1953). *Praxis (Bern)* **142**, 156–158.

Maini, G. (1940). *Giorn. Clin. Med.* **21**, 401–414.

Makino, J. (1924). *Beitr. Pathol. Anat. Allgem. Pathol.* **72**, 808–859.

Malach (1913). Zur Frage der Bedeutung der alimentären Laevolusurie und der Urobilinuria für die Bestimmung der funktionellen Leberinsuffizienz bei chronischer Lungentuberkulose. Inaugural Dissertation (Med.), U. of Basel (28pp.).

Malloy, H. T., and Evelyn, K. A. (1937). *J. Biol. Chem.* **119**, 481–490.

Malloy, H. T., and Evelyn, K. A. (1938). *J. Biol. Chem.* **122**, 597–603.

Malloy, H. T., and Loewenstein, L. (1940). *Can. Med. Assoc. J.* **42**, 112–125.

Maly, R. (1868). *J. Prakt. Chem.* **104**, 28–41.

Maly, R. (1869). *Sitzungsber. Kaiserl. Akad. Wiss. Wien* **59**, Pt. II, 597–606.

Maly, R. (1871a). *Zentr. Med. Wiss.* **9**, 840–850.

Maly, R. (1871b). *Ann. Chem. (Liebigs)* **161**, 368–370.

Maly, R. (1879). *Arch. Ges. Physiol. (Pfluegers)* **20**, 331–338.

Mandel, M., and Decroly, P. (1964). *Nature* **201**, 290.

Mandema, E., de Fraiture, W. H., Nieweg, H. O., and Arens, A. (1960). *Am. J. Med.* **28**, 42–50.

Mandema, E., de Fraiture, W. H., Nieweg, H. O., and Arens, A. (1961). *Ned. Tijdschr. Geneesk.* **105**, 917–924.

Mann, F. C. (1921). *Am. J. Med. Sci.* **161**, 37–42.

Mann, F. C. (1925). *J. Am. Med. Assoc.* **85**, 1472–1475.

Mann, F. C. (1941). *J. Am. Med. Assoc.* **117**, 1577–1582.

Mann, F. C., and Bollman, J. L. (1926). *AMA Arch. Pathol.* **1**, 681–710.

Mann, F. C., and Bollman, J. L. (1935). *J. Am. Med. Assoc.* **104**, 371–374.

Mann, F. C., and Magath, T. B. (1924). *Ergeb. Physiol.* **23**, 212–273.

Mann, F. C., Bollman, J. L., and Magath, T. B. (1924). *Am. J. Physiol.* **69**, 393–409.

Mann, F. C., Sheard, C., Bollman, J. L., and Baldes, E. J. (1925). *Am. J. Physiol.* **74**, 497–500.

Mann, F. C., Sheard, C., Bollman, J. L., and Baldes, E. J. (1926a). *Am. J. Physiol.* **76**, 306–315.

Mann, F. C., Sheard, C., Bollman, J. L., and Baldes, E. J. (1926b). *Am. J. Physiol.* **77**, 219–224.

Mann, J. D., and Koler, R. D. (1951). *Gastroenterology* **17**, 400–405.

Manson, J. S. (1928). *Brit. Med. J.* **I**, 131–132.

Marcussen, S., and Hansen, S. (1918a). *J. Biol. Chem.* **36**, 381–389.

Marcussen, S., and Hansen, S. (1918b). *Ugeskrift Laeger* **80**, 16–23.

Marfori-Savini, L., Stefanini, M., and Bramante, P. (1946). *Policlinico (Rome), Sez. Med.* **53**, 243–273.

Marfori-Savini, L., Stefanini, M., and Bramante, P. (1947). *Am. J. Med. Sci.* **213**, 150–152.

Margadant, F. (1961). *Helv. Med. Acta* **28**, 667–680.

Markowitz, J., Yater, W. M., and Burrows, W. H. (1933). *J. Lab. Clin. Med.* **18**, 1271–1278.

Markson, L. M. (1960). *Proc. Roy. Soc. Med.* **53**, 283–284.

Marshall, F. H. A., and Halman, E. T. (1945). "Physiology of Farm Animals." Cambridge Univ. Press, London and New York (339pp.).

Marsland, E. A., and Gerrard, J. W. (1953). *Brit. Dental J.* **94**, 305–310.

Martin, N. H. (1948). *Biochem. J.* **42**, xv (Proc.).

Martin, N. H. (1949). *J. Am. Chem. Soc.* **71**, 1230–1232.

Martini, G. A. (1957). IV. *Freiburger Symp.* pp. 321–326. Springer, Berlin.

Martini, G. A., and Dölle, W. (1958). *Klin. Wochschr.* **36**, 272–280.

Martini, G. A., von Harnack, G., and Napp, J. (1953). *Deut. Med. Wochschr.* 78, 661.

Marvin, H. C., and Lucy, D. D. (1957). *Acta Haematol.* 18, 239–245.

Massias, P. (1956). "Contribution à l'étude des hyperbilirubinémies provoquées chez l'homme." Foulon, Paris (95pp.).

Mather, A. (1960). *Pediatrics* 26, 350.

Matsui, K. (1959a). *Igaku Kenkyu* 29, 1077–1085 (in Jap., Engl. summary).

Matsui, K. (1959b). *Igaku Kenkyu* 29, 1086–1093 (in Jap., Engl. summary).

Matsui, K. (1959c). *Igaku Kenkyu* 29, 1094–1101 (in Jap., Engl. summary).

Mattei, C. (1946). *Minerva Med.* 37(I), 308–313.

May, C. E., Martindale, R., and Boyd, W. F. (1934). *J. Biol. Chem.* 104, 255–257.

Mayerson, H. S. (1963). *Circulation* 28, 839–842.

Mayerson, H. S., and Wassermann, K. (1950). *Am. J. Med.* 9, 403.

Mayo, C., Jr., and Greene, C. H. (1929). *Am. J. Physiol.* 89, 280–288.

Mazzanti, L., and Lopez, M. (1952). *Arch. Vecchi Anat. Pathol.* (*Firenze*) 17, 825–867.

Meakins, J. C. (1927). *J. Clin. Invest.* 4, 135–148.

Medal, L., Guevara, L., and Quintanar, E. (1958). *Acta Haematol.* 19, 148–155.

Meebold, E. (1938). Quantitative Urobilinbestimmungen im Verlaufe des Cyclus und im Beginn der Schwangerschaft. Inaugural Dissertation (Med.), U. of Hamburg (34pp.).

Meehan, F. P. (1954). *Am. J. Physiol.* 179, 282–284.

Mehaut, M. (1951). *Paris Med.* Suppl. 3, 93–94.

Méhu, M. C. (1878). *J. Pharm. Chim.* (*Paris*) [5] 28, 159–165.

Meinel, A. (1903). *Zentr. Inn. Med.* 24, 321–327.

Meites, S., and Hogg, C. K. (1959). *Clin. Chem.* 5, 470–478.

Meites, S., and Hogg, C. K. (1960). *Clin. Chem.* 6, 421–428.

Melchior, E. (1931). *Zentr. Chir.* 58, 135–138.

Melchior, E., Rosenthal, F., and Licht, H. (1925). *Arch. Exptl. Pathol. Pharmakol.*

Melchior, E., Rosenthal, F., and Licht, H. (1926). *Klin. Wochschr.* 5, 537–541.

Meldolesi, G., Siedel, W., and Möller, H. (1939). *Z. Physiol. Chem.* 259, 137–149. 107, 238–259.

Melichar, V., Poláček, K., and Novák, M. (1962). *Biol. Neonatorum* 4, 94.

Mendioroz, B. A. (1952). *Arch. Soc. Biol. Montevideo* 19, 82–87.

Mendioroz, B. A. (1953a). *Arch. Soc. Biol. Montevideo* 20, 10–14.

Mendioroz, B. A. (1953b). *Arch. Soc. Biol. Montevideo* 20, 14–19.

Mendioroz, B. A. (1953c). *Arch. Soc. Biol. Montevideo* 20, 19–25.

Mendioroz, B. A. (1957). *Anales Fac. Med. Montevideo* 44, 363–375.

Mendioroz, B. A. (1963a). *Anales Fac. Med. Montevideo* 48, 88–96.

Mendioroz, B. A. (1963b). *Anales Fac. Med. Montevideo* 48, 97–103.

Mendioroz, B. A. (1963c). *Anales Fac. Med. Montevideo* 48, 104–117.

Mendioroz, B. A., and Castro, E. (1959). *Anales Fac. Med. Montevideo* 44, 33–35.

Mendioroz, B. A., and Charbonnier, A. (1951). *Compt. Rend. Soc. Biol.* 145, 1480–1483.

Mendioroz, B. A., Charbonnier, A., and Bernard, R. (1951). *Compt. Rend. Soc. Biol.* 145, 1483–1485.

Mendioroz, B. A., Castro, E., and Camiou, M. E. (1953). *Arch. Soc. Biol. Montevideo* 20, 26–34.

Mendioroz, B. A., Charbonnier, A., and Rodriquez, J. V. (1954). *Arch. Soc. Biol. Montevideo* 21, 70–79.

Mensi, E. (1910). *Riv. Clin. Pediat.* 8, 249–313.
Mertens, E. (1934a). *Handb. Allgem. Haematol.* 2, Pt. I, 619–644.
Mertens, E. (1934b). *Handb. Allgem. Haematol.* 2, Pt. II, 923–966.
Mertens, E., and Samlert, H. (1950). *Klin. Wochschr.* 28, 789–790.
Mertens, G. A., and Croal, A. E. (1960). *Can. Med. Assoc. J.* 83, 1148–1150.
Messmer, E., and Dengler, G. (1962). *Acta Hepato-Splenol.* 9, 301–310.
Metcalf, R. L. (1945). *Ann. Entomol. Soc. Am.* 38, 397–402.
Metzger, E. (1927). *Arch. Pathol. Anat. Physiol.* 263, 703–718.
Meulengracht, E. (1918). Studier over den heriditaere haemolytiske Ikterus. Dissertation (Med.), U. of Copenhagen (313pp.).
Meulengracht, E. (1919). *Ugeskrift Laeger* 81, 1785–1799.
Meulengracht, E. (1920). *Deut. Arch. Klin. Med.* 132, 285–301.
Meulengracht, E. (1921). *Deut. Arch. Klin. Med.* 137, 38–46.
Meulengracht, E. (1925). *AMA Arch. Internal Med.* 35, 214–223.
Meulengracht, E. (1938). *Hospitalstidende* 81, Suppl., 117–126.
Meulengracht, E. (1939). *Klin. Wochschr.* 18, 118–121.
Meulengracht, E. (1944). *Ugeskrift Laeger* 106, 355–358.
Meulengracht, E. (1947). *Quart. J. Med.* 40, 83–98.
Meulengracht, E., and Thisted, A. (1925). *Ugeskrift Laeger* 87, 268–270.
Meyer, E. C., and Adler, E. (1924). *Zentr. Gynaekol.* 48, 1514–1520.
Meyer, E. C., and Emmerich, E. (1909). *Deut. Arch. Klin. Med.* 96, 287–327.
Meyer, E. C., and Heinelt, H. (1923). *Deut. Arch. Klin. Med.* 142, 94–109.
Meyer, E. C., and Knüpffer, H. (1922). *Deut. Arch. Klin. Med.* 138, 321–330.
Meyer, K. (1938). Bilirubinbestimmung bei Schlacht- und Klinikpferden. Inaugural Dissertation (Vet.), U. of Hannover (33pp.).
Meyer, K. A., Popper, H., and Steigmann, F. (1949). *Quart. Bull. Northwestern Univ. Med. School* 23, 321–331.
Meyer, W. (1938). Kolidrast-Neu (Bengen) bei Verstopfungskoliken und die Veränderung des Bilirubinspiegels des Blutes im Verlauf der Krankheit. Inaugural Dissertation (Vet.-Med.), U. of Hannover (27pp.).
Meyer, W. C. (1944). *Muench. Med. Wochschr.* 91, 410–411.
Meyer, W. C. (1947a). *Aerztl. Forsch.* 1, 12–22.
Meyer, W. C. (1947b). *Aerztl. Forsch.* 1, 50–64.
Meyer, W. C. (1947c). *Aerztl. Forsch.* 1, 85–97.
Meyer, W. C. (1950). *Deut. Arch. Klin. Med.* 197, 139–147.
Meyer-Betz, F. (1913). *Ergeb. Inn. Med. Kinderheilk.* 12, 733–807.
Meythaler, F., and Jennemann, K. (1936). *Med. Klin.* 32, 1470–1473.
Michaëlsson, M. (1961). Bilirubin Determination in Serum and Urine. Studies on Diazo Method and a New Copperazopigment Method. *Scand. J. Clin. Lab. Invest.*, Suppl. 56 (80pp.).
Michel, H. (1948). *Aerztl. Forsch.* 2, 305–309.
Mikeladse, S. (1928). *Zentr. Gynaekol.* 52, 1461–1469.
Miller, E. B., Singer, K., and Dameshek, W. (1942). *AMA Arch. Internal. Med.* 70, 722–737.
Mills, G. C. (1957). *J. Biol. Chem.* 229, 189–197.
Mills, G. C. (1962). *J. Biochem. (Tokyo)* 51, 41–47.
Mills, G. C., and Randall, H. P. (1958). *J. Biol. Chem.* 232, 589–598.
Minkowski, O. (1892). *Verhandl. Kongr. Inn. Med.* 11, 127–128.
Minkowski, O. (1904). *Z. Klin. Med.* 55, 34–43.
Minkowski, O., and Naunyn, B. (1886). *Arch. Exptl. Pathol. Pharmakol.* 21, 1–33.

Minoru, S. (1958a). *Igaku Kenkyu* **28**, 2540 (in Jap., Engl. summary).
Minoru, S. (1958b). *Igaku Kenkyu* **28**, 2549 (in Jap., Engl. summary).
Mistilis, S., and Schiff, L. (1963). *GUT* (*J. Brit. Soc. Gastroenterol.*) **4**, 13–15.
Mitchell, W. T., and Stifel, R. E. (1916). *Bull. Johns Hopkins Hosp.* **27**, 78.
Mitsuda, T. (1959a). *Okayama Igakkai Zasshi* **71**, 7047 (in Jap., Engl. summary).
Mitsuda, T. (1959b). *Okayama Igakkai Zasshi* **71**, 7057 (in Jap., Engl. summary).
Mittelstrass, H. (1936). *Z. Geburtshilfe Gynaekol.* **112**, 309–318.
Miyai, K., Slusser, R. J., and Ruebner, B. H. (1963). *Exptl. Mol. Pathol.* **2**, 464–480.
Möbius, P. J. (1877). *Arch. Heilkunde* **18**, 83–100.
Möller, H. (1939). Inaugural Dissertation Tech. Hochschule, Munich (quoted in Siedel, 1939, p. 12).
Moeller, J., and Schroeder, R. (1954). *Z. Klin. Med.* **151**, 313–327.
Mogena, H. G. (1929). *Lancet* **I**, 1187–1189.
Mohr, J. L. (1948). *J. Parasitol.* **34**, 2.
Moleschott (1852). *Arch. Physiol. Heilkunde* (*Stuttgart*) **11**, 479–495.
Molinelli, E.-A., and Royer, M. (1929). *Compt. Rend. Soc. Biol.* **102**, 873.
Mollison, P. L. (1948). *Lancet* **I**, 513–515.
Mollison, P. L., and Cutbush, M. (1949a). *Brit. Med. J.* **I**, 123–130.
Mollison, P. L., and Cutbush, M. (1949b). *Arch. Disease Childhood* **24**, 7–11.
Mollison, P. L., Mourant, A. E., and Race, R. R. (1948). The Rh Blood Groups and Their Clinical Effects. *Med. Res. Council Memo.* No. 19 (74pp.).
Monasterio, G., and Giovannetti, S. (1954). *Riv. Gastroenterol.* **6**, 177–190.
Monasterio, G., and Giovannetti, S. (1955). *Minerva Gastroenterol.* **1**, 1–24.
Monasterio, G., and Lattanzi, A. (1947). *Rass. Fisiopatol. Clin. Terap.* **19**, 185–234.
Monasterio, G., and Lattanzi, A. (1948). *Minerva Med.* **39**, 480–485.
Monobe, T. (1959a). *Okayama Igakkai Zasshi* **71**, 6389 (in Jap., Engl. summary).
Monobe, T. (1959b). *Okayama Igakkai Zasshi* **71**, 6399 (in Jap., Engl. summary).
Montagnani, C. A. (1963). *Ann. N.Y. Acad. Sci.* **111** (Art. 1), 121–135.
Montanari, R., and Bracaloni, E. (1931a). *Riv. Clin. Med.* **32**, 401–412.
Montanari, R., and Bracaloni, E. (1931b). *Riv. Clin. Med.* **32**, 480–488.
Moolenar, A. L. (1960). *Clin. Chim. Acta* **5**, 149.
Moore, H. C. (1963). *Lancet* **II**, 57–59.
Moravec, M. (1964). *Z. Klin. Chem.* **2**, 138–141.
Moravec, M., and Netoušek, M. (1963). *Blut* **9**, 182–185.
Moreland, F. B., O'Donnel, W. W., Gast, J. H., and McGinn, M. (1950). *Federation Proc.* **9**, 207.
Morfaux, P. (1899). Recherches sur l'urobilinurie. Thesis (Med.), U. of Paris (72pp.).
Morishima, T. (1930). *Japan. J. Gastroenterol.* **2**, 60–64.
Morris, B. (1956). *Quart. J. Exptl. Physiol.* **41**, 318–340.
Morris, B. (1960). *Australian J. Exptl. Biol. Med. Sci.* **38**, 99–110.
Morrison, D. B., and Anderson, W. A. D. (1942). *Public Health Rept.* **57**, 90–94.
Morrison, D. B., Williams, E. F., Jr., and Anderson, W. A. D. (1940). *J. Biol. Chem.* **133**, lxx–lxxi (Proc.).
Mortimer, P. H., Taylor, A., and Shorland, F. B. (1962). *Nature* **194**, 550–553.
Morton, R. A., and Stubbs, A. L. (1940). *J. Chem. Soc.* (*London*) p. 1347.
Mouchet, S. (1928). *Bull. Soc. Zool. France* **53**, 442–452.
Mozziconacci, P., Attal, C., Pjam, H. T., Malassenet, R., and Bessis, M. (1961). *Nouvelle Rev. Franc. Hematol.* **1**, 832–846.
Müller, A. (1938a). *Z. Physiol. Chem.* **251**, 1–13.

Müller, A. (1938b). Z. Physiol. Chem. **256**, 95–103.

Müller, J. (1844). Handb. Physiol. Mensch. **1**, 131 (4th ed.).

Müller, P., and Engel, L. (1931a). Z. Physiol. Chem. **199**, 117–124.

Müller, P., and Engel, L. (1931b). Z. Physiol. Chem. **200**, 145–152.

Müller, P., and Engel, L. (1931c). Z. Physiol. Chem. **202**, 55–66.

Müller, P., and Engel, L. (1931d). Verhandl. Deut. Ges. Inn. Med. **43**, 393–395.

Müller, W. (1952). Deut. Arch. Klin. Med. **199**, 423–430.

Müller, W. (1954). Deut. Med. Wochschr. **79**, 685–690.

Muir, H. M., and Neuberger, A. (1949). Biochem. J. **45**, 163–170.

Muir, H. M., and Neuberger, A. (1950). Biochem. J. **47**, 97–104.

Mutolo, V. (1948). Acta Med. Scand. **131**, 602–604.

Myers, C. P. (1945). J. Ind. Hyg. **27**, 52–55.

Nabholz, A. (1938). Quantitative Bilirubinbestimmung im Blutserum von Pferd und Rind. Inaugural Dissertation (Vet.), U. of Zurich (35pp.).

Najjar, V. A. (1951). Federation Proc. **10**, 227.

Najjar, V. A. (1952). Pediatrics **10**, 1–10.

Najjar, V. A., and Childs, B. (1951). J. Clin. Invest. **30**, 663.

Najjar, V. A., and Childs, B. (1953). J. Biol. Chem. **204**, 359–366.

Nakadoi, Y. I. (1956a). Igaku Kenkyu **26**, 2544 (in Jap., Engl. summary).

Nakadoi, Y. I. (1956b). Igaku Kenkyu **26**, 2552 (in Jap., Engl. summary).

Nakadoi, Y. I. (1956c). Igaku Kenkyu **26**, 2559 (in Jap., Engl. summary).

Nakajima, H. (1958). Proc. Japan. Acad. **34**, 712–717.

Nakajima, H. (1959). Proc. Japan. Acad. **35**, 144–148.

Nakajima, H. (1963). J. Biol. Chem. **238**, 3797–3801.

Nakajima, H., and Yamaoka, K. (1961). Proc. Japan. Acad. **37**, 640–642.

Nakajima, H., Takemura, T., Nakajima, O., and Yamaoka, K. (1961a). Proc. Japan Acad. **37**, 497–500.

Nakajima, H., Takemura, T., Nakajima, O., and Yamaoka, K. (1961b). Proc. Japan Acad. **37**, 501–504.

Nakajima, H., Takemura, T., Nakajima, O., and Yamaoka, K. (1961c). Proc. Japan Acad. **37**, 579–583.

Nakajima, H., Nakajima, O., and Yamaoka, K. (1961d). Proc. Japan Acad. **37**, 643–644.

Nakajima, H., Takemura, T., Nakajima, O., and Yamaoka, K. (1963). J. Biol. Chem. **238**, 3784–3796.

Nakajima, O. (1962a). Proc. Japan Acad. **38**, 601–606.

Nakajima, O. (1962b). Proc. Japan Acad. **38**, 607–609.

Nakajima, O. (1963). Proc. Japan Acad. **39**, 525–529.

Nakamishi, T. (1956a). Igaku Kenkyu **26**, 807–814 (in Jap., Engl. summary).

Nakamishi, T. (1956b). Igaku Kenkyu **26**, 816 (in Jap., Engl. summary).

Nakamishi, T. (1956c). Igaku Kenkyu **26**, 853–882 (in Jap., Engl. summary).

Nakayama, M. (1902). Z. Physiol. Chem. **36**, 398–400.

Napp, J. H., and Plotz, J. (1949). Arch. Gynaekol. **176**, 781–792.

Nasaralla, M., Gawronska, E., and Hsia, D. Y. Y. (1958). J. Clin. Invest. **37**, 1403.

Naskalski, J., and Szczepkowski, T. W. (1963). Roczniki Chem. **37**, 629–634.

Nath, R. L., Paim, S. K., and Dutt, R. (1960). Bull. Calcutta School Trop. Med. **3**, 61–62.

Naumann, H. N. (1936a). Biochem. J. **30**, 347–351.

Naumann, H. N. (1936b). Biochem. J. **30**, 762–764.

Naumann, H. N. (1936c). Biochem. J. **30**, 1020–1025.

Naumann, H. N. (1947). *Proc. Soc. Exptl. Biol. Med.* **65**, 72–74.

Naumann, H. N., and Young, J. M. (1960). *Proc. Soc. Exptl. Biol. Med.* **105**, 70–72.

Naunyn, B. (1868). *Arch. Anat. Physiol. Wiss. Med.* pp. 401–441.

Naunyn, B. (1869). *Arch. Anat. Physiol. Wiss. Med.* pp. 579–588.

Neefe, J. R., Stokes, J., Jr., Reinhold, J. G., and Lukens, F. D. W. (1944). *J. Clin. Invest.* **23**, 836–855.

Nencki, M., and Sieber, N. (1884). *Arch. Exptl. Pharmakol.* **18**, 401–422.

Nencki, M., and Sieber, N. (1888). *Arch. Exptl. Pathol. Pharmakol.* **24**, 430–446.

Nencki, M., and Zaleski, J. (1900). *Z. Physiol. Chem.* **30**, 384–435.

Nencki, M., and Zaleski, J. (1901). *Ber. Deut. Chem. Ges.* **34**, 997–1010.

Nestlé, L. (1913). Urobilin, eine Monographie nebst klinischen Beiträgen über den Nachweis und das Vorkommen des Urobilins im Pferdenharn. Inaugural Dissertation (Vet. Med.), U. of Stuttgart (85pp.).

Netoušek, M. (1956). *Acta Med. Acad. Sci. Hung.* **9**, 143–151.

Neubauer, C., and Vogel, J. (1858). "Analyse des Harns," 3rd ed., pp. 72–73. Kreidel and Nieders, Wiesbaden.

Neubauer, O. (1903). *Muench. Med. Wochschr.* **50**, 1846.

Neuberger, A. (1951). *Ciba Found Symp. Isotopes in Biochem.* pp. 68–82.

Neuberger, A., Muir, H. M., and Gray, C. H. (1950). *Nature* **165**, 948.

Newburger, R. (1937). *J. Lab. Clin. Med.* **22**, 1192–1195.

Newman, A. J., and Gross, S. (1963). *Pediatrics* **32**, 995–1001.

Newman, C. E. (1928). *Brit. J. Exptl. Med.* **9**, 112–119.

Newns, G. H., and Norton, K. R. (1958). *Lancet* **II**, 1138–1140.

Nicolaus, R. A. (1960). The Chromatographic Study of Pyrrolic Acids Arising from Oxidative Degradation of Natural Pigments. *Rass. Med. Sper.* **7**, Suppl. 2.

Nichols, M. S., and Jackson, J. W. (1930). *J. Lab. Clin. Med.* **15**, 672–677.

Ninger, E., and Továrek, J. (1951). *Acta Med. Scand.* **139**, 242–243.

Nishikawa, S. (1959a). *Okayama Igakkai Zasshi* **71**, 7745 (in Jap., Engl. summary).

Nishikawa, S. (1959b). *Okayama Igakkai Zasshi* **71**, 7753 (in Jap., Engl. summary).

Nishimaru, Y. (1931). *Am. J. Physiol.* **97**, 654–657.

Nissen, K. (1957). *Landartzt (Stuttgart)* **33**, 804–808.

Nizet, E., and Barac, G. (1952a). *Compt. Rend. Soc. Biol.* **146**, 1282–1284.

Nizet, E., and Barac, G. (1952b). *Compt. Rend. Soc. Biol.* **146**, 1285–1286.

Nolli, B. (1938). *Atti XLIV. Congr. Soc. Ital. Med. Int.* (quoted in Bramante, 1948a, pp. 28–29).

Nonnenbruch, W. (1919). *Mitt. Grenzgebieten Med. Chir.* **31**, 470–472.

Noro, T. (1951). *Igaku Kenkyu* **21**, 853–882 (in Jap., Engl. summary).

Nørredam, K. (1962). *Ugeskrift Laeger* **124**, 1351–1363.

Nørredam, K. (1963). *Acta Med. Scand.* **174**, 163–170.

Nosslin, B. (1960). The Direct Diazo Reaction of Bile Pigments in Serum. Experimental and Clinical Studies. *Scand. J. Clin. Lab. Invest.* Suppl. **49** (176pp.).

Nosslin, B. (1963). *Scand. J. Clin. Lab. Invest.* Suppl. **69**, 206–222.

Novák, M., Poláček, K., and Melichar, V. (1962). *Biol. Neonatorum* **4**, 310–315.

Novikoff, A. B. (1959). *J. Histochem. Cytochem.* **7**, 240–244.

Novikoff, A. B., and Essner, E. (1960). *Am. J. Med.* **29**, 102–131.

Obermeyer, F., and Popper, H. (1908). *Wien. Klin. Wochschr.* **21**, 895–902.

Ó'Carra, P. (1962). *Nature* **195**, 899–900.

Ó'Carra, P., and Ó'hEocha, C. (1962). *Nature* **195**, 173–174.

Odell, G. B. (1959a). *J. Pediat.* **55**, 268–279.

Odell, G. B. (1959b). *J. Clin. Invest.* **38**, 823–833.

O'Donnel, J. F., Piller, M. F., and Schiff, L. (1961). *J. Lab. Clin. Med.* **58**, 947 (Proc.).

Oertel, H. (1906). *J. Exptl. Med.* **8**, 103–119.

Oertel, H. (1910). *AMA Arch. Internal Med.* **6**, 293–300.

Ogata, T. (1913a). *Beitr. Pathol. Anat. Allgem. Pathol.* **55**, 236–314.

Ogata, T. (1913b). *Beitr. Pathol. Anat. Allgem. Pathol.* **55**, 315–321.

O'Hagan, J. E., Hamilton, T., Le Breton, E. G., and Shaw, A. E. (1957). *Clin. Chem.* **3**, 609–623.

Ó'hEocha, C. (1958). *Arch. Biochem. Biophys.* **73**, 207–219.

Ó'hEocha, C. (1962a). *Biochem. J.* **85**, 2P–3P.

Ó'hEocha, C. (1962b). *Nature* **195**, 173–174.

Ó'hEocha, C. (1963). *Biochemistry* **2**, 375–382.

Ó'hEocha, C., and Ó'Carra, P. (1961). *J. Am. Chem. Soc.* **83**, 1091–1093.

Ó'hEocha, C., and Haxo, F. T. (1960). *Biochim. Biophys. Acta* **41**, 516–520.

Ó'hEocha, C., and Lambe, R. F. (1961). *Arch. Biochem. Biophys.* **93**, 459–460.

Ó'hEocha, C., Ó'Carra, P., and Carroll, D. (1961). *Biochem. J.* **80**, 25P.

Ohlig, W. (1938). Über das Urobilin im Blutserum. Inaugural Dissertation (Med.), U. of Jena (16pp.).

Ohno, Y. (1931). *Muench. Med. Wochschr.* **78**, 1639–1642.

Okay, S. (1945). *Nature* **166**, 635.

O'Leary, P. A., Greene, C. H., and Rowntree, L. G. (1929). *AMA Arch. Internal Med.* **44**, 155–193.

Opitz, H., and Brehme, T. (1923). *Klin. Wochschr.* **2**, 1269.

Opitz, H., and Brehme, T. (1924a). *Z. Ges. Exptl. Med.* **41**, 681–698.

Opitz, H., and Brehme, T. (1924b). *Klin. Wochschr.* **3**, 2101.

Oppé, T. E., and Valaes, T. (1959). *Lancet* **I**, 536.

Oppenheimer, F. (1885). Über die gelbe Diazo-Reaktion. Inaugural Dissertation (Med.), U. of Berlin. (31pp.).

Orndorf, W. R., and Teeple, J. E. (1905). *Am. Chem. J.* **33**, 215–250.

Orth, J. (1875). *Arch. Pathol. Anat. Physiol.* **63**, 447–462.

Orten, J. M. (1936). *Am. J. Physiol.* **114**, 414–422.

Orten, J. M., and Smith, A. H. (1936). *Proc. Soc. Exptl. Biol. Med.* **34**, 72–74.

Oshima, M. (1930a). *Japan. J. Gastroenterol.* **2**, 81–90.

Oshima, M. (1930b). *Japan. J. Gastroenterol.* **2**, 90–92.

Oshima, M. (1931a). *Japan. J. Gastroenterol.* **3**, 67–70.

Oshima, M. (1931b). *Japan. J. Gastroenterol.* **3**, 137–141.

Oshima, M. (1931c). *Japan. J. Gastroenterol.* **3**, 141–146.

Oshima, M. (1932a). *Japan. J. Gastroenterol.* **4**, 41–51.

Oshima, M. (1932b). *Japan. J. Gastroenterol.* **4**, 100–101.

Oshima, M. (1932c). *Japan. J. Gastroenterol.* **4**, 102–108.

Osipov, L. N. (1962). *Lab. Delo* **8**, 34–39 [quoted from *Biol. Abstr.*, **42**, 1346 (1963)].

Oski, F. A., and Naiman, J. L. (1963). *J. Pediat.* **63**, 1034–1037.

Ostrow, J. D. (1963). *J. Lab. Clin. Med.* **62**, 998.

Ostrow, J. D., Hammaker, L., and Schmid, R. (1961). *J. Clin. Invest.* **40**, 1442–1452.

Ostrow, J. D., Jandl, J. H., and Schmid, R. (1962). *J. Clin. Invest.* **41**, 1628–1637.

Ostrow, J. D., Schmid, R., and Samuelson, D. (1963). *J. Clin. Invest.* **42**, 1286–1299.

Ostrowski, S. (1912). *Jahrb. Kinderheilk.* **76**, 645–653.

Otila, E. (1948). Studies on the Cerebrospinal Fluid in Premature Infants. *Acta Paediat.* 35, Suppl. 7 (100pp.).

Ottenberg, R. (1932). *Contrib. Med. Sci. Honor Dr. Emanuel Libman* III, 917–923.

Ottenberg, R. (1943). *J. Mt. Sinai Hosp., N.Y.* 9, 937–954.

Overbeek, J. T. G., Vink, C. L. J., and Deenstra, H. (1955a). *Rec. Trav. Chim.* 74, 69–76.

Overbeek, J. T. G., Vink, C. L. J., and Deenstra, H. (1955b). *Rec. Trav. Chim.* 74, 81–84.

Overbeek, J. T. G., Vink, C. L. J., and Deenstra, H. (1955c). *Rec. Trav. Chim.* 74, 85–97.

Oviedo Bustos, J. M. (1933). *Semana Med.* 40, 1426–1434.

Oviedo Bustos, J. M. (1934). *Rev. Med. Rosario* 24, 1009–1030.

Pagliardi, E., and Gaidano, G. (1956). *Fegato* 2, 327–344.

Pagliardi, E., and Gaidano, G. (1959). *Fegato* 5, 291–302.

Pagliardi, E., and Penati, F. (1948). *Minerva Med.* 39(II), 477–479.

Pagliardi, E., and Penati, F. (1949). *Minerva Med.* 40(I), 731–734.

Panizon, F., and Meo, R. (1959). *Acta Paediat. Latina* 12, 404.

Parkes Weber, F. (1943). *Brit. Med. J.* II, 690.

Parkes Weber, F. (1946). *Med. Press (London)* 216, 440–441.

Parkes Weber, F. (1948). *Quart. J. Med.* 17, 81.

Paschkis, K. (1933). *Ergeb. Inn. Med. Kinderheilk.* 45, 682–736.

Paschkis, K., and Diamant, M. (1930). *Deut. Arch. Klin. Med.* 169, 180–194.

Pass, I. J., Schwartz, S., and Watson, C. J. (1945). *J. Clin. Invest.* 24, 283–291.

Passama-Vuillaume, M. (1964). *Compt. Rend. Acad. Sci.* 258, 6549–6552.

Patek, A. J., and Minot, G. R. (1934). *Am. J. Med. Sci.* 188, 206–215.

Patrassi, G. (1943). *Z. Klin. Med.* 142, 285–291.

Patterson, J., Swale, J., and Maggs, C. (1952). *Biochem. J.* 52, 100–105.

Patterson, W. H., and Forrester, R. (1953). *Arch. Diseases Childhood* 28, 217–221.

Pauling, L. (1938). "The Nature of the Chemical Bond." Cornell Univ. Press, Ithaca, New York (450pp.).

Paulsmeyer, F. (1937). Quantitative Bestimmung der Urobilin-Farbstoffe in der Milch von Kühen und ihre diagnostischen Wert für den Nachweis des Frischmilchendseins der Kühe. Inaugural Dissertation (Vet. Med.), Tierärztl. Hochschule, Hannover (25pp.).

Pavel, I. (1943a). "Les Ictères," 2nd ed. Institut de Arte gratice "Candida," Anton Richter, Bucharest (189pp.).

Pavel, I. (1943b). *Presse Med.* 64, 1600–1602.

Pavel, I. (1956). *Arch. Maladies App. Digest. Nutr.* 45, 126–146.

Pavel, I. (1957). *IV. Freiburger Symp.* pp. 227–231. Springer, Berlin.

Pavel, I., and Campeanu, S. (1957a). *Presse Med.* 65, 734–735.

Pavel, I., and Campeanu, S. (1957b). *Acta Gastroenterol. Belg.* 20, 179–189.

Pavel, I., and Campeanu, S. (1962). *Semaine Hop. Paris* 38, 1345–1350.

Pavel, I., and Velciu, V. (1951). *Bul. Stiint. Acad. Repub. Pop. Romane. Ser. Stiint. Med.* 3, 1–11.

Pavel, I., and Velciu, V. (1957). *Arch. Maladies App. Digest. Nutr.* 46, 317–328.

Pearson, L. B., and Watson, C. J. (1963). *Proc. Soc. Exptl. Biol. Med.* 112, 756–758.

Peck, O. C., Rey, D. F., and Snell, A. M. (1960). *Gastroenterology* 39, 625–627.

Pedersen, K. O., and Waldenström, J. (1937). *Z. Physiol. Chem.* 245, 152–162.

Peitersen, E. (1959). *Ugeskrift Laeger* 121, 2008–2009.

Pellegrino, E., Patek, A. J., Colcher, A., and Domanski, B. (1947). *J. Lab. Clin. Med.* **32**, 397–402.

Peluffo, E., and Prado, G. M. (1949a). *Arch. Pediat. Uruguay* **20**, 694–707.

Peluffo, E., and Prado, G. M. (1949b). *Arch. Pediat. Uruguay* **20**, 861–872.

Penati, F., and Pagliardi, E. (1943). *Arch. Sci. Med.* **76**, 21–69.

Peremy, G. (1932). *Klin. Wochschr.* **11**, 950–951.

Perkins, F. S. (1927). *AMA Arch. Internal Med.* **40**, 195–202.

Perkoff, G. T., and Tyler, F. H. (1950). *Am. J. Med.* **8**, 542.

Perrin, D. D. (1958). *Biochem. J.* **68**, 314–319.

Perryman, P. W., Richards, D. H., and Holbrook, B. (1957). *Biochem. J.* **66**, 61P.

Peter, J. R. (1933). *Biochem. Z.* **262**, 432–460.

Peterman, E. A., and Cooley, T. B. (1933a). *J. Lab. Clin. Med.* **19**, 723–735.

Peterman, E. A., and Cooley, T. B. (1933b). *J. Lab. Clin. Med.* **19**, 743–748.

Peters, J. A. (1963). *Nature* **200**, 286.

Petersen, K. E. (1964). *Ugeskrift Laeger* **126**, 347–349.

Peterson, R. E. and Schmid, R. (1957). *J. Clin. Endocrinol. Metab.* **17**, 1485–1488.

Petryka, Z., Nicholson, D. C., and Gray, C. H. (1962). *Nature* **194**, 1047–1048.

Pick, E. (1894a). *Wien. Klin. Wochschr.* **7**, 478.

Pick, E. (1894b). *Wien. Klin. Wochschr.* **7**, 500.

Pick, E. (1894c). *Wien. Klin. Wochschr.* **7**, 518.

Pick, E. (1894d). *Wien. Klin. Wochschr.* **7**, 537.

Pilchmayr, I., and Stich, W. (1962). *Klin. Wochschr.* **40**, 665–667.

Piloty, O., Stock. J., and Dormann, E. (1914). *Ber. Deut. Chem. Ges.* **47**, 400–406.

Pitcher, C. S., and Williams, R. (1963). *Clin. Sci.* **24**, 239–252.

Pittera, A., and Cassia, B. (1962). *Boll. Soc. Ital. Biol. Sper.* **38**, 1233–1234.

Pittera, A., and Cassia, B. (1963). *Fegato* **9**, 457–470.

Plachý, O., Kovácz, P., Dzurik, R., and Niederland, T. R. (1961). *Casopis Lekaru Ceskych* **100**, 842–844.

Polack, E. (1930). Den Kliniske Diagnose af Leverparenchymbeskadigelse. Dissertation (Med.), U. of Copenhagen (403pp.).

Pollock, M. R. (1945). *Lancet* **II**, 626–630.

Pollock, M. R. (1951). *Med. Res. Council Spec. Rept. Ser.* **273**, 70–83.

Polonovski, M., and Bourrillon, R. (1952a). *Bull. Soc. Chim. Biol.* **34**, 703–711.

Polonovski, M., and Bourrillon, R. (1952b). *Bull. Soc. Chim. Biol.* **34**, 963–972.

Polonovski, M., and Bourrillon, R. (1952c). *Bull. Soc. Chim. Biol.* **34**, 973–984.

Polonovski, M., and Bourrillon, R. (1952d). *Bull. Soc. Chim. Biol.* **34**, 985–990.

Polonovski, M., Fiessinger, N., and Gajdos, A. (1942). *Bull. Soc. Chim. Biol.* **24**, 221–225.

Popper, H. (1937). *Arch. Pathol. Anat. Physiol.* **298**, 574–593.

Popper, H. (1958). *J. Am. Med. Assoc.* **168**, 2235–2242.

Popper, H., and Schaffner, F. (1957). "Liver: Structure and Function." McGraw-Hill, New York (777pp.).

Popper, H., and Schaffner, F. (1959a). *Proc. Soc. Exptl. Biol. Med.* **101**, 777–779.

Popper, H., and Schaffner, F. (1959b). *Ann. Internal Med.* **51**, 1230.

Popper, H., and Schaffner, F. (1959c). *J. Am. Med. Assoc.* **169**, 1447–1453.

Popper, H., and Schaffner, F. (1963). *Ann. Internal Med.* **59**, 674–691.

Popper, H., and Szanto, P. B. (1956). *Gastroenterology* **31**, 683.

Popper, H., Schaffner, F., Rubin, E., Barka, T., and Paronetto, F. (1963). *Ann. N.Y. Acad. Sci.* **104**, (Art. 3), 988–1013.

Porsche, J. D., Pike, E. F., and Gabby, L. (1939). Quoted in W. Siedel, U.S. Patent 2166073 (1939, Nachtrag).

Posthuma, S. (1931). De bloedafbraek en zijn bepaling in het bijzonder bij aandoningen van de lever. Akad. Proefschrift (Geneesk.), U. of Amsterdam (144pp).

Potter, E. L. (1947). "Rh—Its Relation to Congenital Hemolytic Disease and to Intragroup Transfusion Reaction." Year Book Publishers, Chicago, Illinois (344pp.).

Powell, W. N. (1944). *Am. J. Clin. Pathol., Tech. Sect.* **8**, 55–58.

Pröscher, F. (1900a). *Z. Physiol. Chem.* **29**, 411–415.

Pröscher, F. (1900b). *Z. Physiol. Chem.* **31**, 500–526.

Pröscher, F. (1903). *Deut. Med. Wochschr.* **29**, 927.

Profitt, B. K., and Morrison, D. B. (1949). *Federation Proc.* **8**, 239.

Profitt, B. K., and Morrison, D. B. (1951). *Federation Proc.* **10**, 234.

Pruckner, F., and Stern, A. (1937). *Z. Physik. Chem. (Leipzig)* **A180**, 25–43.

Pruckner, F., and von Dobeneck, H. (1942). *Z. Physik. Chem. (Leipzig)* **A190**, 43–55.

Pullman, B., and Perault, A.-M. (1959). *Proc. Natl. Acad. Sci. U.S.* **45**, 1476–1480.

Quin, J. I. (1933). *Onderstepoort J. Vet. Sci. Animal Ind.* **1**, 501–504.

Quin, J. I. (1936). *Onderstepoort J. Vet. Sci. Animal Ind.* **7**, 351–366.

Quincke, H. (1884). *Arch. Pathol. Anat. Physiol.* **95**, 125–139.

Quincke, H. (1885). *Arch. Exptl. Pathol. Pharmakol.* **19**, 34–38.

Quioc, G. (1909). Examen fonctionelle de la sècretion biliaire chez le nourrison. Thesis (Med.), U. of Paris (66pp.).

Quisling, N. A. (1894). *Arch. Kinderheilk.* **17**, 32–94.

Quodbach, K. (1936). Tagesschwankungen im Urobilinogen- und Farbgehalt des Harns. Inaugural Dissertation (Med.), U. of Rostock (23pp.).

Rabinowitch, I. M. (1932). *J. Biol. Chem.* **97**, 163–175.

Radeff, T. (1943). *Wien. Tieraertzl. Monatsschr.* **21**, 518–522.

Radin, N. S., Rittenberg, D., and Shemin, D. (1950a). *J. Biol. Chem.* **184**, 745–753.

Radin, N. S., Rittenberg, D., and Shemin, D. (1950b). *J. Biol. Chem.* **184**, 755–767.

Raices, A. E., and Velasco Suárez, C. (1935). *Arch. Argent. Enferm. Ap. Digest.* **7**, 115–116.

Ramón Guerra, A. U., Goluboff de Milies, R., and Visca, P. (1948). *Arch. Pediat. Uruguay* **19**, 257–265.

Ramsay, W. N. M. (1946). *Vet. J.* **102**, 206–211.

Rand, R. N., and di Pasqua, A. (1962). *Clin. Chem.* **8**, 570–578.

Ranek, L. (1964). *Ugeskrift Laeger* **126**, 1271–1274.

Raphael (no inits.) (1905). *St. Petersburg Med. Wochschr.* **30**, 128.

Raphaël, C. B. (1936). *Compt. Rend. Acad. Sci.* **202**, 588–590.

Raphaël, C. B. (1939). *Ann. Inst. Oceanogr., Monaco* **19**, 1–78.

Raphaël, C. B. (1948a). *Compt. Rend. Soc. Biol.* **142**, 67–68.

Raphaël, C. B. (1948b). *Compt. Rend. Soc. Biol.* **142**, 69–71.

Rappaport, F., and Eichhorn, F. (1943). *Lancet* **I**, 62–63.

Raule, A., and Grisler, R. (1950). *Osped. Maggiore* **38**, 227–229.

Read, A. E., Harrison, C. V., and Sherlock, S. (1961). *Am. J. Med.* **31**, 249–258.

Redeker, A., and Kahn, A. (1962). *California Med.* **97**, 341–342.

Rees, K. R., and Shotlander, V. L. (1964). *Biochem. Clinics* **3**, 181–188.

Reichardt, H. J. (1931). Der Bilirubinspiegel im Blutserum kolikkranker Pferde, ein prognostisches Hilfsmittel. Inaugural Dissertation (Vet.), U. of Berlin (29pp.).

Reichel, J., Goldberg, S. B., Ellenberg, M., and Schaffner, F. (1960). *Am. J. Med.* **28**, 654–660.

Reiner, M. (1953). "Standard Methods of Clinical Chemistry" (Am. Assoc. Clin. Chemists, eds.), Vol. I, pp. 11–16. Academic Press, New York.

Reiner, M., and Thomas, J. L. (1962). *Clin. Chem.* **8**, 278–283.

Reinert, H. (1948). *Z. Ges. Inn. Med. Grenzgebiete* **3**, 241–242.

Reinhold, J. G., and Fowler, C. B. (1946). *J. Biol. Chem.* **167**, 401–406.

Reinouts, P. van Haga (1963). *Clin. Chim. Acta* **8**, 634–635.

Retzlaff, K. (1923a). *Deut. Med. Wochschr.* **49**, 844–846.

Retzlaff, K. (1923b). *Z. Ges. Exptl. Med.* **34**, 133–196.

Rey, P. (1910). La cholémie familiale. Thesis (Med.), U. of Montpellier (42pp.).

Rezza, E., Felici, W., Colloridi, V., and Natoli, G. (1963). *Helv. Paediat. Acta* **18**, 424–432.

Rich, A. R. (1923). *Bull. Johns Hopkins Hosp.* **34**, 321–329.

Rich, A. R. (1924). *Bull. Johns Hopkins Hosp.* **35**, 415–416.

Rich, A. R. (1925a). *Bull. Johns Hopkins Hosp.* **36**, 233–247.

Rich, A. R. (1925b). *Physiol. Rev.* **5**, 182–224.

Rich, A. R. (1930). *Bull. Johns Hopkins Hosp.* **47**, 338–377.

Rich, A. R., and Bumstead, J. H. (1925a). *Bull. Johns Hopkins Hosp.* **36**, 225–232.

Rich, A. R., and Bumstead, J. H. (1925b). *Bull. Johns Hopkins Hosp.* **36**, 376–380.

Rich, A. R., and Bumstead, J. H. (1925c). *Bull. Johns Hopkins Hosp.* **36**, 437–445.

Rich, A. R., and Resnik, W. H. (1926). *Bull. Johns Hopkins Hosp.* **38**, 75–76.

Ridgway, J. E. (1959). *J. Med. Lab. Technol.* July (quoted from reprint).

Riding, I. M., and Ellis, D. (1963). *Clin. Chim. Acta* **8**, 884–892.

Riegler, E. (1899). *Wien. Med. Bl.* **22**, 271.

Riemerschmied, G., and Quin, J. I. (1941). *Onderstepoort J. Vet. Sci. Animal Husbandry* **17**, 89.

Riggi, S. J., and di Luzia, N. R. (1962). *Nature* **193**, 1292–1294.

Rimington, C. (1943). *Ann. Rev. Biochem.* **12**, 425–446.

Rimington, C. (1951). *Lancet* **II**, 551–556.

Rimington, C. (1952). *Acta Med. Scand.* **143**, 161–196.

Rimington, C. (1955). *Endeavour* **14**, 126–135.

Rimington, C., and Stewart, A. M. (1932). *Proc. Roy. Soc.* **B110**, 75–91.

Rimington, C., Quin, J. I., and Roets, G. C. S. (1937). *Onderstepoort J. Vet. Sci. Animal Ind.* **9**, 225–255.

Rimington, C., Krol, S., and Tooth, B. (1956). *Scand. J. Clin. Lab. Invest.* **8**, 251–262.

Rimington, C., Slater, T. F., Spector, W. G., Sträuli, U., and Willoughby, D. A. (1962). *Nature* **194**, 1152–1153.

Rindone, E., and Mollica, F. (1962). *Pediatria* **70**, 812–823.

Rissel, E. (1939). *Wien. Klin. Wochschr.* **52**, 873–875.

Riva, A. (1896). *Gaz. Med. Torino* **47**, 1–8.

Rivin, A. U. (1959). *J. Am. Med. Assoc.* **170**, 2088–2089.

Roaf, H. E. (1906). *Biochem. J.* **1**, 390–397.

Robbins, W. C. (1951). *Proc. Soc. Exptl. Biol. Med.* **77**, 158–162.

Roberts, M. H. (1925). *J. Am. Med. Assoc.* **85**, 500–502.

Roberts, M. H. (1928). *Southern Med. J.* **21**, 460–464.

Robertson, W. E., Swalm, W. A., and Konzelmann, F. W. (1932). *J. Am. Med. Assoc.* **99**, 2071–2077.

Robinson, D., and Williams, R. T. (1958). *Biochem. J.* **68**, 23P.

Robinson, M. M. (1961). "Antimicrobial Agents and Chemotherapy," Am. Soc. Microbiol., Detroit, Michigan. pp. 394–400.

Robinson, M. M. (1962a). *Am. J. Med. Sci.* **243**, 502–509.

Robinson, M. M. (1962b). *Am. J. Med. Sci.* **244**, 221–224.

Robinson, S., Vamer, T., Desforges, J. F., and Schmid, R. (1962). *New Engl. J. Med.* **267**, 523–529.

Roholm, K., and Iversen, P. (1939). *Acta Pathol. Microbiol. Scand.* **16**, 427–442.

Roholm, K., Krarup, N. B., and Iversen, P. (1942). *Ergeb. Inn. Med.* **61**, 635–679.

Rolleston, H., and McNee, J. W. (1929). "Diseases of the Liver, Gallbladder and Bile Ducts," 2nd ed. Macmillan, New York (884pp.).

Roman, T., and Delluc, G. (1900). *J. Pharm. Chim. (Paris)* [6] **12**, 49–50.

Ronaldson, J. W., Taylor, A., White, E. P., and Abraham, R. J. (1963). *J. Chem. Soc. (London)* pp. 3172–3180.

Rosa, L., and Marchionini, G. (1949). *Bull. Sci. Med. (Paris)* **121**, 293–298.

Rosa, L., and Marchionini, G. (1950). *Riv. Gastroenterol.* **2**, 268–281.

Rosenfeld, M., and Surgenor, D. M. (1950). *J. Biol. Chem.* **183**, 663–677.

Rosenthal, F. (1924). *Ergeb. Chir.* **17**, 308–397.

Rosenthal, F. (1928). *Ergeb. Inn. Med. Kinderheilk.* **33**, 63–142.

Rosenthal, F. (1930). *Klin. Wochschr.* **9**, 1909–1913.

Rosenthal, F. (1932). *Klin. Wochschr.* **11**, 441–446.

Rosenthal, F., and Meier, K. (1921). *Arch. Exptl. Pathol. Pharmakol.* **91**, 246–271.

Rosenthal, F., and Melchior, E. (1922). *Arch. Exptl. Pathol. Pharmakol.* **94**, 28–51.

Rosenthal, F., Licht, H., and Melchior, E. (1926). *Arch. Exptl. Pathol. Pharmakol.* **115**, 138–179.

Rosenthal, I. M., Zimmerman, H. J., and Hardy, N. (1956). *Pediatrics* **18**, 378–386.

Rosin, H. (1893). *Berlin. Klin. Wochschr.* **30**, 106.

Ross, G. R. (1927). *Brit. J. Exptl. Pathol.* **8**, 442–454.

Ross, S. G., Waugh, T. R., and Malloy, H. T. (1937). *J. Pediat.* **11**, 397–408.

Rosta, J. (1962). *Acta Paediat. Acad. Sci. Hung.* **2**, 249–260.

Rothe, G. (1939). *Z. Ges. Exptl. Med.* **106**, 338–351.

Rothemund, P., and Menotti, A. R. (1941). *J. Am. Chem. Soc.* **61**, 2912–2915.

Rotor, A. B., Manahan, L., and Florentin, A. (1948). *Acta Med. Philippina* **5**, 37–48.

Rouiller, C. (1956). *Acta Anat. (Basel)* **26**, 94.

Rous, P., and Larimore, L. D. (1920a). *J. Exptl. Med.* **31**, 609–632.

Rous, P., and Larimore, L. D. (1920b). *J. Exptl. Med.* **32**, 249–272.

Rous, P., and McMaster, P. D. (1921a). *J. Exptl. Med.* **34**, 47–73.

Rous, P., and McMaster, P. D. (1921b). *J. Exptl. Med.* **34**, 75–96.

Rous, P., and McMaster, P. D. (1923). *J. Exptl. Med.* **37**, 11–20.

Rous, P., Broun, G. O., and McMaster, P. D. (1923). *J. Exptl. Med.* **37**, 421–429.

Roy, M., and Boutaric, A. (1941). *Compt. Rend. Acad. Sci.* **213**, 189–191.

Roy, M., and Boutaric, A. (1942). *Compt. Rend. Acad. Sci.* **215**, 425–427.

Royer, M. (1928a). *Compt. Rend. Soc. Biol.* **99**, 1003–1005.

Royer, M. (1928b). *Compt. Rend. Soc. Biol.* **99**, 1006–1007.

Royer, M. (1928c). *Compt. Rend. Soc. Biol.* **99**, 1419–1420.

Royer, M. (1928d). *Compt. Rend. Soc. Biol.* **99**, 1420–1422.

Royer, M. (1929a). *Compt. Rend. Soc. Biol.* **100**, 130–132.

Royer, M. (1929b). *Compt. Rend. Soc. Biol.* **102**, 421–422.

Royer, M. (1929c). *Compt. Rend. Soc. Biol.* **102**, 422–423.

Royer, M. (1929d). *Compt. Rend. Soc. Biol.* **102**, 450–451.

Royer, M. (1929e). *Compt. Rend. Soc. Biol.* **102**, 451–452.

Royer, M. (1932a). *Compt. Rend. Soc. Biol.* 111, 408–409.

Royer, M. (1932b). *Compt. Rend. Soc. Biol.* 111, 466–468.

Royer, M. (1932c). *Compt. Rend. Soc. Biol.* 111, 825–827.

Royer, M. (1938a). *Compt. Rend. Soc. Biol.* 127, 697–700.

Royer, M. (1938b). *Compt. Rend. Soc. Biol.* 127, 701–702.

Royer, M. (1939). *AMA Arch. Internal Med.* 64, 445–456.

Royer, M. (1943). "La urobilina en el estado normal y patologico," 2nd ed. El Ateneo, Buenos Aires (265pp.).

Royer, M., and Bertrand, J. C. (1929a). *Compt. Rend. Soc. Biol.* 100, 130–132.

Royer, M., and Bertrand, J. C. (1929b). *Compt. Rend. Soc. Biol.* 102, 449–450.

Royer, M., and Garay, E. R. (1960). *Rev. Soc. Arg. Biol.* 36, 375–380.

Royer, M., and Noir, B. A. (1962). *Acta Hepato-Splenol.* 9, 164–173.

Royer, M., and Solari, A. V. (1941). *Rev. Soc. Arg. Biol.* 17, 329–335.

Royer, M., Dassen, R., and Martinez, F. (1933). *Compt. Rend. Soc. Biol.* 114, 75–78.

Royer, M., Chiaravalle, A., and Aramburu, H. G. (1941). *Rev. Soc. Arg. Biol.* 17, 208–212.

Royer, M., Garay, E. R., and Argerich, T. (1962). *Acta Physiol. Latinoam.* 12, 84–90.

Royer, M., Lozzio, B. B., and Gorodisch, S. (1964). *Acta Physiol. Latinoam.* 14, 94–98.

Rozdilsky, B. B. (1961a). *AMA Arch. Pathol.* 72, 8.

Rozdilsky, B. B. (1961b). *AMA Arch. Pathol.* 72, 22.

Rozdilsky, B. B., and Olszewski, B. (1961). *J. Neuropathol. Exptl. Neurol.* 20, 193–205.

Rozendaal, H. M., Comfort, M. W., and Snell, A. M. (1935). *J. Am. Med. Assoc.* 104, 374–379.

Rudolph, H. (1951). *Deut. Z. Verdauungs- Stoffwechselkrankh.* 11, 93–95.

Rudolph, H. (1952). "Chemie und Klinik der Bilirubinreduktionsprodukte Urobilin und Sterkobilin." Thieme, Leipzig (61pp.).

Rudra, N. B. (1946). *Biochem. J.* 40, 500–501.

Rüttner, J. R., Rondez, R., and Maier, C. (1962). *Deut. Med. Wochschr.* 87, 1107–1110.

Russel, G. R. (1962). *Nature* 193, 354–356.

Sachs, P. (1931). *Klin. Wochschr.* 10, 1123.

Sackey, M. S., Johnston, C. G., and Ravdin, I. S. (1934). *J. Exptl. Med.* 60, 189–198.

Sacrez, R., Frühling, L., and Rohmer, J. A. (1946). *Arch. Franc. Pediat.* 3, 78–81.

Saiki, S. (1931a). *Japan. J. Gastroenterol.* 3, 192–195.

Saiki, S. (1931b). *Japan. J. Gastroenterol.* 3, 195–197.

Saiki, S. (1931c). *Japan. J. Gastroenterol.* 3, 197–203.

Saiki, S. (1931d). *Japan. J. Gastroenterol.* 3, 203–207.

Saillet (no inits.) (1897). *Rev. Med.* (*Paris*) 17, 109–129.

Sakamoto, T. (1956a). *Acta Med. Okayama* 10, 11–29.

Sakamoto, T. (1956b). *Acta Med. Okayama* 10, 30–46.

Sakamoto, T. (1956c). *Acta Med. Okayama* 10, 47–55.

Sakamoto, T. (1956d). *Acta Med. Okayama* 10, 227–252.

Sakamoto, T. (1956e). *Acta Med. Okayama* 10, 253–260.

Sakamoto, T. (1957). *Igaku Kenkyu* 27, 124–126 (in Jap., Engl. summary).

Sakamoto, T., Komuta, K., Kondo, T., Hirano, H., Monobe, T., and Kaneda, K. (1957a). *Acta Med. Okayama* 11, 81–87.

Sakamoto, T., Yamamoto, S., Yahata, K., and Kondo, T. (1957b). *Igaku Kenkyu* **27**, 121–123 (in Jap., Engl. summary).

Sakurai, H. (1959a). *Okayama Igakkai Zasshi* **71**, 641 (in Jap., Engl. summary).

Sakurai, H. (1959b). *Okayama Igakkai Zasshi* **71**, 651 (in Jap., Engl. summary).

Salén, E. B. (1924). *Acta Med. Scand.* **60**, 291–357.

Salén, E. B., and Enocksson, B. (1927). *Acta Med. Scand.* **66**, 366.

Salmon, G. W., and Richman, E. E. (1943). *J. Pediat.* **23**, 55–58.

Salvini, M. (1947). *Boll. Soc. Ital. Biol. Sper.* **23**, 1181–1184.

Salvini, M., and Feruglio, F. S. (1948). *Boll. Soc. Ital. Biol. Sper.* **24** (quoted from reprint).

Salvini, M., and Feruglio, F. S. (1949). *Arch. Sci. Med.* (*Turin*) **87**, 46–57.

Salvini, M., and Gonzato, P. (1947a). *Boll. Soc. Ital. Biol. Sper.* **23**, 903–905.

Salvini, M., and Gonzato, P. (1947b). *Boll. Soc. Ital. Biol. Sper.* **23**, 906–907.

Salvini, M., and Mantero, O. (1947). *Osped. Maggiore* **35**, 160–167.

Samuels, B. (1961). *Obstet. Gynecol.* **17**, 103–108.

Samson, K. (1930). *Z. Ges. Neurol. Psychiat.* **128**, 494–503.

Sandring, H. (1957). *Nord. Med.* **57**, 715–718.

Sass-Kortsak, A., Bowden, D. H., and Brown, R. J. K. (1956). *Pediatrics* **17**, 383–391.

Satke, O., and Thums, K. (1932). *Z. Klin. Med.* **120**, 386–399.

Sato, T. (1955a). *Hirosaki Med. J.* **6**, 87–90 (in Jap., Engl. summary).

Sato, T. (1955b). *Hirosaki Med. J.* **6**, 177–181 (in Jap., Engl. summary).

Sato, T. (1962). *Tohoku J. Exptl. Med.* **77**, 83–95.

Saudé, A. (1906). Etude sur la cholémie physiologique. Thesis (Med.), U. of Paris (69pp.).

Sauerbruch, F. (1937). Versuche über die Einwirkung von Ascorbinsäure auf Gallen-farbstoff bei experimentellen Ikterus und *in vitro*. Inaugural Dissertation (Med.), U. of Berlin (23pp.).

Saunders, W. (1803). "A Treatise on the Structure, Economy and Diseases of the Liver," 3rd ed. W. Philips, London (342pp.).

Sauvangeau, C. (1907). *Compt. Rend. Soc. Biol.* **62**, 919–921.

Sborov, V. M., and Watson, C. J. (1949). *J. Lab. Clin. Med.* **34**, 1743–1744.

Sborov, V. M., Jay, A. R., and Watson, C. J. (1951). *J. Lab. Clin. Med.* **37**, 52–59.

Schachsuvarly, M. (1927). *Arch. Schiffs.-Tropenhyg.* **31**, 399–413.

Schachter, D. (1957). *Science* **126**, 507–508.

Schachter, D. (1959). *J. Lab. Clin. Med.* **53**, 557–562.

Schaffner, F., and Kniffen, J. C. (1963). *Ann. N.Y. Acad. Sci.* **104** (Art. 3), 847–857.

Schaffner, F., and Popper, H. (1959). *J. Am. Med. Assoc.* **169**, 1447–1453.

Schaffner, F., and Popper, H. (1963). *Gastroenterology* **44**, 239–242.

Schaffner, F., Popper, H., and Steigmann, F. (1949). *Federation Proc.* **8**, 367–368.

Schaffner, F., Popper, H., and Steigmann, F. (1950). *Am. J. Med. Sci.* **219**, 307–315.

Schalm, L. (1951). *Arch. Chir. Neerl.* **3**, 322–332.

Schalm, L. (1953a). *Schweiz. Z. Allgem. Pathol. Bakteriol.* **16**, 470–473.

Schalm, L. (1953b). *Gastroenterology* **24**, 262–266.

Schalm, L., and Hoogenboom, W. A. H. (1952). *Am. Heart. J.* **44**, 517–580.

Schalm, L., and Schulte, M. J. (1950a). *Am. J. Med. Sci.* **219**, 606–616.

Schalm, L., and Schulte, M. J. (1950b). *Ned. Tijdschr. Geneesk.* **94**, 865–873.

Schalm, L., and Schulte, M. J. (1953a). *Ned. Tijdschr. Geneesk.* **97**, 1013–1022.

Schalm, L., and Schulte, M. J. (1953b). *Ned. Tijdschr. Geneesk.* **97**, 1075–1083.

Schalm, L., and Weber, A. P. (1964). *Acta Med. Scand.* **176**, 549–553.

Schalm, L., Schulte, M. J., Bax, H. R., Miete, M., Mansens, B. J., and Rodriguez-Pereira, A. (1952). *Lancet* **II**, 75–81.

Schalm, L., Sluis, S., Witmans, J., and Ruben, A. T. (1962a). *Ned. Tijdschr. Geneesk.* **106**, 870–875.

Schalm, L., Weber, A. P., and Ruben, A. T. (1962b). *Ned. Tijdschr. Geneesk.* **106**, 1079–1084.

Schapiro, R. H., and Isselbacher, K. J. (1963). *New Engl. J. Med.* **268**, 708–711.

Scheel, O. (1911). *Norsk Mag. Laegevidenskab.* [5] **9**, 173–196.

Scheler, W. (1964). *Abstr. 1st Meet. Federation Eur. Biochem. Soc., London* (T. W. Goodwin, ed.), p. 47. Harris and Hartley, London.

Schellong, G. (1963). *Ger. Med. Monthly* **8**, 274–280.

Schenker, S. (1963). *Ann. N.Y. Acad. Sci.* **111**, (Art. 1), 303–305.

Schenker, S., and McCandles, D. W. (1964). *Nature* **202**, 1344.

Schenker, S., and Schmid, R. (1964). *Proc. Soc. Exptl. Biol. Med.* **115**, 446–448.

Schenker, S., Dawber, N. H., and Schmid, R. (1962). *J. Lab. Clin. Med.* **60**, 1015–1016 (Proc.).

Scherer (no inits.) (1845). *Ann. Chem.* (*Liebigs*) **53**, 377–384.

Scherk, G. (1928). *Deut. Med. Wochschr.* **54**, 476.

Schernhardt, J. (1937). *Klin. Wochschr.* **26**, 920–921.

Schettini, F., Meloni, T., Cordan, G., and Mela, C. (1963). *Lancet* **II**, 1012.

Scheunert, G. (1931). *Beitr. Pathol. Anat. Allgem. Pathol.* **86**, 455–464.

Schick, B. (1921). *Z. Kinderheilk.* **27**, 231–250.

Schick, B., Weiner, S. R., and Reiner, M. (1942). *Am. J. Diseases Children* **64**, 655–660.

Schiff, E., and Eliasberg, H. (1922). *Klin. Wochschr.* **38**, 1891–1893.

Schiff, E., and Faerber, E. (1922). *Jahrb. Kinderkheilk.* **97**, 245–258.

Schiff, L. (1927). *AMA Arch. Internal Med.* **40**, 800–817.

Schiff, L. (1946). "Differential Diagnosis of Jaundice," p. 199. Year Book Publishers, Chicago, Illinois.

Schiff, L., and Billing, B. H. (1959). *Gastroenterology* **37**, 595–602.

Schiff, L., Billing, B. H., and Oikawa, Y. (1959). *New Engl. J. Med.* **260**, 1315–1318.

Schilling, E. (1923). *Klin. Wochschr.* **2**, 1552–1553.

Schindel, L., and Barth, E. (1934). *Klin. Wochschr.* **13**, 1329–1355.

Schindeler, T. A. (1870). Beiträge zur Kenntnis der Veränderungen des thierischen Organismus nach Milzexstirpation. Inaugural Dissertation (Med.), U. of Greifswald (30pp.).

Schlesinger, W. (1903). *Deut. Med. Wochschr.* **29**, 561–563.

Schmid, R. (1956a). *Science* **124**, 76–77.

Schmid, R. (1956b). *Schweiz. Med. Wochschr.* **86**, 775–776.

Schmid, R. (1956c). *J. Lab. Clin. Med.* **48**, 940.

Schmid, R. (1957a). *Helv. Med. Acta* **24**, 273–284.

Schmid, R. (1957b). *J. Biol. Chem.* **229**, 881–888.

Schmid, R. (1963a). *Ann. N.Y. Acad. Sci.* **111** (Art. 1), 451–458.

Schmid, R. (1963b). *S. African J. Lab. Clin. Med.* **9**, 276.

Schmid, R., and Hammaker, L. (1962). *Trans. Assoc. Am. Physicians* **75**, 220–227.

Schmid, R., and Hammaker, L. (1963). *J. Clin. Invest.* **42**, 1720–1734.

Schmid, R., Hammaker, L., and Axelrod, J. (1957a). *Arch. Biochem. Biophys.* **70**, 285–288.

Schmid, R., Hammaker, L., Axelrod, J., and Rosenthal, I. M. (1957b). *J. Clin. Invest.* **36**, 927.

Schmid, R., Jeliu, G., and Gellis, S. S. (1958a). *Lancet* I, 855.

Schmid, R., Williams, G. Z., and Clemens, T. (1958b). *Proc. 6th Intern. Congr. Intern. Soc. Hematol., Boston, 1956*, p. 742. Grune & Stratton, New York.

Schmid, R., Axelrod, J., Hammaker, L., and Swarm, R. L. (1958c). *J. Clin. Invest.* **37**, 1123–1130.

Schmid, R., Brecher, G., and Clemens, T. (1959). *Blood* **14**, 991–1007.

Schmid, R., Forbes, A., Rosenthal, I. M., and Lester, R. (1963). *Lancet* II, 938–939.

Schmidt, A. (1895). *Verhandl. Kongr. Inn. Med.* **13**, 320–330.

Schmidt, C. R., Jones, K. K., and Ivy, C. (1936). *Proc. Soc. Exptl. Biol. Med.* **34**, 17–26.

Schmidt, H. (1929). *Muench. Med. Wochschr.* **76**, 1129–1130.

Schmorl, G. (1904). *Verhandl. Deut. Pathol. Ges.* **6**, 109–115.

Schmorl, G. (1910). *Verhandl. Deut. Pathol. Ges.* **14**, 288–293.

Schönfeld, H. (1927). *Jahrb. Kinderheilk.* **116**, 165–176.

Schoenfield, L. J., and Bollman, J. L. (1963). *Proc. Soc. Exptl. Biol. Med.* **112**, 929–932.

Schoenfield, L. J., Grindlay, J. H., Foulk, W. T., and Bollman, J. L. (1961). *Proc. Soc. Exptl. Biol. Med.* **106**, 438–441.

Schoenfield, L. J., Bollman, J. L., and Hoffmann, H. N. (1962). *J. Clin. Invest.* **41**, 133–140.

Schoental, R. (1960). *Proc. Roy. Soc. Med.* **53**, 284–288.

Scholderer, H. (1933a). *Biochem. Z.* **257**, 137–144.

Scholderer, H. (1933b). *Biochem. Z.* **257**, 145–150.

Scholderer, H., and von Ludany, G. (1932). *Schweitz. Med. Woschr.* **13**, 264.

Schorlemmer, R. (1900). *Arch. Verdauungskrankh.* **6**, 263–284.

Schottmüller, H. (1914). *Muench. Med. Wochschr.* **61**, 230–233.

Schreiber, G. (1932). *Pubbl. Staz. Zool. Napoli* **12**, 291–319.

Schrumpf, A. (1932a). *Norsk Mag. Laegevidenskab.* **93**, 1313–1320.

Schrumpf, A. (1932b). *Acta Med. Scand.* Suppl. 50, 264–266.

Schubert, R. (1949). *Klin. Wochschr.* **26**, 143–149.

Schürer, J. (1922). *Deut. Med. Wochschr.* **48**, 593.

Schultz (no inits.) (1904). *Z. Allgem. Physiol.* **3**, 91–130.

Schultz, N., and Becker, M. (1931a). *Z. Physiol. Chem.* **203**, 157–161.

Schultz, N., and Becker, M. (1931b). *Biochem. Z.* **236**, 99–106.

Schumm, O. (1913). *Z. Physiol. Chem.* **87**, 171–181.

Schumm, O. (1916). *Z. Physiol. Chem.* **97**, 32–52.

Schumm, O. (1932). *Handb. Allgem. Haematol.* **1**, Pt. I, 99–222.

Schwalm, H. (1932). *Zentr. Gynaekol.* **56**, 2098–2105.

Schwanda (no inits.) (1865a). *Wien. Med. Wochschr.* **38**, 677–680.

Schwanda (no inits.) (1865b). *Wien. Med. Wochschr.* **38**, 693–697.

Schwartz, S. (1953). *V.A. Tech. Bull.* (TB-10-94) **6**, 1–19.

Schwartz, S., and Watson, C. J. (1942). *Proc. Soc. Exptl. Biol. Med.* **49**, 641–643.

Schwartz, S., Sborov, V., and Watson, C. J. (1942). *Proc. Soc. Exptl. Biol. Med.* **49**, 643–647.

Schwartz, S., Sborov, V., and Watson, C. J. (1944). *Am. J. Clin. Pathol.* **14**, 598–603.

Schwezoff, S. W. (1930). *Z. Ges. Exptl. Med.* **73**, 285–292.

Scott, J. L., Haut, A., Cartwright, G. E., and Wintrobe, M. M. (1960). *Blood* **16**, 1239.

Scott, L. D. (1941). *Brit. J. Exptl. Pathol.* **22**, 17–23.

Segura, R., and Vidal-Sevilla, S. (1964). *Federation Eur. Biochem. Soc., London Abstr. 1st Meet* (T. W. Goodwin, ed.), p. 94. Harris and Hartley, London.

Senator, H. (1872). *Berlin. Klin. Wochschr.* **9,** 615–618.

Sen Gupta, K. P., and Ganguly, N. C. (1955). *Indian J. Med. Sci.* **9,** 760–763.

Sepulveda, B., and Osterberg, A. E. (1943a). *J. Lab. Clin. Med.* **28,** 1359–1368.

Sepulveda, B., and Osterberg, A. E. (1943b). *J. Lab. Clin. Med.* **28,** 1654.

Sereslis, V. (1938). Über die Ursachen der Unterschiede in den Ergebnissen der Bilirubinbestimmung im Serum nach Hijmans van den Bergh und Jendrassik & Cleghorn. Inaugural Dissertation (Med.), U. of Munich (27pp.).

Sergeant, J. J. V. A. (1910). La cholémie simple familiale. Thesis (Med.), U. of Lille (75pp.).

Serrão, D. (1959). Contribuição histopatologica para o estudo das relações hepatobiliares. Dissertation (Med.), U. of Porto (228pp.).

Shafiroff, B. G. P., Doubilet, H., and Rouggiero, W. A. (1939). *Proc. Soc. Exptl. Biol. Med.* **42,** 203–205.

Shafiroff, B. G. P., Doubilet, H., Rouggiero, W. A., Press, A. P., and Tui, C. (1942). *Am. J. Physiol.* **137,** 97–103.

Shafiroff, B. G. P., Doubilet, H., Barcham, I. S., and Tui, C. (1944). *Am. J. Physiol.* **141,** 480–485.

Sheard, C., Baldes, E. J., Mann, F. C., and Bollman, J. L. (1926). *Am. J. Physiol.* **76,** 577–585.

Sheehan, H. L. (1961). *Am. J. Obstet. Gynecol.* **81,** 427–440.

Shemin, D., and Kumin, S. (1952). *J. Biol. Chem.* **198,** 827–837.

Shemin, D., and Rittenberg, D. (1945). *J. Biol. Chem.* **159,** 567–568.

Shemin, D., and Rittenberg, D. (1946a). *J. Biol. Chem.* **166,** 621–625.

Shemin, D., and Rittenberg, D. (1946b). *J. Biol. Chem.* **166,** 627–636.

Shemin, D., and Wittenberg, J. (1951a). *J. Biol. Chem.* **192,** 315–334.

Shemin, D., and Wittenberg, J. (1951b). *Ciba Found. Symp., Isotopes in Biochem.* pp. 41–64.

Sherlock, S. (1951). *Brit. Heart. J.* **13,** 273–293.

Sherlock, S. (1956). *Postgrad. Med. J.* **32,** 460–466.

Sherman, L., and Zak, B. (1953). *Am. J. Clin. Pathol.* **23,** 946–947.

Shigeru, Y. (1958a). *Igaku Kenkyu* **28,** 19–28 (in Jap., Engl. summary).

Shigeru, Y. (1958b). *Igaku Kenkyu* **28,** 29–36 (in Jap., Engl. summary).

Shimizu, I. (1956a). *Igaku Kenkyu* **26,** 2374 (in Jap., Engl. summary).

Shimizu, I. (1956b). *Igaku Kenkyu* **26,** 2384 (in Jap., Engl. summary).

Shimomura, O. (1959a). *Igaku Kenkyu* **29,** 310–317 (in Jap., Engl. summary).

Shimomura, O. (1959b). *Igaku Kenkyu* **29,** 318–325 (in Jap., Engl. summary).

Shindo, M. (1957a). *Igaku Kenkyu* **27,** 1–9 (in Jap., Engl. summary).

Shindo, M. (1957b). *Igaku Kenkyu* **27,** 10–17 (in Jap., Engl. summary).

Shinomura, H. (1930). *Nagasaki Igakkai Zasshi* **8,** 1046–1056 (in Jap., Engl. summary).

Shinowara, G. Y. (1954). *Am. J. Clin. Pathol.* **24,** 696–710.

Shoji, T. (1933). *J. Med. Assoc. Formosa* **32,** 14–15.

Shorter, R. G., Paton, A., and Pinninger, J. L. (1959). *Quart. J. Med.* **28,** 43–58.

Shutkin, M. W., and Caine, D. (1955). *Am. J. Gastroenterol.* **23,** 235–240.

Siede, W., and Schneider, H. (1957). *Med. Klin.* **52,** 940–954.

Siedel, W. (1935). *Z. Physiol. Chem.* **237,** 8–34.

Siedel, W. (1937). *Z. Physiol. Chem.* **245,** 257–275.

Siedel, W. (1939). *Fortschr. Chem. Org. Naturstoffe* **3,** 81–144.

Siedel, W. (1940). *Angew. Chem.* 53, 397–403.
Siedel, W. (1943a). *Chemie (Berlin)* 56, 169–184.
Siedel, W. (1943b). *Chemie (Berlin)* 56, 185–190.
Siedel, W. (1944). *Ber. Deut. Chem. Ges.* A77, 21–42.
Siedel, W. (1957). *IV Freiburger Symp.* pp. 209–211. Springer, Berlin.
Siedel, W., and Fischer, H. (1933). *Z. Physiol. Chem.* 214, 145–172.
Siedel, W., and Fröwis, W. (1939). *Angew. Chem.* 52, 38–39.
Siedel, W., and Fröwis, W. (1941). *Z. Physiol. Chem.* 267, 37–48.
Siedel, W., and Grams, E. (1941). *Z. Physiol. Chem.* 267, 49–78.
Siedel, W., and Meier, E. (1936). *Z. Physiol. Chem.* 242, 101–132.
Siedel, W., and Möller, H. (1939). *Z. Physiol. Chem.* 259, 113–136.
Siedel, W., and Möller, H. (1940). *Z. Physiol. Chem.* 264, 64–90.
Siedel, W., von Pölnitz, W., and Eisenreich, F. (1947). *Naturwissenschaften* 34, 314–315.
Siedel, W., Stich, W., and Eisenreich, F. (1948). *Naturwissenschaften* 35, 316–317.
Siegler, A. M., and Keyser, H. (1963). *Am. J. Obstet. Gynecol.* 86, 1068–1073.
Sigel, B., Acevedo, F. J., and Dunn, M. R. (1963). *Surg. Gynecol. Obstet.* 117, 29–36.
Siggelkow, H. F. (1935). Zur Frage des Ikterus und Leberschädigung bei Pyelitis gravidarum. Inaugural Dissertation (Med.), U. of Hamburg (41pp.).
Silverman, W. A., Andersen, D. H., Blanc, W. A., and Crozier, D. N. (1956a). *Quart. Rev. Pediat.* 11, 152–153.
Silverman, W. A., Andersen, D. H., Blanc, W. A., and Crozier, D. N. (1956b). *Pediatrics* 18, 614–625.
Simmons, S. C. (1963). *Lancet* II, 60–61.
Simon, F. J. (1941). *Schweitz. Med. Wochschr.* 22, 141–142.
Simon, G., and Varonier, H. S. (1963). *Schweitz. Med. Wochschr.* 93, 459–464.
Simon, J. F. (1840). *Arch. Pharm. (Berlin)* 72, 35–40.
Simon, K. T. (1939). *Jahrb. Kinderheilk.* 152, 338–347.
Simpson, G. E. C., and Finckh, E. S. (1963). *J. Pathol. Bacteriol.* 86, 361–370.
Sims, F. H., and Horn, C. (1958). *Am. J. Clin. Pathol.* 29, 412.
Singer, K. (1930). *Wien. Arch. Inn. Med.* 20, 59–79.
Singer, K. (1945). *J. Lab. Clin. Med.* 30, 784–799.
Singer, K., and Kubin, R. (1943). *J. Lab. Clin. Med.* 28, 1042–1049.
Sivo, R., and Forrsi (1927). *Biochem. Z.* 189, 159–161.
Sjöstrand, T. (1952a). *Acta Physiol. Scand.* 26, 328–333.
Sjöstrand, T. (1952b). *Acta Physiol. Scand.* 26, 334–337.
Sjöstrand, T. (1952c). *Acta Physiol. Scand.* 26, 338–344.
Skrijver, D. (1929). *Klin. Wochschr.* 8, 312–313.
Slater, T. F., and Griffiths, D. B. (1963). *Biochem. J.* 88, 60P–61P.
Slater, T. F., Sträuli, U. D., and Sawyer, B. (1964). *Res. Vet. Sci.* 5, 450–472.
Smetana, H. F. (1963). *Ann. N.Y. Acad. Sci.* 104 (Art. 3), 821–846.
Smetana, H. F., and Johnson, F. B. (1955). *Am. J. Pathol.* 31, 747–755.
Smiley, R. K., Campbell, J. S., and Campbell, E. O'F. (1958). *Can. Med. Assoc. J.* 79, 265–268.
Smith, D. S. (1963). *Calif. Med.* 98, 224–226.
Smith, G. D., and Vella, F. (1960). *Lancet* I, 1133–1134.
Smith, T. B., and Richards, J. A. (1963). *Am. J. Med. Technol.* 29, 291–295.
Snape, W. J., Wirts, C. W., and Cantarow, A. (1947). *Proc. Soc. Exptl. Biol. Med.* 66, 468–470.

Snapp, F. E., Li, T. W., Habegger, J. E., and Ivy, A. C. (1944). *Federation Proc.* **3**, 43.

Snapp, F. E., Gutmann, M., Li, T. W., and Ivy, A. C. (1947). *J. Lab. Clin. Med.* **32**, 321–322.

Snelling, C. E. (1933). *J. Pediat.* **2**, 339–413.

Snelling, C. E. (1946). *Can. Med. Assoc.* **56**, 47–51.

Sobotka, H. Luisada-Opper, A. V., and Reiner, M. (1953). *Am. J. Clin. Pathol.* **23**, 607–609.

Sørland, S. (1960). *Nord. Med.* **63**, 86–95.

Soffer, L. J. (1933). *Bull. Johns Hopkins Hosp.* **52**, 365–375.

Soffer, L. J. (1934). *AMA Arch. Internal Med.* **53**, 808–813.

Soffer, L. J., and Paulsson, M. (1936). *Am. J. Med. Sci.* **192**, 535–540.

Soffer, L. J., Dantes, D. A., and Sobotka, H. (1937a). *AMA Arch. Internal Med.* **60**, 509–521.

Soffer, L. J., Dantes, D. A., Newberger, R., and Sobotka, H. (1937b). *AMA Arch. Internal Med.* **60**, 876–881.

Sommerhalder, M., Kuenzle, C., Rüttner, J. R., and Maier, C. (1962a). *Med. Exptl.* **7**, 196–198.

Sommerhalder, M., Kuenzle, C., Rütter, J. R., and Maier, C. (1962b). *Helv. Med. Acta* **29**, 607–610.

Sonnenfeld, A. (1923). *Klin. Wochschr.* **2**, 2124–2126.

Sonnenfeld, A. (1924). *Z. Klin. Med.* **100**, 508–516.

Sorby, H. C. (1875). *Proc. Zool. Soc. London* pp. 351–365.

Sparkman, A. (1939a). *AMA Arch. Internal Med.* **63**, 857–866.

Sparkman, A. (1939b). *AMA Arch. Internal Med.* **63**, 867–871.

Sparkman, A. (1939c). *AMA Arch. Internal Med.* **63**, 872–883.

Spiegelhoff, W., and Gnann, G. (1950). *Klin. Wochschr.* **42**, 719–720.

Spiess, C. (1905). *Compt. Rend. Acad. Sci.* **141**, 506–508.

Sprinz, H., and Nelson, R. S. (1954). *Ann. Internal Med.* **41**, 952–962.

Squarcetta Romano, M. A. (1942). *Riv. Clin. Pediat.* **40**, 65–89.

Sribhishaj, K., Hawkins, W. B., and Whipple, G. H. (1931). *Am. J. Physiol.* **96**, 449–462.

Stadelmann, E. (1881a) *Arch. Exptl. Pathol. Pharmakol.* **14**, 231–237.

Stadelmann, E (1881b). *Arch. Exptl. Pathol. Pharmakol.* **14**, 422–450.

Stadelmann, E. (1882). *Arch. Exptl. Pathol. Pharmakol.* **15**, 336–363.

Stadelmann, E. (1887). *Arch. Exptl. Pathol. Pharmakol.* **23**, 427–452.

Stadelmann, E. (1891). "Der Ikterus und seine verschiedenen Formen." Enke, Stuttgart (287pp.).

Städeler, G. (1864). *Ann. Chem.* (*Liebigs*) **132**, 323–354.

Standards Comm. Coll. Am. Pathologists (1963). *Am. J. Clin. Pathol.* **39**, 90–91.

Stead, E. A., and Warren J. V. (1944). *J. Clin. Invest.* **23**, 283–287.

Stanojević, L., and Arandjelović, R. R. (1937). *Klin. Wochschr.* **16**, 1386–1387.

Stanojević, L., and Petković, S. (1935). *Klin. Wochschr.* **14**, 1146–1147.

Starling, E. H. (1909). "The Fluids of the Body." Constable, London (186pp.).

Steensma, F. A. (1907). *Ned. Tijdschr. Geneesk.* **51**, 273–275.

Steensma, F. A. (1908a). *Zentr. Ges. Physiol. Pathol. Stoffwechsels* **3**, 231–232.

Steensma, F. A. (1908b). *Biochem. Z.* **8**, 209.

Steensma, F. A. (1909). *Ned. Tijdschr. Geneesk.* **53**, 1567–1569.

Steensma, F. A. (1914). *Ned. Tijdschr. Geneesk.* **58**, 248–251.

Steensma, F. A. (1918). Klinische en experimentelle onderzoekingen over urobiline en urobilinurie. Akad. Proefschrift (Geneesk.), U. of Amsterdam (114pp.).

Stefanini, M. (1949). *J. Lab. Clin. Med.* **34,** 1039–1048.

Stefanutti, P. (1940). *Policlinico (Rome), Sez. Prat.* **47,** 169–175.

Stefanutti, P., Ferrara, D., and Ricciardolo, F. (1940). *Policlinico (Rome), Sez. Prat.* **47,** 183–193.

Stehr, K., and Vogt, D. (1962). *Deut. Med. Wochschr.* **87,** 604–606.

Steigmann, F., and Dyniewicz, J. M. (1943a). *Gastroenterology* **1,** 743–764.

Steigmann, F., and Dyniewicz, J. M. (1943b). *Gastroenterology* **1,** 855–875.

Steigmann, F., and Popper, H. (1943). *Gastroenterology* **1,** 645–654.

Steigmann, F., Meyer, K. A., and Popper, H. (1949). *AMA Arch. Surg.* **59,** 101–113.

Stein, A. A., and Wright, A. W. (1956). *J. Am. Med. Assoc.* **161,** 508–511.

Stein, H. B. (1941). *S. African J. Med. Sci.* **6,** 104–115.

Stein, J. (1935). *Compt. Rend. Soc. Biol.* **120,** 1136–1138.

Stein, J. (1937). *Arch. Exptl. Zellforsch.* **20,** 78–81.

Stein, S. (1903). Cholémie simple familiale et grosesse. Thesis (Med.), U. of Paris (110pp.).

Steiner, J. W., and Carruthers, J. S. (1962). *Am. J. Pathol.* **40,** 253–270.

Steiner, J. W., Carruthers, J. S., and Kalifat, S. R. (1962a). *Exptl. Mol. Pathol.* **1,** 162–185.

Steiner, J. W., Carruthers, J. S., and Kalifat, S. R. (1962b). *Exptl. Mol. Pathol.* **1,** 427–456.

Stengle, J. M., and Schade, A. L. (1957). *Brit. J. Haematol.* **3,** 117–124.

Stenhagen, E., and Rideal, E. K. (1939). *Biochem. J.* **33,** 1591–1598.

Stenhagen, E., and Teorell, T. (1938). *Nature* **141,** 415.

Sterling, J. A., and Lowenburg, H. (1963). *Ann. N.Y. Acad. Sci.* **111** (Art. 1), 483–503.

Sterling, S. (1911). *Arch. Exptl. Pathol. Pharmakol.* **64,** 468–488.

Stern, A., and Pruckner, F. (1938). *Z. Phys. Chem. (Leipzig)* **A182,** 117–126.

Stern, F. (1930). Über die Theorien der Gallenfarbstoffbildung mit besonderer Berücksichtigung des Ikterus. Inaugural Dissertation (Med.), U. of Bonn (35pp.).

Stern, H. (1885). *Arch. Exptl. Pathol. Pharmakol* **19,** 39–59.

Stern, K. G. (1935). *J. Biol. Chem.* **112,** 661–669.

Stevens, A. J., Saunders, C. N., Spence, J. B., and Newnham, A. G. (1960). *Vet Record* **72,** 627.

Stevenson, G. W., Jacobs, S. L., and Henry, R. J. (1964). *Clin. Chem.* **10,** 95–102.

Stevenson, I. H., and Dutton, G. J. (1962). *Biochem. J.* **82,** 330–340.

Stewart, A. E. (1960). *Lancet* **II,** 896–897.

Stich, C. (1901). *Muench. Med. Wochschr.* **48,** 1751.

Stich, W. (1946a). *Deut. Med. Wochschr.* **71,** 137–138.

Stich, W. (1946b). *Klin. Wochschr.* **24,** 177–179.

Stich, W. (1948). *Klin. Wochschr.* **26,** 365–367.

Stich, W. (1952a). *Roentgen- Lab. Praxis* **5,** 152–156.

Stich, W. (1952b). *Roentgen- Lab. Praxis* **5,** 174–178.

Stich, W. (1952c). *Roentgen- Lab. Praxis* **5,** 265–269.

Stich, W. (1957). IV. *Freiburger Symp.* pp. 184–188. Springer, Berlin.

Stich, W., and Stärk, G. (1953). *Naturwissenschaften* **40,** 56–57.

Stich, W., Kehl, R., and Walter, H. R. (1953). *Z. Physiol. Chem.* **292,** 178–180.

Stiefel, G. E. (1959). *Schweiz. Med. Wochschr.* **89,** 759.

Stier, E. (1942a). Z. Physiol. Chem. **272**, 239–272.

Stier, E. (1942b). Z. Physiol. Chem. **273**, 47–75.

Stier, E. (1942c). Z. Physiol. Chem. **275**, 155–166.

Stier, E. (1947). Z. Ges. Inn. Med. Grenzgebiete **2**, 257–272.

Still, G. F. (1927). "Common Disorders and Diseases of Childhood," 5th ed., p. 375. Oxford Univ. Press, London and New York.

Stokes, J., Wolman, I. J., Blanchard, M. C., and Farquhar, J. D. (1951). Am. J. Diseases Children **82**, 213–216.

Stokvis, B. J. (1870). Maandblad Naturw. **1**, Nos. 3 and 5 (quoted from Stokvis, 1872b, p. 785).

Stokvis, B. J. (1872a). Maandblad Naturw. **3**, No. 1 (quoted from Stokvis, 1872b, p. 785).

Stokvis, B. J. (1872b). Zentr. Med. Wiss. **10**, 785–788.

Stokvis, B. J. (1872c). Ber. Deut. Chem. Ges. **5**, 583.

Stoner, R. E., and Weisberg, H. F. (1957). Clin. Chem. **3**, 22–35.

Stowens, D. (1963). Ann. N.Y. Acad. Sci. **111** (Art. 1), 337–352.

Strahl, H. (1890). Arch. Anat. Physiol. (Leipzig), Anat. Abt. Suppl., 118–134.

Stransky, E. (1953). Ann. Pediat. (Basel) **175**, 301–307.

Stransky, E. (1955). Lancet I, 1227–1228.

Strasburger, J. (1918). Deut. Arch. Klin. Med. **125**, 108–146.

Strasser, U. (1937). Wien. Arch. Inn. Med. **31**, 267–287.

Strauss, H. (1919). Deut. Med. Wochschr. **45**, 872.

Strausz, L. (1923). Deut. Med. Wochschr. **49**, 376–379.

Strisower, R. (1922). Wien. Arch. Klin. Med. **3**, 153–226.

Strisower, R., and Goldsmidt, W. (1916). Z. Ges. Exptl. Med. **4**, 237–258.

Stroebe, F. (1932a). Z. Klin. Med. **120**, 95–111.

Stroebe, F. (1932b). Klin. Wochschr. **11**, 495–497.

Ströder, J. (1957). IV. Freiburger Symp. pp. 41–48. Springer, Berlin.

Sugar, P. (1961) AMA Arch. Internal Med. **108**, 121–127.

Summerskill, W. H. J., and Walshe, J. M. (1959). Lancet II, 686–690.

Sumner, J. B., and Dounce, A. L. (1938). J. Biol. Chem. **121**, 417–424.

Sunde, A. (1911). Norsk Mag. Laegevidenskab. [5] **9**, 945–950.

Susuki, M. (1958a). Igaku Kenkyu **28**, 2540 (in Jap., Engl. summary).

Susuki, M. (1958b). Igaku Kenkyu **28**, 2549, (in Jap., Engl. summary).

Sutherland, J. M. (1963). Ann. N.Y. Acad. Sci. **111**, (Art. 1). 461–470.

Svanborg, A. (1954). Acta Obstet. Gynecol. Scand. **33**, 434–444.

Svanborg, A., and Ohlsson, S. (1959). Am. J. Med. **27**, 40–49.

Svenneby, G. (1956). Nord. Med. **55**, 765.

Svedberg, A., Maddock, S., and Drury, D. K. (1938). Am. J. Physiol. **121**, 209–214.

Syballa, L. (1904). Folia Haematol. (Leipzig) **1**, 636.

Synge, R. L. M., and White, E. P. (1959). Chem. Ind. (London) pp. 1546–1547.

Szabó, L., and Ebrey, P. (1963). Acta Paediat. Acad. Sci. Hung. **4**, 153–158.

Szabó, L., Kovács, Z., and Ebrey, P. B. (1962). Acta Paediat. Acad. Sci. Hung. **3**, 49–70.

Takaki, N. (1959a). Okayama Igakkai Zasshi **72**, 309 (in Jap., Engl. summary).

Takaki, N. (1959b). Okayama Igakkai Zasshi **72**, 319 (in Jap., Engl. summary).

Takeda, Y. (1959a). Igaku Kenkyu **29**, 2687 (in Jap., Engl summary).

Takeda, Y. (1959b). Igaku Kenkyu **29**, 2698 (in Jap., Engl. summary).

Takemura, T. (1959a). Okayama Igakkai Zasshi **71**, 8343 (in Jap., Engl. summary).

Takemura, T. (1959b). Okayama Igakkai Zasshi **71**, 8353 (in Jap., Engl. summary).

Takemura, T. (1962a). *Proc. Japan Acad.* **38**, 393–396.
Takemura, T. (1962b). *Proc. Japan Acad.* **38**, 591–595.
Takemura, T. (1962c). *Proc. Japan Acad.* **38**, 596–600.
Takeshita, K. (1933). *Mitt. Med. Akad. Kioto* **9**, 750–751.
Takeuchi, R. (1959). *Akayama Igakkai Zasshi* **71**, 7653.
Talafant, E. (1954a). *Collection Czech. Chem. Commun.* **19**, 1344–1347.
Talafant, E. (1954b). *Casopis Lekaru Ceskych* **93**, 582–584.
Talafant, E. (1956a). *Acta Med. Scand.* **156**, 333–335.
Talafant, E. (1956b). *Nature* **178**, 312.
Talafant, E. (1956c). *Chem. Listy* **50**, 817–820.
Talafant, E. (1956d). *Chem. Listy* **50**, 1329.
Talafant, E. (1957). *Nature* **180**, 1051.
Talafant, E. (1959a) *Scripta Med. Fac. Med. Univ. Brun. Olomuc.* **32**, 161–170.
Talafant, E. (1959b). *Scripta Med. Fac. Med. Univ. Brun. Olomuc.* **32**, 201–220.
Talafant, E. (1961). *Nature* **192**, 972–973.
Talafant, E., and Továrek, J. (1959a). *Nature* **183**, 111–112.
Talafant, E., and Továrek, J. (1959b). *Vnitrni Lekar.* **5**, 136–142.
Tallack, J. A., and Sherlock, S. (1954). *Brit. Med. J.* **II**, 212–213.
Tamaki, H. T. and Carfaguo, S. C. (1957). *AMA Arch. Internal Med.* **99**, 294–297.
Taniguschi, K. (1928). *Arch. Exptl. Pathol. Pharmakol.* **130**, 37–48.
Tarchanoff, J. F. (1874). *Arch. Ges. Physiol. (Pfluegers)* **9**, 53–65.
Tat, R. J., Greenwalt, T. J., and Dameshek, W. (1943). *Am. J. Diseases Children* **65**, 558–570.
Taylor, P. M., Bright, N. H., Birchard, E. L., Derinoz, M. N., and Watson, D. W. (1963a). *Biol. Neonatorum* **5**, 299–318.
Taylor, P. M., Wolfson, J. H., Bright, N. H., Birchard, E. L., Derinoz, M. N., and Watson, D. W. (1963b). *Biol. Neonatorum* **5**, 289–298.
Tecon, R. M. (1936). *Rev. Med. Suisse Rom.* **56**, 193–220.
Tecon, R. M. (1938a). *Arch. Maladies App. Digest. Nutr.* **28**, 567–589.
Tecon, R. M. (1938b). *Helv. Med. Acta* **5**, 671–674.
Tefik (no inits.) and Ibrahim (no inits.) (1909). *Z. Urol.* **3**, 703–711.
ten Bokkel Huinink, J. W. G. (1941). *Geneesk. Bladen Klin. Lab. Prakt.* [38] **6**, 177–215.
ten Bokkel Huinink, J. W. G. (1942). *Am. J. Digest. Diseases* **9**, 168–172.
Tenhunen, R., and Torsti, R. (1959). *Scand. J. Clin. Lab. Invest.* **11**, 162–164.
Terwen, A. J. L. (1924). De quantitieve bepaling van urobiline en urobilinogen in urine en feces, Akad. Proefschift (Geneesk.), U. of Amsterdam (79pp.).
Terwen, A. J. L. (1925). *Deut. Arch. Klin. Med.* **149**, 72–101.
Terwen, A. J. L. (1928). *Ned. Tijdschr. Geneesk.* **72**, 128–131.
Thannhauser, S. J., and Andersen, E. (1921). *Deut. Arch. Klin. Med.* **137**, 179–186.
Theile, H., Steiniger, U., and Beyreiss, K. (1963a). *Z. Kinderheilk.* **88**, 144–152.
Theile, H., Steiniger, U., and Beyreiss, K. (1963b). *Monatsschr. Kinderheilk.* **11**, 1–6.
Thoma, G. E., and Kitzberger, D. M. (1948). *J. Lab. Clin. Med.* **38**, 1189–1192.
Thomas, J. E. (1941). *Proc. Soc. Exptl. Biol. Med.* **46**, 260–261.
Thomas, K. (1907a). *Z. Klin. Med.* **63**, 247–252.
Thomas, K. (1907b). Urobilinogen seine klinische Bedeutung, seine chemischen Eigenschaften und seine Farbreaktionen ("Ehrlichsche Aldehyd" und "Eigelbe Diazoreaktion"). Inaugural Dissertation (Med.), U. of Freiburg (49pp.).
Thompson, H. E., and Wyatt, B. L. (1938). *A.M.A. Arch. Internal Med.* **61**, 480–495.
Thorek, P. (1939). *J. Am. Med. Assoc.* **141**, 767–770.

Thorling, L. (1955). Jaundice in Pregnancy. A Clinical Study. *Acta Med. Scand.* Suppl. 302 (123pp.).

Thorpe, W. V. (1955). "Biochemistry for Medical Students." Churchill, London (542pp.).

Thudichum, J. L. W. (1868). *J. Prakt. Chem.* **104**, 193–222.

Thudichum, J. L. W. (1886). "Grundzüge der anatomischen und klinischen Chemie," p. 321. Berlin (quoted in Thudichum, 1897, p. 588).

Thudichum, J. L. W. (1896). "The Progress of Medical Chemistry, Comprising Its Application to Physiology, Pathology, and Practise of Medicine." London (quoted in Thudichum, 1897, p. 588).

Thudichum, J. L. W. (1897). *Arch. Pathol. Anat. Physiol.* **150**, 586–588.

Thureborn, E. (1962). Human Hepatic Bile Composition Changes Due to Altered Enterohepatic Circulation. *Acta Chir. Scand.* Suppl. 303 (63pp.).

Thursfield, H. (1911). *Proc. Roy. Soc. Med.* **5**, Pt. I, 147–148.

Thyman, G. (1950). *Ugeskrift Laeger* **112**, 723–725.

Tiedemann, F., and Gmelin, L. (1826). "Die Verdauung nach Versuchen," 1st ed. Karl Groos, Heidelberg und Leipzig (Vol. I, 280pp.; Vol. II, 279pp.).

Tiedemann, F., and Gmelin, L. (1831). "Die Verdauung nach Versuchen," 2nd ed. Karl Groos, Heidelberg and Leipzig (Vol. I, 280pp.; Vol. II, 279pp.).

Tiesenga, M. F., Neal, R. H., and Hemwall, G. A. (1964). *J. Am. Med. Assoc.* **187**, 367–368.

Tisdale, W. A., and Welch, J. (1962). *J. Lab. Clin. Med.* **59**, 956–962.

Tisdale, W. A., Klatskin, E. D., and Kinsella, E. D. (1959). *Am. J. Med.* **26**, 214–227.

Tissier, P. L. A. (1889). Essai sur la pathologie de la secretion biliaire. Thesis (Med.), U. of Paris (150pp.).

Tixier, R. (1945). *Ann. Inst. Oceanogr.* (*Monaco*) [N.S.] **22**, 343–397.

Tixier, R. (1947). *Compt. Rend. Acad. Sci.* **225**, 508–510.

Tixier, R. (1948). *Compt. Rend. XIII. Congr. Intern. Zool., Paris* pp. 84–85.

Tixier, R., and Lederer, E. (1947). *Compt. Rend. Acad. Sci.* **225**, 508–510.

Tixier, R., and Lederer, E. (1948). *Compt. Rend. XIII. Congr. Intern. Zool., Paris* pp. 85–86.

Tixier, R., and Lederer, E. (1949). *Compt. Rend. Acad. Sci.* **228**, 1669–1671.

Tixier, R., and Tixier-Durivault, A. (1942). *Bull. Soc. Chim. Biol.* **24**, 376–379.

Tixier, R., and Tixier-Durivault, A. (1943). *Bull. Soc. Chim. Biol.* **25**, 98–103.

Tosti, A. (1949). *Minerva Med.* **40**, 203–204.

Tovey, G. H., Gillespie, E. N., Guy, J., Valaes, T., Oppe, T. E., and Lewis, E. F. J. (1959). *Lancet* **I**, 860.

Traina, I. (1941). *Riv. Clin. Pediat.* **39**, 129–160.

Trams, E. G., and Symeonides, A. (1957). *Am. J. Pathol.* **33**, 13.

Treibs, A., and Hermann, E. (1955). *Z. Physiol. Chem.* **299**, 168–185.

Triboulet, H. (1909a). *Bull. Mem. Soc. Med. Hop. Paris* p. 445.

Triboulet, H. (1909b). *Compt. Rend. Soc. Biol.* **66**, 394–395.

Troisier, J. (1909). *Compt. Rend. Soc. Biol.* **66**, 739–740.

Tschirgi, R. D. (1962). *Federation Proc.* **21**, 665–671.

Tsuchiya (no inits.) (1910). *Z. Exptl. Pathol. Therapie* **7**, 352–362.

Tsuchiya, Y., and Nomura, T. (1955). *Tohoku J. Agr. Res.* **6**, 75–83.

Tsuchiya, Y., and Nomura, T. (1958). *Tohoku J. Agr. Res.* **9**, 81–92.

Tsuchiya, Y., and Nomura, T. (1959). *Compt. Rend. Soc. Biol.* **153**, 873–876.

Tsuchiya, Y., and Nomura, T. (1961). *Compt. Rend. Soc. Biol.* **155**, 34–36.

Tsuchiya, Y., and Nomura, T. (1962). *Tohoku J. Agr. Res.* **13**, 49–53.

Tsunoo, S., and Nakamura, H. (1931). *J. Biochem. (Tokyo)* **12**, 133–138.

Tützer, G., and Adler, A. (1924). *Klin. Wochschr.* **3**, 1318–1319.

Tuttle, A. H. (1955). *Am. J. Diseases Children* **89**, 544–552.

Tvaroha, B. (1961a). *Casopis Lekaru Ceskych* **100**, 27–28.

Tvaroha, B. (1961b). *Collection Czech. Chem. Commun.* **26**, 2271–2277.

Tvaroha, B. (1961c). *Naturwissenschaften* **4**, 99.

Tvaroha, B., and Jirsa, M. (1960). *Casopis Lekaru Ceskych* **99**, 252–253.

Tygstrup, N. (1960). *Lancet* **I**, 1171.

Umber, F., and Rosenberg, M. (1928). *Deut. Med. Wochschr.* **54**, 90–91.

Umber, T. (1926). *Handb. Inn. Med.* **3**, Pt. II, 20–36 (2nd ed.).

Ungar, H., Moran, E., Eisner, M., and Eliakim, M. (1962). *AMA Arch. Pathol.* **73**, 427–435.

Uno, S. (1934). *Folia Endocrinol. Japon.* **9**, 108 (in Jap., Ger. summary).

Väyrynen, S. (1934). Untersuchungen über den Bilirubingehalt des Serums bei Gesunden, Nichtschwangeren, Schwangeren, Gebärenden und Wöchnerihnen. *Acta Soc. Med. Fennicae "Duodecim."* **B20**, fasc. 1 (202pp.).

Vahlquist, B. C. (1939). *Acta Paediat.* **25**, 302–330.

Vahlquist, B. C. (1940). *Nord. Med.* **7**, 1516–1521.

Vahlquist, B. C. (1941). Das Serumeisen. *Acta Paediat.* **28**, Suppl. 5 (442pp.).

Valaes, T. (1959). *Lancet* **I**, 208–209.

Valaes, T. (1961). *Cerebral Palsy Bull.* **3**, 431–434.

Valaes, T. (1963). Bilirubin distribution and dynamics of bilirubin removal by exchange transfusion. *Acta Paediat.* Suppl. 149 (117pp.).

Valentini (no inits.) (1888). *Arch. Exptl. Pathol. Pharmakol.* **24**, 412–423.

Van den Bergh, H.: *see* Hijmans van den Bergh.

van de Velde, J. (1927). *Compt. Rend. Soc. Biol.* **97**, 1197–1199.

van de Velde, J. (1929). *Compt. Rend. Soc. Biol.* **100**, 1059–1062.

van Duyne, C. M., and Havel, R. (1959). *Proc. Soc. Exptl. Biol. Med.* **102**, 529.

van Ittalie, L. (1929). *Pharm. Weekblad* **66**, 13–14.

van Leersum, E. C. (1899). *Ned. Tijdschr. Geneesk.* **35**, 1065–1073.

van Leusden, H. A. I. M., and Stolte, L. A. M. (1963). *Acta Physiol. Pharmacol. Neerl.* **12** (quoted from reprint).

van Leusden, H. A. I. M., Bakkeren, J. A. J. M., Zilliken, F., and Stolte, L. A. M. (1962). *Biochem. Biophys. Res. Commun.* **7**, 67–69.

van Putten, L. M. (1958). *Blood* **13**, 789–794.

Varela Fuentes, B. (1943). *Prensa Med. Arg.* **30**, 2091–2117.

Varela Fuentes, B. (1950). *Acta Med. Scand.* **138**, 65–66.

Varela Fuentes, B., and Canzani, R. (1938). "La diazo-reacción amarilla, anormal de algunos sueros ictéricos," Libro de Oro, dedicado al Prof. Dr. Mariano Castex, Vol. III. Buenos Aires (quoted from reprint).

Varela Fuentes, B., and Canzani, R. (1939). *Sang* **17**, 101–106.

Varela, B., and Esculies, J. (1931). *Compt. Rend. Soc. Biol.* **107**, 884–887.

Varela Fuentes, B., and Mendioroz, B. A. (1959). *Arch. Soc. Biol. Montevideo* **24**, 11–16.

Varela Fuentes, B., and Munilla, A. (1934). *Compt. Rend. Soc. Biol.* **117**, 555–557.

Varela Fuentes, B., and Recarte, P. (1934a). *Compt. Rend. Soc. Biol.* **116**, 1193–1196.

Varela Fuentes, B., and Recarte, P. (1934b). *Compt. Rend. Soc. Biol.* **117**, 900–902.

Varela Fuentes, B., and Viana, C. (1933a). *Compt. Rend. Soc. Biol.* **114**, 786–788.

Varela Fuentes, B., and Viana, C. (1933b). *Compt. Rend. Soc. Biol.* **114**, 789–792.
Varela Fuentes, B., and Viana, C. (1935a). *Compt. Rend. Soc. Biol.* **118**, 927–930.
Varela Fuentes, B., and Viana, C. (1935b). *Compt. Rend. Soc. Biol.* **118**, 1518–1520.
Varela, B., Apolo, E., and Viana, C. (1931a). *Compt. Rend. Soc. Biol.* **108**, 1014–1016.
Varela, B., Recarte, P., and Esculies, J. (1931b). *Compt. Rend. Soc. Biol.* **108**, 1009–1013.
Varela, B., Viana, C., and Recarte, P. (1934). *Compt. Rend. Soc. Biol.* **117**, 903–908.
Varela Fuentes, B., Canzani, R., and Graña, A. (1939a). *Arch. Soc. Biol. Montevideo* **9** (quoted from reprint).
Varela Fuentes, B., Canzani, R., and Graña, A. (1939b). *Arch. Pediat. Uruguay* **10**, 389–395.
Varela Fuentes, B., Munilla, A., and Rubira, N. (1944). *Dia medico* **16**, 522–533.
Vaughan, J. M., and Haslewood, G. D. A. (1938). *Lancet* **I**, 113–135.
Vecchio, F., Rigillo, N., and Mela, C. (1963a,b,c). *Boll. Soc. Ital. Biol. Sper.* **39**, 1080–1083(a); 1083–1085(b); 1085–1087(c).
Vegas, F. R. (1963). *Anal. Biochem.* **5**, 465–470.
Vella, F. (1958). *J. Clin. Pathol.* **11**, 87.
Vella, F. (1962). *W. African J. Biol. Chem.* **6**, 1–4.
Verhage, J. C. (1940). *Ned. Tijdschr. Verlosk. Gynaecol.* **43**, 135–159.
Verniory, A. (1946). *Compt. Rend. Soc. Biol.* **140**, 912–915.
Verschure, J. C. M., and Hoefsmit, F. M. C. (1956). *Clin. Chim. Acta* **1**, 38–48.
Verzár, F. (1929). *Z. Ges. Exptl. Med.* **68**, 475–481.
Verzár, F., and Zih, A. (1928). *Klin. Wochschr.* **7**, 1031–1032.
Verzár, F., and Zih, A. (1929). *Biochem. Z.* **205**, 388–401.
Verzár, F., von Arvay, A., Peter, J., and Scholderer, H. (1933). *Biochem. Z.* **257**, 113–129.
Verzár, F., Süllmann, H., and Visscher, A. (1934). *Biochem. Z.* **274**, 7–15.
Vest, M. (1958a). *Arch. Disease Childhood* **33**, 473–476.
Vest, M. (1958b). *Schweiz. Med. Wochschr.* **88**, 59–62.
Vest, M. (1959). "Physiologie und Pathologie des Neugeborenenicterus." Karger, Basel (118pp.).
Vest, M. (1962). *Schweiz. Med. Wochschr.* **92**, 940.
Vest, M., and Fritz, E. (1961). *J. Clin. Pathol.* **14**, 482–487.
Vest, M., and Grieder, H.-R. (1961). *J. Pediat.* **59**, 194–199.
Vest, M., and Streiff, R. R. (1959). *AMA J. Diseases Children* **98**, 688–693.
Vest, M., Kaufmann, H. J., and Fritz, E. (1960). *Arch. Disease Childhood* **35**, 600–604.
Vickers, H. E. (1950a). *St. Mary's Hosp. Gaz.* **56**, 115.
Vickers, H. E. (1950b). *J. Clin. Pathol.* **3**, 270–273.
Vink, C. L. J. (1954). *Maandschr. Kindergeneesk.* **22**, 334–345.
Vink, C. L. J., and Deenstra, H. (1951). *Ned. Tijdschr. Geneesk.* **93**, 3700.
Violet, G. (1880). *Arch. Pathol. Anat. Physiol.* **80**, 353–379.
Virchow, R. (1847). *Arch. Pathol. Anat. Physiol.* **1**, 379–486.
Virtanen, A. I., and Laine, T. (1946). *Nature* **157**, 25–26.
Virtanen, A. I., and Miettinen, J. K. (1949). *Acta Chem. Scand.* **3**, 17–21.
Vitelli, A., Gaidano, G., and Cattaneo, C. (1956). *Fegato* **2**, 408–435.
Vitelli, A., Gaidano, C., Catteneo, C., and Toretta, A. (1957). *Minerva Med.* **48**, 2327.
Voegtlin, W. L. (1947). *Am. J. Clin. Pathol.* **18**, 84–86.
Voegtlin, W. L., Moss, M. H., and March, E. (1950). *Gastroenterology* **14**, 538–540.
Voinov, V. (1928). *Compt. Rend. Soc. Biol.* **99**, 1081–1083.

Voit, C. (1860). *Z. Wiss. Zool.* **10**, 470–475.

von Bergmann, E. (1881). *Volkmann's Samlung Klin. Vortr.* No. 190 (Chir. No. 57), 1540–1574 (1558–1560).

von Bergmann, G. (1927). *Klin. Wochschr.* **6**, 776–780.

von Dobeneck, H. (1941a). *Z. Physiol. Chem.* **269**, 268–270.

von Dobeneck, H. (1941b). *Z. Physiol. Chem.* **270**, 223–232.

von Dobeneck, H. (1942). *Z. Physiol. Chem.* **275**, 1–15.

von Dobeneck, H. (1948a). *Z. Ges. Inn. Med. Grenzgebiete* **3**, 252–254.

von Dobeneck, H. (1948b). *Naturwissenschaften* **35**, 221.

von Dobeneck, H. (1949). *Naturwissenschaften* **36**, 219.

von Dobeneck, H., and Klötzer, E. (1959). *Z. Physiol. Chem.* **316**, 78–82.

von Eck, N. (1877). *Militaer-med. J. St. Petersburg* **130**, 257.

von Fürth, O. (1903). "Vergleichende chemische Physiologie der niederen Tiere," p. 201. Fischer, Jena.

von Gündell, H., and Jacobi, J. (1926). *Deut. Arch. Klin. Med.* **153**, 215–222.

von Jaksch, R. (1890). *Z. Heilkunde* **11**, 417–442.

von Jaksch, R. (1891). *Verhandl. Kongr. Inn. Med.* **10**, 353–354.

von Linden, M. (1903). *Arch. Ges. Physiol. (Pfluegers)* **98**, 1–89.

von Müller, F. (1887). *Z. Klin. Med.* **12**, 45–113.

von Müller, F. (1892). *Jahresber. Schles. Ges. Vaterl.-Cult. (Breslau)* **70** (I. Med. Abt.), 1–13.

von Purjesz, B. (1937). *Med. Klin.* **38**, 1271.

von Recklinghausen, F. D. (1889). *Tagebl. 62. Versamml. Deut. Naturforsch.* pp. 324–325.

von Zeyneck, R. (1901). *Z. Physiol. Chem.* **34**, 148–152.

von Zeyneck, R. (1902). *Z. Physiol. Chem.* **36**, 568–574.

von Zeyneck, R. (1912). *Sitzungsber. Wien. Akad. Wiss.* **121**, Abt. IIb, 1495–1511.

von Zumbusch, L. (1901). *Z. Physiol. Chem.* **31**, 446–459.

Vossius, A. (1879). Über quantitative spektralanalytische Bestimmung des Bilirubins in der Galle. Inaugural Dissertation (Med.), U. of Giessen (29pp.).

Waagstein, P. H. D. (1946). *Nord. Med.* **32**, 2805–2806.

Wagner, R. (1921). *Z. Kinderheilk.* **27**, 251–261.

Wainrach, S. (1956). *Presna Med. Argent.* **43**, 2425–2431.

Wainrach, S., and del Gayso, M. (1958). *Rev. Clin. Espan.* **69**, 14–24.

Waitz, R. (1928). *Rev. Franç. Pediat.* **4**, 1–56.

Wakabayashi, H. (1932). *Trans. Japan. Pathol. Soc.* **22**, 666–668.

Waldeck, F., and Harth, O. (1963). *Klin. Wochschr.* **41**, 825–831.

Waldenström, J. (1937). Studien über Porphyrie. *Acta Med. Scand.* Suppl. **82** (254pp.).

Waldenström, J., and Vahlquist, B. C. (1939). *Z. Physiol. Chem.* **260**, 189–209.

Walker, A. H. C. (1957). *Brit. Med. J.* **II**, 376.

Wallace, G. B., and Diamond, J. S. (1925). *AMA Arch. Internal. Med.* **35**, 698–725.

Wallach, H. F., and Popper, H. (1950). *Arch. Pathol.* **49**, 33–42.

Waller, J. W., Blumgart, H. L., and Volk, M. C. (1940). *AMA Arch. Internal Med.* **66**, 1230–1245.

Walter, H., and Williencourt, J. A. (1928). *Gynécol. Obstet.* **18**, 127–135.

Walzel, P., and Weltmann, O. (1924). *Mitt. Grenzgebieten Med. Chir.* **37**, 437–463.

Wang, C. P. W., and Eastman, N. J. (1936). *Chinese Med. J.* **50**, 53–58.

Warburg, O., and Negelein, E. (1930). *Ber. Deut. Chem. Ges.* **63**, 1816–1818.

Watanabe, H. (1959). *Okayama Igakkai Zasshi* **71**, 6953 (in Jap., Engl. summary).

Waters, W. J., and Britton, H. A. (1955). *Pediatrics* **14**, 45–48.
Waters, W. J., Richert, D. A., and Rawson, H. H. (1953). *Am. J. Diseases Children* **86**, 483.
Waters, W. J., Richert, D. A., and Rawson, H. H. (1954). *Pediatrics* **13**, 319–325.
Waters, W. J., Dunham, R., and Bowen, W. R. (1958). *Proc. Soc. Exptl. Biol. Med.* **99**, 175–177.
Watson, C. J. (1931). *AMA Arch. Internal Med.* **47**, 697–726.
Watson, C. J. (1932a). *Z. Physiol. Chem.* **204**, 57–67.
Watson, C. J. (1932b). *Z. Physiol. Chem.* **208**, 101–119.
Watson, C. J. (1933a). *Z. Physiol. Chem.* **221**, 145–155.
Watson, C. J. (1933b). *Proc. Soc. Exptl. Biol. Med.* **30**, 1207.
Watson, C. J. (1933c). *Proc. Soc. Exptl. Biol. Med.* **30**, 1210.
Watson, C. J. (1934). *J. Biol. Chem.* **105**, 469–472.
Watson, C. J. (1935a). *Proc. Soc. Exptl. Biol. Med.* **32**, 1506.
Watson, C. J. (1935b). *Proc. Soc. Exptl. Biol. Med.* **32**, 1508.
Watson, C. J. (1935c). *Z. Physiol. Chem.* **233**, 39–58.
Watson, C. J. (1936a). *J. Biol. Chem.* **114**, 47–57.
Watson, C. J. (1936b). *Proc. Soc. Exptl. Biol. Med.* **34**, 377–379.
Watson, C. J. (1936c). *Am. J. Clin. Pathol.* **6**, 458–475.
Watson, C. J. (1937a). *AMA Arch. Internal Med.* **59**, 196–205.
Watson, C. J. (1937b). *AMA Arch. Internal Med.* **59**, 206–231.
Watson, C. J. (1938). *In* "Handbook of Hematology" (H. Downey, ed.), Vol. IV, pp. 2446–2580. Hamish Hamilton, London.
Watson, C. J. (1940). *J. Am. Med. Assoc.* **114**, 2427–2432.
Watson, C. J. (1942a). *New Engl. J. Med.* **227**, 665–672.
Watson, C. J. (1942b). *New Engl. J. Med.* **227**, 705–711.
Watson, C. J. (1944). *Gastroenterology* **3**, 296.
Watson, C. J. (1946). *Blood* **1**, 99–120.
Watson, C. J. (1953). *J. Biol. Chem.* **200**, 691–696.
Watson, C. J. (1956a). *Minnesota Med.* **39**, 294–300.
Watson, C. J. (1956b). *Minnesota Med.* **39**, 403–412.
Watson, C. J. (1956c). *Minnesota Med.* **39**, 467–474.
Watson, C. J. (1956d). *Am. J. Med.* **45**, 351–368.
Watson, C. J. (1956e). *Ann. Internal Med.* **45**, 351–368.
Watson, C. J. (1957). IV. *Freiburger Symp.* pp. 41–48 and 188–194. Springer, Berlin.
Watson, C. J. (1958). *Science* **128**, 142–143.
Watson, C. J. (1959). *J. Lab. Clin. Med.* **54**, 1–25.
Watson, C. J. (1963). *J. Clin. Pathol.* **16**, 1–11.
Watson, C. J., and Bilden, E. (1941). *AMA Arch. Internal Med.* **68**, 740–746.
Watson, C. J., and Hawkinson, V. (1946). *J. Lab. Clin. Med.* **31**, 914–915.
Watson, C. J., and Hoffbauer, W. (1946). *AMA Arch. Internal Med.* **25**, 195–227.
Watson, C. J., and Hoffbauer, W. (1947). *AMA Arch. Internal Med.* **26**, 813–842.
Watson, C. J., and Lowry, P. T. (1956). *J. Biol. Chem.* **218**, 633.
Watson, C. J., and Schwartz, S. (1941). *Proc. Soc. Exptl. Biol. Med.* **47**, 393.
Watson, C. J., and Schwartz, S. (1942). *Proc. Soc. Exptl. Biol. Med.* **49**, 636–640.
Watson, C. J., and Weimer, M. (1959). *J. Lab. Clin. Med.* **54**, 1–25.
Watson, C. J., Pass, I., and Schwartz, S. (1941). *J. Biol. Chem.* **139**, 583–591.
Watson, C. J., Sborov, V., and Schwartz, S. (1942). *Proc. Soc. Exptl. Biol. Med.* **49**, 647–651.

Watson, C. J., Schwartz, S., Sborov, V., and Bertie, E. (1944). *Am. J. Clin. Pathol.* **14**, 605–615.

Watson, C. J., Lowry, P. T., Sborov, V. E., Hollinshead, W. H., Kohan, S., and Matte, H. O. (1953). *J. Biol. Chem.* **200**, 697–701.

Watson, C. J., Lowry, P. T., Collins, S., Graham, A., and Ziegler, N. R. (1954). *Trans. Assoc. Am. Physicians* **67**, 242–249.

Watson, C. J., Campbell, M., and Lowry, P. T. (1958). *Proc. Soc. Exptl. Biol. Med.* **98**, 707–711.

Watson, C. J., Weimer, M., and Hawkinson, V. (1960). *J. Biol. Chem.* **235**, 787–794.

Watson, C. J., Hall, J. W., Bossenmaier, I., Weimer, M., and Cardinal, R. (1962). *J. Lab. Clin. Med.* **60**, 1024 (Proc.).

Watson, D. (1960). *Clin. Chim. Acta* **5**, 613–615.

Watson, D. (1961a). *Clin. Chim. Acta* **6**, 737–739.

Watson, D. (1961b). *Clin. Chem.* **7**, 603.

Watson, D. (1962a). *Clin. Sci.* **22**, 435–444.

Watson, D. (1962b). *Clin. Chim. Acta* **7**, 733–734.

Watson, D. (1963). *Australasian Ann. Med.* **12**, 53–69.

Watson, D. (1964a). *Postgrad. Med.* **35**, A46–A55.

Watson, D. (1964b). *Australian New Zealand J. Obstet. Gynecol.* **4**, 121–124.

Watson, D., and Maddison, G. (1962). *Biol. Neonatorum* **4**, 86–93.

Watson, D., and Porter, R. (1963). *Acta Haematol.* **29**, 37–50.

Watson, D., and Rogers, J. A. (1961). *J. Clin. Pathol.* **14**, 271–278.

Watson, J., Meads, M., and Castle, W. B. (1945). *J. Am. Med. Assoc.* **128**, 308.

Watson-James, G., and Abbott, L. D. (1958). *Am. J. Med.* **25**, 124.

Waugh, T. R., Merchant, F. T., and Maugham, G. B. (1940). *Am. J. Med. Sci.* **199**, 9–23.

Weatherall, D. J. (1960). *Lancet* **II**, 835.

Webb, D. A. (1939). *J. Exptl. Biol.* **16**, 499–522.

Weber, A. P., and Schalm, L. (1962). *Clin. Chim. Acta* **7**, 805–810.

Weber, A. P., Schalm, L., and Witmans, J. (1963). *Acta Med. Scand.* **173**, 19–34.

Weech, A. A., Vann, D., and Grillo, R. A. (1941). *J. Clin. Invest.* **20**, 323–332.

Wegmann, R., Rangier, M., Eteve, J., Charbonnier, A., and Caroli, J. (1960). *Semaine Hop. Paris* **36**, 1761–1781.

Wegmann, T., and Marogg, J. (1959). *Schweiz. Med. Wochschr.* **89**, 345.

Weicker, H. (1957). *Deut. Arch. Klin. Med.* **204**, 265–274.

Weinberger, E. (1936). *Z. Physiol. Chem.* **238**, 124–128.

Weinbren, K., and Billing, B. H. (1956). *Brit. J. Exptl. Pathol.* **37**, 199.

Weiner, S. B., and Reiner, M. (1939). *Proc. Soc. Exptl. Biol. Med.* **41**, 83–85.

Weir, J. F. (1932). *Am. J. Surg.* **15**, 494–503.

Weiss, M. (1930). *Wien. Arch. Inn. Med.* **20**, 39–58.

Weiss, P. (1955). *Helv. Med. Acta* **22**, 43–62.

Welin, G. (1945). *Nord. Med.* **25**, 575–581.

Weltmann, O. (1923). *Wien. Klin. Wochschr.* **36**, 389–392.

Weltmann, O., and Hückel, H. (1928). *Med. Klin.* **24**, 1393–1396.

Weltmann, O., and Hückel, H. (1929). *Med. Klin.* **25**, 560–561.

Weltmann, O., and Jost, F. (1928a). *Deut. Arch. Klin. Med.* **161**, 203–226.

Weltmann, O., and Jost, F. (1928b). *Med. Klin.* **24**, 1125–1127.

Werner, E., and Möhlmann, E. (1962). *Klin. Wochschr.* **40**, 972–975.

Werner, L. (1943). *Muench. Med. Wochschr.* **90**, 267–268.

Werner, S. C., Hanger, F. M., and Kritzler, R. A. (1950). *Am. J. Med.* **8**, 325–331.

Wertheimer, E., and Lepage, L. (1897). *Arch. Physiol. Norm. Pathol.* [5] 9, 363–374.
Wertheimer, E., and Lepage, L. (1898). *Arch. Physiol. Norm. Pathol.* [5] 10, 334–346.
Wertheimer, E., and Lepage, L. (1899). *J. Physiol. Pathol. Gen.* 1, 259–267.
Werther, J. L., and Korelitz, B. I. (1957). *Am. J. Med.* 22, 351–366.
Wespi, H. (1935). *Klin. Wochschr.* 14, 1820–1821.
West, E. S., and Todd, W. R. (1956). "Textbook of Biochemistry," 2nd ed. Macmillan, New York (1356pp.).
Wester, J. J. (1912a). *Tijdschr. Veeartsenijk. Veeteelt* 39, 817–834.
Wester J. J. (1912b). *Z. Tiermed.* 16, 467–477.
Westlake, E. K. (1956). *Lancet* II, 146.
Westphal, U., and Gedigk, P. (1948). *Z. Physiol. Chem.* 283, 161–179.
Westphal, U., and Gedigk, P. (1949). *Deut. Arch. Klin. Med.* 195, 445–446.
Westphal, U., Ott, H., and Gedigk, P. (1950). *Z. Physiol. Chem.* 285, 36–50.
Wheeler, H. O. (1963). *Med. Clin. North Am.* 47, 607–620.
Wheeler, H. O., Cranston, W. I., and Meltzer, J. L. (1958). *Proc. Soc. Exptl. Biol. Med.* 99, 11.
Whipple, G. H. (1922a). *AMA Arch. Internal Med.* 29, 711–731.
Whipple, G. H. (1922b). *Physiol. Rev.* 2, 440–459.
Whipple, G. H., and Hooper, C. W. (1913a). *J. Exptl. Med.* 17, 593–611.
Whipple, G. H., and Hooper, C. W. (1913b). *J. Exptl. Med.* 17, 612–635.
Whipple, G. H., and King, J. H. (1911). *J. Exptl. Med.* 13, 115–135.
Whipple, G. H., and Robscheit-Robbins, F. S. (1925). *Am. J. Physiol.* 72, 394–406.
White, D., Haidar, G. A., and Reinhold, J. G. (1958). *Clin. Chem.* 4, 211–222.
White, F. D. (1933). *Brit. J. Exptl. Pathol.* 14, 17–24.
White, F. D., and Duncan, D. (1952). *Can. J. Med. Sci.* 30, 552–560.
Wicke, W. (1858). *Goetting. Gelehrte Anz.* 3, 314–320.
Widal, F., and Abrami, P. (1928). "Les ictères, Nouveau traité de médicine," Vol. XVI, pp. 177–296. Masson, Paris.
Wiechel, K.-L. (1963). Technique and Application of the Percutaneous Transhepatic Cholangiography with Studies of the Hepatic Venous and Biliary Duct Pressures, the Chemical Changes in Blood and Bile, and Clinical Results in a Series of Jaundiced Patients. *Acta Chir. Scand.*, Suppl. 309 (96pp.).
Wieland, H., and Kotzschmar, A. (1937). *Ann. Chem. (Liebigs)* 530, 152–165.
Wieland, H., and Tartter, A. (1940). *Ann. Chem. (Liebigs)* 545, 197–208.
Wiemer, P. (1926). *Deut. Arch. Klin. Med.* 151, 154–171.
Wigglesworth, V. B. (1943). *Proc. Roy. Soc.* B131, 313–339.
Wilbur, A. T., and Addis, T. (1914). *AMA Arch. Internal Med.* 13, 235–286.
Wild, A. E. (1961). *Clin. Sci.* 21, 221–231.
Wildhirt, E. (1955). *Acta Hepatol.* 3, 157–170.
Williams, A. T., and Cabello Ruz, J. (1943). *Rev. Soc. Arg. Biol.* 19, 400–408.
Williams, R., and Billing, B. H. (1961). *Lancet* II, 392–396.
Williams, T. (1953). "An Introduction to Chromatography." Blackie, Glasgow and London (100pp.).
Wilson, M. T., and Davidson, L. S. P. (1949). *Brit. Med. J.* I, 884–887.
Willstaedt, H. (1941). *Enzymologia* 9, 260–264.
Wiss, O. (1942). Die Extraction des Bilirubins aus Blutserum und ihre klinische Verwendung. Inaugural Dissertation (Med.), U. of Basel (15pp.).
Winternitz, M. (1923). *Wien. Arch. Inn. Med.* 7, 201–206.
Wíslański, K. (1930). (Polish with French summary) *Ginekol. Polska* 9, 491–503.

With, T. K. (1942a). *Z. Physiol. Chem.* **275**, 166–175.
With, T. K. (1942b). *Z. Physiol. Chem.* **275**, 176–182.
With, T. K. (1943a). *Z. Physiol. Chem.* **278**, 120–129.
With, T. K. (1943b). *Z. Physiol. Chem.* **278**, 130–135.
With, T. K. (1943c). *Acta Med. Scand.* **115**, 542–553.
With, T. H. (1943d). *Acta Med. Scand.* **114**, 426–441.
With, T. H. (1943e). *Acta Med. Scand.* **114**, 379–382.
With, T. H. (1943f). *Acta Med. Scand.* **116**, 96–114.
With, T. K. (1944a). *Acta Med. Scand.* **119**, 201–213.
With, T. K. (1944b). *Acta Med. Scand.* **119**, 214–248.
With, T. K. (1944c). *Nord. Med.* **21**, 601–604.
With, T. K. (1944d). *Nord. Med.* **22**, 825–832.
With, T. K. (1945a). *Acta Physiol. Scand.* **10**, 172–180.
With, T. K. (1945b). *Acta Physiol. Scand.* **10**, 181–192.
With, T. K. (1945c). *Acta Med. Scand.* **122**, 501–512.
With, T. K. (1945d). *Acta Med. Scand.* **122**, 513–522.
With, T. K. (1945e). *Acta Physiol. Scand.* **10**, 355–365.
With, T. K. (1945f). *Ugeskrift Laeger* **107**, 287–290.
With, T. K. (1946a). *Nature* **158**, 310.
With, T. K. (1946b). *Acta Med. Scand.* **123**, 166–180.
With, T. K. (1946c). *Acta Med. Scand.* **125**, 588–599.
With, T. K. (1947). *Acta Med. Scand.* **128**, 25–41.
With, T. K. (1949). *Acta Med. Scand.* **124**, Suppl. 234, pp. 331–339.
With, T. K. (1954). "Biology of Bile Pigments." A. Frost-Hansen, Copenhagen (523pp.).
With, T. K. (1957a). *IV. Freiburger Symp.* pp. 215–218. Springer, Berlin.
With, T. K. (1957b). *Scand. J. Clin. Lab. Invest.* **9**, 208–209.
With, T. K. (1957c). *IV. Freiburger Symp.* p. 34 (Discussion). Springer, Berlin.
With, T. K. (1958a). *Ann. Biol. Clin.* **16**, 12–20.
With, T. K. (1958b). *Scand. J. Clin. Lab. Invest.* **10**, 188–190.
With, T. K. (1958c). *Scand. J. Clin. Lab. Invest.* **10**, 297–302.
With, T. K. (1958d). *Ugeskrift Laeger* **120**, 843–844.
With, T. K. (1960). "Biologie der Gallenfarbstoffe." Thieme, Stuttgart (377pp.).
With, T. K. (1962). *Spectrum Intern. (Pfizer)* **6**, 77–80.
With, T. K. (1963). *Lancet* **I**, 228.
Witmanns, J., Schalm, L., and Schulte, M. J. (1961). *Clin. Chim. Acta* **6**, 7–15.
Wittenberg, J., and Shemin, D. (1949). *J. Biol. Chem.* **178**, 46–51.
Wittenberg, J., and Shemin, D. (1950a). *J. Biol. Chem.* **185**, 103–116.
Wittenberg, J., and Shemin, D. (1950b). *Federation Proc.* **9**, 247.
Wolf, R. (1935). Untersuchungen über den Bilirubingehalt des Blutes in der Schwangerschaft und im Wochenbett. Inaugural Dissertation (Med.), U. of Jena (27pp.).
Wolf, W. (1956). *Z. Ges. Inn. Med. Grenzgebiete* **11**, 385–388.
Wolff, H. J. (1934). *J Pharmacol. Exptl. Therap.* **50**, 407–419.
Woll, H. O. (1912). Quantitativer Nachweis und Menge des Urobilins im Tierharne mit Hilfe des Descomps'schen Apparats. Inaugural Dissertation (Vet.), U. of Stuttgart (32pp.).
Wooldridge, H., chairman (1962). Report of the Interdepartmental Working Party of the British Government on Groundout Toxicity Research, London.

Woolley, G., and Courtice, F. G. (1962). *Australian J. Exptl. Biol. Med. Sci.* **40**, 121–128.

Worms, R., Bernhard, J., Bessis, M., and Malassenet, R. (1961). *Nouvelle Rev. Franc. Hematol.* **1**, 805–818.

Wright, J. E., and Braithewaite, J. L. (1962). *Nature* **195**, 95–96.

Wyers, H. J., and Bakker, J. C. W. (1954). *Maandschr. Kindergeneesk.* **22**, 253–263.

Yahata, K. (1959). *Igaku Kenkyu* **29**, 2630–2643 (in Jap., Engl. summary).

Yamabuki, T. (1959a). *Okayama Igakkai Zasshi* **71**, 8429 (in Jap., Engl. summary).

Yamabuki, T. (1959b). *Okayama Igakkai Zasshi* **71**, 8445 (in Jap., Engl. summary).

Yamaguchi, M., Nakajima, H., and Yamaoka, K. (1961). *Proc. Japan. Acad.* **37**, 584–588.

Yamamoto, H. (1956a). *Igaku Kenkyu* **26**, 2664 (in Jap., Engl. summary).

Yamamoto, H. (1956b). *Igaku Kenkyu* **26**, 2675 (in Jap., Engl. summary).

Yamamoto, H. (1958). *Okayama Igakkai Zasshi* **70**, 589 (in Jap., Engl. summary).

Yamamoto, Y. (1951). *Igaku Kenkyu* **21**, 1439–1441 (in Jap., Engl. summary).

Yamamoto, Y. (1953). *J. Japan. Soc. Internal Med.* **42**, 531–590.

Yamaoka, K., and Kosaka, K. (1951). *Proc. Japan. Acad.* **27**, 715–721.

Yamaoka, K., and Nakajima, H. (1962). *Japan. J. Med.* **1**, 103–105.

Yamaoka, K., Kosaka, K., and Ariji, S. (1952a). *Acta Med. Okayama* **8**, 84–98.

Yamaoka, K., Kosaka, K., and Shigeru, A. (1952b). *Acta Med. Okayama* **8**, 99–110.

Yamaoka, K., Kosaka, K., Shinamura, T., and Miyake, T. (1952c). *Acta Med. Okayama* **8**, 111–119.

Yamaoka, K., Kosaka, K., and Yamamoto, Y. (1952d). *Acta Med. Okayama* **8**, 120–134.

Yamaoka, K., Kosaka, K., Nakagawa, J., Yada, N., and Hosokawa, M. (1956a). *Proc. Japan. Acad.* **32**, 412–416.

Yamaoka, K., Kosaka, K., and Sakamoto, T. (1956b). *Proc. Japan. Acad.* **32**, 306–310.

Yamaoka, K., Kosaka, K., Nakagawa, J., Yada, N., and Hosokawa, M. (1956c). *Proc. Japan. Acad.* **32**, 417–421.

Ylppö, A. (1913). *Z. Kinderheilk.* **9**, 208–326.

Ylppö, A. (1924). "Eulenburgs Real-Encyklopädie der gesamten Heilkunde," Suppl. 5. Ergeb. Ges. Med., 4th ed. pp. 222–231. Urban & Schwartzenberg, Berlin.

Yokoe, Y. (1957). *Sapporo Med. J.* **11**, 149–180.

Youmans, J. B., and Warfield, L. M. (1926). *AMA Arch. Internal Med.* **37**, 1–17.

Young, L. E. (1947a). *New Engl. J. Med.* **237**, 225–231.

Young, L. E. (1947b). *New Engl. J. Med.* **237**, 261–268.

Young, L. E., Wendell, D. R., and Hogestyn, J. (1949). *J. Lab. Clin. Med.* **34**, 287–291.

Yuasa, D. (1928). *Beitr. Pathol. Anat. Allgem. Pathol.* **79**, 713–727.

Zabel, J. B. (1949). *Ned. Tijdschr. Geneesk.* **93**, 3172–3177.

Zacho, A., and Larsen, E. H. (1946a). *Nord. Med.* **29**, 229–232.

Zacho, A., and Larsen, E. H. (1946b). *Nord. Med.* **32**, 2571–2573.

Zak, B., Moss, N., Boyle, A., and Zlatkis, A. (1954). *Anal. Chem.* **26**, 1220–1222.

Zamorani, V. (1925). *Riv. Clin. Pediat.* **23**, 9–19.

Zeile, K. (1956). *Angew. Chem.* **68**, 193–201.

Zelasco, J. F. (1940). La bilirubinemia normal, Dissertation (Med.), U. of Buenos Aires.

Zelasco, J. F., and Lopez Garcia, A. (1944). *Anales Inst. Invest. Fis. Apl. Patol. Humana* **6**, 1–32.

Zelman, S. (1959). *Am. J. Med.* **27**, 708–729.

Zenglein, G. (1930). Les variations pathologiques de la bilirubinemie chez le cheval. Thesis (Vet.), U. of Strassburg (84pp.).

Zetterqvist, P. (1957). *Nord. Med.* **58**, 1278.

Zetterström, R., and Ernster, L. (1956). *Nature* **178**, 1335–1337.

Ziegelroth, P. (1926). *Muench. Med. Wochschr.* **73**, 1440.

Zieve, L., Hill, E., Hanson, M., Falcone, A. B., and Watson, C. J. (1951). *J. Lab. Clin. Med.* **38**, 446–469.

Zih, A. (1928). *Klin. Wochschr.* **7**, 1155–1156.

Zih, A. (1933). *Arch. Ges. Physiol.* **231**, 502–509.

Zih, A. (1936). *Z. Ges. Exptl. Med.* **99**, 657–663.

Zih, A. (1939). *Z. Ges. Exptl. Med.* **106**, 136–138.

Zimmerman, H. J. (1963). *Ann. N.Y. Acad. Sci.* **104** (Art. 3), 954–987.

Zinkham, W. H., and Lenhard, R. E. (1959). *J. Pediat.* **55**, 319.

Zoja, L. (1938). *Minerva Med.* **14**, 385–387.

Zuelzer, W. W. (1959). *Blood* **14**, 595 (Discussion).

Zuelzer, W. W., and Brown, A. K. (1961). *Am. J. Diseases Children* **101**, 87.

Zuelzer, W. W., and Mudgett, R. T. (1950). *Pediatrics* **6**, 452–474.

Zuelzer, W. W., Reisman, L. E., and Brown, A. K. (1961). *Am. J. Diseases Children* **102**, 815–842.

Zweifel, P. (1875). *Arch. Gynaekol.* **7**, 474–490.

Additional Readings

CHAPTER III

Section B

Root, W. S. (1960). "Methods in Medical Research" (H. D. Brunner, ed.), Vol. 8, pp. 112–118. Year Book Publ., Chicago, Illinois.

Spink, R. R., Malvin, R. L., and Cohen, B. J. (1966). Determination of erythrocyte half life and blood volume in cats. *Am. J. Vet. Res.* **27**, 1041–1043.

CHAPTER V (*continued*)

Section I,1

Gartner, L. M. (1967). The hormonal regulation of hepatic bilirubin excretion. *In* "Bilirubin Metabolism" (I. A. D. Bouchier and B. H. Billing, eds.), pp. 175–182. Blackwell, Oxford.

Phan-The-Tran and Bui-Duy-Tam (1965). Bilirubin blood levels in Vietnamese subjects. *Bull. Soc. Pathol. Exotique* **58**, 108–114.

Section I,2

Alagille, D. (1966). Metabolic jaundice in newborn (in French). *Ann. Biol. Clin.* **24**, 1–13.

Arias, I. M., Wolfson, S., Lucey, J. F., and McKay, R. J., Jr. (1965). Transient familial neonatal hyperbilirubinemia. *J. Clin. Invest.* **44**, 1442–1450.

Bakken, A. F., and Fog, J. (1967). Bilirubin conjugation in newborn rats. *Lancet* **II**, 309–310.

Brodersen, R., Jacobsen, J., Hertz, H., Rebbe, H., and Sørensen, B. (1967). Bilirubin conjugation in the human fetus. *Scand. J. Clin. Lab. Invest.* **20**, 41–48.

Davis, J. A., and Schiff, D. (1966). Bruising as a cause of neonatal jaundice. *Lancet* **I**, 636–638.

Gartner, L. M., and Arias, I. M. (1966). Studies of prolonged neonatal jaundice in the breast-fed infant. *J. Lab. Clin. Med.* **68**, 54–66.

Lu, T.-C., Wei, H., and Blackwell, R. Q. (1966). Increased incidence of severe hyperbilirubinemia among newborn Chinese infants with G-6-P deficiency. *Pediatrics* **37**, 994–999.

Matsuda, I., and Shirato, T. (1967). Bilirubin metabolism in newborns. *Lancet* I, 958–959.
Miller, S., Fonkalsrud, E. W., and Longmire, W. P. (1966). Current concepts in the management of congenital biliary atresia. *Arch. Surg.* 92, 813–817.
Perrin, D., Guimbretière, J., and Harousseau, H. (1966). A new form of foeto-maternal incompatibility, familial neonatal hepatitis (in French). *Presse Med.* 74, 1307–1312.
Smetana, H. F., Edlow, J. B., and Glunz, P. R. (1965). Neonatal jaundice. A critical review of persistent obstructive jaundice in infancy. *Arch. Pathol.* 80, 553–574.

Section J

Natzschka, J. C., and Odell, G. B. (1966). The influence of albumin on the distribution and excretion of bilirubin in jaundiced rats. *Pediatrics* 37, 51–61.

Section K

Brodersen, R., and Tygstrup, N. (1967). Serum bilirubin studies in patients with intermittent intrahepatic cholestasis. *J. Brit. Soc. Gastroenterol.* 8, 46–49.
Butt, H. R., Anderson, V. E., Foulk, W. T., Baggenstoss, A. H., Schoenfield, L. J., and Dickson, E. R. (1966). Studies of chronic idiopathic jaundice (Dubin-Johnson Syndrome). Evaluation of a large family with the trait. *Gastroenterology* 51, 619–630.
Nixon, J. C., and Monahan, G. J. (1967). Gilbert's disease and the bilirubin tolerance test. *Can. Med. Assoc. J.* 96, 370–373.
Toussaint, W., and Gros, H. (1966). Familial jaundice associated with intrahepatic cholestasis. (In German). *Deut. Z. Verdaauungs-Stoffwechselkrankh.* 26, 23–31.

Section L

Adlercreutz, H., Svanborg, A., and Ånberg, Å. (1967). Recurrent jaundice in pregnancy I and II. *Am. J. Med.* 42, 335–340, 341–348.
Lange, F. C., and Ströder, J. (1966). The correlation between the total serum bilirubin and the age in epidemic hepatitis in children (in German). *Klin. Wochschr.* 44, 493–498.
Larsson-Cohn, U. (1967). Jaundice and oral contraceptives. *Lancet* I, 679.
Orellana-Alcade, J. M., and Dominguez, J. P. (1967). Jaundice and oral contraceptive drugs. *Lancet* II, 1278–1280.
Sanderson, R. G., Ellison, J. H., Benson, J. A., Jr., and Starr, A. (1967). Jaundice following open-heart surgery. *Ann. Surg.* 165, 217–224.

Section M

Rutkowski, R. B. (1967). The determination of maximum bilirubin binding capacity of human albumin and serum by a calcium carbonate adsorption technique. *Clin. Chim. Acta* 17, 31–38.

Section N

Fenech, F. F., Bannister, W. H., and Grech, J. L. (1967). Hepatitis with biliverdinemia in association with indomethacin therapy. *Brti. Med. J.* II, 155–156.

Section O

Pethonen, A., Näntö, V., and Brummer, P. (1966). Serum and urinary urobilinoids in hepatic diseases. *Acta Med. Scand.* 180, 235–239.

Supplementary Bibliography

Asterisked reference citations in the text are listed in this bibliography.

Abrahams, C., Wheatley, A., Rubenstand, A. H., and Stables, D. (1963). *Lancet* **II**, 621–622.

Agarawala, O. N., Negi, S. S., and Mahadevan, V. (1962). *Current Sci. (India)* **31**, 506–507.

Albot, G., Partmier-Albot, M., Etienne, J.-P., Barbé, J., Oudea, J., and Housset, E. (1965a). *Pathol. Biol. Semaine Hop.* **13**, 31–42.

Albot, G., Partmier-Albot, M., Housset, E., Etienne, J.-P., and Barbé, J. (1965b). *Pathol. Biol. Semaine Hop.* **13**, 495–505.

Altman, K. I., and Russel, E. S. (1964). *J. Cellular Comp. Biol.* **64**, 293–301.

Ardelt, W., and Pfleiderer, A. (1964). *Klin. Wochschr.* **42**, 971–973.

Arias, I. M., Gartner, L. M., Seifter, S., and Furman, M. (1964). *J. Clin. Invest.* **43**, 2037–2047.

Arias, I. M., Wolfson, S., Lucey, J. F., and McKay, R. J. (1965). *J. Clin. Invest.* **44**, 1442–1450.

Armstrong, P. B. (1964). *J. Exptl. Zool.* **155**, 129–133.

Asscher, A. W., and Jones, J. H. (1965). *Postgrad. Med. J.* **41**, 425–434.

Badger, G. M., Harris, R. L. B., Jones, R. A., and Sasse, J. M. (1962). *J. Chem. Soc.* pp. 4329–4337.

Bailiff, R. N. (1960). *Ann. N.Y. Acad. Sci.* **88**, 3–13.

Barac, G., and Beaumariage, M.-L. (1964). *Arch. Intern. Physiol. Biochim.* **72**, 514–515.

Barbé, J. (1963). Le choleperitoine experimentale, son syndrome biologique, ses rapports avec le syndrome de cholestase. Thèse (Med.), U. of Paris.

Beck, K. (1964). Habilitationsschrift (Med.), U. of Freiburg.

Bennike, K. A., and Hagelsten, J. O. (1964). *Lancet* **II**, 255.

Berendson, S., Lowmann, J., Sundberg, D., and Watson, C. J. (1964). *Blood* **24**, 1–18.

Bergner, P.-E. E. (1965). *Nature* **205**, 975–977.

Bernhardt, F. (1964). *Z. Ges. Inn. Med. Ihre Grenzgebiete* **19**, 824–826.

Bevan, B. R., Holton, J. B., and Lathe, G. H. (1965). *Clin. Sci.* **29**, 353–361.

Billing, B. H., Gray, C. H., Lulczyka, P. M., and Nicholson, D. C. (1964a). *Clin. Sci.* **27**, 163–169.

Billing, B. H., Williams, R., and Richards, T. G. (1946b). *Clin. Sci.* **27**, 245–257.

Billing, B. H., Maggiore, Q., and Goulis, G. (1965). *Minerva Med.* **55**, 2548–2550.

Billing, B. H., Ali, M., and Dunnicliff, M. (1966). *VIth Intern. Congr. Clin. Chem., Munich, 1966* Abstr., p. 234. Karger, Basel.

Blacklidge, V. J. (1963). *J. Pediat.* **62**, 666–686.

Blanck, C., Dahlgren, S., Gullmar-Willcocks, M., and De Hevesy, G. (1966). *Acta Paed. Scand.* **55**, 329–336.

Blažek, Z., Bobek, P., and Dvorsky, A. (1964). *Deut. Z. Verdauungs-Stoffwecheselkrankh.* **24**, 17–21.

Bleyler, J. M., and Steigmann, F. (1958). *Am. J. Digest. Diseases* **3**, 947–952.

Blondheim, S. H., and Kaufmann, N. A. (1965). *J. Lab. Clin. Med.* **65**, 659–664.

Boake, W. C., Schade, S. G., Morissey, J. F., and Schaffner, F. (1965). *Ann. Intern. Med.* **63**, 302–308.

Boerth, R. C., Blatt, A. H., and Spratt, J. L. (1965). *J. Lab. Clin. Med.* **65**, 475–483.

Boggs, T. R., and Bishop, H. (1965). *J. Pediat.* **66**, 349–356.

Bolt, R. J., Dillon, R. S., and Merven-Pollard, H. (1961). *New Engl. J. Med.* **265**, 1043.

Bouchier, I. A. D., and Billing, B. H., eds. (1967). "Bilirubin Metabolism." Blackwell, Oxford (293pp.).

Bouchier, I. A. D., and Cooperband, S. R. (1965). *Gastroenterology* **49**, 354–359.

Boulanger, J.-P., and Fierro, L. (1964). *Am. J. Clin. Pathol.* **42**, 557–558.

Bowman, J. M., and Pollock, J. M. (1965a). *Pediatrics* **35**, 815–835.

Bowman, J. M., and Pollock, J. M. (1965b). *Proc. 10th Congr. Intern. Soc. Blood Transfusion, Stockholm* pp. 912–916. Karger, Basel.

Brauer, R. W., Pessotti, R. L., and Pizzolato, P. (1951). *Proc. Soc. Exptl. Biol. Med.* **78**, 174–181.

Brewer, G. J. (1964). *Am. J. Human Genet.* **16**, 472–476.

Brodersen, R. (1965a). *Acta Paediat. Suppl.* **159**, 15–18.

Brodersen, R., (1965b). *Tijdschr. Gastroenterology* **8**, 194–201.

Brohult, J., and Westgren, A. (1965). *Lancet* **II**, 1344.

Broughton, P. M. G., Rossiter, E. J. R., Warren, C. B. M., Goulis, G., and Lord, P. S. (1965). *Arch. Disease Childhood* **40**, 666–671.

Brown, W. R., Grodsky, G. M., and Carbone, J. V. (1964). *Am. J. Physiol.* **207**, 1237–1245.

Buchanan, K. D., and MacGregor, R. F. S. (1964). *Brit. J. Exptl. Pathol.* **45**, 248–251.

Burka, E. R., Brick, I. B., and Wolfe, H. R. (1961). *Am. J. Med. Sci.* **242**, 746.

Butler, W. L., Hendricks, S. B., and Siegelman, H. W. (1965). In "Chemistry and Biochemistry of Plant Pigments" (T. W. Goodwin, ed.), pp. 197–210. Academic Press, New York.

Cameron, J. L., Stafford, E. S., Schnaufer, L., and Iber, F. L. (1963). *J. Surg. Res.* **3**, 39–42.

Cameron, J. L., Sleeman, H. K., Abei, T. A., and Iber, F. L. (1965). *Surgery* **121**, 291–298.

Cameron, J. L., Filler, R. M., Iber, F. L., Abei, T., and Randolph, J. G. (1966a). *New Engl. J. Med.* **274**, 231–236.

Cameron, J. L., Pulaski, E. J., Ahei, T., and Iber, F. L. (1966b). *Ann. Surg.* **163**, 330–338.

Careddu, P., Sereni, L. P., Giunta, A., and Sereni, F. (1965). *Minerva Med.* **55**, 2559–2562.

Chen, H.-C., Lien, I.-N., and Lu, T.-C. (1965). *Am. J. Pathol.* **96**, 331–338.

Chinard, F. P. (1962). *Bull. N.Y. Acad. Med.* **38**, 375–389.

Christoffersson, E., Edlund, Y., and Kewenter, J. (1965). *Acta Hepato-Splenol.* **12**, 285–292.

Clarke, J. T. (1965). *Clin. Chem.* **11**, 681–690.

Clerici, E., Mocarelli, P., and Provini, L. (1964). *Exptl. Mol. Pathol.* **3**, 569–582.

Cohen, P. J. (1964). *Anat. Record* **150**, 237–242.

Cole, J. R., and Greenough, W. B. (1965). *Lancet* **II**, 972–973.

Cole, K. S. (1966). *Ann. N.Y. Acad. Sci.* **137**, 405–408.

Cole, R. A., Danks, D. M., and Campbell, P. E. (1965). *Lancet* I, 1368–1369.

Cole, W. J. (1965). Dissertation (Ph.D.), U. of London.

Cole, W. J., Gray, C. H., and Nicholson, D. C. (1965). *J. Chem. Soc.* pp. 4085–4091.

Collens, W. S., and Dobkin, G. B. (1965). *N.Y. State Med. J.* 65, 907–909.

Colombo, B., and Bonomo, E. (1965). *Minerva Med.* 55, 2529–2531.

Comparini, L. (1964). *Atti Soc. Ital. Anat., XXIVth Convegno Sociale, Monitore Zool. Ital.* 72, Suppl.

Comparini, L., Fruschelli, C., and Bagnoli, E. (1965a). *Boll. Soc. Ital. Biol. Sper.* 41, 668–673.

Comparini, L., Bagnoli, E., and Fruschelli, C. (1965b). *Boll. Soc. Ital. Biol. Sper.* 42, 673–677.

Cornelius, C. E., Arias, M., and Osburn, N. I. (1965). *J. Am. Vet. Med. Assoc.* 146, 709–713.

Crosby, W. M., and Merrill, J. A. (1965). *Am. J. Ostet. Gynecol.* 92, 53–61.

Cullberg, G., Lundström, R., and Stenram, U. (1965). *Brit. Med. J.* I, 695–697.

Custer, L. E., Abel, T., Chipman, B. R., and Iber, F. L. (1964). *J. Lab. Clin. Med.* 64, 820–827.

Danks, D. M. (1965). *Clin. Pediat.* 4, 499–500.

Das, P. N. (1965). *J. Pathol. Bacteriol.* 90, 135–150.

De Ewenson, I. W., Gianturco, F. A., and Gramaccioni, P. (1966). *Experientia* 22, 14–15.

De Hevesey, G. (1966). *Acta Paediat.* 55, 329–336.

del Piano, E., and Lisi, B. (1964). *Therapeuticon* pp. 438–443.

del Piano, E., Sacco, O., and Palumbo, R. (1962). *Arch. Sci. Med.* 114, 485–492.

De Sandre, G., Leonardi, P., Perona, G., and Frezza, M. (1964). *Acta Med. Pataviana* 24, 1–24.

Diamond, J. R., and Tormey, J. M. (1966). *Nature* 210, 817–820.

Done, J., Mortimer, P. H., and Taylor, A. (1960). *Res. Vet. Sci.* 1, 76–83.

Done, J., Mortimer, P. H., and Taylor, A. (1962). *Res. Vet. Sci.* 3, 161–171.

Doucett, J. A. (1965). *J. Am. Med. Assoc.* 194, 299–300.

Dragovich, A., Kelly, J. A., and Kelly, R. D. (1965). *Nature* 207, 1209–1210.

Du, J. N. H., Stauffer, M. H., Levin, M., and Rogers, A. G. (1965). *Can. Med. Assoc. J.* 92, 839–841.

Dubin, I. N., Czernobilski, B., and Herbst, B. (1965). *Arch. Pathol.* 79, 232–237.

Dutton, E. J., Langelaan, D. E., and Ross, P. E. (1964). *Biochem. J.* 93, 4P–5P.

Dutton, G. J. (1964). *Rept. 10th Anniv. Symp. Glucuronic Acid* pp. 37–45. Tokyo Biochem. Res. Foundation, Tokyo.

Dybkaer, R., and Hertz, H. (1966). *VIth Intern. Congr. Clin. Chem. Munich, 1966* Abstr., p. 207. Karger, Basel.

Einhorn, M., and Davidsohn, I. (1964). *J. Am. Med. Assoc.* 188, 802–806.

Eiseman, B. (1965). *Brit. Med. J.* 2, 127.

Eliakim, M., Šadovsky, E., Stein, O., and Shenter, Y. G. (1966). *A.M.A. Arch. Internal Med.* 197, 696–705.

Elliot, A. J., and Hendry, J. (1965). *Can. Med. Assoc. J.* 92, 344–345.

Fällström, S. P., and Bjure, J. (1965). *Acta Paediat. Suppl.* 159, 25.

Fast, B. B., and Roulston, T. M., (1964). *Am. J. Obstet. Gynecol.* 88, 314–320.

Ferro, P. V., and Ham, A. B. (1965). *Am. J. Clin. Pathol.* 44, 111–113.

Fleming, A., and Woolf, A. J. (1965). *Clin. Chim. Acta* 12, 67–74.

Flint, M., Lathe, G. H., Ricketts, T. R., and Silman, G. (1964). *Quart. J. Exptl. Pathol.* 49, 66–73.

Flitman, R., and Worth, M. H. (1966). *J. Biol. Chem.* 241, 669–672.
Fog, J., and Bakken, A. F. (1967a). *In* "Bilirubin Metabolism" (I.A.D. Bouchier and B. H. Billing, eds.), pp. 85–88. Blackwell, Oxford.
Fog, J., and Bakken, A. F. (1967b). *Scand. J. Clin. Lab. Invest.* 20, 70–72.
Fog, J., and Bugge-Asperheim, B. (1964). *Nature* 203, 756–757.
Foord, L. J. H., and Lawrence, J. A. (1965). *J. Comp. Pathol. Therap.* 75, 185–200.
Freier, S., Mayer, K., Levene, C., and Abrahamov, A. (1965). *Arch. Disease Childhood* 40, 280–283.
Fujimori, E., (1964). *Nature* 204, 1091–1092.
Fulop, M., and Brazeau, P. (1964). *J. Clin. Invest.* 43, 1192–1202.
Fulop, M., Sandson, J., and Brazeau, P. (1965). *J. Clin. Invest.* 44, 666–680.
Gaidano, G., Pagliardi, E., and de Filippo, P. G. (1964). *Boll. Soc. Ital. Biol. Sper.* 40, 651–654.
Garay, E. R., Cantor, D., Argerich, T., and Royer, H. (1964a). *Medicina (Buenos Aires)* 24, 22–25.
Garay, E. R., Lozzio, B. B., O'Donnel, J. C., Toccalino, H., and Emiliani, R. (1964b). *Rev. Intern. Hepatol.* 14, 323–335.
Garay, E. R., Noir, B. A., and Royer, M. (1965). *Biochim. Biophys. Acta* 100, 411–417.
Garay, E. A. R., Owen, C. A., Jr., and Flock, E. V. (1966a). *J. Lab. Clin. Med.* 67, 817–829.
Garay, E. A. R., Flock, E. V., and Owen, C. A., Jr. (1966b). *Am. J. Physiol.* 210, 684–688.
Girard, M.-L., and Paolaggi, F.-M. (1965). *Presse Med.* 73, 2815–2817.
Girard, M.-L., Paolaggi, F.-M., and Rappier, F. (1965). *Ann. Biol. Clin. (Paris)* 23, 279–290.
Glass, G. B. J. (1965). *Am. J. Digest. Diseases* 10, 271–283.
Gliedman, M. L., Girardet, R. E., Schwartz, A., Ryzoff, R., Lerner, B., and Karlson, V. E. (1964). *Surg. Gynecol. Obstet.* 119, 749–757.
Goldberg, A. (1965). *Brit. J. Hematol.* 11, 114–118.
Goldstein, G. W., and Lester, R. (1964). *Proc. Soc. Exptl. Biol. Med.* 117, 681–683.
Gordan, G. S., Lowe, R. C., and Carbone, J. V. (1965). *Arch. Internal Med.* 116, 289–294.
Goresky, C. A. (1965). *Can. Med. Assoc. J.* 92, 851–857.
Goudemand, M., Biserte, G., Habay, D., and Voisin, D. (1964). *Nouvelle Rev. Franc. Hematol.* 4, 487–504.
Grau, H., and Meyer-Lemppenau, U. (1965). *Zentr. Veterinaermed.* 12, 232–242.
Gray, C. H., Kulczycka, A., and Nicholson, D. C., (1961). *J. Chem. Soc.* pp. 2276–2285.
Gray, C. H., Kulczyka, A., Nicholson, D. C., Magnus, I. A., and Rimington, C. (1964). *Clin. Sci.* 26, 7–15.
Gray, O. P., and Saunders, R. A. (1966). *Arch Disease Childhood* 41, 320–328.
Green, J. (1962). *Nature* 196, 1318–1319.
Grinstein, M., Bannerman, R. M., Vavra, J. D., and Moore, C. V. (1960). *Am. J. Med.* 29, 18–32.
Hack, M. H., and Helmby, F. M., (1964). *Acta Histochem.* 19, 316–328.
Haemmerli, U. P. (1966). Jaundice during pregnancy. *Acta Med. Scand. Suppl.* 444 (111pp.).
Haník, L. (1964). *Casopis Lekaru Ceskych.* 103, 708–712.
Hargreaves, T. (1965). *Nature* 208, 154–156.

Hargreaves, T., and Scrimegeour, M. (1966). *Experientia* **22**, 382.

Hargreaves, T., and Thom, B. (1964). *Nature* **206**, 1323.

Harth, O., and Waldeck, F. (1965). *Arch. Ges. Physiol.* **283**, 56–67.

Hassan, G. (1963). *Medicus (Karachi)* **26**, 145–151.

Heirwegh, K., and van Roy, F. (1965). *Clin. Chim. Acta* **12**, 684–689.

Hendricks, S. B., and Borthwick, H. A. (1965). *In* "Chemistry and Biochemistry of Plant Pigments" (T. W. Goodwin, ed.), pp. 405–436. Academic Press, New York.

Heringová, A., Jirsa, M., and Jirsová, V. (1964a). *Casopis Lekaru Ceskych.* **103**, 1132–1135.

Heringová, A., Jirsa, M., and Jirsová, V. (1964b). *Biol. Neonatorum* **6**, 277–284.

Heringová, A., Jirsová, V., and Jirsa, M. (1964c). *Cesk. Pediat., Praha* **19**, 713–716.

Heringová, V., Jirsová, V., and Koldovsky, O. (1965). *Can. J. Biochem. Physiol.* **43**, 173–177.

Herring, P. J. (1965). *Nature* **205**, 103–104.

Hertz, H., and Dybkaer, R. (1966). *VIth Intern. Congr. Clin. Chem., Munich, 1966* Abstr., p. 207. Karger, Basel.

Hibbard, E. (1964). *Science* **144**, 345–346.

Hodges, R., and Taylor, A. (1964). *J. Chem. Soc.* pp. 4310–4314.

Holton, J. B., and Lathe, G. H. (1963). *Clin. Sci.* **25**, 499–509.

Housset, E., Etienne, J.-P., Bonnet, J. L., and Leroy, G. (1962). *Pathol. Biol. Semaine Hop.* **10**, 599–690.

Housset, E., Etienne, J.-P., and Barbé, J. (1965). *Pathol. Biol. Semaine Hop.* **13**, 25–30.

Hsia, D. Y.-Y. (1965). *Pediat. Clin. N. Am.* **12**, 713–722.

Hübner, G. (1965). *Arch. Pathol. Anat. Physiol.* **339**, 187–197.

Huttunen, J. K., and Mittinen, T. A. (1965). *Acta Physiol. Scand.* **63**, 133–140.

Ibbot, F. A., and O'Brien, D. (1964). *Pediatrics* **34**, 418–419.

Ichida, F., and Funahashi, H. (1964). *Acta Hepato-Splenol.* **11**, 332–341.

Ilca, S., Dodiča, C., and Ioanvici, Z. (1965). *Acta Tertii Conventus Med. Hungarici Gastroenterologia* pp. 395–398. Akademia Nyomda, Budapest.

Iwanami, F. (1964). *Rept. 10th Anniv. Symp. Glucuronic Acid* pp. 75–87. Tokyo Biochem. Res. Foundation, Tokyo.

Jackson, A. H., Smith, K. M., Gray, C. H., and Nicholson, D. C. (1966). *Nature* **209**, 581–583.

Jackson, S. H. (1965). *Clin. Chem.* **11**, 1050–1057.

Jäykkä, S. (1964). *Biol. Neonatorum* **7**, 313–318.

Jirsa, M., Heringová, A., and Jirsová, V. (1967). *In* "Bilirubin Metabolism" (I. A. D.) Bouchier and B. H. Billing, eds.), pp. 129–133. Blackwell, Oxford.

Jisová, V., Koldovský, O., Heringová, A., Jirásek, J., and Uher, J. (1965). *Biol. Neonatorum* **8**, 23–29.

Josephson, B., and Furst, P. (1966). *Scand. J. Clin. Lab. Invest.* **18**, 51–63.

Kaern, T. (1966). *Maanedsskr. Prakt. Laegegerning (Copenhagen)* pp. 21–27.

Kahán, I. L., Csernay, L., and Varró, V. (1964). *Clin. Chim. Acta* **7**, 392–397.

Kaneda, K. (1963a). *Okayama Igakkai Zasshi* **75**, 115–124.

Kaneda, K. (1963b). *Okayama Igakkai Zasshi* **75**, 125–137.

Kaneda, K. (1963c). *Okayama Igakkai Zasshi* **75**, 139–144.

Kasza, L., Szilágyi, D., Marer, E. S., Szekely, P., Makai, M., and Palencsár, A. (1965). *Rev. Med. (Tirgu-Mures)* **11**, 27–29.

Katz, H. P., and Robinson, T. A. (1965). *New Engl. J. Med.* **273**, 546–547.

Kaufmann, N. A., and Blondheim, S. H. (1966). *VIth Intern. Congr. Clin. Chem., Munich, 1966* Abstr., p. 239. Karger, Basel.

Keene, W. R., and Jandl, J. H. (1965). *Blood* **26**, 705–719.

Kench, J. E., Gardicas, C., and Wilkinson, B. J., (1950). *Biochem. J.* **47**, 129.

Kikuchi, G., and Rokugo, I. (1961). *J. Biochem. (Tokyo)* **49**, 446–447.

Kikuchi, K. (1961). *Japan. J. Exptl. Med.* **31**, 71–81.

Kirkpatrick, H. F. W. (1953). *Lancet* **I**, 71.

Klaus, D., and Feine, U. (1965). *German Med. Monthly* **10**, 89–93.

Koch, C. A. (1964). *J. Pediat.* **65**, 1–11.

Koch, F., and Rind, H. (1965). *Deut. Med. Wochschr.* **90**, 1358–1363.

Koenig, M. G., Heyssel, R. M., Melly, M. A., and Rogers, D. E. (1965). *J. Exptl. Med.* **122**, 117–142.

Kondo, T. (1964). *10th Anniv. Symp. Glucuronic Acid* Abstr., pp. 21–22. Tokyo Biol. Res. Foundation, Tokyo.

Krebs, J. S., Brauer, R. W., Bollman, J. L., and Leong, G. F. (1964). *Am. J. Physiol.* **207**, 877–882.

Krueger, H., and Higginson, J. (1961). *Proc. Soc. Exptl. Biol. Med.* **107**, 43–47.

Kruijswijk, H., Kennedy, J. C., and Schaap, P. A. H. M. (1966). *Clin. Chim. Acta* **14**, 561–563.

Künzer, W., and Goebels, R. (1964). *Klin. Wochschr.* **42**, 924–925.

Künzer, W., Schenck, W., and Vahlenkamp, H. (1963). *Klin. Wochschr.* **41**, 1108.

Künzer, W., Vahlenkamp, H., and Förster, B. (1965). *Deut. Med. Wochschr.* **90**, 2096–2099.

Künzer, W., Vahlenkamp, H., and Förster, B. (1966). *German Med. Monthly* **11**, 95–100.

Kuenzle, C. C., Sommerhalder, M., Rüttner, J. R., and Maier, C. (1966a). *J. Lab. Clin. Med.* **67**, 282–293.

Kuenzle, C. C., Maier, C., and Rüttner, J. R., (1966b). *J. Lab. Clin. Med.* **67**, 294–306.

Kuma, F. (1966a). *Proc. Japan. Acad.* **42**, 285–290.

Kuma, F. (1966b). *Proc. Japan. Acad.* **42**, 291–294.

Larsson-Cohn, U., and Stenram, U. (1965). *J. Am. Med. Assoc.* **193**, 422–426.

Lathe, G. H. (1965). *Clin. Chem.* **11**, 309–322.

Lausecker, C., Heidt, P., Fischer, D., Hartleyb, H., and Lohr, G. W. (1965). *Arch. Franc. Pediat.* **21**, 789–797.

Leaver, D. D., and Cristie, G. S. (1965). *Australian J. Exptl. Biol. Med. Sci.* **43**, 1–16.

Lee Kavanau, J. (1966). *Federation Proc.* **25**, 1096–1107.

Lester, R. (1964). *Gastroenterology* **47**, 424–427.

Lester, R., and Klein, P. D. (1966). *J. Lab. Clin. Med.* **67**, 1000–1012.

Lester, R., and Schmid, R. (1963). *J. Clin. Invest.* **42**, 736.

Lester, R., and Schmid, R. (1965). *J. Clin. Invest.* **44**, 722–730.

Lester, R., Behrman, R. E., and Lucey, J. F. (1963). *Pediatrics* **32**, 416–419.

Lester, R., Schumer, R., and Schmid, R. (1965). *New Engl. J. Med.* **272**, 939–943.

Levine, R. A., and Klatskin, G. (1964). *Am. J. Med.* **36**, 541–551.

Levrat, M., Brette, R., Tissot, A., Truchot, R., and Moulimer, B. (1964). *Lyon Med.* **212**, 1127–1142.

Lewi, S., Walter, P., Loewe-Lyon, S., and Clarke, T. K. (1965). *Arch. Franc. Pediat.* **22**, 687–695.

Lewis, F., Schulman, H., and Hayashi, T. (1964). *J. Am. Med. Assoc.* **190**, 195–198.

Liley, A. W. (1961). *Am. J. Obset. Gynecol.* **82**, 1359–1370.

Liley, A. W. (1963). *Am. J. Obstet. Gynecol.* **86**, 485–494.

Lozzio, B. B., and Royer, M. R. (1965). *Gastroenterolia* **103**, 65–75.

Lozzio, B. B., Machado, E., Lew, V., and Royer, M. (1964). *J. Reticuloendothelial Soc.* **1**, 293–305.

Lucassen, J. (1961). The diazo reaction of bilirubin and bilirubin diglucuronide. Proefschrift (Wiskunde en Natuurwetenschappen), U. of Utrecht (76 pp.).

Lucey, J. F., Arias, I. M., and McKay, R. J. (1960). *Am. J. Diseases Children* **100**, 787.

Lucey, J. F., Behrman, R. E., and Warshaw, A. L. (1963). *Am. J. Diseases Children* **106**, 350.

Lucey, J. F., Behrman, R. E., Hibbard, E., de Gallardo, E. O., and Windle, W. F. (1964). *Exptl. Neurol.* **9**, 43.

Lüders, D., (1964a). *Z. Kinderheilk.* **91**, 254–264.

Lüders, D. (1964b). *Z. Kinderheilk.* **91**, 338–353.

Lundbergh, P. (1966). *Nord. Med.* **75**, 215–216.

McGill, D. B., Hoffman, H. H., and Bollman, J. L. (1962). *Gastroenterology* **43**, 261–266.

McKay, R. J., Jr. (1964). *Pediatrics* **33**, 763–767.

Maclay, N. M. (1959). *Am. J. Med. Technol.* **25**, 271–279.

Maggiore, Q., and Giovannetti, G. (1965). *Minerva Med.* **55**, 2526–2528.

Maggiore, Q., Cartter, M., and Billing, B. H. (1963a). *Boll. Soc. Ital. Biol. Sper.* **39**, 941–945.

Maggiore, Q., Cartter, M., and Billing, B. H. (1963b). *Boll. Soc. Ital. Biol. Sper.* **39**, 945–947.

Maki, T., Sato, T., and Saitoh, T. (1962). *Tohoku J. Exptl. Med.* **77**, 179–186.

Maki, T., Sato, T., and Saitoh, T. (1964). *Tohoku J. Exptl. Med.* **82**, 117.

Manganelli, G., and Scotti, C. (1964). *Boll. Soc. Ital. Biol. Sper.* **40**, 937–938.

Mangum, C. P. (1962). *Am. Zoologist* **2**, 428.

Marshall, R. W., Moreno, O. M., and Brodie, D. A. (1964). *J. Appl. Physiol.* **19**, 1191–1192.

Martini, G. A., Phear, E. A., Ruebner, B., and Sherlock, S. (1957). *Clin. Sci.* **16**, 35.

Martinek, R. G. (1966). *Clin. Chim. Acta* **13**, 161–170.

Masuda, M. (1965). *Rev. Intern. Hepatol.* **15**, 1227–1231.

Mayer, K., and d'Amáro, J. (1964). *Scand. J. Hematol.* **1**, 331–336.

Medway, W., Schryver, H. F., and Bell, B. (1966). *J. Am. Vet. Med. Assoc.* **149**, 891–895.

Meites, S., and Traubert, W. (1965). *Clin. Chem.* **11**, 691–699.

Mělka J., and Sĭmek, J. (1964). *J. Physiol. (Paris)* **66**, 611–612.

Mendioros, B. A. (1966). Personal communication.

Metge, W. R., Owen, C. A., Foulk, W. T., and Hoffman, H. N. (1964). *J. Lab. Clin. Med.* **64**, 335–341.

Michaëlsson, M., Nosslin, B., and Sjölin, S. (1965). *Pediatrics* **35**, 925–931.

Miller, L. L., and Axelrod, L. R. (1954). *Metab. Clin. Exptl.* **3**, 438.

Moore, R. A., Hellman, L. H., and Jacobius, H. E. (1942). *A.M.A. Arch. Pathol.* **34**, 196–198.

Moravec, M. (1963). *Z. Ges. Inn. Med. Ihre Grenzgebiete* **18**, 471–472.

Morrison, G. R., Karl, I. E., Schwartz, R., and Shank, R. E. (1965). *J. Lab. Clin. Med.* **65**, 248–256.

Mortimer, P. H. (1962). *Res. Vet. Sci.* **3**, 269–286.

Mortimer, P. H. (1963). *Res. Vet. Sci.* **4**, 166–185.

Mortimer, P. H., and Taylor, A. (1962). *Res. Vet. Sci.* **3**, 147–171.

Moscowitz, A. (1961). *Tetrahedron* **13**, 48.

Moscowitz, A., Krueger, W. C., Kay, I. T., Skewes, G., and Bruckenstein, S. (1964). *Proc. Natl. Acad. Sci. U.S.* **52**, 1190–1194.

Murano, G. (1964). *Panminerva* **6**, 299–304.

Murano, G., and Di Toro, R. (1965). *Minerva Med.* **55**, 2562–2570.

Murray, I. M. (1963a). *J. Exptl. Med.* **117**, 139–148.

Murray, I. M. (1963b). *Am. J. Physiol.* **204**, 655–659.

Mushin, W. W., Rosen, M., Bowen, D. J., and Campbell, H. (1964). *Brit. Med. J.* **II**, 229–341.

Natzschka, J. C., and Odell, G. B. (1966). *Pediatrics* **37**, 51–61.

Nepveux, P., Housset, E., Etienne, J.-P., Barber, J., Albot, G., and Wegman, R. (1965). *Pathol. Biol. Semaine Hop.* **13**, 43–45.

Nermark, P., and Thulin, K. E. (1966). *Nord. Med.* **75**, 216.

Netoušek, M., and Moravec, M. (1965). *Med. Klin.* **60**, 1974–1978.

Neumayr, A. A. (1964). *Gastroenterology* **47**, 343–353.

Newbold, B. T., and LeBlanc, G. (1964). *Can. J. Biochem.* **42**, 1697–1702.

Noir, B. A., Garay, E. R., and Royer, M. (1965). *Biochim. Biophys. Acta* **100**, 403–410.

Noir, B. A., Groszman, R. J., and De Walz, A. T. (1966). *Biochim. Biophys. Acta* **117**, 297–304.

Noir, B. A., De Walz, A. T., and Garay, E. R. (1967). *In* "Bilirubin Metabolism" (I. A. D.) Bouchier and B. H. Billing, eds.), pp. 99–102. Blackwell, Oxford.

Nomura, T., Gaudemoer, A., Barbier, M., and Tsuchiya, Y. (1966). *Bull. Soc. Chim. France* 2111–2112.

Nosslin, B., and Morgan, E. H. (1965). *J. Lab. Clin. Med.* **65**, 891–902.

Ó'Carra, P. (1963). Thesis (Ph.D.), Natl. U. of Ireland.

Ó'Carra, P. (1965). *Biochem. J.* **94**, 171–174.

Ó'Carra, P., and Ó'hEocha, C. (1966). *Phytochemistry* **5**, 993–997.

Ó'Carra, P., Ó'hEocha, C., and Carrol, D. M. (1964). *Biochemistry* **3**, 1343–1350.

Odell, G. B. (1965). *Proc. Soc. Exptl. Biol. Med.* **120**, 352–354.

Ó'hEocha, C. (1962). *In* "Physiology and Biochemistry of Algae" (R. A. Lewin, ed.), pp. 421–435. Academic Press, New York.

Ó'hEocha, C. (1963). *Biochemistry* **2**, 373–382.

Ó'hEocha, C. (1965a). *In* "Chemistry and Biochemistry of Plant Pigments" (T. W. Goodwin, ed.), pp. 75–196. Academic Press, New York.

Ó'hEocha, C. (1965b). *Ann. Rev. Plant Physiol.* **16**, 415–434.

Ó'hEocha, C. (1966). *In* "Biochemistry of Chloroplasts" (T. W. Goodwin, ed.), pp. 407–421. Academic Press, New York.

Osipov, L. M. (1964). *Klinich. Med.* **2**, 68–72.

Ostermiller, W., Thompson, R. J., Carter, R., and Hinshaw, D. B. (1965). *Arch. Surg.* **90**, 392–395.

Ostrow, J. D., and Schmid, R. (1963). *J. Clin. Invest.* **42**, 1286.

Ostrow, J. D., Hammaker, L., and Schmid, R. (1961). *J. Clin. Invest.* **40**, 1442.

Otto, J. J., Pender, J. C., Cleary, J. H., Sensenig, D. M., and Welch, C. S. (1958). *Surgery* **43**, 892.

Pagliardi, E., and Gaidano, G. (1965). *Minerva Med.* **55**, 2532–2536.

Panizon, F. (1965). *Lancet* **II**, 495.

Pavel, I., and Campeanu, S. (1965). *Rev. Assoc. Med. Langue Franc.* **1**, 25–31.

Pavel, I., and Pieptea, R. (1966). *Muench. Med. Wochschr.* **108**, 26–30.

Pavone, G., and Pietropaolo, F. (1964). *Clin. Obstet. Gynecol.* **66**, 706–710.

Pearson, L. B., and Watson, C. J. (1963). *Proc. Soc. Exptl. Biol. Med.* **112**, 756–758.

Pennington, G. W., and Hall, R. (1966). *J. Clin. Pathol.* 19, 90–91.

Pereira Lima, J. E., Utz, E., and Roisenberg, I. (1966). *Am. J. Med.* 40, 628–633.

Perona, G., Frezza, M., Furlanello, F., and De Sandre, G. (1964). *Acta Med. Patavia* 24, *Suppl.*, pp. 99–108.

Peters, J. A., and Smith, L. M. (1964). *Biochem. J.* 92, 379–385.

Pittera, A., and Cassia, B. (1964). *Fegato (Rome)* 10, 28–41.

Poland, M. D., Pickett, R. D., and Rosenak, B. D. (1965). *J. Indiana State Med. Assoc.* 58, 429–434.

Poole, H. (1965). *Proc. Soc. Exptl. Biol. Med.* 119, 547–551.

Porter, E. G., and Waters, W. J. (1966). *J. Lab. Clin. Med.* 67, 660–668.

Porush, J. G., Delman, A. J., and Feuer, M. M. (1962). *A.M.A. Arch. Internal Med.* 109, 302–309.

Pruzanski, W. (1965). *Gastroenterologia* 104, 225–235.

Rafferty, M. A., and O'hEocha, C. (1965). *Biochem. J.* 94, 166–170.

Raia, S. (1965). *Nature* 205, 304–305.

Richterich, R. (1963). *Klin. Wochschr.* 41, 778–783.

Rimington, C. (1964). *Clin. Sci.* 26, 7–15.

Robinson, S. H., and Schmid, R. (1964). *Medicine* 43, 667–668.

Robinson, S. H., Vanier, T., Desforgos, J. F., and Schmid, R. (1962). *New Engl. J. Med.* 267, 523.

Robinson, S. H., Owen, C. A., Flock, E. V., and Schmid, R. (1965a). *Blood* 26, 823–829.

Robinson, S. H., Tsong, M., Brown, B. W., and Schmid, R. (1965b). *J. Lab. Clin. Med.* 66, 1015–1016.

Rokugo, I. R. (1962). *Tohoku J. Exptl. Med.* 77, 171–178.

Romano, C. (1965). *Minerva Med.* 55, 2536–2542.

Rosenthal, W. S., Kubo, K., Dolinski, M., Marino, J., Mersheimer, W. L., and Glass, G. B. J. (1965). *Am. J. Digest. Diseases* 10, 279–283.

Rosta, J., and Szöke, L. (1965). *Acta Paediat. Hung.* 6, 221–225.

Roy, A. B. (1956). *Biochem. J.* 62, 41.

Royer, M., Garay, E. R., and Argerich, T. (1962). *Acta Physiol. Latinoam.* 12, 84–95.

Rubin, E. (1964). *Exptl. Mol. Pathol.* 3, 279–286.

Rüttner, J. R., Spycher, M. A., and Kuenzle, C. (1964). *Pathol. Microbiol.* 27, 403–409.

Ruud, J. T. (1965). *Sci. Am.* 213, 108–113.

Sagild, U., Dalgaard, O. Z., and Tygstrup, N. (1962). *Ann. Internal Med.* 56, 308–314.

Sallomi, S. J., and Belew, J. E. (1965). *Obstet. Gynecol.* 25, 264–267.

Sandborn, E., Szeberenyi, A., Messier, P.-E., and Bois, P. (1965). *Rev. Can. Biol.* 24, 243–276.

Sansone, G., and Pick, C. (1965). *Brit. J. Hematol.* 11, 511–517.

Satler, J., (1966). *Acta Hepato-Splenol.* 13, 38–47.

Sato, T., and Saitoh, T. (1965). *Tohoku J. Exptl. Med.* 84, 329–338.

Schaffner, F. (1965). *J. Am. Med. Assoc.* 191, 466–469.

Scheler, W., Graf, W., Scheler, I., and Rahmel, G. (1964). *Acta Biol. Med. Ger.* 13, 126–143.

Schellong, G. (1962). "Ikterus Neonatorum. Untersuchungen über die physiologische Billirubinämine des Neugeborenen." Thieme, Stuttgart (129pp.).

Schellong, G. (1965). *Klin. Wochschr.* 43, 814–816.

Schenker, S., Dawber, N. H., and Schmid, R. (1964). *J. Clin. Invest.* 43, 32.

Schettini, F., and Meloni, T. (1964). *Acta Haematol.* **32**, 35–38.

Schmid, M., and Hefti, M. L. (1966). *Z. Gastroenterol.* **4**, 89–95.

Schmid, M., Hefti, M. L., Gattiuer, R., Kistler, H. J., and Senning, A. (1965). *New Engl. J. Med.* **272**, 545.

Schmid, R., and Hammaker, L. (1962). *J. Clin. Invest.* **42**, 1720–1734.

Schmid, R., Schwartz, S., and Watson, C. J. (1954). *Arch. Internal Med.* **93**, 167–190.

Schmid, R., Diamond, I., Hammaker, L., and Gundersen, C. B. (1965). *Nature* **206**, 1041–1043.

Schmidt, N. A., and Scholtis, R. J. H. (1964). *Clin. Chim. Acta* **10**, 584–586.

Schneider, J. J., and Lewart, M. L. (1956). *J. Biol. Chem.* **222**, 787.

Schoenfield, L. J., Foulk, W. T., and Bollman, J. L. (1964). *Gastroenterology* **47**, 35–40.

Scholtan, W., and Gloxhuber, C. (1966). *Arzneimittel-Forsch.* **16**, 520–528.

Schwartz, S., Ibrahim, G., and Watson, C. J. (1964). *J. Lab. Clin. Med.* **64**, 1003.

Sereni, F., Sereni, L. P., Perletti, L., Livi, E., and Careddu, P. (1964a). *Minerva Med.* **55**, 2550–2554.

Sereni, F., Sereni, L. P., Perletti, L., Appolonio, T., and Careddu, P. (1964b). *Minerva Med.* **55**, 2554–2558.

Shibuya, T. (1964). *Tohoku J. Exptl. Med.* **83**, 29–46.

Siegelman, H. W., and Firer, E. M. (1964). *Biochemistry* **3**, 418–423.

Siegelman, H. W., and Hendricks, S. B. (1965). *Federation Proc.* **24**, 863–867.

Siegelman, H. W., Turner, B. C., and Hendricks, S. B. (1966). *Plant. Physiol.* **41**, 1289–1292.

Singleton, J. W., and Lester, L. (1965). *J. Biol. Chem.* **240**, 4780–4789.

Snyder, A. L., and Schmid, R. (1965). *J. Lab. Clin. Med.* **65**, 817–824.

Soliman, M. K., and Amrousi, S. El (1965). *Vet. Record* **77**, 633–634.

Sotgiu, G. (1965). *Postgrad. Med. J.* **41**, 234–242.

Sova, Z. (1964). *Zentr. Veterinaermed.* **11**, 760–772.

Spiegel, E. L., Schubert, W., Perrin, E., and Schiff, L. (1965). *Am. J. Med.* **39**, 688–692.

Sproul, A., and Smith, L. (1964). *J. Pediat.* **65**, 12–26.

Sternlieb, I. (1965). *J. Microscop.* (*Paris*) **4**, 71–81.

Stickney, J. C., Stewart, P. S., and Collins, J. L. (1965). *Proc. Soc. Exptl. Biol. Med.* **118**, 433–435.

Stiehm, E. R., and Ryan, J. (1965). *Am. J. Disease Children* **109**, 212.

Summerskill, W. H. J. (1965). *Am. J. Med.* **38**, 298–305.

Suzuki, N. (1965a). *Tohoku J. Exptl. Med.* **85**, 238.

Suzuki, N. (1965b). *Tohoku J. Exptl. Med.* **85**, 396.

Talafant, E., and Appelt, G. (1967). *In* "Bilirubin Metabolism" (I. A. D. Bouchier and B. H. Billing, eds.), pp. 103–106. Blackwell, Oxford.

Tarel, I. E. (1964). *Soviet Med.* **10**, 27–32.

Technicon Instruments Corp., Chanuncey, N. Y., Bilirubin Methodology, Notes No. 12, 1960.

Tenhunen, R. (1965a). *Ann. Med. Exptl. Biol. Fenniae Helsinki* **43**, Suppl. 6, 45.

Tenhunen, R. (1965b). *Acta Chem. Scand.* **19**, 1488–1489.

Thaler, M. M. (1964). *Pediatrics* **33**, 721–734.

Thaysen, E. H. (1966). *Ugeskrift Laeger* **128**, 646–651.

Trolle, D. (1965a). *Danish Med. Bull.* **12**, 35–37.

Trolle, D. (1965b). *Acta Obstet. Gynecol. Scand.* **44**, 180–195.

Tumen, H. J., Cain, J. C., Haubrich, W. S., Mellinkoff, S. M., and Mendeloff, A. I. (1965). *J. Am. Med. Assoc.* **191**, 405.

Turay, P., Szórády, T., and Kiss, J. (1964). *Enzymologia* **27**, 281–288.
Tygstrup, I. (1965). *Acta Paediat. Suppl.* **159**, 19–22.
Tygstrup, N., Schiødt, T., and Winkler, K. (1965). *Gut* **6**, 194–199.
Ulstrom, R. A., and Eisenklam, E. (1964). *J. Pediat.* **65**, 27–37.
Van den Bossche, H. (1965). *Clin. Chim. Acta* **11**, 379–381.
van Roy, F., and Heirwegh, K. (1965). *Arch. Intern. Physiol. Biochim.* **73**, 535–536.
Verme, E. G., and Campari, E. (1965). *Minerva Med.* **55**, 2543–2548.
Verzar, F. (1936). "Absorption from the Intestine." Longman, Green, London.
Vest, M. F. (1967) *In* "Bilirubin Metabolism" (I. A. D. Boucher and B. H. Billing, eds.), pp. 47–53. Blackwell, Oxford.
Vest, M. F., Strebel, L., and Haufenstein, D. (1965). *Biochem. J.* **95**, 11C.
Virchow, R. (1865). *Arch. Pathol. Anat. Physiol.* **32**, 117.
Von Dobeneck, H. (1966). *Z. Klin. Chem.* **4**, 137–141.
Von Dobeneck, H., and Brunner, E. (1965a). *Z. Physiol. Chem.* **340**, 157–166.
Von Dobeneck, H., and Brunner, E. (1965b). *Z. Physiol. Chem.* **340**, 200–209.
Von Dobeneck, H., and Klötzer, E. (1959). *Z. Physiol. Chem.* **216**, 78–82.
Von Dobeneck, H., Graf, W., and Ettel, W. (1962a). *Z. Physiol. Chem.* **329**, 168–181.
Von Dobeneck, H., Hägel, E., and Graf, W. (1962b). *Z. Physiol. Chem.* **329**, 182–187.
Von Dobeneck, H., Hägel, E., Schmierle, F., and Brunner, E. (1965). *Z. Physiol. Chem.* **241**, 27–35.
Waldeck, F., and Harth, O. (1965). *Arch. Ges. Physiol.* **283**, 68–74.
Wallace, D. K., and Owen, E. E. (1964). *J. Lab. Clin. Med.* **64**, 741–755.
Ward, P. (1965). *Ugeskrift Laeger* **127**, 227–229.
Waters, W. J., and Porter, E. (1964). *Pediatrics* **33**, 749–757.
Watson, C. J. (1957). *Ann. Internal Med.* **47**, 611.
Watson, C. J. (1960). *J. Biol. Chem.* **235**, 797.
Watson, C. J. (1965). *Ann. Internal Med.* **63**, 931–944.
Watson, C. J. (1966). *Acta Med. Scand.* **445**, Suppl. pp. 25–35.
Watson, C. J., Lowry, P. T., Schmid, R., Hawkinson, V., and Schwartz, S. (1951). *Trans. Assoc. Am. Physicians* **64**, 345.
Watson, C. J., Weimer, M., Krueger, W., Lightner, D. A., and Moscowitz, A. (1965). *Federation Proc.* **24**, 222.
Watson, D. (1967). *Clin. Chim. Acta* **15**, 121–126.
Weber, A. P., and Schalm, L. (1965). *Acta Med. Scand.* **177**, 519–526.
White, F. D. (1932). *Brit. J. Exptl. Pathol.* **13**, 76.
Williams, R., Cartter, M., Sherlock, S., Scheuer, R. J., and Hill, K. R. (1964). *Quart. J. Med.* **131**, 387.
Wilson, T. H. (1962). "Intestinal Absorption," pp. 40–68. Saunders, Philadelphia, Pa.
Winkler, K. (1965). *In* "The Biliary System" (W. Taylor, ed.), pp. 551–566. Blackwell, Oxford.
Winkler, K. (1966). Studier over bromsulfaleineliminationen hos mennesker (Danish with English Summary). Dissertation (Med.), U. of Copenhagen.
Wishingrad, L., Cornblath, M., Takakuwa, T., Rozenfeld, I. M., Elegant, L. D., Kaufman, A., Lassers, E., and Klein, R. I. (1965). *Pediatrics* **36**, 162.
Wong, P. W. K., Burnstine, R. C., and Hsia, D. Y. Y. (1965). *Pediatrics* **36**, 138–140.
Wood, R. L. (1965). *Anat. Record* **151**, 507–530.
Yue, P. C. K., and Strickland, M. (1965). *Lancet* **I**, 350–351.
Zaroda, R. A. (1966). *Am. J. Clin. Pathol.* **45**, 70–74.
Zeckwer, I. T. (1949). *A.M.A. Arch. Pathol.* **47**, 242–248.
Zieve, L. (1964). *Med. Grand Rounds, V. A. Hosp. (Minneapolis)* **33**, 73–99.

Author Index

Numbers in italics refer to pages on which the references are listed.

A

Abbot, A. L., *706*
Abbott, L. D., 97, *739*
Abei, T., 171, 241, 257, 258, 282, *489*, 510, 554, 610, 612, *746*
Abei, T. A., 139, *746*
Abel, T., 17, *747*
Abeloos, M., 653, 654, *671*
Abelson, N., *671*
Aboliņš, L., *647*
Abraham, R. J., 225, 465, *723*
Abrahamov, A., 437, *748*
Abrahams, C., *745*
Abrami, P., 148, *740*
Accame, E., 38, 85, 486, 488, *710*
Acevedo, F. J., 188, *729*
Achard, C., 542, *671*
Acocella, G., *584*
Adame, E., 128, 174, 386, 387, *700*
Adams, N. C., 638, *671*
Addis, T., 531, 596, 607, *740*
Adler, A., 297, 321, 325, 327, 334, 470, 504, 514, 522, 525, 548, 547, 572, 602, 603, *671*, *735*
Adler, E., 494, 525, 587, 590, *714*
Adlercreutz, H., 475, *671*, *744*
Adlersberg, D., 183, *671*
Åkerren, Y., *671*
Ånberg, Å., *744*
Afanassiew, M., 201, 245, *671*
Agarawala, O. N., 220, 413, *745*
Ahrens, E. H., 243, *671*
Aicardi, J., 436, *671*
Aidin, R., 636, 638, *671*
Akagi, K., 116, *671*
Akazaki, K., 127, *671*
Akeroyd, F. H., 167, 555, *706*
Akeroyd, J. H., *682*
Alagille, D., 437, 555, *707*, *743*
Albot, G., 217, 249, *745*, *752*
Aldrich, A., *694*
Aldrich, R. A., 90, 97, 394, 650, *671*, *694*, *706*

Ali, M., 283, *745*
Ali, M. A. H., 257, 258, *489*, 556
Alican, F., 203, 229, 388, 509, 514, *671*
Allen, F. H., 421, 638, 640, *699*
Allessandro, G., 346, *671*
Allies, F., 53, *678*
Alliot, M., 532, *671*
Altman, K. I., 90, 99, *671*
Altschule, M. D., 113, 120, 616, *671*, 692
Alwall, N., 415, 418, 452, 479, *671*
Alzugaray, A. E., 514, *672*
Amada, Y., 29, 59, 64, 567, 568, *672*
Amako, T., *672*
Amatuzio, D. S., 60, 62, 618, *672*
Amrousi, S. El., 413, *754*
Andersch, M., 263, *693*
Andersen, D. H., 112, 643, *729*
Andersen, E., 319, *733*
Anderson, L. A. P., 220, 221, 222, *672*, 678
Anderson, W. A. D., 112, 113, *672*, *715*
Anderson, V. E., *744*
André, R., 556, *672*
Andrewes, C. H., 339, 351, 504, 616, *672*
Andrews, J. T., 258
Andrews, W. H. H., 184, 191, 194, 200, 206, 207, 217, 229, 230, 248, 257, 316, 449, *672*
Anke, N. K., 484, *672*
Antunes, M. L., 85, 331, 424, *675*
Apolo, E., 346, 416, *736*
Appelmans, R., 441, *672*, *677*
Appelt, G., 348, *754*
Appleby, C. A., 662, *687*
Appolonio, T., 135, 197, *754*
Araki, K., 109, *672*
Aramburu, H. G., 413, *724*
Arandjelović, R. R., 411, *730*
Ardelt, W., *745*
Arellano, J. M., 478, *672*
Arens, A., 463, *712*
Argerich, T., 30, 48, 115, 127, 574, *724*, *748*, *753*

757

Subject Index

A

Absorption
 gallbladder, 143
 intestine, 138, 139, 141
 serous cavities, 143
 spectral, *see* specific substances
Acanthocephala, 652
Accelerators (diazo reaction), 295, 324–327
 acetamide, 326
 acetate, 64, 295
 acetone, 64, 325
 activity, relative, 326, 327
 antipyrine, 67, 326
 benzoic acid, 67
 bile salts, 327
 caffeine, 67, 285, 326
 caffeine-sodium benzoate, 326
 diazo reagent, 328
 "direct" sera, action on, 328
 EDTA, 69
 ethanol, 64, 235
 ion, sequence of activity, 327, 328
 methanol, 64, 65, 307, 314, 325
 pH and accelerator action, 321–323, 328
 propanol, 325
 pyridine, 325
 serum, ions of, 328
 urea, 67, 326
Acetate as porphyrin precursor, 90
Acetic acid chains in porphyrins, 1
Acetone, *see* Accelerators
Acetone icterus index, 283
Acidity of bile pigments, 12
Actinidae, 654
Adrenal blocking, 247
Adsorption value (serum bilirubin), 349, 350
Aflatoxin, 253
ALA, 17, 90, 94, 95, 99
Albumin, *see* Serum albumin
Alcohol, *see* Accelerators, ethanol
Aldehyde reaction, *see* Benzaldehyde reaction

Algae, 658–662
 chromatic adaptation, 659
Allium, 394
Allophycocyanin, 657, 659
Amblyostoma, 127
δ-Aminolevulinic acid, *see* ALA
Amniotic fluid, 622–625
Amphibians, 127, 565, 573, 581
Amphipyra, 655
Ampholyte properties of bile pigments, 11
Ampulla of Vater, 243
Ampullas of Hering, *see* Hering's canals
Anasa, 652
Anemia
 aplastic, 97
 dyshematopoietic, 99
 hemolytic, 166, 168, *see also* Jaundice, Hemolysis
 macrocytic in mice, 99
 megaloblastic, 97, 98
 pernicious, *see also* Pernicious anemia
  ineffective erythropoiesis in, 98
 refractory with bile pigment destruction, 134
22β-Angeloyloxyoleanic acid, 221, 222
ANiCT, *see* α-Naphthylisothiocyanate
Animals
 invertebrate, 651–657
 vertebrate, 649, 650, *see also* specific animals
 wild, 649
Annelids, 653
Anodontata, 651
Antelopes, 166
Antibiotics, 145, 146
Anura, 652
Aphrodite, 653
Aplysia, 654–656
Aplysiopurpurin, 656
Aplysioviolin, 656
Apoplexy, cerebral, 478
Arsenic hydride (AsH₃), 406
Arsphenamine, 252
Arthropods, blood sucking, 129
Ascidia, 657

797